42nd European Photovoltaic Solar Energy Conference and Exhibition (EU PVSEC 2025)

Bilbao, Spain
22-26 September 2025

Volume 2 of 6

ISBN: 979-8-3313-2987-7

42nd European Photovoltaic Solar Energy Conference and Exhibition (EU PVSEC 2025)

Bilbao, Spain
22-26 September 2025

Volume 2 of 6

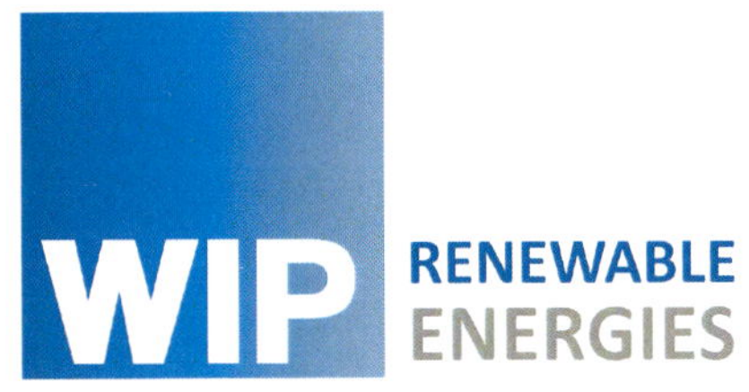

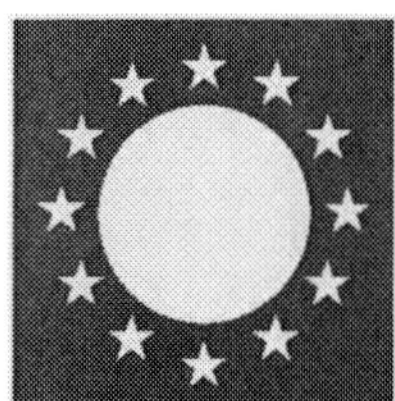

42nd European Photovoltaic Solar Energy Conference and Exhibition

Proceedings of the International Conference

22 September – 26 September 2025

Edited by:

C. DEL CAÑIZO
Solar Energy Institute
UPM
Spain

R. KENNY
European Commission
Joint Research Centre
Italy

J. BERGMILLER
WIP Renewable Energies
Germany

J. DE GREGORIO
WIP Renewable Energies
Germany

Edition Team:

B. Yildiz
L. Großhans
A. Michaelsen
U.E. Birgi
WIP Renewable Energies
Germany

Photos at:

Coordination of the Technical Programme:
European Commission Joint Research Centre
Via E. Fermi 1
21020 Ispra (VA)
Italy

Institutional Support:
European Commission

Institutional PV Industry Cooperation:
SolarPower Europe
ESMC – European Solar Manufacturing Council

Supporting Organisations:
AUSTRALIAN PV INSTITUTE
ASOM – Alliance for Solar Mobility
BASQUE ENERGY CLUSTER
BILBAO CONVENTION BUREAU
EASE – European Association for Storage of Energy
ETIP PV – European Technology & Innovation Platform PV
GÜNDER – Turkish Solar Energy Society
IEA PVPS - IEA Photovoltaic Power Systems Programme
INSTITUTO SOLAR DE ENERGÍA SOLAR
LDES – Long Duration Energy Storage Council
NSEFI – National Solar Energy federation of India
NUS /SERIS – National University of Singapore / Solar Energy Research Institute of Singapore
UPM - Polytechnic University of Madrid

Supporting Associations:
EERA – European Energy Research Aliance
EREF – European Renewable Energies Federation
EUREC – The Association of European Renewable Energy Research Centres
VDMA Photovoltaic Equipment

Local Support:
ENTE VASCO DE LA ENERGÍA
EUH – University of the Basque Country

EU PVSEC 2025 realised by:
WIP Renewable Energies
Sylvensteinstr. 2, 81369 Munich, Germany
Tel: +49 89 720 12 735, Fax: +49 89 720 12 791
Email: pv.conference@wip-munich.de
www.eupvsec.org
www.wip-munich.de

Proceedings produced and published by:
WIP Renewable Energies
Sylvensteinstr. 2, 81369 Munich, Germany
Tel: +49 89 720 12 735, Fax: +49 89 720 12 791
Email: pv.conference@wip-munich.de
www.eupvsec.org
www.wip-munich.de

42nd EUROPEAN PHOTOVOLTAIC SOLAR ENERGY CONFERENCE AND EXHIBITION
22 SEPTEMBER – 26 SEPTEMBER 2025

EU PVSEC 2025 COMMITTEES

INTERNATIONAL SCIENTIFIC ADVISORY COMMITTEE (ISAC)

Chair
P. Szymanski, European Commission Joint Research Centre, Director of Energy, Transport and Climate, Petten, The Netherlands

Committee Members
V. Bermúdez Benito, Founder & Principal Consultant, Berbetin, Antibes, France
G.C. Eder, OFI, Vienna, Austria
P. Frankl, Head of the Renewable Energy Division, International Energy Agency, France
M. Getsiou, European Commission, DG RTD, Brussels, Belgium
S.W. Glunz, Head of Division Photovoltaics - Research, Fraunhofer ISE, Freiburg, Germany
N.M. Haegel, Director of the National Center for Photovoltaics, NREL, Golden, USA
R. Kenny, European Commission Joint Research Centre, Directorate for Energy and Transport and Climate, Ispra, Italy
S. Nowak, Managing Director of NET Nowak Energy & Technology, St. Ursen, Switzerland
R. Schlatmann, Chairman of ETIP PV, Head of the Solar Energy Division at Helmholtz-Zentrum Berlin, Germany
W.C. Sinke, TNO Energy Transition, The Netherlands
M. Topič, Head of Laboratory of Photovoltaics and Optoelectronics of the University of Ljubljana, Slovenia
P. Verlinden, Director at Amrock, Visiting Professor at Sun Yat-Sen University, Guangzhou, China
E. Voroshazi, Head of PV module process laboratory, CEA, Le Bourget-du-Lac, France
J. Bergmiller, Managing Director Events & Knowledge Transfer, WIP Renewable Energies, Munich, Germany
J. de Gregorio, Head of Unit, Scientific Services and Cooperation, WIP Renewable Energies, Munich, Germany

CONFERENCE EXECUTIVE COMMITTEE

Conference General Chair
C. del Cañizo, UPM, Madrid, Spain

Technical Programme Chair
R. Kenny, European Commission Joint Research Centre, Directorate for Energy and Transport and Climate, Ispra, Italy

Committee Members
W.C. Sinke, Program Development Manager, TNO Energy Transition, The Netherlands
S. Nowak, Managing Director of NET Nowak Energy & Technology, St. Ursen, Switzerland
M. Topič, Head of Laboratory of Photovoltaics and Optoelectronics of the University of Ljubljana, Slovenia
V. Bermúdez Benito, BERBETIN, France
E. Voroshazi, Head of PV Module Process Laboratory, CEA, Le Bourget-Du-Lac France

H. Ossenbrink, Former European Commission Joint Research Centre, Germany
J. Bergmiller, Managing Director Events & Knowledge Transfer, WIP Renewable Energies, Munich, Germany
J. de Gregorio, Head of Unit, Scientific Services and Cooperation, WIP Renewable Energies, Munich, Germany

2025 SCIENTIFIC COMMITTEE

Programme Technical Chair
R. Kenny, European Commission, Joint Research Centre, Italy

Topic Chairs

Topic 1: Silicon Materials and Cells
F. Schindler, Fraunhofer ISE, Germany

Topic 2: Thin Films and New Concepts
I. Gordon, imec, Belgium

Topic 3: Photovoltaic Modules and BoS Components
T. Barnes, NREL, USA

Topic 4: PV Systems Engineering, Integrated/Applied PV
A.M. Gracia Amillo, FUNDACION CENER, Spain

Topic 5: PV in the Energy Transition
C. Agraffeil, CEA / INES, France

Topic Organisers and Paper Review Experts

Topic 1: Silicon Materials and Cells
F. Schindler, Fraunhofer ISE, Germany
C. Fischer, Wacker Chemie, Germany
G. Hahn, University of Konstanz, Germany
K. Ding, Forschungszentrum Jülich, Germany
P. Roca i Cabarrocas, CNRS-LPICM, France
A. W. Weeber, TNO Energy Transition, The Netherlands
D. Muñoz, CEA / INES, France
S. W. Glunz, Fraunhofer ISE, Germany
K. Bothe, ISFH, Germany
M. Topic, University of Ljubljana, Slovenia
P. Fath, RCT-Solutions, Germany
S. Peters, Hanwha Q CELLS, Germany

M.P. Bellmann, SINTEF, Norway
A. Ciesla, UNSW, Australia
C. Hagendorf, Freiberg Instruments, Germany
X. Yu, Zhejiang University, China
J.S. Lee, KIER, South Korea
R. Brendel, ISFH, Germany
T. Dullweber, ISFH, Germany
J. Horzel, Fraunhofer ISE, Germany
W. Nemeth, NREL, United States of America
R. Turan, METU, Türkiye
F. Menchini, ENEA, Italy
W. Favre, CEA, France

J. Meier, Meier Technologies, Switzerland
J. Schmidt, ISFH, Germany
M. Wright, University of Oxford, United Kingdom
J. Zhao, CSEM, Switzerland
A. Morisset, CSEM, Switzerland
A. Richter, Fraunhofer ISE, Germany
J. Linke, ISC Konstanz, Germany
B. Geerligs, TNO Energy Transition, The Netherlands
S. Dubois, CEA, France
M. Hermle, Fraunhofer ISE, Germany
B. Terheiden, University of Konstanz, Germany
P. Delli Veneri, ENEA, Italy
T. Matsui, AIST, Japan
Y. Ohshita, Toyota Technological Institute, Japan
E. Bruhat, HOLOSOLIS, France
A. Augusto, Dalarna University, Sweden
F. Ferrazza, ENI S.p.A., Italy
A. Otaegi, UPV/EHU, Spain
M.C. Schubert, Fraunhofer ISE, Germany
H. Duman, KalyonPV, Türkiye
N. Usami, Nagoya University, Japan
Y. Zhu, UNSW, Australia
D. Brunner, RENA Technologies, Germany
A. Danel, CEA, France
C. Gerardi, 3Sun, Italy
H.J. Nonnenmacher, Meyer Burger, Germany
P. Verlinden, AMROCK, Australia
Q. Wang, Wang, Qi, China
W. Zhang, Zhang, Weiming, China
Y. Chen, Trina Solar Energy, China
E. Krassowski, CE Cell Engineering, Germany
M. Foti, 3Sun, Italy
D.L. Bätzner, Meyer Burger Research, Switzerland

Topic 2: Thin Films and New Concepts
I. Gordon, imec, Belgium
J.C. Goldschmidt, Marburg University, Germany
F. Schoofs, Oxford PV, United Kingdom
N. Kyranaki, Hasselt University, Belgium
S. Veenstra, TNO Energy Transition, The Netherlands
T. Aernouts, imec, Belgium
A.N. Tiwari, SOLTIWA, Switzerland
G. Siefer, Fraunhofer ISE, Germany
M. Edoff, Uppsala University, Sweden
A. Marti Vega, UPM, Spain
J. Poortmans, imec, Belgium
I. Ramiro, UPM, Spain
T. Magorian Friedlmeier, ZSW, Germany

S. Albrecht, HZB, Germany
S. Berson, CEA, France
P. Carroy, CEA, France
C. Case, Oxford PV, United Kingdom
G. Coletti, FuturaSun, Italy
S. De Wolf, KAUST, Saudi Arabia
U.W. Paetzold, KIT, Germany
H. Sivaramakrishnan Radhakrisnan, imec, Belgium
P. Schulze, Fraunhofer ISE, Germany
L. Wang, Technology Innovation Institute, United Arab Emirates
Y. Smirnov, Applied Materials, United States of America
B. Stannowski, HZB, Germany
F. Fertig, Hanwha Q CELLS, Germany
L. Lancellotti, ENEA, Italy
S. Cros, CEA, France
S. Hayase, The University of Electro-Communications, Japan
S. Huang, Macquarie University, Australia
M. Khenkin, HZB, Germany
C. Lin, National Taiwan University, Taiwan

M.S.H. Norton, University of Cyprus, Cyprus
P. Pistor, Pablo de Olavide University, Spain
W. Tress, Zurich University of Applied Sciences, Switzerland
A. Aguirre, imec, Belgium
D. Lan, UNSW Sydney, China
M. Saliba, University of Stuttgart, Germany
P. Manshanden, TNO Energy Transition, The Netherlands
L. Vesce, University of Rome II, Italy
I. Dogan, TNO Solliance, The Netherlands
Y. Kuang, imec, Belgium
M. Al Katrib, IPVF, France
M.I. Hossain, QEERI, Qatar
W.H. Chiu, Chang Gung University, Taiwan
C. Chen, Ming Chi University of Technology, Taiwan
C. Fell, CSIRO Energy Technology, Australia
G. Brammertz, imec, Belgium
T. Dalibor, Avancis, Germany
S. Ishizuka, AIST, Japan
A. Redinger, University of Luxembourg, Luxembourg
A. Romeo, University of Verona, Italy
V. Sittinger, Fraunhofer IST, Germany
M. Theelen, TNO/Solliance, The Netherlands
G. Timò, RSE, Italy
A. Kanevce, ZSW, Germany
A. Pérez-Rodríguez, IREC, Spain
R. Gutzler, ZSW, Germany
W. Witte, ZSW, Germany
T. Nishimura, Tokyo Institute of Technology, Japan
C. Qian, University of New South Wales, Australia
J.P. Connolly, CentraleSupelec, France
J.P. Kleider, CNRS/GeePs, France
I. Konovalov, University of Applied Sciences Jena, Germany
Y. Okada, University of Tokyo, Japan
M. Rusu, HZB, Germany
H. Meddeb, DLR, Germany
E. Saucedo, Universitat Politècnica de Catalunya (UPC), Spain
P. Vidal-Fuentes, FUNDACIÓ INSTITUT DE RECERCA EN ENERGIA DE CATALUNYA, Spain
C. Malerba, ENEA, Italy
C. Becker, HZB, Germany
D. Kuciauskas, NREL, United States of America
M. Ochoa, University of Cantabria, Spain
T. Tayagaki, AIST, Japan
S. Wasmer, WAVELABS Solar Metrology Systems, Germany
S. Zandi, UNSW, Australia
C. Messmer, University of Freiburg, Germany
J.B. Puel, Institut Photovoltaïque d'Ile de France (IPVF), France
S. Ternes, University of Rome II, Italy

Topic 3: Photovoltaic Modules and BoS Components
V. Bermúdez Benito, BERBETIN, France
R. Preu, Fraunhofer ISE, Germany
R. Gottschalg, Fraunhofer CSP, Germany
T. Barnes, NREL, United States of America
G. Friesen, SUPSI, Switzerland
G. Bardizza, TÜV Rheinland Solar, Italy

V. Barth, CEA, France
A. Faes, CSEM, Switzerland
A. Lennon, Sundrive Solar, Australia
M. Mittag, Fraunhofer ISE, Germany
M.A. Muñoz-García, UPM, Spain
H. Nagel, Fraunhofer ISE, Germany
S. Pietralunga, CNR, Italy
T. Timofte, ISC Konstanz, Germany

S. Feldbacher, PCCL, Austria
A. Halm, ISC Konstanz, Germany
H. Hanifi, AESOLAR, Germany
E. Warren, NREL, United States of America
S. Zhang, Trina Solar Energy, China
X. Zhen, Canadian Solar, China
G. Beaucarne, Dow Silicones Belgium, Belgium
T. Bejat, CEA, France
C. Camus, LayTec, Germany
U. Jahn, Fraunhofer CSP, Germany
G. Oreski, PCCL, Austria
M. Pander, Fraunhofer CSP, Germany
T. Sample, European Commission JRC, Italy
A. Morlier, imo-imomec, Belgium
C. Barretta, PCCL, Austria
P. Gebhardt, Fraunhofer ISE, Germany
C. Sen, UNSW, Australia
O. Arriaga Arruti, CSEM, Switzerland
X. Gu, NIST, United States of America
C. Xiao, Chinese Academy of Sciences, United States of America
R. Aninat, TNO/Solliance, The Netherlands
S. Mitterhofer, NIST, United States of America
B. Hoex, UNSW, Australia
E. Özkalay, SUPSI, Switzerland
M. Bokalič, University of Ljubljana, Slovenia
S. Bordihn, ISFH, Germany
M. Despeisse, CSEM, Switzerland
J. Govaerts, imec, Belgium
J. Lopez-Garcia, STS-Certified, Spain
M. Pravettoni, Technology Innovation Institute, United Arab Emirates
T. Stoyanova Lyubenova, Joint Research Centre, Italy
C. Ulbrich, HZB, Germany
J. Moereke, Avancis, Germany
Y.S. Long, ITRI, Taiwan
D. Pavanello, European Commission JRC, Italy
A.K. Vidal de Oliveira, UFSC, Brazil
J. Bengoechea, CENER, Spain
M. Ernst, ANU, Australia
H. Ellis, European Commission JRC, Italy
B. Mihaylov, European Commission JRC, Italy
G. Chowdhury, 3E, Belgium
B. Aissa, QEERI - Qatar Environment and Energy Research Institute, Qatar

Topic 4: PV Systems Engineering, Integrated/Applied PV
A. Gracia Amillo, CENER, Spain
W.G.J.H.M. van Sark, Utrecht University, The Netherlands
K. Lappalainen, Tampere University, Finland
J.M. Almeida Serra, University of Lisbon, Portugal
I. Tsanakas, CEA, France
C. Buerhop-Lutz, HI ERN, Germany
D. Moser, Becquerel Institute Italia, Italy
F. Frontini, SUPSI, Switzerland
G.C. Eder, OFI, Austria
A. Scognamiglio, ENEA, Italy
A. Chatzipanagi, European Commission JRC, Italy
I. Antón Hernández, UPM, Spain
R.M.E. Valckenborg, TNO, The Netherlands
T. Reindl, SERIS, Singapore
J.R. Gonzalez, European Space Agency, The Netherlands
G. Mütter, Gerhard Mütter e.U., Austria
T. Merdzhanova, Forschungszentrum Jülich, Germany

V. Lara-Fanego, Solargis, Spain
A. Louwen, Eurac Research, Italy
A. Martinez Fernandez, European Commission JRC, Italy
T. Oozeki, AIST, Japan

J. Remund, Meteotest, Switzerland
M. Sengupta, NREL, United States of America
M. Zehner, Rosenheim Technical University of Applied Sciences, Germany
B. Nouri, German Aerospace Center, Spain
S. Poddar, UNSW, Australia
D. Bachour, HBKU/ Qatar Foundation, Qatar
J. Yang, NREL, United States of America
S. Bouguerra, imo-imomec, Belgium
C. Alonso-Tristán, UBU, Spain
M. Carbone, ENEL Green Power, Italy
M. Dennenmoser, BayWa r.e. Solar Projects GmbH, Germany
C.W. Hansen, Sandia National Laboratories, United States of America
A. Neubert, DNV Maritime Software GmbH, Germany
D. Berrian, Belectric, Germany
M. Oliosi, PVsyst, Switzerland
J. Moschner, KU Leuven / EnergyVille, Belgium
C. Bucher, BUAS, Switzerland
B. Wittmer, PVsyst SA, Switzerland
M. Bolen, SB Energy, United States of America
D. Daßler, Fraunhofer CSP, Germany
R. Einhaus, ZSW, Germany
P. Hacke, NREL, United States of America
A. Heimsath, Fraunhofer ISE, Germany
J. Lin, PV Guider, Taiwan
A. Migan-Dubois, GeePs, France
M. Rinio, University of Karlstad, Sweden
J.S. Stein, Sandia National Laboratories, United States of America
D. Stellbogen, ZSW, Germany
M. Theristis, Sandia National Laboratories, United States of America
A. Virtuani, CSEM, Switzerland
A. Driesse, PV Performance Labs, Germany
M. Øgaard, IFE, Norway
A. Nobre, SERIS, Singapore
T. Trupke, UNSW, Australia
C. Cornaro, University of Rome II, Italy
G. A. dos Reis Benatto, DTU, Denmark
S. Malik, Fraunhofer CSP, Germany
S. Lindig, Univers SAS, France
M.M. Nygård, Institute for Energy Technology, Norway
P. Alonso Gomez, BayWa r.e., Germany
Y. Assoa, CEA, France
P. Bonomo, SUPSI, Switzerland
V. D'Ambrosio, University of Naples Federico II, Italy
E. Román Medina, Tecnalia, Spain
L.H. Slooff, TNO Energy Transition, The Netherlands
S. Villa, TNO, The Netherlands
M. La Rosa, Glass to Power, Italy
T. Del Caño, Onyx Solar Energy, Spain
X. Zhihao, AIST, Japan
P. Sharif, ODTU-GUNAM, Türkiye
K. Umeda, TAISEI CORPORATION, Japan
S. Boddaert, CSTB, France
N. Lysgaard Andersen, DTU, Denmark
K. Meyer, ISFH, Germany
T. Biel, NET Nowak Energy & Technology, Switzerland
F. Colucci, ENEA, Italy
A. Pascaris, NREL, United States of America
C. Dupraz, INRAE, France
C. Alonso-García, CIEMAT, Spain
A. Lefort, BayWa, Germany
H.N. Riise, IFE, Norway
M.A. Schüler, Next2Sun Technology GmbH, Germany
P.J. Pérez-Higueras, University of Jaén, Spain
K. Oda, Agritree,

M. Berwind, Fraunhofer ISE, Germany
M. Dörenkämper, TNO, The Netherlands
M. Heinrich, Fraunhofer ISE, Germany
B. Newman, Lightyear, The Netherlands
A. Reinders, Eindhoven University of Technology, The Netherlands
T. Tanahashi, AIST, Japan
J. Leloux, LuciSun, Belgium
E. Shirazi, University of Twente, The Netherlands
K. Araki, University of Miyazaki, Japan
K. Nishioka, University of Miyazaki, Japan
R. Campesato, CESI, Italy
V. Khorenko, Azur Space, Germany
G. Kakoulaki, European Commission Joint Research Centre, Italy
H. Toyota, JAXA, Japan
P. Garcia-Linares, UPM, Spain
I. Weiss, Weiss, Ingrid, Germany
A. Hensel, Fraunhofer ISE, Germany
J.S. da Fernandes, Hochschule Offenburg, Germany
Y. Ueda, Tokyo University of Science, Japan
J. Braid, Sandia National Laboratories, United States of America

Topic 5: PV in the Energy Transition
J. Stierstorfer, WIP Renewable Energies, Germany
R. Pestana, R&D Nester, Portugal
P.J. Alet, CSEM, Switzerland
C. Agraffeil, CEA, France
K. WAMBACH, Wambach-Consulting, Germany
C. del Cañizo, UPM, Spain
L. Großhans, WIP Renewable Energies, Germany
M. Getsiou, European Commission DG RTD, Belgium
S. Nowak, NET Nowak Energy & Technology, Switzerland
C. Breyer, LUT University, Finland
I. Kaizuka, RTS Corporation, Japan
G. Masson, Becquerel Institute, Belgium
P. Baliozian, VDMA, Germany
L. Großhans, WIP Renewable Energies, Germany
C. Candelise, Bocconi University, Italy
S. Caneva, WIP Renewable Energies, Germany

G. Barchi, Eurac Research, Italy
R. Bründlinger, AIT, Austria
V. Efthymiou, University of Cyprus, Cyprus
M. Centeno Brito, University of Lisbon, Portugal
F. Carigiet, ZHAW, Switzerland
B. Gaiddon, HESPUL, France
F.Z. Ouchani, Green Energy Park, Morocco
M. Rennhofer, AIT, Austria
G. Adinolfi, ENEA, Italy
W. Schaffer, Salzburg Netz, Austria
A. Haber, e-control, Austria
G. Heilscher, Technische Hochschule Ulm, Germany
A. Anctil, Michigan State University, United States of America
S. Arancón, Plug and Play, Spain
S. Capaccioli, ETA - Florence Renewable Energies, Italy
V. Fthenakis, Columbia University, United States of America
G. Heath, NREL, United States of America
K. Komoto, Mizuho Research & Technologies, Ltd., Japan
W. Palitzsch, LuxChemtech, Germany
S. Ovaitt, NREL, United States of America
M. de Wild-Scholten, SmartGreenScans, The Netherlands
S. Herceg, Fraunhofer ISE, Germany
C. Polacchi, Eurac Research, Italy
N. Espinosa, Universidad de Murcia, Spain
E. Drahi, TotalEnergies OneTech, France
S. Guastella, RSE, Italy

H. Ossenbrink, Band Gap, Germany
D. Polverini, European Commission DG GROW, Belgium
N. Taylor, European Commission JRC, Italy
K.A. Weiß, Fraunhofer ISE, Germany
I. Kafedjiska, Helmholtz Zentrum Berlin, Germany
P. Malbranche, Solar Action, France
S. De Iuliis, ENEA, Italy
T. Haarberg, BNW-Energy, Norway
A. Nayfeh, Khalifa University, United Arab Emirates
E. Vartiainen, Fortum Renewables Oy, Finland
E. Veronese, Eurac Research, Italy
P. Sanchez-Friera, Solkeys, Spain
N. Cherradi, Desert Technologies, Saudi Arabia
S. Nold, Fraunhofer ISE, Germany
H.J.J. Yu, CEA, France
M. Beck, U.S. Department of Energy, United States of America
M. Woodhouse, NREL, United States of America
A.B. Cristóbal, UPM, Spain
G. Ruggieri, Insubria University, Italy
S. Tay, NUS, Singapore

Awards Coordinators

Student Awards Coordinator
A.H.M. Smets, Delft University of Technology, The Netherlands

Student Awards Committee
R. Kenny, EU PVSEC Technical Programme Chair, Italy
C. del Canizo, Conference Chair, UPM, Spain
E. Voroshazi, CEA, France
J. Poortmans, imec, Belgium
P.J. Alet, CSEM, Switzerland
S. Caneva, WIP Renewable Energies, Germany
A. Romeo, University of Verona, Italy
G. Friesen, SUPSI, Switzerland
F. Schindler, Fraunhofer ISE, Germany
J.C. Goldchmidt, Marburg University, Germany
D. Moser, Becquerel Institute, Italy
K. Ding, FZJ, Germany
W.C. Sinke, TNO Energy Transition, The Netherlands
M. Topic, University of Ljubljana, Slovenia
R. Schlatman, HZB, Germany
S. Glunz, Fraunhofer ISE, Germany
A.M. Vega, UPM, Spain
I. Kaizuka, RTS, Japan
P.D. Veneri, ENEA, Italy
J. Bengoechea, CENER, Spain

Poster Awards Coordinator
P. Malbranche, Solar Action, France

Poster Awards Committee
R. Kenny, European Commission JRC, Italy
C. del Canizo, UPM, Spain
W. van Sark, Utrecht University, The Netherlands
I. Tsanakas, CEA INES, France
L. Miranda, Oxford PV, United Kingdom
D. Munoz, CEA INES, France
I. Gordon, imec, Belgium
E. Roman, Tecnalia, Spain
G. Eder, OFI, Austria
I. Antón, UPM, Spain
S. Veenstra, TNO, The Netherlands
J.M. Almeida Serra, University of Lisbon, Portugal
T. Magorian Friedlmeier, ZSW, Germany
J. Stierstorfer, WIP Renewable Energies, Germany

SUBJECT INDEX

Silicon Materials and Cells

Sessions 1CP.1, 1EP.3, 1AO.4, 1AO.5, 1AO.6, 1BO.1, 1BO.2, 1BO.3, 1BO.4, 1DO.9, 1BV.5, 1CV.2

Thin Films and New Concepts

Sessions 2CP.2, 2BO.1, 2CO.1, 2CO.2, 2DO.9, 2DO.6, 2DO.7, 2DO.8, 2AO.2, 2AO.3, 2AO.1, 2BO.8, 2BO.9, 2BO.10, 2BV.1, 2BV.2, 2CV.3

Photovoltaic Modules and BoS Components

Sessions 3CP.1, 3CP.3, 3CO.10, 3CO.11, 3DO.12, 3DO.16, 3DO.19, 3DO.20, 3BO.11, 3BO.12, 3BO.14, 3BO.15, 3AV.1, 3AV.2, 3AV.3

PV Systems Engineering, Integrated/Applied PV

Sessions 4AP.1, 4AO.7, 4AO.8, 4AO.9, 4DO.1, 4DO.3, 4BO.6, 4BO.7, 4CO.8, 4CO.9, 4DO.10, 4DO.17, 4BO.5, 4BO.16, 4BO.17, 4DO.2, 4DO.4, 4DO.5, 4CO.3, 4EO.2, 4BV.3, 4BV.4, 4CV.1, 4DV.1, 4DV.4,

PV in the Energy Transition

Sessions 5CP.1, 5CP.2, 5DO.14, 5DO.15, 5CO.4, 5CO.5, 5CO.6, 5DO.18, 5CO.4, 5CO.5, 5CO.6, 5DO.18, 5EO.3, 5EO.1, 5DV.2, 5DV.3,

---

Topic Code	Session Type	Day Codes
1 Silicon Materials and Cells	P = Plenary Session	A = Monday, 22 September 2025
2 Thin-Films and New Concepts	O = Oral Session	B = Tuesday, 23 September 2025
3 Photovoltaic Modules	V = Visual Session	C = Wednesday, 24 September 2025
4 Photovoltaic Systems		D = Thursday, 25 September 2025
5 Photovoltaics in the Energy Transition		E = Friday, 26 September 2025

e.g. 1AO.4 ⇒ 1= Silicon Materials and Cells, A=Monday, O=Oral session, 4=Session 4

FOREWORD

The European Photovoltaic Solar Energy Conference and Exhibition (EU PVSEC) stands as the World's leading and most renowned forum for PV research and development and the biggest conference on PV solar energy. In 2025, celebrating its 42nd edition, the EU PVSEC was the essential meeting and exchanging point for global PV experts from research, development, and industry.

Held from 22–26 September 2025 in Bilbao, Spain, the EU PVSEC 2025 was a resounding success, showcasing a wide range of cutting-edge research results. Bringing together both the Conference and the Exhibition, this edition attracted more than 1600 participants from 61 countries who contributed over 1000 presentations across various fields of science and technology. The event provided an essential platform for the exchange of knowledge and ideas on photovoltaic research, innovations, and applications. In the exhibition area 51 companies from all parts of the world welcomed visitors and presented their products and services.

Conference Highlights

The EU PVSEC covered a broad range of topics with an extensive programme that offers an opportunity for workers from across the entire field of photovoltaics to share their findings, as well as an opportunity for multidisciplinary learning. Rapid advances in materials, designs, and manufacturing processes reflect the accelerating expansion of the global PV market. The programme was arranged into 5 topics as follows:

- Silicon Materials and Cells;
- Thin Films and New Concepts;
- Photovoltaic Modules and Balance of System Components;
- PV Systems Engineering, Integrated/Applied PV;
- PV in the Energy Transition.

Communicating the key messages from the conference, not only to participants, but also to other researchers, key stakeholders, policy makers and the general public was an important added value. We thank the Highlights Committee, composed of selected members of the Scientific Committee, as well as the Session Chairs, for providing a comprehensive summary of the findings and state of the art research that were delivered during this year's event. Some key highlights are listed below, while further details may be found in the dedicated highlights presentation in the annex of these proceedings.

Cross-cutting themes:

- Demonstrated the versatility of solar technologies, spanning traditional and emerging application areas.
- Sustainability and circularity remain central, with research focused on reducing material use, such as replacing silver with copper, and advancing end-of-life management of modules.
- Ensuring long-term stability and predictable energy yield is equally essential, with many examples of studies on degradation mechanisms and efforts to elucidate their root-causes, such as in the case of UVID.

- The role of artificial intelligence across the PV value chain is rapidly expanding, from design to operations and maintenance, including among many others drone applications.

Latest Solar Innovations in Materials, Cells, Modules and PV Systems:

While silicon solar cells remain the cornerstone of PV technology, perovskite solar cells continue to stand out as the leading complementary technology to silicon, both as standalone devices and in tandem configurations. Research efforts are increasingly focused on enhancing stability, understanding degradation mechanisms, improving durability and scalability, and ensuring full industrial compatibility.

Many companies presented impressive results on industrial-size single-junction perovskite modules as well as perovskite-based tandem modules, and several new efficiency records were announced during the event. The rapid pace of innovation in cell and module architecture underscores the need for accelerated and more robust testing and qualification methodologies. Both the industry and the research community are moving swiftly to assess and improve reliability in this fast-evolving PV landscape.

A major focus in module research remains the optimisation of materials and packaging to ensure long lifetimes and predictable energy yields from high-efficiency cells. In parallel, many innovative advances in the operation and maintenance (O&M) of PV systems were presented and discussed.

Applications, Grid Integration and Storage

"PV can be deployed everywhere": from space applications to agrivoltaics, PV noise barriers, building-integrated photovoltaics (BIPV), floating PV systems, and even vehicles. Among these, agrivoltaics is gaining momentum as a promising dual land use approach, offering economic benefits for farmers while increasing resilience to climate change.

Flexibility solutions, particularly through battery storage, were recognised in many technical presentations as essential to accommodate higher PV penetration levels and to reduce energy curtailment. At the same time, strengthening grid infrastructure and enhancing grid management capabilities remain critical to enable the next phase of large-scale PV integration.

Photovoltaics in the Energy Transition

Options for re-establishing competitive module manufacturing in Europe were extensively analysed, including detailed policy recommendations for industrial support and market growth. Currently, a mismatch persists between global PV module installation rates and production rates, resulting in growing inventories and sharply reduced prices.

Finally, inclusiveness, diversity, citizen participation, awareness, education, and social engagement were underlined as vital dimensions of the sector's long-term sustainability and innovation capacity.

EU PVSEC 2025 Proceedings

Selection for inclusion in the conference was made by the Scientific Committee's paper review experts and topic organisers (see the listing on pages 010002-001-005), to whom we express our sincere gratitude for their comprehensive review work and overall contribution to the success of the conference.

The EU PVSEC 2025 Proceedings contain the full papers covering most of the highlights described above and more. The Proceedings provide a comprehensive overview of the PV solar sector, its current status and future prospects in science, research, innovation, development and deployment extending to 3,750 pages. In addition to the 299 submitted papers, the proceedings include 101 presentations (slides) shown during the plenary and oral presentations as well as 176 poster files of the visual presentations. In total this amounts to 576 publications.

The Conference Proceedings are published as downloadable files and are also fully accessible online. A DOI code (Digital Object Identifier) has been assigned to each paper. This ensures unequivocal and permanent identification and full citability. The EU PVSEC 2025 papers can be viewed and downloaded in a full free open access from the EU PVSEC's Proceedings website https://userarea.eupvsec.org/proceedings.

The proceedings of the EU PVSEC 2025 strengthen the commitment to providing quick and open access to high quality scientific results. This is a powerful source for targeted and quick information search and retrieval, enabling you to search by topic, keywords, paper title, DOI, author, or organization.

We are confident that these Proceedings will play an important role in providing a comprehensive overview of the current actors and activities in the global PV sector and that they will disseminate information on the state-of-the-art of technologies and applications. This can generate further research, add momentum to innovation and promote interest in PV worldwide.

We would like to cordially thank all authors and participants of the EU PVSEC 2025 for their contributions and look forward to welcoming you in Rotterdam, The Netherlands from 14 – 18 September 2026 at the EU PVSEC 2026, the 43rd European Photovoltaic Solar Energy Conference and Exhibition

The Editors

TABLE OF CONTENTS OF EU PVSEC 2025 PROCEEDINGS PAPERS

Oral SESSION 1AO.5 Si TOPCon Solar Cells and Related Processing Steps

Oral SESSION 1BO.2 Characterisation and Modelling of Si Solar Cells

Oral SESSION 1BO.3 Si Solar Cell Manufacturing Processes

[1] *Anhalt University of Applied Sciences, Köthen, Germany;* [2] *Fraunhofer CSP, Halle, Germany*

Oral SESSION 2AO.2 Advances in Chalcogenide Devices

2AO.2.3 A New Method for Sb-doped CdSeTe/CdTe Devices with Superior Stability 020057

Elisa Artegiani[1], Mariyam Mukhtar[1], Alessandro Romeo[1]
[1] *University of Verona, Verona, Italy*

Oral SESSION 2AO.3 III-V Based Devices | Tandem and Perovskite Solar Cells

2AO.3.3 Micro-Crystal GaAs Array Sub-Cells for Si Tandem Solar Cells 020058

James Patrick Connolly[1], Ahmed Nejim[2], Alexandre Jaffré[1], José Alvarez[1], Jean-Paul Kleider[1], Denis Mencaraglia[1], Laurie Dentz[3], Géraldine Hallais[3], Frederic Hamouda[3], Laetitia Vincent[3], Daniel Bouchier[3], Charles Renard[3]
[1] *CNRS, Gif-sur-Yvette, France;* [2] *SILVACO, St. Ives, United Kingdom;* [3] *CNRS, Palaiseau, France*

2AO.3.5 Multiscale Models for Perovskite Optimisation 020060

Philippe Baranek[1], James Patrick Connolly[2], Antoine Gissler[1], Philip Schulz[3], Michel Rerat[4], Roberto Dovesi[5]
[1] *EDF R&D, Palaiseau, France;* [2] *CNRS, Gif-sur-Yvette, France;* [3] *IPVF, Palaiseau, France;* [4] *IPREM, Pau, France;* [5] *Academy of Sciences of Turin, Torino, Italy*

2AO.3.6 Modelling Recovery in Perovskite Solar Cells under Light and Dark to Address Stability Challenges 020062

Guillem Álvarez-Pérez[1], Jean Baptiste Puel[1], Jean François Guillemoles [1]
[1] *IPVF, Palaiseau, France*

Oral SESSION 2BO.10 Advanced Modelling and Characterisation of Perovskite Solar Cells

2BO.10.2 On Perimeter Losses in Perovskite Top- and Poly-Si-Passivated Silicon 020063
Bottom Cells – Do Small Area Tandems Reveal the Full Efficiency Potential?

Felix Haase[1], Lukas Brockmann[1], Annika Raugewitz[1], Verena Steckenreiter[1], Verena Barnscheidt[1], Roland Clausing[1], Sara Baumann[1], Joachim Vollbrecht[1], Welmoed Veurman[1], Johannes Löhr[1], Dongyang Liu[1], Mircea Turcu[1], Lasse Nasebandt[1], Udo Römer[1], David Sylla[1], Jessica Strey[1], Martha Löhning[1], Larissa Mettner[1], Renate Winter[1], Anja Christ[1], Heike Kohlenberg[1], Cornelia Marquardt[1], Emanuel Brueckner[1], Hossein Rabiei[1], Michael Rienäcker[1], Sarah Kajari-Schröder[1], Tobias Wietler[1], Robby Peibst[1]
[1] *ISFH, Emmerthal, Germany*

2BO.10.5 In-depth Characterization and Simulation Approach for the Understanding of 020064
In- and Outdoor Degradation of Perovskite Solar Cells

Jonathan Parion[1], Amit Kumar Harit[1], Elias Peraticos[2], Vasiliki Paraskeva[2], Maria Hadjipanayi[2], Aranzazu Aguirre[1], Filip Duerinckx[1], Hariharsudan

Sivaramakrishnan Radhakrishnan[1], Jef Poortmans[1], Johan Lauwaert[3], Bart Vermang[1]
[1] Hasselt Unversity, Genk, Belgium; [2] University of Cyprus, Nicosia, Cyprus; [3] Ghent University, Ghent, Belgium

Oral SESSION 2BO.8 Advanced Conversion Devices

2BO.8.1 Singlet Fission Route for >30% Efficient Solar Cells: Silicon Cell Requirements   020065

Shona McNab[1], Alex J. Baldacchino[1], Pheobe Pearce[1], Alvin Mo[1], Alison Ciesla[1], Bram Hoex[1], Nicholas J. Ekins-Daukes[1], Murad J. Y. Tayebjee[1], Michael P. Nielsen[1]
[1] UNSW, Sydney, Australia

2BO.8.5 Performance of a 4-Terminals Spectral Splitting Asymmetric Solar Concentrator in Diffuse Sunlight: a Numerical Study   020066

Floriana Morabito[1], Daniela Fontani[2], Paola Sansoni[2], Mehdi Ahmadi[3], Salvatore Lombardo[3], Andrea Farina[1], Silvia Maria Pietralunga[1]
[1] CNR-IFN, Milan, Italy; [2] CNR-INO, Florence, Italy; [3] CNR-IMM, Catania, Italy

2BO.8.6 GaAs for Thermophotonics: From Thin-Film Solar Cells to Highly Efficient LEDs   020067

Natasha Gruginskie[1], Peter Mulder[1], Gerard Bauhuis[1], Jani Oksanen[2], John Schermer[1]
[1] Radboud University, Nijmegen, The Netherlands; [2] Aalto University, Espoo, Finland

Visual SESSION 2BV.1 New Materials, Devices and Conversion Concepts | New Modelling and Characterisation Techniques

2BV.1.4 Low-Energy Electron Multiplication on Nanostructured Solar Cells: a Novel Route to Overcome Si-PV Efficiency Limits   020068

Mikaël Hosatte[1], Brice Rouffie[1], Zbigniew T. Kuznicki[1], Frédéric Milesi[2], Bertrand Paviet-Salomon[3], Audrey Morisset[3], Philippe Wyss[3], Lejo Joseph Koduvelikulathu[4], Lazhar Rachdi[4], Lacramioara Popescu[4], Dominik Rudolph[4], Marek Basta[5], Andrzej Miszczuk[5], Martyna Majak[5], Beata Basta[5], Samuel Queste[6]
[1] SEGTON Advanced Technology, Versailles, France; [2] CEA, Grenoble, France; [3] CSEM, Neuchâtel, Switzerland; [4] ISC Konstanz, Konstanz, Germany; [5] Roltec, Poznań, Poland; [6] Marie and Louis Pasteur University, Besançon, France

2BV.1.5 Tailoring CBTSSe Solar Cells for Indoor Photovoltaic Applications   020069

Hitarth Narsi Patel[1], Bindu Pamula[1], Deepak Joshi[1], Vivek Garg[1]
[1] SVNIT, Surat, India

2BV.1.6 Theoretical Insights through DFT into $AgBiS_2$ Thin Films Absorber for Photovoltaic Applications   020071

Dhruv Singh Thakur[1], Rajesh Kumar Sharma[1], Nithin Chatterji[1], Vivek Garg[1], Shivendra Yadav[1]
[1] SVNIT, Surat, India

*Nathan Roosloot[1], Harsha Walpita[2], Christoph Seiffert[1], Jean Thomas[3],
Maarten Dörenkämper[4], Minne M. de Jong[4], Josefine H. Selj[1], Gaute Otnes[1]*
*[1] Institute for Energy Technology, Kjeller, Norway; [2] University of Oslo, Kjeller, Norway; [3]
Ciel et Terre, Lille, France; [4] TNO, Eindhoven, The Netherlands*

**Visual SESSION 3AV.3 PV Modules Characterisation and Performances
Assessment**

*Cristian Terrados¹, Eva de la Viuda¹, Kabir Paul Sulca¹, Julian Anaya¹,
Miguel Ángel González¹, Oscar Martínez¹*
¹ University of Valladolid, Valladolid, Spain

3BO.11.6 Luminescence Measurements of PV Modules with a Cost-Effective and   020206
Small-Sized Hood-Based Tool under Daylight Conditions

*Marc Köntges¹, Michael Siebert¹, Dieter Lorenz², Bernd Kuhrmann², Michael
Fuß²*
¹ ISFH, Emmerthal, Germany; ² MBJ Solutions, Ahrensburg, Germany

Oral SESSION 3BO.12 Characterisation and Energy Rating of PV Modules

3BO.12.1 Developing a New I-V Translation Methodology in Accordance with IEC   020208
60891:2021 Correction Procedure 1 and 2

*Wenhao Xu¹, Yating Zhang¹, Mengdi Liu¹, Christos Monokroussos¹, Werner
Herrmann², Giorgio Bardizza², Harald Müllejans³*
¹ TÜV Rheinland, Shanghai, China; ² TÜV Rheinland Solar, Cologne, Germany; ³ European
Commission JRC, Ispra, Italy

3BO.12.2 Characterization of Vehicle Integrated Photovoltaic Modules   020209

*Ricardo Moruno¹, Francisco José Martín¹, Juan Manuel Redondo¹, Javier
Malo¹, Luis Javier San José¹, Guido Vallerotto¹, Steve Askins¹, Rubén
Núñez¹, César Dominguez¹, Ignacio Antón¹, Rebeca Herrero¹*
¹ UPM, Madrid, Spain

3BO.12.4 Estimating the Energy Yield of Bifacial Photovoltaics with the JRC's   020210
Photovoltaic Geographic Information System

*Nigel Taylor¹, Teodora Lyubenova¹, Lavanya Malarkannan², Nikos
Alexandris¹, Alexandros Falangas³, Robert Kenny¹, Ewan D. Dunlop¹, Blago
Mihaylov¹*
¹ European Commission JRC, Ispra, Italy; ² National Physical Laboratory, Teddington,
United Kingdom; ³ TRASIS International, Brussels, Belgium

3BO.12.5 An Update on Energy Rating Amendments – Integration of Bifacial Modules   020211

*Stefan Riechelmann¹, Hendrik Sträter¹, Ana María Gracia Amillo², Sophie
Pelland³, Anton Driesse⁴*
¹ PTB, Braunschweig, Germany; ² CENER, Pamplona, Spain; ³ Natural Resources Canada,
Varennes, Canada; ⁴ PV Performance Labs, Freiburg, Germany

**Oral SESSION 3BO.14 Characterisation and Outdoor Monitoring of Perovskite-
based PV Modules**

3BO.14.1 Outdoor Measurements of Perovskite Modules   020213

Hanna Ellis¹, Harald Müllejans¹, Ewan D. Dunlop¹, Tony Sample¹
¹ European Commission JRC, Ispra, Italy

**Oral SESSION 3BO.15 Outdoor Performances and Degradation Analysis of PV
Modules**

3CO.11.5 Indoor Characterization and Analysis of Reverse Breakdown Behavior of   020223
Solar Cells with Different Cell Architectures

Bengt Jaeckel[1], Jens Froebel[1], Matthias Pander[1], Andreas Maixner[2], Hamed Hanifi[2]
[1] Fraunhofer CSP, Halle, Germany; [2] AESOLAR, Koenigsbrunn, Germany

Plenary SESSION 3CP.1 Si PV Manufacturing: Pushing the Limits of Performance

3CP.1.2   IBC4EU: European Back Contact Technology   020225

Florian Buchholz[1], Daniel Tune[1], Tobias Meßmer[1], Jonathan Linke[1], Manjunath Prasad[1], Valentin D. Mihailetchi[1], Juras Ulbikas[2], Arne Dahle[3], Martijn Meereboer[4], Francesca Fabris[5], Erik Eikelboom[5], Tom Borgers[6], Rik Van Dyck[6], Filip Duerinckx[7], Hariharsudan Sivaramakrishnan Radhakrishnan[7], Timea Bejat[8], Samuel Harrison[8], Ashish Binani[9], Nicolas Guillevin[9], Jan Kroon[9], Yevgeniya Larionova[10], Thorsten Dullweber[10], Ofer Shochet[11], Isaac Rosen [11], Ingo Röver [12], Wolfram Palitzsch[12], Yasmin Zaror[13], Johannes Stierstorfer[14], Aurimas Radzevicius[15], Julius Denafas[16], Tuomas Vanhanen [17], Tuukka Savisalo[17], Maximilian Pospischil [18], Marian Breitenbücher [18], Özlem Coşkun[19], Melodie de l'Epine [20], Philippe Macé[20], Ian Kenchington[20]

[1] ISC Konstanz, Konstanz, Germany; [2] Protechnology, Vilnius, Lithuania; [3] Norsun, Oslo, Norway; [4] Energyra, Westknollendam, The Netherlands; [5] Futurasun, Citadella, Italy; [6] IMEC, Genk, Belgium; [7] Hasselt Unversity, Genk, Belgium; [8] CEA, Le Bourget-du-Lac, France; [9] TNO, Petten, The Netherlands; [10] ISFH, Emmerthal, Germany; [11] Copprint, Jerusalem, Israel; [12] LuxChemTech, Freiberg, Germany; [13] WIP Renewable Energies, Munich, Germany; [14] WIP - Renewable Energies, Munich, Germany; [15] Valoe Cells, Vilnius, Lithuania; [16] Solitek, Vilnius, Lithuania; [17] Valoe, Mikkeli, Finland; [18] Highline Technologies, Freiburg, Germany; [19] Kalyon PV, Ankara, Türkiye; [20] Becquerel Institute, Brussels, Belgium

Plenary SESSION 3CP.3 Perovskite – Silicon Tandems: Towards Commercialisation | PV Stability in the Field

3CP.3.4   Outdoor Performance and Reliability of Perovskite (Pk)-Silicon (Si)   020226
Tandems: >1 year of Monitoring in the NEXUS Project

Atse Louwen[1], Jordi Veirman[1], Alexander Astigarraga[1], Juan José Stivanello[1], David Moser[2], Perrine Carroy[3], Vincent Barth[3], Delfina Muñoz[3], Markus Lenz[4], Anika Sidler[4], Jorge Ferrando[5], Maximiliano Alejandro Senno[5], Henk J. Bolink[5], Talat Özden[6], Hisham Nasser[6], Shuaifeng Hu[7], Xinyi Shen[7], Henry Snaith[7]

[1] Eurac Research, Bolzano, Italy; [2] Becquerel Institute Italy, Trento, Italy; [3] CEA / INES, Le Bourget-du-Lac, France; [4] School of Life Sciences FHNW, Muttenz, Switzerland; [5] University of Valencia, Paterna, Spain; [6] ODTÜ-GÜNAM, Ankara, Türkiye; [7] University of Oxford, Oxford, United Kingdom

Oral SESSION 3DO.12 Innovative Encapsulation Materials

Nikolina Pervan[1], Jutta Geier[1], Christian Veas[1], Gernot Oreski[1]
[1] PCCL, Leoben, Austria

Oral SESSION 4AO.7 Solar Resource Assessment

Oral SESSION 4AO.8 Solar Irradiance Forecasting

Oral SESSION 4AO.9 Irradiance for PV Design | Shading and Glare Mitigation

Adrián Blanco Aguiar[1], Brais González Rodríguez[2], María Martínez-Barbeito[1], Miguel Sánchez de León Peque[1]
[1] ieco.io, Vigo, Spain; [2] University of Vigo, Vigo, Spain

Plenary SESSION 4AP.1 PV Everywhere

Oral SESSION 4BO.16 Color in Photovoltaics

Oral SESSION 4BO.17 Performance of PV on/in Buildings

Oral SESSION 4BO.5 PV-Products for Buildings

4BV.4.27 Photovoltaic Integration in Football Stadiums: Global Trends, Regional   020309
Disparities, Future Potential

Johanna Buchmann[1], Niels Feuerherdt[1], Bert Stegemann[1]
[1] HTW, Berlin, Germany

Oral SESSION 4CO.8 Soiling and Snow Effects in PV Systems

4CO.8.4 A Tale of Two Dusts: Mimicking Site-Specific Soiling Dynamics and   020311
Cleaning Approaches for PV Plants

Josefa Montoya[1], Douglas Olivares[1], Eric Pilat[2], Jean Patrice Rakotoniaina[2], Aitor Marzo[3], Valeria Del Campo[4], Edward Fuentealba-Vidal[1], Martin Gaete[1], Jérémie Aimé[2], Romain Couderc[2], Delfina Muñoz[2], Ioannis (John) A. Tsanakas[2]
[1] University of Antofagasta, Antofagasta, Chile; [2] CEA / INES, Le Bourget-du-Lac, France; [3] University of Granada, Granada, Spain; [4] Federico Santa María Technical University, Valparaiso, Chile

Oral SESSION 4CO.9 Data-driven and AI-based O&M of PV Systems

4CO.9.1 AI Methods for the Operation and Maintenance of PV Parks with Bifacial   020312
Photovoltaic Modules

Dirk Stellbogen[1], Jonas Petzschmann[1], Timo Freund[2], Jann Wannenwetsch[2], Elena Pabst[1], Ajka Ockert[2], Roland Einhaus[1]
[1] ZSW, Stuttgart, Germany; [2] EnBW, Karlsruhe, Germany

4CO.9.2 A Comprehensive Framework for Accurate Power Degradation Estimation in   020313
Large Photovoltaic Systems Using Machine Learning

Kak Pong Cheung[1], Stephanie Malik[2], David Daßler[2], Carsten Hennig[3], Hauke Nissen[4], Patrick Hennig[1]
[1] Kiel University of Applied Sciences, Kiel, Germany; [2] Fraunhofer CSP, Halle, Germany; [3] saferay holding, Berlin, Germany; [4] Wattmanufactur, Galmsbüll, Germany

4CO.9.3 Use of a Digital Twin to Detect Stalling Tracker Events in Photovoltaic   020314
Power Plant with Horizontal Single-Axis Tracking Systems

Riccardo Adinolfi Borea[1], Matthew Muller[2], Silvana Ovaitt[2], Vincenzo Cirimele[1], Francesco Melino[1]
[1] University of Bologna, Bologna, Italy; [2] NREL, Golden, United States of America

4CO.9.4 Autonomous Multi-AI Agent System for PV Health Monitoring: A Fully   020316
Automated O&M Pipeline with Field Robotics Integration

Mousa Sondoqah[1], David Moser[1], Atse Louwen[2]
[1] Becquerel Institute Italy, Trento, Italy; [2] RISE, Boras, Sweden

4CO.9.5 Predictive Modelling and Analysis of Soiling Losses in PV Plants through a   020317
Hybrid Data-Driven Approach

Ioannis (John) Tsanakas[1], Eric Pilat[1], Sebastien Arbaretaz[1], Minh Thong Doi[1], Filipa Monteiro Martins[2], Jorge Veludo[2], Christophe Ménézo[3]
[1] CEA / INES, Le Bourget-du-Lac, France; [2] Galp Energia, Lisbon, Portugal; [3] LOCIE, Le Bourget-du-Lac, France

Anastasios Kladas[1], Bert Herteleer[1], Jan Cappelle[1]
[1] *KU Leuven, Ghent, Belgium*

Oral SESSION 4DO.1 PV Tracking and Simulation

*Marcus Rennhofer[1], Philipp Mayer-Ullmann[1], Diana Maria Krainer[1],
Gusztav Ujvari[1], Janine Lichtenberger[1], Konrad Kainz[1], Vassilissa Neussl[1],
Bernhard Kubicek[1]*
[1] AIT, Vienna, Austria

Visual SESSION 4DV.4 PV System Engineering

[1] Luxembourg Institute of Science and Technology, Esch-sur-Alzette, Luxembourg; [2] University of Lisbon, Lisbon, Portugal

Oral SESSION 5CO.4 Life Cycle Assessment of Silicon and Perovskite-based Cells and Modules

Oral SESSION 5CO.5 Life Cycle Assessment of New PV Applications and Recycling

OPTIMIZATION OF SOXHLET EXTRACTION PARAMETERS FOR GEL CONTENT DETERMINATION OF CO-EXTRUDED EPE

A. Trefzer[1], A.K. Öz[1], J. Forster[1], C. Wellens[1], M. Çalışkan[2], C. Düz[2]
[1]Fraunhofer Institute for Solar Energy Systems ISE, Heidenhofstraße 2, 79110 Freiburg, Germany
[2]Kalyon PV Solar Technologies Factory, Başkent Osb, Şaditürk Blv., 06909 Malıköy, Sincan, Ankara / Türkiye
Corresponding Author: Aksel Kaan Öz | +49 (0) 761 4588-2556 | e-mail: aksel.kaan.oez@ise.fraunhofer.de

ABSTRACT: With the transition to TOPCon technology raising several challenges regarding reliability and long-term stability of PV modules, tailored encapsulant solutions like EPE (EVA+POE+EVA) are more commonly used in PV module production due to their advantageous properties. The optimization and adaptation of precise quality control is hereby most important. While the measurement of Gel Content (GC) with DMA, DSC and FTIR are relative methods, Soxhlet offers a more accurate and reliable quantitative alternative. This study focuses on optimizing Soxhlet extraction parameters for GC measurements of co-extruded EPE encapsulants. The influence of various extraction cycle times as well as number of cycles and resting time in cooling solvent on GC values is investigated. Furthermore a sweep of extraction time from 8-24 h is performed for two different EPE and POE encapsulants to identify the point at which the change in GC saturates. At this point any further increase in extraction time will not lead to significant changes in GC values. With EPE this point of saturation was found at 22-24 h while POE exhibits this saturation behavior at 20-26 h minimum extraction time highly depending on the specific material.

Keywords: Soxhlet extraction, degree of cross-linking, gel content, co-extruded EPE, quality control

1 INTRODUCTION

With the progressive transition from PERC (Passivated Emitter and Rear Cell) to TOPCon (Tunnel Oxide Passivated Contact) several challenges regarding reliability, long-term stability and failure modes of TOPCon came to light [1]. TOPCon is much more susceptible to high humidity, contamination and PID (potential-induced degradation) than PERC as *C. Sen et al.* have shown [1]. According to forecasts from the International Technology Roadmap for Photovoltaic (ITRPV 2025), the market share of TOPCon technology is expected to rise to up to almost 70 % by 2029, thereby replacing PERC as the dominant cell technology [2]. The development of tailored encapsulants and corresponding BOMs is therefore most important [1].

S.K. Chunduri and *M. Schmela* also reached a similar conclusion in the TaiyangNews Market Survey 2022-2023 suggesting the usage of co-extruded EPE consisting of a multilayer system of EVA+POE+EVA [3]. This material combines the advantageous mechanical properties of EVA (ethylene-vinyl acetate) with the low water vapor permeability of POE (polyolefin elastomer) and is priced between these two [4–6].

Due to this combination of properties, the market share of co-extruded EPE encapsulants is expected to rise to up to about 45 % by 2035 according to forecasts from the ITRPV 2025, thus replacing EVA as the dominant encapsulant material [2]. Therefore EPE will be the alternative encapsulant for bifacial products in GG (glass-glass) combinations [2].

For quality control of laminated PV modules DMA (Dynamic Mechanical Analysis), DSC (Differential Scanning Calorimetry) and FTIR (Fourier Transform Infrared Spectroscopy) are commonly used methods for determining GC (Gel Content) of cross-linked encapsulant material [7]. In comparison to these methods, Soxhlet extraction is based on washing out non-cross-linked monomers using a suitable solvent [8]. On the one hand this process is significantly more time-consuming, on the other hand it is a quantitative method and more precise and reliable [8]. In case of EVA a Soxhlet extraction time of up to 16 hours can be expected while POE needs up to 24 hours highly depending on the specific material [8]. Since there is no recommendation for determining the GC of co-extruded encapsulants, the optimization of Soxhlet extraction parameters for GC determination is essential to reliably assess the quality of laminated PV modules using these encapsulant solutions.

The goal of this study is to find suitable process parameters for determining the GC using Soxhlet extraction for co-extruded EPE. For this, the total extraction time as well as cycle time and number of extraction cycles are varied in case of POE and EPE with a high degree of cross-linking. The extraction time is varied from 8-24 h in 1 h increments. The recommended extraction time is determined at which the change in the measured GC saturates. At this point a complete extraction is ensured and any further increase in extraction time no longer has a significant effect on the measured GC.

2 MATERIALS AND METHODS

To compare the GC behavior of POE and EPE using Soxhlet extraction, the materials *POE-A* and *EPE-A* of a Turkish solar encapsulant film manufacturer were used, as well as *POE-B* and *EPE-C* from two different Chinese solar encapsulant film manufacturers. For producing samples for the Soxhlet extraction with a high degree of cross-linking, the POE and EPE materials were laminated according to their longest recommended datasheet processes using a *Ypsator* PV-module laminator from *Robert Bürkle GmbH*. The used materials are listed in Table 1 along with their respective thicknesses.

To be able to extract the double layer of cross-linked encapsulant from the mini – GBS (glass-backsheet) laminates (280x250 mm) for Soxhlet measurements, Teflon sheets are added in between the different layers as seen in Figure 1.

Table 1: List of used materials and their specifications.

Layer	Material	Thickness [mm]
POE-A	POE	0.740
POE-B	POE	0.500
EPE-A	EPE	0.650
EPE-C	EPE	0.550
Glass	Solar glass	3.000
Backsheet	PET/Primer	0.218
Teflon sheet	Polytetrafluoroethylene (PTFE)	0.080

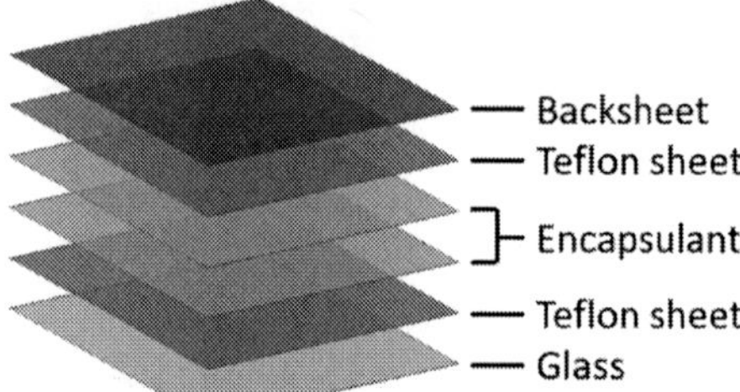

Figure 1: Module lay-up without cells for Soxhlet sample preparation.

In addition to the gel content determination by Soxhlet extraction, the performance of mini-modules with *EPE-A* and *POE-A* encapsulants was evaluated after reliability tests. *Damp Heat* (DH), *Thermal Cycling* (TC) and *Ultraviolet* (UV) aging tests were conducted in accordance with *IEC 61215-2* using the parameters stated in Table 2.

Table 2: Reliability test parameters for mini-modules with *EPE-A* and *POE-A*.

Test	Parameters
***Damp Heat* (DH)**	1000 h at 85 °C / 85 % RH
***Thermal Cycling* (TC)**	200 cycles from -40 °C to 85 °C
DH200 + UV60	200 h DH + 60 kWh/m² UV

2.1 Soxhlet Extraction

For Gel Content determination via Soxhlet extraction a *Behrotest* Soxhlet extraction unit was used in accordance with *IEC 62788-1-6*. Each sample was measured 3 separate times. Each datapoint of the results represents the mean value of these separate measurements. Unless stated otherwise a cycle time of 3.5 min is used resulting in about 17 extraction cycles per hour implemented by an integrated siphon-system to continuously cycle fresh solvent. The Gel Content was calculated by the following formular [9,10]:

$$GC\ [\%] = \left(\frac{M_2 - M_0}{M_1 - M_0}\right) * 100,\ M_2 \leq M_1 \quad [9,10]$$

Each sample was weighed in to 1±0.05 g and placed in a cylindrical stainless steel mesh tube. M_0 represents the pre-determined weight of the tube with M_1 representing the total weight of the sample including the tube before the extraction process. M_1 represents the total weight of sample and tube after extraction and subsequent drying in a vacuum oven at 100 °C for 7 h.

3 RESULTS AND DISCUSSION

3.1 Influence of Soxhlet cycle time and number of cycles

The influence of Soxhlet cycle time on the measured GC was tested by varying the cycle time from 2-5 min (30-12 cycles/hour) with intervals of 1.5 min. The results are shown in Table 3 for EPE-C after a constant extraction time of 6 h therefore effectively varying the total amount of extraction cycles.

Decreasing the cycle time from 5 to 2 min leads to a change of only -0.43 % in measured GC. The influence of varying the Soxhlet cycle time on the measured GC with a constant extraction time is therefore not significant.

Table 3: GC values of EPE-C after 6 h extraction with different cycle times.

Cycle time [min]	No. of extraction cycles [ ]	Gel Content [%]
2	180	91.57
3.5	~100	91.67
5	72	92.00

To further test the influence on the measured GC a Soxhlet extraction was carried out with a constant number of 100 cycles while varying the cycle time from 2-5 min with intervals of 1.5 min therefore varying the total extraction time from 200-500 min as shown in Table 4.

Decreasing the number of cycles from 500 to 350 and to 200 leads to significant changes of +1,23 % and +2,68 % in measured GC respectively. Since the number of cycles was held constant, this change in GC can be explained by the total extraction time. A longer extraction time necessarily leads to more non-cross-linked monomers and/or low molecular weight polymer chains being washed out therefore resulting in a decrease in measured GC.

Table 4: GC values of EPE-C after 100 extraction cycles with different cycle times.

Cycle time [min]	Total extraction time [min]	Gel Content [%]
2	200	94.42
3.5	350	92.97
5	500	91.74

3.2 Influence of resting time in cooling Soxhlet solvent

To investigate the influence of additional resting time in the cooling solvent after a finished Soxhlet extraction a 6 h extraction of *EPE-C* was performed. After the finished extraction the samples were taken out of the Soxhlet apparatus and dried in a vacuum oven after different resting times. The first sample was taken out after 0.75 h (45 min) while the second sample rested in the solvent for 3 h (180 min). The third sample was taken out on the following day after a total amount of 18 h (1080 min) of resting time in the solvent. In Table 5 the measured GC values are shown. Due to the heating plates of the *Behrotest* Soxhlet apparatus needing to cool down, the usual amount of resting time is about 20-30 min before being able to take out samples.

After 45 min a GC of 91.78 % was measured. After a resting time of +3 h a decrease of 1.39 % could be measured compared to the initial GC value of 91.78 %.

When comparing the measured GC values after +3 h and +18 h of resting time this initial decrease of GC is no longer visible. In this case no significant change on GC can be measured.

This behavior can be explained by the remaining temperature of the solvent. Until it cools down non-cross-linked monomers and/or low molecular weight polymer chains are still being extracted from the sample since the diffusion coefficient is still high enough for effectively washing out compounds. With a decrease in temperature this diffusion process slows down heavily resulting in no more significant changes in GC after +18 h resting time at room temperature.

Table 5: GC values of EPE-C after additional resting time in cooling solvent after a finished 6 h extraction.

Resting time [h]	Gel Content [%]
+ 0.75	91.78
+ 3	90.39
+ 18	90.47

Lust et. al. encountered a similar effect in their study [11]. In their case a 5 h extraction was conducted with additional heating/cooling steps with 15 h of overnight resting time resulting in a significant decrease of 8.1 % compared to a 5 h extraction without resting time [11]. This highlights the importance of a set amount of time until taking out the samples. Otherwise, the results can become highly distorted and will no longer be reproducible.

3.3 Variation of Soxhlet extraction time

To determine suitable process parameters for GC measurement of co-extruded EPE using Soxhlet the extraction time was varied from 8-24 h in 1 h increments. To ensure a complete extraction another set of samples was measured after 32 h extraction. An EVA encapsulation film of a Chinese solar encapsulant film manufacturer is used as reference and is therefore listed as *EVA ref* in the following diagrams. The results of this extraction time sweep from 8-24 h can be seen in Figure 2 for both *EPE-A* and *EPE-C*. The material *EPE-A* was laminated at 155°C for 20 min while *EPE-C* was laminated at 150°C for 18 min. These lamination parameters represent the longest recommended datasheet processes.

Both EPE encapsulants exhibit considerably higher GC values than the *EVA ref* material. At the lowest extraction time of 8 h *EPE-A* and *EPE-C* reach GC values of 93.8 % and 92.51 % respectively while *EVA ref* reaches 86.51 %. At the highest extraction time of 24 h 90.57 % and 86.03 % are reached. Over the period of the 8-24 h extraction time sweep *EPE-A* therefore shows a decrease of 3.23 % while *EPE-C* shows a decrease of 6.48 % which is twice as high. After 32 h extraction time a decrease of 0.15 % in case of *EPE-A* and 0.3 % in case of *EPE-C* can be seen in comparison with the GC values after 24 h. Since 8 h more extraction time leads to an insignificant decrease in GC for both EPE encapsulants a complete extraction can be assured.

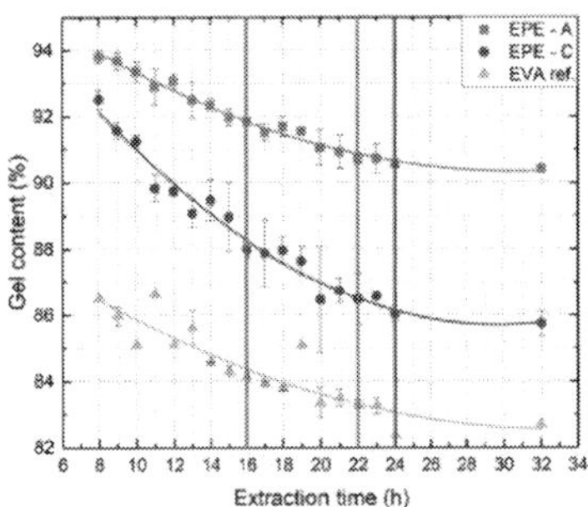

Figure 2: Measured gel content of EPE encapsulants as function of extraction time (3 samples per data point) with fitted curves and calculated minimum extraction time (green & blue line) in comparison with recommended extraction time for POE [12] (red line).

The changes in GC values of both EPE encapsulants are shown in Figure 3. The measured data exhibits volatile jumps in GC values above and below the 0 %-line due to unavoidable measurement inaccuracies. This is exceptionally true for *EPE-C* which shows several jumps above the line at high extraction times as seen in Figure 3. To be able to graphically determine the extraction time where the GC saturates, the curves of both EPE encapsulants were individually fitted as shown in Figure 4 in case of EPE-A.

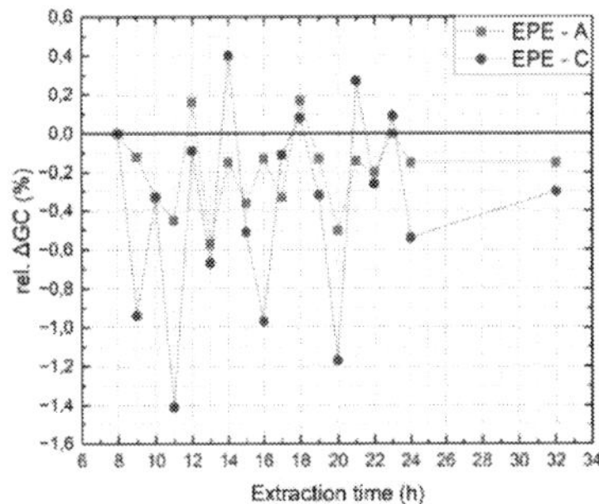

Figure 3: Relative change in measured gel content of co-extruded EPE encapsulants as function of extraction time (3 samples per data point).

The data of these individually fitted curves was then used to calculate the change in GC values of both EPE encapsulants as seen in Figure 5. To determine the gel content at the saturation point the change of GC was analyzed at the intersection with the 0 %-line.

In case of *EPE-A* this saturation is reached at 31 h of calculated extraction time with a GC value of 90.34±0.52 % which is well above the recommended extraction time for POE of 16 h [12]. Taking the calculated standard deviation of 0.52 % into account the minimum extraction time to reach the measured GC value of 90.34 % is 22 h.

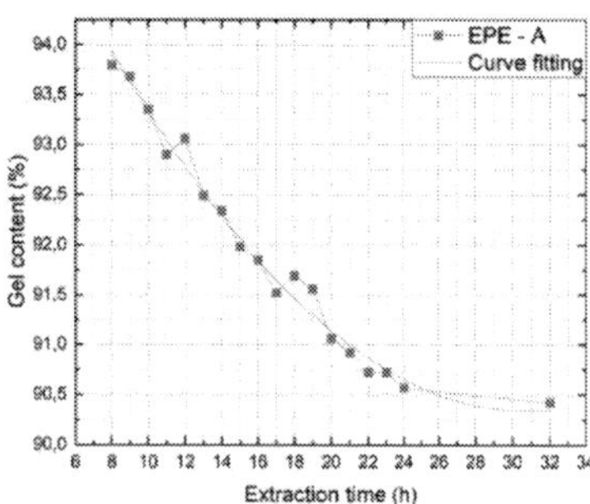

Figure 4: Measured gel content of co-extruded *EPE-A* as function of extraction time (3 samples per data point) with fitted curve.

In case of *EPE-C* the point of saturation is reached at 30 h of calculated extraction time with a GC value of 85.70±0.52 % as seen in Figure 5. With the standard deviation of 0.52 % the GC value of 85.70 % can already be reached at 24 h of Soxhlet extraction. This coincides with the recommended 24 h for certain POE encapsulant materials [8]. It should be noted that this might not be the case for badly cross-linked material. Since the recommended extraction time for EVA encapsulants with a low degree of cross-linking is 12 h compared to samples with high degree of cross-linking with 8 h, the GC values of badly cross-linked EPE encapsulants are expected to saturate at higher extraction times than shown here [13].

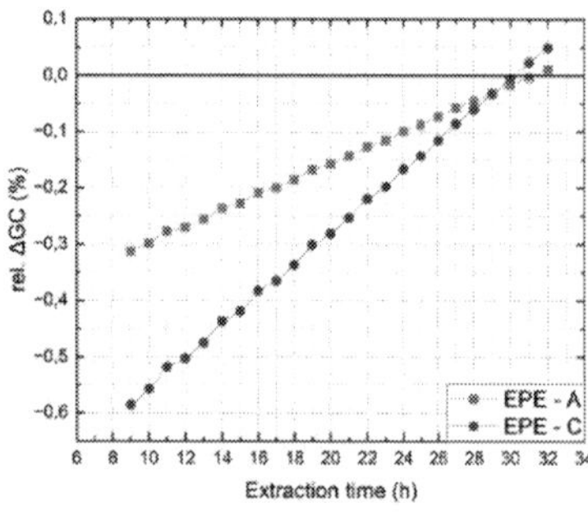

Figure 5: Calculated relative change in gel content of co-extruded EPE encapsulants as function of extraction time (3 samples per data point) using individually fitted curve data.

To further determine suitable process parameters for GC measurement of *POE-A* and *POE-B* using Soxhlet extraction the extraction time was varied similarly to both EPE encapsulants. The results of this extraction time sweep from 8-24 h can be seen in Figure 6 for both *POE-A* and *POE-B*. Both POE materials were laminated at 155°C for 20 min. These lamination parameters represent the longest recommended datasheet process.

POE-A exhibits high GC values starting at 87.35 % after 8 h extraction and decreasing to 82.48 % after 24 h with a total decrease of 4.87 % showing a similar behavior in GC changes compared to *EVA ref.* After 8 h extraction *POE-B* exhibits a measured GC value of 80.35 %

decreasing to 73.16 % after 24 h with a total decrease in GC of 7.19 %. After 32 h extraction a change in GC of 0.1 % in case of *POE-A* and 0.02 % in case of *POE-B* can be measured in comparison to 24 h extraction. Since 8 h more extraction time leads to an insignificant change in GC for both POE encapsulants a complete extraction can be assured similar to the extraction time sweep for both EPE encapsulants.

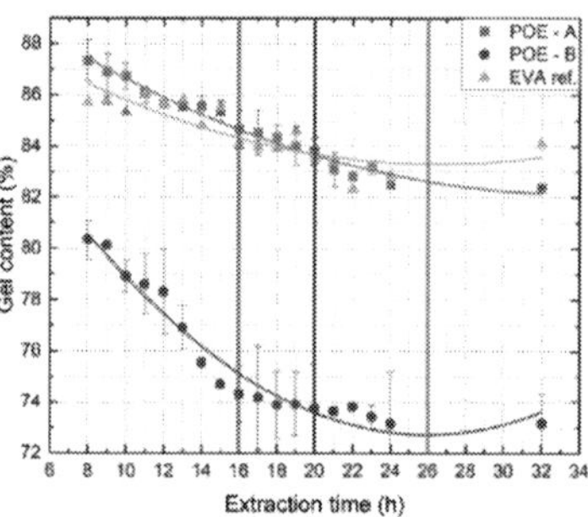

Figure 6: Measured gel content of POE encapsulants as function of extraction time (3 samples per data point) with fitted curves and calculated minimum extraction time (green & blue line) in comparison with recommended extraction time for POE [12] (red line).

The changes in GC values of both POE encapsulants are shown in Figure 7. Similar to the measured data of both EPE encapsulants in Figure 3 volatile jumps in GC values can be seen in case of both POE encapsulants. For graphical determination of the saturation point both POE encapsulants are individually fitted as shown in Figure 8 in case of *POE-B*.

The data of these individually fitted curves was then used to calculate the change in GC values of both POE encapsulants as seen in Figure 9. When analyzing for intersection with the 0 %-line *POE-A* exhibited saturation at 32 h of calculated extraction time with a GC value of 82.16±0.52 %, leading to a minimum extraction time of 26 h when considering standard deviation.

As seen in Figure 9 *POE-B* shows saturation at 26 h of calculated extraction time with a GC value of 73.17±0.52 % which corresponds to a minimum extraction time of 20 h. It should be noted that the influence of specific material on the minimum extraction time is more noticeable in case of POE with a difference of 6 h between *POE-A* and *POE-B* compared to a difference of 2 h with *EPE-A* and *EPE-C* as shown in Figure 2 and Figure 6 with vertical lines. This dependance on the specific POE encapsulation material was already mentioned by *Öz et al* [12].

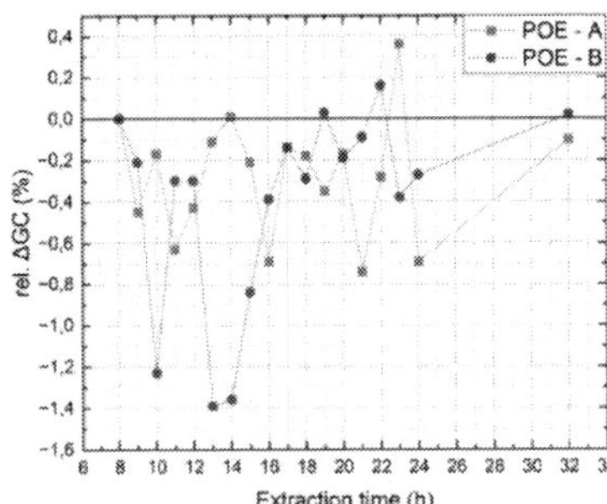

Figure 7: Relative change in measured gel content of POE encapsulants as function of extraction time (3 samples per data point).

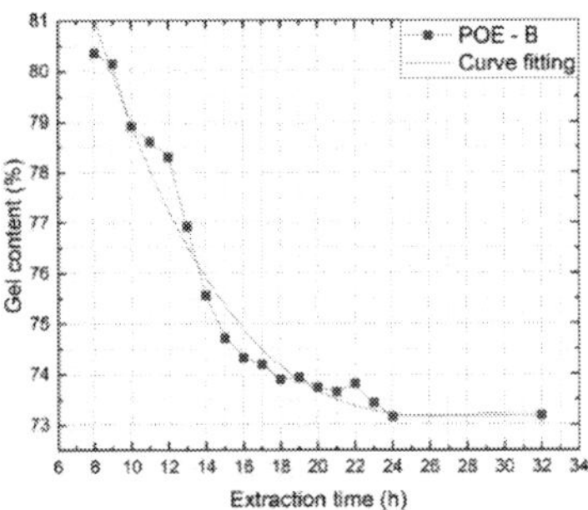

Figure 8: Measured gel content of *POE-B* as function of extraction time (3 samples per data point) with fitted curve.

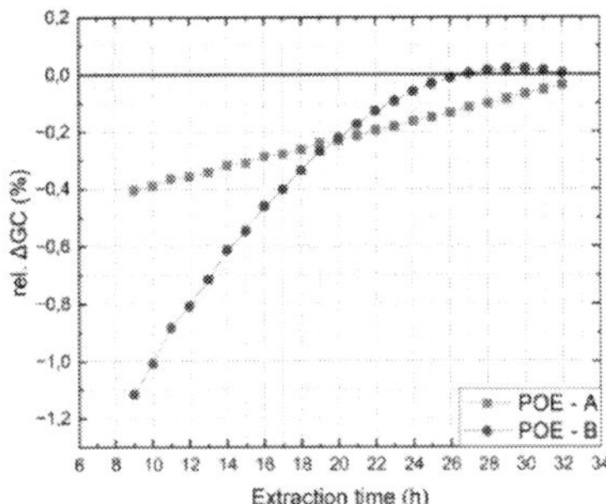

Figure 9: Calculated relative change in gel content of POE encapsulants as function of extraction time (3 samples per data point) using individually fitted curve data.

3.4 Mini-module reliability (*EPE-A & POE-A*)

In Figure 10 the power losses of mini-modules comprised of *EPE-A* and *POE-A* after different reliability tests are shown. DH1000 and TC200 tests resulted in average below -1.15 % power loss at MPP (*Maximum Power Point*) with the highest loss of -1.73 % in case of

DH1000_2. After UV exposure the modules initially show power losses of up to -10 % in case of *UV60_1*. After stabilization (*stab_1*/stab_2, see Figure 10) by light soaking the modules show an average of -3 % in P_{mpp}. This so called *dark storage effect* is known for TOPCon modules and can be recovered by a light soaking process just prior to the power measurement as reported by *Gebhardt et al.* [14].

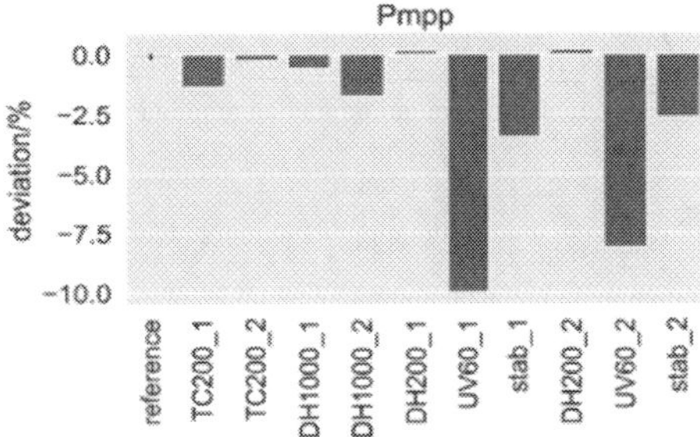

Figure 10: Power loss (ΔPmpp) of mini-modules (A-series encapsulants) after reliability tests.

In Figure 11 the captured EL images before and after DH1000 are shown. No significant visible damage can be observed which is consistent with the low power loss of -1.15 % in average.

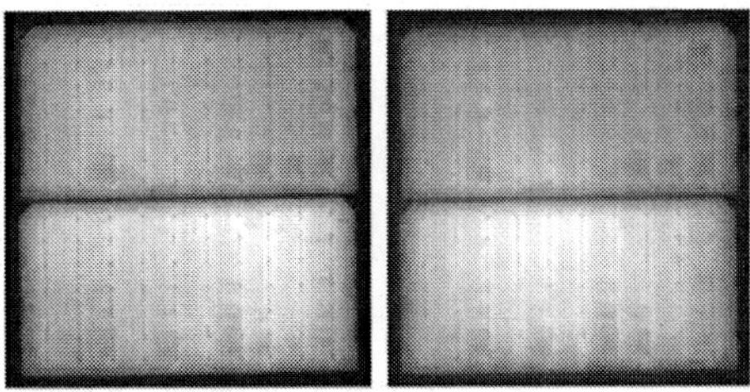

Figure 11: EL images of mini-module (A-series encapsulants) before and after DH1000.

4 CONCLUSION AND OUTLOOK

This study recommends suitable process parameters for Gel Content determination using Soxhlet extraction for co-extruded EPE. By systematically varying process parameters like extraction cycle time, number of extraction cycles and total extraction time a recommendation can be given for complete extraction of EPE and POE encapsulant films with a high degree of cross-linking. The point of complete extraction is determined as the extraction time at which the change in measured GC saturates. At this point an increase in extraction time will no longer have significant effects on the measured GC of the cross-linked encapsulant.

By variation of cycle time from 2-5 min in 1.5 min intervals the measured GC of *EPE-C* was analyzed regarding changes in GC values. Since decreasing the cycle time from 5 min to 2 min resulted in only - 0.43 % change in measured GC it can be concluded that the variation of cycle time in the tested range has no significant influence on the measured GC. Further testing showed that an increased number of extraction cycles and therefore a higher total amount of extraction time led to lower GC values. Due to this increase in extraction time more non-cross-linked compounds are being washed out resulting in a decrease in measured GC.

For testing the influence of resting time in the cooling solvent samples of *EPE-C* were taken out of the Soxhlet apparatus after different amounts of resting time after a finished extraction. Between the samples taken out after + 45 min and + 3 h of resting time a decrease of 1.39 % in GC was measured. Comparing the samples taken out after + 3 h and + 18 h of resting time no more significant changes in GC could be measured. This is explained by the remaining high temperature of the solvent and therefore higher diffusion coefficient allowing non-cross-linked compounds to diffuse out until the solvent cools down. After cooling down the diffusion process slows down heavily resulting in no more significant changes in measured GC. Due to this effect the resting time in the cooling solvent is highly important to accurately measure GC values. When being inconsistent with this parameter the results can become highly distorted and will no longer be reproducible.

To determine the minimum extraction time for EPE and POE with a high degree of cross-linking a sweep from 8-24 h extraction time was performed to analyze the change in GC for the point of saturation where a further increase in extraction time no longer significantly affects the measured GC. For *EPE-A* this point of saturation was found at 31 h (GC of 90.34±0.52 %) while *EPE-C* saturates at 30 h (GC of 85.70±0.52 %). Taking the standard deviation of 0.52 % into account yields a minimum extraction time of 22 h and 24 h for *EPE-A* and *EPE-C* respectively. The necessary extraction time needed for EPE samples with a low degree of cross-linking are expected to saturate at higher extraction times due to a higher percentage of non-cross-linked compounds needed to be washed out. Analyzing the POE samples, it was found that *POE-A* reaches saturation at 32 h (GC of 82.16±0.52 %) with a minimum extraction time of 26 h. *POE-B* exhibits saturation at 26 h (GC of 73.17±0.52 %) with a minimum extraction time of 20 h.

The tested mini-modules with *EPE-A* and *POE-A* encapsulants exhibited high stability with power losses of -1.15 % in average after DH1000 and TC200 tests and no visible damage in EL images. Initial UV-induced losses recovered after light soaking, stabilizing at around -3 % in average.

In further experiments the GC measurements for both POEs and EPEs conducted in this study will be analyzed in case of low degree of cross-linking. Since the recommended extraction time for EVA encapsulants differs from 8-12 h depending on the degree of cross-linking according to *IEC 62788-1-6* the GC values of EPE encapsulants with a low degree of cross-linking are expected to exhibit a similar behavior due to the multilayer EPE encapsulant being comprised partly of EVA encapsulant films [13]. With this a better understanding of the correlation between GC and necessary extraction time can be achieved.

5   ACKNOWLEDGEMENTS

We would like to thank *Kalyon PV* for their collaboration and support in this study.

6   REFERENCES

[1]   C. Sen, H. Wang, M. U. Khan et al., "Buyer aware: Three new failure modes in TOPCon modules absent from PERC technology," *Solar Energy Materials and Solar Cells*, vol. 272, p. 112877, 2024.

[2]   M. Fischer, M. Woodhouse, P. Baliozian et al., "International Technology Roadmap for Photovoltaics (ITRPV): 2024 Results," 16. Edition, May 2025.

[3]   S. K. Chunduri and M. Schmela, "Market Survey on Backsheets and Encapsulation 2022-2023," 2023.

[4]   G. Cattaneo, A. Faes, H.-Y. Li et al., "Lamination process and encapsulation materials for glass–glass PV module design," *Photovoltaics International*, 2015.

[5]   N. T. Dintcheva, E. Morici, and C. Colletti, "Encapsulant Materials and Their Adoption in Photovoltaic Modules: A Brief Review," *Sustainability*, vol. 15, no. 12, p. 9453, 2023.

[6]   S. K. Chunduri and M. Schmela, "Market Survey on Backsheets and Encapsulation 2024-2025," 2025.

[7]   M. L. Pliquet, T. Béjat, M. Sérasset et al., "Standardized cross-linking determination methods applied to POE encapsulants in lamination recipe development," *40th European Photovoltaic Solar Energy Conference and Exhibition*, 2023.

[8]   S. Lust, N. Schnitzler, A. Brendler et al., "Challenges for Quality Control Posed by New PV Encapsulation Materials," *40th European Photovoltaic Solar Energy Conference and Exhibition*, 2023.

[9]   C. Hirschl, L. Neumaier, S. Puchberger et al., "Determination of the degree of ethylene vinyl acetate crosslinking via Soxhlet extraction: Gold standard or pitfall?," *Solar Energy Materials and Solar Cells*, vol. 143, pp. 494–502, 2015.

[10]   A. K. Öz, J. Vasani, C. Reichel et al., "Temperature Distribution during the Lamination Process of PV Modules and its Influence on the Degree of Crosslinking for EVA-Simulation vs Test Results," *40th European Photovoltaic Solar Energy Conference and Exhibition*, 2023.

[11]   S. Lust, T. Weber, S. R. Kuntamukkula et al., "Update of quality control tests for new PV encapsulation materials," *EPJ Photovoltaics*, vol. 15, p. 5, 2024.

[12]   A. K. Öz, J. Vasani, C. Reichel et al., "Simulation and Experimental Analysis of Temperature Profiles and Crosslinking in PV Module Lamination," *IEEE Journal of Photovoltaics*, vol. 14, no. 5, pp. 777–784, 2024.

[13]   VDE Verlag GmbH, "Measurement procedures for materials used in photovoltaic modules - Part 1-6: Encapsulants: Test methods for determining the degree of cure in Ethylene-Vinyl Acetate," IEC 62788-1-6.

[14]   P. Gebhardt, U. Kräling, E. Fokuhl et al., "Reliability of Commercial TOPCon PV Modules—An Extensive Comparative Study," *Progress in Photovoltaics: Research and Applications*, 2024.

Transforming Industrial Façades with Integrated Photovoltaics

N. Pervan[1,2], C. Veas[1,2], S. Feldbacher[1], L. Geymayer[3], G. Kitzberger[3], M. Fleischanderl[3], H. Kurz[3], F. Füreder-Kitzmüller[3], G. Oreski[1,2]

[1] Polymer Competence Center Leoben GmbH (PCCL), Leoben, Austria – nikolina.pervan@pccl.at
[2] Chair of Materials Science and Testing of Polymers, Montanuniversität Leoben, Leoben, Austria
[3] voestalpine Stahl GmbH, 4020 Linz, Austria

INTRODUCTION AND OBJECTIVES

> The integration of photovoltaics (PV) into infrastructures, especially in buildings, is an important factor for achieving the targets for the expansion of renewable energies without the additional use of green spaces.

> Building integrated photovoltaic (BIPV) modules serve as both building element and an energy generation source.[1]

> In addition to the efficiency of the PV modules, BIPV modules must meet the architectural and structural requirements of buildings, including mechanical stability, thermal insulation and fire retardancy. The final product must have a service life of more than 30 years, and standardization should align with both building and electrical norms.[2]

> The objectives of the project "PV- Industrial Façade" are:

>> to develop a glass - free PV module concept for integration into large-scale steel façade elements

>> to identify, modify and qualify solutions for the polymeric frontsheet (FS), encapsulant and backsheet (BS) foil.

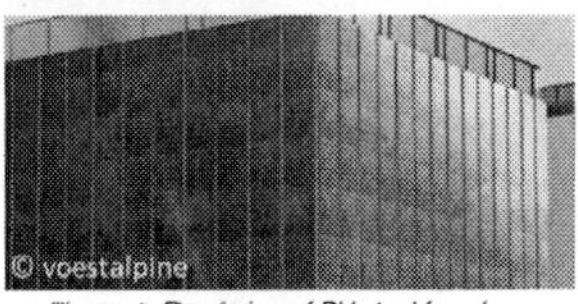

Figure 1. Rendering of PV steel façade.

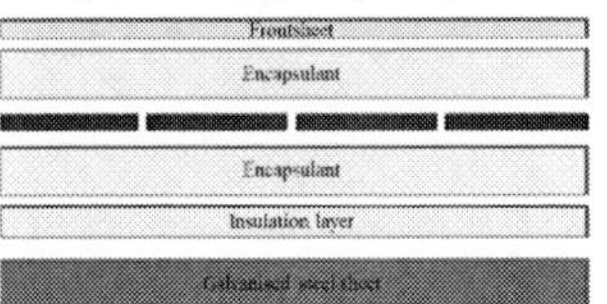

Figure 2. Material lay-up of BIPV module structure.

EXPERIMENTAL PART

POLYMER MATERIAL CHARACTERISATION

Melting temperature (DSC)

Thermal stability (TGA)

Coefficient of thermal expansion (CTE)

ADHESION OF BACKSHEET TO GALVANIZED STEEL (GS) + DAMP HEAT (DH) AGING

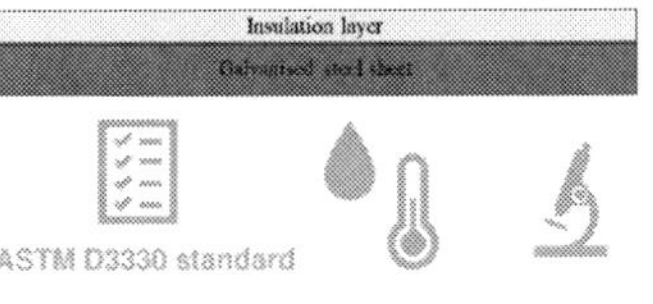

ASTM D3330 standard

ADHESION AND INTERACTION OF FS – ENCAPSULANT (POE and TPO) - BS

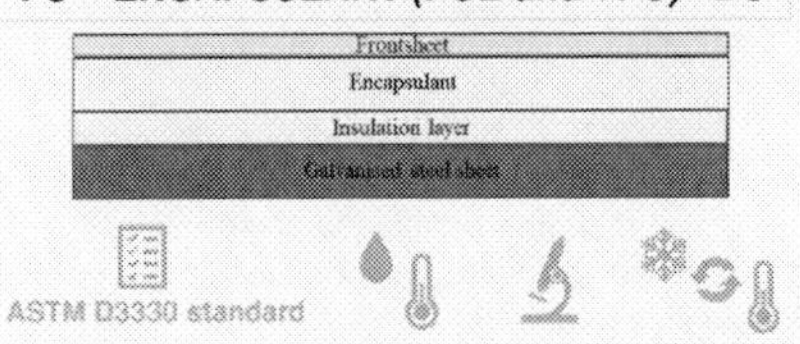

ASTM D3330 standard

PV MODULE ASSEMBLY [3]

RESULTS AND DISCUSSION

BACKSHEET (BS) FOIL THERMAL PROPERTIES

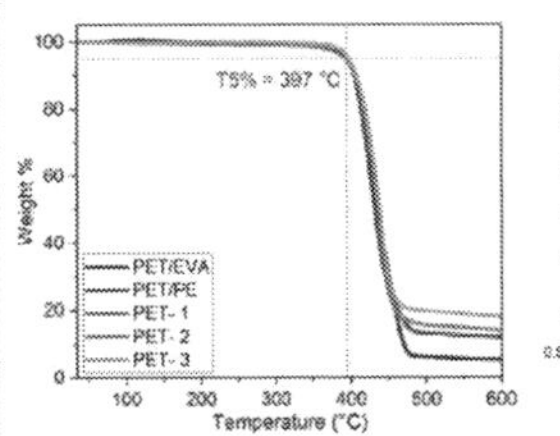

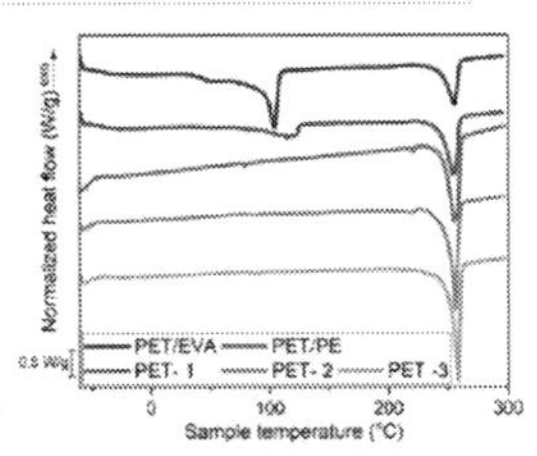

Figure 3. TGA (T5% - on the left) and DSC 1st heating curves (melting peaks – on the right) of BS foils.

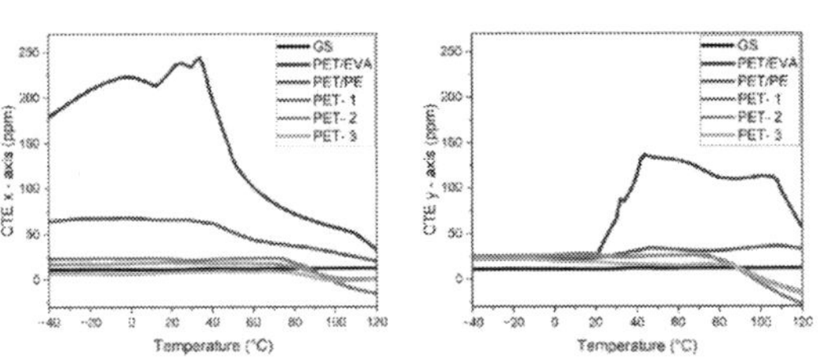

Figure 4. CTE curves in x- and y- direction of galvanized steel (GS) and BS foils.

BS/GS – PEEL MECHANISM

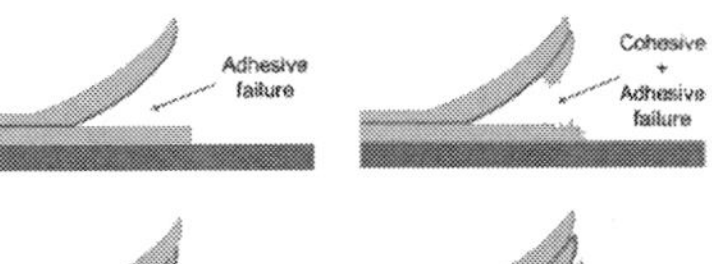

Figure 5. Peel test - delamination mechanisms between BS foil (blue) and GS substrate (grey).

INTERLAYER - PEEL STRENGTH

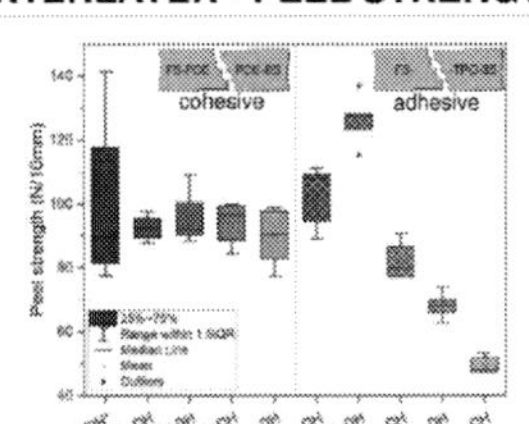

Figure 6. Peel test – peel strength between FS-encapsulant-BS + DH exposure.

> All backsheets - thermally stable up to 397 °C – fit in the production process of steel sheets.

> Best match in the CTE values between GS and BS is with PET 1-3 BS. Presence of EVA and PE in the BS results in higher CTE values.

> Delamination mechanism between GS and BS – for all, but PET/EVA BS was cohesive within the BS layer. For PET/EVA BS galvanized steel developed corrosion in the interface layer and this resulted in reduced adhesion.

> Interlayer adhesion tests shown good adhesion between POE and BS since delamination was mostly in the encapsulant layer – cohesive failure type.

> Coupons with POE maintain the same adhesion strength even after 1000 h in the DH, while the adhesion of coupons with TPO is decreased gradually.

CONCLUSIONS AND OUTLOOK

- PET backsheets have good thermal properties and fit in the production process of the steel sheets.

- Polymeric foils with EVA component are not suitable for the PV modules on top of the galvanized steel plate due to the corrosion development.

- POE maintains same adhesion strength even after 1000 h in the damp heat, while TPO is being affected by the humidity.

- Mini and full size PV modules have been prepared for aging and performance tests – results by the end of the year.

REFERENCES

1. IEA-PVPS T15-04: 2018, International definitions of "BIPV", https://iea-pvps.org/wp content/uploads/2020/02/IEAPVPS_Task_15_Report_C0_International_definitions_of_BIPV_hrw_18082 3.pdf
2. http://dx.doi.org/10.3390/buildings14061510
3. Copilot AI image creation – August 2025.

ACKNOWLEDGMENT

This work was conducted as part of the Austrian "efMISSION.at – Energy Mission Austria" project "PV Industriefassade" (FFG No. FO999915002) funded by the Austrian Climate and Energy Fund and the Austrian Research Promotion Agency (FFG).

020136-00
ORCID

This presentation was selected by the Sc. Committee of the EU PVSEC 2025 for submission of a full paper to one of the EU PVSEC's collaborating peer-reviewed journals.

Indoor Characterization and CTM Evaluation of Photovoltaic Modules with Colored Backsheets and Rear-Side Glazed Glasses

Pouya Pourshafi[1*], Alexander Protti[2], Max Mittag[2], Christian Reichel[2], Andreas Maixner[1], Hamed Hanifi[1]
[1] AESOLAR, Messerschmittring 54, Koenigsbrunn, Germany
[2] Fraunhofer Institute for Solar Energy Systems (ISE), Freiburg, Germany
*Corresponding Author: p.pourshafi@ae-solar.com

ABSTRACT: The photovoltaic (PV) industry operates in a highly price-sensitive market, necessitating continuous advancements and optimizations to enhance module efficiency and power output. Traditionally, the primary approach to increasing the power output of PV modules has been the incorporation of high-efficiency solar cells. However, alternative strategies exist that focus on minimizing energy losses and optimizing other module components to improve overall performance. After integrating solar cells into a module stack, several loss mechanisms occur, typically resulting in a lower output power compared to the theoretical sum of the individual cell powers. These losses are generally classified into two categories: optical losses and electrical losses. As a result, photovoltaic (PV) manufacturers experience financial challenges due to cell-to-module (CTM) losses. By adopting strategies to improve optical gains and reduce electrical losses, the CTM ratio can be significantly enhanced. In this study, we systematically evaluate the impact of different back cover materials on CTM gains and the overall power output of PV modules. Methodology of this work involves the characterization and assessment of the transmission and reflection properties of polymer-based backsheets in white, black, and transparent variants. Additionally, transparent, black, and white-colored rear-side glass configurations are investigated. These materials are analyzed in terms of their influence on CTM gains and their overall contribution to the module's power output. The raw measurement data obtained from these characterizations were processed using SmartCalc.Module, an analytical software tool for CTM analysis. This study offers valuable insights into the optimization of back cover materials for enhanced PV module performance.

1 INTRODUCTION

In recent years, declining production costs and the maturation of the photovoltaic supply chain have positioned photovoltaic technology as a major contributor to global energy supply. By 2024, photovoltaic systems accounted for 81% of newly installed renewable capacity [1]. Along with the expansion of photovoltaic systems, their efficiency is also continuously increasing. Over the past decade, the efficiency of commercial solar modules has increased from approximately 16% to over 22% [2]. In the laboratory test, silicon cells achieved a record efficiency of 27.8%, while the efficiency of silicon modules has reached 26% [3]. Although efficiency continues to improve, physical, electrical, and optical factors cause Cell-to-Module (CTM) losses. Identifying these losses is essential for enhancing performance under both standard and real operating conditions. To this end, detailed models incorporating optical, electrical, thermal, and environmental effects were developed, enabling precise assessment of module performance in practice [4], [5].

Researchers have concentrated on various aspects of CTM losses in their studies. Guo et al. [6] and Jung et al. [7] have investigated the mechanisms behind CTM losses, with a particular focus on resistive and mismatch effects— meanwhile, Dasary et al. [8] have focused on optimizing the number and width of busbars to reduce CTM resistive losses. Hanifi et al. [9] developed a practical optical– electrical model that enables a detailed quantification of losses and highlights the potential for achieving optical gain at the module level. Another work by Haedrich et al. [10] introduced a unified methodology for determining CTM ratios, providing a systematic approach to predict module power by analyzing optical, electrical, and geometrical loss and gain mechanisms. This methodology has become a cornerstone for subsequent research and practical applications in PV module design. Haedrich et al. [11] enhanced the framework to estimate annual yield losses and gains due to solar module design and materials in real-world conditions, moving from predictions under

STC to actual field exposure. A similar approach was followed by Shen et al. [12], [13] who adopted a more comprehensive perspective, analyzing electrical and thermal performance as well as loss mechanisms under real environmental conditions. Additional refinements to Haedrich's methodology have been proposed, incorporating new loss factors, additional components such as junction boxes and ribbon geometries, and extensions tailored to specific module concepts such as shingled and overlapping cells [14]-[17].

The CTM methodology is widely used in the analysis of different module concepts and has been applied to different cell designs, module concepts, applications, and even historical analysis of module development [18]-[24].

Based on the reviewed literature in the evolving landscape of photovoltaic technology, one of the main challenges is maximizing the energy conversion efficiency from individual solar cells to fully assembled solar modules. Recent studies have highlighted important strategies to reduce CTM losses by implementing innovative modeling and optimization techniques. From a different perspective, this study aims to improve module efficiency by enhancing optical gain and reducing the performance gap between the cell and the module.

2 METHODOLOGY

This work aims to characterize, evaluate, and analyze the effect of the backsheet color on the CTM gains and total power of PV modules. For this purpose, in the first place, all module components are characterized optically and electrically with a spectrometer and a sun simulator. The characterization includes interconnecting tabs, solar cells, encapsulation materials, front side glasses, and three standard backsheets with black, white, and transparent colors. In the second step, the measurement data are evaluated with SmartCalc.Module, a CTM analysis software developed by Fraunhofer ISE [25], is used to determine the CTM losses and gains for each module. In the final step, the losses and gains for modules with each back cover type are compared.

The experimental methodology is focused on characterizing and assessing the transmission and reflection properties of glass-based and polymer-based backsheets available in white, black, and transparent variants. The influence of these materials on CTM gains and their overall contribution to module power output is analyzed. Furthermore, a thorough evaluation is conducted on other critical components of photovoltaic (PV) modules—including solar cells, encapsulation materials, interconnection tabs, and front-side glass—from both electrical and optical perspectives. The analyses performed focus on the reflection of the rear cover and the subsequent power gain from increased irradiance on the solar cell. The gain mechanism is called "k11" following the nomenclature by Haedrich et al. **Figure 1**.

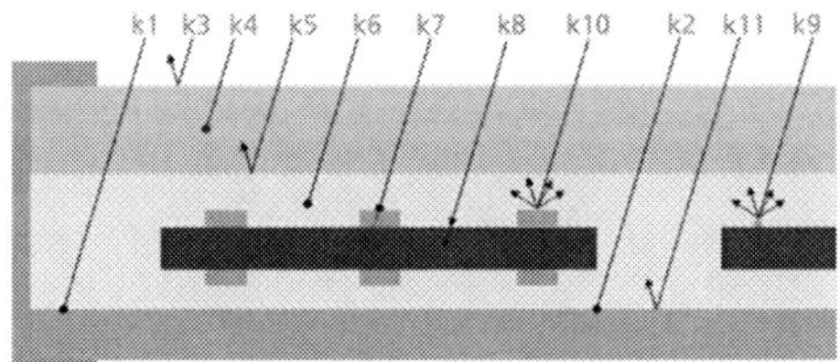

Figure 1: Detailed analysis of gain and loss mechanisms. k11 represents the optical gain obtained from the module back cover.

2.1 Materials

In this study, three glass-glass PV modules with white and black glazing, as well as without glazing, were examined (**Figure 2**).

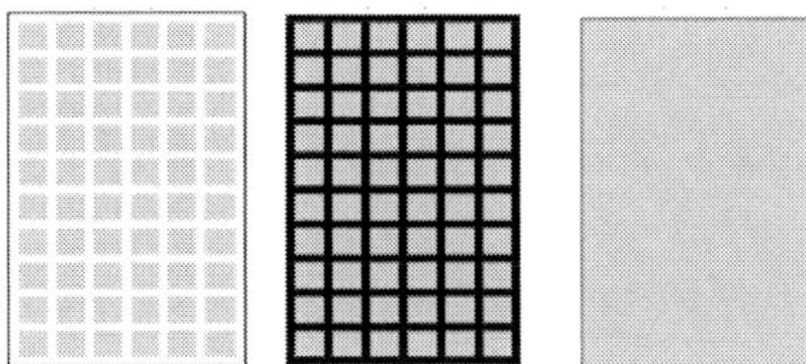

Figure 2: Schematic drawing of the rear side glass with (left) white-glazed, (middle) black-glazed, and (right) transparent glasses on the rear side of the PV module.

In addition, three modules with white, black, and transparent backsheets were examined (**Figure 3**).

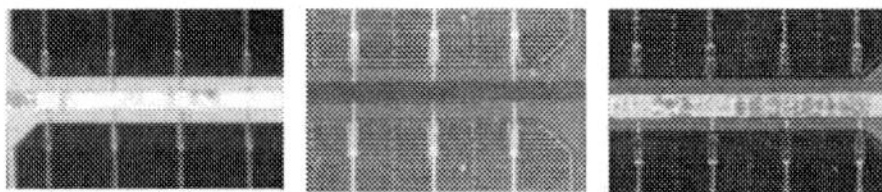

Figure 3: Close-up Image of the modules with (left) white, (middle) black, and (right) transparent backsheet.

2.2 Modelling

In 2016, Mittag et al. [26] developed CTM software, offering the photovoltaic community a precise, user-friendly, and standardized tool for CTM analysis. This software has been developed based on a comprehensive methodology for CTM analysis provided by Haedrich et

al. in 2014 [10]. Important input parameters for the modelling are listed in **Table 1**.

Table 1: Characteristics of the analyzed module

Layout	Module area = 2.856 m²
Cell	Cell type: half-cut 182x91 mm, Pseudo-square diameter: 247 mm Efficiency = 23.7% Bifaciality = 75% Number of busbars: 10
Cover	Front: 2.0 mm clear glass with ARC Rear: 2.0 mm clear glass
Encapsulant	Front: UV blocking POE Rear: UV blocking EVA
Cell interconnectors	Resistivity = 1.8 µΩ-cm Diameter = 250 µm
String interconnectors	Resistivity = 1.8 µΩ-cm Width = 5.072 mm Thickness = 0.472 mm
Junction box	Number: 2 Internal resistance = 0.5 mΩ
Cables	Length = 0.5 m Cross section = 4 mm² Specific resistance = 0.02 Ω-mm²/m Contact resistance plug/jack=0.3mΩ

3 RESULTS

3.1 Characterization

Initially, all components of the photovoltaic module both electrically and optically were characterized using a spectrometer and a solar simulator. These components include solar cells, front side glasses, encapsulation materials, interconnecting tabs, and three standard backsheets with black, white, and transparent colors and three rear glasses in white glazed, black glazed and transparent. Since the number of resulting graphs from this characterization is considerable, only one representative example is presented here. Specifically, **Figure 4** illustrates the reflectance of backsheets with different colors, serving as a demonstration of the obtained results. **Figure 4** indicates that the white backsheet exhibits higher reflectance compared to the black and transparent variants, suggesting a stronger contribution to the optical gain of the module.

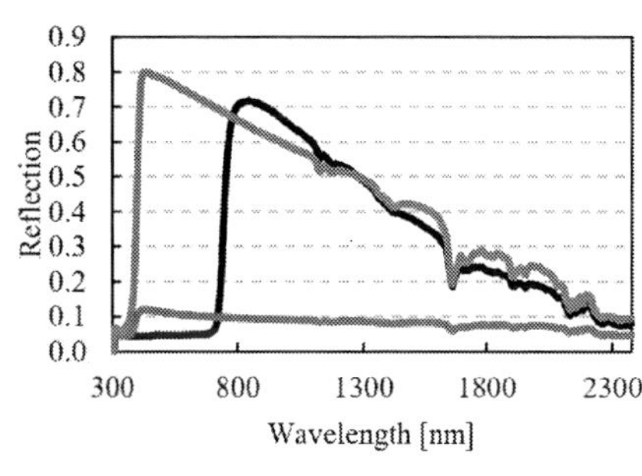

Figure 4: Hemispheric reflection data for polymer based backsheets in white, black and transparent

3.2 CTM analysis

All backsheets show very different optical properties in the visible and the infra-red spectrum (**Figure 4**). Worth noting is also the difference between the reflection of the inner side and the outer side of the white backsheet. While the inside is highly reflective, the outside has a low reflection reducing energy input into the module and lowering module temperature.

Figure 5 illustrates the results of CTM simulations conducted for polymeric backsheets in white, black, and transparent configurations. The findings reveal that the primary distinction among these variants is associated with differences in optical gain, which are quantified by the k11 coefficient. This coefficient serves as an indicator of the backsheet's positive contribution to enhancing optical gain at the module level.

The white backsheet provides the highest contribution, with a positive effect of 0.59%, increasing the overall optical gain to 1.67%. This is followed by the black backsheet, which enhances the optical gain by 0.33%, reaching a total of 1.41%. As shown in the results, the use of a transparent backsheet yields no significant impact on the optical gain.

Figure 6 illustrates the CTM simulation results obtained for three types of rear glass configurations: white-glazed, black-glazed, and transparent. The comparison highlights how different rear-glass glazing influence the optical behavior of the module and, consequently, its overall performance.

The results for the black glazing and no glazing modules are the same, because black glazing does not significantly contribute to the rear-cover coupling gains, as does the very low reflection of the transparent rear glass. It is worth noticing that an analysis with more decimals would show a difference because the black layer is not a perfect absorber. Here, the efficiency and power gains caused by the rear cover of 0.03% absorption is due to the reflection of light that passes through the cell and is reflected.

Regarding the white glazing, it caused an increment of 0.10% abs. in the simulated module efficiency. These gains are mostly due to the scattered reflection of light in the inactive module area between the cells and strings (k1 and k2, **Figure 1**).

These CTM gains are lower than the benefits from having a fully white backsheet instead of white glazing, which increases the reflected light not only from the inactive module area, but also from the transmitted light in the cell module area. But the module would be monofacial with a fully white backsheet, while the glazing allows for bifaciality. This will significantly affect the energy yield depending on the installation site, as well as the tilt and orientation of the module.

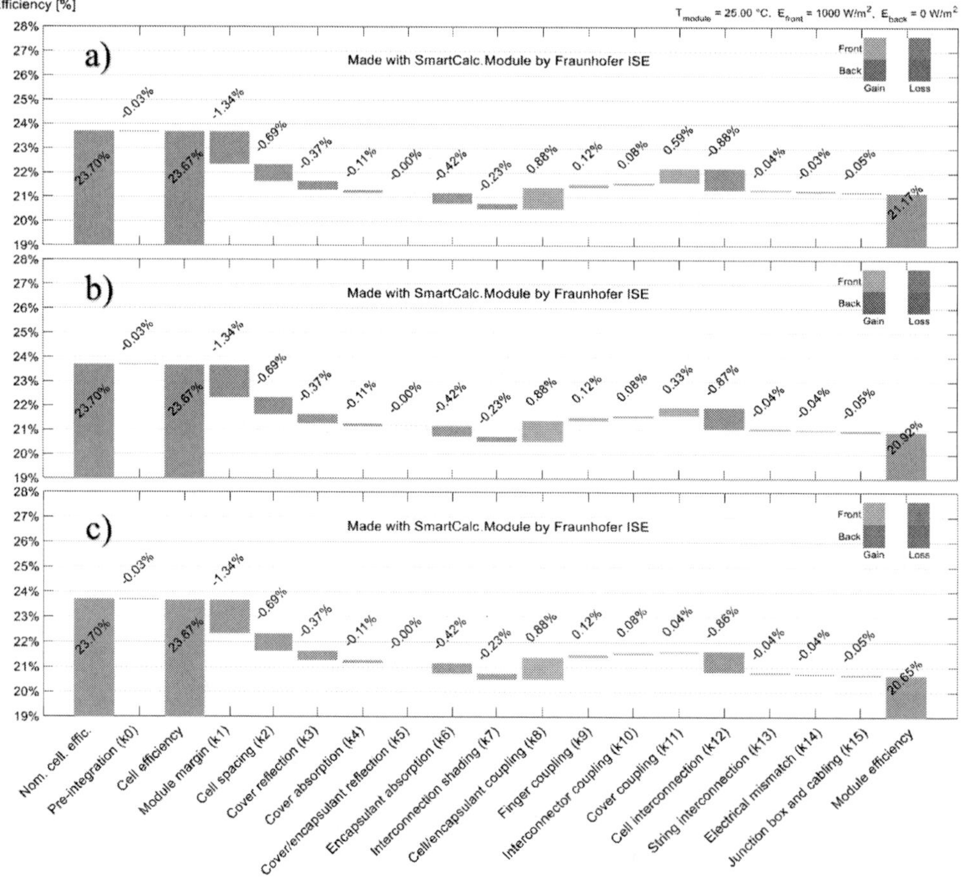

Figure 5: Cell to module efficiency loss analysis of the: a) white, b) black, and c) transparent backsheet

Efficiency loss analysis shows no significant loss for the black backsheet compared to the white backsheet. The high IR-reflection of the black backsheet compensates for losses in the visible spectrum. The transparent backsheet shows significant losses in the range of 0.2%abs but allows for a bifacial module. A further assessment on the yield of the modules in operation is necessary to quantify benefits.

Figure 7 provides a comprehensive summary of the effect of different backsheet types on the optical gain of the module. In both cases, whether using glass or polymeric materials, the incorporation of a white-colored backsheet consistently results in an increased optical gain. This highlights the significance of backsheet color selection in enhancing module performance, particularly through its contribution to the optical gain component.

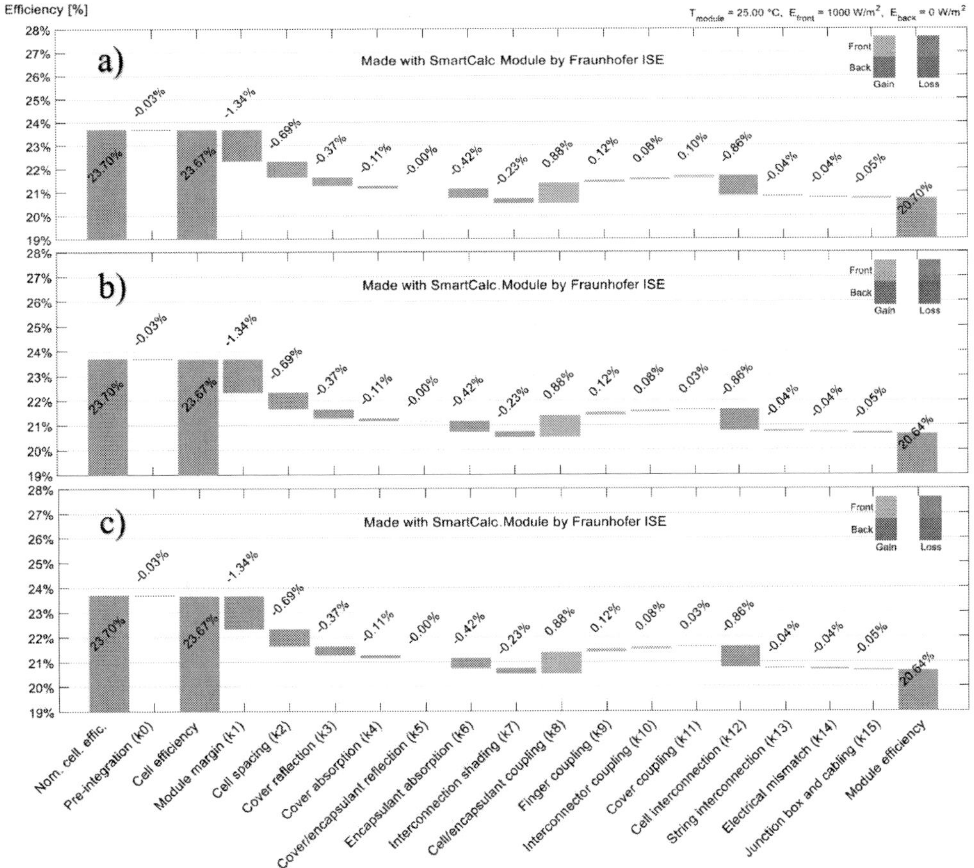

Figure 6: Cell to module efficiency loss analysis of the: a) white, b) black, and c) transparent backsheet

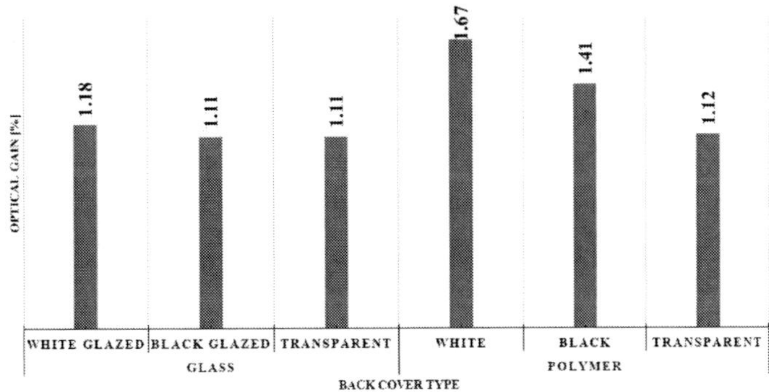

Figure 7: Calculated optical gain for different types of back cover materials, white colored back covers perform better in both polymer and glass.

4   DISCUSSION

Photovoltaic (PV) modules are subject to significant cell-to-module (CTM) losses arising from optical, electrical, and thermal mechanisms. Accurate modeling of these losses is therefore essential for predicting real-world module performance. While previous studies have primarily focused on quantifying and mitigating various CTM loss mechanisms, the present study shifts the focus toward the positive contribution of optical gain. In particular, the effects of different backsheet and rear-glass materials—including polymeric and glass variants with varying colors—on module optical gain were investigated.

Based on the results shown in **Figures 5–7**, backsheet and rear-glass selection strongly influence the optical gain of PV modules. White backsheets, whether polymeric or glass, provide the largest enhancement, increasing optical gain by 0.55% absolute over transparent and 0.26% over black backsheets. In comparison, white-glazed rear glass offers a smaller improvement of 0.07% absolute. These findings indicate that backsheet color has a greater impact on module optical gain than rear-glass glazing, highlighting the importance of reflective backsheets for maximizing monofacial performance. However, while backsheets enhance optical gain, they limit bifacial operation. Conversely, color-glazed rear glass, although contributing less to CTM gains, allows bifacial modules to capture additional irradiance from the rear, potentially increasing overall energy yield under real-world conditions.

Future work will focus on developing a more detailed CTM model for glazed glass, incorporating additional optical, electrical, and geometrical factors to better predict module performance under real operating conditions.

5   CONCLUSION

This study examines rear glass with different glazes (white, black, and transparent) and backsheets of corresponding colors. Their influence on cell-to-module (CTM) efficiency and the overall power output of photovoltaic (PV) modules is evaluated. Using spectroscopic analysis and CTM modeling via the SmartCalc.Module software, the study evaluates the contributions of these materials to CTM gains.

The study demonstrates that the choice of rear-side glazing material significantly influences the CTM efficiency and power output of PV modules. While white backsheet offers the highest CTM gains due to enhanced light scattering, modules become monofacial. High infrared reflection of black backsheets shows significant benefits but also results in monofacial modules. Glazed glass yields in lower CTM gains but provides module bifaciality which results in higher energy production in operation.

These findings underline the need for tailored material selection to optimize PV module performance based on application and environmental factors. Future work should focus on real-world operational assessments to quantify long-term energy yield benefits.

Acknowledgment

The authors thank the German Federal Ministry of Economics and Energy, BMWE, for the project MiMoRisk with the contract number 03EE1149A.

6   References

[1] REN21.2025, "Renewables 2025 Global Status Report Collection, Global Overview (Paris: REN21 Secretariat)."

[2] S. W. W. Philipps, "Photovoltaics Report," May 2025. Accessed: Aug. 26, 2025. [Online]. Available: https://www.ise.fraunhofer.de/content/dam/ise/d e/documents/publications/studies/Photovoltaics-Report.pdf

[3] M. A. Green et al., "Solar Cell Efficiency Tables (Version 66)," Progress in Photovoltaics: Research and Applications, vol. 33, no. 7, pp. 795–810, Jul. 2025, doi: 10.1002/pip.3919.

[4] L. Shen, Z. Li, and T. Ma, "Analysis of the power loss and quantification of the energy distribution in PV module," Appl Energy, vol. 260, Feb. 2020, doi: 10.1016/j.apenergy.2019.114333.

[5] T. Ma et al., "Performance modelling of photovoltaic modules under actual operating conditions considering loss mechanism and energy distribution," Appl Energy, vol. 298, Sep. 2021, doi: 10.1016/j.apenergy.2021.117205.

[6] S. Guo, J. P. Singh, M. Peters, A. G. Aberle, and J. Wong, "Two-dimensional current flow in stringed PV cells and its influence on the cell-to-module resistive losses," Solar Energy, vol. 130, pp. 224–231, Jun. 2016, doi: 10.1016/j.solener.2016.02.012.

[7] T. hee Jung, H. eun Song, H. keun Ahn, and G. hwan Kang, "A mathematical model for cell-to-module conversion considering mismatching solar cells and the resistance of the interconnection ribbon," Solar Energy, vol. 103, pp. 253–262, May 2014, doi: 10.1016/j.solener.2014.01.032.

[8] S. M. Dasari, P. Srivastav, R. Shaw, S. Saravanan, and P. Suratkar, "Optimization of cell to module conversion loss by reducing the resistive losses," Renew Energy, vol. 50, pp. 82–85, Feb. 2013, doi: 10.1016/j.renene.2012.05.022.

[9] H. Hanifi, C. Pfau, M. Turek, and J. Schneider, "A practical optical and electrical model to estimate the power losses and quantification of different heat sources in silicon based PV modules," Renew Energy, vol. 127, pp. 602–612, Nov. 2018, doi: 10.1016/j.renene.2018.04.060.

[10] I. Haedrich, U. Eitner, M. Wiese, and H. Wirth, "Unified methodology for determining CTM ratios: Systematic prediction of module power," Solar Energy Materials and Solar Cells, vol. 131, pp. 14–23, 2014, doi: 10.1016/j.solmat.2014.06.025.

[11] I. Haedrich, D. C. Jordan, and M. Ernst, "Methodology to predict annual yield losses and gains caused by solar module design and materials under field exposure," Solar Energy Materials and Solar Cells, vol. 202, Nov. 2019, doi: 10.1016/j.solmat.2019.110069.

[12] T. Ma et al., "Performance modelling of photovoltaic modules under actual operating conditions considering loss mechanism and energy distribution," Appl Energy, vol. 298, Sep. 2021, doi: 10.1016/j.apenergy.2021.117205.

[13] L. Shen, Z. Li, and T. Ma, "Analysis of the power loss and quantification of the energy distribution

in PV module," Appl Energy, vol. 260, Feb. 2020, doi: 10.1016/j.apenergy.2019.114333.

[14] J. Shahid and A. Ö. Karabacak, "Presented at the 30th PV Solar Energy Conference, 08 th-13 th," 2020.

[15] M. Mittag, T. Zech, M. Wiese, D. Bläsi, M. Ebert, and H. Wirth, "Cell-to-Module (CTM) Analysis for Photovoltaic Modules with Shingled Solar Cells."

[16] M. Mittag, C. Kutter, S. Hoffmann, P. Romer, A. J. Beinert, and T. Zech, "ELECTRICAL AND THERMAL MODELING OF JUNCTION BOXES."

[17] M. Mittag, A. J. Beinert, L. C. Rendler, M. Ebert, and U. Eitner, "TRIANGULAR RIBBONS FOR IMPROVED MODULE EFFICIENCY."

[18] H. Hanifi, D. Dassler, J. Schneider, M. Turek, S. Schindler, and J. Bagdahn, "Optimized Tab Width in Half-cell Modules," Energy Procedia, vol. 92, pp. 52–59, Aug. 2016, doi: 10.1016/j.egypro.2016.07.009.

[19] H. Hanifi, C. Pfau, M. Turek, and J. Schneider, "A practical optical and electrical model to estimate the power losses and quantification of different heat sources in silicon based PV modules," Renew Energy, vol. 127, pp. 602–612, Nov. 2018, doi: 10.1016/j.renene.2018.04.060.

[20] J. Schneider, J. Bagdahn, H. Hanifi, and J. Bagdahn, "REDUCED SHADING EFFECT ON HALF-CELL MODULES-MEASUREMENT AND SIMULATION," 2015. [Online]. Available: https://www.researchgate.net/publication/28348 8492

[21] I. Haedrich et al., "How cell textures impact angular cell-to-module ratios and the annual yield of crystalline solar modules," Solar Energy Materials and Solar Cells, vol. 183, pp. 181–192, Aug. 2018, doi: 10.1016/j.solmat.2018.04.006.

[22] A. Tummalieh and A. Pfreundt, "TREND TRACKING OF EFFICIENCY AND CTM RATIO OF PV MODULES."

[23] M. Mittag, A. Pfreundt, and J. Shahid, "Presented at the 30th PV Solar Energy Conference, 08 th-13 th," 2020.

[24] M. Mittag, A. Pfreundt, J. Shahid, N. Wöhrle, and D. H. Neuhaus, "TECHNO-ECONOMIC ANALYSIS OF HALF CELL MODULES-THE IMPACT OF HALF CELLS ON MODULE POWER AND COSTS."

[25] "Fraunhofer Institute for Solar Energy Systems ISE, SmartCalc.Module." Accessed: Sep. 01, 2023. [Online]. Available: http://www.cell-to-module.com

[26] M. Mittag, "Systematic PV module optimization with the cell-to-module (CTM) analysis software," vol. 5, pp. 97–105, 2017. [Online]. Available: www.ise.fraunhofer.de

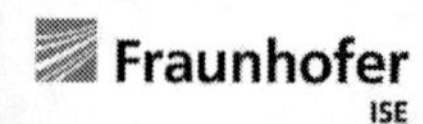

Indoor Characterization and CTM Evaluation of Photovoltaic Modules with Colored Backsheets and Rear-Side Glazed Glasses

Pouya Pourshafi[1*], Alexander Aguilar Protti[2], Max Mittag[2], Christian Reichel[2], Andreas Maixner[1], Hamed Hanifi[1]

1 AESOLAR, Messerschmittring 54, 86343 Königsbrunn, Germany
2 Fraunhofer Institute for Solar Energy Systems (ISE), Heidenhofstraße 2, 79110 Freiburg, Germany
*Corresponding author: p.pourshafi@ae-solar.com

MOTIVATION

- PV modules experience significant **cell-to-module (CTM) losses** due to optical, electrical, and thermal mechanisms.
- Accurate CTM modeling is essential for predicting real-world PV module performance.
- Previous studies have focused on various loss mechanisms.
- This study shifts focus from losses to optical gain using different back cover materials including polymer and glass with different coloring on the cell side.

METHODOLOGY

- Back cover materials:
  - Glass: White-glazed, black-glazed, transparent

| White-glazed | Black-glazed | Transparent |

- Polymer Backsheet: white, black, transparent

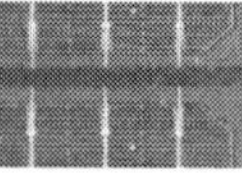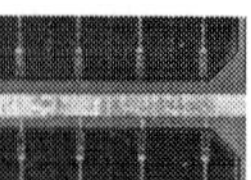

| White | Black | Transparent |

- Optical and electrical Characterization:
  - Optical characterization of module components with a focus on back cover
  - Assessment of electrical and optical contributions
- Comparative analysis:
  - Processing with SmartCalc.Module[1]
  - Comparison of CTM ratios & power output across materials variations

SUMMARY

- **CTM Loss Challenge:** PV modules deliver less power than the sum of the power of their solar cells due to optical and electrical losses ➡ Financial loss for producers
- Optical gains:
  - White backsheet: 0.55% abs. and 0.26% abs. extra optical gain compared to transparent and black backsheets
  - White-glazed glass: 0.07% abs. extra gain compared to other glass types
- Key Insight:
  - White back cover materials (polymer or glass) increase optical gain compared to black or transparent counterparts.
  - Backsheets outperform the color-glazed glasses in optical gains. However, the module will be limited to monofacial design and the bifaciality is compromised
  - Color-glazed glasses contribute less to CTM gains compared to the backsheets but the module can produce more yield because of bifaciality
- The bifacial design ultimately leads to a higher annual energy yield, which in turn improves the economic performance of the PV system.

Outlook: The CTM model for glazed glass with more details will be developed.

[1] Fraunhofer ISE, www.cell-to-module.com

The authors thank the German Federal Ministry of Economics and Energy, BMWE, for the project MiMoRisk with the contract number 03EE1149A

020138-001

RESULTS

- CTM analysis of the modules with different back cover is shown as following:

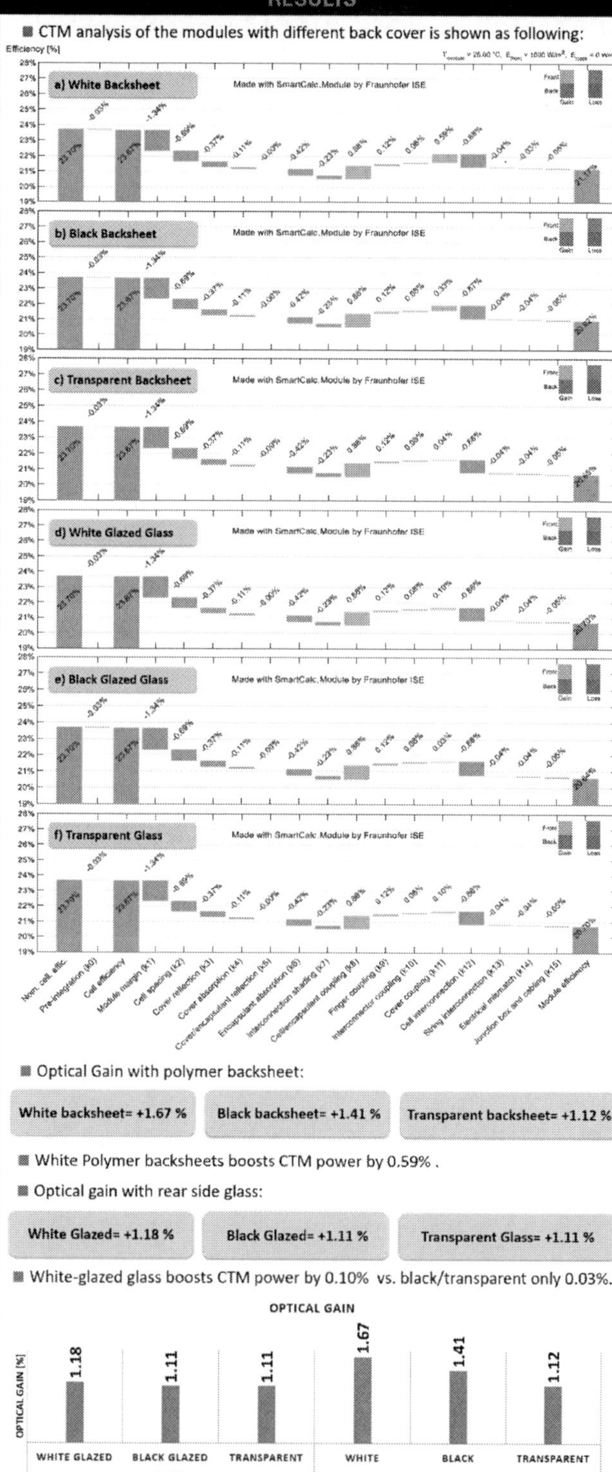

- Optical Gain with polymer backsheet:

| White backsheet= +1.67 % | Black backsheet= +1.41 % | Transparent backsheet= +1.12 % |

- White Polymer backsheets boosts CTM power by 0.59% .
- Optical gain with rear side glass:

| White Glazed= +1.18 % | Black Glazed= +1.11 % | Transparent Glass= +1.11 % |

- White-glazed glass boosts CTM power by 0.10% vs. black/transparent only 0.03%.

FIBER REINFORCED COMPOSITE PHOTOVOLTAIC MODULES BY HP-RTM MANUFACTURING PROCESS

Jon Aizpurua, Igor Arrizabalaga, Leire Herrero, Unai Iglesias, Oihane Echeverria, Eduard Bellvert, Sonia Garcia, Olatz Ollo, Maikel Mugica, Werther Cambarau, Francisco J. Cano, Eduardo Roman, Oihana Zubillaga*
TECNALIA, Basque Research and Technology Alliance (BRTA); *oihana.zubillaga@tecnalia.com

ABSTRACT: Lightweight photovoltaic (PV) modules made of continuous fiber reinforced transparent composite are promising for BIPV, VIPV and other urban applications. The present work compiles the recent results obtained for composite module manufacturing through high-pressure resin transfer moulding (HP-RTM), regarding process quality and durability of corresponding modules. Minimodules were manufactured with successful mould filling and demoulding step, while maintaining the integrity of the cells and module quality. Regarding reliability of the modules, after 200 thermal cycles, a power and short-circuit current loss of 2.3% and 2.8% were observed respectively, with a colour change of 27% in b* chromatic coordinate. The power and short-circuit losses were more pronounced after 1000 hours in damp-heat exposure, reaching values of 3.0 and 4.0% respectively. The colour change was also higher in this last case, with a 123% increase in b*, suggesting that optical losses may be affecting the electrical performance. With power losses detected due to aging below 5%, the modules would meet the PV standard requirements. The study concluded that the HP-RTM is a promising approach to advance towards a composite PV module manufacturing process with higher automation level, repeatability and precision, leading finally to an increased throughput and cost reduction.
Keywords: Composite encapsulant, HP-RTM process, PV module, performance stability, PV integration

1 INTRODUCTION

Photovoltaic modules made of continuous fiber composite have been developed for BIPV, VIPV and other urban applications using vacuum assisted resin infusion (VARI) as manufacturing process [1,2].

An approach to a process of higher automation level comprises module manufacturing by high-pressure resin transfer moulding (HP-RTM).

The inherent challenges of HP-RTM include tackling with fast-curing resins and the interaction between PV cells and process parameters. Advancing in the automation of composite PV module manufacturing will allow not only increasing throughput and reducing costs, but also improving repeatability and precision.

Recent advances carried out on back-contact silicon cell encapsulation by HP-RTM and stability performance of resulting PV modules are presented.

2 EXPERIMENTAL

2.1 Materials and module manufacturing

PV modules were manufactured with back-contact silicon solar cells using as encapsulant continuous E-type glass fiber fabric and fast-curing clear bisphenol-A epoxy resin. Research on process parameters and module configuration was carried out until complete mould filling was reached while maintaining the integrity of cells and electrical connections.

2.2 Module characterization

The modules were characterized by current-voltage (I-V) curves carried out by solar simulator and electroluminescence (EL) images.

The reliability of the modules was studied in accelerated aging tests comprising exposure to damp-heat and thermal cycling, under conditions indicated in IEC 61215 standard. The damp-heat test was performed in a climatic chamber and the modules were exposed to 85°C and 85% relative humidity for 1000 hours. The thermal cycling test covered 200 cycles between -40°C and 85°C. The weathering progress was evaluated by I-V curves carried out by solar simulator, EL images and colour analysis under CIE system. For colour analysis, b* chromatic coordinate in the blue-yellow axis was measured. A higher b* value corresponds to yellower composite and may indicate potential power decrease due to optical losses.

3 RESULTS AND DISCUSSION

3.1 Module manufacturing and characterization

Minimodules consisting of four, six and nine crystalline silicon cells were manufactured with successful mould filling and demoulding step, while maintaining the integrity of the cells and module quality. A picture of a module and corresponding EL image are presented in figure 1. Suitable process parameters and module configuration were identified to avoid cell breakage.

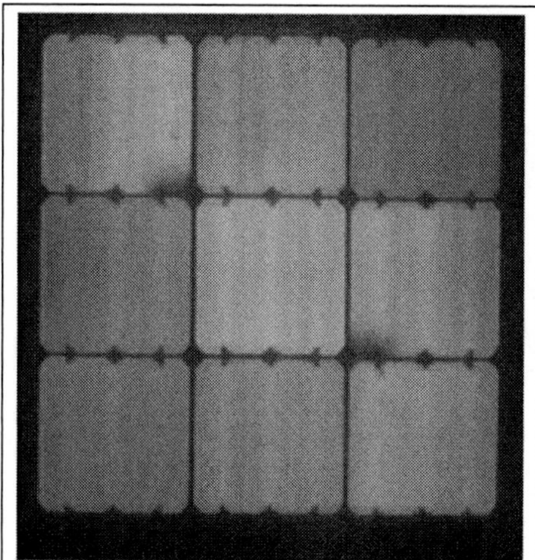

Figure 1: Picture and EL image of a composite PV module with 9 cells manufactured by HP-RTM.

3.2 Accelerated aging test results

After 200 thermal cycles, a power and short-circuit current loss of 2.3% and 2.8% were observed respectively, with a colour change of 27% in b* CIE parameter, showing a slightly yellowish appearance at naked-eye (figure 2). The power and short-circuit losses were more pronounced after 1000 hours in damp-heat exposure, reaching values of 3.0 and 4.0% respectively (figure 3). The colour change was also higher in this case, with a 123% increase in b* and more accused yellow appearance of the samples, suggesting that optical losses may be affecting the electrical performance (figure 2). No significant damage was observed in EL analysis after thermal cyclaing or damp-heat exposure. With power losses due to aging below 5%, the modules would meet the IEC standard requirements.

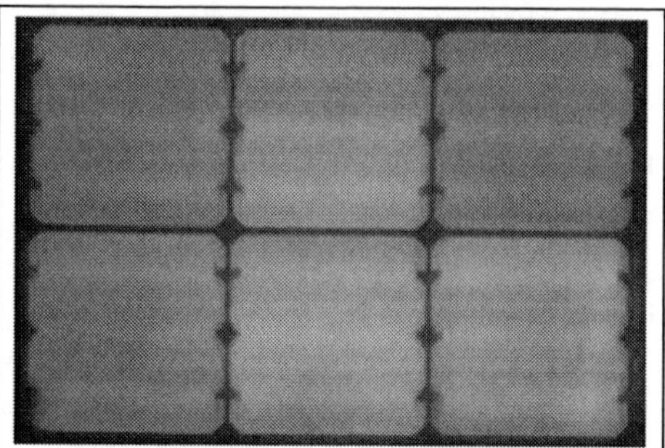

Figure 2: Picture and EL image of a composite PV module after exposure to 200 thermal cycles.

4 CONCLUSIONS

Suitable process parameters and module configuration were found to manufacture minimodules of 4, 6 and 9 cells, with successful mould filling while maintaining cell integrity. The manufactured modules showed good performance stability in damp-heat and thermal cycling exposure. Further accelerated aging tests are on going under PV standards and regulatory framework of PV integrated applications.

The study concluded that the HP-RTM process is a promising approach to advance towards a composite PV module manufacturing with higher automation level. This process may allow tackling particular cases requiring tailored designs usually found in integrated photovoltaics, while target throughput and cost values are achieved.

Figure 3: Picture and EL image of a composite PV module after 1000 hours damp-heat exposure.

5 ACKNOWLEDGEMENTS

This work was supported by the European Union's Horizon Europe research and innovation programme under SEAMLESS project [grant agreement number 101096126].

6 REFERENCES

[1] N. Yurrita, J. Aizpurua, W. Cambarau, G. Imbuluzqueta, J.M. Hernández, F.J. Cano, O. Zubillaga, Photovoltaic modules encapsulated in composite material modified with ultraviolet additives, Solar Energy Materials and Solar Cells 230 (2021) 111250.
[2] E. Rico, I. Huerta, T. del Caño, L. Villada, Á. Gallego, V. Velasco, O. Zubillaga, J.M. Vega de Seoane, I. Arrizabalaga, N. Yurrita, J. Aizpurua, G. Imbuluzketa, F.J. Cano, "PVCOM Project: Manufacture of PV Modules Encapsulated in Composite Materials for Integration in Urban Environments", Communications in computer and information science 978 (2019), 38-52.

OPTICAL CHARACTERISATION OF PV GLASSES WITH VARYING ANTIMONY CONTENTS

Oliver Pfeiffer[1], Alexander Aguilar Protti[2], Christian Reichel[2], Bengt Jaeckel[3] Thomas Sauer[4],
Holger Neuhaus[2], Ulf Blieske[1]
[1]University of Applied Sciences Cologne, [2]Fraunhofer ISE, [3]Fraunhofer CSP, [4]EXXERGY
alexander.aguilar.protti@ise.fraunhofer.de, christian.reichel@ise.fraunhofer.de, bengt.jaeckel@csp.fraunhofer.de,
tcs@exxergy.com, holger.neuhaus@ise.fraunhofer.de, ulf.blieske@th-koeln.de
*oliver.pfeiffer@th-koeln.de (Tel: 0049 221 8275 4993), Betzdorfer Str. 2, 50679 Cologne

ABSTRACT: Antimony pentoxide is often added during the production of rolled solar glass to reduce light absorption in the near-infrared spectrum. However, this compound is toxic, poses environmental risks, and restricts the recycling of antimony-containing solar glass. This study examines the optical properties of solar glasses with varying antimony concentrations to determine how much the content can be reduced without compromising the optical performance of PV glass. An antimony-free float glass was compared with four rolled (textured) glass samples containing antimony levels from 10 ppm to 1240 ppm. Optical quality was assessed through transmittance, reflectance, and IAM measurements. These results were then used to calculate the linear absorption coefficient and to simulate PV module performance with SmartCalc.Module. The rolled glass samples showed better transmittance than the float glass, but no advantage in reflectance. IAM performance was slightly higher for the rolled glasses, though this was due to the textured surface rather than the antimony content. When normalized for thickness using the linear absorption coefficient, the rolled glasses showed lower absorption than the float glass. Surprisingly, no clear correlation was found between antimony concentration and absorption behaviour. Overall, the superior optical properties of the rolled glasses translated into a rated energy yield about 1% higher than that of the float glass. It is important, that it is difficult to generalise these results without knowing the exact chemical composition or the production process of the glasses. However, a key finding is, that high-quality rolled solar glass can be produced without the need of adding antimony.
Keywords: Antimony, solar glass, optical characterisation, rated energy yield

1 INTRODUCTION

High optical transmission is a key requirement for PV module front covers to maximise the amount of light available to the solar cells. The most common front cover material is soda-lime glass because of its low cost. Since the raw material (sand) is gained in natural mining, it can contain a significant amount of iron in the form of FeO. The not fully oxidized iron has the disadvantage of absorbing light in the near infrared band, critically decreasing a PV module's efficiency. Therefore, the solar glass industry hasdeveloped two strategies for reducing iron-induced absorption of light: The usage of low iron natural materials, and further, the oxidation of FeO into Fe_2O_3 which only insignificantly absorbs light in the near UV and blue range. The oxidation of FeO is performed by adding antimony pentoxide (Sb_2O_5) during the glass melting process.

$$Sb_2O_5 + 4FeO \rightarrow Sb_2O_3 + 2Fe_2O_3 \qquad (1)$$

Using Sb_2O_5 as an additive is, however, only common in the production of patterned solar glass, since it is suspected to react with the tin bath during float glass production causing a poor glass surface. In the float glass production, molten (low iron) glass flows onto a molten tin bath, resulting in advantages related to production yield and process stability, producing a glass with a mirror-like surface. However, it is challenging to use Sb_2O_5 in float glass since the molten glass can possibly interact with the liquid tin bath. In the patterned glass production, molten glass is formed between two rollers into a flat sheet. The rollers imprint a texture onto the glass defined by the roller structure; the texture can create a light trapping function. Since adding Sb_2O_5 does not lead to interactions and since there is no tin layer on the glass surface, patterned glass usually has a higher transmission than float glass. [1] Nonetheless, antimony is toxic for humans [2] and can potentially contaminate soil and groundwater if not disposed properly [3]. When melted, toxic emissions

impose the risk of negative respiratory, skin and gastrointestinal effects for industry workers and furthermore, its reaction with tin bath limits the use of recycled glass cullet in the float glass production [4].
Therefore, in the context of the EU Ecodesign Directive, limiting the content of antimony could be an interesting option for improving the sustainability ratings of PV modules, since disclosing the content of materials is a key recommendation of leading institutions for a future ecolabel [5]. Thus, it is expected that the market share of antimony-free glass in PV modules may increase from ~5% to ~18% between 2025 and 2035 [6].
This work builds on the study by Glaubitz et al. [7], who concluded that the positive optical effects are not linear to the antimony content of the glass. However, it further analyses how the antimony content affects the optical properties of glass samples, in particular the hemispherical spectral transmittance, reflectance and absorbance, as well as the angular behaviour of the transmittance, by means of the incidence angle modifier (IAM). Furthermore, the impact of these properties on the rated energy yield [8] is determined.

2 MATERIAL AND METHODS

2.1 Glass samples

Five glass types with varying antimony content and from two European producers were tested. Table I summarizes the main properties of the samples. It is important to mention that the samples are hand-made specimen without thermal curing and without anti-reflective coating. Besides the thickness and the antimony content, the glass surface roughness differs due to the different hot-forming process.

Table I: Glass sample characteristics

Producer	Thickness [mm]	Sb$_2$O$_5$ content [ppm]	Glass type
1	3.2	0	Float (low iron)
2	4	10	Rolled
2	4	290	Rolled
2	4	660	Rolled
2	2	1240	Rolled

The glass roughness was measured, using a "hommel etamic w10" device as summarized in Table II. While the float glass has an average roughness value of R_a=0,008-0.009 µm, the roughness of front and rear side from the rolled glasses is higher and differs since usually, the counter-rotating rollers have a different texture. For the optical characterisation of the samples, the textured front side is directed to the light source.

Table II: Average roughness value of front and rear side of the glass samples

Sample	R_a – front [µm]	R_a – rear [µm]
Float 3.2mm	0.008	0.009
Rolled 4mm	1.614	3.126
Rolled_2mm	1.153	1.579

2.2 Transmittance measurements

Transmittance measurements were carried out at TH Köln in accordance with DIN EN 62805-2 [9]. This comprises a xenon arc lamp as the light source, small-band optical filters (monochromator) and an integrating sphere in which a C-Si sensor measures the light intensity, as displayed in Figure 1 a). Further information about the measurement system are given in [7]. During a measurement, the light intensity in the sphere is measured at each wavelength interval when a glass sample is placed in front of the sphere's entrance (allowing light to pass through the glass) and when there is no glass present. Transmission $\tau_i(\lambda)$ is obtained by dividing the light intensity in the sphere with glass, $I_i(\lambda)$, by the light intensity in the sphere without glass, $I_0(\lambda)$. In total, 40 wavelength intervals between 300 nm and 1200 nm are measured. Ten measurements are taken and averaged for each glass sample.

$$\tau_i(\lambda) = \frac{I_i(\lambda)}{I_0(\lambda)} \qquad (2)$$

2.3 Reflectance measurement

The reflectance measurement was also carried out at TH Köln in accordance with DIN EN 62805-2 [9] with a similar setup as for the transmittance measurements, as seen in Figure 1 b). However, this time the samples are placed inside the integrating sphere on a sample holder that has a high absorbing surface. The reflected part of the light is measured by the sensor. Light that is transmitted through the glass sample is absorbed by the absorber. Reflectance $\varrho_i(\lambda)$ is obtained by dividing the light intensity in the sphere with glass and absorber, $I_i(\lambda)$, by the light intensity in the sphere without glass and without absorber, $I_0(\lambda)$.

$$\varrho_i(\lambda) = \frac{I_i(\lambda)}{I_0(\lambda)} \qquad (3)$$

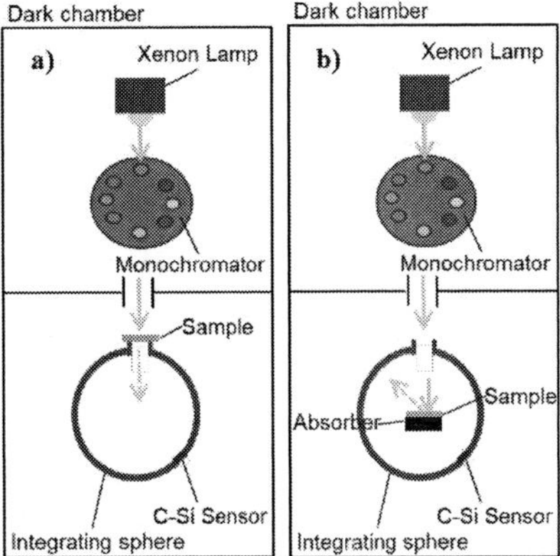

Figure 1: Schematic representations of the measurement setup at TH Köln for: a) the transmittance measurement and b) the reflectance measurement

2.4 Absorption coefficient

The absorbance characteristics of the glass samples were analysed using the spectral absorption coefficient, enabling a comparison independent of glass thickness. The spectral absorption coefficient α describes the loss of light intensity which is transmitted through a thin layer of homogeneous medium and can be derived from the Beer-Lambertian law. [10]

$$I(d) = I_0 * e^{-\alpha d} \qquad (4)$$

In this Equation (4), I_0 refers to the initial light intensity, $I(d)$ to the light intensity after traveling the distance d through the medium, and α is the absorption coefficient, which is occasionally referred to as linear attenuation coefficient or extinction coefficient in other contexts [11]. To calculate the spectral absorption coefficient for a glass sample $\alpha_i(\lambda)$, the following equation is used.

$$\alpha_i(\lambda) = -\ln\left(\frac{\tau_i(\lambda)}{1 - \varrho_i(\lambda)}\right) * d_i^{-1} \qquad (5)$$

In this Equation (5), $\tau_i(\lambda)$ corresponds to the light intensity $I(d)$ in the Beer-Lambertian law. The term $1 - \varrho_i(\lambda)$ is analogous to to I_0, as the light that passes through the glass sample consists of the incident light from the light source that is reduced by reflection losses. The parameter d_i corresponds to the thickness of the glass sample in centimetre.

2.5 IAM measurement

IAM measurements were carried out in accordance with IEC 61853-2 [12] at the TH Köln laboratories. The setup included a xenon arc lamp as the light source, an aperture to adjust the size of the light spot, and an automatically angle-adjustable sample holder, and is displayed in Figure 2. Mini-modules were built for measuring the IAM. For this, two glass/glass mini-modules were manufactured using M6 PERC half cells and EVA as the encapsulant. To assess whether the antimony content influences the IAM, the sample with the lowest content was compared to the sample with the highest content. Consequently, measurements were taken on a mini-module with low-iron float glass containing 0 ppm of antimony and a mini-module with 2 mm rolled glass containing 1240 ppm of antimony. The short-circuit current was measured using a "Keithley 2700" data logger. Fifteen measurements were taken per angle and averaged. The mini-module was underexposed during the measurement, as can be seen in the following figure.

Figure 2: IAM measurement setup at TH Köln

2.6 Module performance

This study evaluates the impact of antimony content in glass on the performance of photovoltaic (PV) modules, specifically in terms of rated module power and rated energy yield. The rated power at Standard Test Conditions (STC) was determined using CTM simulations, while the rated energy yield was assessed through the Virtual Energy Rating method, both implemented in the SmartCalc.Module software [13]. For this analysis, an exemplary module with a total cell power of 644.63 Wp was selected. Additional specifications are provided in Figure 3 and Table III. To account for the fact that the glasses have different thicknesses, the refractive and extinction coefficients are extracted from the optical measurements as specified in [14] and the thickness is then normalized to 2 mm for all simulations.

For the energy yield calculations, the angular loss coefficient (a_r) of the Martin-Ruiz model [15] is extracted from the IAM measurements by applying a least-squares fitting. Since only one sample with antimony (rolled glass) is measured, the same a_r value is assumed for all the simulations with rolled glass (10, 290, 660 and 1290 ppm).

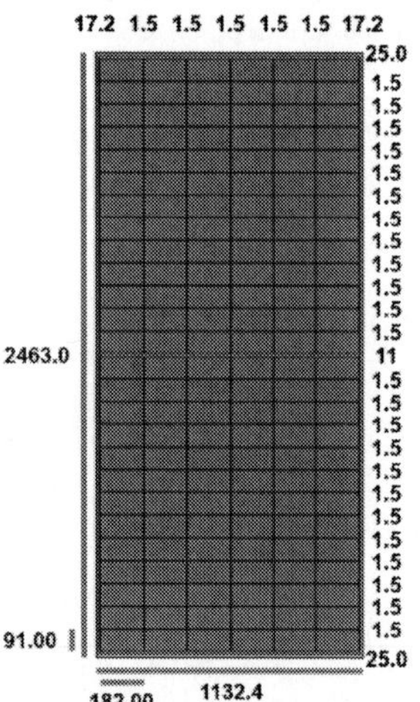

Figure 3: Layout of the simulated PV module

Table III: Characteristics of the simulated module

Layout	Cell spacing: 1.5 mm String spacing: 1.5 mm Top and bottom margins: 25 mm Side margins: 17.2 mm Number of cells: 156 Module length = 2.46 m Module width = 1.13 m Module area = 2.789 m²
Cell	Cell type: half-cut M10 HJT Efficiency = 25.0% Bifaciality = 90% Number of fingers = 78/90 (front/bottom) Number of busbars = 16
Cover	Front: 2.0 mm clear glass with ARC Rear: 2.0 mm clear glass with ARC
Encapsulant	Front: UV transmitting POE Rear: UV blocking POE Thickness = 600 μm
Cell connectors	Resistivity = 1.8 μΩ-cm Diameter: 0.25 mm
String connectors	Resistivity = 1.8 μΩ-cm Width = 5.072 mm Thickness = 0.472 mm
Junction box	Quantity = 2 Internal resistance = 0.03 mΩ
Cables	Length = 1.3 m Cross section = 4 mm² Specific resistance = 0.02 Ω-mm²/m Contact resistance plug/jack = 2mΩ

3 RESULTS

3.1 Transmittance

The results of the transmittance measurements are displayed in Figure 4. While low iron glass without antimony showed the lowest overall transmittance, decreasing from 92% at wavelength of 600 nm to 90.6% at 1100 nm, the transmittance of the 2 mm rolled glass with the highest antimony stayed constant over 92% for all wavelengths down to approx. 500 nm. The transmittance of all 4mm rolled glass was very similar, decreasing around 0.5 percent points from 92% at 600 nm to 91.5% at 1100 nm. It should be mentioned that the results at wavelengths below 400 nm and above 1150 nm were highly uncertain which is due to the low sensitivity of the c-Si optical sensor. They were therefore not included in the diagram. However, the trend of decreasing transmittance below 400 nm is generally established for soda-lime glass. The same is true for the reflectance measurement results and therefore also for the calculated absorption coefficient.

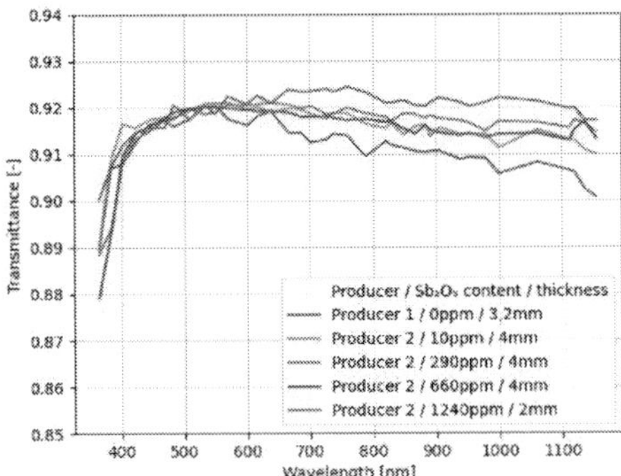

Figure 4: Transmittance results

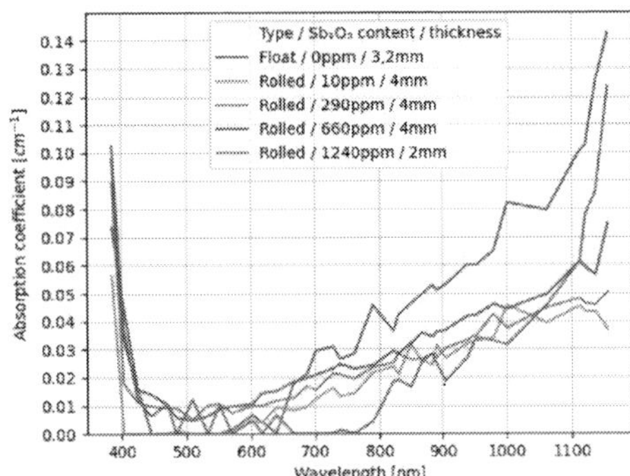

Figure 6: Absorption coefficient results

3.2 Reflectance

The reflectance measurements in Figure 5 show no significant differences between the different glass samples. At small wavelengths between 400nm and 500nm, the reflection is between 8-8.5% and decreases steadily to 6.5-7% at 1100 nm.

3.4 IAM

The IAM measurements revealed a slight difference between the low iron float and the high antimony rolled glass at high angles, as illustrated Figure 7. The discrepancy can be attributed to the different surface textures of float and rolled solar glass that are detailed in section 2.1. To confirm this, the results from the float glass were compared to a synthetic IAM curve resembling pure Fresnel reflections. As the graphs are coherent, it can be concluded that the higher reflections at higher angles are due to the low surface roughness of the float glass. The slightly rougher texture of the rolled glass decreases reflections at high angles, meaning that the IAM is higher for higher angles compared to the float-glass.

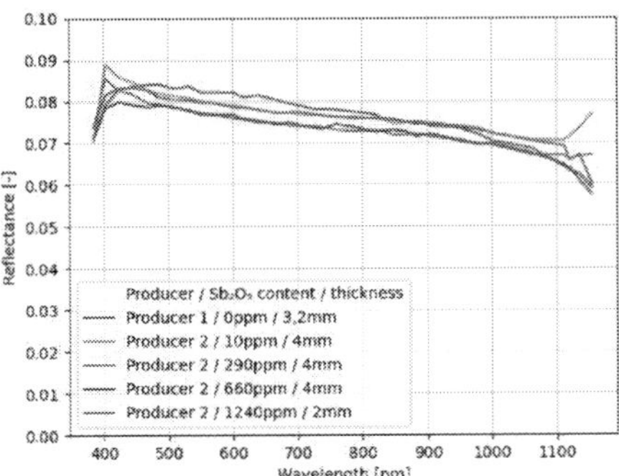

Figure 5: Reflectance results

3.3 Absorption coefficient

When calculating the absorption coefficient with equation 3, results can be displayed as in Figure 6. For all glasses an absorption coefficient between 0-0.01 cm^{-1} can be seen at wavelengths to around 650 nm. Then, it steadily increases over the whole wavelength range. While the rolled glass results show high coherence regardless of the antimony content, absorbing between 4-6% of the light per centimetre at 1100 nm, the low iron float glass has a significantly higher absorbance of 9.8% per centimetre. This result can mainly be attributed the lower transmittance of this glass in the corresponding wavelength range.

It should be noted that the calculated absorption coefficients in a range between 400-650 nm and for the 2 mm rolled glass additionally between 650-780 nm, was at some points slightly below zero. Since these results are not valid and can be explained by uncertainties in the transmittance and reflectance measurements, they were artificially changed to zero.

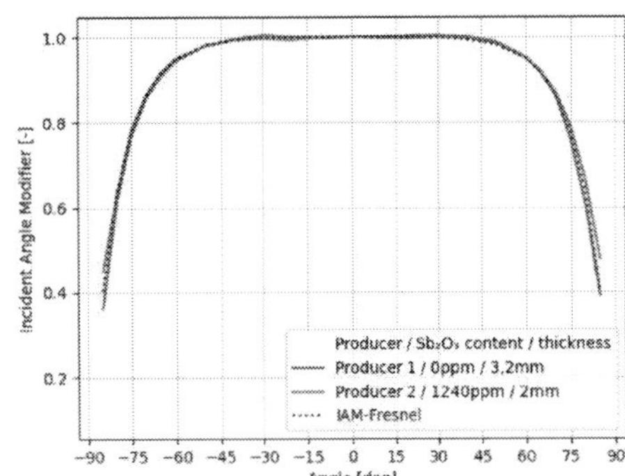

Figure 7: IAM results

The angular loss coefficients that minimize the difference between the measurements and the Martin-Ruiz model are $a_r = 0.1812$ for the 0 ppm (float) glass and $a_r = 0.1685$, for the rolled glass.

3.5 Module performance

The impact of antimony content in glass on module rated power is illustrated in Figure 8. For rolled glasses, no discernible trend is observed between antimony content and rated power, with an average module power of 589.98 Wp. This value is 3.32 Wp (0.4%) higher than the 587.58 Wp recorded for float glass, primarily attributable to increased glass absorption.

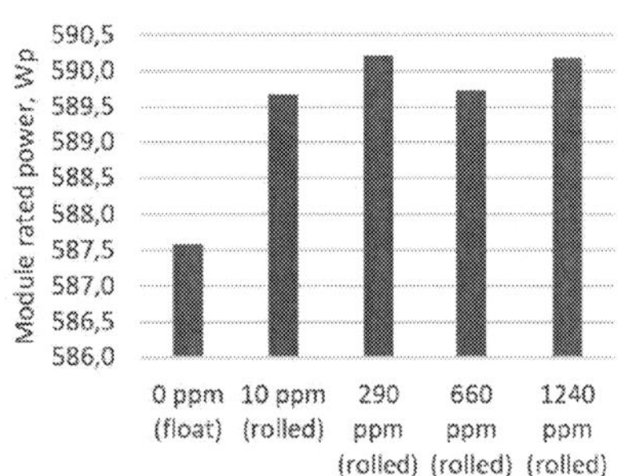

Figure 8: Impact of the antimony content on the rated power of a 156 M10 half-cell module

Figure 9 depicts the effect of glass antimony content on average rated energy yield. Similarly, no trend is evident between antimony content in rolled glass and energy yield. The rolled glass demonstrates an average yield of 341.58 kWh/m²/yr, which is 1% higher than the 338.26 kWh/m²/yr achieved with float glass. The improved incident angle modulation (IAM) of the rolled glass, owing to its textured surface, is the primary factor contributing to this difference compared to the results at Standard Test Conditions (STC).

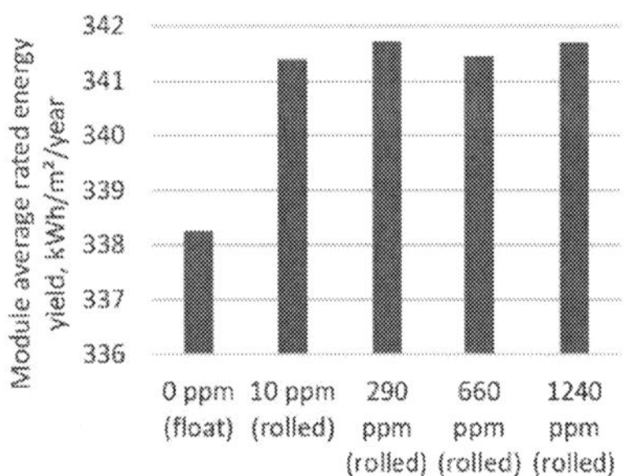

Figure 9: Rated energy yield of an exemplary PV module (average of 6 climatic regions)

4 DISCUSSION

The results are validated by comparing the measurements presented in this study with literature values.

Regarding the transmission, Babin et al. measured transmissions of around 91.5% - 92% over a similar wavelength range for low-iron glass with a slight texture [16]. This result is coherent with the measurement conducted on the rolled glass samples. Blieske and Stollwerck also report that a transmission of 91.5% can be expected for antimony containing glasses [1].

In terms of the reflectance, slightly lower values were published by Starowicz et al. [17]. However, these were measured on laminated mini-modules and not on glass sheets, as in this study. Since a glass/EVA junction will alter the reflection behaviour compared to a glass/air junction, different results can be expected.

Comparable absorbances were published by Allsopp et al.

[18], who experimented with different glass recipes and glass dopants such as Fe_2O_3 and Bi_2O_3. Since the exact chemical composition of the samples used in this study is not known, the applicability of these results remains uncertain.

Regarding the IAM, the measured values are of high certainty, especially those for the flat mirror-like surface glass, who were coherent with a synthetical curve for Fresnel reflections.

The energy yield simulations are based on measured data, so the results are consistent with the findings presented earlier. The rated energy yield was approximately 1% higher for textured glass than for flat glass. This finding is comparable to the results of a real-world study which compared textured and flat glass modules over a six-month period, finding that textured glass had a 1.4% higher optical gain than flat glass [19].

Surprisingly, the antimony content of the glass does not seem to influence the absorption. An earlier study conducted on different glass samples using a different method observed such an effect [7]. As there are no other studies that have conducted a similar analysis to quantify the effect of distinct antimony contents (to the best of the authors' knowledge), the results cannot be directly compared. As outlined, aside of the known Sb_2O_3 content, the glass chemistry is unknown. This might explain why the antimony did not affect the absorption as expected. Another possible explanation is that the effect of the surface texture, which increases transmission, outweighs the optical effect caused by antimony. This would mean that reducing the antimony content would not compromise the optical quality of solar glass, paving the way for more eco-friendly solar modules.

5 CONCLUSION

This study involved the optical characterisation of glass samples with different antimony contents. Five samples were compared in total: a float glass without antimony and four rolled glasses with antimony contents ranging from 10 ppm to 1,240 ppm. The samples were characterised using total transmission and reflection measurements, which were then used to calculate absorption. IAM measurements were also performed, and these results were then used alongside the others to calculate the energy annual yield of a module containing these glasses using the SmartCalc.Module software.

While the rolled, antimony-containing glasses outperformed the float glass (with transmission values of 91.5% to slightly over 92% compared to 90% at 1100 nm), reflectance was unaffected. Similarly, the IAM was not influenced by the antimony content but rather by the texture of the glass surface, resulting in lower IAM values at high angles for textured glass.

The energy yield simulations were also found to be influenced mainly by the glass texture rather than the antimony content, leading to a 1% higher rated energy yield of the textured glasses compared to the flat glass.

To the authors' surprise, the antimony content in the rolled glasses did not affect the absorption when normalised for glass thickness. As this result is novel and unlikely to be due to a measurement error, it suggests that high-quality solar glass can be produced without the need for antimony. However, without knowing the exact chemical glass composition of the glass substrates used in this study, this conclusion may deserve further investigation.

ACKNOWLEDGEMENTS
This work is part of the Green Solar Modules Project (ID: 03EE1161B) which is funded by the Federal Ministry for Economic Affairs and Energy (BMWE) and managed by Projektträger Jülich (PtJ).

6   REFERENCES

[1]   U. Blieske and G. Stollwerck, Eds., *Advances in photovoltaics: Chapter Four: Glass and other Encapsulation Materials,* 1st ed. Amsterdam: Elsevier, 2013.

[2]   S. Sundar and J. Chakravarty, "Antimony toxicity," (eng), *International journal of environmental research and public health,* vol. 7, no. 12, pp. 4267–4277, 2010.

[3]   P. A. Nishad and A. Bhaskarapillai, "Antimony, a pollutant of emerging concern: A review on industrial sources and remediation technologies," (eng), *Chemosphere,* vol. 277, p. 130252, 2021.

[4]   EUROPEAN SOLAR PV INDUSTRY ALLIANCE, "Addressing uncertain antimony content in solar glass for recycling," [Online] Available: https://solaralliance.eu/wp-content/uploads/2023/10/Recommendation-on-Addressing-uncertain-antimony-content-in-solar-glass-for-recycling.pdf. Accessed on: Jun. 30 2025.

[5]   "Expert Input Paper – Eco Design and Energy Labelling for Photovoltaic Modules, Inverter and Systems in the EU, ETIP PV, SolarPower Europe, PVthin, European Solar Manufacturing Council, IECR," 2021. [Online] Available: https://pvthin.org/wp-content/uploads/2021-02-ETIP-PV-Report-expert-input-paper.pdf. Accessed on: Jun. 30 2025.

[6]   VDMA, "International Technology Roadmap for Photovoltaics (ITRPV) 16th. Edition," May. 2025.

[7]   A. Glaubitz, S. Grüttner, S. Yagci, O. Pfeiffer, and U. Blieske, "Optimizing Sustainability: Balancing Antimony Content for Enhanced Optical Properties and Environmental Impact in Solar Glass," in 2024.

[8]   International Electrotechnical Commission, "Photovoltaic (PV) module performance testing and energy rating," Geneva, International standard / International Electrotechnical Commission IEC 61853-3, 2018.

[9]   *Method for measuring photovoltaic (PV) glass – Part 2: Measurement of transmittance and reflectance (IEC 62805-2:2017),* DIN EN 62805-2, 2018.

[10] T. G. Mayerhöfer, S. Pahlow, and J. Popp, "The Bouguer-Beer-Lambert Law: Shining Light on the Obscure," (eng), *Chemphyschem : a European journal of chemical physics and physical chemistry,* vol. 21, no. 18, pp. 2029–2046, 2020.

[11] J. D. Jackson, *Classical electrodynamics,* 2nd ed. New York: Wiley, 1975.

[12] *Photovoltaic (PV) module performance testing and energy rating – Part 2: Spectral responsivity, incidence angle and module operating temperature measurements (IEC 61853-2:2016),* DIN EN 61853-2 (VDE 0126-34-2), 2017.

[13] A. Protti, J. Shahid, M. Mittag, D. H. Neuhaus, U. Kräling, and M. Kaiser, "Virtual Energy Rating: a Method for Optimizing Module Performance Through Cell-To-Module Analysis," (eng), 2022.

[14] I. Haedrich, U. Eitner, M. Wiese, and H. Wirth, "Unified methodology for determining CTM ratios: Systematic prediction of module power," *Solar Energy Materials and Solar Cells,* vol. 131, pp. 14–23, 2014.

[15] N. Martín and J. M. Ruiz, "A new model for PV modules angular losses under field conditions," *International Journal of Solar Energy,* vol. 22, no. 1, pp. 19–31, 2002.

[16] M. Babin, A. Bertomeu i Baldé, S. V. Spataru, M. L. Jakobsen, and S. Thorsteinsson, "Study of Optical Transmission Losses of Satinated PV Glass," (eng), 2022.

[17] Z. M. Starowicz, K. Drabczyk, K. Gawlińska, and P. Zięba, "METROLOGICAL ASPECTS OF EVALUATION OF GLASS TYPES USED IN PHOTOVOLTAIC MODULES IN LABORATORY SCALE," *Metrology and Measurement Systems,* 2018.

[18] B. L. Allsopp, R. Orman, S. R. Johnson, I. Baistow, G. Sanderson, P. Sundberg, C. Stålhandske, L. Grund, A. Andersson, J. Booth, P. A. Bingham, and S. Karlsson, "Towards improved cover glasses for photovoltaic devices," *Progress in Photovoltaics,* vol. 28, no. 11, pp. 1187–1206, 2020.

[19] Y. S. Khoo, J. P. Singh, T. M. Walsh, and A. G. Aberle, "Comparison of Angular Reflectance Losses Between PV Modules With Planar and Textured Glass Under Singapore Outdoor Conditions," *IEEE J. Photovoltaics,* vol. 4, no. 1, pp. 362–367, 2014.

TOWARDS CIRCULAR SOLAR TECHNOLOGIES: NOVEL BIO-BASED POLYMERS AS NEXT-GENERATION ENCAPSULANTS

Kristina Maliutina[1], Oliver Pfeiffer[1], Matthias Eisenacher[1], Martin Bonnet[1], Ulf Blieske[1]
[1]Cologne Institute for Renewable Energy (CIRE), University of Applied Science Cologne, Betzdorfer Straße 2, 50679 Cologne, Germany
Email: kristina.maliutina@th-koeln.de

ABSTRACT: Conventional photovoltaic (PV) encapsulants such as ethylene-vinyl acetate (EVA) suffer from yellowing, delamination, irreversible crosslinking, and poor recyclability, limiting module lifetimes and sustainability. To enable a circular economy (CE) for PV modules, new encapsulants must combine long-term stability with programmed end-of-life (EoL) pathways. This review critically evaluates recent progress in bio-based polymers synthesized via ring-opening metathesis polymerization (ROMP) and alternating ROMP (AROMP) as candidates for next-generation encapsulants. Compared to EVA, these systems offer modular design flexibility, renewable feedstock origins, and recyclability potential. Key challenges remain, including long-term UV and moisture stability, lack of standardized testing, and limited scalability. Future work should prioritize in situ aging, quantitative benchmarking of barriers and optical properties, and module-level validation. Building on these insights, we outline design principles for circular encapsulants: thermomechanical tuning via modular monomers, incorporation of aromatic blocks for UV stability, and degradable motifs as "molecular fuses" to reconcile durability with recyclability. This study emphasizes catalyst footprint minimization, continuous-flow synthesis for scalability, and standardized durability testing. By integrating renewable precursors (aromatics, furans, saccharides) with precision polymerization, a pathway toward closed-loop PV encapsulants that combine reliable performance with sustainable EoL recovery is presented.

Keywords: bio-based polymers, ROMP, AROMP, circular economy, photovoltaic encapsulation

1. INTRODUCTION

Durability challenges of conventional encapsulants are central to PV module degradation. Sunlight, humidity, and chemically aggressive environments induce glass corrosion, backsheet photo-oxidation, encapsulant yellowing as well as delamination, leading to power losses [1]. Long-term stability therefore remains the primary bottleneck, demanding new materials with improved UV and hydrolytic resistance. From a life-cycle perspective, Abian et al. showed that although PV systems reduce emissions compared to fossil energy, manufacturing and end-of-life stages still contribute significantly to the overall footprint. Energy payback time (EPBT) and global warming potential (GWP) vary strongly across technologies: crystalline silicon PV panels have high burdens, while perovskite and organic PV modules offer shorter EPBT but suffer from insufficient stability [2]. Extending service lifetimes and developing scalable recycling solutions are thus critical strategies for sustainability.

EVA remains the benchmark encapsulant due to its low cost and adequate performance, but it suffers from irreversible crosslinking, poor recyclability, and degradation pathways such as yellowing and delamination that limit module lifetime [1, 3]. To align with CE strategies, novel non-crosslinking and recyclable encapsulants are needed. Renewable polymers synthesized via precision polymerization, ring-opening metathesis polymerization (ROMP) and alternating ROMP (AROMP) attract interest of researchers nowadays [4–7]. These materials offer tunable structure–property relationships and inherent recyclability, making them prospective candidates to compete with EVA in both durability and CE compatibility.

Recent progress in continuous-flow ROMP further strengthens this direction. Flow setups enable faster polymerizations, improved molecular weight control, higher reproducibility, and easier scale-up compared to batch systems [8, 9]. These features are particularly relevant for translating bio-based ROMP/AROMP polymers from laboratory concepts to industrial encapsulants. By connecting advances in polymer design with requirements for PV reliability and circularity, this review highlights both the opportunities and the outstanding challenges for next generation encapsulant development. The urgent demand for systematic and comprehensive evaluation drives interest of researchers and represents the biggest interdisciplinary gap between materials, synthetic approaches and practical applications within CE goals.

2. METHODOLOGY

This multidisciplinary review follows four steps:

1. The study is based on an extensive literature synthesis of polymer chemistry and encapsulant requirements for the potential application in PV.
2. Benchmarking of current advances of ROMP/AROMP polymers derived from bioresources and their precursors against EVA with respect to transparency, glass transition temperature (Tg), thermal stability, recyclability, and UV resistance.
3. CE assessment prospectives, including degradability pathways and recycling strategies.
4. The study is finalized by a gap analysis and discussion to identify limitations and define future research opportunities.

3. RESULTS AND DISCUSSION

3.1 State of the art of ROMP/AROMP Polymers

The development of bio-based ROMP and AROMP polymers has expanded rapidly in recent 5 years, driven by the need for sustainable functional materials in various fields of applications [10]. It can be associated with unique features, such as:

1. **Versatility of monomers.** This enables integration of renewable feedstocks directly into high-performance polymers [11].
2. **Precision in structure–property control.** Advanced strategies such as AROMP or living ROMP enable sequence control and

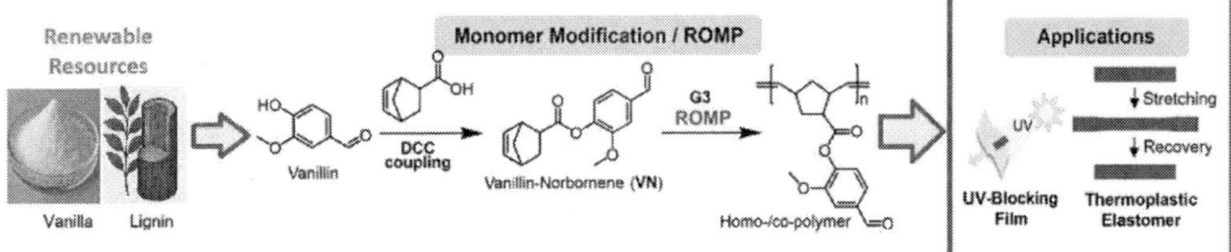

Figure 1: Overview of B. Koo´s study [16]. These materials were evaluated for use in UV-blocking films and TPEs [16].

programmed degradability [12–14].

3. **Compatibility with CE goals and needs.** ROMP polymers can be designed for chemical recyclability (via acid-triggered depolymerization or mechanochemical scission) [10].

4. **Demonstrated performance in functional materials.** ROMP-based systems already exhibited UV resistance, optical clarity, and tunable mechanical strength across different studies [5, 13, 15]. Therefore, their properties are directly transferable to PV encapsulant requirements. Although comprehensive datasets on long-term durability, moisture ingress, and standardized PV qualification testing are still limited, the reported results clearly demonstrate the potential of these materials to meet encapsulant performance demands.

The comparison of benchmarking EVA, vanillin-derived ROMP and furan/maleic anhydride-derived AROMP polymers is represented in Tab 1. Vanillin, derived from lignin biomass, has been functionalized as a ROMP monomer [16]. It can be seen from Tab.1, that the resulting polymer exhibited glass transition temperatures (Tg) up to 95 °C, high optical transparency, and mechanical flexibility [16]. In addition, vanillin-derived polymers have been processed into UV-blocking films with enhanced thermal and mechanical properties compared to conventional thermoplastic elastomers (TPEs) [16]. It can be seen in Fig 1, that lignin-derived vanillin, was chemically modified via DCC coupling to attach a norbornene group, forming the monomer VN. This VN was polymerized using a G3 catalyst to create pVN and block copolymers. These findings highlight the potential of lignin-derived feedstocks to combine sustainability with performance in PV encapsulants (Fig. 1).

Sun et al. introduced an elegant strategy to access degradable polymers by AROMP of biomass-derived exo-oxanorbornenes and cyclic enol ethers (Fig. 2) [17]. Exo-oxanorbornenes were synthesized from furan and maleic anhydride via a Diels–Alder reaction, followed by acyl substitution, providing thermodynamically stable monomers resistant to retro-Diels–Alder processes [17]. The resulting copolymers showed >94% alternation, tunable molecular weights, and Tg values from 11 to 98 °C, with imide-containing monomers yielding the highest stability [17]. Crucially, the alternating architecture enabled acid-triggered depolymerization into low-molecular-weight fragments (<1000 Da), while homopolymers remained stable, proving that degradability originates from enol ether units [17]. This work highlights how renewable monomers and precision polymerization can deliver programmed chemical recycling while maintaining versatile thermal and mechanical properties, aligning with CE goals.

themselves are critical for circular encapsulant design. Aydonat et al. demonstrated that mechanochemistry using mechanical force to trigger chemical reactions, can induce controlled bond scission and depolymerization in otherwise robust polymer networks [18]. This approach offers an attractive route for prospective PV encapsulants, as it provides energy-efficient recycling pathways that avoid harsh solvents or extreme processing conditions. Integrating mechanochemical recycling into the life cycle of ROMP/AROMP materials could therefore further enhance their alignment with CE principles.

3.2 Molecular design strategies in ROMP

Molecular design in ROMP and alternating ROMP enables a wide range of strategies to balance in-use stability with programmed EoL degradation.

An entirely different class of monomers was recently introduced by Jiang et al., who developed monosaccharide-derived cyclic ketene acetals (CKAs) from glucose, mannose, and galactose [19]. These CKAs undergo fully quantitative, regiospecific, and stereoselective radical ring-opening polymerization (rROP), yielding degradable polyesters with high glass transition temperatures (Tg = 104 °C for P(Glu-CKA); 102 °C for P(Man-CKA); 72 °C for P(Gal-CKA)) and decomposition temperatures up to 228 °C [19]. Degradation studies confirmed complete hydrolytic cleavage to lactones under acidic or basic conditions [19]. Moreover, copolymerization with methacrylates and maleimides enabled uniform incorporation of Glu-CKA, producing degradable terpolymers that fully depolymerized upon alkaline hydrolysis [19]. This sugar-based approach opens a new dimension for bio-based encapsulants, combining high Tg, service stability, and programmed degradability.

ROMP-derived polymers have demonstrated high versatility in biomedical contexts, including drug release, sensing, and cellular uptake. As summarized by Gandra et al., ROMP enables precise functionalization with hydrophilic, hydrophobic, and bioactive groups; self-assembly into stable nanostructures; and incorporation of cleavable units for programmable degradation [20]. These attributes, such as functional tunability, self-assembly, stability, and controlled degradability are promising transfer to PV encapsulation. In principle, such design strategies could be exploited to introduce UV stabilizers or adhesion promoters, build nanoscale barriers against

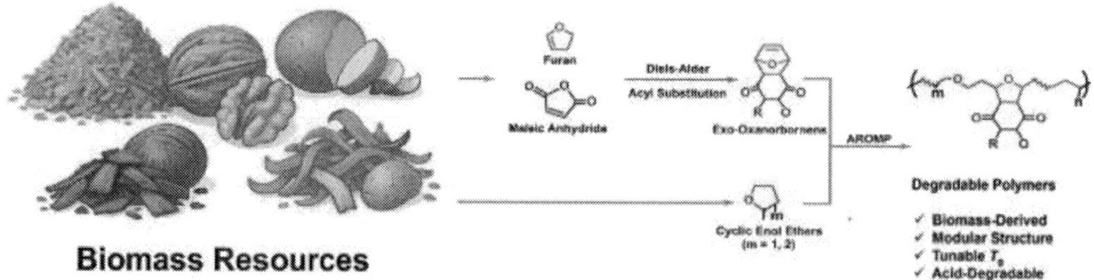

Figure 2: Degradable polymers were synthesized via AROMP using biomass-derived exo-oxanorbornenes and cyclic enol ethers [17]. Two enol ethers: 2,3-dihydrofuran and 3,4-dihydropyran were explored to tune the polymer properties such as thermal stability and degradability [17].

moisture ingress, and encode EoL into encapsulant architectures. Recent progress in living ROMP has shown that it is possible to precisely control polymer architecture at the monomer-sequence level. Elling et al., demonstrated that single monomer units can be placed at defined positions within ROMP chains [21]. This opens opportunities to embed functional units, for instance, UV stabilizers or cleavable linkers directly in situ into the backbone. Such precision design could be exploited to tailor encapsulants for both long-term stability and controlled EoL degradation, bridging performance requirements with recyclability.

Microstructural engineering has recently emerged as a powerful strategy to tune polymer performance for energy and environmental applications. Starvaggi et al., extended this concept by incorporating dihydrofuran (DHF) into ROMP of cyclooctadiene (COD) and cyclooctene (COE). The resulting alternating copolymers featured regularly distributed acetal linkages in the backbone, which acted as programmed weak points [22]. Such design illustrates how degradability can be encoded directly into otherwise robust polyolefin-like materials, advancing the vision of recyclable encapsulants for PV modules. Xue et al., demonstrated that controlling chain length distribution, stereo- and regioregularity, and sequence architecture enables tailoring of crystallinity, Tg, permeability, and degradation kinetics without altering overall chemical composition [23]. These insights are highly relevant for engineering of PV encapsulants: microstructural control in ROMP and AROMP systems could be exploited to balance optical transparency, mechanical stability, and durability, while encoding programmed EoL degradation.

In addition to degradable systems, reversible alternating copolymerizations represent another path towards sustainable materials. Zhang et al. (2023) reported aldehyde–anhydride alternating copolymers that are chemically recyclable back to monomers under acidic conditions [24]. A recent comprehensive review by Purohit et al., synthesizes the state of the art in degradable and chemically recyclable polymers enabled by ROMP and AROMP for CE [25]. Two pillars emerge: (i) backbone-degradable ROMP via monomer design that embeds acid/base-labile motifs (acetal/ketal, orthoester, silyl ether, phosphoramidate, enol ether), and (ii) chemically recyclable POs analogues engineered through ring-strain energy (RSE) and ceiling-temperature (Tc) control [25].

However, current limitations include bench-scale demonstrations, multistep monomer synthesis, energy-intensive conditions, the cost and toxicity of Ruthenium-based (Ru) catalysts. Authors emphasized the need for organocatalytic or non-toxic alternatives and for systematic durability assessments, including hydrolytic and photostability tests directly relevant to PV encapsulants [25].

Collectively, these strategies show that ROMP/AROMP can integrate renewable feedstocks, functional tunability, precision sequence control, degradable linkages, and reversible thermodynamics to deliver bio-derived that are transparent, mechanically stable, UV-resistant and recyclable at EoL of PV modules.

4. CRITICAL PERSPECTIVES: DESIGN STRATEGY FOR CIRCULAR PV ENCAPSULANTS

The transition from EVA to truly circular bio-based encapsulants requires balancing in-use reliability (optical clarity, UV/moisture stability, adhesion, Tg) with EoL pathways (chemical recycling, hydrolytic or acid/base degradation, and even upcycling). Recently overviewed studies demonstrate that such balance is achievable through molecular design in ROMP and AROMP systems [11, 16, 17, 26, 27].

Lessons from POs, and TPOs degradation underline the need for multi-parameter optimization [3]. Future bio-based encapsulants must integrate:

(i) Thermomechanical tuning: AROMP copolymers and vanillin-based ROMP segments provide Tg ranges from 11 to 98 °C, enabling design of multiphase systems for adhesion and service stability.

(ii) Optical/UV control: lignin biomass derived ROMP forms UV-blocking films, while alternating architectures enable precise integration of stabilizers without sacrificing transparency.

(iii) Programmed degradation: acetal- or ester-rich AROMP backbones undergo predictable acid/base cleavage, with sequence-defined placement of labile units ensuring recyclability without premature hydrolysis .

(iv) Renewable sourcing and scalable synthesis: oxanorbornene monomers from furans and itaconic anhydride demonstrate solvent-free, atom-economic routes, aligning material innovation with supply sustainability.

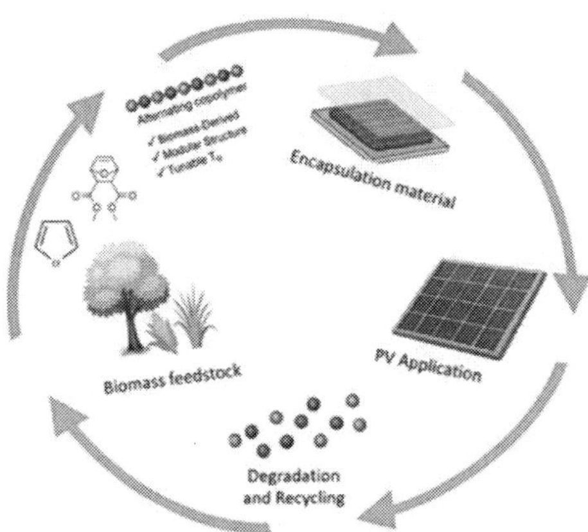

Figure 3: A schematic diagram of the proposed closed-loop model for novel bio-based PV encapsulation materials.

Yet, vulnerabilities remain. As Oladele et al. emphasized, environmental factors (UV radiation, humidity, chemical exposure) continue to challenge durability, requiring stabilizer chemistry and surface modifications [5]. Moreover, high density of degradable motifs may compromise service stability, demanding careful spatial distribution of cleavable units.

Looking forward, the rational design of circular encapsulants will hinge on the choice of precursors and functional groups. Biomass-derived aromatics such as vanillin offer rigid, conjugated structures that enhance UV resistance, transparency, and thermal stability, while hydroxyl and methoxy groups provide handles for functionalization and adhesion to glass. Furan- and itaconic-derived oxanorbornenes contribute to ROMP reactivity and enable incorporation of acetal or enol-ether motifs, which act as acid/base-labile linkages for programmed degradation. Cyclic enol ethers such as 2,3-dihydrofuran provide enthalpy-driven ROMP pathways with tuneable depolymerization kinetics, critical for chemical recycling. Sugar-derived cyclic ketene acetals add another dimension: they combine high Tg with ester backbones that undergo hydrolytic cleavage, ensuring service stability and recyclability.

By combining these biomass-derived precursors, i.e. aromatics for stability and optical clarity, enol ethers and acetals for degradability, and saccharide-derived esters for high-Tg tunability, a new bunch of engineered encapsulants can be tailored to satisfy the stringent demands of photovoltaics.

Fig. 3 illustrates the proposed closed-loop concept for bio-based PV encapsulants. Renewable feedstocks such as lignin, furans, oils and saccharides are converted into ROMP/AROMP monomers, enabling precision polymerization into encapsulants with tailored stability and recyclability. After service, programmed degradation pathways (acid/base cleavage, mechanochemical scission, reversible depolymerization) allow recovery of monomers or value-added fragments, which can be reintegrated into the material cycle. This model highlights how molecular design strategies translate into a practical CE framework for PV encapsulation.

5. CONCLUSIONS AND OUTLOOK

Bio-based ROMP and AROMP polymers offer a credible route to circular PV encapsulants by combining durability with programmed recyclability. Vanillin-derived systems provided high transparency, UV resistance, flexibility, and Tg up to 95 °, while AROMP copolymers from furan/enol ethers show tunable Tg (11–98 °C) and complete acid-triggered degradability. Mechanochemistry enables solvent-free recycling, precision ROMP/AROMP allows embedding stabilizers or cleavable units, and reversible copolymerizations demonstrate true closed-loop pathways.

To transfer these concepts into PV encapsulation practice, several priorities emerge:

1. Catalyst footprint minimization: residual Ru (from Grubbs catalyst systems) must be reduced to sub-ppm levels via short-residence synthesis, scavenging, and post-polymerization deactivation.
2. Flow manufacturing: continuous-flow ROMP/ROP offers faster kinetics, narrower dispersities, safer operation, and better scalability.
3. Architectural strategies: low-density cleavable motifs (acetal, enol-ether) act as "molecular fuses" maintaining in-service stability but enabling mild depolymerization at EoL
4. Benign catalysis: development of organocatalytic or non-toxic metal pathways is critical to overcome cost and toxicity concerns.

Remaining challenges include lack of long-term durability data under UV, humidity, and thermal cycling; absence of standardized encapsulant testing protocols; limited module-level demonstrations; and uncertainties in scalability and economy.

In conclusion, ROMP/AROMP bio-polymers establish a materials design toolbox for circular PV encapsulation. By integrating thermomechanical tuning, UV/moisture resistance, and programmed degradation, these systems can merge operational reliability with CE goals.

ACKNOWLEDGMENTS

This contribution has been developed in the project PLan_CV. Within the funding programme FH-Personal, the project PLan_CV (reference number 03FHP109) which is funded by the Federal Ministry for Economic Affairs and Energy (BMWE) and Joint Science Conference (GWK).

6. REFERENCES

1   A. I. Abian, S. Azam, D. Ompong, D. Mathur, *Solar Energy* 2025, *301*, 113927.

2   A. Mdallal, A. Yasin, M. Mahmoud, M. A. Abdelkareem, A. H. Alami, A. G. Olabi (2025), *Sustainable Horizons*, 13, Elsevier B.V.

3   A. K. Schnatmann, F. Schoden, E. Schwenzfeier-Hellkamp (2022), *Sustainability (Switzerland)*, 14, MDPI.

4   Francis O. Boadi, Jingling Zhang, Xiaoxi Yu, Surita R. Bhatia, Nicole S. Sampson, *Macromolecules* 2020, *53* (14), 5857–5868.

5   I. O. Oladele, V. O. Oki, T. F. Omotosho, M. B. Adebanjo, O. T. Ayanleye, S. A. Adekola (2025), *Next Materials*, 8, Elsevier B.V.

6   Benjamin R. Elling and Yan Xia, *Journal of the American Chemical Society* 2015, *137* (31), 9922–9926.

7   U. R. Gandra, S. K. Podiyanachari, H. S. Bazzi, M. Al-Hashimi (2022), *ACS Omega*, 8, American Chemical Society.

8   Y. Liu, S. Ou, J. Wu, R. Zhao, R. Hou, X. Li, Y. Sun, Y. Li, X. Hu, N. Zhu, K. Guo, *European Polymer Journal* 2024, *216*, 113288.

9   M. G. Banwell, X. Liu, L. A. Connal, M. G. Gardiner, *Macromolecules* 2020, *53* (13), 5308–5314.

10   V. B. Purohit, M. Pięta, J. Pietrasik, C. M. Plummer (2024), *European Polymer Journal*, 208, Elsevier Ltd.

11   T. Ibrahim and H. Sun, *ACS Applied Polymer Materials* 2024, *6* (23), 14076–14083.

12   Na Chuan Jiang, Zefeng Zhou, Jia Niu, *Journal of the American Chemical Society* 2024, *146* (8), 5056–5062.

13   S. Aydonat, Adrian H. Hergesell, Claire L. Seitzinger, R. Lennarz, G. Chang, C. Sievers, J. Meisner, I. Vollmer, R. Göstl (2024), *Polymer Journal*, 56, Springer Nature.

14   K. A. Parker and N. S. Sampson (2016), *Accounts of Chemical Research*, 49, American Chemical Society.

15   Y. Xue, M. Cao, C. Chen, M. Zhong (2023), *JACS Au*, 3, American Chemical Society.

16   Byungjin Koo, *ACS Applied Polymer Materials* 2024, *6* (3), 1653–1661.

17   H. Sun, T. Ibrahim, A. Ritacco, K. Durkee, *ACS Macro Letters* 2023, *12* (12), 1642–1647.

18   S. Aydonat, A. H. Hergesell, C. L. Seitzinger, R. Lennarz, G. Chang, C. Sievers, J. Meisner, I. Vollmer, R. Göstl, *Polymer Journal* 2024, *56* (4), 249–268.

19   N.-C. Jiang, Z. Zhou, J. Niu, *Journal of the American Chemical Society* 2024, *146* (8), 5056–5062.

20   U. R. Gandra, S. K. Podiyanachari, H. S. Bazzi, M. Al-Hashimi, *ACS Omega* 2023, *8* (2), 1724–1738.

21   B. R. Elling, J. K. Su, J. D. Feist, Y. Xia, *Chem* 2019, *5* (10), 2691–2701.

22   F. A. Starvaggi, B. A. Suslick, Y. Xia, *ACS Macro Letters* 2024, *13* (3), 296–301.

23   Y. Xue, M. Cao, C. Chen, M. Zhong, *JACS Au* 2023, *3* (5), 1284–1300.

24   X. Zhang, W. Guo, C. Zhang, X. Zhang, *Nature Communications* 2023, *14* (1), 5423.

25   V. B. Purohit, M. Pięta, J. Pietrasik, C. M. Plummer, *European Polymer Journal* 2024, *208*, 112847.

26   Kelly A.E. Amorim, Virgínia C.A. Martins, Benedito S. Lima-Neto, *Polymer* 2025, *317*.

27   Benjamin R. Elling, Jessica K. Su, John D. Feist, Yan Xia, *Chem* 2019, *5* (10), 2691–2701.

RELIABILITY OF ELECTRICALLY CONDUCTIVE ADHESIVE JOINTS FOR PERC AND HJT-BASED BUILDING-INTEGRATED PHOTOVOLTAIC FACADE ELEMENTS

R. Koepge, S. Jahreis, J. Froebel, N. Schröter, M. Pander, S. Großer, B. Jaeckel
Fraunhofer Center for Silicon Photovoltaics CSP
Otto-Eissfeldt-Strasse 12, 06120 Halle, Germany
ringo.koepge@csp.fraunhofer.de

ABSTRACT: Integrating photovoltaic solutions directly into building facades presents a crucial strategy for achieving Europe's goal of climate neutrality by 2050. A widespread adoption of building-integrated photovoltaics (BIPV) can bolster energy security, diversify the energy mix, and create new green jobs. By seamlessly integrating renewable energy generation into our cities, BIPV becomes a cornerstone of a sustainable future for Europe and keeping aesthetic and functional benefits, such as providing shade, mitigating heat gain, and enhancing the overall building envelope performance. To achieve such goals, especially the building and construction sectors needs to be facilitated to adapt photovoltaic technologies into their production and value chains. With the results of the AluPV project, we will demonstrate how PV production processes and material combination can be adapted to realize PV-integrated aluminum facades as building-integrated photovoltaics elements. One main objective is to adapt the manufacturing process to handle redesigned photovoltaics modules, in terms of electrical adaptation due to other dimensional and architecture constraints and mechanical structures due to direct incorporation with Al-façade elements. Therefore, suitable material combinations and process parameters were studied, with particular attention to reducing mechanical stress and utilizing cost-effective standard PV production equipment. Within the paper, we demonstrate our findings to successfully use commercially available aluminum façade elements as backside encapsulation and solar cell string material layer. Standard industrial lamination equipment was demonstrated to be suitable for cost-efficient production and rapid implementation of the prototype into the production line. A material study will show an optimum of material types and layers for reliable façade modules. Test sequences according to IEC are performed and performance measurements as well as electroluminescence (EL) images were applied to quantify our findings. In summary, multiple challenges related to manufacturing and material selection were addressed, especially the differences in the thermal expansion of the materials. Modules with an aluminum back sheet show less moisture ingress than those with a polymer back sheet, because moisture can only enter through the edges. This effect is independent of cell technology; there is no observed difference between PERC cells and HJT cells. This investigation will give significant feedback regarding reliability of façade solar modules to improve manufacturing processes. and increase the acceptance of building integrated PV on the market.

1 INTRODUCTION

The EU has set itself the binding target of achieving climate neutrality by 2050 - emissions are to be reduced by at least 55% by 2030 [1]. Globally, it is important to align development, economic, financial, energy and transport policies with climate protection goals. Energy generation from photovoltaic systems plays a decisive role in achieving the desired goals. A current draft of the European Commission has targeted a 90% share of EU electricity from renewables by 2040 – mostly solar and wind – and complemented by nuclear energy. BIPV market is still rising, and the potential is currently hardly used. The current market share is less than 3% [2]. Challenging is the requirement of reliable and in shape integration into existing architectural elements [3]. One aspect is the development of BIPV facade elements. The evaluation of suitable material combinations and economic manufacturing process parameters plays an important role in the implementation of prototypes for industrial series production.

Within this work PV solar cell strings and encapsulation were integrated into commercially available aluminum façade elements. Suitable material combinations and processes have been studied. Approaches for mechanical stress reduction and the use of economic standard PV production equipment were successfully evaluated [4]. We implemented different electrically conductive adhesive (ECA) strings and different solar cell technology (PERC and HJT) strings and performed a material variation to identify suitable and reliable façade modules.

Current investigations address the reliability of façade modules that were manufactured by direct lamination. The production of PV integrated aluminum façades places high demands on the material composite. Due to the different coefficients of thermal expansion, internal stresses are introduced into the façade solar module. Cracks can occur in the cell connectors joints, in the glass and delamination of the encapsulation can take place. A manufacturing process will be presented that shows a defective free aluminum façade element ready for application in BIPV. Delamination issues as well as module bending caused by different thermal expansions during the manufacturing are not detected. Smart pressure distribution during the lamination process is the key for flawless manufacturing. Electroluminescence (EL) images give evidence for properly working solar cell strings without cell breakage. Magnetic field imaging (MFI) was also used for investigation, which provided evidence of properly functioning solar cell strings without interconnector failures [5]. It is shown that standard industrial lamination equipment can be used to ensure cost-efficient production and rapid implementation of the prototype into the production line. To overcome the high different coefficients of thermal expansion two major paths are followed. On the one hand a variation of materials was performed. On the other hand, two different types of electrically conductive adhesive were used to see the influence of reliability. In addition, HJT cells strings are compared to reliability of PERC cell strings in façade modules.

2 MATERIALS & METHODS

2.1 Manufacturing

Different material combinations were used to investigate the influence of thermal cycling on the reliability of the solar modules. The Table 1 shows the bill of material (BOM) for each module batch. Batch B0 was the reference batch, a glass back sheet module with a standard solder cell connection. The batches from B1 to B6 are facade solar modules with an aluminum facade as back sheet. Material component substitutions take place. Thus, a change from solder to ECA connection (B2), a change of the encapsulant from POE to EVA (B6), the electrical isolation was changed from polyester foil (modified polyester - MPE) to a polymer fiber mesh (B7), a change of cell type from PERC to HJT (B8) and finally the acrylic based ECA instead of epoxy bases ECA was used (B9). The material stack is illustrated in Figure 1.

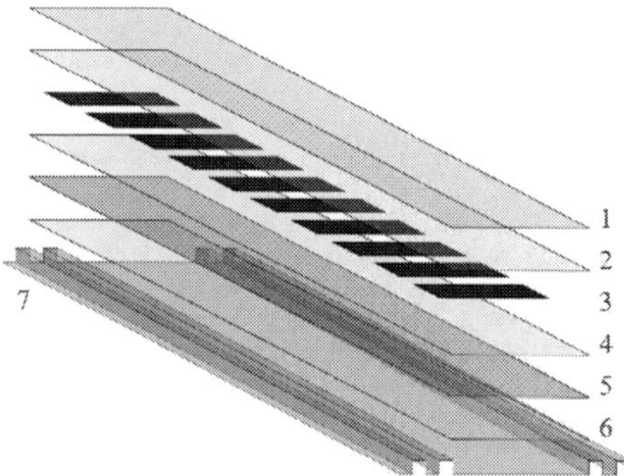

Figure 1 BIPV module, a) layup stack of module materials (1 – Front Glass, 2 – Encapsulant, 5 – Insulation Layer, 4 – Encapsulant, 3 – Cell String, 6 - Encapsulant, 7 - Facade)

The cell connectors are not shown as well as the back sheet at layer position seven, the figure shows the aluminum facade at layer number seven. On the top of the Solar panel an Opti-White glass with a thickness of 3 mm was used, without any anti reflection coating. The encapsulants (EVA and POE) were commercial materials from the market. The cell strings were manufactured with 9BB PERC and 0BB HJT cells with Team Technik TT Lab i8 ECA stringer. The solder string batch B1 was manufactured with a Komax Solar's Xcell X3 Stringer with 5BB PERC. The aluminum facade sheet was provided by project partner MN Metall. Finally, the layup was made manually before the material stack runs into the lamination process. The Lamination takes place at a vacuum laminator ICOLAM 28/26 from SM Inno Tech GmbH & Co. KG. The following Figure 2 shows a aluminum facade with a PV activation after lamination process.

Figure 2 BIPV module, a PV activated aluminum facade after lamination process.

2.2 Treatment

After manufacturing the modules are tested by accelerated ageing test according to the IEC standard [6, 7]. The major focus is on the thermal cycling (sequence E) of the modules. Caused by the huge thermal deformation of the aluminum facade at the back side of the module, a connector fail between the cells is assumed. In addition, a multiple stressor test (sequence B) was performed for all batches, and a damp heat test (sequence D) was performed on a selection of samples. The following Table 2 shows an overview of the batch treatment.

Table 1 Sample Overview for reliability testing (POE – Polyolefin Elastomer, PERC - Passivated Emitter and Rear Cell, MPE – Modified Polyester, PF – Polymer Fiber, EVA - Ethylenvinylacetat, HJT - Heterojunction Solar Cell, SnPb – Tin Lead, ECA – Electrically Conductive Adhesive)

Batch		B1	B2	B3	B4	B5	B6	B7	B8	B9
Material layer	1	Glass	Glass	Glass	Glass	Glass	Glass	Glass	Glass	Glass
	2	POE	EVA	POE	POE	POE	EVA	POE	POE	POE
	3	M3-10HC PERC	M6-6HC PERC	M6-6HC PERC	M6-10HC PERC	M6-6HC PERC	M6-10HC PERC	M6-10HC PERC	M6-6HC HJT	M6-10HC PERC
	4	POE	EVA	POE	POE	POE	EVA	POE	POE	POE
	5	MPE	-	BS	MPE	MPE	MPE	PF	MPE	MPE
	6	POE	-	Adhesive	POE	POE	EVA	POE	POE	POE
	7	Facade	BS	Facade	Facade	Facade	Facade	Facade	Facade	Facade
Connection		SnPb Solder	ECA1 Epoxy based							ECA2 Acrylic-based

2.3 Characterization

Module characterization was done using a HALM Cetis PV-Moduletest 4 A+A+A+ Solar simulator. The repeatability of the system is usually better than 0.15 % for maximum power determination. Flash measurements were done at STC conditions and 200 W/m². For the HJT cells hysteresis compensation is performed by incorporating a forward and backward measurement. Electroluminescence images were taken in a commercial EL system from Halm with a cooled CCD camera. The injection current was set close to ISC (5 A) and at 10 % ISC (500 mA). Since there were no issues related to shunting that are more pronounced under low irradiance and low current injection, we limit the presented results to the STC characterization. In addition, magnetic field imaging (MFI) was performed at sample with an abnormal performance drop. Magnetic field imaging visualizes the current flow in photovoltaic modules in a non-invasive manner by measuring triaxial magnetic fields above the glass during a constant current injection (e.g., ISC = 5 A). Using a DENKWEIT B-LAB with a 160 mm magnetically sensitive line sensor on a motorized x-y-z table scans are created at a constant distance spatial maps of B_x, B_y, B_z in micro tesla.

Table 2 Overview of applied test sequences according to IEC 61730 and IEC 61215 standards

	Sequence B Multiple Tests	Sequence D Damp Heat	Sequence E Thermal Cycling
B1	2 Samples	2 Samples	2 Samples
B2	0 Samples	2 Samples	2 Samples
B3	0 Samples	2 Samples	2 Samples
B4	2 Samples	2 Samples	2 Samples
B5	0 Samples	2 Samples	2 Samples
B6	2 Samples	0 Samples	2 Samples
B7	1 Samples	0 Samples	2 Samples
B8	0 Samples	2 Samples	2 Samples
B9	2 Samples	0 Samples	2 Samples

After offset/background correction and filtering, false-color maps of the field components (often B_y) co-registered with EL images qualitatively show the current paths without requiring a full inversion. Defects such as desoldering, misalignments, or broken connections disturb the otherwise uniform field and create local inhomogeneities, enabling rapid, non-contact diagnosis, with the resolution determined by the sensor spacing and distance.

3 RESULTS

The following chapter contains the relative power loss of solar modules after damp heat (Seq. D), thermal cycling (Seq. E) and multiple stressor testing (Seq. B). In addition, electroluminescence images were made of all modules and abnormal modules with increased power loss are presented in the following chapter. Magnetic field measurements were performed on abnormal modules, which are also shown.

3.1 Performance Loss

Damp Heat | The duration of each test of this study is not equal, caused by delays in manufacturing. The results of the damp heat treatment are shown in Figure 3. We can see the time of duration versus the relative power loss. Batches B1 (Solder) and B5 (ECA1) have the highest duration time of 3000 hours. Both batches pass the IEC 5% limit at 1000 hours.

With an increase in damp heat duration time, we see an increase of the power loss up to almost minus 3 and minus 7 percent for the ECA batch B4. In comparison the solder batch shows less power loss. This is attributed to cell batch and metallization paste which is more stable for the older M3 cells of B1. Further it can be correlated to a smaller cell size, that means a bigger distance from the facade edges to the solar cells. Diffusion of water from the outside to the cells is impeded. The other batches are still pending. Currently Batches B5 and B8 show equally stable

behavior with less than 1.2 % power loss after 1000 h. The B3 batch is on the faster degradation path with 2.2 and 2.8 % after 1000 h. B2 shows the strongest degradation with 2.6 and 3.4 % already after 1000 h and more than 15 % after 2000 h. The test was stopped after 2250 h with a power loss of more than 20 %. This demonstrates the susceptibility of these cells to humidity related degradation.

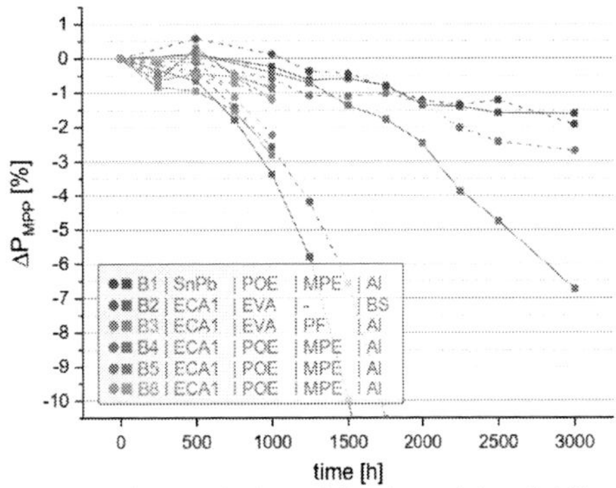

Figure 3 Characterization of facade module reliability. Damp Heat results, Reference Batches of solder connection (B1) and ECA connection (B4) finished at 3000 hours. B2 is finished after 2250 hours because of too high degradation

Thermal Cycling | The highest mechanical stress was caused by the thermal cycling test. Again, non-equal number of cycles are caused by different finishing times in manufacturing. Differences in thermal expansion of the aluminum facade at the backside and the rest of solar module materials stress the cell connectors. The power loss after thermal cycling is shown in Figure 4.

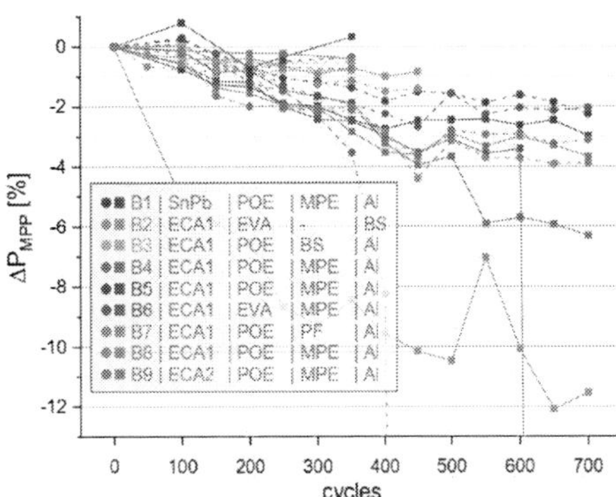

Figure 4 Characterization of facade module reliability. Results of thermal cycling tests after 350 and 700 cycle treatment.

All batches pass the IEC standard of 200 cycles with a power loss of less than 5 percent. The most abnormal facade module behavior until 700 cycles was observed for batch B7 (polymer fiber mesh) and batch B4 (ECA1 facade reference). A drop of 4 to 12 percent was detected for batch B7 and a drop of 6 percent to total failure was observed for batch B4. All the other batches show almost equal behavior. The batches finishing the 700 cycles show a drop of maximum 4 percent apart from the abnormal module batches. The batches of 350 cycles are still pending till reaching the 700 cycles but, the current drop in power loss is lower in comparison to the finished batches (B1, B4, B6, B7, B9).

Multiple Stressor | The last aging test was a multiple stressor sequence. Only five batches were tested. Figure 5 shows the results. For efficiency reasons, no UV60 treatment was carried out on the reverse side, as irradiating aluminum from behind in the desired application is not necessary. Almost all samples with the exception Batch B7 shows a power loss of less than 1.5%, which is an excellent result. The highest power loss is recorded in sample B7. The cause of the 2.5% is unclear. Approximately 1% is attributable to a loss in I_{sc} and 1% to a lower FF. The following Table 3 shows an overview of the final performance drop of each facade module after treatment.

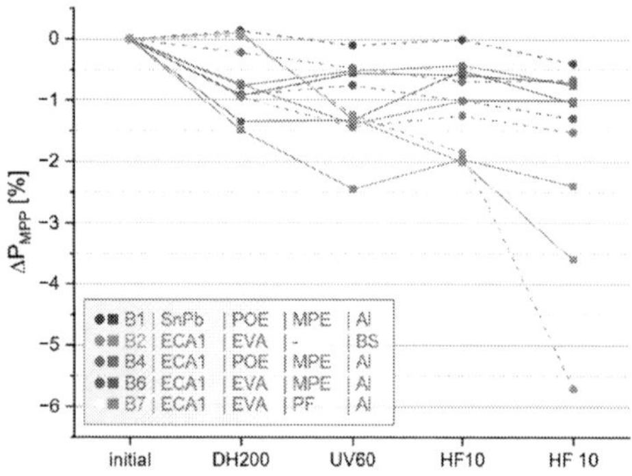

Figure 5 Characterization of facade module reliability. Results of multiple stressor tests after Damp Heat, UV60 and humidity Freeze treatment.

Table 3 Overview of relative module degradation at the end of testing

	Damp Heat	Thermal Cycling	Multiple Stressor
B1	-1.6 | -1.9	-2.2 | -3.0*	-0.4 | -0.7
B2	-21.2 | -32.7	-1.0 | -1.8*	-3.6 | -5.7
B3	-1.1 | -1.5*	-0.5 | -0.8*	not tested
B4	-2.7 | -6.7	-6.3 | fail	-0.7 | -0.8
B5	-0.5 | -0.5	-0.3 | -0.4	not tested
B6	not tested	-2.0 | fail	not tested
B7	not tested	-3.9 | -11.5	-2.4
B8	-0.5 | -0.7*	-0.4 | -0.8*	not tested
B9	not tested	-3.1 | -3.7	-1.0 | -1.5
*Treatment not finished			

3.2 Module Fails

The aluminum facade modules do not show a clear trend of degradation regarding the bill of materials. The Table 3 shows an overview of facade module degradation. The modules with the highest degradation are investigated in more detail by EL and MFI.

Damp Heat | There is a problem with the cross connection at solder joint in Batch B1, which is unusual for DH and could indicate a cold solder joint. The existing cracks remain stable, see Figure 6. Otherwise, there are hardly any anomalies. A performance change of around 1.5%

seems plausible. It is noteworthy that another cross-connection failed after approximately 4,250 operating hours (not shown in the graph), indicating a potential systematic problem with the connections.

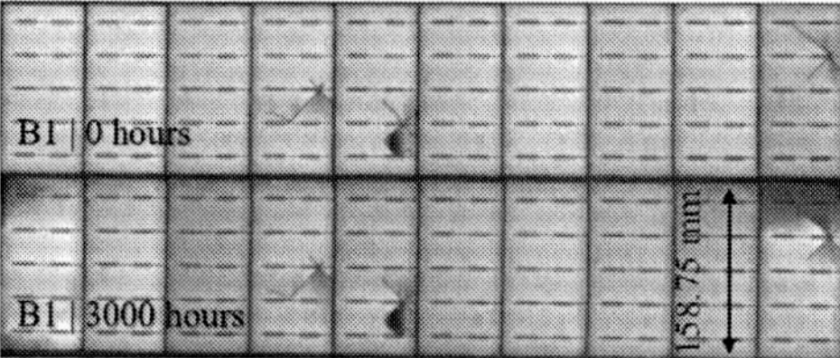

Figure 6 EL Images of one Module of Batch B1

With Charge B2, the power loss for the DH1000 remains below 5%, but a negative trend is already apparent. In the following stages, the loss increases disproportionately. With the DH2000, the power reduction is already more than 15%. EL images correlate to the power loss, see Figure 7. In batch B4 (ECA1 facade reference) see Figure 8, the cracks remain stable. There are slight anomalies at the connection ends, and a performance change of approximately 1.5% appears plausible.

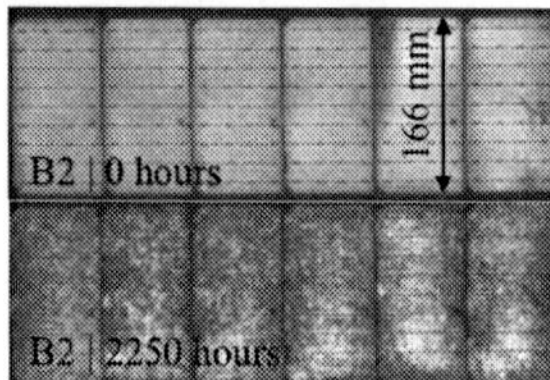

Figure 7 EL Images of one Module of Batch B2

The edges of the bottom and top cells are affected by corrosion. After 1,000 operating hours, moisture-induced degradation, which begins at the edges, is clearly visible and continues to spread, indicating that these cells are more susceptible than soldered cells. The sample is significantly more affected than the parallel sample. After 4,500 hours (not shown here), the sample looks worse than the comparison sample, although the power loss is still moderate at around 3.7%. The areas with connection problems have increased slightly. Once corrosion has set in, the degradation of the cells progresses steadily.

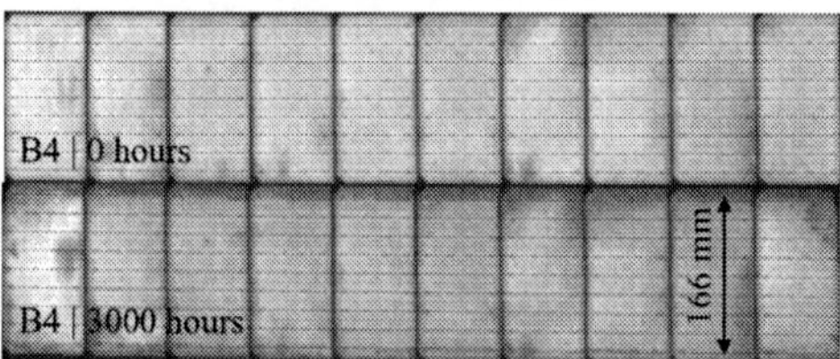

Figure 8 EL Images of one module of Batch B4

Thermal Cycling | We consider 3 times IEC (600 cycles) to be completely sufficient for reliable applications in central Europe. The most important points are that the solder connection is not optimal in all samples and even the soldered samples exhibit problems. Smaller M3 cells may have an advantage over M6 in terms of fatigue, so it should be checked whether 5 mm instead of 10 mm distance between the cell and the cross connection offers an advantage. worse the batches, B7 clearly performs worst, and B4 is scorched at the cross connection equal to a Module of Batch B6, see Figure 9.

Figure 9 Cross connection fail by thermal cycling and current flow

The changes to the BOM have not made much difference so far, and an important lever for noticeable improvements is missing. The modules of batch B9 also shows initial problems, but the dark areas remain stable. Significant anomalies in the lower cross connection. The upper and lower cross connections are also conspicuous in EL and MFI, see Figure 10. A higher magnetic flux density correlates with a higher current density, caused by intact connections covering the defective ones. Thus, not all cell connectors show a proper connection to the cross connector (marked in red), the current flow is strongly inhomogeneous. Two cell connectors have detached from a solar cell and no longer make electrical contact (marked in blue).

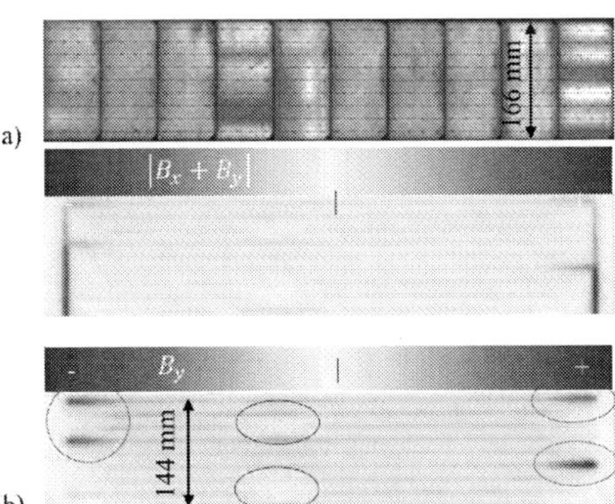

Figure 10 Comparison of EL (a) and Magnetic Field (b) image with failed cross connections of Batch B9

Multiple Stressor | The EL images show no abnormal modules apart from batch B2. The maximum power loss was detected for batch B2 and the EL images correlate to them, see Figure 11.

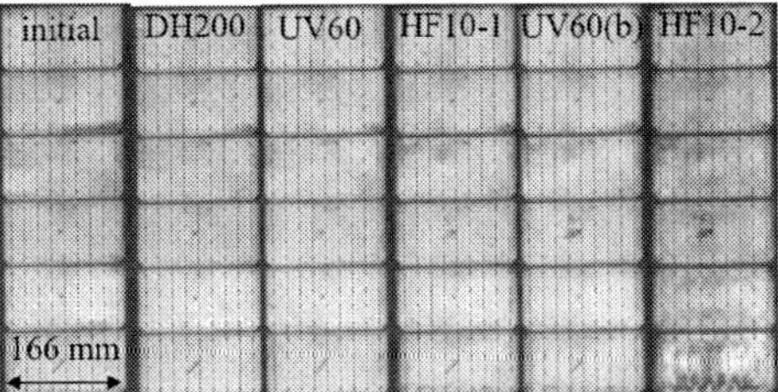

Figure 11 EL Images of Batch B2 for all multiple stress sequences

Crack and Surface artifacts stay stable. A degradation of the entire cells takes place by multiple stressor testing.

4 SUMMARIZE

The evidence was given that aluminum facade modules are ready to use in BIPV application. Less moisture penetration for aluminum facade modules in comparison to back sheet modules was detected. Moisture, and the degradation associated with it, can only enter through the module edge and the junction box. The Facade module degradation of HJT cells and PERC cells are equal and almost independent from material selection, apart from back sheet batch and polymer fiber mesh batch. Magnetic field imaging was used to confirm the cross-connector failure that has been seen in EL imaging and to get more information about current flow.

5 ACKNOWLEDGEMENTS

Financial support by the Federal Ministry for Economic Affairs and Energy funded project "AluPV" (FKZ: 03EN1069B) is gratefully acknowledged.

6 REFERENCES

[1] Document 32021R1119, Regulation (EU) 2021/1119 of the European Parliament and of the Council of 30 June 2021 establishing the framework for achieving climate neutrality and amending Regulations (EC) No 401/2009 and (EU) 2018/1999 ('European Climate Law'), http://data.europa.eu/eli/reg/2021/1119/oj

[2] International Technology Roadmap for Photovoltaics (ITRPV) 2024, Results 16. Edition, May 2025

[3] Wiebke Wirtz, Kevin Meyer, Rolf Brendel, Henning Schulte-Huxel, "Improved robustness against thermal stress for building-integrated PV modules built on aluminum façade elements", Progress in Photovoltaics: Research and Applications, 2025, Vol. 33, Page 717–725, https://doi.org/10.1002/pip.3915

[4] Ringo Koepge, Matthias Pander, Stephan Großer, Bengt Jaeckel, "Process Development and Material Evaluation of Photovoltaic Aluminum Facade Element for BIPV Application", Proceedings, 41st EU PVSEC, 2024

[5] Dominik Lausch, Marcus Patzold, Maik Rudolph, Chia-Mei Lin, Jens Froebel, Kai Kaufmann, "Magnetic Field Imaging (MFI) of Solar Modules", Proceedings, 35th EU PVSEC, 2018

[6] IEC 61215-2:2021, Terrestrial photovoltaic (PV) modules – Design qualification and type approval – Part 2: Test procedures

[7] IEC 61730-2:2023, Photovoltaic (PV) module safety qualification - Part 2: Requirements for testing

Reliability of Electrically Conductive Adhesive Joints for PERC and HJT-based Building-integrated Photovoltaic Facade Elements

Fraunhofer Center
for Silizium Photovoltaik CSP

R. Koepge, S. Jahreis, J. Froebel, N. Schröter, M. Pander, S. Großer, B. Jaeckel

3AV.2.1

Motivation

- The **potential of building integrated PV** is currently hardly used, less than 3% market share[1]

- **Building facades have high potential** to increase the share of PV application **beside the standard PV module** applications on roof tops.

- **Evaluation of suitable material combinations** plays an important role in the implementation of facade modules

- **Prevent material-induced module** failures to secure long-term reliability

Scope of this Study

- Accelerated climate stress testing of different material combinations to demonstrate high reliability of facade solar modules and identify weaknesses

	Reference module	Variation encapsulant (2,4,6) | cell type (3) | electrical insulation layer (5) | back sheet / plate (7) and cell connection type (8)							
Batch	**B1**	**B2**	**B3**	**B4**	**B5**	**B6**	**B7**	**B8**	**B9**	
Material layer 1	Glass	Glass	Glass	Glass	Glass	Glass	Glass	Glass	Glass	
2	POE	EVA	POE	POE	POE	EVA	POE	POE	POE	
3	M3-10HC PERC	M6-6HC PERC	M6-6HC PERC	M6-10HC PERC	M6-6HC PERC	M6-10HC PERC	M6-10HC PERC	M6-6HC HJT	M6-10HC PERC	
4	POE	EVA	POE	POE	POE	EVA	POE	POE	POE	
5	MPE	-	BS	MPE	MPE	MPE	PFM	MPE	MPE	
6	POE	-	Adhesive	POE	POE	EVA	POE	POE	POE	
7	Facade	BS	Facade	Facade	Facade	Facade	Facade	Facade	Facade	
Connection 8	SnPb Solder	Epoxy ECA1							Acrylic ECA2	

Table 1 Overview of manufactured facade modules (POE – Polyolefin Elastomer, PERC – Passivated Emitter and Rear Cell, MPE – Modified Polyester, PF – Polymer Fiber Mesh, EVA - Ethylenvinylacetat HJT - Heterojunction Solar Cell, SnPb – Tin Lead, ECA – Electrically Conductive Adhesive)

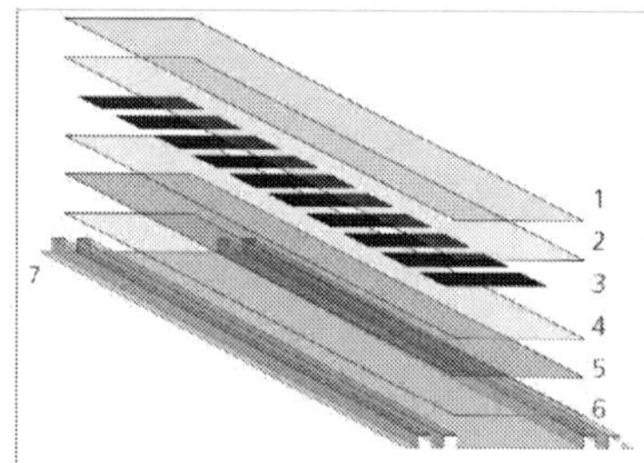

Figure 1 Material stack of facade modules

Results

Damp Heat

- All material are within the IEC pass criteria, less than 5 percent power loss[2]

- All aluminum facades demonstrate better moisture barrier compared to polymer BS

- Higher distance between cell-module edge, B1 compared to B4, increase moisture barrier

Thermal Cycling

- Almost all materials combinations pass the IEC TC200[2]

- Apart from B7 all facade modules pass the TC600 with a power loss of 2 to 4 %[2]

- BS module slightly better than façade module[2]

Manufacturing

- Successful manufacturing of photovoltaic activated building facades

- Optimized manufacturing processes by Fraunhofer CSP

- Ready to hand over to industry

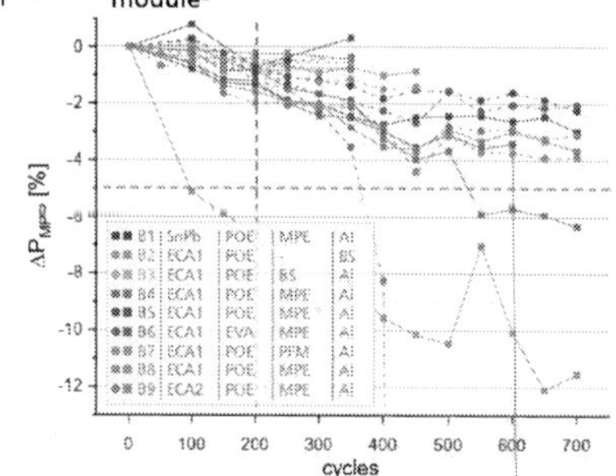

Figure 2 Power loss of each facade module after damp heat treatment

Figure 3 Power loss of each facade module after thermal cycling treatment

Figure 4 Aluminum facade solar module

Ringo Koepge
PV Modules, Components and Manufacturing
Tel. +49 345 5589-5311
Ringo.Koepge@csp.fraunhofer.de
Fraunhofer Center für Silicon Photovoltaics CSP
Otto-Eissfeldt-Strasse 12
06120 Halle
www.csp.fraunhofer.de

Summary

- Evidence was given that **aluminum facade modules are ready to use in BIPV** application

- **Less moisture penetration** for aluminum facade modules in comparison to back sheet modules

- Facade module **degradation of HJT cells and PERC cells are equal and almost independent** from material selection, apart from back sheet batch and polymer fiber mesh batch

[1] *International Technology Roadmap for Photovoltaics (ITRPV) 2024, Results 16. Edition, May 2025.* [2] *Tests have not yet been completed.*

Financial support by the Federal Ministry for Economic Affairs and Energy funded project » AluPV « (grant no.: 03EN1069B) is gratefully acknowledged.

DURABILITY AND RELIABILITY: A CROSS-TECHNOLOGICAL STABILITY ANALYSIS OF SILICON PHOTOVOLTAICS

Mengdi Liu[1], Wenhao Xu[1], Yating Zhang[1], Giorgio Bardizza[2], Christos Monokroussos[1]

[1]TÜV Rheinland (Shanghai) Co., Ltd., No.177, Lane 777, West Guangzhong, 200072, Shanghai, P.R. China

[2]TÜV Rheinland Solar GmbH, Am Grauen Stein, 51105, Cologne, Germany

ABSTRACT: Due to environmental concerns and the depletion of fossil fuels, photovoltaics (PV) is set to play a significant role in meeting future energy demands. For PV technology to be economically feasible, maintaining high efficiency over the typical 25-year lifespan of PV modules is critical. This study examines the reliability of advanced solar cell technologies, namely Passivated Emitter Rear Cell (PERC), Tunnel Oxide Passivated Contact (TOPCon), Heterojunction with Intrinsic Thin layer (HJT), and Back-Contact (BC). Additionally, it compares the durability of different module structures like Glass/Backsheet (G/BS) and Glass/Glass (G/G) under extensive standardized reliability tests according to IEC standards, covering thermal cycling (TC), damp heat (DH), potential induced degradation (PID), light- and elevated temperature-induced degradation (LETID), and ultraviolet-induced degradation (UVID).

The results show that PERC cells exhibit degradation, with a median decrease of approximately 2.0% and 2.3%, after TC600 and DH1000 stress tests, respectively. BC and HJT cells demonstrate low degradation levels, approximately 1.0%, following post-TC200 conditions. BC technology shows the lowest median degradation, around 1.2%, following DH1000 exposure. TOPCon cells exhibit lower degradation rate under thermal cycling and PID. It is particularly notable that in TC600 a mean degradation of 0.3% was observed, while after 96h of PID test the mean degradation stayed below 0.5%. However, they experience higher degradation under UVID, with a median rate of 1.5%. Regarding LETID, both technologies, TOPCon and BC, exhibit low sensitivity, with median degradation levels of 0.3% and 0.1%, respectively. Overall, these results highlight the performance differences between cell technologies and the importance of comprehensive stress testing for informed selection and implementation to enhance the longevity and performance of photovoltaic systems.

Keywords: Reliability, Silicon Photovoltaics,

1 Introduction

As environmental concerns grow and fossil fuel reserves continue to deplete, the generation of electricity via renewable energy sources becomes essential for fulfilling future energy requirements. While a diverse mix of renewable resources will likely satisfy our energy needs, photovoltaic (PV) technology is expected to play a pivotal role. For PV to be commercially viable and sustainable, it is imperative that modules sustain high efficiency over operational durations exceeding 25 years. Therefore, enhancing module reliability is paramount for reducing the Levelized Cost of Energy (LCOE) and ensuring the long-term success of solar energy.

A critical pathway to improving reliability lies in understanding degradation mechanisms. Accelerated stress tests, standardized by the International Electrotechnical Commission (IEC), are indispensable for this purpose, as they simulate years of field exposure in a condensed timeframe. For instance, Thermal Cycling (TC) can identify thermo-mechanical fatigue issues such as cell soldering defects and interconnect failures, while Damp Heat (DH) exposes susceptibility to corrosion and delamination. The continuous evolution of cell technologies—from the industry-dominant Passivated Emitter and Rear Cell (PERC) to advanced designs like Tunnel Oxide Passivated Contact (TOPCon), Heterojunction (HJT), and Back-Contact (BC)—introduces new materials and structures whose long-term behavior must be rigorously compared. Furthermore, module construction elements, such as the choice between Glass/Backsheet (G/BS) and Glass/Glass (G/G) configurations and advanced encapsulants like Polyolefin Elastomer (POE), are increasingly recognized as critical factors influencing longevity.

This study conducts a direct comparison of the degradation behavior of leading commercial cell technologies (PERC, TOPCon, HJT, and BC) and module structures under a comprehensive suite of IEC-standardized tests, including TC, DH, Potential Induced Degradation (PID), and Light- and Elevated Temperature-Induced Degradation (LETID). The findings provide valuable insights into the relative resilience of these technologies. By linking specific degradation signatures to cell technology and module architecture, this work provides critical data to guide the development of more reliable and durable PV modules for the future.

2 Methodology

2.1. Sample Description and Preparation

A set of commercial photovoltaic (PV) modules representing leading cell technologies was selected for this accelerated lifetime testing study. The sample cohort included modules fabricated using PERC, TOPCon, HJT, and BC technologies. To investigate the role of module construction, samples with different structural configurations—specifically G/G and G/BS—and encapsulants (Ethylene-Vinyl Acetate (EVA) and POE) were incorporated.

It is important to note that the sample sizes for certain technologies, particularly PERC and BC, were limited. While sufficient for identifying dominant degradation trends, this limitation precludes definitive statistical conclusions for these groups and indicates a need for further investigation with a larger dataset. All modules underwent initial flash testing (I-V curve measurement) under Standard Test Conditions (STC: 1000 W/m², 25°C, AM1.5G spectrum) to establish a baseline maximum power (Pmax).

10.4229/EUPVSEC2025/3AV.2.3
020144-001

2.2. Stress Testing Protocols

The modules were subjected to a sequence of accelerated stress tests, following relevant portions of the IEC standards [1, 2], to simulate long-term field degradation. The specific tests conducted were:

- Thermal Cycling (TC): Modules underwent 200, 400, and 600 cycles. This test evaluates the resistance to thermo-mechanical stress by cycling the chamber temperature between -40°C and 85°C.

- Damp Heat (DH): Modules were exposed to 1000 hours of damp heat conditions at 85°C and 85% relative humidity to assess the susceptibility to moisture ingress and corrosion.

- Potential Induced Degradation (PID) Testing: PID sensitivity was evaluated under both positive and negative polarities at a voltage of ±1500V, applied for a defined period at 85°C. This test identifies vulnerabilities to ion migration driven by high system voltages.

- Ultraviolet Irradiation and Light- and Elevated Temperature-Induced Degradation (UVID & LETID): Modules were subjected to a prescribed dose of ultraviolet (UV) irradiation. Subsequently, LETID testing was performed by exposing the modules to light at an elevated temperature to activate and monitor this specific degradation mechanism.

Following each stress test sequence (post-TC200, post-TC400, etc.), the modules were removed from the environmental chambers, and their maximum power output (Pmax) was re-measured under STC.

2.3. Measurement and Data Analysis

The power degradation for each module was calculated as the percentage change in Pmax from its initial baseline value. The results are presented using box plots to show the median degradation, variance, and potential outliers for each technology group and test condition. To ensure the reported degradation signals were not artifacts of measurement variance, the uncertainty of the flash tester was rigorously characterized. The expanded measurement uncertainty (k=2) for Pmax was determined to be ±2.0%, with a reproducibility (k=2) of ±0.6%. This high level of reproducibility confirms that the observed degradation trends are indicative of actual module performance changes rather than measurement noise.

3 Results

This section presents the key findings from a series of accelerated stress tests designed to evaluate the reliability and degradation behavior of various PV cell technologies and module configurations. The results highlight significant differences in degradation rates between PERC, TOPCon, HJT, and BC technologies, and further demonstrate the critical influence of module construction, such as glass-glass configuration and POE encapsulant, in mitigating certain stress-induced losses.

3.1 Thermal Cycling

Figure 1 presents the results of power degradation under post-TC at 200, 400, and 600 cycles. In the results, PERC technology showed a more pronounced reduction in power output with a degradation of ~1.5% after 200 and 400 cycles, and up to ~2.0% after 600 cycles. This is an improvement to the degradation rates that PV modules sustained after TC200; on average 4.0% 10 years ago [3, 4]. This is primarily attributed to the novel metallization concepts, which have been implemented [5]. On the other hand, both BC and HJT technologies exhibited a moderate median degradation of about 1.0%, but the larger variance seen in BC could imply a need for enhanced manufacturing consistency to mitigate the risk of performance outliers. Notably, TOPCon PV-modules emerged with the least degradation after TC600 with a median degradation of 0.4%. It is important to note that the sample sizes for PERC and BC technologies were not sufficient to draw definitive conclusions, indicating a need for further investigation with a larger dataset.

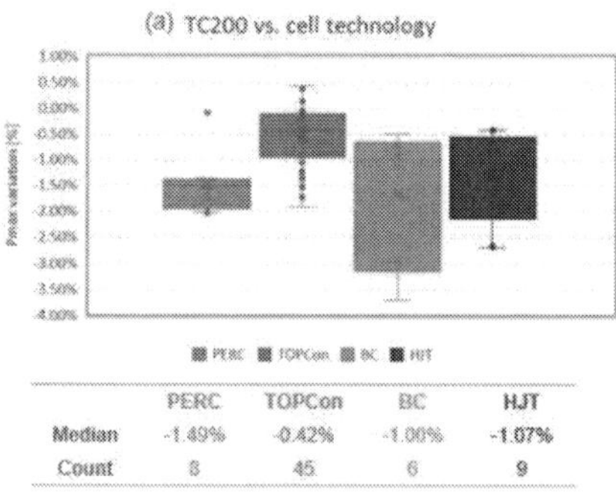

	PERC	TOPCon	BC	HJT
Median	-1.49%	-0.42%	-1.00%	-1.07%
Count	8	45	6	9

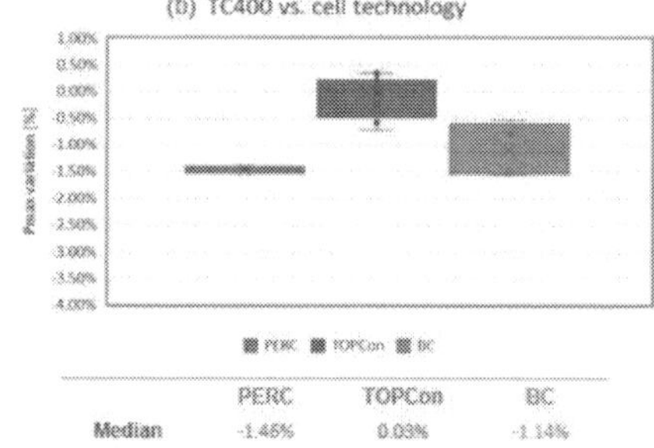

	PERC	TOPCon	BC
Median	-1.46%	0.03%	-1.14%
Count	2	15	4

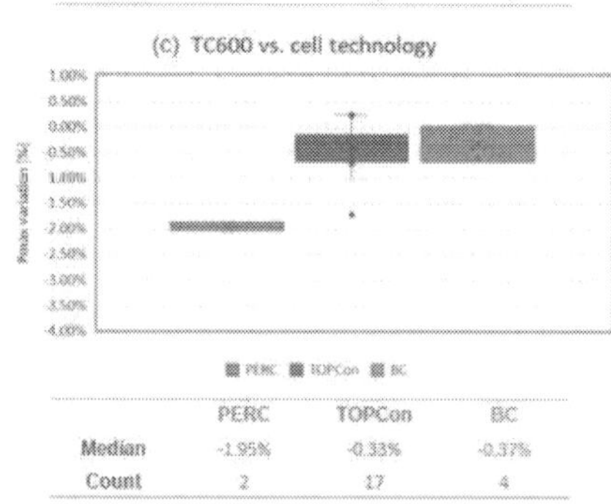

	PERC	TOPCon	BC
Median	-1.95%	-0.33%	-0.37%
Count	2	17	4

Figure 1: power variation of different cell technologies under post-TC at 200 (a), 400 (b), and 600 (c) cycles

3.2 Damp Heat

The impact of damp heat (DH) on maximum power

output of different cell technologies is depicted in Figure 2 (a). On average, PERC technology exhibited a median degradation of approximately 2.3%, compared to TOPCon and BC technologies, which showed median degradations of roughly 1.3% and 1.2%, respectively. Additionally, modules with G/G configurations demonstrated enhanced resistance to DH-induced power degradation, with performance losses approximately 50% lower than those noted in G/BS structures shown in Figure 2 (b). This suggests that while choice of technology is critical, module configuration plays a significant role in the longevity and reliability of solar cells under DH conditions. Particularly noteworthy is the shift from EVA to POE as the preferred encapsulant in newer PV module designs. This change mitigates the tendency of EVA to release acetic acid, which contributes to the degradation process. Modern modules that employ POE, especially combined with the improved moisture sealing of G/G configurations, could result in the reduced susceptibility to these detrimental effects, thereby enhancing the overall reliability of the modules.

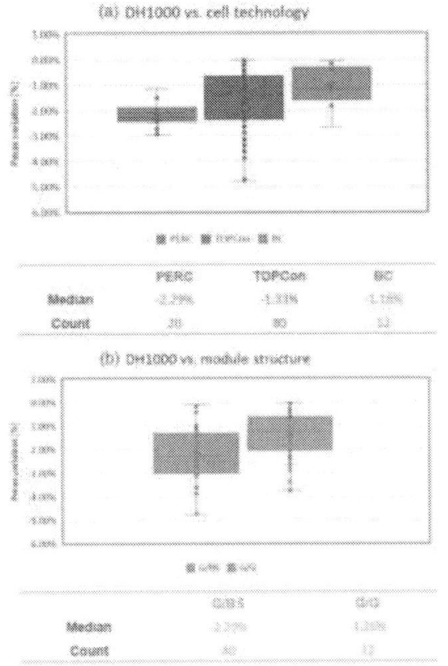

Figure 2: power variation under post-DH1000 condition for different cell technologies (a) and different module structures (b).

3.3 Potential Induced Degradation

Figure 3 illustrates the variations in power degradation across different cell technologies under post-PID conditions. From the results, BC showed greater resilience against both positive and negative PID stress in comparison to TOPCon and PERC, with a median degradation rate of approximately 0.5% at +1500V and around 0.8% at -1500V. Conversely, PERC cells exhibited higher degradation, trailing BC by an estimated 0.6% under both polarity stress conditions. Generally, there are several PID phenomena such PID-s and PID-p and the magnitude of degradation appears to be particularly

sensitive to module type than cell technology. These findings highlight the critical need to factor in PID effects during the selection and implementation of solar cells to ensure sustained long-term performance.

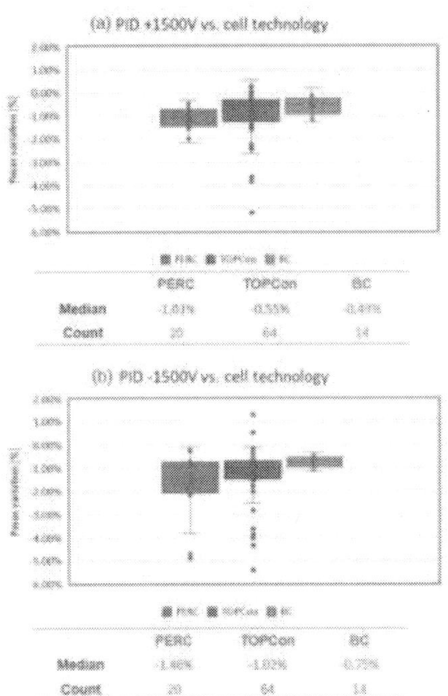

Figure 3: power variation of different cell technologies under post-PID at +1500 V (a), and -1500 V (b)

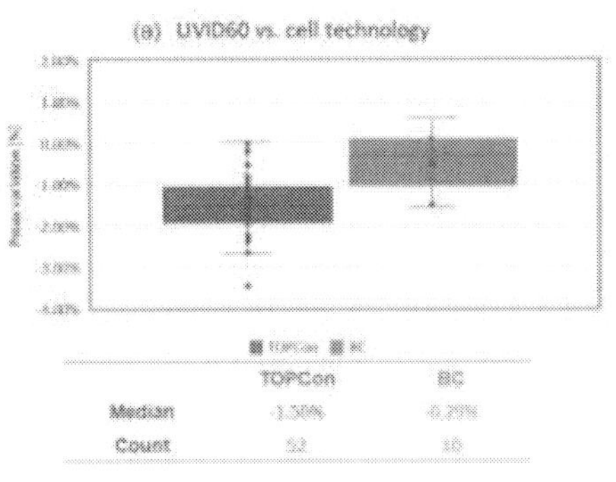

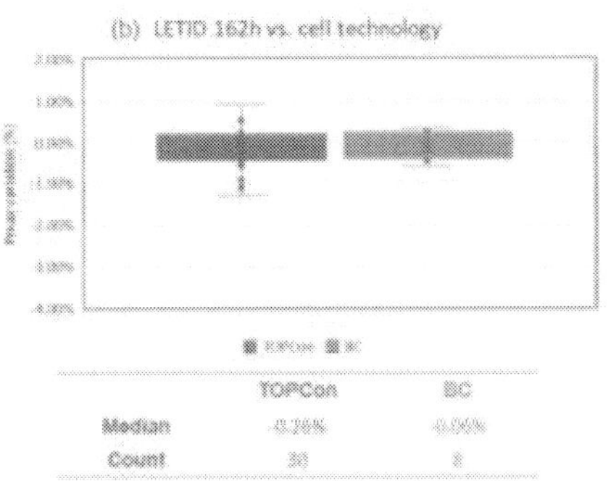

Figure 4: power variation of different cell technologies under post-UVID (a), and post-LETID (b)

3.4 Ultraviolet-induced Degradation and Light- and Elevated Temperature-Induced Degradation

Figure 4 provides evidence of the differentiated impact that post-UVID (a) and LETID (b) conditions have on TOPCon and BC cell technologies. TOPCon cells exhibit significantly greater degradation under UVID, with an estimated decrease of around 1.5%, which is notably five times higher than that observed in BC. In contrast, both cell types demonstrate less sensitivity to LETID, with TOPCon and BC showing median degradations of approximately 0.3% and 0.1%, respectively. These findings underscore the necessity of considering encapsulation material performance in harsh environmental conditions to ensure the longevity and efficiency of solar cell technologies.

Notably, degradation rates have been observed to be small, and as such, it becomes imperative to differentiate the effects of measurement uncertainty from the actual degradation phenomena. We have determined that the measurement uncertainty associated with our testing is ±2.0%, k=2 and the reproducibility ±0.6%, k=2 This emphasis on reproducibility serves to corroborate that the degradation signals we report are not artifacts of measurement variance but are indeed indicative of the modules' performance over time.

4   ConclusionThis study provides a comparative analysis of the reliability of leading PV cell technologies—PERC, TOPCon, HJT, and BC—under a comprehensive set of accelerated stress tests. The results clearly demonstrate that the degradation behavior is highly dependent on both the cell technology and the module's construction, with no single technology exhibiting superiority across all conditions.

PERC cells exhibit considerable degradation, with recorded losses of approximately 2.0% and 2.3% after TC600 and DH1000 stress tests, respectively, which lower the confidence of the suitability for long-term application. Conversely, BC and HJT cells demonstrate markedly less degradation, around 1.0%, following TC600 testing. Specifically, BC technology shows low degradation of approximately 1.2% at post-DH1000 condition. Notably though, the BC cells display a relatively broad distribution of degradation rates. This variability may suggest that while certain manufacturers have optimized their production processes for BC cells, yielding high reliability, others may benefit from further refinement in their manufacturing techniques to achieve consistent quality and reduce variability across the board. TOPCon cells are distinguished by their exceptional thermal stability and lower degradation rates, particularly during TC (~0.3%), DH (~1.3%) and PID (~0.5% positive stress) assessments, yet they exhibit increased sensitivity to UVID, with an average degradation of 1.5%. Regarding LETID results, both TOPCon and BC technologies tested show limited impact, with median degradations of 0.3% and 0.1%, respectively.

Overall, these findings indicate that while there is no one-size-fits-all solution, the selection of solar cell technology and module design must be tailored to specific environmental conditions to ensure the maximum efficiency and longevity of solar power systems. Applying

these insights can guide manufacturers, designers, and consumers in making informed decisions for sustainable and reliable solar energy solutions.

References

[1] IEC61215, "Crystalline Silicon terrestrial photovoltaic (PV) modules- design qualification and type approval," The International Electrotechnical Commission (IEC), 2021.

[2] IECTS63202-4, "Photovoltaic cells - Part 4: Measurement of light and elevated temperature induced degradation of crystalline silicon photovoltaic cells," The International Electrotechnical Commission (IEC), 2022.

[3] K. Morita, P. Sochor, Y. Tsuno, Y. Yasuda, S. Kera, T. Kohno and M. Fujimori, "Correlation between Thermal Cycling Test and Outdoor Exposure for Major Degradation Modes of PV modules," in WCPEC6, Kyoto, Japan, 2014.

[4] P. Hacke, K. Terwilliger, S. Glick, R. Smith, G. Perrin and S. Kurtz, "Application of the terrestrial photovoltaic module accelerated test-to-failure protocol," in 2014 IEEE 40th Photovoltaic Specialist Conference (PVSC), Denver, CO, USA, 2014.

[5] N. C. A Ebong, "Metallization of crystalline silicon solar cells: A review," High capacity optical networks and emerging/enabling technologies, pp. 102-109, 2012.

Durability and Reliability:
A Cross-Technological Stability Analysis of Silicon PV

Mengdi Liu[1], Wenhao Xu[1], Yating Zhang[1], Giorgio Bardizza[2], Christos Monokroussos[1]

[1] TÜV Rheinland (Shanghai) Co., Ltd., No.177, Lane 777, West Guangzhong, 200072, Shanghai, P.R. China

[2] TÜV Rheinland (Italy), Via E. Mattei, 3 - 20005, Pogliano Milanese, Italy

Why Reliability Matters in PV Technology

- Maximizing Energy Performance
- Withstanding Extreme Conditions
- Protecting Investments
- Energy Independence
- Cost Savings
- Sustainability

PID Performance of Cost-effective Material

EPE (EVA/POE/EVA) sandwich structure may not have sufficient diffusion resistance with power loss >10% after PID 96 exposure.

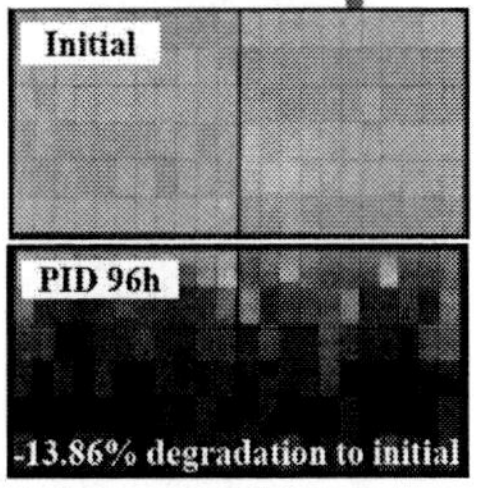

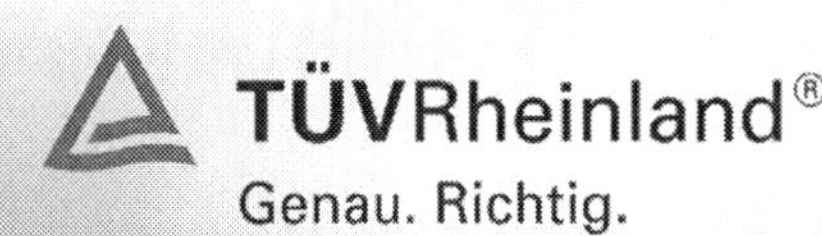

Reliability Analysis

Sequence 1: Thermal Cycling

Sequence 2: Damp Heat

Sequence 3: Potential Induced Degradation

Sequence 4: UV-Induced Degradation

Sequence 5: Light- and elevated Temperature-Induced Degradation

TC 200 — -40°C to +85°C for 200 temperature cycles

DH 1000 — 85°C and 85% RH for 1000 h

PID 96 — 85°C, 85% RH, V_{sys} [(+) and (-)] for 96 h

UVID 60 — 60kWh/m², 60°C

LeTID 162 — 1000W/m², 162h, 75°C

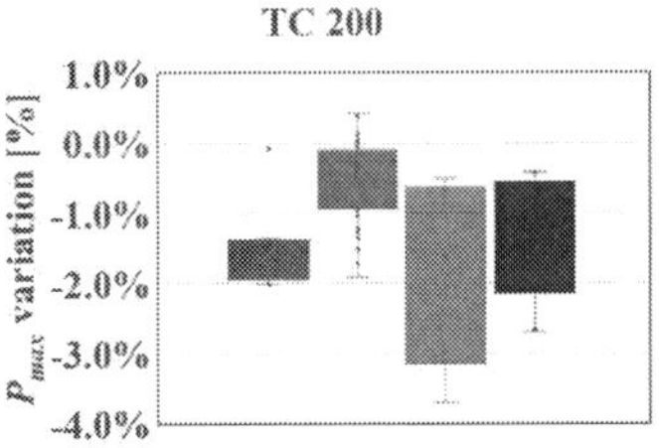

TC 200

	PERC	TOPCon	BC	HJT
Median	-1.49%	-0.42%	-1.00%	-1.07%
Count	8	45	6	9

Measurement Reproducibility: ±0.6 %, k=2

DH 1000

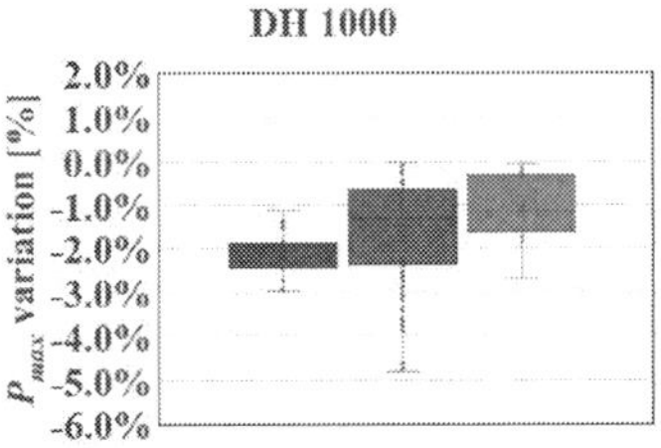

	PERC	TOPCon	BC
Median	-2.29%	-1.33%	-1.16%
Count	20	80	12

Measurement Reproducibility: ±0.6 %, k=2

PID 96

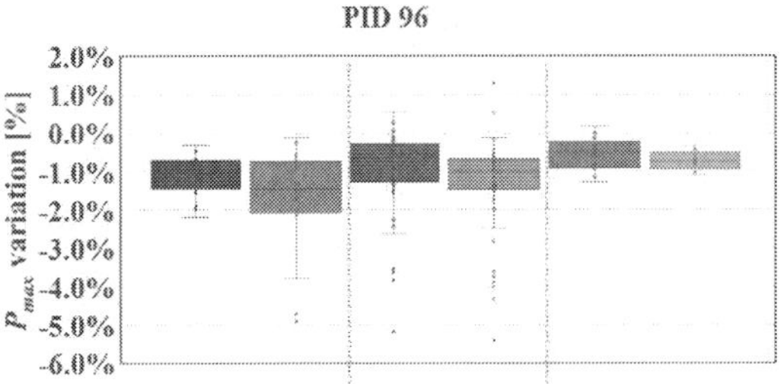

	PERC		TOPCon		BC	
	+	-	+	-	+	-
Median	-1.03%	-1.46%	-0.55%	-1.02%	-0.49%	-0.75%
Count	20		64		14	

Measurement Reproducibility: ±0.6 %, k=2

UVID 60

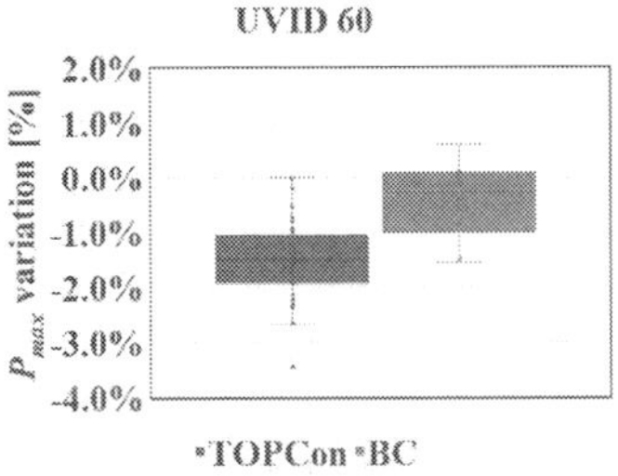

	TOPCon	BC
Median	-1.50%	-0.29%
Count	52	10

Measurement Reproducibility: ±0.6 %, k=2

LeTID 162

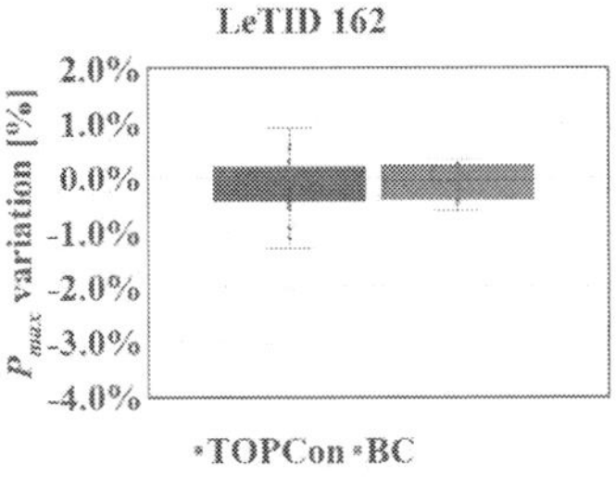

	TOPCon	BC
Median	-0.26%	-0.06%
Count	30	8

Measurement Reproducibility: ±0.6 %, k=2

Key Points

- TOPCon modules displayed excellent reliability with particular low degradation in the TC 200 test.
- BC modules exhibited strong resistance to DH, PID, LeTID and UVID.
- Today's modules exhibit significantly less degradation than those Al-BSF modules a decade ago.
- Individual module types need to be analyzed case-by-case.

Corresponding author: Dr. Mengdi Liu
Email: mengdi.liu@tuv.com

TÜVRheinland®
Genau. Richtig.

SILICA COATING WITH OPTIMIZED OPTICAL AND MECHANICAL PROPERTIES FOR ANTI-REFLECTION AND DUST RESISTANCE IN HARSH DESERT ENVIRONMENTS

Brahim Aïssa*, Mohammad I. Hossain, Atef Zekri, Amir Abdallah, Veronica Bermudez Benito
Qatar Environment and Energy Research Institute (QEERI), Hamad Bin Khalifa University (HBKU), Qatar Foundation,
Doha, 5825, Qatar
* baissa@hbku.edu.qa

ABSTRACT: This research directly addresses the persistent challenges encountered in desert environments, where solar energy systems, optical devices, and building surfaces are continuously exposed to two harsh stressors: intense ultraviolet (UV) radiation and heavy dust deposition. Both factors significantly degrade performance, leading to efficiency losses, higher maintenance requirements, and reduced operational lifetimes. To mitigate these environmental impacts, a specialized silica-based coating was developed, designed not only to enhance optical performance but also to provide long-term durability under extreme conditions. The coating, produced via reactive RF magnetron sputtering using high-purity SiO_2 targets, was fabricated under carefully controlled conditions. By varying the oxygen-to-argon flow ratios during deposition, researchers were able to finely tune the microstructural and surface properties of the films. Systematic testing revealed that higher oxygen content during sputtering resulted in coatings with improved smoothness and enhanced hydrophilicity (water-attracting behavior). This property plays a key role in the coating's self-cleaning functionality, as it facilitates water spreading and the removal of dust particles from the surface. Beyond optical and wetting properties, the mechanical robustness of the coatings was rigorously assessed. Mechanical tests demonstrated that the films remained structurally stable and mechanically strong even after 24 months of continuous outdoor exposure to desert conditions. Furthermore, the hardness of the coatings could be effectively tailored by adjusting oxygen content, offering a pathway for optimizing both strength and resilience. Notably, coatings deposited at higher oxygen flow ratios exhibited a reduced tendency for dust accumulation, confirming their dual role as both anti-reflective and anti-soiling layers. Collectively, these findings highlight the promise of silica coatings engineered for desert environments as a durable, eco-friendly, and multifunctional solution. By simultaneously reducing sunlight reflection, improving light absorption, resisting mechanical degradation, and suppressing dust buildup, such coatings extend the performance and operational lifetime of solar panels, optical devices, and building-integrated surfaces. This approach not only supports the deployment of renewable energy technologies in harsh climates but also aligns with the broader vision of sustainable and low-maintenance materials for energy and environmental applications.

1 INTRODUCTION

Significant advancements have been achieved in the design and fabrication of anti-reflection (AR) and anti-soiling (AS) coatings, given their broad impact across industries such as photovoltaic (PV) solar energy, laser optics, automotive components, architectural glass, and high-performance optical devices. These coatings play a pivotal role in enhancing efficiency and durability, particularly in PV systems where environmental dust accumulation can lead to severe performance losses. For instance, dust storms can reduce module efficiency by up to 22%, while even a thin, ~1 μm layer of dust deposited on crystalline silicon (c-Si) modules can cause a 25% efficiency drop [1–3]. Such statistics underline the urgency of developing advanced thin-film coatings that combine both AR and AS functionalities in order to mitigate performance degradation and reduce maintenance demands.

Self-cleaning AR–AS coatings have emerged as one of the most promising approaches to address these dual challenges. Achieving optimal AR performance typically requires destructive interference of reflected light at the glass/coating and coating/air interfaces, which is usually obtained by tailoring the film thickness to approximately one-quarter of the wavelength of incident light. Conventional approaches employ porous coatings to lower the refractive index and minimize reflection, or stacked SiO_2/TiO_2 bilayers to enhance transmission. However, these designs often face practical limitations: stacked systems, while optically efficient, may suffer from scalability issues, reduced self-cleaning performance, higher refractive indices, and

elevated fabrication costs [4,5]. Thus, the challenge lies in striking a balance between durability, optical efficiency, surface functionality, and cost-effectiveness. Among available materials, silicon dioxide (SiO_2) stands out for its exceptional optical transparency, low refractive index, mechanical strength, and chemical stability. Its high transmission across the near-ultraviolet to near-infrared spectrum makes it an ideal candidate for AR–AS coatings. Beyond photovoltaics, SiO_2 thin films are widely employed in flexible displays, protective coatings, bioengineering, and ophthalmic applications, owing to their robustness and optical clarity. A wide range of deposition techniques has been explored for SiO_2 thin films, including electron-beam evaporation, ion-assisted deposition, magnetron sputtering, sol–gel processing, and atomic layer deposition. Among these, RF magnetron sputtering is often considered the most suitable for industrial-scale applications due to its excellent reproducibility, precise control over microstructural properties, and low defect rates. In particular, reactive sputtering has been extensively adopted in the PV industry for fabricating SiO_2-based AR coatings, though further work is still required to establish a comprehensive correlation between deposition parameters, film microstructure, and functional performance.

In the present study, 100 nm-thick SiO_2 thin films were deposited via RF sputtering under varying oxygen flow rates (0–50 sccm) at a controlled substrate temperature of 200 °C. The influence of the oxygen-to-argon flow ratio [$r(O_2) = O_2/Ar$] on the structural, optical, and surface properties of the films was systematically investigated. The coatings were characterized using a suite of techniques:

- Ellipsometry and UV–Vis spectroscopy to evaluate refractive index, extinction coefficient, and optical transmittance,
- Contact angle measurements to probe wettability and self-cleaning potential,
- 3D stylus profilometry for surface roughness quantification, and
- Field-emission scanning electron microscopy (FESEM) to assess surface morphology and microstructural features.

The findings demonstrated that oxygen flow is a critical tuning parameter in controlling film performance. Higher oxygen content during sputtering resulted in smoother, more uniform films with enhanced hydrophilicity, which in turn promoted self-cleaning behavior by reducing dust accumulation. Interestingly, the coatings also exhibited hydrophobic contributions under certain oxygen flow conditions, further improving resistance to particulate adhesion. Together, these properties enabled the SiO_2 films to significantly improve the optical and environmental stability of PV modules, particularly in dust-prone desert climates.

This work underscores the immense potential of SiO_2 coatings to combine AR and AS functionalities into a single, scalable thin-film solution. By enhancing light transmission, suppressing dust buildup, and maintaining long-term mechanical integrity, such coatings represent a durable and eco-friendly pathway to boost both the performance and lifespan of solar modules and other optoelectronic devices in harsh environments.

Looking ahead, future research should aim to refine deposition techniques, optimize oxygen-to-argon ratios, and explore the interplay between film microstructure, surface chemistry, and functional response. A deeper understanding of these relationships will be crucial for pushing the boundaries of next-generation AR–AS coatings, ultimately enabling self-sustaining, high-performance solar energy systems that thrive even under the most demanding environmental conditions.

2 METHODOLOGY

Silica thin films were deposited onto soda lime glass (SLG) substrates (dimensions: $1'' \times 3''$) using a Torr Magnetron Sputtering Tool™ under carefully controlled conditions to ensure high-quality coatings with tunable properties. The sputtering chamber was evacuated to a base pressure of 5×10^{-5} Torr prior to deposition, minimizing contamination and ensuring reproducibility. A reactive sputtering configuration was employed, utilizing high-purity (99.995%) argon and oxygen gases. Substrate rotation was continuously applied during deposition to guarantee uniform film coverage across the glass surface. The sputtering target consisted of a high-purity SiO_2 source (99.995%, Kurt J. Lesker), ensuring consistent stoichiometry and purity in the deposited films. All depositions were performed at a constant substrate temperature of 200 °C and a stable deposition rate of 0.5 Å/s, providing controlled growth conditions for uniform thin films. The argon flow rate was fixed at 200 sccm to sustain plasma ignition and stabilize sputtering, while the oxygen flow rate was systematically varied between 0 and 50 sccm. This adjustment enabled oxygen-to-total gas flow ratios

ranging from 0% to 25%, allowing precise tuning of the thin film's optical and surface characteristics as a function of deposition chemistry. Following deposition, the silica-coated samples were transferred to the Outdoor Testing Facility (OTF) for real-world environmental evaluation. To examine the role of surface orientation on dust accumulation and self-cleaning behavior, the samples were mounted at five different tilt angles (0°, 22°, 45°, 60°, and 90°). All samples were exposed simultaneously to identical desert outdoor conditions, ensuring a fair comparison of soiling dynamics across the tested geometries. This experimental design provided critical insights into the influence of tilt angle on dust deposition, removal, and overall performance stability, directly relevant to optimizing photovoltaic (PV) module performance in dust-prone environments.

3 RESULTS AND DISCUSSION

Fig. 1. X-ray Photoelectron Spectroscopy (XPS) survey spectra of silica thin films deposited with varying oxygen flow ratios (0%–25%) at a substrate temperature of 200 °C. The survey includes the Si 2p and O 1s core-level peaks acquired after monatomic etching, complemented by oxygen depth profiling across the films. To ensure accurate quantification, oxygen bound to carbon-related contaminants was subtracted, and the remaining oxygen signal was attributed to oxide-related bonds such as oxygen–metal linkages. The dominant peaks corresponding to silicon and oxygen confirmed the formation of SiOx chemical states. Notably, the Si 2p peak consistently appeared at ~103 eV, indicative of stable silicon–oxygen bonding. The calculated stoichiometry of the films ranged from $SiO_{1.85}$ to $SiO_{1.91}$, depending on the oxygen flow ratio. Both cluster ion and monatomic ion etching were employed to cross-validate results, ensuring reliable assessment of the films' chemical composition.

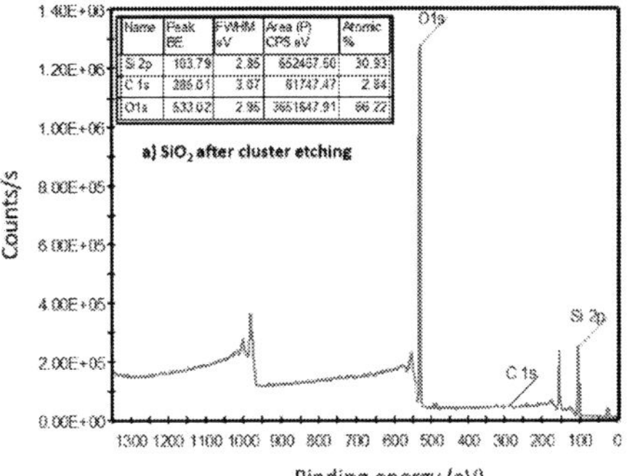

Name	Peak BE	FWHM eV	Area (P) CPS eV	Atomic %
Si 2p	103.79	2.85	652467.50	30.93
C 1s	285.01	3.07	61747.47	2.84
O1s	533.02	2.95	3651647.91	66.22

Figure 1: X-ray Photoelectron Spectroscopy (XPS) survey spectrum of silica thin films deposited at an oxygen flow ratio of $r(O_2) = 0\%$ and a substrate temperature of 200 °C. The survey highlights the elemental composition of the as-deposited films, with clear signals corresponding to silicon (Si 2p) and oxygen (O 1s), confirming the presence of SiOx-related chemical states. Minor carbon peaks are also observed, attributed to surface contamination during sample handling. The analysis establishes a baseline for subsequent comparisons with oxygen-enriched films, providing insight into the evolution of chemical bonding

and stoichiometry as a function of deposition parameters.

Fig. 2. Correlation between the refractive index and the wettability properties (hydrophobic/hydrophilic behavior) of the silica thin films as a function of oxygen flow ratio ($r(O_2)$). The results demonstrate that higher oxygen content enhances film transparency while simultaneously modifying surface morphology and wetting properties. Surfaces with increased oxygen content exhibited greater hydrophilicity, supporting water spreading and potential self-cleaning behavior. Conversely, lower oxygen ratios yielded more hydrophobic surfaces, where water droplets resisted spreading and remained pinned to the surface. These trends suggest that silica films with optimized oxygen incorporation not only enhance optical transmission but also display functional wetting characteristics suited to dust mitigation. The interplay between chemical composition and surface roughness was evident: hydrophilicity was linked to hydroxyl (–OH) group formation and three-dimensional capillary action within rougher surfaces, whereas hydrophobicity arose from reduced substrate effects and lower surface energy. Further surface roughness characterization is recommended to validate the strong influence of morphology on wettability transitions.

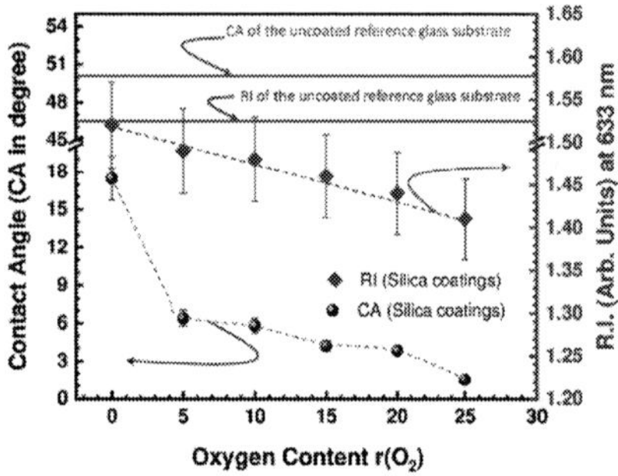

Figure 2: Summary of contact angle (CA) measurements for sputtered silica thin films deposited at varying oxygen flow ratios ($r(O_2)$), with a reference uncoated glass sample included for comparison. Dashed lines are provided as visual guides to highlight the observed trends. The results reveal a clear dependence of wettability on oxygen incorporation: as the oxygen content increases, the coatings exhibit progressively lower contact angles, indicating enhanced hydrophilicity. This transition reflects changes in surface chemistry (e.g., hydroxyl group formation) and morphology, which play a crucial role in enabling self-cleaning and anti-soiling properties for applications such as PV modules in desert environments.

Fig. 3a. Comparative micromechanical hardness of uncoated soda-lime glass and silica-coated samples fabricated under different oxygen concentrations, measured using the Vickers indentation method. Results confirmed that silica coatings maintained substantial hardness, approximately 10% lower than bare glass, demonstrating their structural robustness. Increasing oxygen content correlated with a slight reduction in hardness, consistent with enhanced porosity and surface hydroxylation.

Fig. 3b. Mechanical degradation of silica films over time, plotted as hardness reduction as a function of oxygen flow ratio ($r(O_2)$). After two months of outdoor exposure, no measurable hardness loss was observed, while after 24 months, only a ~5% reduction was recorded, confirming the films' exceptional long-term durability and stability. These findings highlight that oxygen-rich silica coatings can combine mechanical integrity with functional hydrophilicity, making them well-suited for durable AR–AS applications in harsh desert conditions.

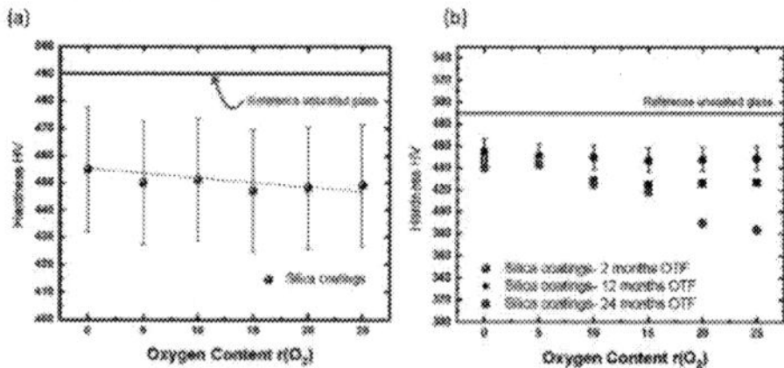

Figure 3: (a) Comparative hardness measurements of reference uncoated glass and silica thin films deposited with varying oxygen flow ratios ($r(O_2)$). The results highlight the influence of oxygen incorporation on the micromechanical properties of the coatings, with increased oxygen content generally leading to slightly reduced hardness values relative to bare glass. (b) Long-term assessment of mechanical stability, showing the evolution of hardness as a function of exposure time under outdoor conditions for different $r(O_2)$. The data demonstrate the excellent durability of silica coatings, with only marginal degradation observed after extended exposure. Even after 24 months, hardness reduction remained within ~5%, underscoring the coatings' ability to retain their mechanical integrity while simultaneously delivering optical and anti-soiling functionalities.

Fig. 4. Scanning Electron Microscopy (SEM) images of the front surfaces of silica-coated glass coupons after two months of outdoor exposure at the Outdoor Test Facility (OTF). Dust accumulation was quantified by calculating the surface coverage (SC) of particles, enabling direct comparisons across different oxygen flow ratios ($r(O_2)$) and tilt angles. The results showed a clear angular dependence: higher tilt angles reduced dust deposition, with soiling behavior scaling proportionally to the cosine of the tilt angle (θ). Moreover, coatings deposited with higher oxygen content exhibited superior hydrophilicity, which substantially reduced dust retention without the need for manual cleaning. In contrast, coatings fabricated at lower oxygen flow rates accumulated significantly more dust, highlighting the importance of optimized oxygen incorporation. Collectively, these results demonstrate that hydrophilic silica films not only enhance transparency but also offer self-cleaning functionality by resisting dust buildup, thereby mitigating one of the most critical performance losses for PV modules and optical devices in desert climates.

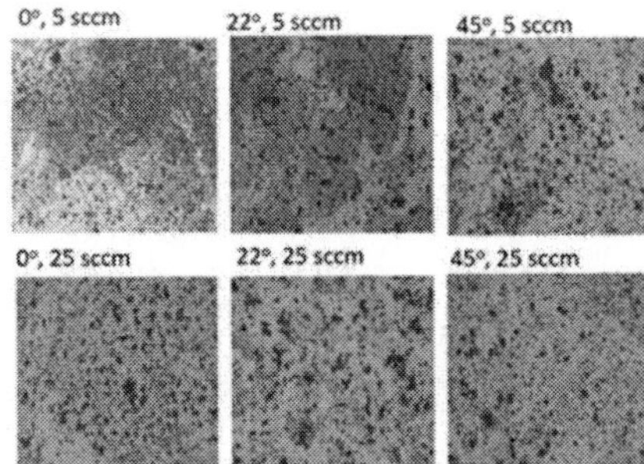

Figure 4: Representative optical microscope images of the front surfaces of silica-coated glass coupons after two months of outdoor exposure at the Outdoor Test Facility (OTF). The images illustrate characteristic soiling patterns and dust accumulation on the coatings, enabling qualitative comparison of surface coverage across different oxygen flow ratios and tilt angles. Distinct differences in particle adhesion and distribution are observed, reflecting the role of oxygen content in governing the films' hydrophilicity and self-cleaning performance. These visual observations support quantitative analyses of dust coverage, confirming that oxygen-rich silica coatings exhibit reduced dust retention and enhanced resistance to environmental soiling.

4 CONCLUSIONS

This research provides a comprehensive investigation into the optical and morphological properties of silica thin films fabricated via reactive RF magnetron sputtering using high-purity SiO_2 targets. By systematically varying the oxygen-to-total-flow ratios between 0% and 25%, the deposition process enabled precise tailoring of film properties to achieve multifunctional performance. The resulting silica coatings demonstrated exceptional optical clarity, with transmittance values exceeding 90% across the visible spectrum, confirming their suitability for transparent applications such as protective and anti-reflective (AR) layers. Ellipsometric analysis revealed refractive index values in the range of 1.4–1.5, closely matching those of high-quality AR coatings, thereby validating the films' potential to minimize reflection losses and enhance light harvesting in photovoltaic and optical devices. Surface analyses provided further insights into the influence of oxygen incorporation. Contact angle measurements showed that films deposited with higher oxygen flow ratios displayed markedly improved hydrophilicity, while surface roughness characterization indicated subtle morphological adjustments that promoted self-cleaning behavior. These surface properties directly translated into enhanced anti-soiling performance during real-time outdoor exposure tests. Indeed, a clear correlation was observed between oxygen content and dust resistance: films fabricated under oxygen-rich conditions exhibited significantly reduced dust accumulation, whereas oxygen-deficient films were more prone to particulate deposition. Collectively, these findings underscore the dual functionality of silica thin films as both anti-reflective and anti-soiling coatings. Their ability to combine high optical transmission, tunable refractive indices, hydrophilic surface properties, and environmental durability highlights their value for solar modules deployed in harsh desert environments, where dust accumulation and reflection losses remain critical challenges. Beyond photovoltaics, such coatings hold promise for broader applications in lasers, optical sensors, architectural glass, and automotive systems. By bridging fundamental material characterization with real-world outdoor testing, this study establishes silica-based coatings as a scalable, robust, and eco-friendly solution for next-generation energy and optical technologies. Future work should focus on refining deposition parameters, exploring multi-layer or doped silica architectures, and investigating the long-term stability of AR–AS properties under prolonged desert exposure to further enhance their practical viability.

5 REFERENCES

[1] I. Arabatzis, N. Todorova, I. Fasaki, C. Tsesmeli, A. Peppas, W. X. Li, and Z. Zhao, "Photocatalytic and self-cleaning coatings for solar applications," Solar Energy, vol. 159, pp. 251–259, 2018.

[2] K. Nishioka, S. P. Moe, and Y. Ota, "Performance evaluation of photovoltaic modules with anti-reflection coatings," Coatings, vol. 9, no. 1, p. 49, 2019.

[3] T. Shao, F. Tang, L. Sun, X. Ye, J. He, L. Yang, and W. Zheng, "Nanostructured coatings for enhanced optical and surface properties," Nanomaterials, vol. 9, no. 2, p. 180, 2019.

[4] T.-C. Chen, T.-W. Kuo, Y.-L. Lin, C.-H. Ku, Z.-P. Yang, and I.-S. Yu, "High-transmittance hydrophobic coatings for photovoltaic protection," Coatings, vol. 8, no. 12, p. 418, 2018.

[5] L. L. Lebel, B. Aïssa, M. A. El Khakani, and D. Therriault, Composites Science and Technology, vol. 70, no. 3, pp. 518–524, 2010.

[6] W. Julia, C. Luis, R. Federico, et al., Advanced Functional Materials, vol. 23, pp. 5591–5598, 2013.

[7] D. T. H. Dalir, R. D. Farahani, V. Nhim, and B. Aïssa, et al., Langmuir, vol. 28, no. 1, pp. 791–803, 2011.

[8] A. Ali, F. El-Mellouhi, A. Mitra, and B. Aïssa, Nanomaterials, vol. 12, no. 5, p. 788, 2022.

[9] R. D. Farahani, D. T. H. Dalir, V. Le Borgne, A. Loick, et al., Composites Science and Technology, vol. 72, no. 12, pp. 1387–1395, 2012.

[10] N. M. H. Gavi, B. D. Ngom, A. C. Beye, A. M. Strydom, B. Aïssa, V. V. Srinivasu, and M. Chaker, Journal of Magnetism and Magnetic Materials, vol. 324, no. 6, pp. 1172–1176, 2012.

[11] B. Aïssa and M. A. El Khakani, Nanotechnology, vol. 20, no. 17, p. 175203, 2009.

[12] M. A. Habib, M. Barkat, B. Aïssa, and T. Denidni, Progress in Electromagnetics Research, vol. 88, pp. 135–148, 2008.

[13] H. Zhao, H. Kimura, Z. Cheng, X. Wang, and T. Nishida, Applied Physics Letters, vol. 95, p. 232904, 2009. https://doi.org/10.1063/1.3271032.

PLASMONIC-DECORATED TIO₂ THIN FILMS AS PHOTOCATALYTIC ANTI-SOILING COATINGS

Brahim Aïssa*, M.I. Hossain and Adnan Ali
Qatar Environment and Energy Research Institute (QEERI), Hamad Bin Khalifa University (HBKU), Qatar Foundation,
Doha, 5825, Qatar
* baissa@hbku.edu.qa

ABSTRACT: Soiling of solar collectors represents one of the most pressing challenges for the reliability and efficiency of solar energy systems, particularly in arid and semi-arid regions such as the Middle East and North Africa (MENA). The accumulation of dust, sand, and organic residues on solar surfaces leads to substantial reductions in power output and escalates operational and maintenance (O&M) costs, often making soiling the single largest contributor to performance losses in photovoltaic (PV) plants. Soiling on PV modules is broadly categorized into inorganic and organic components, each posing distinct challenges. Inorganic soiling, typically derived from mineral-rich sources such as desert sand, sea salt, and suspended mineral particles, tends to be less adhesive and can often be removed through routine cleaning or wind action. In contrast, organic soiling, originating from airborne dust mixed with pollen, microbial deposits, and biological residues such as bird droppings, exhibits strong adhesion to surfaces. Organic matter is particularly problematic as it not only resists removal but can also serve as a substrate for microbial growth, leading to corrosive byproducts that degrade encapsulants, coatings, and even glass surfaces over time. To address this critical issue, the present study investigates the use of plasmonic metal nanoparticles (NPs) as a strategy for mitigating the impact of organic dust deposition on solar surfaces. Specifically, the work evaluates the role of localized surface plasmon resonance (LSPR) in enhancing photocatalytic degradation of organic contaminants. Gold (Au) nanoparticles were deposited onto plain glass and TiO₂-coated glass substrates via the solid-state dewetting (SSD) process, which enables the formation of uniformly distributed nanoscale particles with strong plasmonic activity. The SSD approach also maximizes the nanoparticle–substrate interface, thereby promoting efficient charge transfer and improved catalytic reactivity under solar illumination. The experimental results demonstrated that the incorporation of Au nanoparticles significantly enhances the photocatalytic activity of TiO₂, leading to a pronounced reduction in the organic fraction of deposited dust. This effect is attributed to the excitation of LSPR in Au NPs, which increases light absorption and generates hot electrons that actively participate in photocatalytic reactions at the surface. As a result, organic contaminants decompose more efficiently, reducing adhesion and facilitating easier removal. These findings highlight the potential of plasmonic nanostructures to serve as the foundation for next-generation anti-soiling coatings, combining optical transparency with self-cleaning functionality. By targeting the persistent problem of organic soiling, often the most difficult to mitigate in real-world PV deployments, this approach provides a promising pathway toward reducing cleaning frequency, lowering O&M costs, and ensuring higher long-term energy yields in desert and coastal environments.

1 INTRODUCTION

A phenomenon known as localized surface plasmon resonance (LSPR) emerges when incident electromagnetic radiation interacts with metallic nanoparticles confined on a surface. This interaction arises because the oscillating electric field of light induces a collective motion of mobile charge carriers within the nanoparticles, driving coherent electron oscillations relative to the fixed ionic lattice. The displacement of these electrons generates restoring Coulomb forces, and under the right conditions, resonance is established between the external electromagnetic field and the natural oscillation frequency of the conduction electrons [1,2]. This resonant interaction gives rise to strongly enhanced optical absorption and scattering, along with intensified near-field effects, which are the hallmarks of plasmonic nanostructures.

The LSPR effect is highly sensitive to multiple factors, including the size, distribution, morphology, and dielectric environment of the nanoparticles [1,3,4]. By carefully tuning these parameters, the plasmonic response can be engineered across a wide spectral range. Gold (Au) and silver (Ag) nanoparticles are among the most widely employed materials due to their superior plasmonic efficiency in the visible range and their chemical stability, although other metals can also exhibit plasmonic activity [3]. While LSPR is most commonly observed in the visible spectrum, it can be deliberately extended into the ultraviolet (UV) and infrared (IR) regions through appropriate material choices and nanostructuring. For example, aluminum nanoparticles have been shown to support UV plasmonics, while compound semiconductors such as GaAs and InP, or transparent conducting oxides like indium-doped tin oxide (ITO), enable plasmonic resonances that extend well into the near-infrared (NIR) [5]. The resonance frequency of LSPR is governed by several key parameters. Nanoparticle size is particularly influential: as particle diameter increases, the resonance intensity is amplified, often accompanied by red-shifts in the spectral response [7]. Similarly, inter-particle spacing and arrangement critically affect resonance conditions. When the distance between nanoparticles increases, the plasmon resonance typically shifts toward shorter wavelengths (blue-shift), whereas strong electromagnetic coupling between closely spaced particles may induce energy splitting or hybridization effects, producing multiple resonance modes [6]. Geometrical factors such as nanoparticle aspect ratio, shape (spheres, rods, triangles), and orientation relative to the incident field further expand the tunability of LSPR, making it a versatile platform for tailoring optical functionalities. [7-11]

One practical route to fabricating plasmonic nanoparticles is the solid-state dewetting process, which transforms thin continuous films into discrete nanoscale islands upon thermal treatment. Dewetting typically progresses through three stages: (i) the initial formation

10.4229/EUPVSEC2025/3AV.2.5

of voids in the nanofilm, (ii) the lateral growth and coalescence of these voids, and (iii) the eventual breakup of the film into nanoparticles driven by Rayleigh instability. These self-assembled nanoparticles naturally exhibit size distributions and inter-particle spacings determined by the initial film thickness, annealing temperature, and substrate properties. [12-15]

In the present work, we systematically investigate the dewetting behavior of thermally evaporated Au nanofilms deposited on TiO_2 thin films supported by quartz glass substrates. A series of experiments were conducted by varying both the annealing temperature and the initial thickness of the Au layers, enabling us to study their influence on nanoparticle evolution. The properties of the underlying TiO_2 films—including crystallinity, surface energy, and morphology, also played a significant role in guiding nanoparticle nucleation and growth. The resulting Au nanostructures were characterized in terms of their average particle size, surface density, and inter-particle distance, providing a quantitative understanding of how processing parameters dictate LSPR-active nanostructures. [16-21]

Beyond fundamental insights into nanoparticle formation, this study explores the functional application of plasmonic metal nanoparticles for mitigating the effects of soiling on solar energy devices. Specifically, Au nanoparticles supported on both glass and TiO_2-coated substrates were evaluated for their ability to reduce organic dust deposition through a photocatalytic mechanism. By leveraging the enhanced light absorption and hot-electron generation associated with LSPR, the Au/TiO_2 nanocomposites facilitate more efficient decomposition of organic matter, thereby reducing adhesion and promoting self-cleaning behavior under solar illumination [22].

Taken together, this investigation not only deepens the understanding of LSPR tuning via dewetting processes but also highlights its potential as a practical tool for developing next-generation anti-soiling coatings for photovoltaic and optoelectronic systems operating in challenging desert environments.

2 METHODOLOGY

Thin films of titanium oxide (TiOx) were deposited using electron beam (e-beam) evaporation under carefully optimized conditions to ensure high-quality growth. The depositions were performed at room temperature with a meticulously controlled deposition rate of 1 Å/s. To achieve stoichiometric oxide formation, a constant oxygen flow was introduced, maintaining a stable deposition pressure of 2×10^{-4} Torr throughout the process. For comparison, thin metallic layers of gold (Au) were also deposited under identical conditions using the same e-beam evaporation system and deposition rate. In this case, however, oxygen flow was excluded to preserve the metallic state and avoid unwanted oxidation.

To prevent electrical arcing caused by excess free charge carriers in the presence of oxygen, the oxygen flow rate was capped at 20 standard cubic centimeters per minute (sccm). This limit ensured stable plasma conditions and uninterrupted deposition. The use of a Denton Vacuum Explorer™ evaporator allowed sequential deposition of multilayer stacks without breaking vacuum, thereby minimizing interfacial contamination and preserving the structural and chemical integrity of the layers.

Prior to deposition, substrates (glass slides, 1 inch × 1 inch) were prepared by ultrasonic cleaning in successive baths of deionized (DI) water, acetone, and isopropanol, followed by drying under an inert nitrogen stream to eliminate residual contaminants and moisture. For multilayer configurations, TiOx and Au were alternately deposited in stacked sequences, with individual layer thicknesses systematically adjusted to tune the resulting optical and structural properties.

The deposited thin films were subjected to post-deposition annealing in a programmable muffle furnace. Annealing was carried out at temperatures ranging from 300 °C to 900 °C for one hour in ambient air. This thermal treatment was employed to enhance film crystallinity, stabilize the stoichiometry, and improve overall film quality, with particular attention to tailoring grain structure and optical performance.

A comprehensive suite of characterization techniques was used to evaluate the deposited films:

- Optical properties were investigated using UV–Vis spectroscopy to extract transmittance, reflectance, and absorption spectra over the 200–2000 nm wavelength range.

- Wetting behavior was assessed by static contact angle measurements, providing insights into hydrophilicity and potential anti-soiling performance.

- Surface topology was examined with both a 3D stylus profilometer (Dektak) and atomic force microscopy (AFM) to quantify surface roughness and morphological features.

- Microstructural analysis was conducted using field-emission scanning electron microscopy (FESEM), enabling visualization of film density, uniformity, and nanoscale features.

- Chemical composition and bonding states were determined using X-ray photoelectron spectroscopy (XPS), which confirmed the oxidation state of Ti in TiOx films and the purity of Au layers.

High-purity precursors (99.9995% Ti and Au pellets, Kurt J. Lesker) were employed to minimize impurities and ensure reproducibility. The combination of controlled deposition, in-situ vacuum stacking, and systematic annealing produced thin films with tunable optical and structural properties suitable for integration into infrared-filtering, anti-soiling, and plasmonic optoelectronic applications.

3 RESULTS AND DISCUSSION

Figure 1 presents the grazing-incidence X-ray diffraction (GIXRD) patterns of Au–TiOx thin films annealed at temperatures ranging from 300 °C to 900 °C, measured within the 2θ range of 20°–80°. The as-deposited TiOx films exhibited an amorphous nature, showing no discernible diffraction peaks, which is typical for films grown at room temperature without post-deposition treatment. Upon thermal annealing, however, distinct phase transformations were observed. The emergence of the anatase phase of TiOx was confirmed by characteristic diffraction peaks at 25° (101) and 47° (200), while the rutile phase appeared at higher temperatures, with reflections identified at 65° (310) and 70.1° (301). The coexistence of anatase and rutile phases at elevated annealing temperatures indicates a temperature-driven structural transition, consistent with the known polymorphic behavior of TiO_2. In the case of gold, the GIXRD patterns revealed well-defined crystalline features across all samples, confirming the formation of a face-centered cubic (FCC) lattice structure. Four prominent Bragg reflections were identified at 38.1° (111), 44.3° (200), 64.5° (220), and 77.7° (311). Among these, the sharp and intense (111) peak at 38.1° suggests a preferred orientation along the (111) plane, which is commonly reported for thin Au films due to its lowest surface energy configuration.

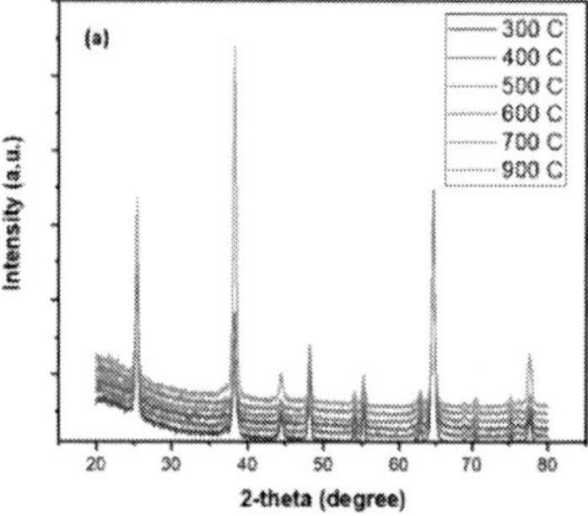

Figure 1: Grazing-incidence X-ray diffraction (GIXRD) patterns of Au/TiOx thin films annealed at temperatures ranging from 300 °C to 900 °C. The as-deposited TiOx films exhibit an amorphous structure, while post-annealing treatments induce crystallization into the anatase phase with characteristic peaks at 25° (101) and 47° (200), and the rutile phase with reflections at 65° (310) and 70.1° (301). The Au layers display a face-centered cubic (FCC) structure with prominent Bragg reflections at 38.1° (111), 44.3° (200), 64.5° (220), and 77.7° (311), with the (111) peak indicating preferential orientation. Increasing annealing temperature enhances the crystallinity of both TiOx and Au, as evidenced by sharper and more intense diffraction peaks, consistent with grain growth and improved structural ordering.

A clear correlation between annealing temperature and crystallinity was observed: with increasing temperature, the intensity and sharpness of the diffraction peaks for both TiOx and Au became more pronounced, indicative of enhanced crystallite size and improved structural ordering. This trend is in strong agreement with complementary morphological studies, which showed that higher annealing temperatures facilitate the formation of larger crystallites through grain coalescence. Overall, the XRD results confirm that annealing serves as a key parameter in tailoring the phase composition, crystallinity, and preferential orientation of Au–TiOx thin films.

Figure 2 presents the surface morphology of evaporated Au/TiOx thin films subjected to post-deposition annealing at six different temperatures, ranging from 300 °C to 900 °C, with TiOx serving as the seed layer. The microstructural evolution clearly reveals that with increasing annealing temperature, the TiOx films deposited on quartz substrates undergo grain growth, leading to the formation of progressively larger crystallites. This coarsening behavior is consistent with thermally driven diffusion processes, which promote atomic rearrangement and grain boundary migration. Correspondingly, the Au thin films exhibit enhanced

crystallinity, as evidenced by the development of larger grains and more pronounced grain boundaries.

In general, seed layers characterized by smaller grains possess a greater density of grain boundaries, which act as energetically favorable sites for diffusion and nucleation. At the highest annealing temperature of 900 °C, a marked increase in particle density along grain boundaries was observed. This phenomenon is attributed to the migration of atoms from grain edges toward surface pits, resulting in localized nanoparticle formation and surface texturing. Importantly, despite these morphological changes, the analysis confirmed that all evaporated layers remained dense, uniform, and free from pinholes, thereby ensuring excellent structural integrity. The TiOx films provided complete and uniform surface coverage, a feature that is indispensable for advanced optoelectronic devices, where defects such as cracks or voids can severely compromise both optical and electronic performance.

Beyond structural quality, the study also highlights the functional significance of incorporating noble metal nanoparticles, particularly gold (Au), into oxide thin films. Gold nanoparticles are well known for their unique optical and photocatalytic properties, which arise from the phenomenon of localized surface plasmon resonance (LSPR). When illuminated, the oscillating electromagnetic field of incident light couples with the collective oscillations of free electrons in the nanoparticles, generating localized electromagnetic "hotspots." These hotspots create highly reactive sites that can degrade organic matter deposited on surfaces while simultaneously loosening dust particles.

When Au nanoparticles are integrated into TiO_2 thin films, the intrinsic photocatalytic activity of TiO_2 is significantly amplified under both UV and visible illumination, owing to synergistic charge transfer effects between the semiconductor and the plasmonic metal. This dual mechanism, LSPR-induced plasmonic enhancement coupled with TiO_2 photocatalysis, results in surfaces with powerful anti-dust and self-cleaning functionalities. Such plasmonic coatings not only mitigate the accumulation of both organic and inorganic dust but also ensure the breakdown of adherent contaminants over time, maintaining surface transparency and performance.

These characteristics are especially valuable for solar energy systems deployed in arid and dust-prone environments, where soiling is a major contributor to power loss. By leveraging LSPR and photocatalytic mechanisms, plasmonic coatings provide a sustainable and energy-efficient approach to dust mitigation, thereby improving both the efficiency and the operational lifetime of solar panels and other optoelectronic devices exposed to harsh outdoor conditions.

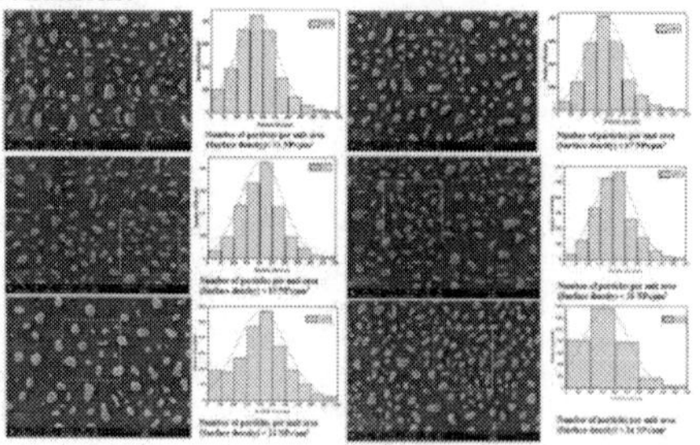

Figure 2: Morphological characterization of Au/TiOx thin films annealed at six different temperatures ranging from 300 °C to 900 °C. The images illustrate the progressive grain growth and surface evolution of both TiOx seed layers and Au films with increasing annealing temperature. At higher temperatures, Au crystallites become larger and more defined, with pronounced grain boundaries and increased particle density along these regions, attributed to thermally driven diffusion. The TiOx films provide uniform surface coverage, ensuring dense and pinhole-free layers, which is critical for maintaining structural integrity. These results confirm that annealing temperature strongly influences nanoparticle size, surface density, and grain separation, thereby enabling precise control of film morphology for applications in plasmonic and optoelectronic devices.

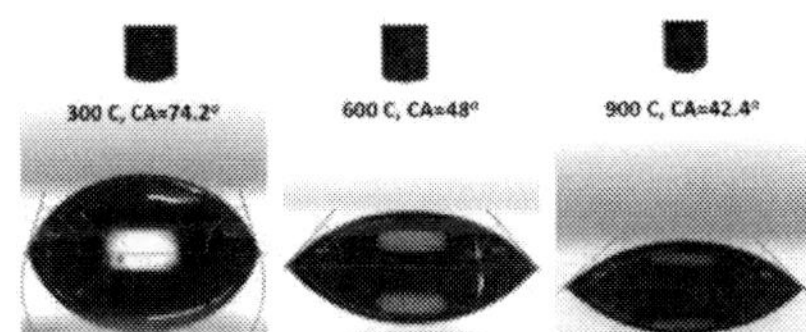

Figure 3: Wettability study of Au/TiOx thin films obtained by e-beam evaporation and subsequent annealing. Static contact angle measurements reveal the evolution of surface hydrophilicity with increasing annealing temperature, showing a decrease in contact angle from 74.2° to 42.4°. This change is attributed to the dewetting-driven transformation of Au into nanoparticle islands, which alters surface roughness and interfacial energy. The results demonstrate the strong correlation between annealing-induced morphological changes and surface wettability, underscoring the potential of Au/TiOx films for applications requiring tailored wetting behavior, such as self-cleaning and anti-soiling coatings.

The surface tension dynamics of Au thin films are strongly governed by the surface energy of the underlying TiO_2 seed layers, which dictates the nucleation and growth behavior of Au during thermal treatment. This interplay leads to the formation of Au particles with systematically varying sizes, surface densities, and grain separations, depending on the annealing conditions. The wettability of the resulting films was evaluated through static contact angle measurements, as illustrated in Figure 3, which revealed a pronounced evolution in surface properties as a function of annealing temperature.

Specifically, the contact angle decreased from 74.2° to 42.4° with increasing annealing temperature, signifying a substantial transition from moderately hydrophobic to more hydrophilic behavior. This shift in wettability can be directly correlated with the nanostructural transformation of the Au layers: the continuous Au films progressively evolve into discrete nanoparticle islands through solid-state dewetting, thereby increasing surface roughness and altering the surface energy landscape. The emergence of well-separated Au nanoparticle domains enhances the interaction of water molecules with the substrate, effectively reducing the interfacial tension between the liquid droplet and the film surface. These observations highlight the critical role of annealing in modulating both surface morphology and wettability, offering a versatile pathway for tailoring thin-film properties. By controlling annealing temperature and thereby tuning particle formation dynamics, it is possible to engineer films with customized surface energies suited to specific functionalities. Such tunability is particularly relevant for applications where precisely controlled wettability is essential, including anti-soiling coatings, photocatalytic self-cleaning surfaces, and biointerface engineering.

4 CONCLUSIONS

In conclusion, this study underscores the critical challenge that soiling poses to the long-term performance and reliability of solar collectors, particularly in the Middle East and North Africa (MENA) region where high dust loads and frequent deposition events are prevalent. The accumulation of dust and particulate matter on photovoltaic (PV) modules and solar thermal collectors not only reduces power generation efficiency but also drives up operational and maintenance (O&M) costs, often becoming one of the most significant barriers to the widespread deployment of solar energy technologies in desert climates. Importantly, this work highlights the necessity of distinguishing between inorganic and organic soiling mechanisms: while inorganic particles such as sand and mineral dust tend to be less adhesive and easier to remove, organic soiling—comprising pollen, microbial residues, and biological contaminants—presents a more persistent and damaging challenge due to its strong adhesion and potential to catalyze corrosive processes through microbial activity. To address this challenge, the study investigated the integration of plasmonic metal nanoparticles, with a focus on gold (Au), onto both bare glass and TiO_2-coated glass substrates. By leveraging the phenomenon of localized surface plasmon resonance (LSPR), it was demonstrated that Au nanoparticles can significantly enhance the photocatalytic activity of the underlying TiO_2 layer. The use of the solid-state dewetting (SSD) technique to deposit and self-assemble Au nanoparticles proved particularly effective, as this method maximizes the nanoparticle–substrate interface and ensures well-distributed nanostructures capable of resonant optical excitation. Under illumination, the resulting plasmonic substrates exhibited superior performance in degrading and mitigating the organic fraction of dust, thereby reducing adhesion and facilitating self-cleaning behavior.

The findings presented here contribute to the advancement of next-generation anti-soiling coatings that combine optical transparency, plasmonic activity, and photocatalytic self-cleaning capabilities. By effectively targeting the more problematic organic component of dust deposition, these coatings offer a pathway to significantly improve solar energy yield, reduce cleaning frequency, and lower O&M costs for solar plants deployed in harsh desert and coastal environments. Beyond their immediate application in PV modules and solar collectors, the concepts demonstrated here open avenues for multifunctional surface coatings in broader optoelectronic and environmental applications, positioning plasmonic nanostructures as a versatile tool for sustainable energy technologies in dust-prone regions.

5 REFERENCES

[1] E. Petryayeva, U.J. Krull, Anal. Chim. Acta 706 (1) (2011) 8–24, https://doi.org/10.1016/j.aca.2011.08.020.
[2] K.L. Kelly, E. Coronado, L.L. Zhao, G.C. Schatz, et al., J. Phys. Chem. B 107 (3) (2003) 668–677, https://doi.org/10.1021/jp026731v.
[3] J.N. Anker, W.P. Hall, O. Lyandres, N.C. Shah, J. Zhao, R.P. Van Duyne, et al., Nat. Mater. 7 (6) (2008) 442–453, https://doi.org/10.1038/nmat2162.
[4] T. Chung, Y. Lee, M.S. Ahn, W. Lee, S.I. Bae, C.S.H. Hwang, K.H. Jeong, et al., Nanoscale 11 (18) (2019) 8651–8664, https://doi.org/10.1039/c8nr10539a.
[5] G.V. Naik, V.M. Shalaev, A. Boltasseva, Alternative Plasmonic Materials: Beyond Gold and Silver (2013). URL www.MaterialsViews.com. https://doi.org/10.1002/adma.201205076.
[6] M.M. Jiang, H.Y. Chen, B.H. Li, K.W. Liu, C.X. Shan, S. De Zhen, et al., J. Mater. Chem. C 2 (1) (2014) 56–63, https://doi.org/10.1039/c3tc31910e.
[7] M.B. Ross, J.C. Ku, M.G. Blaber, C.A. Mirkin, G.C. Schatz, et al., Proc. Natl. Acad. Sci. U.S.A. 112 (33) (2015) 10292–10297, https://doi.org/10.1073/pnas.1513058112.
[8] L.L. Lebel, B. Aïssa, M.A. El Khakani, D. Therriault, Compos. Sci. Technol. 70 (3) (2010) 518–524.
[9] W. Julia, C. Luis, R. Federico, et al., Adv. Funct. Mater. 23 (2013) 5591–5598.
[10] D.T.H. Dalir, R.D. Farahani, V. Nhim, B. Aïssa, et al., Langmuir 28 (1) (2011) 791–803.
[11] A. Ali, F. El-Mellouhi, A. Mitra, B. Aïssa, Nanomaterials 12 (5) (2022) 788.
[12] R.D. Farahani, D.T.H. Dalir, V. Le Borgne, A. Loick, et al., Compos. Sci. Technol. 72 (12) (2012) 1387–1395.
[13] N.M.H. Gavi, B.D. Ngom, A.C. Beye, A.M. Strydom, B. Aïssa, V.V. Srinivasu, M. Chaker, J. Magn. Magn. Mater. 324 (6) (2012) 1172–1176.
[14] B. Aïssa, M.A. El Khakani, Nanotechnology 20 (17) (2009) 175203.
[15] M.A. Habib, M. Barkat, B. Aïssa, T. Denidni, Prog. Electromagn. Res. 88 (2008) 135–148.
[16] M.I. Hossain, B. Aïssa, A. Samara, S.A. Mansour, C.A. Broussillou, V. Bermudez Benito, ACS Omega 6 (8) (2021) 5276–5286.
[17] L.L. Lebel, B. Aïssa, M.A. El Khakani, D. Therriault, Compos. Sci. Technol. 70 (3) (2010) 518–524.
[18] W. Julia, C. Luis, R. Federico, et al., Adv. Funct. Mater. 23 (2013) 5591–5598.
[19] D.T.H. Dalir, R.D. Farahani, V. Nhim, B. Aïssa, et al., Langmuir 28 (1) (2011) 791–803.
[20] A. Ali, F. El-Mellouhi, A. Mitra, B. Aïssa, Nanomaterials 12 (5) (2022) 788.
[21] R.D. Farahani, D.T.H. Dalir, V. Le Borgne, A. Loick, et al., Compos. Sci. Technol. 72 (12) (2012) 1387–1395.
[22] H. Zhao, H. Kimura, Z. Cheng, X. Wang, T. Nishida, Appl. Phys. Lett. 95 (2009) 232904, https://doi.org/10.1063/1.3271032.

Plasmonic-Decorated TiO2 Thin Films as Photocatalytic Anti-Soiling Coatings

Brahim Aissa*, Mohammad I. Hossain, Adnan Ali and
Qatar Environment and Energy Research Institute (QEERI)- Hamad Bin Khalifa University (HBKU),
Doha, 34110, Qatar

*Contact: baissa@hbku.edu.qa

Abstract

The overall objective of this work is to fabrication plasmonics Au nanostructures on the surfaces of TiO2 thin films by a solid state thermal dewetting for solar cells applications.

More specifically:

- Developing efficient and cheap designs to optimize light management in optoelectronic devices.
- Considering the utilization of abundant and cheap materials to ensure cost-effectiveness.
- Developing multi-physics tool for solar cell design considering comprehensive and interactive optical, thermal, and electrical analyses.
- Experimental realization and proof-of-concept.

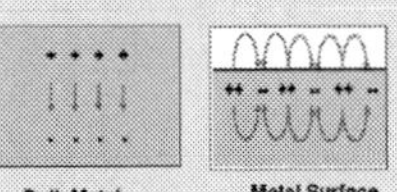

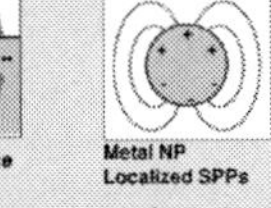
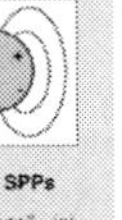
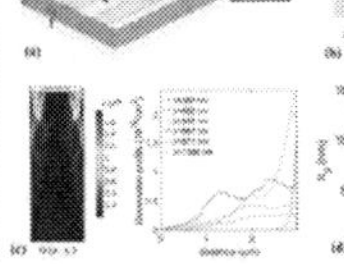
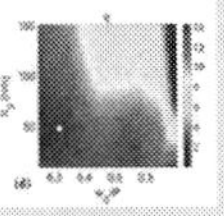
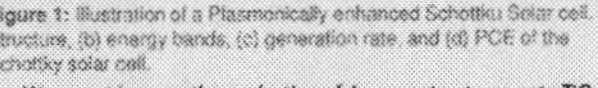
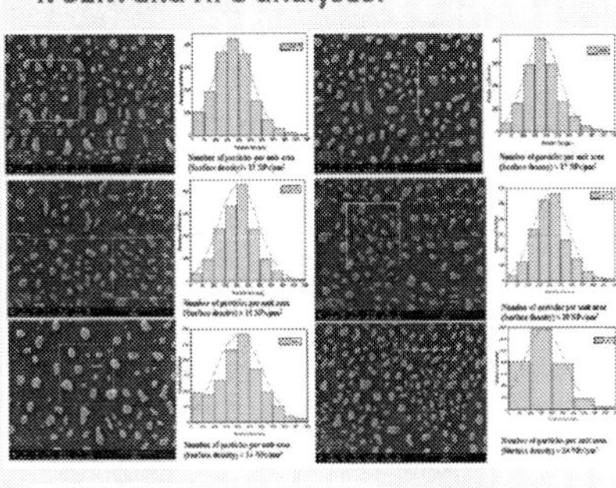

Figure 1: Illustration of a Plasmonically enhanced Schottku Solar cell. (a) Structure, (b) energy bands, (c) generation rate, and (d) PCE of the Schottky solar cell.

We report here on the nucleation of Au nanostructures onto TiOx thin films surfaces which occurred in consecutive steps.

Firstly, TiOx thin films were grown on quartz substrates reactively by e-beam evaporator and then thermally annealed at different temperatures, starting from 300 to 900 °C.

Subsequently, a nano-film of Au was deposited on the top of these TiOx surfaces.

The stacked Au/TiOx samples were post-annealed using muffle furnace at a temperature of 600°C for 1 hour, to study the thermal dewetting properties and the controlled growth of the different TiOx morphologies on the formation of Au nanoparticles and their plasmonic response.

The average surface roughness also increased significantly with respect to the TiOx annealing temperature, which is mainly attributed to the porosity of the films.

Finally, the absorption peak for Au nanostructures has shown a localized surface plasmon resonance close to 520 nm, along with a broad shoulder peak with a strong tail thereby reflecting the wide distribution of the formed Au nanoparticles sizes.

1. Experimental Setup

Metal oxide thin films (TiO$_x$) were grown using e-beam evaporation of Ti pellet at room temperature under a constant oxygen flow rate to maintain a deposition pressure of 2×10^{-4} Torr. Metal layers (Au) were also grown on quartz substrates using the same e-beam evaporation, at room temperature(Denton Vacuum Explorer™ evaporator). Pristine TiO$_2$ films were annealed at different temperatures ranging from 300 °C to 900 °C, using muffle furnace for 1 hour, whereas annealing temperature for Au/TiO$_2$ films was kept at 600 °C.

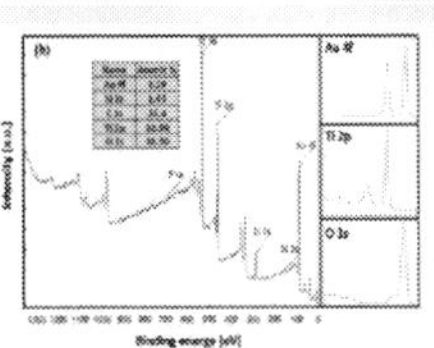

Figure 1: Schematic of the e-beam evaporation process

Figure 2: (a) XRD patterns of the Au/TiO$_x$ thin films with 300°C-900 °C annealing temperature of TiO$_x$ films.

Samples were optically measured using ultraviolet-visible (UV-Vis) spectroscopy. The wetting behavior was characterized using contact angle measurements. Dektak™ 3D stylus and Bruker™ atomic force microscopy (AFM, Fig. 6) were used to characterize surface topology. JEOL 7610™ field-emission scanning electron microscopy (FESEM) was engaged to study the microstructure of the films. Structural characterization of the grown films was carried out using x-ray photoelectron spectroscopy (XPS) and Bruker™ X-ray diffraction (XRD).

2. Results. Morphological and Surface properties:

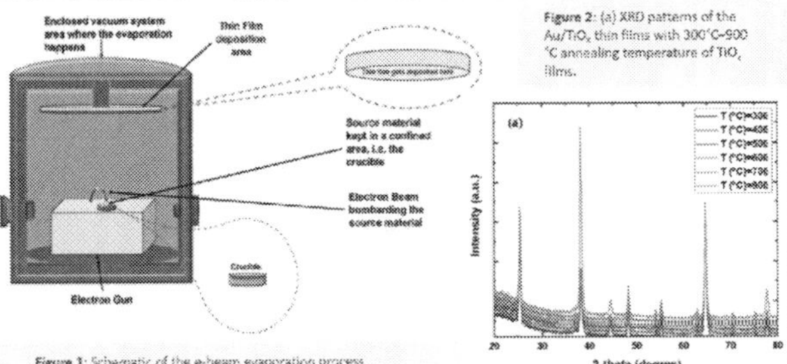

The surface tension dynamics of gold (Au) films significantly depends on the surface kinetics of TiOx films, which leads to the formation of Au particles with various shapes and sizes, different densities, and different grain distances.

Figure 3: AFM analysis showing a topological study of Au/TiO$_x$ systems with TiO$_x$ at three different surface densities.

Figure 4: Wettability study of Au/TiOx structures

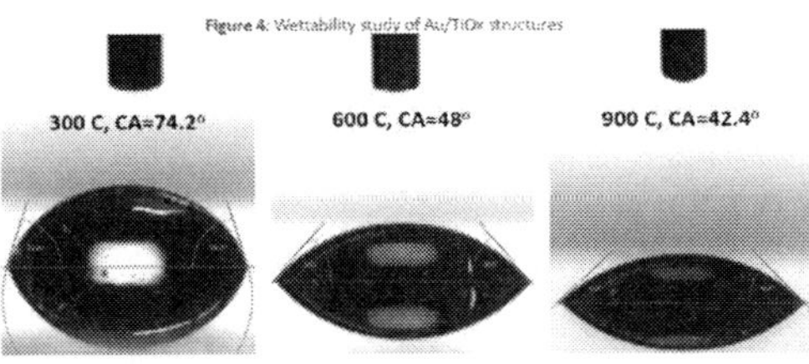

As confirmed by the wetting technique using contact angle measurement shown in Figure 4, surface wettability has changed significantly, and the CA has decreased from 74.2° to 42.4° with respect to the annealing temperature. The samples became more hydrophilic.

4. SEM and XPS analyses:

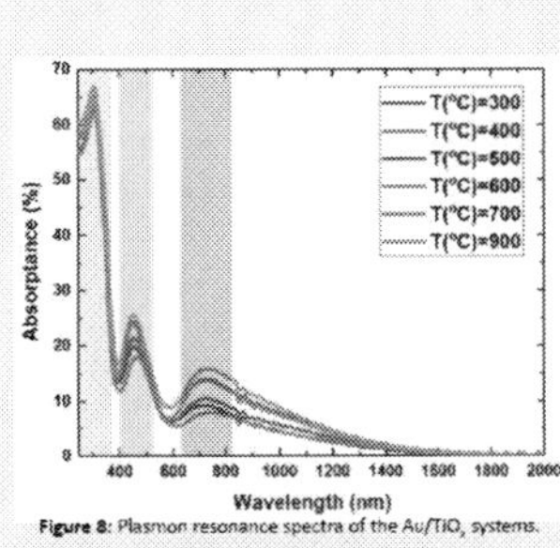

Figure 5: SEM morphological results of Au/TiO$_x$ systems with TiO$_x$ films annealed at six different temperatures, from 300 C to 900 °C. The size distribution and surface density of the Au NPs is associated with their respective histograms. Figure 5. AFM analysis showing a topological study of Au/TiOx systems with TiOx annealed at three different temperatures, namely 300, 600 and 900 °C.

Figure 6: XPS survey of the Au/TiO$_2$ system (TiO$_2$ annealed at 900 °C, Au/TiO$_x$ annealed at 600 °C) along with Au 4f, Ti 2p and O 1s spectra.

5. Optical properties and plasmonic responses:

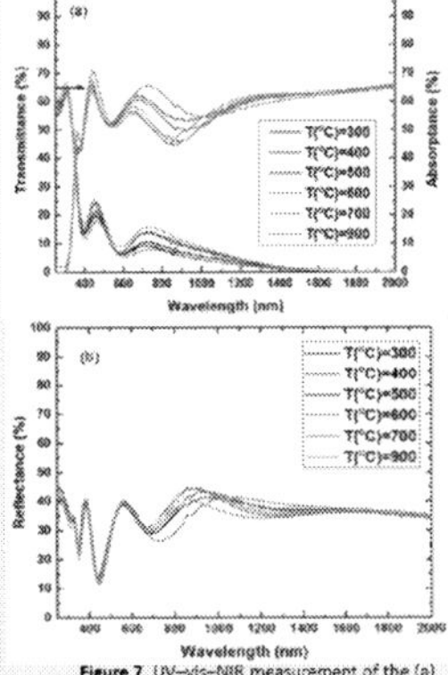

Figure 8: Plasmon resonance spectra of the Au/TiO$_x$ systems.

The absorption peak for Au nanostructures has shown a localized surface plasmon resonance close to 520 nm, along with a broad shoulder peak with a strong tail thereby reflecting the wide distribution of the formed Au nanoparticles sizes, highlighting the evidence of a thermal dewetting efficiency for large scale and high-throughput fabrication.

Figure 7: UV–vis–NIR measurement of the (a) transmittance and absorptance spectra for the annealed samples and (b) reflectance spectra of the annealed samples.

6. Conclusions

- ✓ The correlations between soldi state thermal dewetting temperatures and Au/TiOx systems properties have been established in this work.
- ✓ Sharp peak intensity has been observed of all the films with the highest dewetting temperature and attributed to the crystallinity of the films.
- ✓ It was found that crystallinity of Au NPs depended significantly on the TiOx seed layer surface properties.
- ✓ The optical measurements showed that transmission shifts to a higher range with > 65%, while reflectance ranges below < 40% in the visible range as the dewetting temperature increased, confirming thereby that the Au/TiOx systems become more transparent.
- ✓ Finally, the absorption peak for Au nanostructures has shown a localized surface plasmon resonance close to 520 nm, along with a broad shoulder peak with a strong tail thereby reflecting the wide distribution of the formed Au nanoparticles sizes, highlighting the evidence of a thermal dewetting efficiency for large scale and high-throughput fabrication.

References:

1. Naik, Gururaj, Jongbum Kim, Nathaniel Kinsey, and Alexandra Boltasseva. "Alternative plasmonic materials." In Handbook of Surface Science, vol. 4, pp. 189-221. North-Holland, 2014.
2. Khurana, Kanika, and Neena Jaggi. "Localized surface plasmonic properties of Au and Ag nanoparticles for sensors: A review." Plasmonics 16, no. 4 (2021): 981-999.
3. Kotni, Tirumala Rao, Jayati Sarkar, and Rajesh Khanna. "Dewetting of thin wetting film supported by different solid substrates: a review." Phase Transitions 95, no. 8-9 (2022): 551-566.
4. Rudakova, Aida V., Alexei V. Emeline, Andrey I. Romanychev, and Detlef W. Bahnemann. "Photoinduced hydrophilic behavior of TiO2 thin film on Si substrate." Journal of Alloys and Compounds 872 (2021): 159746.

Acknowledgments
This publication was made possible by NPRP grant # NPRP11S-0117-180330 from the Qatar National Research Fund (QNRF), a member of Qatar Foundation. The findings herein reflect the work and are solely the responsibility of the authors. The authors acknowledge the technical support from colleagues who exchanged constructive discussions about the topic of this research. The authors are also grateful for the support from QEERI CORE Labs and Thin Films Lab for material deposition and characterization.

EVALUATING CLIMATE-SPECIFIC DEGRADATION OF PV MODULES BY SPECTRAL UV-FLUORESCENCE MAPPING

Oleksandr Stroyuk[1], Oleksandra Raievska[1], Oleksandr Mashkov[1], Carlos D. Rodríguez-Gallegos[2],
Claudia Buerhop[1], Jens Hauch[1], Ian Marius Peters[1]
[1]Forschungszentrum Jülich GmbH, Helmholtz-Institut Erlangen Nürnberg für Erneuerbare Energien
(HI ERN), 91058 Erlangen, Germany, o.stroyuk@fz-juelich.de
[2]Solar Energy Research Institute of Singapore, National University of Singapore, Singapore 117574,
cardarod88@gmail.com

ABSTRACT: Spectral mapping of the UV-excited fluorescence (UVF) band maximum is introduced as a universal approach to evaluate the degradation status of PV modules exposed to different climatic conditions and aging periods. The UVF band maximum maps are independent of the excitation conditions, enabling direct comparisons of the degradation state of PV modules exposed to different environments. A distinct correlation between the UVF band position and oxidative degradation of EVA encapsulants, of PV modules revealed by near-infrared absorption spectroscopy allows spectral UVF mapping to be applied for very fast comparative field evaluation of the degradation of PV polymers in different climates.
Keywords: fluorescence; spectral mapping; polymer degradation; near-infrared absorption spectroscopy

1 INTRODUCTION

Degradation of encapsulants and backsheets is a major cause of premature PV module failures. The evaluation of the degradation status of polymer packaging requires the development of new non-invasive characterization methods that are upscalable for high-throughput deployment and allow the comparability of the data collected in different climates. UV-excited fluorescence (UVF) imaging of aged encapsulants has emerged as an informative and fast diagnostic tool, providing new insights into polymer degradation depending on the bill-of-materials (BOM) and climate [1, 2]. At the same time, the potential of using spectral parameters of UVF emission, such as UVF band position or emission lifetime, to provide additional meaningful information on polymer degradation, remains largely unexplored and under-appreciated.

Here, we introduce spectral mapping of the UVF band maximum as a universal approach for evaluating polymer degradation in PV modules. In a case study of PV modules exposed to a tropical climate, a distinct correlation between the UVF band position and oxidative degradation of ethylene vinyl acetate (EVA) copolymer encapsulants of PV modules was found, the latter expressed as a carbonyl index (CI) determined by near-infrared absorption (NIRA) spectroscopy [3]. This correlation is assumed to reflect a competition between primary EVA photodegradation, generating emissive species, and secondary oxidative degradation resulting in UVF quenching and an increase of CI. The interrelation between spectral UVF parameters and CI allows spectral UVF mapping to be introduced together with NIRA as a fast tool for field evaluation of the degradation of PV polymers [1, 2, 4], even at very early stages [5]. The feasibility of such comparison was exemplified by spectral datasets collected for PV modules with the same BOM and age but exposed to different climates, moderate European and tropical in Singapore.

2 SAMPLES AND METHODS

2.1 Samples

The spectral measurements were performed on a set of 34 coupon samples and extracted from 15-year-old PV modules installed as a rooftop system in a tropical climate of Singapore. The coupons were 8 per 7 cm in size, cut between four adjacent cells (Figure 1) from laminates detached from the frontal glass.

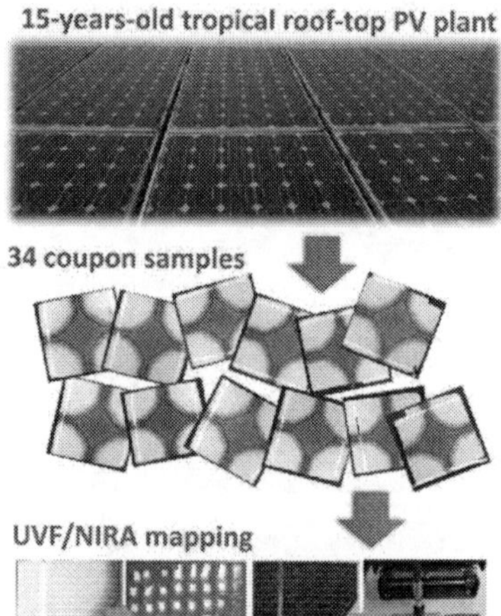

Figure 1: Illustration of the tested samples and workflow (photos of coupons were taken under UV illumination, 350-370 nm)

A cross-sectional Raman study (reported in detail in 3AV.2.10) of coupons showed them to contain a Tedlar-like BSh with symmetrical air- and inner-side 30-mkm layers of rutile-filled polyvinyl fluoride (PVF) and a 280-mkm core layer of polyethylene terephthalate (PET). The coupons also included two layers of EVA encapsulant and residuals of Si cells.

2.2 Methods

Carbonyl indices were measured in two modes.

Single-point CI measurements were performed for a set of PV modules (in the lower left corner of each module [3]) and for coupons (in the center between the cell fragments). For a selected sample, the frontal EVA layer was detached from the rest of the coupon (see Fig. 1), mounted on an Al mirror, and subjected to point-wise NIRA measurements using a Y-shaped optical fiber (Fig. 1) with a step of 5 mm along both X and Y axes. The point-wise measurements resulted in a set of 64 NIRA spectra, used to calculate CI and WI for each point and map them as a function of the coordinates. NIRA measurements were performed with a fiber-coupled FT-NIR Rocket 2.6 spectrometer (Arcoptix) in a spectral range of 900-2600 nm (3800-11000 cm^{-1}) with a resolution of 8 cm^{-1}. The samples were excited by a stabilized fiber-coupled SLS201/M NIR lamp (Thorlabs). Typically, 20 reflectance spectra were averaged for noise reduction. Carbonyl index was calculated as a ratio of integral intensities of a C=O-related band at 2140 nm and a reference C-H first-overtone vibrational band at 1730 nm [3]. Similarly, the water index WI was calculated as a ratio of integral intensities of the water-related O-H vibrational band at 1910 nm and the reference band at 1730 nm [6].

Fluorescence spectra were collected point-wise for the detached frontal layer of EVA of a selected sample, similar to the point-wise NIRA measurements, with steps of 5 mm along the X and Y axes. The sample was excited by a fiber-coupled 365-nm LED (Thorlabs), and the emission was detected by a Black Comet diode-array-based UV-Vis spectrometer (StellarNet) in the range of 400-800 nm with a resolution of ca. 1 nm. Afterwards, the detached EVA sample was cut into a set of 8 by 8 pieces and arranged as a rectangular array (see Fig. 1). The array was used to collect a set of fluorescence and fluorescence excitation spectra using a plate-reading monochromator-based Tecan spectrometer with an excitation wavelength of 370 nm.

3 RESULTS AND DISCUSSION

Spectral measurements were performed on a series of 34 samples, provided by the Solar Energy Research Institute of Singapore (SERIS), extracted from silicon PV modules exposed to the tropical climate of Singapore in a rooftop installation for 15 years starting in 2008. The samples were produced by delaminating the stack of backsheet and cells sandwiched between two encapsulant layers from the front glass and cutting to have an intercell void and corner fragments of four neighboring cells in each sample. A cross-sectional Raman analysis (see more details in 3AV.2.10) showed the samples to be composed of Tedlar-like tri-layer PVF-PET-PVF backsheet and EVA co-polymer encapsulant.

Under UV excitation (360–370 nm), samples showed strong fluorescence (UVF), with intensity highest over Si cells, quenched between cells, and intermediate at cell corners. (Figure 2a). Spectral measurements in different points showed that UVF band center (UVF$_{max}$) shifts from ca. 550 nm for the sample center to 570-580 nm for the cell corner to 600-610 nm for the brightest areas over cells (Fig. 2b). To quantify the distribution of UVF$_{max}$, the UVF spectra were measured grid-wise for the sample shown in Fig. 1a, taking 5 mm steps along X and Y axes, resulting in a UVF$_{max}$ distribution map (Fig. 2c).

The UVF measurements were performed using two types of UV-Vis spectrometers, diode-array-based and monochromator-based, yielding identical UVF spectra. The attempt to collect fluorescence excitation spectra

yielded no meaningful results due to the dominance of artifacts in the UVF excitation spectra, most probably due to the antireflective geometry of the tested EVA samples.

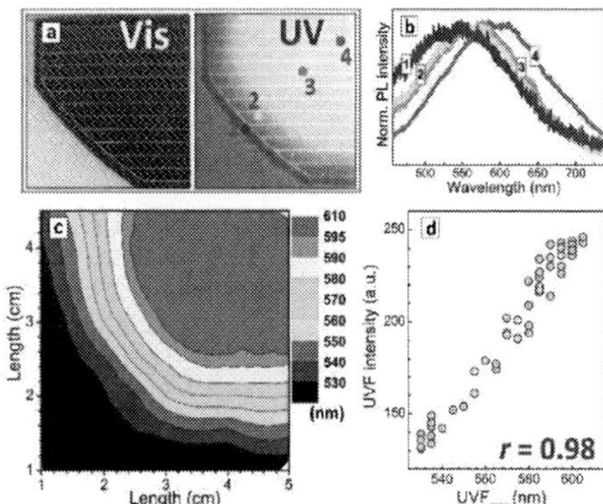

Figure 2: (a) Photographs of the mapped sample fragment made under visible (Vis) and UV illumination. (b) Normalized UVF spectra registered at the points numbered in (a, UV). (c,d) UVF$_{max}$ band mapping and correlation between the UVF intensity and UVF$_{max}$ (d) for a 5×5 cm sample fragment in (a). R is Pearson's correlation coefficient

The UV$_{max}$ distribution was found to mimic the emission intensity distribution observed in the UVF images, showing a positive correlation between the UVF$_{max}$ position and emission intensity (Fig. 2d). In this view, the UVF$_{max}$ mapping can be used as an alternative to conventional UVF imaging, allowing direct comparison between different samples, while UVF imaging is dependent on the excitation intensity and angle, requiring additional measurements of emissive reference to enable comparisons between different sites and/or climates.

Along with the spectral UVF$_{max}$ mapping, the samples were subjected to NIRA mapping performed similarly to our recent reports [2, 6] with the same spatial resolution. The NIRA mapping produces spatial maps of CI and WI distributions (Figure 3a,b), both parameters serving as degradation markers in EVA encapsulants. The distributions of CI and WI were found to be negative reflections of the corresponding UVF$_{max}$ distribution and UVF image, with higher UVF$_{max}$ wavelengths and emission intensities corresponding to lower CI/WI values, that is, to a lower depth of oxidative degradation.

Overall, CI values collected over the entire sample surface showed a clear inverse correlation to the UVF band maxima collected from the same spots (Fig. 3c). This correlation reflects a competition between primary photochemical and secondary oxidative degradation modes. The photodegradation of EVA generates emissive species with longer UVF$_{max}$ wavelengths corresponding to deeper degradation, while the secondary degradation by air oxygen results in gradual UVF quenching and oxidation of EVA with shorter UVF$_{max}$ wavelengths and higher CIs corresponding to deeper degradation. These observations indicate that more deeply oxidized sections of the sample located on cell edges and between the cells are characterized by strongly quenched UVF and UVF band maxima at shorter wavelengths, with an almost linear relationship between CI and UVF$_{max}$ determined by two different spectroscopic approaches. Considering this correlation, the UVF spectroscopy of EVA encapsulant emerges as a feasible method for field evaluation of oxidative degradation in PV modules, providing the same level of detail and confidence as NIRA spectroscopy.

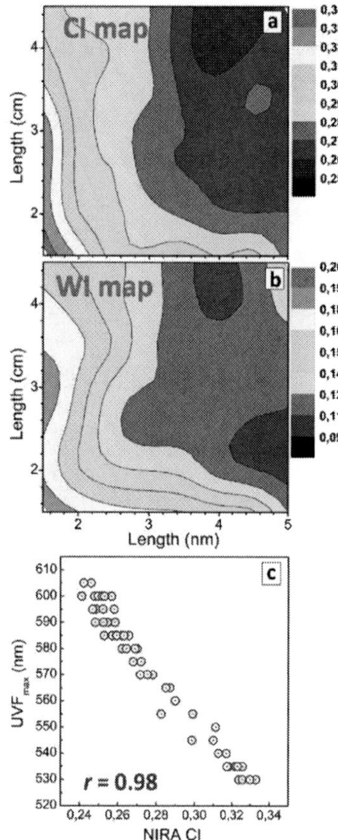

Figure 3: (a) Carbonyl index CI (a) and water index WI (b) mapping by NIRA and correlation between the CI values and UVF_{max} (d) for a 5×5 cm sample fragment in Fig. 1a

As reported in [2], the CI values measured in the inter-cell spots of field-aged PV modules, where the oxidative degradation of EVA is maximal, are inversely proportional to the "wet" leakage resistance R_{iso}, with higher CIs corresponding to lower R_{iso}. This correlation allows the CI distributions measured in the field for a statistically significant number of modules (more than 20 per field) to be used to evaluate the isolation integrity and degradation of the tested modules and compare different fields without making actual electrical measurements.

Here, we further extend this approach by replacing NIRA measurements of CI for multiple modules with the measurements of UVF_{max} that can be done for a single representative module. The evaluation of the feasibility of this approach was performed for a set of samples with the same PVF-type backsheet type and age, but installed in two different climatic zones, in Germany (PVF-G) and Singapore (PVF-S).

Spectral UVF_{max} measurements made for several representative areas of both module types showed a strong

difference in the position and shape of UVF_{max} distribution (Figure 4a, left column), the PVF-G modules showing a narrow UVF_{max} group centered at ca. 500 nm, while the PVF-S samples revealed a broadened bi-modal distribution with two apparent peaks at ca. 540 nm and 590 nm. These data show that despite the very similar BOM and age, UVF_{max} distributions of PVF-G and PVF-S samples do not even overlap, indicating an advanced degradation state of PVF-S modules subjected to harsher climatic conditions and stronger irradiation.

To provide additional emphasis on the difference in spectral UVF properties between the two climates, we collected UVF_{max} distribution from a historic module with a PET-type backsheet and EVA encapsulant exposed to field aging in Germany (PET-G) for more than 30 years, showing the highest UVF emission of all samples available in our lab. Figure 4 shows that the UVF_{max} distribution for this module type only partially overlaps with the UVF_{max} distribution of PVF-S, showing the advanced degradation state of the latter samples.

The right column in Fig. 4 shows distributions of CI values measured in the most oxidized inter-cell spots for multiple modules of PVF-G (59 modules), PET-G (22), and PVF-S (34) types. These distributions follow the same trend as UVF_{max} distributions (left column), centering at CI ca. 0.20 for PVF-G, ca. 0.24 for PET-G, and extending from 0.28 to 0.32 for the most degraded PVF-S.

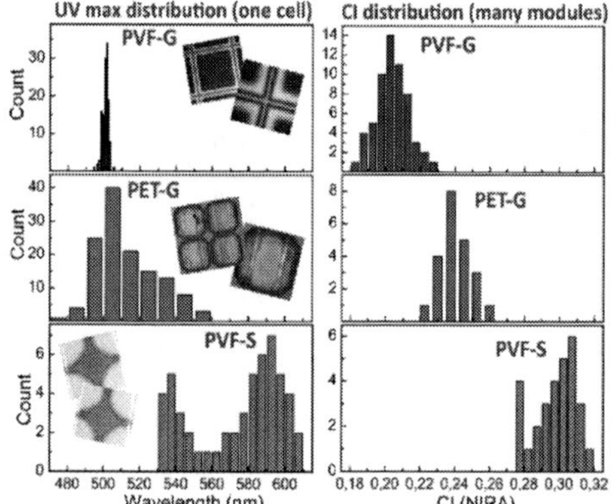

Figure 4: Distributions of UVF_{max} collected for a single particular cell area (left column) and distributions of CI measured between the cells from numerous module samples (right column) for samples with PVF-type backsheet aged in the field for 10 years in Germany (PVF-G) and in Singapore (PVF-S), as well as for the samples with PET-based backsheet aged for more than 30 years in Germany (PET-G). Insets in the left column show photographs of the samples under UV illumination

Similar evolution of the relative positions of UVF_{max} and CI distributions stems from the inherent relationship between the depth of primary photochemical degradation of EVA (expressed in terms of UVF_{max}) and the secondary oxidative degradation (expressed in terms of CI). While both parameters can be used to compare the degradation state of PV modules of different ages and in different climatic conditions, the UVF measurements can be collected from a single module and require a shorter time.

4 CONCLUSION

The feasibility of using spectral mapping of UVF emission band maximum for the evaluation of the degradation status of encapsulants in field-aged PV modules is shown. Based on a set of strongly degraded samples from a tropical climate of Singapore, we found a distinct positive correlation between the UVF emission intensity and UVF maximum wavelength, as well as an inverse correlation between the CI and UVF max values. PV modules exposed to different climates, moderate European and tropical in Singapore, showed distinctly different UVF band maximum distributions, illustrating the potential of the spectral UVF imaging for the comparative evaluation of the degradation progress in different climatic zones.

This work was funded by the German Federal Ministry for Economic Affairs and Climate Action (BMWK) by the project "dig4morE" (FKZ: 03EE1090B) and by the WIPANO project "PolymAERA" (FKZ: 03TN0053E). The samples were collected in the frame of the international PV Camper initiative.

References
[1] C. Buerhop, O. Stroyuk, O. Mashkov, J. Hauch, I.M. Peters, Sol. RRL, 8 (2024) 2400566.
[2] C. Buerhop, O. Stroyuk, O. Mashkov, A. Barabash, J.A. Hauch, I.M. Peters, Sol. Energy Mater. Sol. Cells, 277 (2024) 113111.
[3] O. Stroyuk, C. Buerhop, E. Wittman, O. Mashkov, P. Stephan, J.L. Crozier McCleland, M. Vumbugwa, F.J. Vorster, E.E. van Dyk, J. Hauch, C.J. Brabec, I.M. Peters, Sol. RRL, 8 (2024) 2301022.
[4] C. Buerhop, E. van Dyk, F.J. Vorster, O. Stroyuk, O. Mashkov, J.L. Crozier McCleland, M. Vumbugwa, J. Hauch, I.M. Peters, IEEE J. Photovoltaics, 15 (2024) 30.
[5] A.A. Abdallah, M. Kivambe, M. Abdelrahim, M. Elgaili, A. Ahmed, K. Mroue, O. Stroyuk, O. Mashkov, I.M. Peters, C. Buerhop-Lutz, Sol. Energy Mater. Sol. Cells, 294 (2026) 113899.
[6] O. Mashkov, O. Stroyuk, C. Buerhop, S. Bind, D. Clark, J. Hauch, I.M. Peters, Sol. RRL, 2025, 202500499.

IDENTIFICATION OF SPECTRAL INDICATORS OF DEGRADATION IN TEDLAR-TYPE BACKSHEETS: A CASE STUDY OF PV MODULES AGED IN TROPICAL CLIMATE

Oleksandr Stroyuk[1], Oleksandr Mashkov[1], Carlos D. Rodríguez-Gallegos[2],
Claudia Buerhop[1], Jens Hauch[1], Ian Marius Peters[1]
[1]Forschungszentrum Jülich GmbH, Helmholtz-Institut Erlangen Nürnberg für Erneuerbare Energien
(HI ERN), 91058 Erlangen, Germany, o.stroyuk@fz-juelich.de
[2]Solar Energy Research Institute of Singapore, National University of Singapore, Singapore 117574,
cardarod88@gmail.com

ABSTRACT: Degradation of backsheets and encapsulants induces significantlosses in insulation resistance, often decreasing it below the allowed threshold and inducing inverter shut-offs. The deterioration of polymer packaging can be reliably detected by measurements of the insulation resistance, which, however, are resource-demanding and limited to wet periods. In this connection, alternative non-invasive and resource-efficient methodologies are highly demanded. Recently, we showed that insulation resistance can be indirectly evaluated by near-infrared absorption spectroscopy, using an inverse correlation between the insulation resistance and spectrally identified carbonyl index, which indicates the depth of oxidative degradation of ethylene vinyl acetate copolymer encapsulation. In the present contribution, we extend this spectral approach by applying Raman spectroscopy to identify spectral features of the polymer degradation in Tedlar-type backsheet components of PV modules aged in a tropical climate. We report several spectral parameters that correlate with the carbonyl index of the encapsulant and can be used as substitute for the measurements of the insulation resistance, including the ratio of C=O- and C=C-related vibrational bands in polyethylene terephthalate core layer, the ratio of polyvinyl fluoride- and rutile-related bands in Raman spectra of the air layer, as well as the integral photoluminescence of the air layer. The relevance of the selected spectral parameters as descriptors of degradation events in Tedlar-like backsheets was further confirmed by artificial UV aging tests. This demonstrates Raman-based field diagnostics as a practical complement to insulation resistance and NIRA methods.
Keywords: polymer degradation; backsheets; encapsulants; climate-dependent degradation; Raman spectroscopy

1 INTRODUCTION

Degradation of backsheets and encapsulants can induce severe losses in insulation resistance of PV modules, compromising operational safety and inducing inverter shut-offs. The deterioration of polymer packaging can be reliably detected by measurements of the insulation resistance R_{iso} on the module level. However, such measurements are resource-demanding and weather-dependent. For these reasons, alternative, non-invasive approaches for reliable field evaluation are urgently needed.

Recently, we showed that the insulation resistance of PV modules can be evaluated indirectly and contactless by near-infrared absorption (NIRA) spectroscopy, using an inverse correlation between R_{iso} and spectrally identified carbonyl index (CI). The later indicates the depth of oxidative degradation of ethylene vinyl acetate (EVA) copolymer encapsulants and, in general, the extent of PV module degradation [1]. This correlation was confirmed for several backsheet (BSh) types, highlighting CI as a viable "proxy" indicator of the quality of polymer PV packaging [2-4].

Here, we further extend this spectral approach by identifying new spectral features of BSh components that correlate with the CI of EVA encapsulant and can be used as additional "proxies" proportional to R_{iso}, measurable by field-ready Raman spectroscopy from the air side of PV modules. These spectral indicators can provide additional insights into the degradation status of PV modules, complementing other approaches, such as electrical R_{iso} measurements, spectral evaluations by NIRA, and UV-excited fluorescence imaging [1, 5, 6]. The relevance of the selected spectral parameters as descriptors of degradation events in Tedlar-like (PVF/PET/PVF) backsheets was further confirmed by artificial UV aging tests.

2 SAMPLES AND METHODS

2.1 Samples

The spectral measurements were performed on a set of 34 coupon samples, provided by SERIS and extracted from 15-year-old PV modules installed as a rooftop system in a tropical climate of Singapore. The coupons were 8 per 7 cm in size, cut between four adjacent cells (Figure 1) from laminates detached from the frontal glass. The coupons contained the whole stack of backsheet, inner EVA encapsulant, silicon cell fragment, and external EVA encapsulant layers.

Figure 1: Illustration of the samples used in the present study

2.2 Methods

Carbonyl indices were measured by NIRA spectroscopy in the center of every coupon, that is, on the silicon-free BSh/encapsulant spots between the four adjacent cell fragments. NIRA spectra were collected in a reflectance mode and converted into absorption spectra using the spectrum of lamp irradiation reflected from an Al mirror. Measurements were performed with a fiber-coupled FT-NIR Rocket 2.6 spectrometer (Arcoptix) in a spectral range of 900-2600 nm (3800-11000 cm^{-1}) with a resolution of 8 cm^{-1}. The samples were excited by a

10.4229/EUPVSEC2025/3AV.2.10

stabilized fiber-coupled SLS201/M NIR lamp (Thorlabs). Typically, 20 reflectance spectra were collected consecutively and averaged for noise reduction. Carbonyl index was calculated as a ratio of integral intensities of a C=O-related band at 2140 nm and a reference C-H first-overtone vibrational band at 1730 nm [1, 7].

Raman measurements were performed pointwise on cross-sections of the coupons produced by cutting 1 per 2 cm corner fragments from each of the coupons. Raman spectra were detected on a WITec alpha700 confocal Raman microscope equipped with a UHTS 300 spectrometer in a spectral range of 130-3700 cm^{-1} and a resolution of 3 cm^{-1}. The samples were excited by a 532-nm laser with the maximum power of 50 mW [7].

Artificial UV ageing tests were carried out using a commercial Atlas UVTest weathering setup (Ametek) equipped with UVA-340 fluorescent lamps. The coupons of BShs (PVF/PET/PVF) and BSh components (PET) were supplied by Sunset company (Germany) and subjected to 4000 h of UV weathering at ambient relative humidity (50-60%) and 40-42 °C.

3 RESULTS AND DISCUSSION

The identification of spectral degradation markers was performed on a series of 34 coupon samples, provided by SERIS and extracted from 15-year-old PV modules installed as a rooftop system in a tropical climate of Singapore and showing an advanced state of degradation. A cross-sectional Raman study showed that the samples have a Tedlar-like BSh (Figure 2a) with identical air-side and inner 30-mkm layers of rutile-filled polyvinyl fluoride (PVF) and a 280-mkm core layer of polyethylene terephthalate (PET), as well as EVA encapsulant. The degradation state of the samples was evaluated by measuring the carbonyl index (CI) by NIRA of the frontal EVA layer [1] in the central spots between four neighboring Si cells.

The samples showed a rather broad distribution of CI values as well as Raman features indicative of a broad variation of the degradation depth among the tested samples. Distributions of various spectral Raman parameters collected for both PVF layers and PET cores, with the CI distribution among the tested samples, were compared, with the aim of finding Raman indicators correlating with CI and, therefore, with R_{iso} [2-4].

3.1 Degradation markers for the PET layer

Cross-sectional Raman spectra of the PET core layer reveal "fingerprint" vibrational bands at ca. 1620 and 1740 cm^{-1} assigned to C=C and C=O bonds in PET, respectively (Fig. 2b) [7]. The oxidation state of PET evaluated as a ratio of integral intensities, $R_{C=O/C=C}$, showed a distribution of values among the tested samples, indicating a variation of oxidative degradation depth of the PET core layer. A comparison of $R_{C=O/C=C}$ values with corresponding CIs of EVA measured by NIRA (NIRA CI) [1] revealed a positive correlation between both datasets (Fig. 2c). This correlation indicates that $R_{C=O/C=C}$ measured by Raman spectroscopy is a meaningful descriptor of PET degradation, proportional to EVA CI and R_{iso} [2-4].

3.2 Degradation markers for the PVF layers

Cross-sectional Raman spectra of PVF layers of non-aged BSh show a characteristic PVF C-H vibration band at 2800-2900 cm^{-1} and strong signals of rutile titania (R)

pigment at 200-700 cm^{-1} (Figure 3a) [7]. The air layers of field-aged samples were strongly degraded, showing only a photoluminescence (PL) background with no detectable PVF-related features (Fig. 3b).

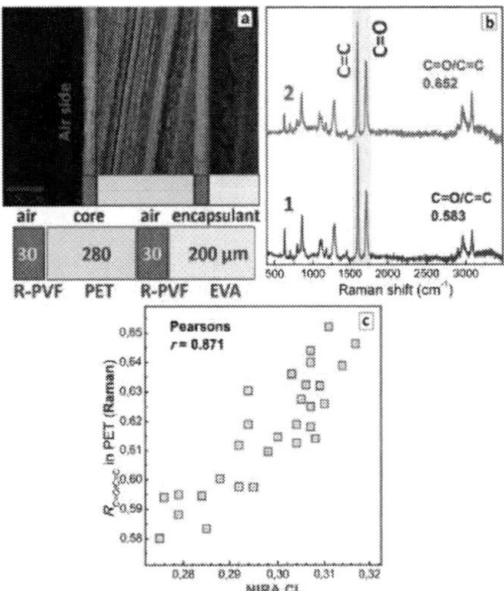

Figure 2: (a) Cross-sectional photograph and schematic of BSh structure; (b) Exemplary Raman spectra of PET layers with lower (1) and higher (2) depth of oxidation; (c) correlation between $R_{C=O/C=C}$ and NIRA CI

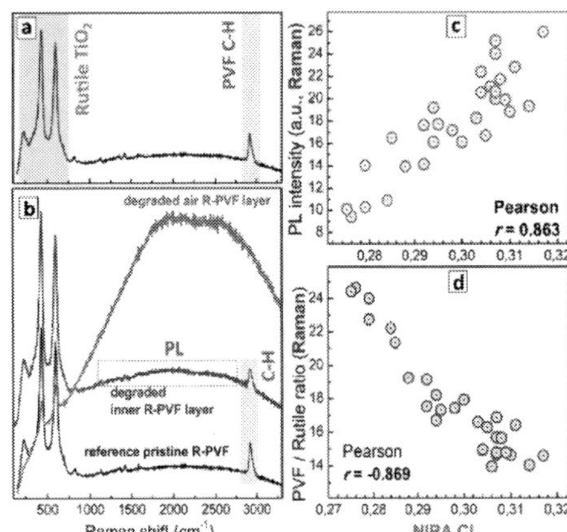

Figure 3: (a) Exemplary Raman spectrum of pristine rutile-PVF layer; (b) Raman spectra of pristine and field-aged inner and air layers of rutile-PVF; (c,d) Correlations between NIRA CI and the integral PL intensity of air rutile-PVF layers (c) and PVF/Rutile peak intensity in the inner rutile-PVF layers (d) of field-aged samples

The degradation depth of the inner rutile-PVF layer is lower, allowing both rutile and PVF-related features to be observed, along with a moderate PL background. At that, the ratio of integral intensities of PVF C-H peak to rutile-related peaks is lower for field-aged inner layers as compared to the pristine one, indicating partial decomposition of the PVF component. Considering these observations, both the integral intensity of the PL background and PVF/Rutile peak intensity ratio can be used to evaluate the degradation state of PVF layers. Indeed, both PL intensity and PVF/Rutile peak ratio were found to correlate with the NIRA CI values.

Higher PL intensities of air rutile-PVF layers correspond to higher NIRA CI values of EVA encapsulant with Pearson's correlation coefficient of 0.863 (Fig. 3c). Lower PVF/Rutile ratios in the inner PVF layers correspond to higher NIRA CI, in line with the expectedly higher degradation depth of such samples (Fig. 3d). These data show the relevance of both PL intensity and PVF/Rutile ratio in PVF layers as spectral descriptors of the degradation.

3.3 Artificial UV degradation

The relevance of the above-discussed spectral markers for assessments of the field degradation of polymer packaging was supported by the outcomes of artificial UV degradation of selected pristine samples, including pure PET film and a Tedlar-like R-PVF/PET/R-PVF BSh. The samples were characterized by cross-sectional Raman and FTIR spectroscopies before and after the test, while a combination of NIRA, Raman, and PL spectroscopies was applied to monitor the UV aging continuously.

The UV aging of PET film was found to result in distinct evolutions in the Raman spectrum, including an increase in $R_{C=O/C=C}$ and a rise of a PL background (Figure 4a, upper part). The integral PL intensity increases with exposure, showing some acceleration at the initial stage (Fig. 4b, scatter 1), most probably due to the photoinduced formation of new chromophores capable of absorbing additional UV light and accelerating UV degradation.

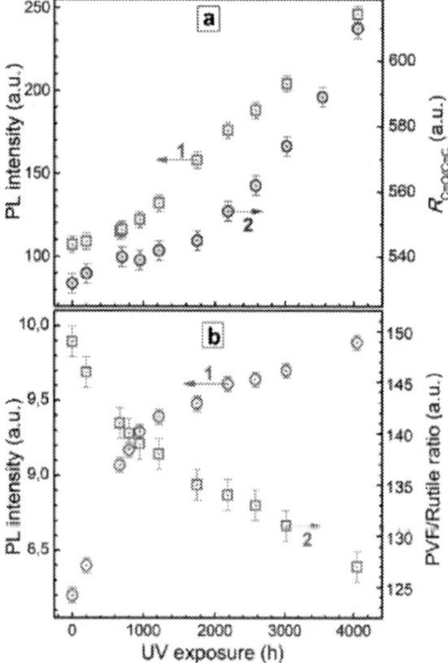

Figure 4: Evolution of degradation markers during artificial UV exposure of PET (a) and R-PVF/PET/R-PVF (b) samples. In (b) scatter 1 – PL intensity, 2 – $R_{C=O/C=C}$; in (c) scatter 1 – PL intensity, 2 – PVF/Rutile ratio

The increase of $R_{C=O/C=C}$ with UV exposure also shows an auto-catalytic character (Fig. 4b, scatter 2), indicating the participation of the photodecomposition products in light absorption and further photodegradation. Summarizing, the UV degradation of PET results in the decomposition and oxidation of the polymer, with the integral PL intensity and

$R_{C=O/C=C}$ ratio proportional to the UV exposure, showing both spectral parameters to be adequate descriptors for the degradation processes in PET.

Similar to the case of PET, the UV degradation of R-PVF/PET/R-PVF BSh results in noticeable changes in the Raman spectra of the illuminated air layer, in particular, in a decrease of the ratio of PVF/Rutile peak intensities and a rise of a PL background (Fig. 3a, lower part). The integral PL intensity showed a gradual increase with UV exposure, slowing down at longer illumination times (Fig. 4c, scatter 1), most probably due to the gradual depletion of the surface layer with PVF and the UV light filtering effect of rutile deposits. The assumption of the surface polymer decomposition is also supported by a decrease in the PVF/Rutile ratio with exposure (Fig. 4c, scatter 2). Both observations, the growth of PL intensity and the decrease of the PVF/Rutile ratio, indicate that these spectral descriptors are relevant for tracking the degradation of PVF-based BSh layers.

4 CONCLUSIONS

Several new spectral indicators measurable by Raman spectroscopy from the BSh surface that can be used to evaluate the degradation of PV modules with Tedlar-type BShs are reported. In particular, the ratios of PVF/Rutile Raman peaks, integral PL intensity of the PVF layer, and C=O/C=C signal ratio in the underlying PET layer were found to correlate with CI values measured by NIRA spectroscopy for EVA encapsulant, which, in turn, correlates with insulationresistance of tested PV modules. These spectral indicators are readily measurable in the field with portable Raman and UV-Vis spectrometers and can provide additional insights into the degradation status of PV modules, complementing spectral evaluations by NIRA, R_{iso} measurements, and UV-fluorescence imaging [1, 5, 6]. Artificial UV aging reproduced the same spectral trends as field samples, confirming the robustness of these Raman markers as general descriptors of polymer degradation.

This work was funded by the German Federal Ministry for Economic Affairs and Climate Action (BMWK) by the project "dig4morE" (FKZ: 03EE1090B) and by the WIPANO project "PolymAERA" (FKZ: 03TN0053E). The samples were collected in the frame of the international PV Camper initiative.

References

[1]. O. Stroyuk, C. Buerhop, E. Wittman, O. Mashkov, P. Stephan, J.L. Crozier McCleland, M. Vumbugwa, F.J. Vorster, E.E. van Dyk, J. Hauch, C.J. Brabec, I.M. Peters, Solar RRL, 8 (2024) 2301022.

[2]. C. Buerhop-Lutz, O. Stroyuk, J. Zöcklein, T. Pickel, J. Hauch, I.M. Peters, Progr. in Photovolt., 30 (2022) 938.

[3]. C. Buerhop, L. Lüer, O. Stroyuk, J. Hauch, I.M. Peters, Sol. Energy Mater. Sol. Cells, 257 (2023) 112398.

[4]. C. Buerhop-Lutz, T. Pickel, O. Stroyuk, J. Hauch, I.M. Peters, Sol. Energy Mater. Sol. Cells, 246 (2022), 111913.

[5] C. Buerhop, O. Stroyuk, O. Mashkov, J. Hauch, I.M. Peters, Solar RRL, 8 (2024), 2400566.

[6]. C. Buerhop, O. Stroyuk, O. Mashkov, A. Barabash, J.A. Hauch, I.M. Peters, Sol. Energy Mater. Sol. Cells, 277 (2024) 113111.

[7]. O. Stroyuk, C. Buerhop-Lutz, A. Vetter, J. Hauch, C.J. Brabec, Sol. Energy Mater. Sol. Cells, 216 (2020) 110702.

PVDF-BASED SOLUTION FOR USE AS A DIELECTRIC LAYER IN BACKSHEET CRACKINGS

C. Montes[1], L. Ocaña[1], B. González-Díaz[2], S. González-Pérez[3], E. Llarena[1].
[1]Instituto Tecnológico y de Energías Renovables, S. A. (ITER)
Pol. Industrial de Granadilla, s/n, E 38600 Granadilla de Abona, Spain.
Ph. +34 922 747 700 / Fax +34 922 747 701 / E-mail cmontes@iter.es
[2]Departamento de Ingeniería Industrial. Universidad de La Laguna.
Camino San Francisco de Paula, s/n, 38206 San Cristóbal de La Laguna. S/C de Tenerife. Spain.
[3]Departamento de Didácticas Específicas. Universidad de La Laguna.
c/ Pedro Zerolo, s/n, Edificio Central Planta 2. Apartado 456, 38200 San Cristóbal de La Laguna. S/C de Tenerife.
Spain.

ABSTRACT: Backsheet cracking is a critical reliability issue in photovoltaic (PV) modules, often leading to leakage currents and module failure. This study presents the development and characterization of a PVDF-based fluoropolymer solution designed to act as a dielectric repair layer for damaged backsheets.
Various formulations using N-Methyl-2-pyrrolidone (NMP) as the main solvent and acetone or diethyl ether as co-solvents were prepared and evaluated. The most promising formulation (PVDF:NMP:Ac = 21.5:48.7:29.7 wt%) demonstrated good stability, adhesion, and ease of application. Morphological analysis revealed a porous structure with embedded air bubbles and gaps ranging from 20 μm up to several millimeters.
Initial electrical insulation tests showed resistance values exceeding 100 MΩ. However, due to the material's porosity, localized dielectric breakdown occurred under high-voltage stress tests.
To enhance performance, several strategies are proposed, such as multilayer deposition, the incorporation of hydrophobic additives, and the application of superhydrophobic protective topcoats.
This approach offers a practical, field-deployable method for extending the service life of PV modules affected by backsheet degradation.
Keywords: PV module reliability, backsheet,cracking, fluoropolymer materials, characterization.

1 INTRODUCTION

As of November 2024, the global installed photovoltaic (PV) capacity has surpassed 2 terawatts (TW) [1], with the majority of systems utilizing photovoltaic modules encapsulated with backsheet layers composed of polymer films such as Polyethylene Terephthalate (PET), Polyvinyl Fluoride (PVF), Polyvinylidene Fluoride (PVDF), and Polyamide (PA) [2], [3]. Backsheet cracking is a significant reliability concern in PV modules. A 2019 study by DuPont revealed that 14% of examined modules exhibited backsheet defects, with cracking accounting for 66% of these issues [4], [5]. Further research analyzing 26 power plants found that 67% of polyamide-based backsheets developed cracks, particularly in cell gap areas [6]. These findings underscore the prevalence of backsheet cracking, especially in certain material types, highlighting the need for ongoing monitoring and maintenance, as well as finding ways to address this kind of issues, to ensure long-term PV module performance [7].

The photovoltaic cell laboratory at the Instituto Tecnológico y de Energías Renovables (ITER, SA, Tenerife, Spain), with the support of the University of La Laguna (ULL, Tenerife, Spain), has been working for years on the development of thin-film perovskite photovoltaic cells. In one iteration of this research, solutions with high concentrations of PVDF were developed and used as a binding agent [8].

Although various solutions have been proposed to address backsheet cracking in PV modules [9], [10], to the best of our knowledge, the development of a PVDF-based compound for this purpose is a novel approach. If proven effective, this compound could restore functionality to modules typically deemed unusable due to backsheet cracking. Notably, it would enable on-site repairs without requiring the removal of the affected modules, significantly simplifying maintenance procedures.

This article presents the development of a PVDF-based solution designed to cover damaged areas in the backsheet of photovoltaic modules. In the specific case studied, the damage observed in the backsheet is not primarily due to material aging or typical cracking phenomena. Instead, it results from poor handling during the "string soldering" stage of module manufacturing. This type of defect manifests as a perforation in the backsheet, typically near the aluminum frame, which creates an unintended electrical bridge that leads to leakage currents.

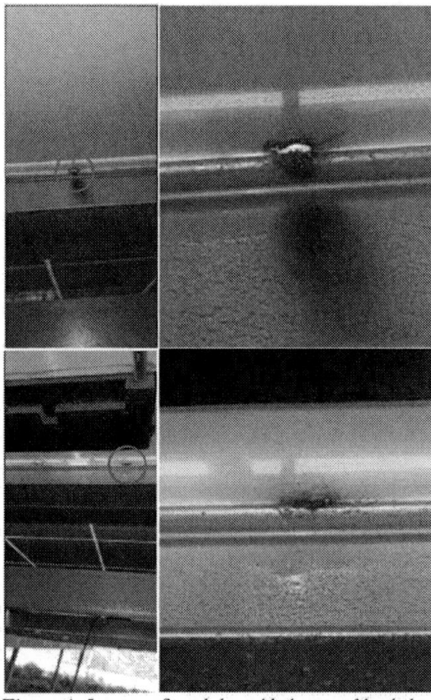

Figure 1: Images of modules with damaged backsheet (left) and close-up of the damaged areas (right).

2 METHODOLOGY

The following table shows the most relevant physical properties of the substances considered for our purposes:

Table I: Physical properties of the materials used. ρ = density (g/ml), Bp = boiling point (ºC), ε = dielectric contact.

	ρ	Bp	ε	Origin
PVDF [11]	1.77–1.79	173 140	10	KF Polymer W#1700 by KUREHA
NMP [12]	1.028	202–204	33	Sigma-Aldrich 328634
Acetone [13]	0.7845	55–57	20.7	Honeywell 32201
Diethyl Ether [14]	0.7134	34.6	4.3 [15]	Merck 1.00921

The study was divided into two parts.

First, using PVDF powders and based on the studies by A. Bottino et al. [15], that investigates the solubility of PVDF in 50 different solvents, as well as the work by Mengyuan Li et al. [16], in which PVDF is dissolved in DMF at a specific temperature, we have established a course of action to create PVDF solutions based on the following principles:

- Use a single polar solvent, in our case NMP.
- Perform the mixing process at 200 ºC, which is close to the boiling point of NMP (and well above the melting point of PVDF).
- Stir the mixture 200 rpm to ensure homogeneity. A speed that is too low can lead to the mixture splitting into two phases, while excessive stirring can introduce turbulence and drag the solution.
- Test two co-solvents of different natures:
  o Acetone (Ac): The relatively high dielectric constant of acetone should help NMP dissolve the PVDF. Its low boiling point also promotes agitation of the material during mixing and facilitates faster drying of the solution.
  o Diethyl Ether (DE): Having a very low dielectric constant, it should not contribute much as a solvent. However, its very low boiling point should make its contribution during both stirring and drying considerably better than that of acetone.

Once the best solution candidate was obtained—that is, the one that accommodates the largest amount of PVDF while remaining in a liquid state for a long time—the second part of the study consisted of putting it to the test:

- Drying and adhesion on samples of backsheet material from photovoltaic modules (typically Tedlar-Polyester-Tedlar or TPT type laminates [17]).
- Performing layer thickness measurements on conductive material.
- Taking images with a microscope (looking for porosity).
- Performing electrical measurements on conductive material: Continuity tests, estimation of volume resistance, and electrical insulation tests.

3 PVDF solutions in NMP with Ac and DE as Co-solvents

Table II shows the relevant information of the different solutions prepared by mixing PVDF with NMP and Ac, while Table III is for the ones made with PVDF, NMP and DE:

Table II: Solutions of PVDF in NMP and Ac.

Vial	PVDF Wt%	PVDF g	NMP Wt%	NMP ml	NMP g	NMP V%	+Ac Wt%	+Ac ml	+Ac g	+Ac V%
1	11.2%	1.3	61.9%	7	7.196	63.6%	27.0%			36.4%
3	15.0%	1.64	56.3%	6	6.168	60.0%	28.7%			40.0%
5	18.5%	1.88	50.6%				30.9%			
7	19.5%	2	50.0%				30.5%	4	3.138	
8	20.5%	2.14	49.3%	5	5.140	55.6%	30.1%			44.4%
9	21.5%	2.27	48.7%				29.7%			
10	22.5%	2.4	48.1%				29.4%			

Table III: Solutions of PVDF in NMP and DE.

Vial	PVDF		NMP				+DE			
	Wt%	g	Wt%	ml	g	V%	Wt%	ml	g	V%
2	11.2%	1.011	57.1%				31.7%			
4	15.0%	1.41	54.7%	5	5.140	55.6%	30.3%	4	2.854	44.4%
6	18.5%	1.81	52.4%				29.1%			

Where:
- Wt% refers to the weight percentage of each element.
- V% refers to the volume percentage of the solvents.

Figure 2 shows the weight percentage (Wt%) of PVDF relative to the mass of the material used, as a function of the solvent combination.

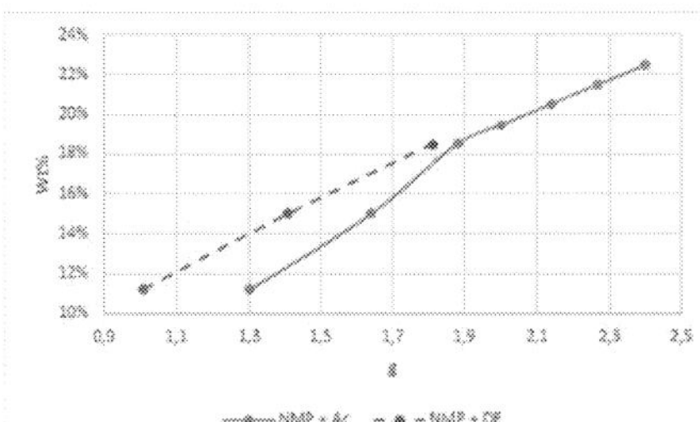

Figure 2: Weight percentage (Wt%) of PVDF relative to the total mass of this material, when using NMP+Ac (blue line) or NMP+DE (green dashed line).

All solutions were liquid when freshly made. A month later, however, their condition had changed, and the results can be seen in Figure 3.

Figure 3: Appearance of the solution vials one month after fabrication, in normal orientation (top) and inverted (bottom).

As it can be seen in Figure 3:

- Vials 1, 2, and 3 contained perfectly liquid solutions.
- The solutions in vials 4, 6, and 10 were almost completely gelled.
- The solutions in vials 5, 7, 8, and 9 were mostly liquid but contained gel agglomerations. The proportion of these agglomerations increased with the amount of PVDF added to the mixture.

Based on these results, the solution from Vial 9, with a PVDF:NMP:Ac mixture of 21.5:48.7:29.7%, was selected for morphological characterization and electrical performance studies.

3 MORPHOLOGICAL AND ELECTRICAL ANALYSIS

The initial deposition of the solution was carried out via a spatula. This method was later deemed impractical for subsequent field trials, leading to the adoption of a brush for application.

3.1 Drying and Adhesion with spatula deposition

Using a spatula, a small amount of the solution from Vial 9 was deposited onto a TPT sheet to estimate the drying time and degree of adhesion. It was also poured onto a copper tape to estimate the deposited layer thickness.

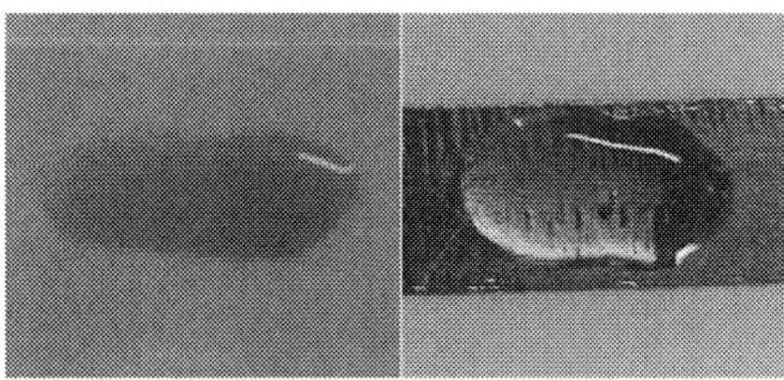

Figure 4: Deposition of the solution onto a TPT sheet (left) and a TPT sheet with copper tape (right) for subsequent analysis.

Two days later, the substance was observed to have dried, though it retained a faint yellowish color. Furthermore, it showed strong adhesion to the TPT when scraped with a spatula, but weaker adhesion to the copper tape, as shown in Figure 5.

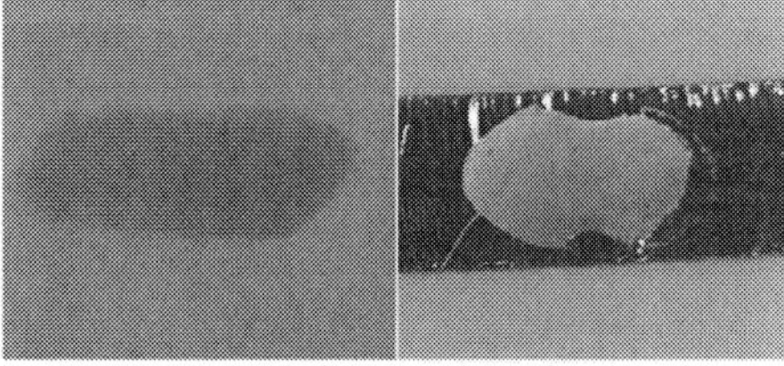

Figure 5: Dried solution, two days after deposition, showing good adhesion to the TPT substrate (left) and poor adhesion to the copper tape (right).

3.2 Thickness measurement with spatula deposition

Using a PCE-CT 28 thickness gauge, a measurement of the deposited layer thickness was taken on the copper tape. As shown in the following illustration, the layer thickness was estimated to be around 640 µm.

3.3 Drying and adhesion with brush deposition

In order to obtain better statistical data on thickness measurements and to have enough substrates for the electric tests, a small amount of the Vial 9 solution was deposited with a brush onto a set of six copper tapes adhered to a glass slide, as it can be seen in Figure 6.

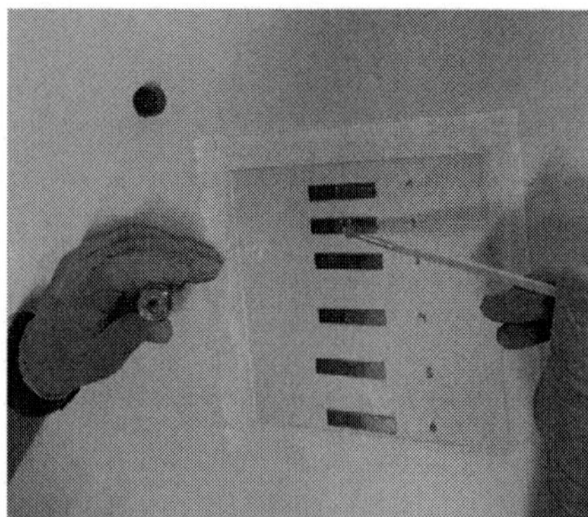

Figure 6: Deposition of PVDF solution from Vial 9 onto pieces of copper tape adhered to glass, using a brush.

Upon deposition of the solution onto the copper tapes, the samples were imaged using a recently acquired electronic microscope with the following specifications:

- Objective Magnification (and C-Mount) with a manual optical zoom ranging from 0.7X to 4.5X.
- Camera Sensor: The microscope is equipped with a Sony IMX224, a 1/3-inch color CMOS sensor. The diagonal of this sensor is approximately 6 mm (0.236 inches). This is a crucial detail for calculating the system's theoretical magnification, which, when paired with a 24" monitor, ranges from 71.2X to 457.7X [16].

To avoid the "empty magnification" effect inherent to this type of microscopy imaging technique [17], we limited the optical zoom up to 3.5X, which corresponds to a theoretical magnification of 350X. Figure 7 shows images taken with the microscope, displaying their appearance immediately after deposition.

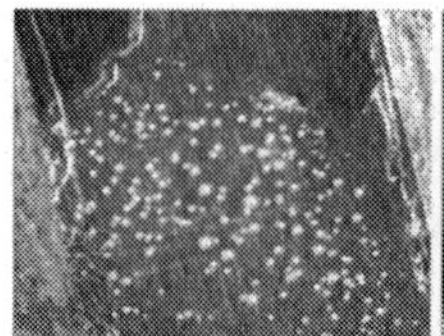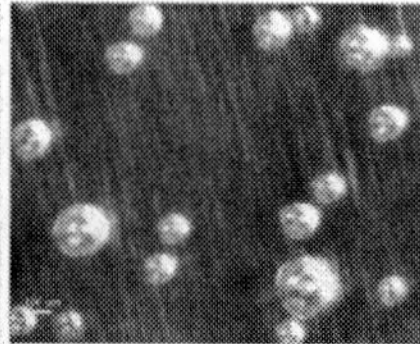

Figure 7: Microscopic image of deposition 5 at 0.7X (left) and at 3.5X optical zoom (right).

As seen in Figure 7, the chosen deposition method (brush) leaves a large number of spherules, between 100 and 200 µm in size, embedded within the material. These spherules appear to be air or solvent vapor bubbles. Five days later, the PVDF solution depositions from Vial 9 were observed to be perfectly dry. The images obtained with the microscope confirm the porous appearance of the deposited material and that the observed spherules were, in fact, bubbles of air trapped in the solution, as it can be seen in Figure 8.

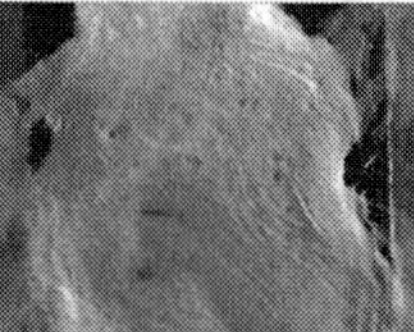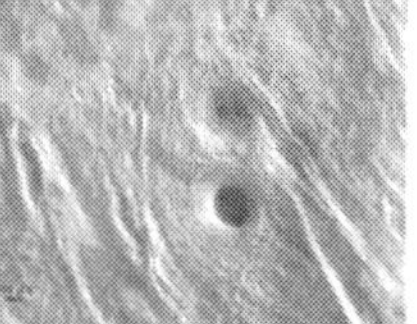

Figure 8: Microscopic image of dried deposition 5 at 0.7X (left) and at 3.5X optical zoom (right).

To ensure the reliability of our results, we prepared a new solution with a PVDF concentration identical to that of Vial 9, which was 30 days old and had begun to semi-gel. This fresh solution, labeled Vial 11, allowed us to replicate the experiment and ensure accurate data for the subsequent thickness measurements and electrical tests. Figure 9 provides a visual comparison of the two solutions.

Figure 9: Image showing the PVDF solutions in Vial 9 (left) and Vial 11 (right).

Next, we repeated the PVDF deposition process on six copper tapes adhered to glass. The new samples were labeled sequentially, continuing from the last Vial 9 sample, starting with numbers 7, 8, up to 12. Microscopic images of these freshly prepared depositions were then taken, as shown in Figure 10.

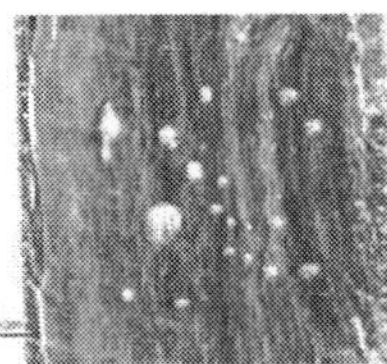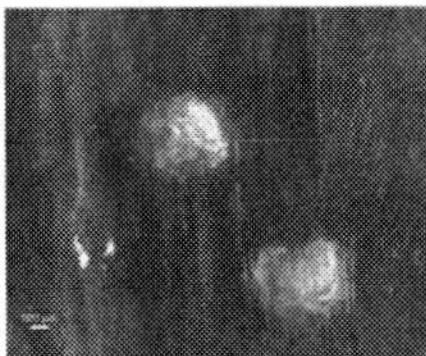

Figure 10: Microscopic images of deposition 10 at 0.7X (left) and at 3.5X optical zoom (right).

A comparison of the brush-deposited samples shows that the freshly prepared solution also produced air bubbles, with some reaching up to 1 mm in diameter. After two days, the PVDF samples were visibly dry but had a more distinct yellow hue than the earlier samples (deposited with the aged solution).

As it can be seen in Figure 11, the microscope images confirm the porous nature of the deposited material, which was also observed in previous depositions. With the current optical system's resolution, the overall granularity is deemed to be below 20 μm. Additionally, we can see fractures over 100 μm thick, which in some cases extend across most of the sample in the direction of the brush application. This is a critical factor for the material's intended application, as porosity affects absorption, liquid diffusion, and mechanical strength [18].

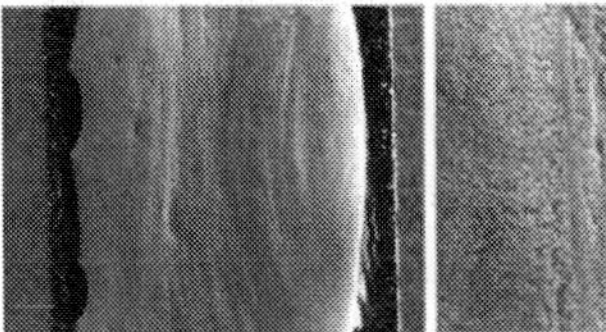

Figure 11: Microscopic images of dried deposition 10 at 0.7X (left) and at 3.5X optical zoom (right).

The obtained images reveal that the deposited material has a rough surface morphology, characteristic of a layered polymer network. The formation of this irregular topography is a common phenomenon in thin polymer films, resulting from the kinetics of deposition, the solvent's evaporation rate, or the interaction between polymer chains during the drying process [19]. These morphological features are critical as they directly influence the material's properties, including adhesion, optical properties, and conductivity [20], [21], [22].

For a more precise characterization of the distribution, size, and interconnectivity of these pores, a higher-resolution microscope is required. Alternatively, we propose the use of techniques such as scanning electron microscopy (SEM), which is a standard tool for this type of analysis in polymer materials science [23], [24].

3.4 Thickness measurement with brush deposition

Table IV shows the thickness measurements of the deposited layers, which were obtained using a PCE-CT 28 thickness gauge.

Table IV: Measured thicknesses of the deposited samples. All values are in μm.

	Vial 9						Vial 11					
Sample	1	2	3	4	5	6	7	8	9	10	11	12
10/09/2025	93.5	89.1	134.0	193.0	213.0	136.0	-	-	-	-	-	-
12/09/2025	116.0	65.4	72.4	176.0	100.0	123.0	290.0	305.0	341.0	253.0	360.0	448.0
16/09/2025	115.0	60.5	117.0	201.0	189.0	123.0	288.0	320.0	280.0	250.0	356.0	420.0
Avg. value per sample	108.2	71.7	107.8	190.0	167.3	127.3	288.0	312.5	310.5	251.5	353.0	434.0
Avg. value	128.7						325.1					

As it can be seen, there is a clear difference in the average thickness of the deposited layers. Samples prepared with the Vial 9 solution had an average thickness of 129 μm, whereas those from the fresh Vial 11 solution averaged 325 μm. This last value is also approximately half the thickness of the sample deposited with a spatula, indicating that brush application results in a thinner coating. Also, when comparing only the brush-deposited samples, those from Vial 11 were 2.5 times thicker than those from Vial 9. This finding, along with the visible non-uniformity of the Vial 9 solution, leads us to hypothesize that the PVDF within the solutions undergoes progressive gelation over time. As a result, less solute remains in the effectively dissolved liquid phase, which is the main component transferred by the brush during application.

3.5 Electrical studies

Using a TENMA 72-2600 multimeter, we first performed continuity tests and estimated the bulk resistance. For all deposited samples, the multimeter was unable to detect continuity, with measured bulk resistances exceeding 20MΩ.

Next, using the HT PV-ISOTEST multifunction instrument in its insulation resistance measurement configuration, insulation resistance tests were conducted on the deposited samples. The tests were performed in accordance with IEC/EN 62446-1 and IEC/EN 61557 standards. Due to the material's porosity, we took special care to position the electrode as horizontally as possible on the surface, as shown in Figure 12.

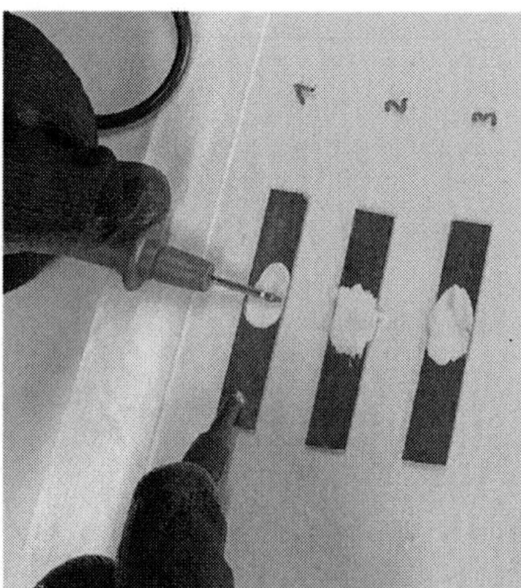

Figure 12: Close-up view showing the positioning of the electrodes for the electrical insulation test.

The tests were conducted at 250V (with a max of 260V), 500V (with a max of 520V), and 1000V (with a max of 1039V). In all cases, the results were positive ("OK"), and the volume resistance (Ri) was estimated to be greater than 100 MΩ.

Finally, in order to evaluate the worst-case scenario, the insulation test was repeated, this time pressing the electrode point first onto the coating's surface and applying the highest voltage setting (1000V). This time the test resulted in an insulation failure. An electrical arc was generated, which carbonized the area surrounding the point of contact, as shown Figure 13. This outcome is highly significant, as it underscores the critical need to implement strategies to reduce the material's porosity to enhance its electrical robustness.

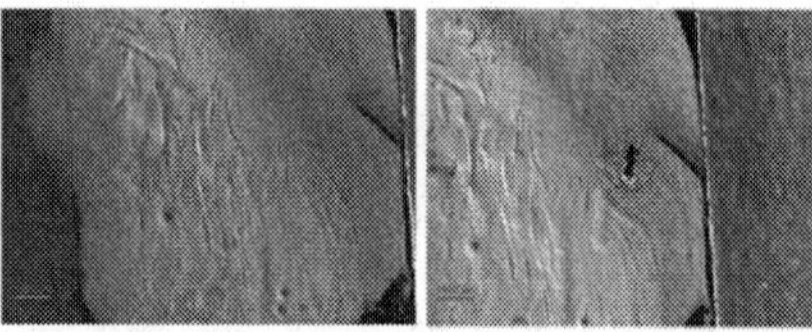

Figure 13: Microscopic images of deposition 3 taken at 0.7X optical zoom before (left) and after the stress test (right).

4   CONCLUSIONS AND DISCUSSION

This study successfully developed and characterized various PVDF solutions with NMP and co-solvents such as acetone and diethyl ether, intended for use as insulating coatings on the backsheets of solar modules damaged by bypass diodes. Through systematic testing of preparation, deposition, drying, morphology, and electrical insulation, we identified that the porosity of the deposited material—estimated to be below 20 µm, though with fractures up to several millimeters in some areas—is a critical factor that compromises its effectiveness as a dielectric barrier.

Insulation tests showed that while the samples exhibit high bulk resistance (>100 MΩ), the presence of pores and shear fractures can induce insulation failure under high voltage.

A practical solution could be to simply apply multiple deposition layers, with sufficient time between each application to allow the previous layer to dry completely. This technique has been shown to improve the structural integrity and dielectric properties of porous polymer films [25].

Additionally, incorporating hydrophobic materials, such as nanocomposites of silicon dioxide (SiO_2) [26], [27], [28], into the PVDF solution could be a promising approach.

Finally, adding hybrid coatings of titanium dioxide and silicon dioxide (TiO_2–SiO_2) have demonstrated superhydrophobic properties, high mechanical strength, and excellent adhesion [29], [30]. These characteristics would make them suitable for application on top of our PVDF layers, acting as a protective topcoat.

The proposed strategies will be a focus of future work. Should they prove successful in laboratory trials, the resulting material will undergo field testing directly on damaged photovoltaic modules to validate its performance and durability under realistic operating conditions.

5   ACKNOWLEDGMENTS

This study was conducted within the SIROCO project (code CPP2023-010858), and is co-funded by the Ministerio de Ciencia e Innovación and the Agencia Estatal de Investigación (under code /10.13039/501100011033), and by the European Union within the framework of the EU NextGenerationEU Recovery Plan and the Plan de Recuperación, Transformación y Resiliencia de España (PRTR).

6   REFERENCES

[1]   "Global installed PV capacity tops 2 TW – pv magazine International." Accessed: Sep. 17, 2025. [Online]. Available: https://www.pv-magazine.com/2024/11/13/global-installed-pv-capacity-tops-2-tw/

[2]   "International Technology Roadmap for Photovoltaic (ITRPV) - vdma.eu - VDMA." Accessed: Sep. 17, 2025. [Online]. Available: https://www.vdma.eu/en-GB/international-technology-roadmap-photovoltaic

[3]   "Solar Backsheets & Encapsulants Market Survey 2022/23." Accessed: Sep. 17, 2025. [Online]. Available: https://taiyangnews.info/reports/solar-

backsheets-encapsulants-market-survey-2022-23

[4] "DuPont module reliability study finds that backsheet defects are increasing." Accessed: Sep. 17, 2025. [Online]. Available: https://www.solarpowerworldonline.com/2019/06/dupont-module-reliability-study-finds-that-backsheet-defects-are-increasing/

[5] M. Kempe, D. Miller, A. Zielnik, D. Montiel-Chicharro, J. Zhu, and R. Gottschalg, "Survey of Mechanical Durability of PV Backsheets," *2017 IEEE 44th Photovoltaic Specialist Conference, PVSC 2017*, pp. 3208–3213, 2018, doi: 10.1109/PVSC.2017.8366198.

[6] J. Markert, S. Kotterer, D. E. Mansour, D. Philipp, and P. Gebhardt, "Advanced analysis of backsheet failures from 26 power plants," *EPJ Photovoltaics*, vol. 12, p. 7, 2021, doi: 10.1051/EPJPV/2021006.

[7] M. Waqar Akram, G. Li, Y. Jin, and X. Chen, "Failures of Photovoltaic modules and their Detection: A Review," *Appl Energy*, vol. 313, p. 118822, May 2022, doi: 10.1016/J.APENERGY.2022.118822.

[8] E. Llarena, C. Montes, L. Ocaña, B. González-Díaz, S. González-Pérez, "REVIEW OF A RESEARCH CARRIED OUT TO PRODUCE CONDUCTIVE INKS AND AGGLOMERATES THAT MAKE USE OF NON-PRECIOUS MATERIALS TOGETHER WITH VEHICLES COMPATIBLE WITH THIN LAYERS OF PEROVSKITE." in *40th European Photovoltaic Solar Energy Conference and Exhibition*, 2023, pp. 020105-001-020105–006. doi: 10.4229/EUPVSEC2023/2BV.2.12.

[9] W. M. Guy Beaucarne, Gabriele Eder, Emmanuel Jadot, Yuliya Voronko, "REPAIR AND PREVENTIVE MAINTENANCE OF PV MODULES WITH DEGRADING BACKSHEETS USING FLOWABLE SILICONE SEALANT," in *38th European Photovoltaic Solar Energy Conference and Exhibition*, 2021, pp. 1051–1053. doi: 10.4229/EUPVSEC20212021-5DO.2.6.

[10] Y. Voronko *et al.*, "Repair options for PV modules with cracked backsheets," *Energy Sci Eng*, vol. 9, no. 9, pp. 1583–1595, 2021, doi: 10.1002/ese3.936.

[11] Kureha Co, "KF POLYMER Poly(vinylidene fluoride) (PVDF)", Accessed: Sep. 17, 2025. [Online]. Available: https://www.kureha.co.jp/

[12] "N-Methyl-2-pyrrolidone - Wikipedia." Accessed: Sep. 17, 2025. [Online]. Available: https://en.wikipedia.org/wiki/N-Methyl-2-pyrrolidone

[13] "Acetone | 32201 | Honeywell Research Chemicals." Accessed: Sep. 17, 2025. [Online]. Available:

https://lab.honeywell.com/shop/acetone-32201

[14] "Diethyl ether - Wikipedia." Accessed: Sep. 17, 2025. [Online]. Available: https://en.wikipedia.org/wiki/Diethyl_ether

[15] "Liquids - Dielectric Constants." Accessed: Sep. 17, 2025. [Online]. Available: https://www.engineeringtoolbox.com/liquid-dielectric-constants-d_1263.html

[16] I. Rasnik, T. French, K. Jacobson, and K. Berland, "Electronic Cameras for Low-Light Microscopy," *Methods Cell Biol*, vol. 114, pp. 211–241, Jan. 2013, doi: 10.1016/B978-0-12-407761-4.00010-5.

[17] Greenfield. Sluder and D. E. . Wolf, "Digital microscopy," p. 697, 2013.

[18] P. Colombo, D. C. Dunand, and V. Kumar, "ADVANCES IN THE SYNTHESIS, CHARACTERIZATION, AND PROPERTIES OF BULK POROUS MATERIALS," 2017, doi: 10.1557/jmr.2013.232.

[19] S. Suprapto, G. S, S. R, and J. Jubaidah, "Fabrication and Characterization of PVDF Thin Film," no. Il, pp. 2–9, 2022, doi: 10.4108/eai.11-10-2022.2325314.

[20] M. Sharma, P. Chauhan, R. Sharma, and D. Kumar, "Materials and Chemistries of Polymers," *Specialty Polymers*, pp. 15–28, Dec. 2022, doi: 10.1201/9781003278269-2/MATERIALS-CHEMISTRIES-POLYMERS-MANSI-SHARMA-PRAGATI-CHAUHAN-REKHA-SHARMA-DINESH-KUMAR.

[21] R. K. Gupta, "Specialty Polymers," *Specialty Polymers*, Dec. 2022, doi: 10.1201/9781003278269/SPECIALTY-POLYMERS-RAM-GUPTA.

[22] R. O. Ebewele, *Polymer science and technology*. 2000. doi: 10.1016/0261-3069(95)90127-2.

[23] "Introduction to the Scanning Electron Microscope," 1997.

[24] P. M. V Raja and A. R. Barron, "Physical methods in chemistry," *Nature*, vol. 134, no. 3384, pp. 366–367, 1934, doi: 10.1002/jctb.5000533702.

[25] B. Qiu, Y. Gao, P. Gorgojo, and X. Fan, "Membranes of Polymer of Intrinsic Microporosity PIM-1 for Gas Separation: Modification Strategies and Meta-Analysis," *Nanomicro Lett*, vol. 17, no. 1, pp. 1–33, Dec. 2025, doi: 10.1007/S40820-024-01610-2/FIGURES/5.

[26] X. Tan *et al.*, "A simple fabrication of superhydrophobic PVDF/SiO2 coatings and their anti-icing properties," *J Mater Res*, vol. 36, no. 3, pp. 637–645, Feb. 2021, doi: 10.1557/S43578-020-00034-Z/FIGURES/8.

[27]   Q. Wu *et al.*, "Dual hydrophilic/hydrophobic SiO2 transparent super-hydrophobic coating with good interfacial adhesion and high mechanical robustness," *J Mater Sci*, vol. 59, no. 46, pp. 21294–21309, Dec. 2024, doi: 10.1007/S10853-024-10470-5/FIGURES/8.

[28]   X. Gong and S. He, "Highly Durable Superhydrophobic Polydimethylsiloxane/Silica Nanocomposite Surfaces with Good Self-Cleaning Ability," *ACS Omega*, vol. 5, no. 8, pp. 4100–4108, Mar. 2020, doi: 10.1021/ACSOMEGA.9B03775.

[29]   Q. Li, F. Qian, K. Yuan, W. Dong, Y. Han, and J. Lu, "Properties of superhydrophobic filter media prepared by TiO2–SiO2@PDMS coating," *J Solgel Sci Technol*, vol. 107, no. 1, pp. 178–189, Jul. 2023, doi: 10.1007/S10971-022-05871-4/METRICS.

[30]   Z. Jin *et al.*, "Preparation and characterization of Superhydrophilic TiO2-SiO2 films for double-layer broadband antireflective coating," *Journal of Porous Materials*, vol. 31, no. 6, pp. 1955–1964, Dec. 2024, doi: 10.1007/S10934-024-01648-Y/FIGURES/12.

PVDF-BASED SOLUTION FOR USE AS A DIELECTRIC LAYER IN BACKSHEET CRACKINGS

INTRODUCTION

From the Lab to the Field: Building on our expertise in thin-film perovskite cells, we've adapted our high-concentration PVDF solutions for a new purpose: repairing damaged PV module backsheets.

Addressing a Manufacturing Flaw: The focus is on a unique problem: perforations caused by faulty soldering. This defect creates an electrical bridge, leading to harmful leakage currents.

A Simple, Practical Repair: Develop a PVDF-based solution to be painted directly onto the damaged areas using a simple brush-based method, making it a practical and accessible fix for on-site repairs.

Reliability focus: Through detailed characterization and rigorous testing, investigate how this coating performs. Such analysis will determine if and how the solution seals defects, prevents further damage, and contributes to the module's electrical integrity.

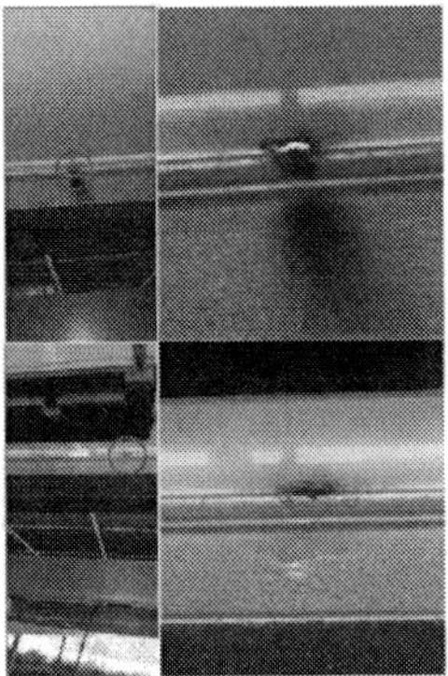

Modules with damaged backsheet (left) and close-up of the damaged areas (right).

Authors:

C. Montes[1], L. Ocaña[1], B. González-Díaz[2], S. González-Pérez[3], E. Llarena[1].
[1]Instituto Tecnológico y de Energías Renovables, S. A. (ITER)
Pol. Industrial de Granadilla, s/n, cp. 38600 Granadilla de Abona, Spain.
Ph. +34 922 747 700 / Fax +34 922 747 701
E-mail cmontes@iter.es
[2]Departamento de Ingeniería Industrial. Universidad de La Laguna.
Camino San Francisco de Paula, s/n, cp. 38206, S/C de Tenerife, Spain.
[3]Departamento de Didácticas Específicas. Universidad de La Laguna.
C/ Heraclio Sánchez, s/n. Apartado 456. cp. 38200, San Cristóbal de La Laguna. S/C de Tenerife. Spain.

METHODOLOGY

Solution Preparation
- PVDF dissolved in NMP as a single polar solvent.
- Mixing performed at 200 °C (near NMP boiling point).
- Stirring speed set to 200 rpm for optimal dissolution.
- Two co-solvents tested:
    - Acetone (Ac): High dielectric constant, promotes dissolution and fast drying.
    - Diethyl Ether (DE): Low dielectric constant, enhances agitation and drying due to low boiling point.

Solution Selection Criteria
- Chosen solution must:
    - Dissolve maximum PVDF.
    - Remain liquid for extended periods.

Characterization and Testing
- Applied solution to photovoltaic backsheet samples (TPT laminates) and copper tape, via *brush deposition*.
- Measured:
    - Drying and adhesion.
    - Layer thickness on conductive material.
    - Porosity via microscopy.
    - Electrical properties: continuity, volume resistance, insulation.

EXPERIMENTAL

Appearance of the solution vials one month after fabrication, in normal orientation (top) and inverted (bottom).

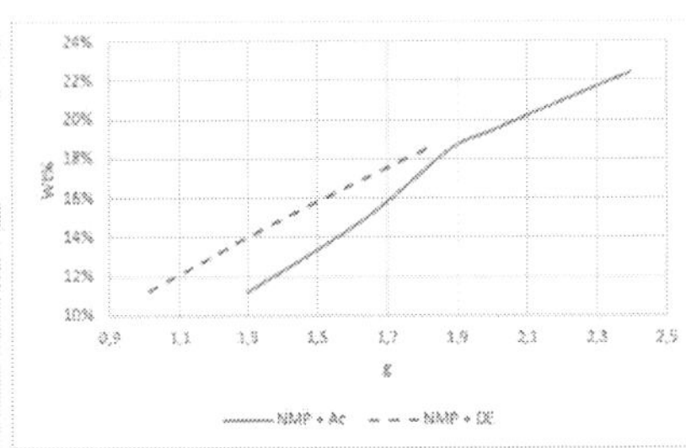

Weight percentage (Wt%) of PVDF relative to the total mass of this material, when using NMP+Ac (blue line) or NMP+DE (green dashed line).

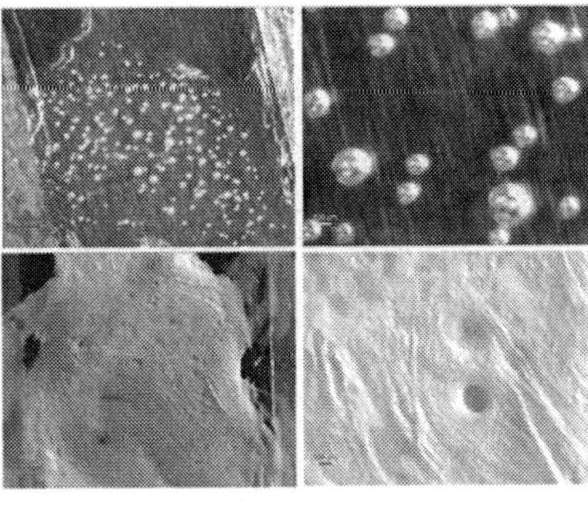

Microscopic image of fresh (above) and dried (below) deposition #5 at 0.7X (left) and at 3.5X optical zoom (right).

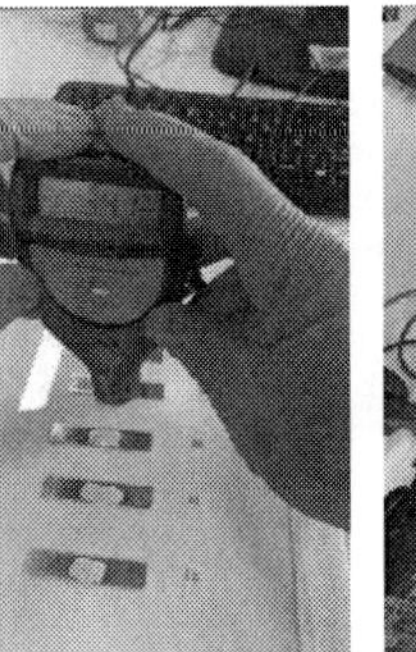

Thickness measurement (left) and insulation test (right).

RESULTS

- **Optimal Formulation:** A 21.5:48.7:29.7 wt% PVDF:NMP:Ac ratio proved most stable.
- **Progressive Gelation:** Brush-deposited layers were **325 μm** thick, while aged solutions created a thinner **129 μm** layer.
- **Porous Structure:** Coatings showed embedded air bubbles and fractures (**>100 μm**), with higher porosity in aged samples.
- **Electrical Performance:** While exhibiting high bulk resistance (**>100 MΩ**), the coatings suffered dielectric breakdown under high-voltage stress, highlighting porosity as a key issue.
- **Conclusion:** PVDF-based coatings show promise for PV module repair, with future work focused on multilayer deposition and hydrophobic topcoats.

CRITICAL ANALYSIS OF THE PROTECTION OFFERED BY BYPASS DIODES IN CURRENT MODULES

Eneko Cereceda [1], Nekane Azkona [1], Yeray Mateos, Alona Otaegi [1], Vanesa Fano [1], Eneko Ortega [1],
Jose Ruben Gutierrez [1] and Juan Carlos Jimeno [1]
1 Technological Institute of Microelectronics, University of the Basque Country UPV/EHU, 48013, Bilbao, Spain
nekane.azkona@ehu.eus

ABSTRACT: Bypass diodes are integral components of photovoltaic (PV) modules. Their function is to protect these modules from the adverse effects of partial shading by providing an alternative path for the current. This allows shaded or defective cells to be bypassed, thus maintaining the performance and longevity of the module. In the photovoltaic industry, it is common practice to incorporate three bypass diodes per module, regardless of the number and type of solar cells that comprise it. As a result, the module is divided into three substrings, which prevents a single shaded cell from causing the loss of energy from the entire module. Numerous studies have explored various configurations and quantities of bypass diodes within photovoltaic modules, seeking to optimise energy production under different shading conditions. However, there is a notable lack of research dedicated to evaluating the protective function of bypass diodes in relation to the physical integrity of solar cells in shaded situations. This article aims to address this gap with the objective of verifying whether this three-diode configuration offers sufficient protection to new cell models.

Keywords: bypass diodes, partial shading, thermal stress

1 INTRODUCTION

Installed photovoltaic capacity has increased significantly in recent years, and is expected to continue to do so in the future [1], as it offers the best alternative for generating clean energy, at least for the time being, in line with policies such as the European Green Deal [2]. The cost per kWh of solar photovoltaic energy has shown an exponential downward trend [3], due in part to improvements in cell efficiency. A longer module lifespan also influences the Levelized Cost of Electricity (LCOE). In this regard, there are many studies on the different types of failures in solar modules, depending on the type of cell or the environment in which the modules are installed, among others [4].

One of the components that protect the module from degradation is the bypass diode. Although the cells in a module will have virtually identical characteristics when they leave the factory, some shading is inevitable, causing an imbalance between cells in the same module. If the module is located in a place where it is shaded by nearby buildings, for example, the repetitive module's operation under thermal stress will eventually degrade the shaded cells. Even in an open-air location, vegetation can cast shadows or release leaves or pollen that stain the module. This is why bypass diodes are necessary.

Bypass diodes play a key role in photovoltaic (PV) modules, as they provide alternative current paths that bypass shaded or damaged cells. This alternative current path has a dual advantage: on the one hand, it prevents the loss of the entire module's generation. On the other hand, when a cell enters reverse bias due to shading or mismatch, bypass diodes limit the voltage in the cell, reducing power dissipation and the risk of overheating and localised failures.

The effect of these diodes has been extensively analyzed, especially with regard to the number of diodes used and the different connection configurations with the module [5]. In most of these studies, the objective is to maximize output power [6], [7]. In some cases, the failure of the bypass diode itself and its effect on the module have been studied [8].

Although less common, there are also studies that characterize the temperature increase generated by partial shades and its distribution in the module [9], and relate the area of the shaded with the risk hot spot generation [10]. However, despite the studies on this subject, it seems that the use of three bypass diodes is common practice in the photovoltaic market.

Given that improved cell efficiency is linked to higher photocurrent, it is worth asking whether the configuration of three bypass diodes per module continues to offer the necessary protection against thermal stress in cases of partial shading. This paper aims to offer some thoughts on this issue.

2 HOMOGENEOUS SHADING SIMULATIONS

We carried out simulations using Matlab. We created a module by connecting several cells in series. One of the cells simulated the shaded cell, so different percentages of irradiance were applied to it: from 100% for an unshaded cell, decreasing to 0% when the cell was completely shaded.

Next, we connected three bypass diodes, each in parallel with a set of cells in series, dividing the module into three substrings. The measurements were repeated for the different percentages of shading.

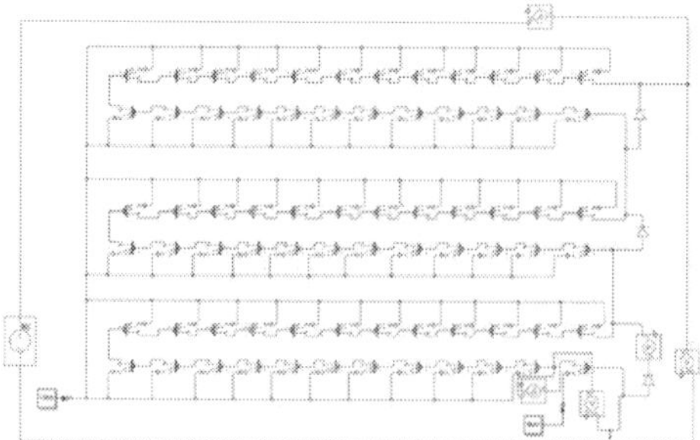

Figure 1: Simulation in Matlab of a module with 72 cells in series, with 3 bypass diodes and a shaded cell.

10.4229/EUPVSEC2025/3AV.2.17
020153-001

Figure 1 shows the resulting circuit with the cells in the substring protected by the bypass diodes. As expected, when a cell is shaded, the current through this cell limits the current through the entire module until at a given point the bypass diode is activated. This means that, although the generation of the string in which the shaded cell is located is lost, at least that of the other two strings is not.

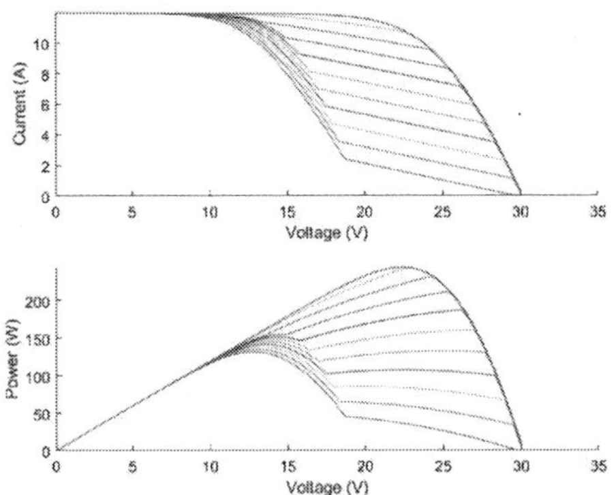

Figure 2: IV and PV curves of the module with 3 bypass diodes and a cell homogeneously shaded to different percentages (0% to 100% in 10% increments).

To see the degree of stress to which the shaded cell is subjected, we look at the power dissipated in it for different percentages of shading. Figure 3 shows the module current (blue), the current through the bypass diode (green) and the power dissipated in the shaded cell (red, right axis) for four different shading conditions, including no shade. It can be seen that for a small amount of shading, the overall generated power loss is small, but the power that the shaded cell must dissipate is high. The worst-case scenario corresponds to shading values between 5% and 25%. The exact value will depend on the design of the module, such as the number of cells in each string or the value of their parallel resistance.

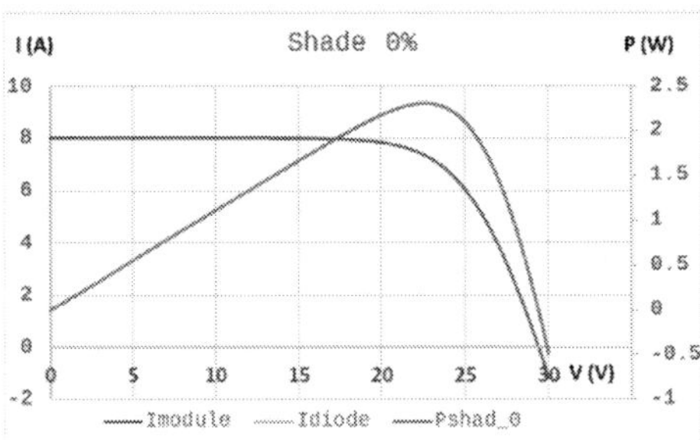

Figure 3: Photocurrent in the module (blue), current in the BPD (green) and power in the shaded cell (red), for 0% shade situation.

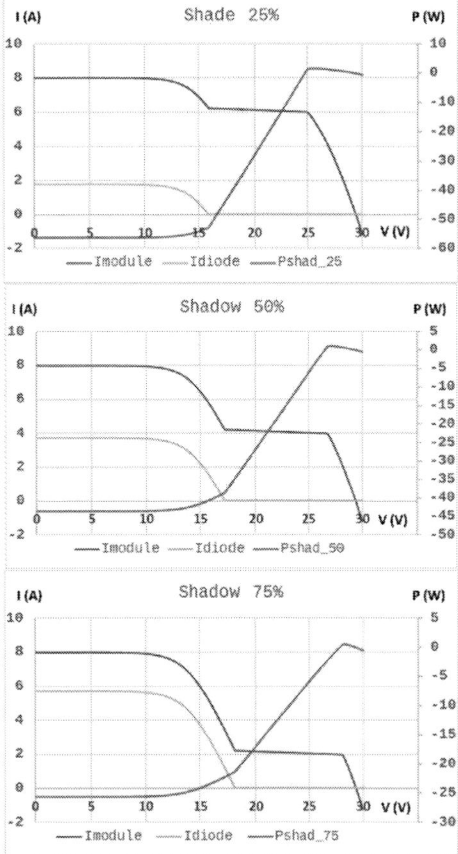

Figure 4: Photocurrent in the module (blue), current in the BPD (green) and power in the shaded cell (red), for a module with 3 bypass diodes and shade of 25% (up), 50% (middle) and 75% (down).

These results seem to indicate that tiny debris, such as a flower petal or a bird dropping, could be the more harmful than a leaf or a building shadow, and lead to increased temperatures in the shaded cell. However, these simulations, although common, are unrealistic, since reducing the irradiance by 5% across the entire area of a cell or reducing the irradiance by 100% in 5% of the cell area are totally different situations. In fact, the former is highly unrealistic, as it would be equivalent to having a cloud the exact size of the cell that attenuates the irradiance it receives.

3 INHOMOGENEOUS SHADING SIMULATIONS

To simulate the effect of partial shading more realistically, a photovoltaic module with three strings of 20 cells in series was simulated using LTSpice. Each string had a bypass diode in parallel. These cells are small blocks containing the equivalent circuit of the cells. The equivalent circuit of a diode was used for this purpose.

In one of the strings, one of these cells was replaced by a set of 20 small subcells in parallel, representing the shaded cell. This allows different portions of a cell to be completely shaded, with a resolution of 5%. More cells could be placed in parallel if greater precision were considered necessary. We are aware that this diagram greatly simplifies the physical behaviour of a partially shaded cell, but we believe it is a good approximation for better understanding the most compromising situation.

Figure 5 shows the circuit representing the entire module, with three strings each with a BPD in parallel and a cell that can be partially shaded.

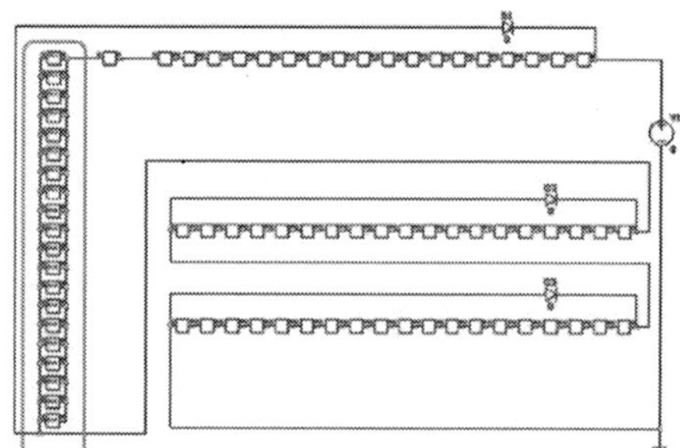

Figure 5: Equivalent circuit of the module with a partially shaded cell (in the orange box) in LTspice.

We have used for our model a general cell with I=6A, Rs=0.01Ω, and Rp=100Ω. For the subcells that compose the shaded cell, the values have been scaled according to the divisions. In this first case, they have been calculated for an area 20 times smaller. Assuming that the conclusions regarding the current and power generated by the module obtained with the homogeneous shadow simulation are valid, we now focus on analysing what happens in the shaded cell. In this regard, figure 6 shows the IV and PV curves for the entire shaded cell (including the 20 subcells in parallel). In contrast, figures 7 and 8 analyse the effect of shading on different parts of that same cell. Shading percentages corresponding to 5%, 25%, 50% and 75% have been selected for comparison.

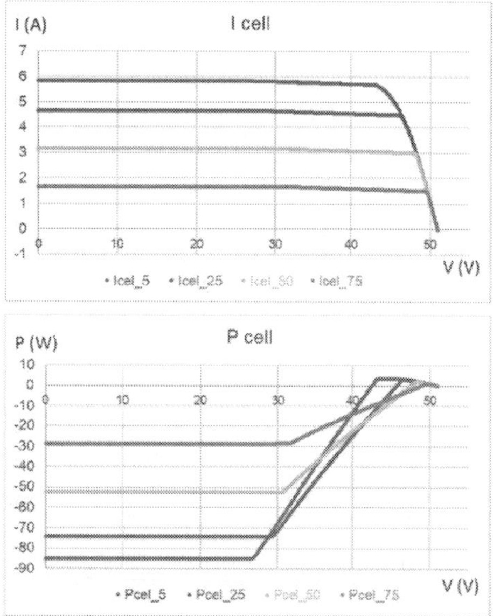

Figure 6: IV and PV curves in the shaded cell as a whole for shading percentages of 5%, 25%, 50% and 75%.

Figures 7 shows the same IV and PV curves but for an illuminated subcell, i.e. one portion of the partially shaded cell that fells into illumination. Finally, fiigure 8 shows the same curves in a shaded subcell.

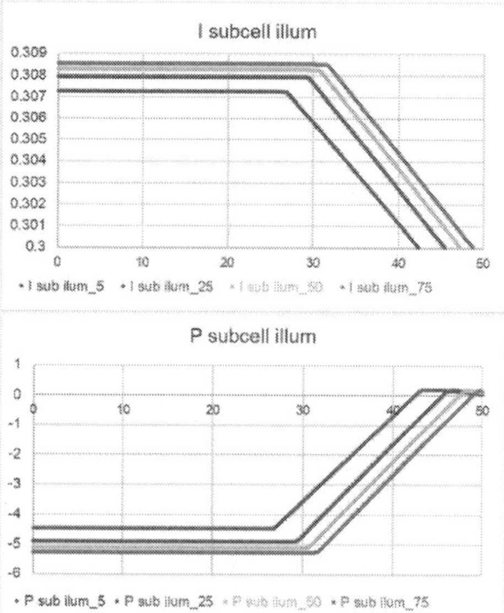

Figure 7: IV and PV curves in an illuminated subcell unit of the shaded cell for shading percentages of 5%, 25%, 50% and 75%.

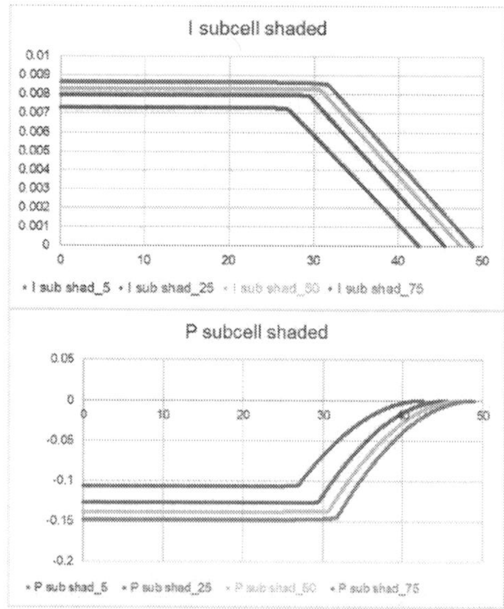

Figure 8: IV and PV curves in a shaded subcell unit of the shaded cell for shading percentages of 5%, 25%, 50% and 75%.

From the simulations with the subdivided cell, it can be concluded that:
- For values close to V_{OC}, the shaded cell also contributes to generation. The lower the percentage of shading, the longer it takes to start consuming.

- If we look at the values for the entire cell (Figure 6), the smaller the shadow, the greater the power dissipated in that cell.

However, if we observe the behaviour in the illuminated and shaded areas of a partially shaded cell, we see that:

- In both the shaded and illuminated areas, the greater the shade, the more power is dissipated. It should also be noted that the difference is quite small.
- Based on the dissipated power values obtained, it can be deduced that it is the illuminated part of the partially shaded cell that is suffering, and not the shaded part. The difference in power here is considerable (about forty times greater).

Considering that a shaded subcell and an illuminated subcell are two parts of the same size of the cell, the values obtained will be proportional to current and power densities, so greater heating is to be expected in the areas under illumination of the cells with most of their area shaded.

4 CONCLUSIONS AND DISCUSION

Simulations of partial shading have been performed in two ways: shadow of the total area of the cell with partial irradiance, and total shadow of only a part of the cell. From the first simulations, the conclusion that the worst-case scenario happens for a small percentage of shading is derived. From the second simulations on the contrary, the conclusion is that the worst-case scenario occurs when almost all the cell is covered, and the part that handles the thermal stress is the illuminated part of the shaded cell.

These simulations have considered a short-circuit current of 6A, so it can be said that we have been quite conservative. In conclusion, we would say that, although bypass diodes prevent total loss of generation, they do not seem to offer an adequate protection to the cells from excessive heating in a realistic case of partial shading.

We believe that in order to determine the relationship with cell heating, the parameter to be taken into consideration is not the total power consumed by the shaded cell, but rather the current and power density, which will be distributed unevenly across the cell area.

ACKNOWLEDGEMENTS

This work was funded by the *Ministerio de Ciencia, Innovación y Universidades* of Spain within the project MCIU-O23/P45 (reference: PID2023-148369OB-C42) under the scheme *Proyectos de Generación de Conocimiento 2023*.

REFERENCES

[1] International Energy Agency (IEA)
Task 1 Strategic PV Analysis and Outreach – 2025 Snapshot of Global PV Markets
https://iea-pvps.org/wp-content/uploads/2025/04/Snapshot-of-Global-PV-Markets_2025.pdf

[2] European Commission
The European Green Deal. Striving to be the first climate-neutral continent
https://commission.europa.eu/strategy-and-policy/priorities-2019-2024/european-green-deal_en

[3] Our Worl in Data
Solar panel prices have fallen by around 20% every time global capacity doubled
https://ourworldindata.org/data-insights/solar-panel-prices-have-fallen-by-around-20-every-time-global-capacity-doubled

[4] Al Mahdi, H., Leahy, P. G., Alghoul, M., & Morrison, A. P. (2024, January). A review of photovoltaic module failure and degradation mechanisms: Causes and detection techniques. In *Solar* (Vol. 4, No. 1, pp. 43-82). MDPI.

[5] Vieira, R. G., de Araújo, F. M., Dhimish, M., & Guerra, M. I. (2020). A comprehensive review on bypass diode application on photovoltaic modules. *Energies*, *13*(10), 2472.

[6] Silvestre, S., Boronat, A., & Chouder, A. (2009). Study of bypass diodes configuration on PV modules. *applied energy*, *86*(9), 1632-1640.

[7] Pannebakker, B. B., de Waal, A. C., & van Sark, W. G. (2017). Photovoltaics in the shade: one bypass diode per solar cell revisited. *Progress in photovoltaics: Research and Applications*, *25*(10), 836-849.

[8] Lee, C. G., Shin, W. G., Lim, J. R., Kang, G. H., Ju, Y. C., Hwang, H. M., ... & Ko, S. W. (2021). Analysis of electrical and thermal characteristics of PV array under mismatching conditions caused by partial shading and short circuit failure of bypass diodes. *Energy*, *218*, 119480.

[9] Mohammed, H., Kumar, M., & Gupta, R. (2020). Bypass diode effect on temperature distribution in crystalline silicon photovoltaic module under partial shading. *Solar Energy*, *208*, 182-194.

[10] Gao, C., Liang, P., Ren, H., & Han, P. (2018). Experimental research on the relationship between bypass diode configuration of photovoltaic module and hot spot generation. *Journal of Semiconductors*, *39*(12), 124014.

BREAKAGE IN BIFACIAL PV MODULES

Rodrigo P. Maruyama, Adnei Melges de Andrade, Roberto Zilles
Institute of Energy and Environment, University of São Paulo
Av. Prof. Luciano Gualberto, 1289 - 05516-050 - São Paulo - Brazil

ABSTRACT: This work presents the occurrence of glass cracking in bifacial photovoltaic modules installed at the São Paulo campus of University of São Paulo. One of the systems consists of 78 bifacial modules (545 Wp) arranged in six strings connected to a 35 kW inverter with a single-axis tracker. Within the first month of operation, two modules exhibited cracks in the rear glass. Over the following months the number of PV modules with cracks increased to 20 (25.6%) in 14 months. To gain understanding of the reasons for the glass cracking events, after discussions with the supplier and manufacturer, a second system with 30 modules (545 Wp) of the same maker and model was installed on a fixed-tilt structure. In the fixed-tilt system cracks were observed in nine modules after 10 months of installation (30%). This study documents the cracking patterns in both systems and compares their occurrence to better understand the underlying causes.
Keywords: bifacial PV modules, glass cracking, solar panel reliability, module design.

1 INTRODUCTION

The global solar photovoltaic (PV) market has grown rapidly over the past decade, driven by cost reductions and a variety of technological changes. In Brazil, PV has become one of the most dynamic energy sources, supported by abundant solar resources and favorable policies that enabled fast deployment of distributed generation, strengthening the diversification of the national energy mix.

While the Brazilian electric capacity remains dominated by hydropower, renewable sources account for about 90% of the national electricity mix. Within this context, solar PV participation has already reached nearly 23,5%. This rapid growth of solar PV capacity, however, also raises the need to ensure the reliability, performance, and safety of PV systems.

Reports of spontaneous glass breakage in photovoltaic modules, often referred to as "spontaneous cracking," have been increasingly reported worldwide. Recent studies highlight that thinner glass, evolving module designs, and inadequate adaptation of qualification standards have created a scenario in which thin glass used in large-area bifacial modules is particularly vulnerable. Field observations show that modules can crack prematurely, sometimes even before commissioning, raising significant concerns about long-term reliability and the adequacy of current testing protocols.

Several research groups [1,2,9-12] have reported glass failures in bifacial modules tested under local weather conditions and some large power plants. The study carried on by Nascimento e Silva et al. [1] investigated premature glass cracking in large-area bifacial glass/glass photovoltaic modules (2 mm thick) installed at a 100 kWp test plant in Florianópolis, Brazil, where approximately 50% of the modules exhibited cracks within nine months of operation. Using scanning electron microscopy (SEM), the research analyzed both the glass thickness and the glass–frame interface, identifying regions with thickness below the manufacturer's specifications (up to 8% reduction) and defects such as voids or improper polyurethane filling along the aluminum frame interface.

A study from NREL [2] highlights broader interacting factors, including reduced surface compression, edge flaws, lamination "edge pinch," frame contact, and stresses from larger module sizes. Both studies point to the vulnerability of 2 mm thick glass.

Together, they show that premature breakage arises from combined mechanical and manufacturing issues rather than a single cause.

2 PV SYSTEMS DESCRIPTION

The studied systems are installed on the University of São Paulo campus, in the city of São Paulo, Brazil. According to the Köppen–Geiger classification [8], the site is characterized as a humid subtropical climate (Cfa). The single-axis tracker PV system and the fixed-tilt PV system are shown in Figures 1 and 2, respectively.

Figure 1: Single tracker PV system. Cracked modules marked yellow (adapted from Google Earth).

Figure 2: Fixed-tilt PV system. Cracked modules marked yellow (adapted from Google Earth).

The single axis tracking system consists of three sets, each comprising two strings of 13 modules arranged sequentially from right to left and connected to a 35 kW inverter. The tracker operates based on solar time at the site's geographic location, with an angular range of +55° (east) to –55° (west). It is equipped with a wind protection mechanism that is automatically activated after sustained wind speeds exceeding 60 km/h for more than one minute.

The fixed-tilt system consists of a single set with two rows of 13 modules each, along with four additional non-connected modules mounted on the same racking structure in the front row. The array is installed at a tilt angle of 24° and oriented toward geographic north.

The photovoltaic modules employed in the systems under study are bifacial silicon monocrystalline n-type PERC devices, each composed of 144 half-cut cells. Their main electrical parameters include a maximum power (P_{MAX}) of 545 W, an open-circuit voltage (V_{OC}) of 49.75 V, a short-circuit current (I_{SC}) of 13.93 A, and a temperature coefficient of power (γ) of $-0.35\%/°C$. Furthermore, the modules exhibit a bifaciality factor of 70% ±10%.

Figure 3 shows the mounting position of the PV modules and in the images in Figures 5 and 6 these positions are identified by blue dots.

Figure 3: PV module mounting position. a) Tracker PV system and b) Fixed-tilt PV system.

The module's dimensions are 2,278 × 1,134 × 30 mm (L×W×H), a total mass of 31.8 kg, and a double-glass structure composed of 2.0 mm glass on both the front and rear sides. They are designed to withstand static mechanical loads, with maximum tolerances of 5,400 Pa (112 lb/ft²) applied on the front surface and 2,400 Pa (50 lb/ft²) on the rear surface.

In terms of reliability assurances, the manufacturer provides a product warranty of 12 years and a linear performance warranty of 30 years. According to this guarantee, the modules are warranted to deliver at least 85% of their initial nominal power output by the 30th year of operation, corresponding to an average annual degradation rate of approximately 0.45%.

In addition to the mechanical parameters described above, the glass layers play a central role in the structural integrity of photovoltaic modules. Commercial PV modules typically employ one of two glass types: rolled (patterned) glass or float glass. Rolled glass is produced by drawing molten glass through water-cooled rollers, which imprint a dimpled inner surface and leave a relatively smooth outer surface; it is frequently used on the front and rear sides of c-Si modules. Float glass, on the other hand, is manufactured on a molten tin bath, resulting in very smooth surfaces free of dimples.

Although both technologies are widely adopted, rolled glass has not demonstrated consistent optical or adhesion advantages, and the dimples introduced during manufacturing may act as stress concentrators that slightly reduce mechanical strength compared to float glass [4]. The manufacturer's datasheet of the studied module does not indicate all the characteristics of the employed glass, introducing an additional layer of uncertainty to the failure analysis.

3 CRACK OBSERVATION

In the tracker system, installed in November 2023, the first cracks were observed in two modules as early as 10 days after installation (2.56% of the modules). The number of affected modules continued to grow, reaching 20 cracked units after 14 months, corresponding to 25.64% of the modules.

In the Fixed-tilt system, where less cracking was expected, the first glass crack was recorded after three months of installation. After six months of operation, 30% of the modules had cracks.

The comparative analysis showed that both systems had similar failure rates: 20/78 modules (25.64%) in the tracker system and 9/30 modules (30%) in the fixed system. Different crack patterns, however, were observed; in the fixed system, cracks displayed periodic-like waviness, while in the tracker system no periodic-like waviness was observed.

Crack formation was recorded over time in order to understand its dynamics, as shown in Figure 4. In this example the cracks in three modules are illustrated.

In Figure 4a the cracking evolution is recorded at two different moments. The first record, shown in red, corresponds to the initial observation, while the yellow markings indicate the cracking evolution pattern after approximately 100 days. Figures 4b and 4c show the cracks in modules 01 and 02 of the bottom string and were observed 8 months and 9 months after installation startup, respectively. The red line marks the initial crack observation, while the yellow line indicates the second observation.

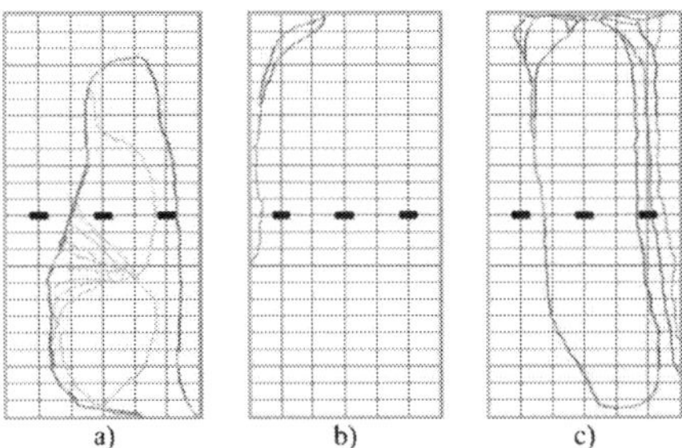

Figure 4: Example of recorded cracking patterns. a) Top String module 01, b) Bottom string module 01 and c) Bottom string module 02.

Data registration was performed for all 29 cracked modules, 20 of them located in the single-axis tracking PV system and 9 in the fixed-tilt PV system. For each cracked module, the cracking records were mapped into a matrix of 24 rows by 6 columns, corresponding to the physical position of each half-cell within the module. Initially, the matrices were filled with zeros, and whenever a glass crack was identified, the value at the corresponding position was set to 1. This procedure was repeated for every cracked module, and the resulting matrices were subsequently combined to generate the aggregated crack distributions presented in Figure 5. The color scale represents the frequency of cracks at each cell position. Darker shades indicate a higher concentration of cracks in that specific location.

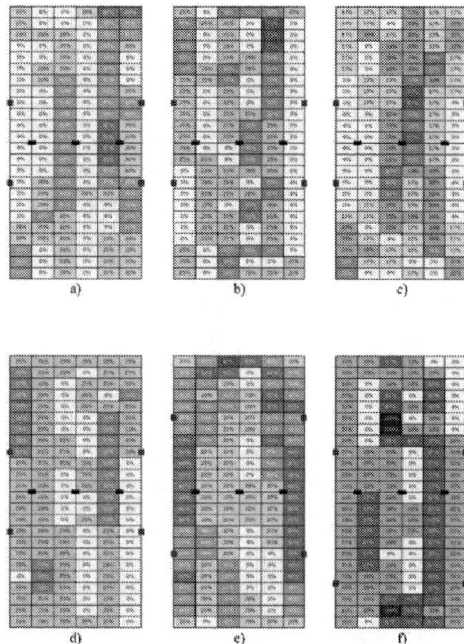

Figure 5: Matrix combination for strings in both PV systems. a) String 1, b) String 02, c) String 03, d) String 05, e) Bottom string and f) Top string.

To get a broader view of each system analyzed, the matrices were summed for all modules in each system. The results can be seen in Figure 6.

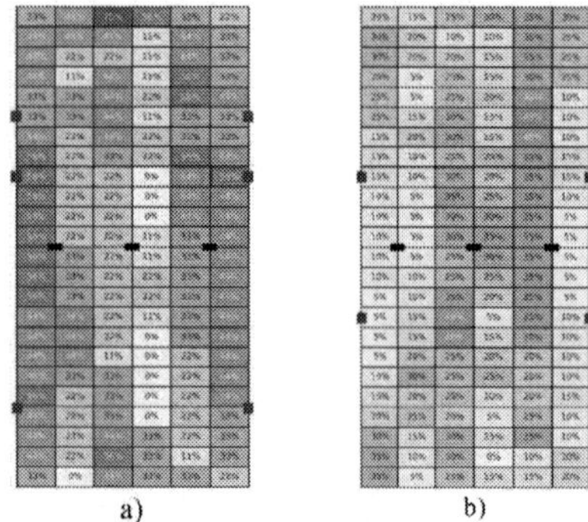

Figure 6: Matrix sum of all cracked modules, a) Fixed-tilt and b) Tracker PV system.

The observation of crack initiation and growth shows a clear difference between the single-axis tracker PV system and the fixed-tilt PV system. In the tracker system, cracks occur more often in the middle of the module, whereas in the fixed-tilt system they tend to form close to the edges. It is also important to highlight that in the tracker system, cracks are rarely found close to the clamps in the mounting, which rules out the assembly clamps as a possible cracking initiation cause.

The observed mechanical behavior of the module frame under static load can be explained by its boundary conditions and structural constraints. When the module is fixed at the 400 mm mounting position, the frame in the immediate vicinity of the mounting point remains largely prevented from torsional deformation. However, as the distance from the mounting point increases, the frame exhibits a tendency to twist. This torsional movement propagates along the frame until it approaches the corner region. At this point, the corner geometry and the rigidity of the frame prevent further torsional displacement, leading instead to localized stress concentration. These concentrated stresses at the corners provide a plausible explanation for the high frequency of cracks observed in Figure 6b.

A graphic of the local ambient temperature is shown in Figure 7. To seek the understanding of crack evolution, the dates of the observation were plotted on the graph. It should be noted that the recording dates may not correspond to the exact day of the crack's initiation or growth.

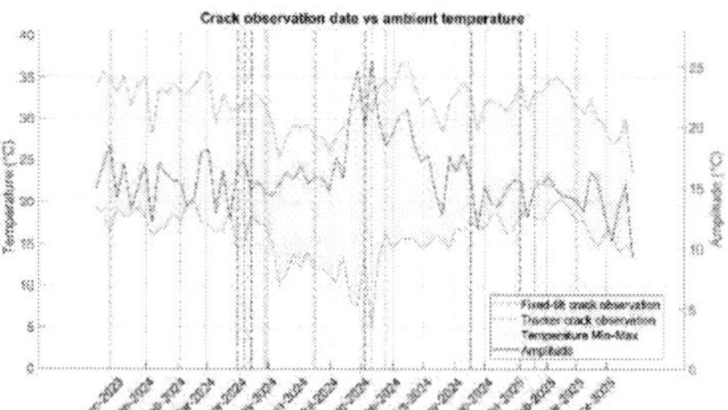

Figure 7: Temperature (min, max, thermal amplitude) and timestamps of new cracks.

4 EVALUATION TECHNIQUES

In addition to recording and organizing the collected data, technical analyses were carried out, namely electroluminescence (IEC 60904-13), IV Curve (IEC 60904-1), dry (IEC 61215 - MQT 03) and wet (IEC 61215 - MQT 15) insulation resistance, and measurements of module deflection (sagging).

The tests were performed in our laboratory, which is signatory of the ILAC Mutual Recognition Arrangement (ILAC-MRA), ensuring that the results are internationally recognized for their technical competence, impartiality, and compliance with ISO/IEC 17025 requirements.

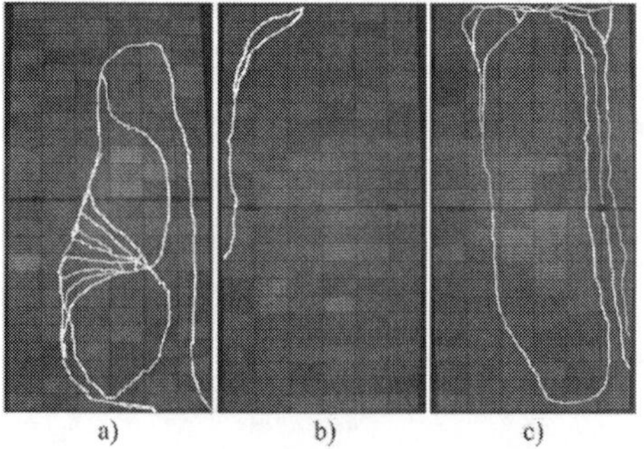

Figure 8: Electroluminescence in the modules seen in Figure 4. a) Top String module 01, b) Bottom string module 01 and c) Bottom string module 02.

4.1 Electroluminescence evaluation

Test was carried out following IEC TS 60904-13. Figure 8 shows the electroluminescence generated by the cracked modules previously seen in Figure 4.

4.2 IV Curve

Modules in Figure 9 are coded by their exposure history and mounting scheme: **UNExp** (unexposed) is a reference module that has never been exposed to real-world sunlight and is kept stored as a testimonial sample; **Exp** denotes a module that has been field-exposed but was not electrically connected; **Conn** indicates a module in normal operation with no cracks; and **ConnCrack** designates a module in operation that exhibits glass cracks.

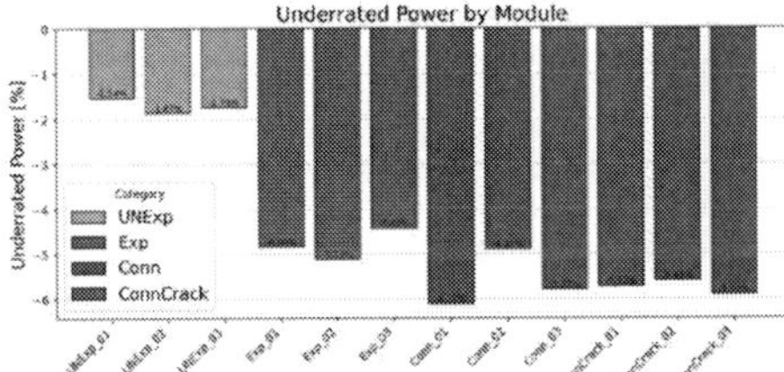

Figure 9: Underrated power by module.

Average power loss from the 545 W nameplate is: **UNExp** 1.72% (9.4 W), **Exp** 4.80% (26.2 W), **Conn** 5.61% (30.6 W), **ConnCrack** 5.75% (31.3 W). Loss increases from unexposed to exposed to operating modules. The solar simulator has an uncertainty of ±2%, so **Exp**, **Conn**, and **ConnCrack** are statistically indistinguishable from each other in these tests. The observed power losses, ranging from 5.61% to 5.75%, significantly exceed the degradation rate outlined in the manufacturer's datasheet. For the 16-month period of use, the manufacturer specifies a linear degradation rate of 0.45% per year, which would result in an expected loss of 2.6%.

4.3 IEC 61215:2021 MQT 03 and MQT 15

The tests were carried out following IEC 61215:2021 [7] with calibrated equipment with traceable calibration certificates linked to national and international standards.

The MQT 03 test verifies the insulation resistance of the photovoltaic module under dry conditions. It ensures that the insulation between the active electrical circuits and the metallic frame can withstand the system's maximum voltage without excessive leakage current. The result is expressed in $G\Omega$ and normalized by the module area ($G\Omega \cdot m^2$). The results are shown in Table I.

The MQT 15 test verifies the insulation resistance of the photovoltaic module under wet conditions as specified in this standard. The results are shown in Table I.

Three tests were conducted: one for MQT 03; two for MQT 15 in two different moments. Test 3 was conducted 2 hours after test 2. The results are shown in Table I.

The module showed very high insulation resistance under dry conditions (7.13 $G\Omega \cdot m^2$), well above the minimum limit of 40 $M\Omega \cdot m^2$ required by IEC 61215:2021. In the two wet leakage current tests, the insulation resistance showed to be between 2.78 $G\Omega \cdot m^2$ and 3.09 $G\Omega \cdot m^2$, demonstrating stability and electrical safety under humidity. The module was considered PASSED in the Insulation Resistance (MQT 03) and Wet Leakage Current (MQT 15) tests, according to IEC 61215:2021.

Table I: MQT 03 and MQT 15 test results.

Parameter	Test 1 – MQT 03	Test 2 – MQT 15	Test 3 – MQT 15
Ambient temperature	26.2 °C	16.1 °C	16.1 °C
Relative humidity	35 %	NA*	NA*
Water temperature	NA*	14.9 °C	15.4 °C
Applied voltage	1544 V (2 min)	1544 V (2 min)	1544 V (2 min)
Insulation resistance	18.4 GΩ	7.17 GΩ	7.99 GΩ
Module area	2.58 m²	2.58 m²	2.58 m²
Normalized insulation value	7.13 GΩ·m²	2.78 GΩ·m²	3.09 GΩ·m²
Conclusion	PASSED	PASSED	PASSED

*Not applicable.

4.4 Deflection measurement

Shortly after the tracking system installation was completed, module deflection was observed, caused by the combined effects of gravity and temperature variations.

Figure 10 illustrates how the span progressively bends under varying environmental and operational conditions. The reference values d', d'' and d''' are not measured data but schematic indicators, highlighting the relative increase in mid-span deflection as the day advances and external factors such as temperature, irradiance, and wind loading change.

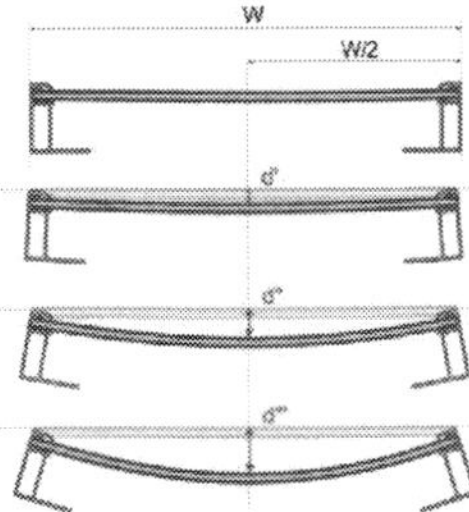

Figure 10: Transverse deflection.

Considering this information extremely relevant to investigation the cause of the cracks in the rear glass, measurements of this deflection were conducted throughout the day on four modules. Two modules in the single-axis tracker PV system and another two in the fixed-tilt PV system. The results of these measurements are presented in the graph shown in Figures 11 and 12.

The collected results demonstrate that deflection varies throughout the day. In Figure 11 the deflection is shown for modules 1 and 5 on string 01 in the single-axis tracker PV system. Glass deflection is higher in the early morning and late afternoon. Although deflection decreases during the day, a slight increase is observed around solar noon, likely due to the combination of tilt position at 0° with thermal and irradiance stress at that time. Deflection likely begins at a higher value because the tracker "sleeps" at an almost horizontal 9°, which is almost horizontal.

In the fixed-tilt PV system, deflection varies less during the day but is still influenced by temperature. Since the tilt angle remains constant, the gravitational effect contribution to sagging does not change. This behavior may be different in modules installed in different geographical locations.

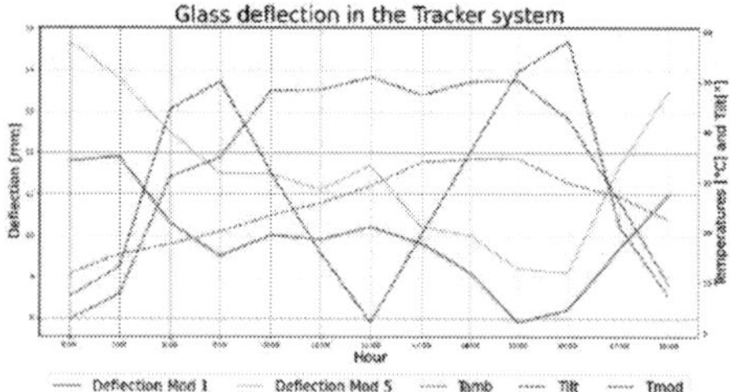

Figure 11: Tracker PV module deflection. Deflection of Modules 1 and 5 measured in mm. Tamb is the ambient temperature, Tilt is the module angle with respect to the ground plane, and Tmod is the module temperature.

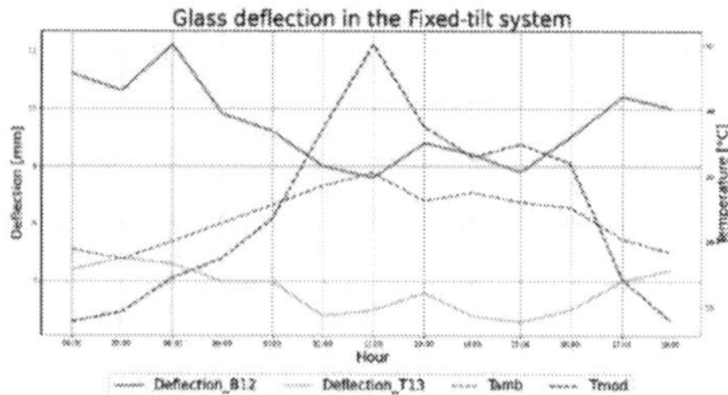

Figure 12: Fixed-tilt PV module deflection. Deflection of Modules B12 and T13 measured in mm. Tamb is the ambient temperature, and Tmod is the module temperature.

5 RESULTS AND DISCUSSION

The comparative monitoring of the two systems, fixed-tilt and tracker, revealed that glass cracking in bifacial modules is not limited to a specific mounting configuration, although different crack distribution patterns were observed. In the tracker system, 20 out of 78 modules (25.64%) exhibited cracks within 14 months of operation, whereas the fixed-tilt system showed 9 failures among 30 modules (30%) in just over one year. Although the absolute numbers differ, both systems converged toward similar failure rates, suggesting that glass laminate fragility is intrinsic rather than driven by the mounting scheme.

In the fixed system, cracks exhibited a periodic-like waviness, a feature often attributed in the literature [3] to the crack propagation speed: when propagation occurs rapidly, the crack tends to deviate upon encountering local resistance, producing a wavy-like track. Conversely, tracker-mounted modules developed cracks without a clear periodic pattern, possibly reflecting the continuous movement and the dynamic stresses imposed by daily sun-tracking.

Although many cracks were initially observed after periods of high thermal stress, timely crack observations in relation to ambient temperature indicate that their occurrence cannot be attributed solely to thermal conditions.

Complementary laboratory tests indicated that individual cracked modules continued to meet IEC 61215:2021 requirements. Both MQT 03 and MQT 15 insulation tests yielded values well above the minimum thresholds.

IV Curve results show that the average power loss relative to the 545 W nameplate ranged from 1.72% in testimonial sample modules and from 5.61% to 5.75% in modules exposed to sunlight but not electrically connected and operating. Since simulator uncertainty (±2%) makes exposed, connected, and cracked connected modules statistically similar, their actual losses, well above the expected 2.6% after 16 months (0.45%/year), indicate significantly faster degradation than specified by the manufacturer.

Electroluminescence imaging shows cells mismatch that can explain the power loss verified in IV curve tests results.

Although the highest deflection is expected to occur around solar noon, when irradiance can reach its maximum and the module is positioned almost horizontally, so that the gravity vector acts fully normal to the glass surface, the collected data reveal a different behavior. At the start of the monitoring period (~6:00 AM), Module 1 in the tracker system already shows its largest deflection, 11.8 mm, while Module 5 starts even higher, at 14.7 mm.

This discrepancy underscores the importance of integrating field-representative mechanical stress scenarios, such as catenary deflection, dynamic wind loading, and thermal cycling with constrained edges, into bifacial module reliability protocols and highlights the necessity of updating normative testing procedures and criteria.

6 CONCLUSIONS

This study documented extensive rear-glass cracking in bifacial PV modules under both tracker and fixed-tilt installations at the University of São Paulo, São Paulo, Brazil. In less than 14 months, over one-quarter of the modules in both systems exhibited cracking, despite passing the IEC 61215:2021 tests.

The convergence of crack incidence across mounting configurations suggests that the problem is systemic to module design and manufacture rather than module mounting schemes. The distinct crack morphologies point to interactions between structural boundary conditions and environmental stresses.

The IV curve test clearly shows that the measured modules exhibit electrical behavior that deviates more strongly and rapidly than predicted on the manufacturer's datasheet. The lack of significant difference between intact and cracked operating modules suggests that performance deviations are more closely related to exposure and operation than to cracking itself. Further tests will be performed to evaluate the evolution and condition of the electrical characteristics of these modules.

These findings demonstrate the urgent need to refine existing qualification standards to better reflect real-world operating conditions of bifacial modules. Future work should focus on (i) improved mechanical testing protocols that account for bifacial modules, (ii) correlation of crack initiation with structural deflection and thermal cycles, (iii) long-term monitoring of power degradation in cracked modules, and (iv) accelerated degradation studies such as MQT 16 and MQT 20 of IEC 61215:2021 to verify whether cracks contribute to faster degradation than guaranteed by the manufacturer. By bridging the gap between laboratory tests and field reality, more reliable evaluation frameworks can be established, ultimately supporting the secure deployment of bifacial PV at scale.

7 ACKNOWLEDGMENTS

This research was supported by the National Council for Scientific and Technological Development (CNPq/MCTI/Brazil), which funding the project "Real-World Characterization of Bifacial Photovoltaic Modules and Generators.", through process No. 406711/2022-5. We also thank the Photovoltaic Systems Laboratory (LSF-IEE/USP) for technical analysis and support.

8 REFERENCES

[1] Nascimento e Silva, B., Matos, M. F. A., Lira, A. L. O., Alves, C. G. L., Ferreira, D. A., de Sousa, A. R., & Emiliavaca, S. A. S. (2024). Análise da espessura dos vidros e da interface moldura-vidro em módulos fotovoltaicos bifaciais com uso de microscopia eletrônica de varredura. Revista Brasileira de Energia Solar, 15(1), 46–53.

[2] Silverman, T. J., Palmiotti, E. C., Springer, M., Bosco, N., Deceglie, M., Repins, I., & Gaulding, A. (2024). Tough break: Many factors make glass breakage more likely (NREL/TP-5K00-91695). National Renewable Energy Laboratory.

[3] Quinn, G. D. (2020). Fractography of ceramics and glasses (Special Publication 960-16e3). National Institute of Standards and Technology. https://doi.org/10.6028/NIST.SP.960-16e3

[4] E. C. Palmiotti, M. Springer, J. Zuboy, T. J. Silverman, J. L. Braid, D. C. Jordan, S. Rabade, and T. M. Barnes. Growing Panes: Investigating the PV Technology Trends Behind Frequent Early Failures in Modern Glass–Glass Modules. IEEE Journal of Photovoltaics, vol. 15, no. 2, pp. 297–306, Mar. 2025.

[5] J. Markert, A. G. Belawadi, E. Job, I. Hädrich, and D. Philipp. What Can We Learn from the Comparison of Glass Breakage between Lab and Field?. in Proc. SOPHIA Workshop 2025, DTU Risø Campus, Denmark, Apr. 29, 2025.

[6] D. Wang, A. Hermawan, and E. Woolard. Wind Speed and Rear Glass Breakage on Bifacial PV Modules Mounted on Trackers. DNV White Paper, Utrecht, The Netherlands, 2024.

[7] IEC 61215-1:2021 – Terrestrial Photovoltaic (PV) Modules – Design Qualification and Type Approval – Part 1: Test Requirements, International Electrotechnical Commission, Geneva, Switzerland, Apr. 2021.

[8] KOTTEK, Markus; GRIESER, Jürgen; BECK, Christoph; RUDOLF, Bruno; RUBEL, Franz. World Map of the Köppen-Geiger climate classification updated. Meteorologische Zeitschrift. v. 15, n. 3, p. 259-263, 2006.

[9] M. Braga, G. X. A. Pinto, A. M. Pires, A. H. Zamboni, L. R. Nascimento, and R. Rüther. Investigating the causes and consequences of glass cracks on double-glass large area bifacial PV modules. Poster presented at PV Research Workshop, Florianópolis, Brazil, Mar. 2023. [Online].

[10] Barnes, T. (ed.). DuraMAT FY 2023 Annual Report: Toward Reliability Forecasting. Durable Module Materials Consortium (DuraMAT), National Renewable Energy Laboratory (NREL), Sandia National Laboratories, Lawrence Berkeley National Laboratory, 2023.

[11] Wang, D.; Hermawan, A.; Woolard, E. Wind Speed and Rear Glass Breakage on Bifacial PV Modules Mounted on Trackers. Whitepaper, DNV Netherlands B.V., Arnhem, 2024.

[12] Pilliod, M. Central Tension – Glass Durability and Breakage. Presented at the NREL Photovoltaic Reliability Workshop (PVRW 2024), Glass Durability and Breakage session, February 28, 2024, Golden, CO, USA.

DAMP HEAT TEST ON TOPCON MODULES MADE WITH GLASS/BACKSHEET

Author(s): Alessandro Anderlini
Company / Institute(s): Coveme Spa
Address(es): Via Emilia 288, 40068 -San Lazzaro di Savena (BO)- Italy, aanderlini@coveme.com

ABSTRACT:
Given the rising market share of TOPCon cell technologies, where the typical PV module configuration is Glass/Glass, there is a need to prove that also Glass/Backsheet can be considered as a valid alternative in terms of performance and reliability.
On the one hand these backsheets need to have a high resistance towards water ingress; a factor which gains increasing importance with latest developments in cell technologies like TOPCon which are assumed to be more sensitive to humidity.[1] On the other hand, the combination of different BOM and different production processes, suggests to investigate the reliability of backsheets, combined with different encapsulants and running through different production process, towards environmental stresses with a common test procedure following the existing standards.
In order to test for the general backsheet durability, 8 modules have been tested in a standardized (IEC61215, MQT13) damp heat test (1000 h) in the TestLab PV Modules at Fraunhofer Institute for Solar Energy Systems ISE. The modules were built by two third-party module manufacturers. The module compositions are depicted in Table 01 and Table 02. The test consisted of a total of 1000 h damp heat exposure, The difference between the modules was the encapsulant supplier both being POE based. The aim was to understand differences in PV modules performance that might arise from various material combinations and different production process.
At the end of the test all PV modules except one passed the test, remaining below the 5% power loss limit according to IEC 61215. The Glass/Glass module obtained the best result with only 1.68% power loss. The Glass/Backsheet modules power loss was between 3.0 % and 4.3% for all PV modules except one. In addition the backsheets employed remained clear and free of cracks. Only one module lost more then 5% but it is likely that the higher degradation of this module was not due to the backsheet, but rather associated with the difference in encapsulant. Another possibility could be a variation in module manufacturing quality.

1 AIM AND APPROACH

The major aim of his work is to understand more about the reliability of PV modules with TOPCon cell technologies in Glass/Backsheet configuration compare to Glass / Glass and specifically the behaviour of different moisture barrier backsheet types, combined with 2 types of encapsulants in different production process towards environmental stresses with a common test procedure following the existing standards.

The 1000h damp heat test was conducted with full size PV modules produced by known PV module producers from their standard production process.

All modules were exposed to the following test sequence:

- Power measurement at STC acc. to IEC 61215, MQT02
- EL imaging
- Damp Heat test acc. to IEC 61215, MQT13
- Power measurement at STC acc. to IEC 61215, MQT02
- EL imaging

Manufacturer	Module ID	front side	cells	Encapsulant front/back	Backside	Pmpp_[W] %	stress test
A	M06	Glass	16BB TOPCon	Brand A - POE/POE	Glass	-1,68	DH 1000h
A	M07	Glass	16BB TOPCon	Brand A - POE/POE	COVEME dyMat HDPYE SPV L (370 µm / white)	-3,26	DH 1000h
A	M08	Glass	16BB TOPCon	Brand A - POE/POE	COVEME dyMat HDPYE SPV LDO (420 µm / white)	-3,17	DH 1000h
A	M09	Glass	16BB TOPCon	Brand A - POE/POE	COVEME dyMat HDPYE SPV C (314 µm / white)	-4,26	DH 1000h
Manufacturer	Module ID	front side	cells	Encapsulant front/back	Backside	Pmpp_[W] %	stress test
B	M02	Glass	16BB TOPCon	Brand B - POE/POE	COVEME dyMat HDPYE SPV L (370 µm / white)	-3,22	DH 1000h
B	M03	Glass	16BB TOPCon	Brand B - POE/POE	COVEME dyMat Clr HDPYE F (320 µm / Clear)	-5,87	DH 1000h
B	M04	Glass	16BB TOPCon	Brand A - POE/POE	COVEME dyMat Clr HDPYE F (320 µm / Clear)	-3,39	DH 1000h
B	M05	Glass	16BB TOPCon	Brand A - POE/POE	COVEME dyMat HDPYE SPV L (370 µm / white)	-3,72	DH 1000h

Table I: List of tested modules

2   RESULTS (OR PRELIMINARY RESULTS) AND CONCLUSIONS

2.1 Manufacturer A

All modules passed the DH1000 test according to the pass/fail criteria of less than 5 % power loss. In the electroluminescence images the GBS modules revealed dark features after DH1000 located on the cell edges. The origin of the features is likely related to tapes used for string fixing.

FIGURE 01 - DEVIATION IN POWER OUTPUT FROM INITIAL VALUES

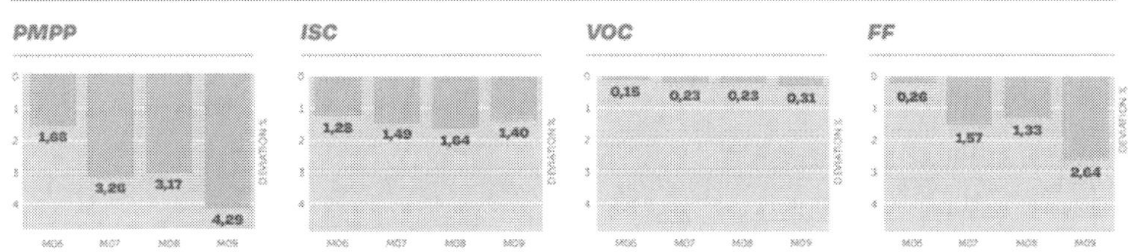

2.2 Electroluminescence Imaging

The GBS modules revealed dark features on the cell edges after damp heat exposure. A possible explanation is that they result from tapes that are often used to fix the module strings. M08 and M09 additionally reveal darker areas on some cells after DH1000. M08 exhibits a vertical darker strip after the damp heat exposure. The origin is unknown. It is not visible on the module with the bare eye.

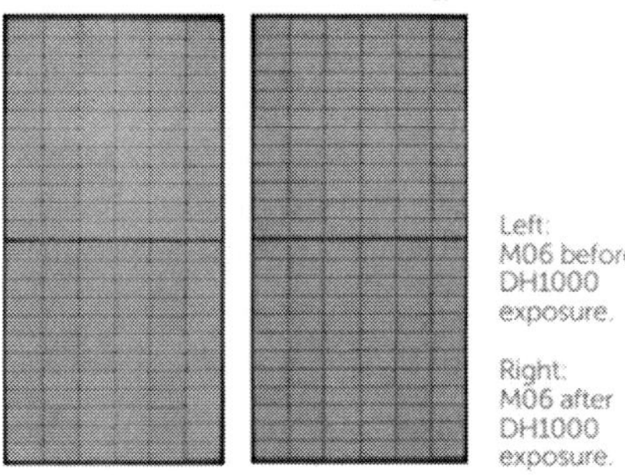

Left:
M06 before DH1000 exposure.

Right:
M06 after DH1000 exposure.

2.3 Manufacturer B

With exception of M03 all modules passed the DH test. M03 has the same BS as M04, which passed the test, but is constructed with a different encapsulant. Therefore, it is likely that the higher degradation of M03 is not due to the backsheet, but rather associated with the difference in encapsulant. Another possibility could be a variation in module manufacturing quality. The electroluminescence images revealed slightly impaired solder connections of the grid fingers around the cell edges. This issue is particularly pronounced in M03 after DH1000. This suggests that the module manufacturing quality may be a

contributing factor to the higher power loss observed in M03.

FIGURE 02 - DEVIATION IN POWER OUTPUT FROM INITIAL VALUES

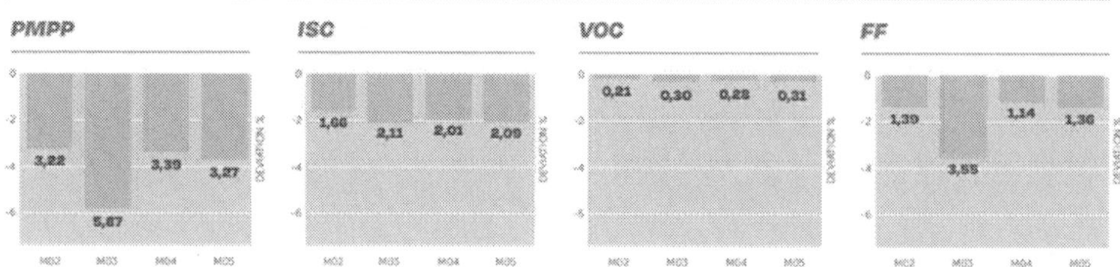

2.4 Electroluminescence Imaging

The electroluminescence (EL) images in the initial condition exhibit some darker areas around the cell edges, which are likely associated with an impaired solder connection of the fingers. After DH1000 more such dark areas are developed in particular in M03. This is an indication that the module quality is the major reason for the relatively higher power loss of M03.

After damp heat exposure in particular M05 exhibits dark features on the cell edges, which most likely stem from tapes used for string fixing.

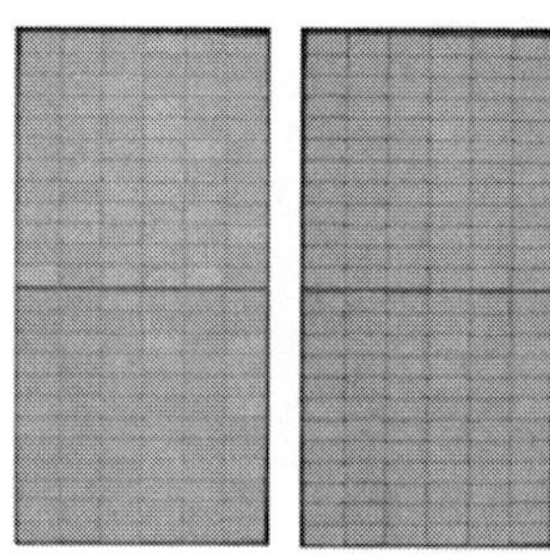

Left:
M02 before
DH1000
exposure.

Right:
M02 after
DH1000
exposure.

3 COMPARATIVE AGING TEST FROM FRAUNHOFER ISE

Coveme backsheets have also been tested at 1000 h damp heat in a comparative analysis of 20 TOPCon PV module types in the Test- Lab PV Modules at Fraunhofer Institute for Solar Energy Systems ISE, showing a superior performance compared to all other backsheets tested [2]

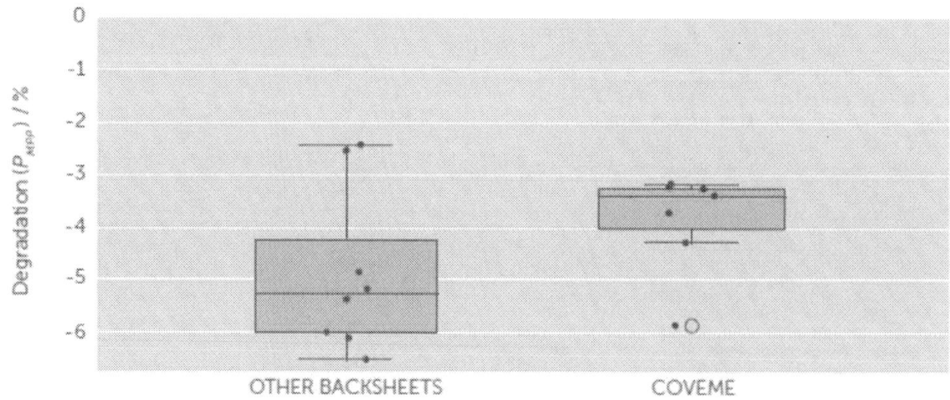

4 SCIENTIFIC INNOVATION AND RELEVANCE

At the end of the test all PV modules except one passed the test, remaining below the 5% power loss limit according to IEC 61215. The Glass/Glass module obtained the best result with only 1.68 % power loss. The Glass/Backsheet modules power loss was between 3.0 % and 4.3% for all PV modules except one. In addition the backsheets employed remained clear and free of cracks. Only one module lost more then 5% but it is likely that the higher degradation of this module was not due to the backsheet, but rather associated with the difference in encapsulant. Another possibility could be a variation in module manufacturing quality.

The Glass/Glass module performed quite well with minimum power loss. Also the Glass/backsheet modules passed the aging test, except one which shows that encapsulant material choice and production process are key factors to reach optimum performance. In addition, a comparative analysis of 20 TOPCon PV module types demonstrated that COVEME backsheets perform better than other backsheets. Finally Glass/backsheet configuration can be considered a valid alternative to Glass/Glass for specific installations where light module weight, lower cost and high resistance to hail are considered winning factors.

References

[1]   O. Arriaga Arruti, A. Virtuani, C. Ballif, Long-term performance and reliability of silicon heterojunction solar modules, Prog. Photovolt: Res. Appl. 31 (2023) 664–677.

[2] Paul Gebhardt, Ulli Kräling, Esther Fokuhl, Ingrid Hädrich, Daniel Philipp Reliability of Commercial TOPCon PV Modules—An Extensive Comparative Study, Progress in Photovoltaics: Research and Applications, 2024; 0:1–9

The influence of angle of incidence on the reliability of photovoltaic modules: Lessons Learned

N. Kyranaki [1,2,3], I. Kaaya [1,2,3], M. Adnan Hameed [4,5,6], R. de Jong [1,2,3], S. Bouguerra [1,2,3], A. Morlier [1,2,3], M. Daenen [1,2,3]

[1] Hasselt University, Institute for Materials Research (imo-imomec), Hasselt, Belgium, [2] imec, imo-imomec, Thor Park, Genk, Belgium, [3] EnergyVille, imo-imomec, Thor Park, Genk, Belgium, [4] Martin-Luther-University Halle-Wittenberg, Halle, Germany, [5] Ministry of Oil -SCOP, Baghdad, Iraq, [6] Fraunhofer Center for Silicon Photovoltaics CSP, Halle, Germany

Motivation

- Photovoltaic (PV) system designers optimize parameters that **enhance plane-of-array irradiance**, to **maximize energy yield**.
- **However, higher irradiation raises UV levels and operating temperatures**, leading to accelerated PV module degradation.
- An **indoor accelerated aging test** is presented, replicating variations in UV exposure linked to tilt angle.

Methodology

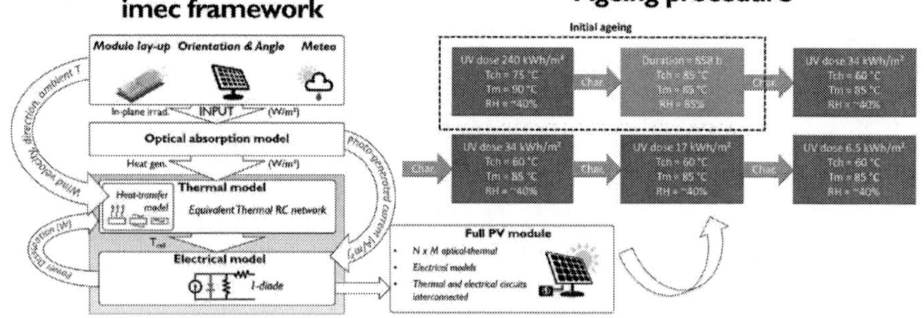

- Estimating variation in climate stressors with tilt angle using the imec PV simulation framework [1]
- Modelling acceleration factor of degradation for different tilt angles according to:

$$\mathrm{AF} = \left(\frac{\mathrm{UV}_A}{\mathrm{UV}_F}\right)^y \cdot \left(\frac{1+\mathrm{RH}_A^n}{1+\mathrm{RH}_F^n}\right) \cdot \exp\left(\frac{-E_{aF}}{k_B}\left(\frac{1}{T_A}-\frac{1}{T_F}\right)\right)$$

- Designing a relevant ageing sequence accounting for varied tilt angle, including electrical (I-V measurements) and optical (EL, visual inspection) characterization (Char.). Tch and Tm were the chamber and module temperature, respectively.

Results

- **First UV ageing 240 kWh/m²** (Fig. 1): $P_{max} \downarrow$ **0.79%** (mainly $V_{OC} \downarrow$ 0.97%); $I_{SC} \uparrow$ 0.11%
- **Damp-heat** (DH, Fig. 1): P_{max} **loss**; all electrical parameters↓
- **2nd UV** (Fig. 1): Full recovery after initial (34 kWh/m²) → degradation resumes after further 34 kWh/m²
- **Trend:** Cyclic degradation–regeneration ↔ BO-LID/LeTID; + encapsulant discoloration & photobleaching (Fig. 2)
- **Activation energy** (Fig. 3): ~0.54 eV ≈ BO-LID [2] (LeTID cannot be excluded)
- **UV dose sensitivity** (Fig. 3): Strongly module-quality (or activation energy) dependent

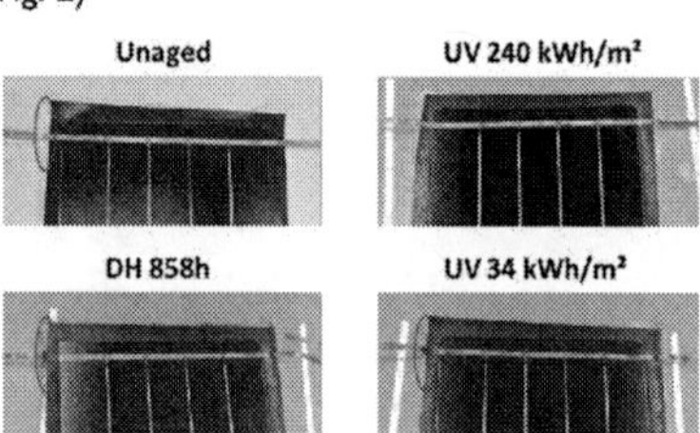

Fig. 2: Encapsulant discoloration

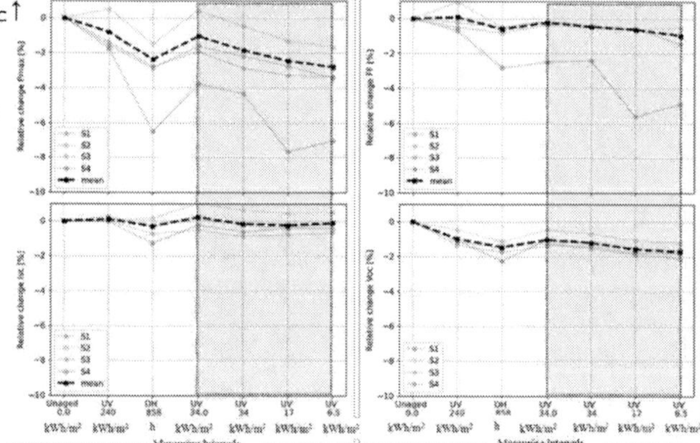

Fig. 1: Electrical performance parameters from I-V measurements

LESSONS LEARNED!!!

Exposure	34 kWh/m²	17 kWh/m²	6.5 kWh/m²
P_{max} drop	0.79%	0.61%	0.35%

- **Correlation of accelerated aging to tilt & outdoor effects:** further study needed ⚠. No BO-LID stabilization was performed so the impact of the various degradation mechanisms (LeTID and encapsulant discoloration/photobleaching) could not be distinguished
- **BO-LID/LeTID behavior:** PERC c-Si PV ⟶ requires further investigation and outdoor validation ✔

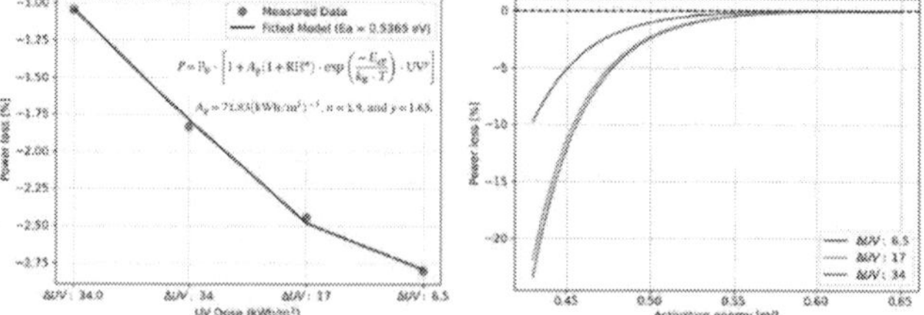

Fig. 3: Fitted model to experimental data (left) and simulated dose sensitivity for different activation energies

References

[1] SIMULATION OF PHOTOVOLTAIC MODULES, https://data.epo.org/publication-server/rest/v1.0/publication-dates/20170705/patents/EP2998756NWB1/document.html, accessed December 15, **2023**

[2] Woodhouse et. al, https://www.nrel.gov/docs/fy21osti/78629.pdf

020156-001

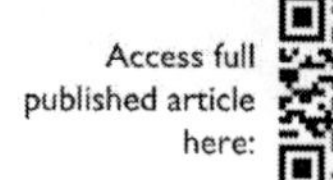

Access full published article here:

DETECTION OF TRANSFORMATIONS IN ENCAPSULANTS
AFTER MODULE LAMINATION PROCESS

V. Ulbikaitė[1], J. Donėlienė[1], P. Dubravskij[1], A. Galdikas[1], J. Devenson[2], V. Vaičikauskas[2], V. Nargelienė[2], A. Šetkus[2]
[1] Applied Research Institute for Prospective Technologies, Vilnius, Lithuania
[2] Center for Physical Sciences and Technology (FTMC), Vilnius, Lithuania
<vaidvile.ulbikaite@protechnology.lt>, <arunas.setkus@ftmc.lt>

ABSTRACT: Lamination of the PV-modules based on the thermal treatment of the encapsulants is primarily accepted to enhance the stability and durability of the module functioning. However, the encapsulants are modified due to transformations in polymers during the lamination process. In spite of the optimized conditions of the process, there is a lack in clear understanding about these modifications even if there were reliable proofs about a significant influence of the quality of the encapsulant on the characteristics of the PV-modules especially in the long-term exploitation. There is no reliable description of the parameters acceptable to characterize the polymer transformations in correlation with the lamination process conditions. In addition, an absence of informative parameters significantly diminishes possibilities to identify the encapsulation related problems in the long-term functioning of the PV-modules.
Keywords: solar modules, encapsulant defects, polymer properties, modules testing

1 AIM AND APPROACH

The module lamination process is worthy to investigate aiming to enhance the reliability and long-term stability of the PV-modules that directly makes significant impact on sustainability and recyclability [1]. Improvements of PV module durability and reliability include diverse aspects and depends on series of the technological processes and materials. Lamination of the PV modules is supposed to protect the functional parts from the surrounding influence. The transformations in the encapsulant determines the quality of the protection [2] and, therefore, this aspect is worthy to study in more details filling in the gaps in existing knowledge.

The characteristics acceptable to identify the transformations in the encapsulant during the lamination process have to be studied in details aiming to combine the most informative parameters into a model description of a relationship between the conditions of the lamination process and the properties of the encapsulant.

In this work, a novel approach was introduced acceptable to combine the infrared spectroscopy characteristics with the information extracted from the polarized light-based experiments. For this, the lamination process was reproduced by manufacturing double-side glass polymer models. The ethylene vinyl acetate (EVA) and polyolefin elastomer (POE) films were used in these models. The reflectance and transmittance spectra were measured, and the absorbance bands were analyzed in the near- and mid-infrared (NIR and MIR) intervals. Large area images were produced for the models in a polarized light (wight) illumination with a polarizing filter (analyzer) and a camera. In addition, the rotation of the light polarization plane was quantitatively measured along selected areas of the double-side glass polymer models.

2 METHODS AND TESTS

2.1 Sample modules
The EVA and POE films were purchased from three diverse companies that were not disclosed in this text. For the experiments, the samples of the films were produced as the square shape pieces with the dimensions about 10 x 10 cm^2. The PV-module lamination process were simulated by producing the double-side glass polymer samples. The lamination process for the EVA and POE was conducted using a standardized approach with the laboratory laminator ICOLAM 18/11 (Germany). EVA and POE films were used for this.

The gel content was obtained by the Soxhlet method [3] as the marker of the process. Two specimens (~ 1 g each) were cut from two diverse areas in each of the EVA or POE test square samples with dimensions 10 x 10 cm^2. All specimens were weighed by precision balance before (the initial weight W_{ini}) and after (the final weight W_F) the extraction. Each specimen was cut into 1×1 cm^2 pieces and put into a sample flask with organic solvent. To determine the gel content of cured EVA film specimens were used ~100 ml toluene (p.a., Chempur, Poland) with 10% of butylated hydroxytoluene – BHT (≥99.7%. Carl Roth GmbH+Co. KG, Germany) antioxidant. Flasks with the contents/substance were kept in the oven at 60±1 °C for 24 h. The solvent was then decanted and all specimens were dried in an oven at 105±1 °C temperature for 4 hours. Xylene (Reag.Ph.Eur., CARLO ERBA Reagents S.A.S., France) solvent extractions were performed for the determination of the gel content of the cured polymer films.

2.2 Methods and tests
The NIR absorbance spectra were obtained from the transmittance and reflectance measurements. The spectra of optical absorbance were obtained from the measurements using a Bruker Vertex 80 spectrometer in three modes: Attenuated Total Reflectance (ATR), specular Reflectance (R), and Transmittance (T). The aluminum-coated mirror optics of the spectrometer was used for the measurements in the interval of the wavelengths from 400 nm to 60 μm. Depending on the task of the experiment, individual sets of the beam splitters and the detectors were included into the active configuration of the spectrometer.

The model samples were also analyzed in the polarized white light illumination. Large area photographs were obtained by placing the sample module between the light source and a camera with a standard polarizing filter. Before the experiments the analyzer (polarizing filter) was rotated around the central axis until the polarized light was completely quenched. In addition, the module samples were scanned point-by-point with a laser beam. The scanning was performed along the top of the sample surface and perpendicular to the sample boundaries. In these tests, the polarization plane rotation angle was measured quantitatively for the light laser light beam.

3 RESULTS AND DISCUSSIONS

3.1 Polarized light images

Large area images of the model samples visually displayed large scale deformations. Typical large area images were illustrated in Fig.1 for the model samples.

The clear and transparent image in the day light transformed into non-homogeneous picture of the combined dark-shadow-bright zones images if the deformations were presented in the polymer film. The brightness of the zones depended on the strengths of the deformations. Novel aspects about a relationship between the lamination conditions and the polymer transformations were described by combining the results of the polarized light tests and the absorbance band analysis.

The intensity of the transmitted polarized light in Fig. 1 was dependent on the rotation of the light polarization plane in the polymer film. Deep dark (even black) areas corresponded to the completely quenched illumination zone that represented the preparatory state of the experimental setup. The arrangement of the polarized light source, polarizing filter (analyzer) and camera was fixed so that the light was completely quenched after the polarizing filter and a black screen was seen without the model sample. After the sample was placed between the source and the analyzer, the bright zones appeared.

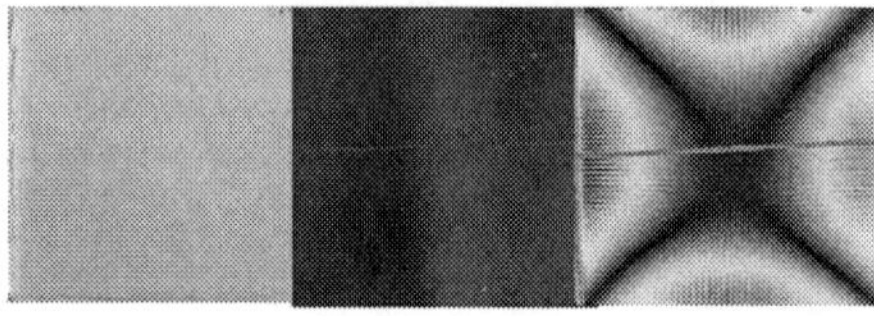

Figure 1: Model samples 10x10 cm2. Photos: in non-polarized day-light illumination (left), polarized white light (center and right)

3.2 Rotation of the polarization plane

The rotation of the polarization plane was measured using a laser beam. A profile of the rotation angle was measured by scanning the sample surface along a straight line. A sample line of such scans corresponded with the red and green lines in Fig. 1.

In these tests the laser beam was focused on the sample. Reflected beam passed through the polarizing filter (analyzer) and was pointed to the photodetector. The starting arrangement of the setup was accepted being with the analyzer position when the signal of the detector was negligible. In this case, rotation of the analyzer wit the sample fixed in the setup was equal to the polarization rotation angle produced by the sample module. Typical profiles were illustrated in Fig. 2.

It followed from the rotation angle profiles, that the deep dark zones in the polarized light images

corresponded to the negligible rotation of the polarization plane by the polymer. These zones were represented by $U_{detector} = 0$ V in Fig. 2 whereas the bright areas corresponded to high the detector responses. The rotation of the polarization plane angle was higher for the higher detected signal.

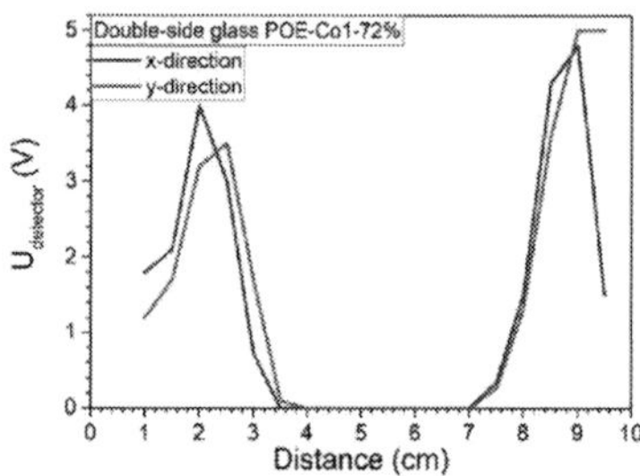

Figure 2: Signal proportional to rotation of the light polarization angle vs. distance: x-direction is along green line (right-to-left) in Fig. 1; y-direction is perpendicular to the green line

3.3 Spectra of optical absorbance

The spectra of optical absorbance were obtained from the measurements using a Bruker Vertex 80 spectrometer. During the measurements in mid-infrared interval, the setup included a Bruker A225/Q Platinum ATR single reflection diamond ATR accessory with a crystal of 2.35 mm × 2.35 mm surface area. A high-pressure clamp was employed to ensure the contact between the ATR crystal and the polymer films. The spectra were measured in the range of the wavenumbers from 8000 cm⁻¹ to 650 cm⁻¹ with the scanning step 2 cm⁻¹. A KBr beam splitter and a Globar light source were included in the setup.

It must be noted here, that 6-8 spectra were measured for each of the samples in diverse freely selected spots on the surface of an individual sample. For the spots with practically the same polarization rotation angle, the scattering of the experimental spectra obtained at the diverse spots of the same sample was lower than the differences between the samples with individual gel content. It was not applicable to the results obtained in the spots with obvious polarization angle rotation. Typical experimental results were illustrated by the NIR absorbance bands in Fig. 3.

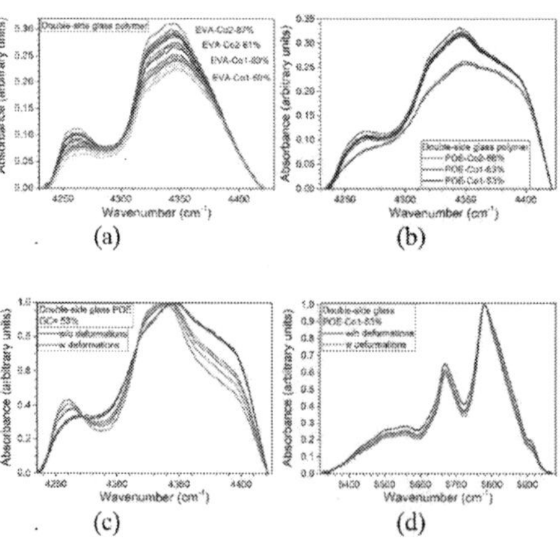

Figure 3: Near-infrared absorbance bands for (a, b) the double-side glass polymer films ((a) EVA and (b) POE) without deformations with individual gel (%) content from diverse producers (Co1 and Co2); (c, d) POE films with (w) and without (w/o) deformations.

The absorbance bands in Figs. 3(a) and 3(b) demonstrated few important aspects of the polymer transformations in the homogeneous non-deformed film zones. First, the absorbance band only slightly depended on the position across the dark area. The lines of the absorbance spectra that were quite close one to another for the same model sample. Second, the absorbance band shape was sensitive to the gel content. Third, the absorbance band shape was individual for the polymer films produced by separated companies. Fourth, the band shape was individual for EVA and POE films.

The bright zone absorbance bands proved the fact that the film deformations produced significant distortions in the band shape. The distortions were larger than the differences attributed to the properties of the polymer films.

3.4 Point defects

In addition to the large area deformations, small area defects were also detected. We used microscope with polarized light source for imaging of the pont defects in the encapsulants after the lamination.

Typical results of more precise study of the dark areas were illustrated in Fig. 4.

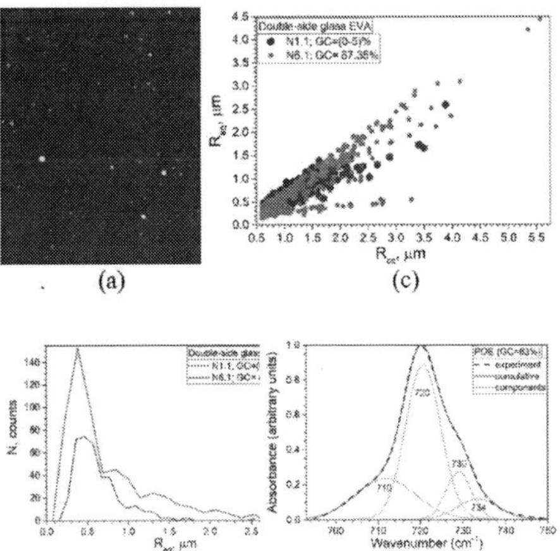

Figure 4: (a) Polarized light double-side glass EVA image in 90x90 μm² area. (b) Distribution of equivalent disc radius R_{eq} of the bright spots for two EVA model samples with individual gel content. (c) Correlation between the radius R_{eq} and minimum circumcircle radius R_{cc} of the bright spots for the EVA films. (d) Deconvolution of the absorbance band 720 cm⁻¹ with the 730 cm⁻¹ component as the crystallinity marker.

The small area images under the polarized light illumination (Fig. 4(a)) visualized the polymer crystallites as the bright spots. The distribution of the dimensions (Fig. 4(c)) proved that the density and the diameter of the crystallite increased with an increase n

the gel content after the lamination process. In addition, appearance of specific groups were detected by analysis of the correlation Req vs. Rcc in Fig. 4(c). The deconvolution of the 720 cm-1 absorbance band (Fig. 4(d)) proved an increase in the density of the polymer crystallites in the films after the lamination process.

4   SUMMARY AND CONCLUSIONS

The combinations of the characteristics extracted from the polarized light images and the absorbance bands were acceptable to identify mechanical deformations and the related mechanisms in the encapsulants after the lamination process. The detailed analysis of the properties can be carried out using the optical reflection mode. The combined description can be acceptable for control of lamination process as well as to analyze the drifts and degradation in the long term periods by non-destructive trials of the PV-modules.

It was proved that the crystallinity of the polymers increased with an increase in the gel content that depended on the lamination conditions. The crystallinity was detected from the component analysis of the absorbance band at the wavenumber 720 cm-1. The density and dimensions of the polymer crystals were evaluated from the analysis of the large area images. In these images, the polymer deformation zones were also visualized. The degree and the extent of the deformations were quantitatively described by the dependences of the polarization angle on the coordinate of the probing spot on the model surface. The MIR absorbance bands were highly dependent on the deformation suggesting a non-homogeneous transformations in the polymer encapsulants during the lamination process.

5   REFERENCES

[1] V. Fiandra, L. Sannino, C. Andreozzi, G. Flaminio, M. Pellegrino, Polymer Degradation and Stability 220 (2024) 110643.
[2] M. Landa-Pliquet, T. Bejat, M. Serasset, A. Descormes, E. Mofakhami, E. Voroshazi, Solar Energy Materials & Solar Cells, 267 (2024) 112725
[3] Ch. Hirschl et al. Solar Energy Materials & Solar Cells, 116 (2013) 203.

6   ACKNOWLEDGMENTS

This work has been co-funded under Horizon Europe project IBC4EU (GA: 101084259). Views and opinions expressed are however those of the author(s) only and do not necessarily reflect those of the European Union or CINEA. Neither the European Union nor the granting authority can be held responsible for them.

IMPROVING ULTRAVIOLET FLUORESCENCE ANALYSIS FOR PHOTOVOLTAIC ENCAPSULANT ASSESSMENT

Zonghan Jiang[1], Hugo Sanchez[1,2], Leila Mortazavifar[1,2], Ralph Gottschalg[1,2]
[1]Hochschule Anhalt University of Applied Sciences
[2]Fraunhofer Center for Crystalline Silicon Photovoltaics CSP
zonghan.jiang@hs-anhalt.de

ABSTRACT: Fluorescence spectroscopy could be used for lamination control of the PV module, but the mapping is time-consuming. Camera-based ultraviolet fluorescence (UVF) imaging has potential for rapid crosslinking degree mapping but is unreliable due to the lack of uncertainty control. Temporal instability and spatial non-uniformity of UV excitation, camera nonlinearity and noise, keep current UVF largely qualitative and limit reliable per-location quantification of lamination quality from fluorescence intensity. To address these issues, an improved methodology is presented: multi-frame acquisition and averaging reduce camera-noise uncertainty by approximately 10 times; an automated saturation-avoidance algorithms prevents the sensor from entering nonlinear response; 1 hour pre-operation of the UV excitation reduced a maximum of 18.4% fluorescence change during measurement. Furthermore, with the per-location linear response model and uniform-field simulation, errors driven by excitation-field non-uniformity are reduced from up to 60.72% (worst-case responsivity) to near zero. These combined improvements provide a reliable foundation for mapping local encapsulant crosslinking using camera-based UVF.

Keywords: Ultraviolet fluorescence, Non-uniform UV illumination, semi-quantitative UVF, Crosslinking

1 INTRODUCTION

Ultraviolet fluorescence (UVF) technology has been widely applied in the photovoltaic (PV) industry. Camera-based UVF systems with UV LEDs excitation are widely used as rapid and non-destructive tools for defect inspection [1–4], whereas UV laser excitation coupled with spectrometric detection enables more detailed monitoring of lamination quality in PV modules [5, 6]. Morlier et al. demonstrated the potential of camera-based UVF for rapid assessment of lamination quality [7], and showed that in-line monitoring in production environments is feasible.

However, current camera-based UVF systems remain predominantly qualitative and are still not able to achieve the mapping of the crosslinking degree. The previous study demonstrated that the detected fluorescence intensity is strongly dependent on local UV excitation irradiance [8]. Due to the non-uniformity of the UV illumination field, differences in fluorescence signals may arise from variations in excitation rather than intrinsic material properties. This limitation has been the primary obstacle preventing camera-based UVF from mapping the crosslinking degree of the PV module.

In addition, the limited linear range of camera sensors can cause signal saturation when fluorescence intensity exceeds the upper end of the linear range, making accurate measurement impossible [8], while the intrinsic noise of the camera leads to fluctuations in the acquired signal and leads to the wrong prediction of the crosslinking degree. Morlier et al. and Jiang et al. further reported that temperature significantly affects UVF results, introducing reproducibility issues under varying testing conditions [8, 9]. Collectively, these limitations hinder the quantitative determination of the pointwise crosslinking degree of PV module encapsulants using UVF.

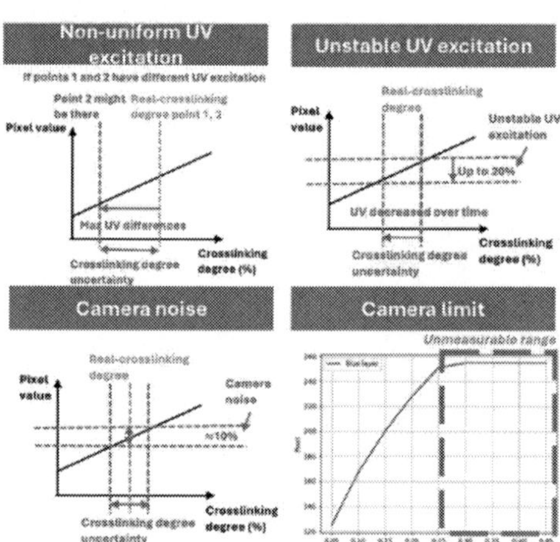

Figure 1: Uncertainty-driven variations in crosslinking degree

This work presents a comprehensive methodology to enhance the accuracy and reliability of camera-based UVF for PV encapsulant analysis. An excitation-fluorescence response model was established by capturing images under varying UV excitation levels. This mitigates the effects of spatial non-uniformity in the UV illumination field without requiring uniform illumination. Furthermore, an automated threshold-detection system was developed to prevent sensor saturation, temperature control was implemented to minimize thermally induced variations, and multi-frame averaging was employed to reduce camera noise fluctuations. These improvements enable the camera-based UVF for the crosslinking mapping, providing a foundation for inline monitoring of lamination quality and uniformity in PV module manufacturing.

2 EXPERIMENTAL SETUPS

A camera-based ultraviolet fluorescence (UVF) measurement system was developed for the experiments. The system was equipped with a 365 nm LED array combined with a bandpass filter (Peak 360nm) as the excitation light source and a Basler ace 2 a2A3840-45ucBAS camera for image acquisition. To prevent ambient light interference, the entire setup is enclosed with black blackout cloth to ensure light isolation (detailed configuration can be found in [8]). The camera operated in Bayer RG10 mode with 10-bit pixel values (0–1023). To obtain raw image data, automatic gain control, automatic white balance, and automatic exposure adjustment were all disabled, and demosaicing/color space processing was turned off. Color channel gains were set to unity (R = G = B = 1) to avoid white balance bias.

The experimental samples consist of mini-PV modules exhibiting ring-shaped UVF patterns that had undergone damp heat (DH) and UV aging to simulate encapsulant degradation.

To characterize the uniformity and stability of the illumination field, a spectrometer coupled with an XY scanning stage covering an effective area of 500 mm × 500 mm was employed to measure the light intensity distribution across the field. Additionally, a fixed UV sensor read out via an Arduino microcontroller was integrated into the UVF system to monitor illumination stability in real time.

Three temperature sensors were installed to monitor the internal environment temperature of the UVF setup as well as the sample temperature, thereby addressing temperature-induced measurement variations. The laboratory ambient temperature was strictly controlled within 20–22 °C (Sample temperature 20 – 24°C) to ensure stable experimental conditions.

The output intensity of the UV-LEDs array was regulated by an adjustable converter to allow flexible excitation control. The measurement and data acquisition process was automated via Python scripts, improving experimental efficiency and repeatability.

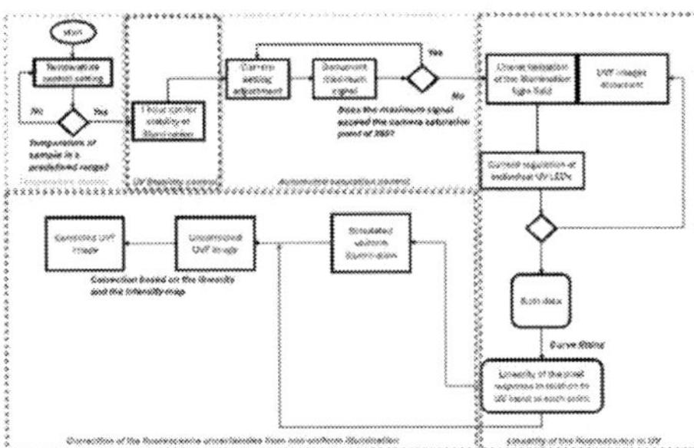

Figure 2: Workflow of the uncertainty correction

3 AUTOMATED AVOIDANCES OF SIGNAL SATURATION

Previous work established the camera's linear response range [8]; when fluorescence signals exceed this range, pixel values saturate and enter a nonlinear, non-measurable regime. To prevent such saturation, an automated exposure-control algorithm was implemented. For each acquisition, the frame-maximum pixel value is computed; if this maximum exceeds a predefined threshold (set inside the camera's linear operating region),

the exposure time is iteratively reduced to another predefined value until all pixel values fall within the linear range, and the corresponding fluorescence-crosslinking model will be selected. This procedure ensures that fluorescence measurements remain within the sensor's linear response range, preserving quantitative integrity and preventing bias introduced by nonlinear sensor behaviour.

4 CHARACTERIZATIONS OF CAMERA NOISE AND STABILITY

Camera fluctuations originate from the combined effects of various noise sources, including shot noise due to the random arrival of photons, readout noise, and dark current noise, etc, which will cause the uncertainties of the crosslinking prediction. In this study, all noise contributions are aggregated into a single total-noise term for analysis. To emulate a near worst-case noise scenario while avoiding saturation, the exposure time was set to the maximum allowable value (1s) under constant illumination and stable temperature conditions.

The camera noise level was characterized by acquiring 100 consecutive images under the constant illumination and controlled temperature, using the maximum exposure time of 1 s.

The standard deviation of pixel values was calculated according to Eq. (1), yielding σ = 169.23 DN. The average noise-signal percentage is approximately 10%.

$$s = \sqrt{\frac{1}{N-1}\sum_{i=1}^{N}(x_i - \bar{x})^2} \qquad (1)$$

If 100 images are captured and averaged per measurement, the standard error of the mean (SEM) can be estimated σ/√N (with N = 100), according to Eq. (2) [10]:

$$u = \frac{\sigma}{\sqrt{N}} \qquad (2)$$

where σ is the standard deviation (169.23 DN), and N=100 is the number of images averaged. Thus, the standard error standard error of the mean is 16.92 DN, indicating a significant reduction in measurement uncertainty through averaging.

5 UNCERTAINTIES DUE TO EXCITATION INSTABILITY AND NON-UNIFORMITY

In camera-based UVF measurement systems, the instability and non-uniformity of the UV illumination are the main reasons that make the mapping of crosslinking impossible. As a result of the mutual interactions among the intrinsic characteristics of LEDs, variations in operating temperature, and the temperature-dependent behaviour of the bandpass filter, the intensity of the UV excitation source gradually decreases during operation, thereby affecting the stability of the detected fluorescence signal and bringing uncertainty to the crosslinking degree detection.

In addition to this temporal instability, the spatial non-uniformity of the excitation field introduces another critical limitation. While the fluorescence intensity is approximately proportional to the excitation irradiance, achieving a perfectly uniform excitation field is nearly impossible in practice. Consequently, two regions with identical inherent material properties may exhibit significantly different fluorescence intensities solely due to variations in local UV excitation. Because the signal intensities at different positions cannot be reliably compared, this limitation has constrained the camera-based UVF measurements to the mapping of the crosslinking degree.

To address this issue, we propose a correction method based on the relationship between local excitation irradiance and the measured fluorescence signal. Specifically, for each spatial location, the actual excitation irradiance is measured under multiple illumination levels, while the corresponding UVF images are acquired. A linear fit between the fluorescence pixel values and the measured excitation intensity is then performed for each location. The resulting fit parameters will be used to simulate the fluorescence results for each point in the UVF images under uniform illumination conditions. The adjustable uniform illumination range defined as the maximum excitation in the weakest field to the minimum excitation in the strongest field.

5.1 Stability of the illumination field

Since the temporal stability of the excitation source is a prerequisite for reliable spatial characterization, the stability of the illumination field was first evaluated over time. A spectrometer and a fixed-position UV sensor read out via an Arduino unit were employed to continuously monitor the UV irradiance. The measurements indicated that the UV irradiance decayed by a maximum of 20% (see Fig. 3) in the 1-hour run (which could cause a maximum of 18.4% fluorescence change at the most responsive location, a 1% change in UV excitation produces a 0.92% change in fluorescence per channel pixel values), and the excitation UV source required ≈1 h after activation to reach a stable output. Consequently, all subsequent experiments were performed following a warm-up period of one hour. During data acquisition, the fixed-position UV sensor remained active to ensure consistency of the illumination field throughout the measurements.

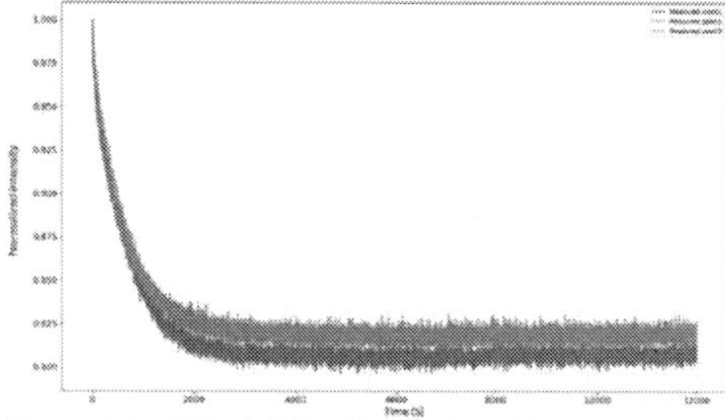

Figure 3: Stability of the illumination field over time at three points within the field

5.2 Non-uniformity of the illumination field

To quantify the impact of excitation-field non-uniformity on fluorescence measurements, spatial mapping of the UV irradiance distribution was performed. Before mapping, the UV source was preheated for one hour, and measurements were initiated only after

the UV sensor confirmed irradiance stability. The spectrometer was positioned at the same height used during UVF image acquisition to ensure consistency between fluorescence detection and excitation measurements. The UVF image resolution (3840 × 1920 pixels) was divided into a 32 × 16 measurement grid, yielding 120 × 120 pixels per cell, which is sufficient for mapping. At each grid position, the excitation intensity was recorded with the spectrometer. Since the LED spectral profile remained invariant across different output levels, the peak spectral value was taken as the representative UV excitation intensity. To suppress measurement noise, five repeated measurements were conducted at each position, and the across-repeats value was used for analysis.

The excitation-field intensity was varied by adjusting the driving current of the UV-LED source (1 A, 1.3 A, 1.5 A, 1.7 A, and 2 A). For each illumination level, 100 UVF images were acquired and averaged to determine the mean fluorescence pixel value. To ensure repeatability, a fixed-position UV sensor continuously monitored overall field stability during data acquisition.

The resulting intensity map was scaled by the same factor (i.e., 120 per axis) to match the UVF image resolution.

By multiple UV illumination level and the corresponding UVF images, a per-location linear response model (pixel value vs. excitation irradiance) is first established (see Fig. 4). Using the determined linear calibration parameters, the fluorescence images are subsequently corrected for spatial non-uniformity, thereby enabling direct and quantitative comparison of fluorescence signals across the entire field of view.

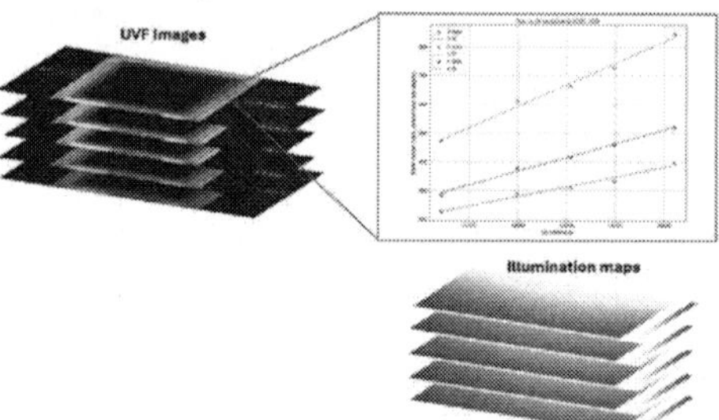

Figure 4: Per-location linear response model of fluorescence versus excitation based on multi-image UVF data and excitation-field measurements

The test results reveal pronounced non-uniformity in the UV excitation field, with the maximum-to-minimum illumination ratio reaching ≈ 166% Because the fluorescence–excitation responsivity varies across spatial locations, we adopt the maximum measured responsivity for a conservative assessment. At the most responsive location, a 1% change in UV excitation produces a 0.92% change in fluorescence per channel pixel values. Under this worst-case responsivity, the observed illumination non-uniformity can propagate to pixel-level deviations of up to 60.72% in the final image, posing a substantial risk to quantitative interpretation. This upper bound (60.72%) follows from ((Maximum-to-minimum illumination ratio − 1) * maximum local slope), using maximum-to-minimum illumination ratio R = 166% and the maximum local slope S = 0.92% (0.92%-pixel variation per 1% change in UV intensity).

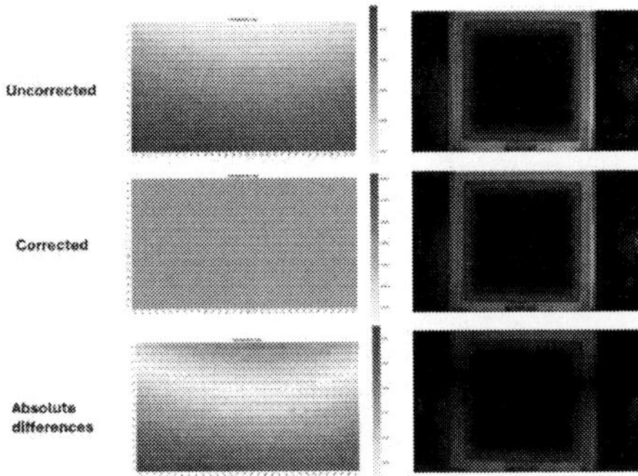

Figure 5: UV excitation irradiance maps (left) and UVF images (right), shown uncorrected, corrected, and as absolute-difference images; the absolute-difference row is displayed at 2× brightness for visibility

Figure 5 shows the uncorrected UVF image, the corrected UVF image, and the absolute-difference map between them. The correction is based on a pixel-wise linear model that captures the local dependence of fluorescence intensity on UV excitation. As evidenced by the substantial reduction in absolute differences, this approach effectively compensates for fluorescence pixel deviations arising from non-uniform excitation, producing a UVF image that is functionally equivalent to one acquired under spatially uniform UV illumination, which was achieved without physical homogenization of the UV field and provides a foundation for the mapping of the crosslinking degree of encapsulant via camera-based UVF.

6 SUMMARY

This work presents a methodology to enable camera-based UV fluorescence used for the mapping of the crosslinking degree.

The approach couples automated saturation prevention, multi-image averaging noise reduction, pre-operation of the UV excitation light source and the per-location linear response model and uniform-field simulation.

The multi-image averaging yielding ≈10× camera-noise reduction, 1 hour pre-operation of the UV excitation reduced a maximum of 18.4% fluorescence change during measurement, furthermore, with the per-location linear response model and uniform-field simulation, errors driven by excitation-field non-uniformity are reduced from up to 60.72% (worst-case responsivity) to near zero, substantially mitigating spatial bias. These combined improvements provide a reliable foundation for mapping local encapsulant crosslinking using camera-based UVF.

7 ACKNOWLEDGEMENTS

This work is supported by the Deutsche Forschungsgemeinschaft (DFG, German Research Foundation) – 467133067.

8 REFERENCES

[1] M. Köntges, A. Morlier, G. Eder, E. Fleis, B. Kubicek, and J. Lin, "Review: Ultraviolet Fluorescence as Assessment Tool for Photovoltaic Modules," *IEEE J. Photovoltaics*, vol. 10, no. 2, pp. 616–633, 2020, doi: 10.1109/JPHOTOV.2019.2961781.

[2] A. Morlier, M. Siebert, I. Kunze, G. Mathiak, and M. Kontges, "Detecting Photovoltaic Module Failures in the Field During Daytime With Ultraviolet Fluorescence Module Inspection," *IEEE J. Photovoltaics*, vol. 7, no. 6, pp. 1710–1716, 2017, doi: 10.1109/JPHOTOV.2017.2756452.

[3] C. Buerhop, O. Stroyuk, T. Pickel, J. Hauch, and I. M. Peters, "Identification of solar module behavior originating from backsheet failure - from lab studies to field tests," in *2021 IEEE 48th Photovoltaic Specialists Conference (PVSC)*, Fort Lauderdale, FL, USA, 2021, pp. 831–834.

[4] M. Köntges, S. Kajari-Schröder, and I. Kunze, "Crack Statistic for Wafer-Based Silicon Solar Cell Modules in the Field Measured by UV Fluorescence," *IEEE J. Photovoltaics*, vol. 3, no. 1, pp. 95–101, 2013, doi: 10.1109/JPHOTOV.2012.2208941.

[5] J. C. Schlothauer, C. Peter, C. Hirschl, G. Oreski, and B. Röder, "Non-destructive monitoring of ethylene vinyl acetate crosslinking in PV-modules by luminescence spectroscopy," *J Polym Res*, vol. 24, no. 12, 2017, doi: 10.1007/s10965-017-1409-y.

[6] J. C. Schlothauer, R. M. Ralaiarisoa, A. Morlier, M. Köntges, and B. Röder, "Determination of the cross-linking degree of commercial ethylene-vinyl-acetate polymer by luminescence spectroscopy," *J Polym Res*, vol. 21, no. 5, 2014, doi: 10.1007/s10965-014-0457-9.

[7] A. Morlier, M. Köntges, S. Blankemeyer, and I. Kunze, "Contact-free Determination of Ethylene Vinyl Acetate Crosslinking in PV Modules with Fluorescence Emission," *Energy Procedia*, vol. 55, pp. 348–355, 2014, doi: 10.1016/j.egypro.2014.08.101.

[8] Z. Jiang, C. Meza, H. Sanchez, and R. Gottschalg, "Evaluation of the Impact of the UV Excitation Intensity on the Ultraviolet Fluorescence Measurement System for Photovoltaics," *41st European Photovoltaic Solar Energy Conference and Exhibition*, 2024, doi: 10.4229/EUPVSEC2024/3AV.2.35.

[9] A. Morlier, M. Siebert, I. Kunze, S. Blankemeyer, and M. Kontges, "Influence of environmental conditions on UV fluorescence imaging in the field," in *2018 IEEE 7th World Conference on Photovoltaic Energy Conversion (WCPEC) (A Joint Conference of 45th IEEE PVSC, 28th PVSEC & 34th EU PVSEC)*, Waikoloa Village, HI, 2018, pp. 1309–1312.

[10] J. Lisiecki and S. Kłysz, "Estimation of Measurement Uncertainty," *Research Works of Air Force Institute of Technology*, vol. 22, no. 1, 2007, doi: 10.2478/v10041-008-0004-4

IMPROVING ULTRAVIOLET FLUORESCENCE ANALYSIS FOR PHOTOVOLTAIC ENCAPSULANT ASSESSMENT

Zonghan Jiang[1], Hugo Sanchez[1,2], Leila Mortazavifar[1,2], Ralph Gottschalg[1,2]

E-Mail: zonghan.jiang@hs-anhalt.de
[1]Hochschule Anhalt University of Applied Sciences, Bernburger Str. 55, 06366, Köthen, Germany
[2] Fraunhofer-Center for Silicon Photovoltaics CSP, Halle (Saale), Germany

Motivations

Challenge:
- ❖ Fluorescence intensity via fluorescence spectroscopy could be used for lamination control of the PV module, but the mapping is time-consuming [1].
- ❖ Camera-based UVF has potential for rapid crosslinking degree mapping, but is not yet reliable due to the lack of uncertainty control. [2].

Goal:
- ❖ Develop a methodology to enable reliable mapping of local crosslinking degree via camera-based UV fluorescence.

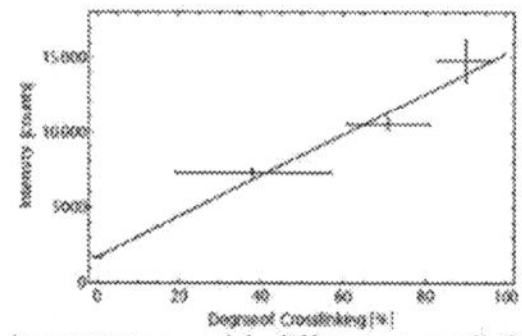

Fig. 1: Fluorescence intensity at 450 nm with different crosslinking degree and linear fit [1]

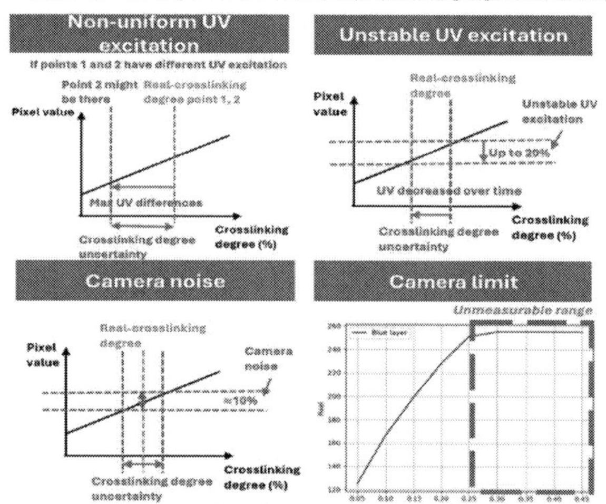

Fig. 2: Uncertainty-Driven Variations in Crosslinking Degree

Camera-related uncertainties

Solution
- ❖ Automated saturation-avoidance algorithms.
- ❖ Multi-frame acquisition (e.g., 100 frames) with averaging reduce camera-noise uncertainty by approximately a factor of 10.

UV illumination-related uncertainties

Solution for the instability of the UV illumination caused uncertainties

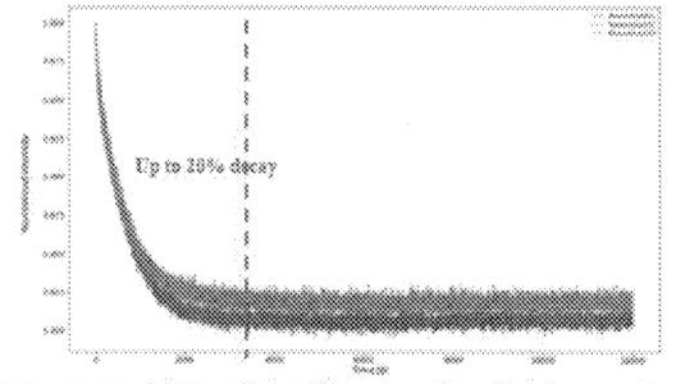

- ❖ The UV light source should be operated until the LED output stabilizes (typically ~1 hour).
- ❖ Control sensor to monitor the UV illumination stability during the measurement.

Fig. 3: Stability of the illumination field over time at three points within the field of view

Solution for non-uniform illumination caused uncertainties

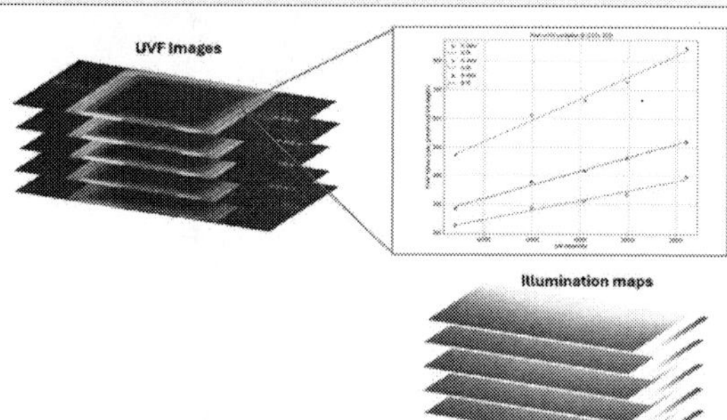

Fig. 4: Per-location linear response model of fluorescence versus excitation based on multi-image UVF data and excitation-field measurements

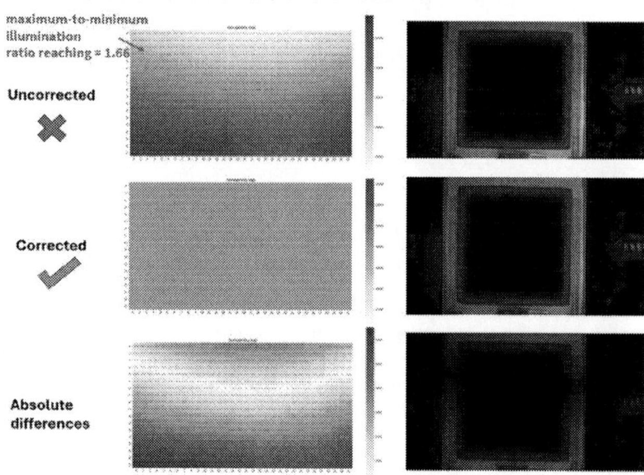

Fig. 5: UVF images and UV excitation fields before correction, after correction, and their absolute differences (Absolute-difference image displayed with brightness scaled by 2× for visualization.)

Conclusions / Key findings

- ❖ **Noise reduction:** *Multi-frame averaging decreased camera noise by 10x.*
- ❖ **UV stability:** *Pre-operating the UV source ensured stable illumination.*
- ❖ **Spatial correction:** *The per-location linear response model and uniform-field simulation corrected the uncertainties caused by non-uniform UV illumination. Enable the mapping of the crosslinking degree.*
- ❖ **Implication for crosslinking:** *These combined improvements provide a reliable foundation for mapping local encapsulant crosslinking using camera-based UVF.*

References

[1] J. C. Schlothauer, R. M. Ralaiarisoa, A. Morlier, M. Köntges, and B. Röder, "Determination of the cross-linking degree of commercial ethylene-vinyl-acetate polymer by luminescence spectroscopy," J Polym Res, vol. 21, no. 5, 2014, doi: 10.1007/s10965-014-0457-9

[2] Z. Jiang, C. Meza, H. Sanchez, and R. Gottschalg, "Evaluation of the Impact of the UV Excitation Intensity on the Ultraviolet Fluorescence Measurement System for Photovoltaics," 41st European Photovoltaic Solar Energy Conference and Exhibition, 2024, doi: 10.4229/EUPVSEC2024/3AV.2.35.

ACKNOWLEDGEMENT This work is supported by the Deutsche Forschungsgemeinschaft (DFG, German Research Foundation) – 467133067.

020159-001

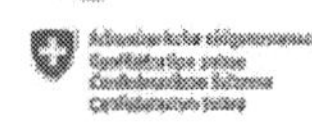

SUPSI

Institute for Applied Sustainability to the Built Environment

Evaluating Hot-Spot Stress in PV Modules under Shading: from PV System and Laboratory Data

Ebrar Özkalay[1]*, Anika Gassner[2,3], Gabriele C. Eder[2], Gabi Friesen[1], Markus Feichtner[4]

1 – SUPSI, University of Applied Sciences and Arts of Southern Switzerland, Mendrisio, Switzerland; 2 – OFI, Austrian Research Institute for Chemistry and Technology, Vienna, Austria; 3 – TU Wien, Institute for Material Scien- ce and Technology, Vienna, Austria; 4 – Sonnenkraft Energy GmbH, St.Veit a.d. Glan, Austria

Corresponding author: ebrar.oezkalay@supsi.ch

Motivation

- **Shading in the built environment** exposes PV modules to frequent and localized hot-spot stress, unlike open-field systems—raising reliability concerns beyond energy yield loss.
- **Current standard hot-spot endurance testing** (IEC 61512-2, MQT09) may underestimate real-world stress (especially in residential PV): long-term repetitive shading can cause more severe material degradation than observed in standard 1-hour to maximum 5-hour lab tests.

Indoor Hot-Spot Endurance Test

- **Hot-Spot (HS) test** performed at **standard** ($55 \pm 15\ °C$) and **extended** ($75 \pm 15\ °C$) temperature conditions
- Each module tested 3× for 5 hours → 15 hours total HS test

Module Technology	Indoor – Hot-spot endurance		Outdoor (3 years)
	55°C; 3 x 5h	75°C; 3 x 5h	BIPV & shadow mask
G/PERC/BS-1	1	1	1 (Insulated)
G/IBC/BS	1	1	1 (Insulated)
G/HJT/BS	1	1	1 (Insulated)
G/PERC/G	1	1	-
G/PERC/BS-2	1	1	-
G/TOPCon/G	1	1	-

Outdoor Accelerated Ageing using Shadow Mask

- **Outdoor accelerated ageing** using a **36% transmittance shadow mask**
- Shadowing adjusted to achieve **10 ± 5% difference** between global maximum power (low V) and local maximum power (high V) → **diode activation**

PV System—Field Experience

- **G/EVA/BS Al-BSF modules** after **11 years** of rooftop operation in Cfb Köppen-Geiger climate (warm, humid, warm summer)
- **Regular partial shading** on some modules due to rooftop signage

Temperature Analysis of Indoor Hot Spot Endurance Test

- **HJT & TOPCon:** Highest hot spot temperatures → higher power dissipation in reverse
- **IBC:** Lowest hot spot temperature → low breakdown voltage (V_{BR}) limits dissipation [1]
- **PERC:** Hot spot-to-module ΔT increases with temperature → V_{BR} becomes more negative (see the I–V curves below)

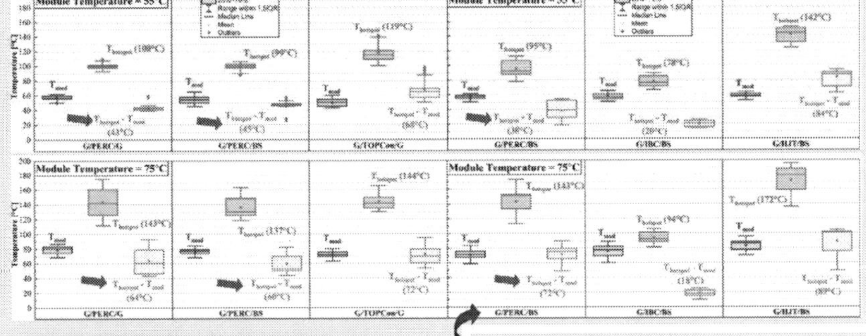

Degradation Analysis:

- **EVA Discolouration:** Significant yellowing observed in the shaded module (ΔE = 4, Δb > 3) compared to the non-shaded module (ΔE < 1).
- **Chemical Analysis:** Acetate compounds detected in the shaded area via thermal desorption (TC GC/MS), indicates higher operating temperatures.
- **Front Metallization Corrosion:** Corrosion visible in the shaded region, confirmed by EL imaging.
- **Backsheet Degradation:** PVDF outer layer shows more pronounced degradation in the shaded area (not shown).

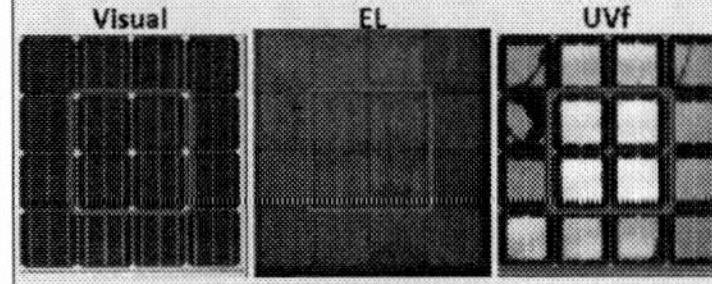

I–V curves of individual cells measured under shadow mask conditions used in the hot spot test:

Temperature increase cause more negative V_{BR}

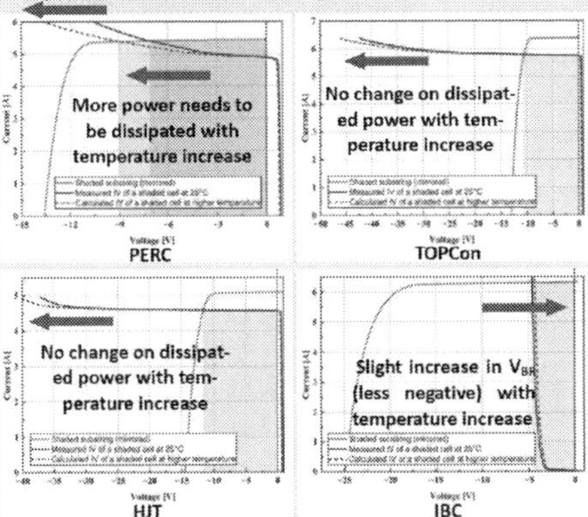

- **Avalanche breakdown (PERC, TOPCon and HJT):** $V_{BR} \downarrow$ with ↑ temperature (positive temp. coefficient) [2]
- **Zener breakdown (IBC):** $V_{BR} \uparrow$ with ↑ temperature (negative temp. coefficient) [1]

G/PERC/BS-1 Module

- **Discolouration i n outdoor shadow-masked module:**
  - **EVA:** ΔE = 7.7, Δa > 2.3 (red)
  - **PVDF/PET/PE backsheet:** ΔE = 12.5, Δb > 11.5 (yellowing)
  - ΔE < 1 in non-shaded and indoor HS-tested modules
- **PET layer:** Thermal degradation of the PET core layer can be detected after outdoor shadow mask and, to lower extent, for the HS test 143°C (see PET core layer spectra)
- **Adhesive degradation:** The adhesive layer between PVDF and PET is degrading in parallel to the thermal stress applied leading to delamination after outdoor shadow mask for 3 years [3, 4] (see ATR, attenuated total reflectance images)

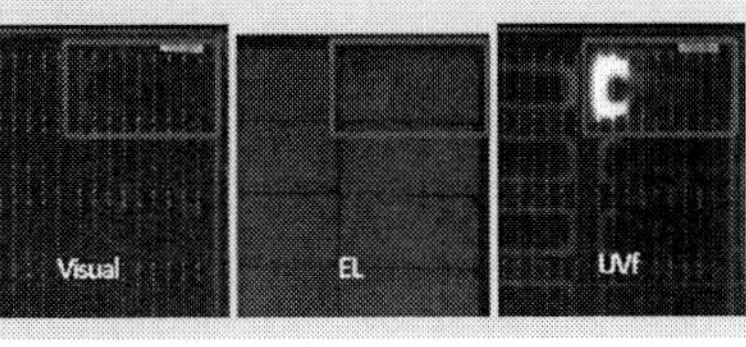

PET Core Layer Spectra

ATR Image of the backsheets: Compare correlation with adhesive spectra

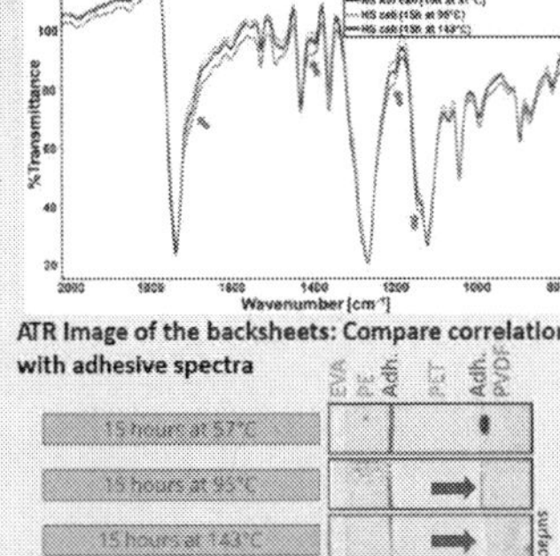

Summary

- **Persistent shading** leads to **gradual degradation** of encapsulant and backsheet materials, increasing long-term **reliability risks** in PV modules.
- **Indoor HS tests**, even at 75°C for 15 hours, **fail to replicate** the degradation observed in real-world or outdoor accelerated ageing — **except for backsheet adhesive degradation** after 15 hours at 75°C.
- **PERC modules** may reach **higher hot spot temperatures** with increasing operating temperatures if their breakdown voltage falls within the series-connected substring voltage range.
- **Ongoing analysis** focusses on identifying a **reliable degradation indicator** aligned with observed **outdoor module behavior.**

References:
[1] H. Chu et al (2015), 10.1016/j.egypro.2015.07.006
[2] F. Fertig et al. (2013), 10.1016/j.egypro.2013.07.246
[3] Y. Voronko et al. (2014), 10.1366/13-07291
[4] Y. Voronko et al. (2015), 10.1002/pip.2580

SALT SPRAY CORROSION RESISTANCE TESTING AND RELIABILITY EVALUATION OF LARGE-SIZE SOLAR MODULES AND METAL COMPONENTS

3AV.2

San-Yu Ting, Huan-Wu Lu, Syh-Homg Chen, Min-An Tsai, Cho-Fan Hsieh
Center for Measurement Standards, Industrial Technology Research Institute, Hsinchu 310, Taiwan
jackting@itri.org.tw; kuanwu@itri.org.tw; shuhing@itri.org.tw, MATsai@itri.org.tw; hsiehchofan@itri.org.tw

This study evaluates salt spray resistance of large PV modules (M6, M10, BIPV) and fasteners under IEC 60068-2-52. M10 showed higher power loss, while BIPV performed better. Stainless steel resisted corrosion best but caused galvanic effects; galvanized steels sacrificed protection but corroded faster; zinc-tin alloy was moderate. Improving encapsulation, sealing, and using coated or insulated fasteners can enhance durability in coastal environments.

Keywords: Large-Size PV Modules, Salt Spray Corrosion, Durability Enhancement.

Aim and Approach

This study evaluates the corrosion resistance and reliability of large-size PV modules and metal fasteners in salt spray environments, offering insights into long-term stability in high-salinity regions. Test samples include M6, M10 (single/dual glass), and BIPV corrugated modules, along with electro-galvanized, hot-dip galvanized, zinc-tin alloy, and stainless steel fasteners. Following IEC 60068-2-52, a platform was developed for modules over 2.1 m, simulating cyclic salt spray, drying, and humidity.

The testing process—from sample installation (Figure 1) to reliability evaluation (Figure 2)—assesses power degradation, insulation resistance, and structural integrity. Corrosion analysis of fasteners includes weight loss and surface deterioration. Findings highlight the importance of optimizing encapsulation, improving sealing, and selecting durable materials to enhance long-term reliability of PV systems in coastal environments.

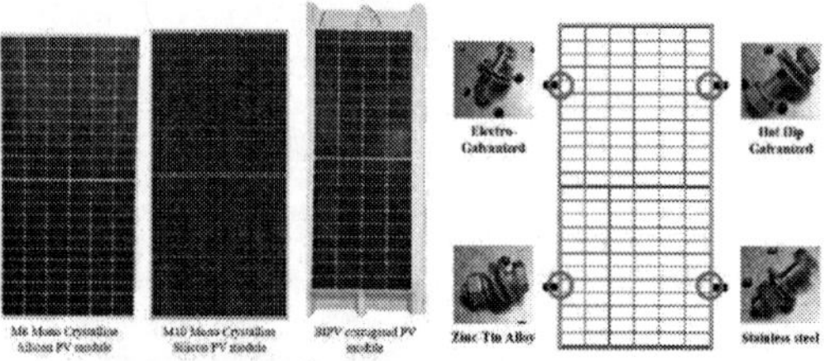

Figure 1: Large size PV module and metal component erection

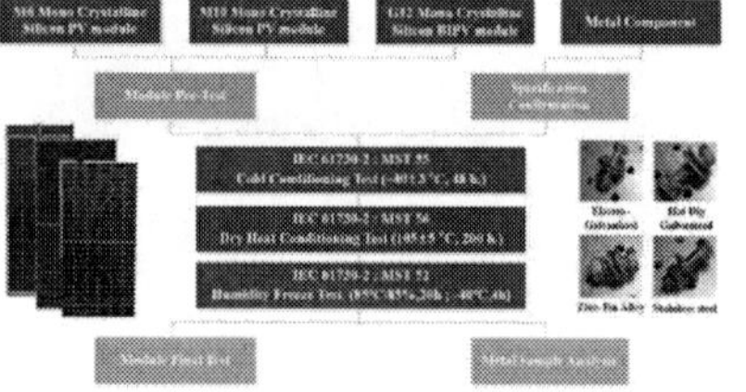

Figure 2: Flowchart of large size PV module and component reliability evaluation testing

Research Results

Preliminary results show that large-size PV modules degrade in salt spray environments, with durability strongly influenced by module type and encapsulation materials. As shown in Figure 3, M10 modules suffered greater power loss than M6 due to encapsulant deterioration and chloride infiltration, while BIPV modules maintained better stability, underscoring the value of optimized encapsulation.

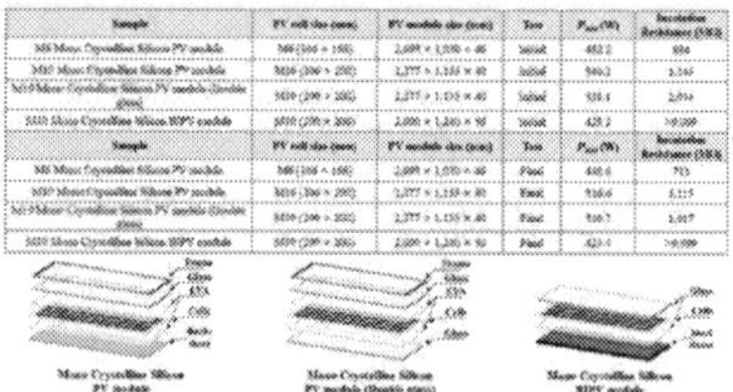

Figure 3: Power measurement results before and after testing for large-size modules

For fasteners, four common metals were tested. As shown in Figure 4, hot-dip and electro-galvanized fasteners provided sacrificial protection but corroded heavily, stainless steel offered the best resistance yet caused localized galvanic corrosion, and zinc-tin alloy demonstrated relatively stable performance, making it a suitable option for high-salinity environments.

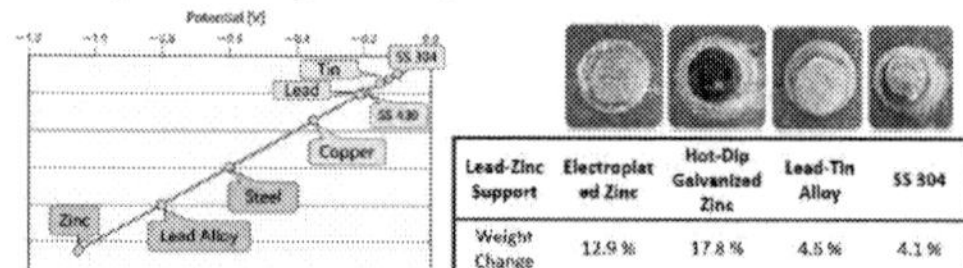

Lead-Zinc Support	Electroplated Zinc	Hot-Dip Galvanized Zinc	Lead-Tin Alloy	SS 304
Weight Change	12.9 %	17.8 %	4.5 %	4.1 %

Figure 4: Before and after weight comparison of commonly used metal fasteners in testing

Acknowledgments

This study was successfully conducted with the support of Energy Administration, Ministry of Economic Affairs, R.O.C., for which we express our sincere gratitude.

References

1. IEC 61730-2:2023, Photovoltaic (PV) module safety qualification – Part 2: Requirements for testing.
2. IEC 61215-2:2021, Terrestrial photovoltaic (PV) modules - Design qualification and type approval - Part 2: Test procedures.
3. CNS 14122, Corrosion of metals and alloys-Removal of corrosion products from corrosion test specimens
4. CNS 15753, Corrosion of metals and alloys-Corrosivity of atmospheres-Classification, determination and estimation

Conclusion

Power stability of large-size PV modules in salt spray conditions depends on encapsulation quality and frame sealing, while fastener durability relies on material and surface protection. Optimizing encapsulation, enhancing sealing, and selecting corrosion-resistant fasteners such as stainless steel or zinc-tin alloy with protective coatings can effectively extend service life and ensure reliable operation in high-salinity environments.

Analysis of Performance Loss in PV Systems due to Cracked Backsheets and Insulation Problems

Raffael Schifferegger [1,2], Yuliya Voronko [1], Anika Gassner [1,3], Gabriele C. Eder [1]
[1] OFI, Austrian Research Institute for Chemistry and Technology, Vienna, Austria;
[2] TU Wien, Institute of Applied Physics, Vienna, Austria;
Corresponding author: gabriele.eder@ofi.at

Motivation

See also Poster 3.AV2.14 on „Restoring the Functionality of Damaged PV-Backsheets"

While PV systems generate clean energy throughout their operational lifetime, their sustainability across the full lifecycle requires further attention. Manufacturing remains resource-intensive, but todays modules with m-cry Si-technology installed and manufactured in Europe can achieve a energy payback time of round one year. However, dealing with early-failing modules, potential repair and reuse as second-life modules, and end-of-life (EOL) management are becoming increasingly challenging—especially as PV waste volumes are expected to rise sharply in the coming decades.

Addressing module failures through repair strategies can extend module lifetimes, reduce waste, and decrease the need for premature replacements.

One major failure type of PV modules is the degradation of the backsheet, which serves as an electrical insulator and protective layer of a PV module laminate. Cracks in the backsheet can lead to reduced insulation resistance ($R_{iso\,wet}$), triggering inverter shutdowns to prevent electrical hazards on the one hand but resulting in reduced energy production on the other hand.

Thus, a study was performed investigating the occurrence of insulation-related inverter failures and quantifies their impact on energy production.

A	As good as new, only small scratches etc.
B	Encapsulant and/or backsheet discoloration, minor delamination
C	Snail trails with < 10% module power loss
D	Cracked cells with < 10% module power loss
E	Failed bypass diode(s) that can be replaced (no potting)
F	Damaged junction boxes and/or cabling that should be replaced
G	Modules with severe power loss caused by PID
H	Cracked back sheet/severe scratches in back sheet that could be repaired
I	Unacceptable module damage that cannot be repaired: broken glass, hot spots / burn marks, excessive delamination, broken interconnects or poor soldering, corrosion, cracked cells with > 10% module power loss.

Table 1: Classification matrix for PV modules triage and eligibility for repair/reuse.
Toward Reuse-Ready PV: A Perspective on Recent Advances, Practices, and Future Challenges
Wiley; Adv Energy and Sustain Res, 2024, DOI: 10.1002/aesr.202400237

Approach

The polymeric backsheet of a PV-module protects the internal components from environmental stresses and provides electrical insulation. Over time, environmental stressors such as UV radiation, temperature fluctuations, and mechanical loads can degrade the backsheet (dependent of the materials used), leading to delaminations, discolouration, cracks and insulation failures. Some failures impact the systems safety leading to inverter shutdowns and - on the long run – to underperformance.

→ A more detailed understanding of these inverter failures/shutdowns can help estimate the potential power loss and costs (financial impact of downtime) associated with not repairing defective modules and provides a clear economic rationale for repair strategies.

Repairing backsheets presents a viable solution to extend module lifetimes and reduce environmental impact by delaying the need for new materials and energy-intensive replacements.

Figure 1: PV-System in Koper/Slovenia with cracked backsheets; Monitoring data for the period 2016-2024; BAPV system

Analysis of Monitoring Data / Inverter Failures

Insulation resistance ($R_{iso\,wet}$) measures the ability of the module's encapsulation and backsheet to prevent leakage currents between the active electrical components and the grounded frame. Cracks in the backsheet reduce insulation resistance, especially in high humidity, and increase the likelihood of leakage currents that trigger the inverter's safety shutdown.

Safety-related inverter shutdown due to too low insulation resistance leads to power outages

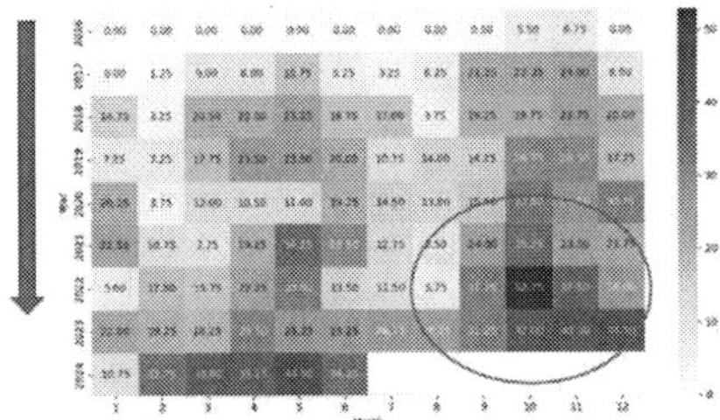

Figure 2: Monthly downtime (in hours) for inverter 1. The color intensity represents the magnitude of downtime, with darker colors indicating longer durations.

Downtime caused by inverter shutdown (Error 41)

Measurement period: 01.2016 - 07.2024 :

- increasing frequency of inverter failure E41
- Increased occurrence from 2020 (5-6 y of operation)
- Seasonality: more downtime in spring and especially fall

Comparison of humidity before the occurrence of the inverter error

- Humidity significantly higher on downtime days
- downtime days vs. reference days H: 83% vs. 65%

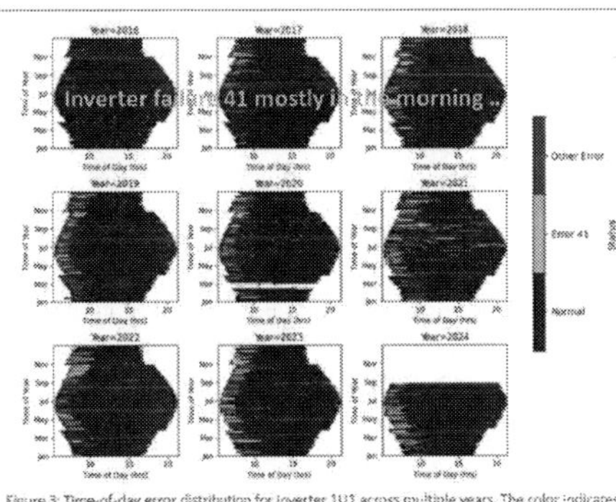

Figure 3: Time-of-day error distribution for inverter 1U1 across multiple years. The color indicates the inverter status: normal operation (blue), error 41 (orange), and other errors (purple).

Calculated Energy loss → Underperformance

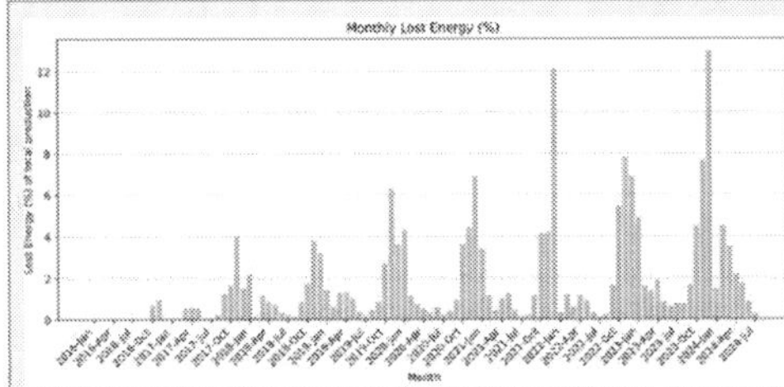

Figure 4: Calculated energy loss due to inverter shutdown; data available 2016 - 07.2024, Error 41 = inverter shutdown

Underperformance not very high (1,7% / year) BUT: safety issues !

Figure 5: Yearly energy production and lost energy due to the inverter shutdown under low insulation resistance. Percentage values indicate lost energy as a fraction of total production.

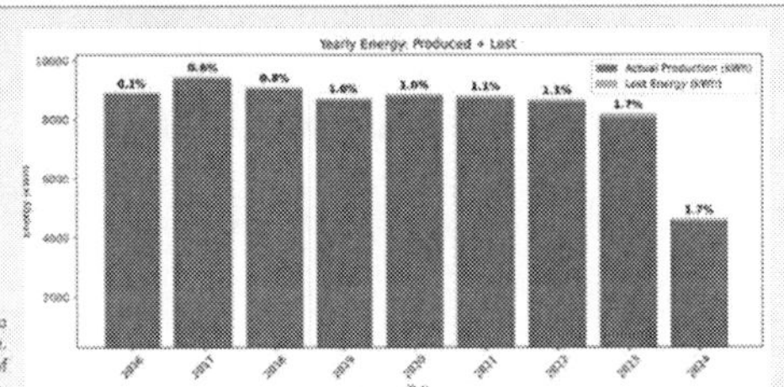

Conclusions

Serious defects (deep cracking) in the polymer backsheet of a PV module can

- pose a serious safety risk (loss of insulation strength; $R_{iso\,wet}$ breakdown),
- reduce the electrical performance of a PV module (penetration of water vapor and oxygen into the encapsulation -> solar cell -> corrosion of cell; degradation of encapsulant),
- lead to financial losses (increased inverter downtime) – especially under humid/wet conditions

Thus, the effected modules have to be replaced (and sent as EoL module to recycling) or can be repaired.

A specific repair technology or approach that can offer backsheet repair without compromising the module's performance, can be a game-changer for the PV industry. Repair coatings and tapes/foils have been developed and tested for their long-term stability:

- Repair options for PV modules with cracked polyamide backsheets; Yuliya Voronko, et al.; Energy Science & Engineering 2021 DOI: 10.1002/ese3.936; and IEEE PVSC 48 2021.
- Repair and Preventive Maintenance of PV Modules with Degrading Backsheets Using Flowable Silicone Sealant; Guy Beaucarne, et al., EU PVSEC 2021 5.DO.2.6. and PIP3492; DOI: 10.1002/pip.3492
- Towards reuse-ready PV: A perspective on recent advances, practices and future challenges; I.A. Tsanakas, et al., Adv Energy Sustainability Res. 2024; doi.org/10.1002/aesr.202400237

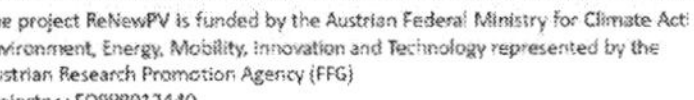

The project ReNewPV is funded by the Austrian Federal Ministry for Climate Acti Environment, Energy, Mobility, Innovation and Technology represented by the Austrian Research Promotion Agency (FFG)
Projectnr.: FO999912440

RESEARCH ON THE IMPACT OF OUTDOOR DUST ACCUMULATION AND COPPER-ACCELERATED ACETIC ACID SALT SPRAY ON SOLAR PHOTOVOLTAIC MODULES

3AV.2

San-Yu Ting, Yung-Jen Shyong, Min-An Tsai, Cho-Fan Hsieh

Center for Measurement Standards, Industrial Technology Research Institute, Hsinchu 310, Taiwan

jackting@itri.org.tw; ryanshyong@itri.org.tw; MATsai@itri.org.tw; hsiehchofan@itri.org.tw

With limited land, Taiwan increasingly adopts water-based PV. The 100 MW Changbin plant faces humidity, salt, and coastal dust, causing faster efficiency loss than inland sites. This study establishes an outdoor platform to evaluate dust and humidity effects, verify cleaning methods, and reduce costs. CASS accelerated corrosion tests further reveal dust–material interactions. Results on power loss, corrosion, and insulation aim to guide durable PV design for offshore use and provide industry strategies for cleaning and maintenance.

Keywords: Dust Accumulation, Corrosion Resistance, PV Reliability.

Aim and Approach

The primary objective of this research is to assess the impact of environmental stressors, such as dust accumulation and salt corrosion, on the long-term reliability of PV modules deployed in high-risk coastal areas. The study aims to:

a. Evaluate power loss and efficiency degradation caused by prolonged outdoor dust exposure and re-accumulation cycles.
b. Investigate corrosion mechanisms of different metallic components through accelerated CASS testing under simulated harsh conditions.
c. Identify effective mitigation and cleaning strategies to enhance module durability, reduce maintenance frequency, and optimize lifecycle costs.

To achieve these objectives, an experimental platform was established, combining long-term outdoor exposure testing with laboratory-based CASS testing. PV modules were systematically exposed to coastal environments characterized by high humidity, salt-laden air, and dust-laden winds, followed by corrosion resistance evaluation under controlled CASS testing conditions (Refer to Figure 1). The study integrates power performance measurements, electroluminescence (EL) imaging, insulation resistance evaluation, and structural integrity analysis to provide comprehensive insights into degradation pathways. These results are expected to support the development of more resilient PV designs and inform industry stakeholders in formulating practical maintenance and reliability strategies.

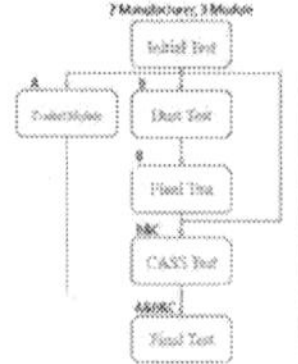

Figure 1: Experimental Procedure of this Study (Left), Outdoor Dust Test (Center), CASS Test Records (Right)

Research Results

The experimental results indicate that outdoor dust accumulation leads to a measurable decline in power generation efficiency. Manufacturer A's modules exhibited a 3% power loss, while Manufacturer B's modules showed a 1.5% loss after one month of exposure (Refer to Figure 2). This suggests that dust accumulation affects different module designs to varying extents, potentially due to differences in surface coatings, frame materials, or encapsulation methods. Post-CASS testing, no significant electrical degradation was observed; however, visual inspections revealed varying degrees of corrosion on metal frames and module surfaces, particularly in areas where dust had accumulated before exposure to the corrosive environment (Refer to Figure 3). The presence of fine dust particles may have enhanced the retention of moisture and corrosive agents, accelerating material degradation.

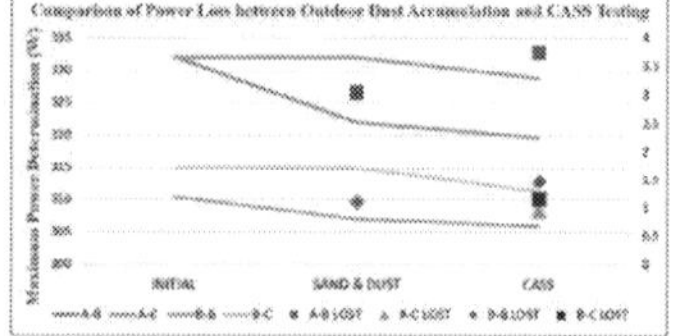

Figure 2: Power measurement results before and after testing for large-size modules

Figure 3: From Left to Right: (1) A Manufacturer Dust + CASS, (2) A Manufacturer CASS Only, (3) B Manufacturer Dust + CASS, (4) B Manufacturer CASS Only

Acknowledgments

This study was successfully conducted with the support of Energy Administration, Ministry of Economic Affairs, R.O.C., for which we express our sincere gratitude.

References

1. IEC 60068-2-68:1994, Environmental testing - Part 2-68: Tests - Test L: Dust and sand.
2. ISO 9227:2022, Corrosion tests in artificial atmospheres Salt spray tests
3. Hussain, Athar, Ankit Batra, and Rupendra Pachauri. "An experimental study on effect of dust on power loss in solar photovoltaic module." Renewables: Wind, Water, and Solar 4.1 (2017): 9.

Conclusion

This study demonstrates that while dust alone has limited short-term effects, its interaction with salt-laden environments significantly accelerates corrosion, particularly in aluminum frames, and contributes to insulation decline. These findings highlight the need for periodic cleaning, protective measures, and alternative materials to ensure durability in coastal PV systems. Future work will refine predictive models and explore advanced anti-corrosion treatments to further enhance long-term reliability.

TEXT-TO-IMAGE AND IMAGE-TO-IMAGE AUGMENTATION AND CLASSIFICATION OF DEFECTS IN PHOTOVOLTAIC MODULES

M. Waqar Akram[a,b*], Jianbo Bai[a*], Anees Ur Rehman[c]
[a]School of Renewable Energy, Hohai University, Changzhou, Jiangsu, China
[b]School of Electrical and Power Engineering, Hohai University, Nanjing, Jiangsu, China
[c]College of Mechanical and Electrical Engineering, Hohai University, Changzhou, Jiangsu, China
*Correspondence: waqarakramuaf@gmail.com, (M. W. Akram), bai_jianbo@hhu.edu.cn (J. Bai)

ABSTRACT: The autonomous photovoltaic (PV) monitoring is an emerging field with potential application in large-scale PV farms to maximize their output and reliability. However, it experiences several critical challenges like limited data constraints, intricate data collection and insufficient performance on unseen data in unknown working conditions. Addressing these challenges, the present study explores text-to-image and image-to-image synthetic data generation methods. The synthetic electroluminescence (EL) images are generated using Stable Diffusion (text-to-image) and Style Generative adversarial Networks, StyleGAN (image-to-image) variants. The real and synthetic data combinations are then used for solo and mixed training experiments that demonstrated enhanced (highest) classification performance with text-to-image data augmentation followed by image-to-image augmentation and real data. Moreover, a hybrid classification architecture based on MobileNetv3 small and YOLOv11 is proposed that achieved enhanced precision, recall and accuracy of 94.3 %, 87.3 % and 91.3 % respectively compared to baseline and other models. The introduction of inverse and effective sampling along with class weighting is also studied to handle class imbalance. This study explored synthetic data generation methods and proposed a classification architecture to improve the performance of autonomous PV monitoring as well as addresses limited volume and diverse data constraints, simplifying the data acquisition process.
Keywords: Photovoltaic (PV) modules, Defect detection, Generative AI, Text-to-image generation, Electroluminescence (EL) images

1 INTRODUCTION

With the exponential global expansion of Photovoltaic (PV) technology and ongoing development of large-scale PV farms, the autonomous and intelligent monitoring has become an integral aspect of PV systems to optimize their operation, performance and reliability [1,2]. The PV systems require continuous and fast monitoring as they are exposed to several environmental and climatic stresses and factors throughout their entire life. Regarding this, PV systems intelligence has caught significant attention of researchers globally and has been studied widely using classical computer vision and deep learning based methods [3]. The classical computer vision usually includes image processing and feature engineering based methods, that were mainly studied for classification of defects [4]. They can also be adapted for detection or localization and segmentation of defects [5]. However, they offered limited and multi-stage (fragmented) applications. These methods lack generalization, wide defects coverage, large-scale application, and real-time inference [6].

In recent years, deep learning based methods demonstrated broad prospects and achieved remarkable progress in PV systems intelligence [7]. They overcome many existing limitations and widely applied for classification [8,9], detection [10,11] and segmentation [12,13] tasks of defects as well as studied for real-time application and deployment on edge devices [14,15]. As a fundamental component of these systems, the robustness and generalization of models trained for these systems has a direct and significant impact on their practical and in-field applications. In practical and outdoor environments, PV cells and modules often experience multiple degradation stages, multi-scale defects, susceptibility to interference with examination background, complex lighting conditions, unseen rare data and other detection challenges [16]. Moreover, there are different types and designs of cells, modules and other components that make

detection more challenging.

One of the factors behind these challenges is volume and diversity limited data available for training these models, as these methods are data-driven and heavily relies on data size, diversity and other characteristics for their robust and generalized application. Data collection is an intricate and costly process requiring expertise, specific conditions, and instrumentation, particularly for Electroluminescence (EL) imaging, which is considered as one the most-effective methods. These factors, in turn, leads to limiting the diversity and size of data, which has a significant impact on training, robustness and generalization of detection systems. They particularly suffer with performance constraints upon application on unseen data in unknown working conditions, limiting their application in the field.

Consequently, these data and practical limitations have become a critical issue in this field. In recent years, synthetic data generation through integration of language (textual descriptions) with images (visual) data marked several advancements and achieved highly realistic generation, simplifying data acquisition and related constraints [17,18]. These advancements are associated with capturing long-range dependencies through introduction of self-attention mechanism and transformer model [19], which has enabled to manage the generation and understanding in Large Language Models (LLMs) and Natural Language Processing (NLP). These developments lead to highly realistic images generation by text-to-image models like Recraft, DALL-E, Ideogram, Midjourney, Flux, and Stable Diffusion, that have learnt millions and billions of text-image pairs [20]. These models are widely used in many domains for data creation and performance augmentation including Agriculture, Remote sensing, Digital Media, Medical, and others. Similarly, there are wide prospects for text-to-image models application in PV intelligence, but they need to be explored yet. On the other hand, image-to-image models also have potential application for synthetic PV data creation. Image-to-image models like Generative adversarial network (GAN) based methods were developed in few studies and demonstrated performance gains in PV monitoring intelligence [21–23]. Both these text-to-image and image-to-image models uses deep learning for generating images and their difference lies in the architectures, algorithms and inputs. They offered different output quality, source replication, resemblance, variability, object coverage, customization, control, usability, and resource efficiency in different contexts of real data like image complexity, presence of multiple objects and backgrounds, data size, and others [24,25]. These factors, in turn demand the exploration of their application in PV domain and evaluation of generated data to assess their representation of real environment.

In this light, this study aims to explore text-to-image and image-to-image synthetic data generation methods for their application in autonomous PV monitoring. It explores Stable Diffusion and StyleGAN variants for text-to-image and image-to-image generation of EL images of PV modules respectively. The generated and real data is then used for mixed and solo training experiments. Moreover, a hybrid classification architecture based on MobileNetv3 and YOLOv11 is proposed that achieved enhanced accuracy of 91.3 %. The proposed architecture is compared with baseline and several other models i.e. MobileNetv3, YOLOv11, EfficientNet, ConvNext, Vision Transformer, Swin Transformer, ResNet, YOLOv8, and YOLOv12. The introduction of inverse and effective sampling along with class weighting is also studied to handle class imbalance.

2 METHODOLOGY

2.1 Text-to-image generation

For text-to-image generation, Stable Diffusion models [17,18] from study [26] are used for generation of images including stable diffusion iterations v1, 2, and XL. These models are based on forward diffusion and reverse diffusion i.e. denoising processes which are carried out in latent space, and guided by text prompt-to-image conditioning. The supervised real data in text-image pairs form i.e. textual descriptions along with corresponding images is used to train these networks. Seed, guidance scale, inference steps, mixed/blended prompts, and negative prompts are used for generating diverse data. For instance, the seed, guidance scale, and inference steps are varied between 0 to 200, 5 to 15, and 20 to 60 respectively. Additionally, mixed prompts mentioning multiple defects with variations in numbers and severities of defects, and negative prompts mentioning low quality, unclear, blurriness, and other undesired guiding words are used.

2.2 Image-to-image generation

For text-to-image generation, StyleGAN [27] iterations from study [23] including StyleGAN2, and StyleGAN3-T (Translation equiv.), and StyleGAN3-R (Rotation and Translation equiv.) are used for generation of images. These models are based on generator and discriminator networks. They are trained from unsupervised real EL images data of normal operating and defective PV modules. Truncation and seeds are varied between 0.3 to 1.7 and 0 to 999 respectively to generate large number of images by these models.

2.3 Classification

2.3.1 Training data

This study used real data, text-to-image generated data (section 2.1) and image-to-image generated data (section 2.2) for training experiments. The real data used in this study consists of total 964 images including 472 defective and 492 normal operating modules. 836 images are taken from a from a public dataset [28] and remaining 128 images are collected from EL imaging experiments. The complete data is openly shared on Kaggle data hub [See data availability statement]. These modules are of different brands having different designs of cells, modules and other components. The defective modules cover multiple defects including cracks, black edges, low cells, finger or grid interruptions, dark cells, breaks, contamination, and backsheet scratches.

Each text-to-image and image-to-image generated data consists of total 600 images of normal and defective modules. The incremental augmentation (training with incremental data proportions from 100 to 600 in steps of 100) for both synthetic datasets lead to selection of only defective images (300 for each case). The text-to-image generated module images have cracks, black edges, low cells, black cells and breaks. The image-to-image generated module images have black edges, low cells, contamination, black cells, and breaks.

The synthetic datasets are then used to augment real data. The real and synthetic images are used for solo and mixed training experiments in following solo and mixed formations i.e. (1) real data (2) real+text-to-image synthetic mix, and (3) real+image-to-image synthetic mix. The details of each data category or combination are given in table I.

Table I: Data combinations used for solo and mixed training experiments

Module/ Data category	Real image data (solo)	Text-to-image data	Image-to-image data	Real+ Text-to-image	Real+ Image-to-image
Total	964	300	300	1264	1264
Normal	492	0	0	492	492
Defective	472	300	300	772	772

2.3.2 Proposed classification architecture

Initially, we studied YOLOv11 variants for classification of PV modules, which results in higher efficiency by YOLOv11 Nano variant when trained from pre-trained ImageNet weights. Focusing further on improved feature extraction, subtle defects, light-weight application, and better generalization, we studied different architectural backbones i.e. ConvNeXt, EfficientNetV2, Swin Transformer, Vision Transfomer, MobileNetV3, ShuffleNetV2, and ResNet. Moreover, we also carried out experimentation with other YOLO family models whose classification pipelines are available. Based on the above models training, error analysis from the misclassifications by the models and limitation by the data size, we proposed a hybrid architecture based on MobileNetv3 [29] and YOLOv11 [30], which is shown in figure 1.

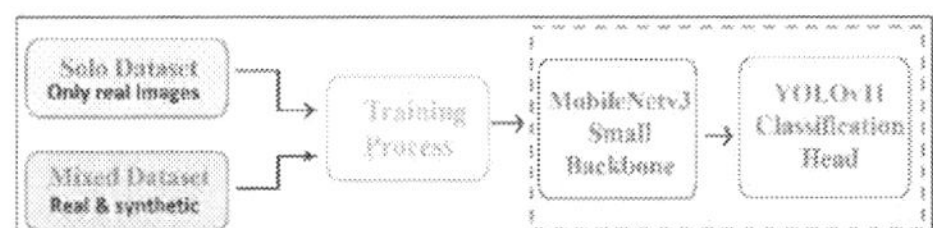

Figure 1: Overall methodology of this study and proposed architecture

This proposed architecture employs a MobileNetv3-Small backbone which makes it efficient as well as light weight. Originally the MobileNet introduced a depth-wise separable convolution technique consisting of depth-wise and point-wise convolution layers for filtering the input channels and combining their output to create a new feature respectively, which results in reduced computation and model size compared to conventional convolution operation. Later the MobileNetv2 introduced inverted residuals blocks and linear bottlenecks that further improve the efficiency as well as reduce the complexity. The inverted residuals block starts with a bottleneck having a smaller number of channels followed by expansion to larger number of channels instead of direct connection with layers having large number of channels. The MobileNetv3 combines the existing versions and uses Platform-aware NAS, NetAdapt, Squeeze-and-Excite (SE) modules, and H-Swish activation for developing an enhanced network. It has two large and small versions and we used MobileNetV3-Small in our proposed architecture as it provides excellent results with low resources compared to MobileNetV3-Large.

The platform-aware neural architecture search (NAS) helps in optimization of the architecture complimented with NetAdapt to fine-tune the layers. The Squeeze-and-Excite (SE) modules improves feature learning and network accuracy with a small increase in number of parameters. The nonlinearity H-Swish activation, a harder version of swish function improves the model efficiency as the original Swish function is computationally expensive for edge or embedded environments.

We used TorchVision library to load the MobileNetV3-Small model with pretrained ImageNet weights. The classifier layers of MobileNetV3 are truncated, which is handled by YOLO head as discussed later. During loading, the feature width of MobileNet is aligned with YOLO head.

The MobileNetV3-Small backbone is then followed by YOLOv11 classification head. YOLOv11 is designed to handle diverse computer vision challenges of classification in addition to detection, segmentation, and other tasks. It has different classification variants which are trained on ImageNet data with 1000 classes. The architectural changes in these variants lies in depth, width and maximum channels having different number of layers, parameters, gradients and GFLOPs.

The YOLOv11 classification head used in proposed architecture takes the input channels from backbone and reduces the final layer to number of classes n_c. It adds an extra 1x1 convolution layer prior to final classification and includes global average pooling. Global average pooling computes the average of every value in entire feature map and give a single output for each channel. This reduces the dimensionality as well as maintain classification efficiency. The YOLOv11 used SiLU activation instead of H-Swish used by MobileNetv3 as mentioned earlier. Moreover, it does not used dropout for regularization as used by MobileNetv3, it uses other regularization methods

instead. The final layer is followed by softmax activation to produce probability distribution.

For handling data imbalance, a data-level approach of class-balanced sampling is used in this study. A weighted random sampling strategy based on class weights w for n_c number of sample images in class c is used, which helps to create approximately class-balanced mini batches in an epoch during training. While, natural data distribution is used during validation to prevent biasness. For class weighting, inverse-frequency and effective-number rules are studied and inverse frequency class weighting is found as more robust and it is also simple, therefore, used in final architecture.

The model is trained for 100 epochs with a batch size of 4 and image size of 640x640. The initial and final learning rates are 0.01 with a momentum of 0.937.

3 RESULTS AND DISCUSSION

3.1 Text-to-image data

These images are generated using different text-prompts, seeds, guidance scales. negative prompts, and inference steps, as shown in figure 1. It can be observed that the generated images have diverse characteristics with different cell and module designs and have multiple defect types. There are multiple instances and severities of the defects appeared in many of the images, leading to robust model development. The text-to-image synthetic data includes cracks, low cells, dark cells, black edges and breaks. The contamination and finger interruptions are not well preserved in the generated images.

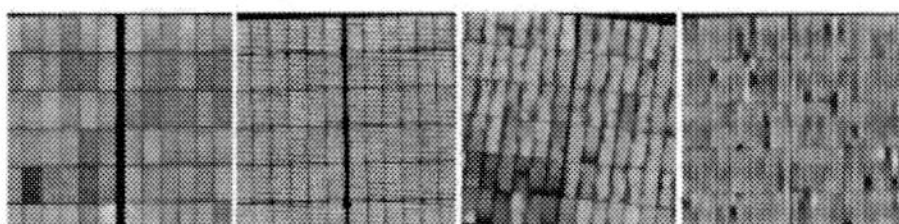

Figure 2: Text-to-image synthetic data generated by different iterations and variants of stable diffusion

3.2 Image-to-image data

These images are generated using different truncation and seed variations. The images generated by different iterations and variants of StyleGAN are shown in figure 2. Similar to above, the generated images have diverse characteristics with different cell and module designs and have multiple defect types. However, the variation is less compared to stable diffusion based models. There are multiple instances and severities of the defects appeared in many of the images. The image-to-image synthetic data includes low cells, dark cells, black edges, breaks, and contamination. The cracks and finger interruptions are not well preserved in the generated images.

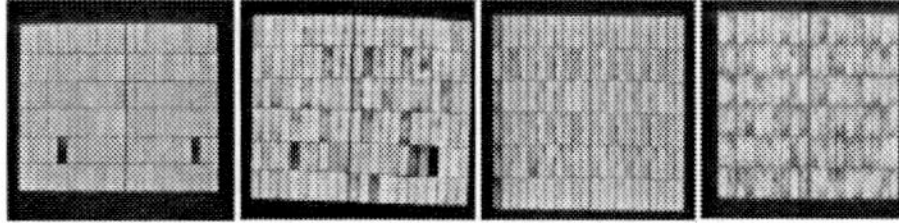

Figure 3: Image-to-image synthetic data generated by different StyleGAN iterations

3.3 Classification results

In present study, we studied different architectures and training strategies tailored for enhanced performance, real-time speed and data imbalance. Firstly, YOLOv11-n classification network is trained on solo and real-synthetic data combinations from pre-trained weights. The training experiments demonstrates highest results for real+text-to-image synthetic data mix followed by real+image-to-image mix and real data. These results are given in table II.

Table II: Classification results with different data combinations

Training Data	Precision	Recall	Accuracy
Real data	0.919	0.842	0.887
Real+Image-to-image	0.895	0.905	0.902
Real+Text-to-image	0.913	0.894	0.908

Following above results, the remaining experiments are carried out with real+text-to-image synthetic data mix. These include training of proposed network, baselines and other models. The proposed architecture obtained Precision, Recall and Accuracy of 94.3 %, 87.3 % and 91.3 % respectively. It shows that 94.3% of modules predicted as defective were actually defective. However, the recall value is a bit low that shows 87.3 % correct predictions for defective modules.

The proposed method is compared with baseline and several state-of-the-art and widely used architectures as discussed earlier. This also includes training with YOLOv11-s, and YOLOv11-m models that shows similar results as by YOLOv11-n at higher computational cost. Therefore, we continue to choose YOLOv11-n for further architectural and training changes tailored for enhanced performance, real-time speed and data imbalance; which results in proposed architecture and training methods. The comparison is given in table III.

Table III: Results of different architectures trained on real+text-to-image data mix

Networks	Precision	Recall	Accuracy
YOLOv11-s	0.918	0.831	0.882
YOLOv8-n	0.903	0.884	0.897
YOLOv12-n	0.862	0.926	0.892
ResNet-18	0.919	0.843	0.887
EfficientNetv2-s	0.881	0.928	0.907
Convnext tiny	0.836	0.805	0.820
Vision Vit-l-16	0.767	0.484	0.676
YOLOv11-n	0.913	0.894	0.908
MobileNetV3-s	0.897	0.897	0.897
Proposed Architecture	0.943	0.873	**0.913**

It can be seen from table 3 that the proposed architecture demonstrates enhanced performance compared to baseline and other models. However, the recall value is found higher for other models. The EfficientNetv2-s achieved highest recall value of 0.928 with an overall accuracy of 0.907 indicating highest correct prediction rate for defective modules followed by YOLOv12-n with recall value of 0.926. Here, the baseline models are trained with original heads and architectures using different training formations like training of head with frozen base, training of n base layers and training entire model.

The training and validation losses for the proposed model are shown in figure 4. Their curves show a steady decline that indicates effective model learning. The validation loss value was initially around 0.6 which first decreases rapidly to value around 0.5, followed by progressive decrease to value around 0.3. Similar pattern is observed for training loss. Both the losses eventually remained between a small range with slight fluctuations, indicating training stability.

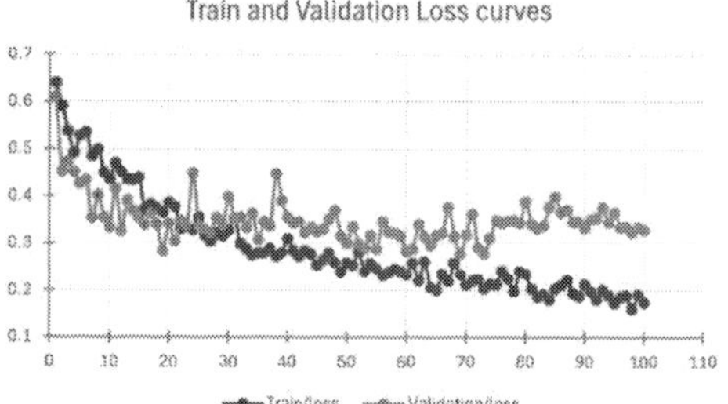

Figure 4: Training and validations losses over 100 epochs.

The confusion matrix analysis shows that the model is hardly classifying the defective class comparatively. Few defective images are misclassified as normal which is further analyzed with inference results. The inference results of proposed network are shown in figure 5. There was misclassification problem mainly observed for the module images having low cell defects with low contrast. Their color and texture are very similar to normal cells creating confusion for the model. This problem can be further analyzed with global or local/selective contrast adjustment.

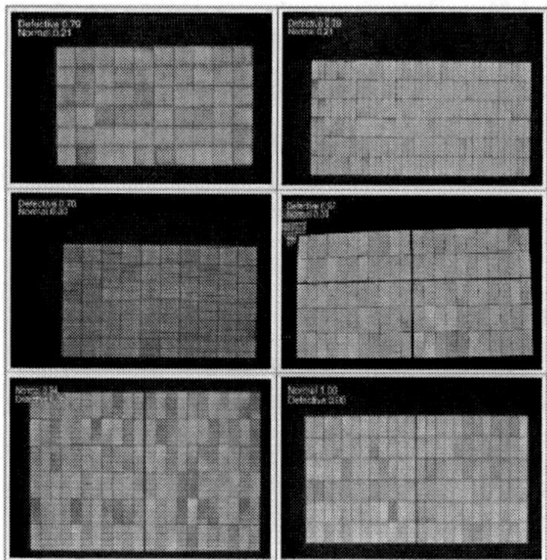

Figure 5: Inference results of proposed method (Last row shows incorrect predictions)

4 CONCLUSIONS

This study proposed a hybrid architecture integrating MobileNetv3 small backbone and YOLOv11 classification head for enhanced classification of normal and defective PV modules. The proposed architecture outperforms baseline and other architectures in terms of precision and accuracy. This study also investigated text-to-image and image-to-image synthetic data generation and the mixed data training results demonstrates highest results for real+text-to-image synthetic data mix followed by real+image-to-image mix and real data. Furthermore, the inverse weighted sampling is found robust in handling class imbalance.

The integration of MobileNet and YOLO head is easy and consistent with Ultralytics YOLO framework and training pipeline, and the experiments demonstrates the adaptability and robustness of YOLOv11 classification head. This is an easy-to-use and end-to-end pipeline in which Ultralytics framework deals with all steps.

ACKNOWLEDGEMENTS

This research work was supported by "The Fundamental Research Funds for the Central Universities Program, China Project Number B250201205".

REFERENCES

[1] Solar Farm Automation Market: Global Forecast From 2025 To 2033 - Dataintelo Report (2024).

[2] Databridge. Global Solar Farm Automation Market - Industry Trends and Forecast to 2029. DATA BRIDGE (2021).

[3] Buratti Y, Javier GMN, Abdullah-Vetter Z, Dwivedi P, Hameiri Z. Machine learning for advanced characterisation of silicon photovoltaics: A comprehensive review of techniques and applications. Renewable and Sustainable Energy Reviews 202 (2024) 114617.

[4] Mahdavipour Z. Defect inspection of photovoltaic solar modules using aerial electroluminescence (EL): A review. Solar Energy Materials and Solar Cells 278 (2024) 1-28.

[5] Akram MW, Li G, Jin Y, Chen X, Zhu C, Ahmad A. Automatic detection of photovoltaic module defects in infrared images with isolated and develop-model transfer deep learning. Solar Energy 198 (2020). https://doi.org/10.1016/j.solener.2020.01.055.

[6] Waqar Akram M, Li G, Jin Y, Chen X. Failures of photovoltaic modules and their detection: A Review. Applied Energy 313 (2022) 118822. https://doi.org/10.1016/j.apenergy.2022.118822.

[7] Masita K, Hasan A, Shongwe T, Hilal HA. Deep learning in defects detection of PV modules: A review. Solar Energy Advances 5 (2025).

[8] Akram MW, Li G, Jin Y, Chen X, Zhu C, Zhao X. CNN based automatic detection of photovoltaic cell defects in electroluminescence images. Energy (2019) 116319. https://doi.org/10.1016/j.energy.2019.116319.

[9] Zhang J, Chen X. Wei H, Zhang K. A lightweight network for photovoltaic cell defect detection in electroluminescence images based on neural architecture search and knowledge distillation. Applied Energy 355 (2024).

[10] Ramadan EA, Moawad NM, Abouzalm BA, Sakr AA, Abouzaid WF, El-Banby GM. An innovative transformer neural network for fault detection and classification for photovoltaic modules. Energy Conversion and Management 314 (2024).

[11] Liu Q, Liu M, Wu QMJ, Shen W. A novel few-shot detector for rare defect localization in photovoltaic cells using electroluminescence images. Solar Energy 296 (2025).

[12] Zhou P, Wang R, Wang C, Chen H, Liu K. SIIF: Semantic information interactive fusion network for photovoltaic defect segmentation. Applied Energy 371 (2024) 123643.

[13] Mahboob Z, Khan MA, Lodhi E, Nawaz T, Khan US. Using SegFormer for Effective Semantic Cell Segmentation for Fault Detection in Photovoltaic Arrays. IEEE Journal of Photovoltaics (2024)1-12.

[14] Tang W, Yang Q, Hu X, Yan W. Deep learning-based linear defects detection system for large-scale photovoltaic plants based on an edge-cloud computing infrastructure. Solar Energy 231 (2022) 527-35.

[15] Di Renzo AB, de Morais HRF, Lazzaretti AE, de Arruda LVR, Lopes HS, Martelli C, et al. Edge Device for the Classification of Photovoltaic Faults Using Deep Neural Networks. Journal of Control, Automation and Electrical Systems 35 (2024) 861-9.

[16] Waqar Akram M, Bai J, Xuan C, Xiaotuo X, Hu J, Wu S. Advancing photovoltaic cells defect detection in electroluminescence images through exploring multiple object detectors. Solar Energy Materials and Solar Cells 292 (2025) 113777. https://doi.org/https://doi.org/10.1016/j.solmat.2025.1137 77.

[17] Ho J, Jain A, Abbeel P. Denoising diffusion probabilistic models. Adv Neural Inf Process Syst (2020).

[18] Podell D, English Z, Lacey K, Blattmann A, Dockhorn T, Müller J, et al. Sdxl: Improving Latent Diffusion Models for High-Resolution Image Synthesis. 12th International Conference on Learning Representations, ICLR (2024).

[19] Vaswani A, Shazeer N, Parmar N, Uszkoreit J, Jones L, Gomez AN, et al. Attention is all you need. Advances in Neural Information Processing Systems (2017).

[20] Schuhmann C, Beaumont R, Vencu R, Gordon C, Wightman R, Cherti M, et al. LAION-5B: An open large-scale dataset for training next generation image-text models. Advances in Neural Information Processing Systems 35 (2022) 1-50.

[21] Luo Z, Cheng SY, Zheng QY. GAN-based augmentation for improving CNN performance of classification of defective photovoltaic module cells in electroluminescence images. IOP Conference Series: Earth and Environmental Science 354 (2019).

[22] Lu F, Niu R, Zhang Z, Guo L, Chen J. A Generative Adversarial Network-Based Fault Detection Approach for Photovoltaic Panel. Applied Sciences 12 (2022).

[23] Akram MW, Bai J. Defect detection in photovoltaic modules based on image-to-image generation and deep learning. Sustainable Energy Technologies and Assessments 82 (2025).

[24] Wang H. Comparative Analysis of GANs and Diffusion Models in Image Generation. Highlights in Science, Engineering and Technology 120 (2024) 59-66.

[25] Peng Y. A Comparative Analysis Between GAN and Diffusion Models in Image Generation. 2nd International Conference on Artificial Intelligence, Database and Machine Learning (AIDML), Vol. V (2024) 189-95.

[26] M. Waqar Akram. PVEL-Text-to-image-Generator. Hugging Face Model Hub (2025). https://huggingface.co/mwaqarakram/PVEL-Text-to-image-Generator-1 or https://huggingface.co/mwaqarakram/PVEL-Text-to-image-Generator-2

[27] Karras T, Laine S, Aila T. A Style-Based

Generator Architecture for Generative Adversarial Networks. IEEE Transactions on Pattern Analysis and Machine Intelligence 43 (2021).

[28]   M. Waqar Akram. Solar PVMEL-Solar PV module-level EL images data (2025). https://kaggle.com/datasets/b6ebe1ef566cc298a4173b697 c121f1a49234762d24910982a530d73bd30a8ca   or https://www.kaggle.com/datasets/waqarakram/solar-pvmel-solar-pv-module-level-el-images-data

[29]   Howard A, Sandler M, Chu G, Chen L-C, Chen B, Tan M, et al. Searching for MobileNetV3. ArXiv ID 190502244 (2019).

[30]   Khanam R, Hussain M. YOLOv11: An Overview of the Key Architectural Enhancements. ArXiv ID 241017725 (2024).

Text-to-Image and Image-to-Image Augmentation and Classification of Defects in Photovoltaic Modules

M. Waqar Akram, Jianbo Bai, Anees Ur Rehman
School of Renewable Energy, Hohai University, Changzhou, Jiangsu, China

Introduction

The autonomous and intelligent monitoring has become an integral aspect of photovoltaic (PV) systems to optimize their operation, performance and reliability. Deep learning demonstrated broad prospects and achieved remarkable progress in PV systems intelligence. However, the detection systems face different detection challenges in outdoor and practical applications concerning appearance of multiple degradation stages, multi-scale defects, susceptibility to interference with examination background, complex lighting conditions, unseen diverse cell and module designs, and others. One of the factors behind these challenges is volume and diversity limited data available for training these data-driven and data-reliant models, as data collection is an intricate and costly process. This study explored text-to-image and image-to-image synthetic data generation methods for their application in autonomous PV monitoring. Moreover, it proposes a hybrid classification architecture based on MobileNetv3 and YOLOv11 for enhanced performance.

Text-to-Image Generation

It used stable diffusion models based on forward diffusion and reverse diffusion processes in latent space, and guided by text prompt-to-image conditioning. The text-image pairs i.e. textual descriptions along with corresponding images are used for training these networks. Seed, guidance scale, inference steps, mixed/blended prompts, and negative prompts are varied to generate diverse data.

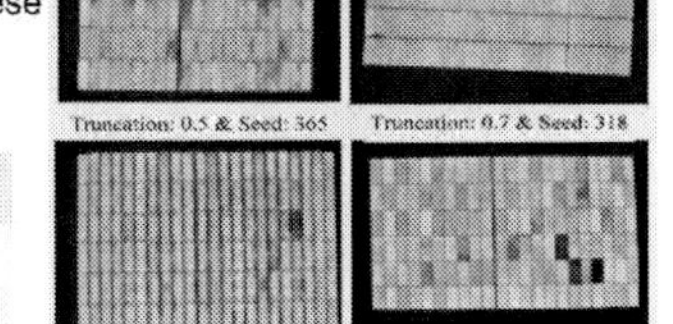

Fig 1. Text-to-Image generated images

Image-to-Image Generation

It used StyleGAN3 variants i.e. Translation and Rotation-Translation equivalent based on generator and discriminator networks. The unsupervised images data of normal operating and defective PV modules is used for training these StyleGAN3 variants .

Table 1. Data combinations used for solo and mixed training experiments

Modules / Data category	Real images data (solo)	Text-to-image data	Image-to-image data	Real+Text-to-image (mixed)	Real+Image-to-image (mixed)
Total	964	300	300	1264	1264
Normal operating	492	000	000	492	492
Defective modules	472	300	300	772	772

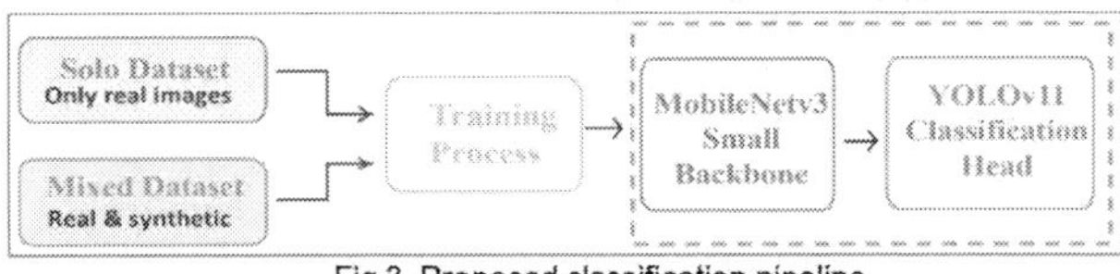

Fig 2. Image-to-Image generation

Classification

The real data used in this study is collected from the electroluminescence imaging of PV modules having diverse designs and characteristics exposed to accelerated ageing. The synthetic datasets are used to augment real data, and solo and mixed training experiments are performed, with data combinations shown in table 1. A hybrid classification architecture based on MobileNetv3 and YOLOv11 is proposed that employs a MobileNetv3-Small backbone followed by YOLOv11 classification head, as shown in figure 3.

Fig 3. Proposed classification pipeline

Table 2. Classification results with different data combinations

Training Data	Precision	Recall	Accuracy
Real data	0.919	0.842	0.887
Real+Image-to-image	0.895	0.905	0.902
Real+Text-to-image	0.913	0.894	0.908

Results

Firstly, YOLOv11-s classification network is trained on the data combinations of solo and synthetic data from pre-trained weights. The training results showed best results for real+text-to-image synthetic data mix followed by real+image-to-image mix and real data, given in table 2. Following above results, several architectures including the proposed network and baselines models are trained on real+text-to-image data mix. The proposed architecture obtained Precision, Recall and Accuracy of 94.3 %, 87.3 % and 91.3 % respectively. The results of proposed method is compared with baseline models and other networks as shown in figure 4. The inference results of proposed architecture are shown in figure 5.

Conclusions

Mixed training with text-to-image synthetic augmentation demonstrates enhanced (highest) performance followed by image-to-image augmented training compared to solo data training.

The proposed hybrid architecture integrating MobileNetv3 and YOLOv11 demonstrates highest classification accuracy compared to baseline and other networks. This integration is an end-to-end pipeline, which is easy-to-use and consistent with Ultralytics framework and training script.

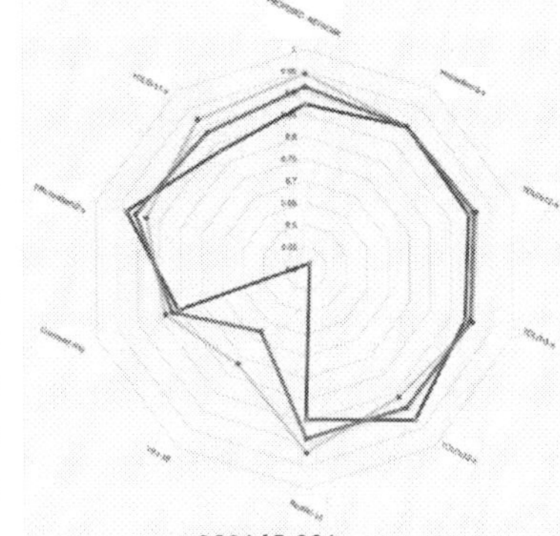

020165-001

Fig 4. Comparison with baseline & other models

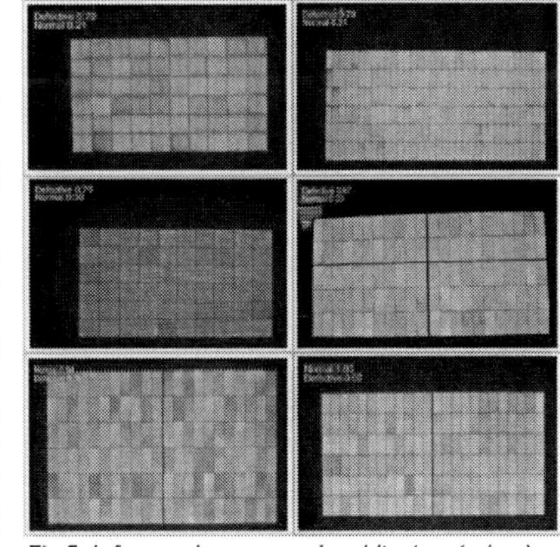

Fig 5. Inference by proposed architecture trained on real+synthetic mix data (Last row: misclassification)

UV FLUORESCENCE IMAGING OF DEFECTS AND BILL OF MATERIALS VARIATIONS IN BIFACIAL SOLAR PANELS

Andrew M. Gabor[1], Maulid Kivambe[2], Mohamed Abdelrahim[2], Mohamed Elgaili[2], Amir A. Abdallah[2]

[1] BrightSpot Automation, Boulder Colorado, USA; gabor@brightspotautomation.com
[2] Qatar Environment & Energy Research Institute (QEERI), Hamad Bin Khalifa University (HBKU), Doha, Qatar

ABSTRACT: UV Fluorescence (UVF) is a high-throughput, non-contact method of imaging defects and bill of material variations in solar panels. Cracks in silicon solar cells are easily seen by this technique since oxygen can diffuse through polymer backsheets, through the cracks in the cells, and then quench the fluorescence in the front encapsulant above the crack lines. Most of the reported data on UVF imaging in the literature shows images of panels with polymeric backsheets, but bifacial panels with rear glass layers are steadily taking market share, and oxygen cannot penetrate the rear glass in such panels except through the junction box penetrations and the perimeter edges. We therefore ask the question, "Does UVF have a useful role in imaging glass/glass panels?" Here we present data from several different glass/glass bifacial panels installed in desert climate (Qatar), showing effective UVF imaging of varying levels of oxygen ingress from the frame edges, varying oxygen ingress from the junction box penetrations, encapsulant bill of materials variations, hot spots, and cell cracks. We therefore conclude that a use case does exist for UVF in at least certain glass/glass solar panel models.

Keywords: UV Fluorescence, Characterization, Defects

1 INTRODUCTION

UV Fluorescence (UVF) is a powerful imaging technology for revealing defects and bill of materials variations in solar panels [1-5]. In this technique, the panels are illuminated with UV light in the dark, and the encapsulant and/or polymer backsheet fluoresce in the visible spectrum. The longer the field exposure or environmental chamber exposure, the stronger the encapsulant will fluoresce. The benefits of the technique include its non-contact and high throughput nature, adaptability to drone imaging, and ability to see a wide range of defects. Such defects include 1) solar cell cracks, 2) edge and junction box sealing failures, 3) hot spots (regions that had run hot during the panel lifetime), 4) cracked glass, and 5) gridline corrosion. Bill of materials (BOM) variations in the panel construction that can be seen directly or indirectly include: 1) encapsulant, 2) polymer backsheet, and 3) metallization paste. An important mechanism for seeing some of these defects involves the diffusion of oxygen into the panel to quench the fluorescence of the encapsulant. In panels with polymer backsheets, the oxygen can diffuse into the panel continuously over the entire back surface. In the case of detecting cracked solar cells, the oxygen can diffuse through the cracks and then spread laterally a few mm's to either side of the crack lines to create a vivid image of the crack locations as dark lines against a brighter background.

Over the last several years, the market share of bifacial panels has steadily grown due to the importance of gains in energy delivery. A majority of these bifacial panels use rear glass layers rather than transparent polymer backsheets. Oxygen cannot penetrate the rear glass in such panels except through the junction box penetrations and the perimeter edges, and thus any defect imaging that relies on oxygen quenching may be less effective with such panels as compared to polymer backsheet panels. We therefore ask the question, "Does UVF have a useful role in imaging glass/glass panels?"

The literature mentions only a few examples of glass/glass UVF imaging. Koentges showed an example of ring pattern fluorescence in a panel that incorporated a metal foil oxygen barrier on the rear side, and showed an example of a cell crack which fluoresced brightly due to fluorophores diffusing through the crack from the back encapsulant [2]. Although this panel did not use rear glass, the use of a similar oxygen barrier suggests that bright crack lines might be visible in glass/glass panels for certain bill of material combinations. Sinha showed ring pattern fluorescence in glass/glass modules indicating that fluorophores could migrate though the gaps between cells from a rear encapsulant rich in fluorophores to the front encapsulant with a low fluorophore concentration, but no defects were found in this case [3]. Gilleland showed the quenching of fluorescence near the short edges of a glass/glass panel as is shown below in Figure 1, which may indicate greater diffusion of oxygen through the edge seals on the short edges of that panel type than the long edges [4]. Although not explicitly mentioned in their paper, there is observable darkening near several interconnect wires which could be due to quenching from oxygen diffusing through cell cracks commonly found by the interconnect wires. Most recently, Buerhop showed small bright spots in UVF images over interconnect wire locations where intense resistive heating was taking place in panels with cracked glass [5].

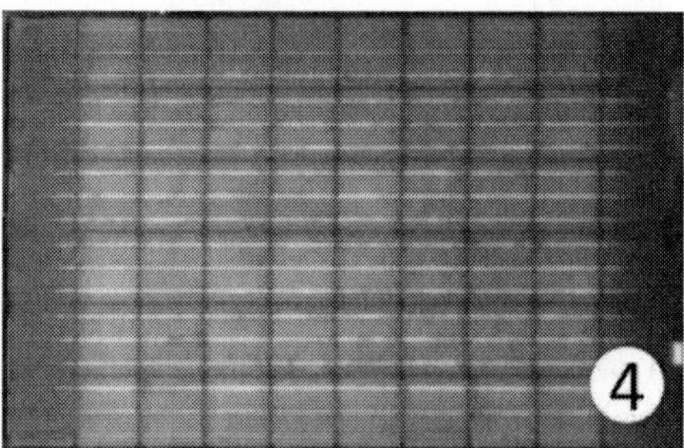

Fig. 1: Taken from [4]. UVF image of a glass/glass panel with oxygen quenching near the short ends and apparently by some interconnect wires.

In order to add to the body of literature on UVF imaging of glass/glass panels, we imaged several different glass/glass panel models installed at the QEERI outdoor test facility in Qatar.

2 UVF IMAGING METHOD

The panels imaged were installed outside for varying amounts of time at the Qatar Environment and Energy Research Institute (QEERI) OTF Outdoor Testing Facility at GPS coordinates 25.326661, 51.432340. Most panels were installed on single axis trackers.

The hardware used for imaging was a **UVF-Spot**™ system from BrightSpot Automation [6]. The system components included a broadband flash head with filters to allow only the UV light to be transmitted, a full-frame sensor consumer camera with a UV cut filter and a 28mm lens, a tall monopod to elevate the camera and flash above the panels for frontside imaging, a remote eyelevel display to see the captured UVF images or the field of view of the camera prior to imaging, and a remote trigger to focus and capture images.

For panels that were imaged outdoors, the images were all taken at least 45 minutes after sundown to reduce noise light effects. An initial image was captured for each panel type, and then the camera gain was adjusted to give good brightness for that panel type. The f-stop of the camera was kept constant at 2.0. The field of view of the camera varied but was generally at least as wide as the panel under test. The monopod pole was employed for imaging the front side of some panels, but in a few cases, the camera was removed from the pole for rear-side imaging underneath the racking.

No post processing was performed for any of the images presented here, but in general, post processing can be valuable to allow certain defects to appear more clearly or to remove perspective distortion. Images shown below are cropped to show the regions of interest.

In addition to the UVF data, in some cases the Performance Ratio (PR) of the panels was measured where PR is defined as the Pmax measured indoors with an IV flash tester divided by the nameplate Pmax value.

3 UVF IMAGES AND COMPLEMENTARY DATA

Panels displaying different types of UVF signatures are grouped into the following subsections.

3.1 Bill of Materials Variations

Figure 2 shows UVF images of two Heterojunction (HJT) panels with identical model numbers but which show the incorporation of a different front encapsulant layer. The panel on the left has a front encapsulant which fluoresces strongly and where oxygen is apparently diffusing inward both from the panel edges as well as from the gaps between the cells to produce a darker ring around each cell where the fluorophores are partially quenched. It is unclear why oxygen diffuses so uniformly through these gap regions when the source of the oxygen is presumably only from the perimeter of the panels. In contrast, the panel on the right displays ring pattern fluorescence, where the front encapsulant did not incorporate UV absorbing additives, but where fluorophores from the rear encapsulant are diffusing through the gaps and across the surface of the cells. In both cases, oxygen has diffused in

from each long edge up to the first interconnect wire to produce a dark band along each long edge. It is unclear whether the abrupt ending of oxygen quenching at the first interconnect wire is a coincidence, or whether perhaps the thinner region of encapsulant between the glass and wire reduces the inward diffusion of the oxygen. If the kinetics of oxygen diffusion can indeed be affected in this manner, perhaps this effect could be intentionally designed into oxygen and moisture sensitive panels.

Fig. 2: UVF images showing BOM variations in the front encapsulant layer for the same model number of HJT panels installed in 2020. PR = 92.7%.

3.2 Sealing Failures

Figure 3a shows a UVF image taken from the back side a different HJT panel type where oxygen is diffusing inward from both the edge perimeter regions as well as through the 3 junction box penetrations. It is interesting to note that the diffusion front from each long edge shows that oxygen appears to have diffused inward faster over the middle regions of the cells. In contrast, the UVF image taken from the front side in Figure 3b shows the oxygen diffusing inward more strongly from the gaps between cells, but overall that the quenched regions reach less far inward than on the backside, perhaps due to the differences in UV additives within the encapsulant layers or the different UV aging doses experienced on the front and back sides. Also, there are some scattered dark spots seen on the rear side that are unexplained. It is possible that these correspond to cell crack locations, but it is not clear why enhanced oxygen diffusion would take place from the front side.

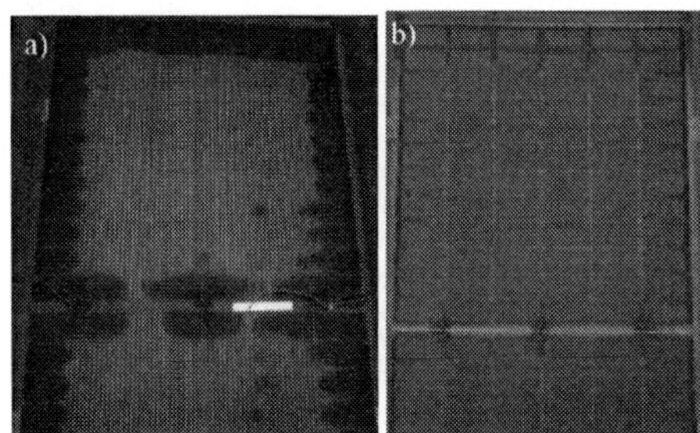

Fig. 3: a) UVF image from the rear side of a HJT panel showing oxygen diffusing through holes in the glass for junction box penetrations, varying degrees of oxygen diffusion from the perimeter, and a few unexplained dark spots; b) UVF image from the front side of a panel of the same model. Panels installed in 2020. PR = 94.7%

Fig. 4 shows another example of strong rear side fluorescence where oxygen is seen diffusing inward from the perimeter in a PERC panel. In contrast with the panel shown in Figure 3, there the diffusion appears to be occurring more rapidly in the gaps between cells. Also, here the sealing around the junction box penetrations appears to be more effective.

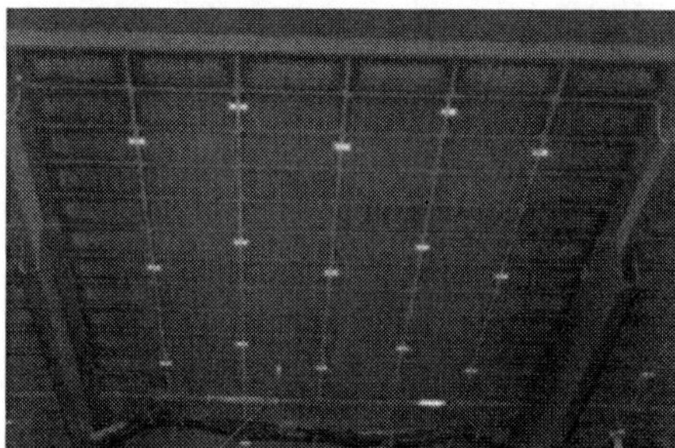

Fig. 4: UVF image from the rear side of a PERC panel showing oxygen diffusing inward from the perimeter. Panels installed in 2018.

We also collected UVF images from thin-film CIGS panels. Although these panels were not of a bifacial design, these data points have high importance in evaluating the potential for UVF in imaging thin-film panel defects. Figure 5 shows the UVF image of panels where the CIGS is deposited on the rear glass in a substrate type configuration and the encapsulant between the CIGS and the top glass is fluorescing brightly. Each panel displays some degree of sealing problems on the edges, but in 3 of the panels, there are large dark regions emanating from an edge which incur deeply into the panel central regions. In some cases narrow dark lines extend down the length of the scribed cells. It is not clear why oxygen can diffuse down the length of a cell, but perhaps the scribing process in some cases leaves channels that are not fully filled with encapsulant or where delamination is occurring. These correspond to white regions by eye. Each panel also displays some large brighter regions that can be seen by eye as light brown spots where perhaps hot spot heating has occurred.

Fig. 5: UVF image of CIGS panels showing likely sealing failures and possible delamination (dark spots) and bright regions where possible hot spot heating has occured. Panels installed in 2015.

3.3 Cracked Cells

Figure 6 shows a UVF image of a TOPCon panel with ring pattern fluorescence where variations in the ring pattern likely correlate to cell crack locations. Most cracks appear to be near interconnect wire locations where the oxygen quenching leads to dips in the outer perimeter of the rings near the wire locations. In a few examples, diagonal cracks

show bright lines in the center of the cells where fluorophores are diffusing through the cracks from the rear encapsulant and where oxygen has not diffused in from the cell perimeter to quench that fluorescence.

Fig. 6: UVF image of a TOPCon panel where breaks and variations in the ring patterns likely correspond to cell cracks. Yellow arrows show cracks that may lie underneath busbars, while red arrows show cracks that propagate between busbars. Panels installed in 2022 at a fixed tilt southward of 22 degrees. PR = 96.0%.

3.4 Hot Spots

Figure 7 shows a UVF image of a PERC panel with no visible fluorescence anywhere except near the junction boxes and the perimeter frame. We assume the fluorescence has evolved preferentially in these locations due to resistive heating in the junction boxes and due to regions near the frame running hotter than elsewhere. The competing kinetics of fluorescence activation from heat and fluorescence quenching from oxygen diffusion through glass penetrations and edges give rise to complex patterns.

Fig. 7: UVF image showing the effect of hotter regions near the junction boxes and the perimeter of a PERC solar panel. The competing kinetics of fluorescence activation from heat and fluorescence quenching from oxygen diffusion through glass penetrations and edges give rise to complex patterns. Panels installed in 2018.

Figure 8a shows frameless PERT panels where some clamping positions where shifted after some years of operation and where there may be local heating near the clamp positions. The regions around both the old and new clamping positions shows visible browning above the white regions at the perimeter of the panels. The glass surface was manually scrubbed to verify that the discoloration was not due to residue on the top surface of the glass. Possible causes of the discoloration are due to hotter internal panel temperature under the clamp positions or diffusion of some chemical species from the polymer used in the clamps. Figures 8b and 8c show UVF images of the panels where the browned regions fluoresce strongly but where there is little other fluorescence in the panel. The fluorescence appears quite strong over the cell regions close to the clamps, and it is possible that the strong fluorescence correlates to hot spot regions.

Fig. 8: a) RGB image of frameless PERT panels where some clamp positions had been shifted after some years of field operation; b) a UVF image of the same panels, and c) a closeup UVF image near a clamp position. Panels were installed in 2020.

Finally, we show in Figure 9 a UVF image of the rear side of a Series 4, First Solar CdTe panel installed for >10 years in Ohio. Strong fluorescence is seen along both edges of the bussing wire near the edge of panel. We assume that some local heating had occurred in this location, but do not understand the origin of the heating or the reliability/performance impacts.

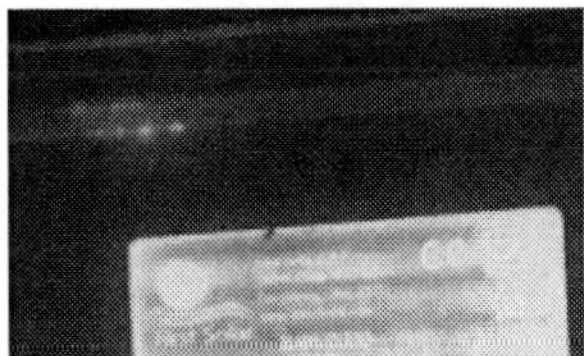

Fig. 9: a) UVF image of the rear side of a Series 4 First Solar panel showing strong fluorescence along a bussing wire, potentially due to local heating (poor TCO connection?).

4 DISCUSSION

As a field testing technique, UVF suffers from its high dependency on bill of materials, panel design, installation location, and panel history. Encapsulants that have no UV absorbing additives do not fluoresce unless fluorophores diffuse from other layers. When fluorophores are present, it can take years of field exposure for sufficiently strong fluorescence to evolve. Oxygen diffusion barriers such as rear glass can reduce the effectiveness of seeing cracked cells. However, the strengths of UVF lie in its high throughput, non-contact nature, and ability to image problems not otherwise seen by EL and thermal IR imaging. The data presented above demonstrate that even for the most challenging cases of relatively new glass/glass panels, useful defect imaging can occur.

Despite the rear glass acting as an oxygen diffusion barrier, the diffusion of oxygen from panel edges and junction box penetration still occurs in glass/glass panels, as does the diffusion of oxygen from the rear encapsulant layer to the front encapsulant layer both in the gaps between cells as well as through cracks in the cells. For most silicon based panels, such sealing failures may not represent a significant durability problem, and in the context of UVF imaging, may present an opportunity for more informative imaging of other defect types where oxygen ingress has occurred. However, in more sensitive thin-film panels such as those based on Perovskites, such sealing failures may be catastrophic, and their detection critical. Our observation here of oxygen possibly diffusing preferentially down the scribe lines of the monolithically integrated thin film cells points to a potential problem deserving attention.

While the successful imaging here of the superstrate type CIGS thin-film panels is promising for UVF imaging of thin-film panels, we note that the vast majority of monolithically integrated thin-film panel produced to date (CdTe panels from First Solar) are of the superstrate variety with no encapsulant to image from the front side except in the narrow regions between scribe lines. The emerging field of Perovskite PV is of varied designs with most monolithically integrated panels having a superstrate front cell, while the Perovskite on Si-wafer designs are more promising for front-side UVF imaging with encapsulant between the cells and the front glass. Our finding here of successful UVF imaging from the rear side may find application in superstrate type thin-film panels depending on their bill of materials. While high throughput UVF imaging by pole-mounted or drone-mounted camera imaging may not obviously be applicable to rear-side imaging, such rear side imaging may still be conveniently performed by systems that are hand held or mounted to vehicles, robots, and even drones, especially for tracker systems that could be tilted to nearly vertical for better access to the rear side.

The overall trend over the last decade for glass/glass panels of using encapsulants with no UV absorbers bodes poorly for universal application of UVF to such panels, but our findings here give promise that for some significant number of GWs of panels, UVF will find useful applications. In particular, based on our finding here in Figures 7, 8, and 9 and in Buerhop's investigations [5], the imaging of hot spots may be effectively performed even in panels with no fluorescence elsewhere in the panel. Operations and Maintenance groups and field testing companies can use UV flashlights to assess any site for UVF imaging potential, and then where applicable follow up with high throughput imaging tools [6].

A summary of the different panel problems that may be visible with UVF imaging in glass/glass panels is shown in Table I with very rough estimates of the probability that UVF can see the problem and amount of field exposure time needed for the fluorescence to be strong enough to image the problem.

Table I. UVF effectiveness for defects in glass/glass panels

Problem	UVF Imaging Probability	Field exposure time needed
Encapsulant BoM variation	High	0-3 yrs
Local heating	High	0-1 yrs
Sealing failures	Med	2-5 yrs
Cracked Cells	Low	2-5 yrs

5   CONCLUSIONS

Despite the relatively few examples in the literature of UVF being used to characterize glass/glass solar panels, we have found multiple examples of useful applications over a range of different PV technologies in panels fielded for 5-10 years. We demonstrated detection of 1) front encapsulant bill of material variation between panels of the same model number, 2) sealing failure at the panel perimeter edges and at the junction box penetrations, 3) possible hot spot heating near junction boxes, frames, clamping positions, and 4) cell cracking. We also demonstrated useful imaging of the rear side for three panel types.

The emerging technology of Perovskite solar cells is particularly sensitive to sealing failures, and the ability of UVF to image such failures from either the front or rear sides could be helpful for both product development after chamber testing and for field testing.

6   REFERENCES

[1] D. J. Colvin *et al.*, "Ultraviolet Fluorescence Imaging for Photovoltaic Module Metrology: Best Practices and Survey of Features Observed in Fielded Modules," in *IEEE Journal of Photovoltaics*, vol. 15, no. 3, pp. 465-477, May 2025, doi: 10.1109/JPHOTOV.2025.3545825.

[2] M. Kontges, A. Morlier, G. Eder, E. Fleis, B. Kubicek, and J. Lin, "Review: Ultraviolet fluorescence as assessment tool for photovoltaic modules," *IEEE J. of Photovolt.*, vol. 10, no. 2, pp. 616–633, 2020.

[3] A. Sinha, D. B. Sulas-Kern, M. Owen-Bellini, L. Spinella, S. Ulicna´, S. Ayala Pelaez, S. Johnston, and L. T. Schelhas, "Glass/glass photovoltaic module reliability and degradation: a review," *J. Phys. D: Appl. Phys.*, vol. 54, no. 41, p. 413002, 2021.

[4] B. Gilleland, W. B. Hobbs, and J. B. Richardson, "High throughput detection of cracks and other faults in solar PV modules using a high-power ultraviolet fluorescence imaging system." IEEE, 2019, pp. 2575–2582.

[5] C. Buerhop et al., "Combined Non-Destructive Techniques for On-Site Failure Analysis -Showcase of Glass Cracks with Burn Marks in a PV Power Station," 2025 IEEE 53rd Photovoltaic Specialists Conference (PVSC), Montreal, QC, Canada, 2025, pp. 0526-0529, doi: 10.1109/PVSC59419.2025.11132595.

[6] UVF-Spot.   Available: brightspotautomation.com/products/ultraviolet-fluorescence/uvf-spot/. [Accessed: Sep. 12, 2025].

DETERMINATION THE RELIABLITY OF SOLAR MODULES
IN ANALOGY TO GLASS IN BUILDINGS

Ruth Kasper*, Hannah Reichart
University of Applied Sciences Cologne (TH Köln)
Betzdorfer Str. 2, 50679 Köln, Germany
*Contact: ruth.kasper@th-koeln.de, +49 221-8275-2791

ABSTRACT: In recent years, photovoltaic (PV) module designs have doubled in size, introducing XXL modules, with approximately 3 m². Meanwhile, the single glass height of glass-glass modules has decreased from 3.2 mm to 2 mm or less. This reduction, coupled with decreased frame stiffness, raises concerns about load-bearing capacity and modules increasingly show damage like glass and frame breakage in the field.

PV module load bearing capacity is determined via MQT 16, a static mechanical load test in accordance with IEC 61215. This test inadequately represents real damage scenarios as it does not consider material strength variability and time-temperature behavior of the interlayer.

Instead, the design method from the construction industry can be used to determine the static reliability of solar modules. Regardless of the material, the partial safety concept is used, which considers variations in loading and material. Components or structures can then be dimensioned using a suitable mechanical model. For many years, glass has been used in façades and roof structures without frequent breakage due to static overloading.

This paper describes the current problems related to unexpected solar module damage, illustrates load-bearing behavior of glass-glass modules considering material, mounting, and mechanics, and presents the construction industry design method.

Keywords: PV-module reliability, partial safety concept, mechanical load test, glass stress, Eurocode

1 INTRODUCTION

The design of photovoltaic (PV) modules has undergone continuous development in recent years. In addition to improvements in cell structure, designs are trending toward larger modules. Over the last 10 years, these modules have grown on average, to twice their original size, and new XXL modules (approximately 3 m²) are reaching significantly larger dimensions [1]. Additionally, the application of glass-glass modules is reaching a new high, with an expected market share of over 50% in 2024 and a continued upward trend [2]. However, this has resulted in a significant increase in weight. To counteract this, there has been a reduction in height decreased from 3.2 mm to 2 mm [1]. For small module dimensions, glass heights up to 1.6 mm are also found [3]. This results in a significant reduction in stiffness and load-bearing capacity, leading to the moniker "big, floppy modules" [1].

The load-bearing capacity of PV modules is determined by the static mechanical load test (MQT 16) according to IEC 61215 [4]. However, while modules had high load-bearing reserves in the past, many modern PV modules have difficulty passing the minimum load requirement of 2.4 kN/m² according to the standard [1]. Concurrently, there has been an increase in glass breakage in PV modules despite prior type testing in accordance with IEC 61215. In some cases, this can be attributed to extreme weather events such as hail or storms, but spontaneous glass breakage is also frequently observed, mainly in the first few years after installation [5].

This has a significant impact not only on the economic efficiency of solar parks but also on their safety standard.

This paper examines how to ensure the load resistance of PV modules. In this regard, the current state of the art

in the PV industry is explained in greater detail in Chapter 2. Sample calculations are used to illustrate the mechanical principles of load transfer and the impact of changes in glass height, frame stiffness, and support conditions (see Chapter 3). Additionally, the design concept in construction is presented in Chapter 4. The Eurocode 10 [10] is available in draft form as a European harmonized standard for designing and dimensioning structural glass components. As with building materials such as steel, reinforced concrete, or wood, the partial safety concept is applied here as well, covering variations on the impact and material sides. For many years, glass has been used in façades and roof structures without an increase in breakage due to static overload due to a proper design based on the Eurocode safety concept [11].

2 STATE OF THE ART IN THE PV INDUSTRY

2.1 Static mechanical load test according to IEC 61215

In the PV industry, the load bearing capacity of PV modules is ensured by mechanical load testing MQT 16, which is conducted in accordance with the International Electrotechnical Commission (IEC) standard 61215. This process involves simulating wind and snow loads using a constant load structure. The load is typically generated with sandbags or pneumatic cylinders. The manufacturer may determine the design situation. The load consists of a design load and a safety factor of 1.5:

$$Test\ load = \gamma_M \cdot design\ load = 1.5 \cdot design\ load$$

According to the standard, the minimum test load is 2.4 kN/m². Usual pressure levels are 2.4 kN/m² for wind loads (suction) and up to 5.4 kN/m² for snow loads (pressure). Each level is maintained for one hour. The module is mounted on a rigid test frame in the most unfavorable support situation and is subjected to alternating positive (pressure) and negative (suction) loads. Three load cycles are performed. After each cycle, the module undergoes a visual inspection for damage and electrical tests to detect breaks or performance losses. To pass type approval, one module must be tested according to MQT 16. There are no specifications for maximum deflection or plastic deformation of the frame to pass the load test. [4]

2.2 Criticism of the testing procedure

The test procedure according to IEC 61215 has been the subject of criticism for several years. A significant point of criticism is the inadequate consideration of the diverse real-world conditions under which photovoltaic modules are operated. The test conditions are considerably simplified, and thus, they are unable to fully reflect the complex environmental interactions to which modules are exposed. This encompasses, among other considerations, the selection of an appropriate load level. The modules are frequently found to be significantly overloaded at an external load of 5.4 kN/m², a condition that invariably results in a change to the static system. The large deformations that result from this force cause the glass pane to rest on the substructure, thereby fundamentally altering the static system [13]. The load paths that occur - in some cases also via unspecified load-bearing elements under the solar module - correspond to an overloaded system and do not reflect the realistic load and bearing situation in the installed state. Only in the event of an once-in-a-century storm or exceptional snowfall under special installation conditions due to characteristic loads of up to 5.4 kN/m² and the associated deformations occur. Therefore, it is not advisable to determine the "design load" by means of testing.

The assumption of a uniform load also results in simplifications that do not accurately reflect the complexity of the situation. The typical mounting of PV modules at a defined angle results in inhomogeneous snow and wind loads. Studies have demonstrated that greater stresses emerge from an asymmetric distribution of loads in comparison to a uniform distribution. These assumptions entirely exhaust the safety factor of 1.5 [14], [15].

However, the failure to consider material dispersion has a particularly significant effect. In modules with larger dimensions, the primary load transfer occurs through the glass pane. Consequently, the load-bearing capacity of the module is determined by the strength of the used glass. The theoretical strength of glass is very high; however, due to its brittle behavior and material variability, the actual strength of glass depends heavily on the condition of the surface and any irregularities present. Consequently, the strength of glass is subject to a very high degree of variation. In the field of construction, the characteristic strength of glass is evaluated by the 5th percentile value, with a 95% probability [16], [17]. It is generally accepted that a minimum of 30 samples, which must be identical and undamaged, are required to ensure the production of representative results for the characteristic strength. The MQT 16 load test does not consider this material variation. According to IEC 61215, the successful completion of a single module's load test is sufficient for the attainment of type approval. In conjunction with this phenomenon, the process of tempering thin glass is notably more challenging than that of thicker panes. This discrepancy may lead to the occurrence of irregular tempering values across the surface of the pane [1]. Consequently, the load test does not yield any information regarding the general load-bearing capacity of the modules; it provides a single, non-representative spot value.

Moreover, end users are frequently confronted with a lack of congruent information. The data sheet for photovoltaic (PV) modules typically provides insufficient information regarding their load-bearing capacity. If a statement is made regarding the load-bearing capacity, the maximum tested load situation is specified without any information about the mechanical system [3]. Information about the mounting arrangement or support can only be found in the user manual. It is evident that the specified maximum load depends on the mounting situation, and the design situation mentioned in the data sheet is only applicable to specific, optimal mounting conditions [20]. This phenomenon is especially evident in conjunction with a tracking system. Large solar parks primarily utilize single-axis trackers, which facilitate the optimal alignment of the PV modules with the sun's position throughout the day [21]. In this case, a combination of substructure and modules is subjected to rigorous testing. However, it was observed that none of the combinations were able to achieve the maximum load specified in the data sheet. The actual load levels are significantly lower [20].

3 MECHANICAL AND GEOMETRICAL FACTORS INFLUENCING THE STRESS STATE

3.1 Load bearing elements of a PV-System

A PV-System consists of three different main parts. First, the PV-modul composed of the PV-laminate containing the glass and the interlayer in connection with the frame. For the determination of the load bearing capacity, the cells themselves can be neglected. Second, the clamping system and third, the tracing system.

Starting with the behavior of glass-glass-laminate, the main influences on the stress state in the glass are demonstrated in the following.

3.2 Load-bearing behavior of a glass plate

3.2.1 Influence of the glass height and the span

The load-bearing behavior of a component is largely determined by a variety of influencing parameters [25]. In addition to material-related factors such as the modulus of elasticity E, the geometric influences play a decisive role. These include in particular:

- the mechanical system with its load transfer and
- the geometry of the cross-sections and the resulting moments of resistance.

A glass pane with a height h linearly supported on two sides can be described mechanically using linear beam theory (see Figure 1). Here, the static system is defined by its support conditions and external loads, which result in internal forces such as normal force, shear force and moment (N, V and M) (see Figure 2). The glass in solar modules is mainly subjects to bending, so only the internal moment M is relevant.

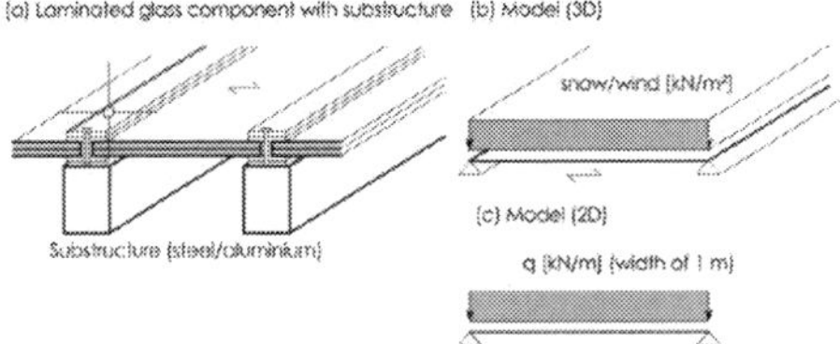

Figure 1: 2-sided linear supported glass plate

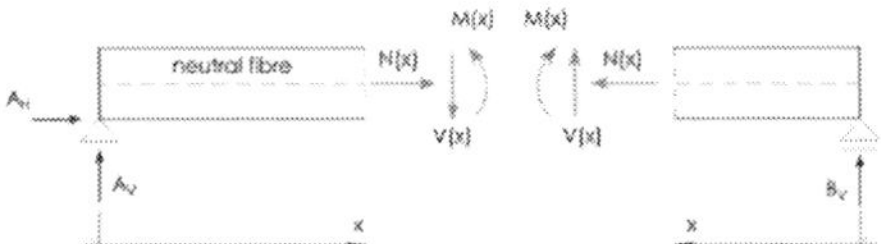

Figure 2: Section forces in a beam (general mechanical definition)

There are three basic types of bearings in the two-dimensional plane: roller bearings, fixed bearings and clamping bearings, which differ in terms of their degree of retention. While a roller bearing absorbs only vertical forces, a fixed bearing is capable of bearing vertical and horizontal forces. A clamp can also absorb a moment. The arrangement of the supports and the type of loading have a significant influence on the resulting internal forces. The simplest static system is the single-span beam under a constant load, which can be used to describe the load-bearing behavior of a glass plate supported on both sides by linear bearings. Given a line load q [kN/m] and a span L, the internal moment M [kNm] for a beam with free rotation at the supports is calculated as follows

$$M = q \cdot L^2 / 8 \qquad (1)$$

with

q line load

L span

Figure 3 shows the shear force and moment distribution for a simple beam under line load for two different kinds of bearing arrangements. In these cases, the internal normal forces N are zero.

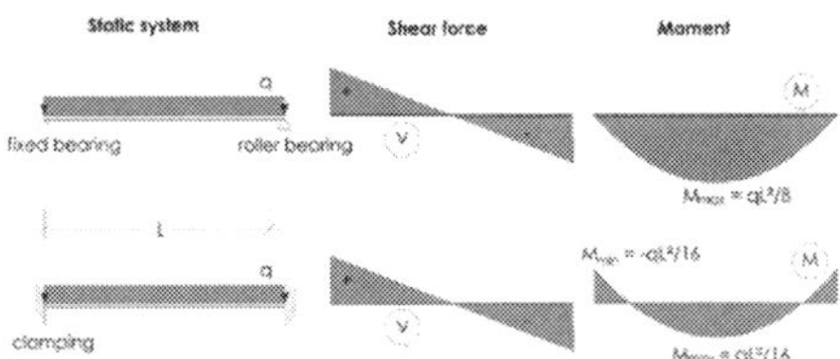

Figure 3: Shear force and Moment for a single beam

The internal forces are for such simple case independent from the type of material. Glass components usually fail when a critical normal stress level is reached on the glass surface. The normal stress on the glass surface is influenced by the internal force M as well as by the geometry of the cross-section. For a rectangular cross-section, the maximum normal stresses (surface) can be calculated by (see Figure 4):

$$\sigma = \frac{M}{W} = \frac{M}{\frac{1}{6} b \cdot h^2} \qquad (2)$$

with

M Internal bending moment

h height of the section (here: plate thickness)

b width of the section (we assume a glass component with a width of 1000 mm equal to the supported length)

The main factor influencing the determination of normal stresses is therefore the height of the component.

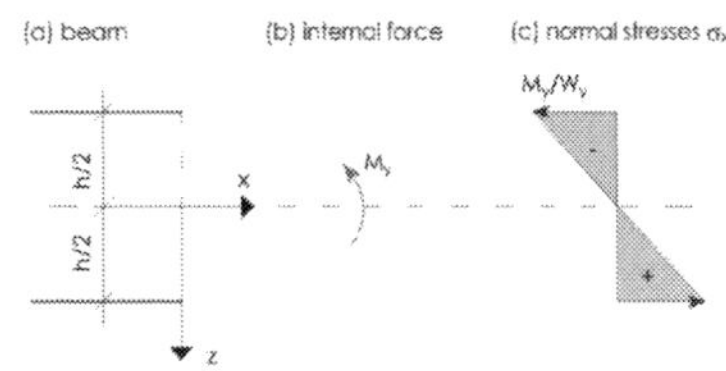

Figure 4: Relation between internal force M and normal stresses

With the moment of resistance W for the glass heights 3.2 mm and 2 mm

$$W_{(3.2\ mm)} = \frac{(3.2\ mm)^2 \cdot 1000\ mm}{6} = 1.71 \cdot 10^3\ mm^3 \quad (3)$$

$$W_{(2\ mm)} = \frac{(2\ mm)^2 \cdot 1000\ mm}{6} = 0.67 \cdot 10^3\ mm^3 \quad (4)$$

and the corresponding stresses in [N/mm²]

$$\sigma_{(3.2\ mm)} = M / W_{(3.2\ mm)} \qquad (5)$$

$$\sigma_{(2\ mm)} = M / W_{(2\ mm)} \qquad (6)$$

the increase in normal stress can be determined for an identical span L and the load q when the glass height changes from 3.2 to 2 mm:

$$\sigma_{(2\ mm)} / \sigma_{(3.2\ mm)} = 1.71 / 0.67 = 2.55 \quad (7)$$

A reduction in glass height of 37.5 %, therefore results in 2.55 times the normal stress on the glass surface.

This calculation only applies to a monolithic glass panel, but the effect is the same for any type of bearing.

In addition to normal stress, the deformation of a component also plays a central role in load-bearing capacity considerations. An additional factor for the deformation is the stiffness of the material. It is defined by the product $(E \cdot I)$, which is composed of the modulus of elasticity E and the second-degree moment of inertia I. For the example described above of a glass component linearly supported on two sides under uniform load respectively line load, the following deformations result:

$$w = \frac{q \cdot L^4}{76,8 \cdot E \cdot I} \qquad (8)$$

with

q line load

L span

E modulus of elasticity

I second-degree moment of inertia

The second-degree moment of inertia I for a glass plate with a width of 1 m and the glass heights of 3.2 mm or 2 mm is equal to:

$$I_{(3.2\ mm)} = \frac{(3.2\ mm)^3 \cdot 1000\ mm}{12} = 2.73 \cdot 10^3\ mm^4 \quad (9)$$

$$I_{(2\,mm)} = \frac{(2\,mm)^3 \cdot 1000\,mm}{12} = 0.67 \cdot 10^3\ mm^4 \qquad (10)$$

By changing the glass height from 3.2 to 2 mm, the deformation increases by a factor of

$$w_{(2\,mm)}/w_{(3,2\,mm)} = 2.73/0.667 \approx 4.1 \qquad (11)$$

The example illustrates the influence on the normal stresses due to bending because of material reduction.

3.2.2 Stiffness of the composite material

The normal stress distribution in glass-glass modules depends on the stiffness of the composite material and equation (2) is no longer valid here. The normal stress distribution in the cross-section lies between the boundary cases 'with and without full shear connection'.

For a structure consisting of two glass layers with height h, the normal stresses on the surface in [N/mm²] for the boundary case 'with connection' are equal to:

$$\sigma_{(2\,x\,h)} = \frac{M}{W_{(2\,x\,h)}} = \frac{M}{(\frac{2}{3}h^2 \cdot b)} \qquad (12)$$

with

$$W_{(2\,x\,h)} = (2\,h)^2 \cdot b/6 = 2/3\,h^2 \cdot b \qquad (13)$$

or 'without shear coupling' (the load q is divided equally between the individual glass layers):

$$M_{(h)} = \frac{(\frac{q}{2})L^2}{8} = \frac{q\,L^2}{16} = \frac{M}{2} \qquad (14)$$

$$W_{(h)} = (h)^2/6 = 1/6\,h^2 \qquad (15)$$

$$\sigma_{(h)} = \frac{M_{(h)}}{W_{(h)}} = \frac{M/2}{1/6\,h^2} = 3\,M/h^2 \qquad (16)$$

The normal stress ratio is equal to:

$$\sigma_{(h)}/\sigma_{(2h)} = 2 \qquad (17)$$

This simple mechanical derivation shows that without shear effect, the normal stresses in the glass are twice as high as with full lamination. The truth lies somewhere between these two extremes and is determined by the stiffness of the composite material, the temperature and the duration of the loading (see Figure 5). In structural glass construction in Germany, for example, the shear composite approach is only permitted if the shear composite properties of the intermediate material data have been evaluated by testing.

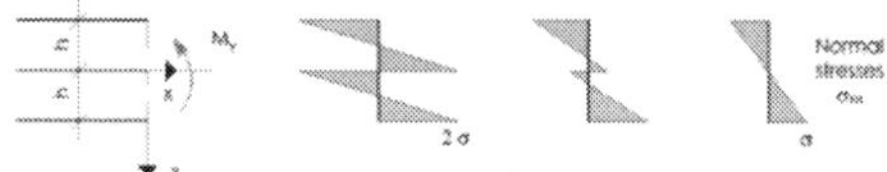

Figure 5: Normal stress distribution due to bending for the limits "no shear coupling", "partial shear coupling" and "full coupling"

Additionally, to the parameters "system span" and "glass height" (exponent 2), the coupling effect of the interlayer may influence the normal stresses in the glass in the factor equal to 2.

3.2.3 Four-sides linearly supported plate

The module frame changes the load transfer of the laminated glass from a single-axis to a two-axis load transfer. Assuming that the module frame is sufficiently rigid, the bearing is assumed to be a stiff roller bearing. The effect of multi-axial load transfer is present up to an aspect ratio of the edge lengths of 1:3. After that, single-axis load transfer resumes.

For small deformations, the load-bearing behavior of the glass plate can be described by *Kirchhoff's* linear plate theory. Linear plate theory loses its validity as soon as the deformations w of the glass pane exceed the glass height h. This case occurs with the glass heights used in the PV industry even under very low loads and is therefore always be applicable. A membrane load-bearing behavior then occurs, comparable to the load transfer in a rope. The center of the glass pane 'hangs' in the rigid glass plate edge and causes a load transfer via a combination of normal stresses due to bending and membrane effects (see Figure 6). This significantly reduces the stresses and deformations in the glass pane. Another effect is that the relationship between the load q and the stresses and deformation is not directly proportional. Stresses and deformation increase more slowly than the external load q. Neglecting this favorable membrane load-bearing behavior, glass panes in construction often cannot be dimensioned economically.

The membrane effect generally depends on:

- the height of the pane: the thinner, the greater.

- the aspect ratio: the greater, the lower.

- the loading: the higher the loading q, the stronger the effect.

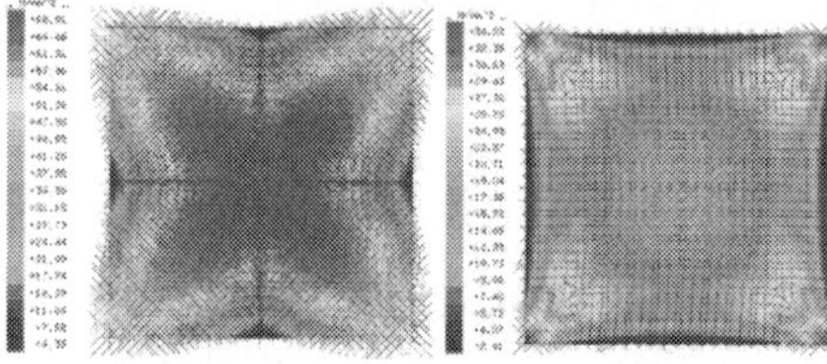

Figure 6: Membrane effect of a four-sides supported plate

Taking into consideration the linear plate theory, the maximum principal (normal) stresses occur at the middle of the plate. In contrast, when the membrane theory is considered the maximum principal (normal) stresses shift to the corners of the plate. Figure 7 compares the distribution and values of the maximum principal stresses for a rectangular 4-sided linear supported plate.

Figure 7: Maximum principal stresses with vector plots indicating the direction (left side: linear plate theory, right side: membrane theory), dimension 1000 mm x 1000 mm, glass height 2 mm, 4-sides linear supported, q = 1 kN/m²

3.3 Variation of support conditions

The influence of the support conditions has been analyzed for the following parameters:

- Dimension 1000 mm x 1000 mm

- Laminated glass of 2 x 1.6 mm, no shear coupling

- Constant distributed loading of 1 kN/m²

In glass in building, a prerequisite for accepting a linearly supported plate is a deformation restriction of the support. The supports (equal to the frame of a PV-module) may only deflect by L/200 (L = span) [30]. After that, the deflection of the substructure must be included in the design model. Figure 8 shows the influence on stress and deformation depending on the frame stiffness EI (E-modulus · area moment of inertia I). The span of the plate is equal to 1000 mm, so the deflection limit might be L/200 = 1000 mm / 200 = 5 mm.

The diagrams show that this deformation limit marks the transition between a single-axis to a two-axis load transfer. The results shown in Figure 8 are calculated with the finite element program SJ MEPLA PRO [26]. This tool includes a shell laminate element to examine the stresses of a laminate depending on the shear stiffness of the interlayer. The module frame can be modelled with an edge beam. A disadvantage of SJ MEPLA PRO is that the edge beam does not include torsional stiffness so that an analyzation of restraint effects at the frame support is not possible.

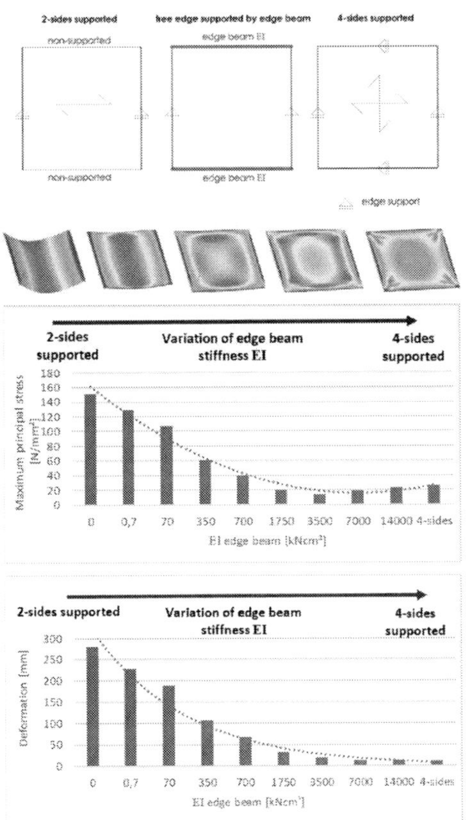

Figure 8: Maximum principal stresses and deformation depending on the bending stiffness EI of the frame

(dimension 1000 mm x 1000 mm, laminate of 2 x 1.6 mm, no shear coupling, q = 1 kN/m²)

In the next step the linear support is replaced by four springs acting vertical to the plate simplifying the effect of four edge clamping's (see results in Figure 9). The change of the maximum principal stresses (top and bottom side) and deflections are shown in Figure 9 depending on bending stiffness EI of the edge beam (= module frame). Caused by the local springs, stress concentrations occur next to the springs. With increasing edge beam stiffness, the maximum principal stresses occur at the edge.

Considered that the characteristic bending strength of solar glass is about 70 N/mm², the edge stiffness of the frame has a significant influence on the load carrying capacity of a solar module. Having in mind that the presented values are calculated for the parameters mentioned above.

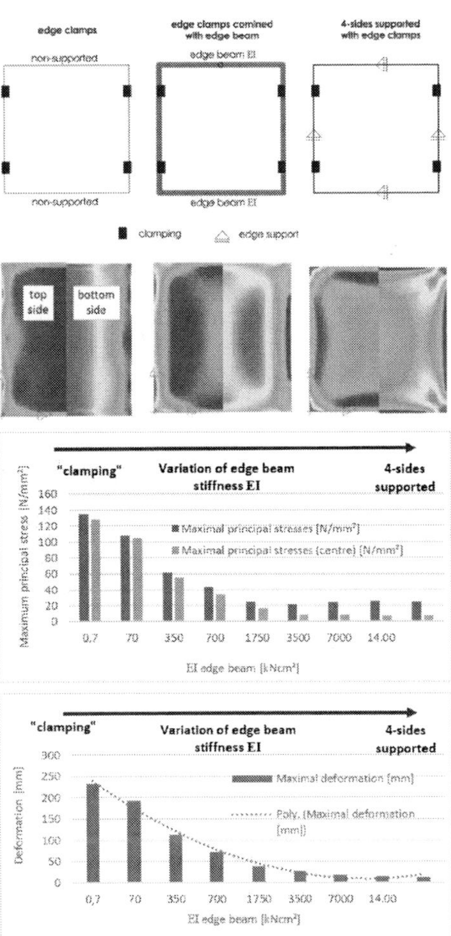

Figure 9: Maximum principal stresses and deformation depending on the bending stiffness EI of the frame (dimension 1000 mm x 1000 mm, laminate of 2 x 1.6 mm, no shear coupling, q = 1 kN/m²)

Using the FEM-program ANSYS the edge beam can be modelled with volume elements according to the real geometry of the module frame.

Figure 10 shows the results for the dimension of 1000 mm x 1000 mm, monolithic pane of 2.5 mm with a constant distributed load of 2 kN/m². The results are influenced by the chosen boundary conditions between the glass and the module frame. In glass in building restraints from the edge cover of a façade plate is generally neglected, due to thicker glass plates (height ≥ 3 mm) the influence of the edge cover on the stress distribution is low. However, in case of a PV-element, the edge cover has in combination with the bending and torsional stiffness of the frame a significant influence on the stress distribution in the glass (see Figure 10).

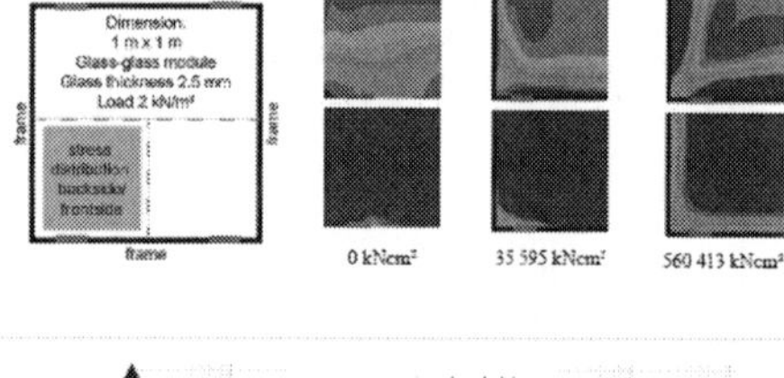

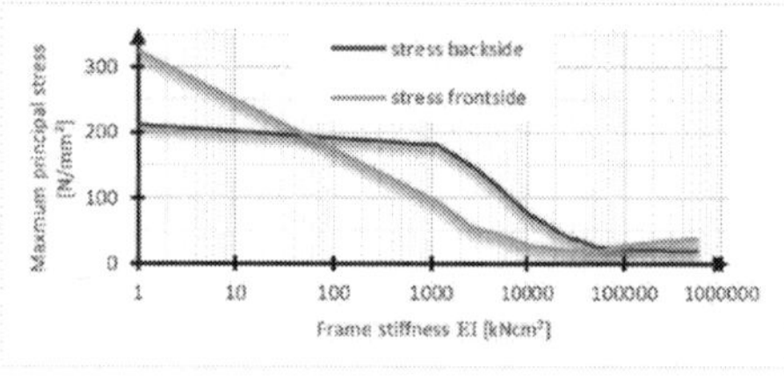

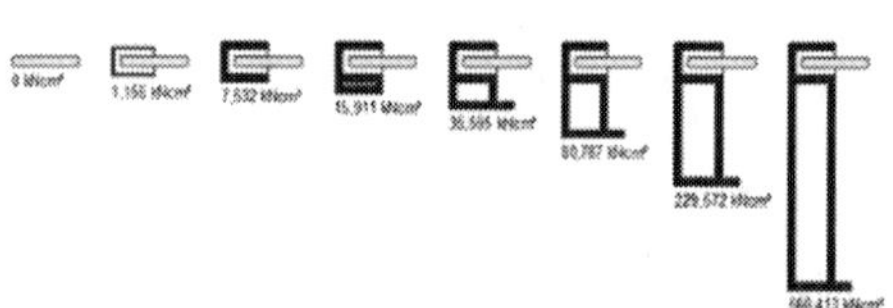

Figure 10: Maximum principal stresses depending on the bending stiffness EI of the frame (dimension 1000 mm x 1000 mm, monolithic pane of 2 mm, q = 2 kN/m²) [29]

3.4 Influence of frame stiffness and module mounting

The results shown in Chapter 3.3 are related to a module fixed with four clamps at two opposite edges. These results cannot be transferred to arbitrary mounting situation. For example, stress and deformation for a mounting situation with an overhang (mechanically equal to a cantilever) are shown in Figure 11. For the mounting situation and dimension analyzed in Chapter 3.3, a beam bending stiffness of EI = 14000 kNcm² gives a stress distribution similar to a 4-sided-suppported pane. Here, the determined span is the length of the cantilever: maximum deformation of the frame L/200 = 700 mm/200 = 3.5 m. The value of the maximum deformation of the cantilever is with 50 mm a multiple of this value, so that the deformation of the substructure (here the frame) has influence on the stress distribution which is approximately 30% higher compared to a stiff support.

3.5 Conclusions

The parameters demonstrated above have a large impact on the load bearing capacity of a PV module. The parameters are:

- glass height and span,
- stiffness of the interlayer (material, load duration, temperature),
- span,
- bending and torsional stiffness of the module frame and
- support conditions of the PV-module,

For example, the stiffness of the interlayer is a major factor which cannot be evaluated by a single load test. The question is how to define the "load bearing capacity" of a PV-module. The target is to find a method to give a design load or module properties which can be the basis for a reliability evaluation to ensure solar systems with a minimal breakage risk.

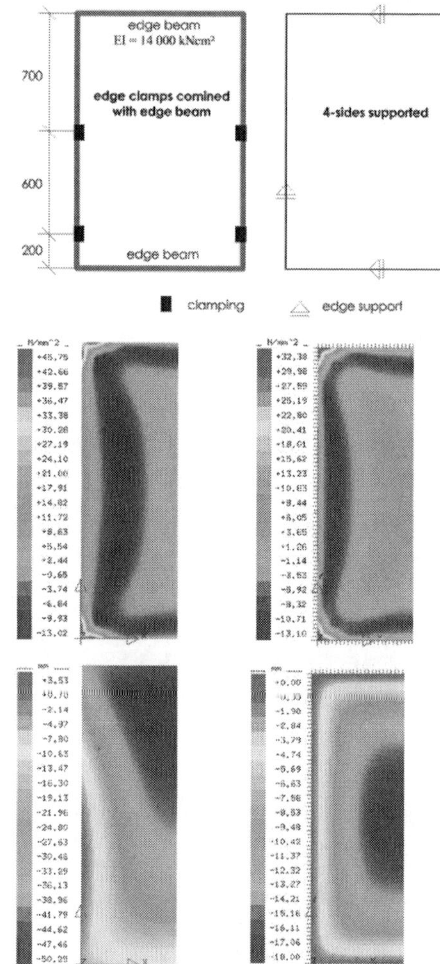

Figure 11: Maximum principal stresses and deformation (dimension 1000 mm x 1500 mm, laminate of 2 x 1.6 mm, no shear coupling, q = 1 kN/m², EI = 14,000 kNcm²)

4 SAFETY CONCEPT ACCORDING TO EUROCODE

4.1 General verification concept

The development of harmonized European design standards began 50 years ago [11]. For the past 20 years, Eurocodes (EC) have formed the basis for designing structures and their associated components, such as façades and glass components.

EC 0 describes the fundamentals of structural design by the partial safety concept [27]. This concept aims to ensure the safety and serviceability of structures by using differently weighted safety factors. This concept separates effects (loads, "E") and resistances (material properties, "R") for safety assessments. Rather than using a uniform global safety factor, a differentiated approach is employed, wherein separate safety factors are defined for actions (γ_F) and material resistances (γ_M). These factors account for uncertainties in actions that can affect a structure. Actions can be permanent or variable and include loads such as dead loads, live loads, wind loads, snow loads, and others. The magnitude of the safety factor reflects the variability and uncertainty of these loads. Material safety factors account for uncertainties in material properties and manufacturing processes. These factors vary depending on the material, for example, steel, aluminum or glass, and address variations in material strength due to manufacturing tolerances or natural variability. The basic idea behind the partial safety concept is to convert characteristic values into design values. For design purposes, the characteristic value of an action is multiplied by the corresponding safety factor, while the characteristic resistance value is divided by its safety factor. The design formula is generally written to:

$$E_k \cdot \gamma_F \geq \frac{R_k}{\gamma_M} \qquad (18)$$

with

E_k characteristic effects (stresses)

γ_F partial safety factor on the load side (F = "forces")

R_k characteristic resistance

γ_M material partial safety factor

The global safety of the structures is equal to:

$$\gamma_{global} = \gamma_F \cdot \gamma_M \qquad (19)$$

and respect a variation of external loading and variation of material data.

Considering the variation of the effects and the variation of the loading in a load test, it leads to an overloaded system with unrealistic deformation and mechanical conditions (e.g. unwanted load paths or similar). It is more appropriate to carry out a calculation with characteristic load combination and multiplying the result with the corresponding partial safety factor. The result is then compared with the characteristic strength divided by the material partial factor γ_M.

4.2 Wind and snow loading and design load combination

Wind and snow loading are regulated by the National Annexes of the Eurocode. Clearly, the climatic conditions at building sites differ depending on climate in the northern Europe, next to the sea, or in the Mediterranean. For this reason, every nation defined wind and snow zones.

For example, a gust speed pressure (mean value over gust period of 2-4 seconds, annual probability of occurrence of 2%) is assigned to the wind zones depending on the wind speed. The acting wind pressure is calculated depending on the geometry and the height of the building, the installation position (façade or roof) and the size of an element. Due to the small dimension of a solar element (2-3 m²), the mean wind value is higher than the mean value for a dimension larger than 10 m².

In analogy snow zone maps localize the characteristic snow loads (98% fractal value with an annual exceedance probability of 0.02 and a return period of 50 years). The geometry of the roof must be respected to consider slipping or drifting effects.

Clearly, the worst snow event and the worst storm will not occur simultaneously. The combination factors Ψ_i take this effect into account: $\Psi_{1,wind} = 0.6$ and $\Psi_{1,snow} = 0.5$.

The design load according to Eurocode is written to:

$$q_d = max \begin{vmatrix} 1{,}35\ g + 1{,}5\ (w_{pressure} + 0.5\ s) \\ 1{,}35\ g + 1{,}5\ (s + 0.6\ w_{pressure}) \\ g + 1{,}5\ w_{suction} \end{vmatrix} \qquad (20)$$

with

g   self weight

s   snow

g   wind

Conversely, for standardized elements the maximum design load q_d can be defined.

Table 1 exemplary shows how the requirements vary considerably depending on the construction site. Important for a better understanding is that the design load $q_{d,max}$ does not correspond to a test load.

Table 1 Examples: Design load due to wind and snow loading for two different construction sites in Germany

	Cologne (snow zone and wind zone 1)	Sylt (snow zone 2 and wind zone 4)
S_k *	0,65 kN/m²	0,85 kN/m²
$w_{k,suction}$ **	-1,0 kN/m²	-2,8 kN/m²
$w_{k,pressure}$ **	0,55 kN/m²	1,7 kN/m²
$q_{d,max}$	1,5 kN/m²	4,2 kN/m²

* characteristic snow load on the ground without snow accumulation

** Assumptions: building height < 10 m, flow conditions of the wind comparable to canopies

4.3 Calculation of the effects

After evaluation of the design load q_d, the effects due to the loading E_d can be calculated. In case of a thin glass plate with favorable membrane effects, the partial safety factor should be applied after the calculation of the stresses in the system. Because of the small ratio g/q_d the characteristic stresses may be multiplied on the safe side with the partial factor $\gamma_F = 1.5$.

As shown in Chapter 3, multiple parameters are influencing the value and distribution of the maximum principal stresses, which are the determined fracture criterion for glass.

4.4 Design value

The expression

$$R_d = \frac{R_k}{\gamma_M} \qquad (21)$$

with

R_d design value

γ_M material partial factor

is a general definition for all type of construction materials and it is defined in the material codes (e.g. EC3 for steel or EC9 aluminum). Because of the small variation in strength the material partial factor of steel is equal to $\gamma_M = 1.0$ the material partial factor for aluminum is equal to $\gamma_M = 1.1$.

The design value for pre-stressed glass is more sophisticated because of the influence of the pre-stress. Furthermore, the material partial safety factor is higher compared to aluminum because of the large variation in strength:

$$R_d = f_{gd} =$$

$$k_e \cdot k_{mod} \cdot \frac{k_{sp} \cdot f_{g,k}}{\gamma_M} + k_p \cdot k_{e,p} \cdot \frac{f_{b,k} - f_{g,k}}{k_i \gamma_p} \qquad (22)$$

with

k_e edge or hole finishing factor

k_{mod} modification factor on load duration

k_{sp} surface treatment factor

$f_{g,k}$ characteristic value of bending strength of annealed glass

γ_M material partial factor

k_p coefficient accounting for the reduction of the process-induced prestress

$k_{e,p}$ edge or hole prestress factor

$f_{b,k}$ characteristic value of bending strength of annealed glass

k_i interference factor

γ_p partial safety factor for prestress on the surface

Clearly, proofed material data are necessary to determine a design value.

Since glass has a very wide range of strengths due to its material properties, the characteristic strength is described using the 5% quantile with a confidence level of 95%. Figure 12 shows the frequency distribution of 2 mm thick solar glass from Glasmanufaktur Brandenburg (GMB) [28]. The strength range shown there (119 N/mm² - 198 N/mm²) is typical for glass as a material and clearly illustrates the large variations.

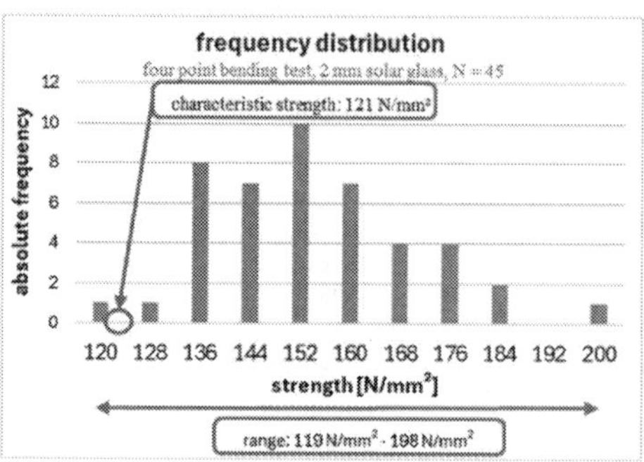

Figure 12: frequency distribution of solar glass by GMB [28]

Considering material data from test of solar glass (GMB), the design value is written according to EC10 to:

$$R_d = f_{gd} =$$

$$0.8 \cdot 1.0 \cdot \frac{0.75 \cdot 45}{1.8} + 1.0 \cdot 1.0 \cdot \frac{120 - 45}{1.0 \cdot 1.2} = 77.5 \ \text{N/mm}^2 \qquad (23)$$

The effects E_d in the glass due to the design load q_d must be smaller than the design value R_d.

5 COMPARISON AND GUIDELINE

Finally, the procedures of Eurocode and IEC 61215 are illustrated and compared in Figure 13. The design method of the Eurocode from material and the loading side is based on statistical basis and proofed values are available for the load (EC1) and the material side (e.g. EC10 for glass in building). For a reliable design of solar modules, strength values for PV modules are always necessary. In comparison, the informativeness of the test method of IEC is limited due to the small number of tests and the unknown breakage stress and therefore unknown breakage strength. Additionally, there is no informativeness about the input data which have to be compared with the design load according to Chapter 4.2.

In first instance, the procedure according to Eurocode seems not appropriate for "systems". But inversely, by a calculative optimization a maximum design load can be given in combination with the system data and support conditions. Finally, the usability of a solar system can be checked depending on the construction site and if necessary, targeted reinforcement of the system can be developed to avoid cost intensive replacement of modules and waste of resources after damage.

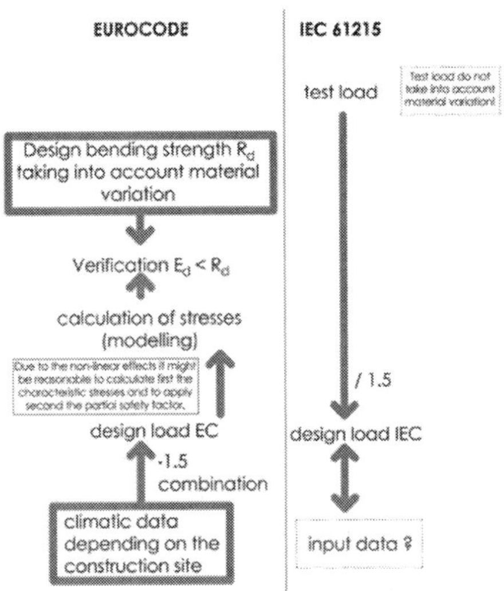

Figure 13: Comparison of Eurocode and test method of IEC 61215

6 OUTLOOK

The application of the Eurocode method might be appropriate to avoid cost intensive damage cases. The given values of the Eurocode e.g. concerning the safety level, the building geometries for the determination of the wind load etc. have to be analyzed to adapt the given rules for the special need of the solar industry.

The paper has the aim to raise awareness in the solar industry to change the planning process and the product quality control.

ACKNOLEDGEMENTS

This publication was funded by the Federal Ministry for Economic Affairs and Energy in the project Green Solar Modules under grant number **00EE1161A** and **03EE1161B**. The findings herein reflect the work, and are solely the responsibility, of the authors.

REFERENCEE

[1] Palmiotti, E. C., Springer, M., Zuboy, J., Silverman, T. J., Braid, J. L., et al., "Growing Panes: Investigating the PV Technology Trends Behind Frequent Early Failures in Modern Glass–Glass Modules," IEEE Journal of Photovoltaics, Vol. 15, No. 2, 1 Jan. 2025, pp. 297–308. doi: 10.1109/JPHOTOV.2025.3526170.

[2] International Technology Roadmap for Photovoltaic (ITRPV), 15th Edition, 1 Jan. 2024.

[3] JinkoSolar, "JinkoSolar module datasheet JKM420-440N-54HL4-BDV-D1-EN," URL: https://jinkosolar.eu/wp-content/uploads/JKM420-440N-54HL4R-BDV-F1.2-EN-4.pdf [retrieved 3 June 2025].

[4] International Electrotechnical Commission, "Terrestrial photovoltaic (PV) modules - Design qualification and type approval: Part 2: Test procedures," IEC 61215-2, Feb. 2022.

[5] PV magazine USA, "Spontaneous glass breakage on solar panels on the rise," URL: https://www.pv-magazine.com/2024/06/24/spontaneous-glass-breakage-on-solar-panels-on-the-rise/ [retrieved 14 July 2025].

[6] Silverman, T., Palmiotti, E., Springer, M., Bosco, N., Deceglie, M., et al., "Tough Break: Many Factors Make Glass Breakage More Likely," National Renewable Energy Laboratory, Jan. 2024, URL: https://www.nrel.gov/docs/fy25osti/91695.pdf

[7] T. Weber et al., Glass breakage: A growing phenomenon in largescale PV, PV magazine webinar, 20th Jan. 2023

[8] Solar Builder, "Solar module glass is 'spontaneously breaking' in the field," URL: https://solarbuildermag.com/featured/solar-module-glass-is-spontaneously-breaking-in-the-field/ [retrieved 3 June 2025].

[9] The American Ceramic Society, "Solar panel breakage on the rise as glass thickness decreases and hail severity increases - The American Ceramic Society," URL: https://ceramics.org/ceramic-tech-today/solar-panel-breakage-on-the-rise-as-glass-thickness-decreases-and-hail-severity-increases/ [retrieved 3 June 2025].

[10] "Eurocode 10 – Design of glass structures," prEN 19100 (all parts), Jan. 2024.

[11] https://eurocodes.jrc.ec.europa.eu/ [retrieved 19 September 2025].

[12] International Electrotechnical Commission, "Terrestrial photovoltaic (PV) modules - Design qualification and type approval: Part 1: Test requirements," IEC 61215-1, Feb. 2022.

[13] Matthias Pander, The increasing importance of the substructure for PV modules under high mechanical loads, 40. PV- Symposium 2025, Bad Staffelstein, March 2025. DOI: https://doi.org/10.52825/pv-symposium.v2i

[14] Romer, P., Pethani, K. B., and Beinert, A. J., "Effect of inhomogeneous loads on the mechanics of PV modules," Progress in Photovoltaics: Research and Applications, Vol. 32, No. 2, 1 Jan. 2024, pp. 84–101. doi: 10.1002/pip.3738.

[15] Dietrich, S., Zeller, U., Pander, M., and Ebert, M., "Evaluation of non-uniform mechanical loads on solar modules," 2013 IEEE 39th Photovoltaic Specialists Conference (PVSC), IEEE, 16 Jun. 2013, pp. 2998–3003.

[16] "Glass in Buildings - Design and construction rules: Part 1: Termes and general bases," DIN 18008-1, 1 May 2020.

[17] "Eurocode: Basis of structural design," EN 1990 (all parts), 1 Jan. 2021.

[18] Markert, J., Ensslen, F., Rist, T., Beinert, A. J., Job, E., et al., "Mechanical Stability of PV Modules," PV-Symposium Proceedings, Vol. 1, 1 Jan. 2024. doi: 10.52825/pv-symposium.v1i.1237.

[19] CSI Solar Co. Ltd., "CS-Datasheet-TOPBiHiKu7(Topcon)_CS7N-TB-AG_Bifacial

High efficiency," URL:
https://static.csisolar.com/wp-content/uploads/2025/05/14135820/CS-Datasheet-TOPBiHiKu7_CS7N-TB-AG_v1.9_EN.pdf [retrieved 4 August 2025].

[20] JinkoSolar, "JinkoSolar Photovoltaic Modules Installation Manual," URL: https://jinkosolarcdn.shwebspace.com/uploads/JinkoSolar%20Global%20Installation%20Manual_202506_A1.5.pdf [retrieved 31 July 2025].

[21] Valentín, D., Valero, C., Egusquiza, M., and Presas, A., "Failure investigation of a solar tracker due to wind-induced torsional galloping," *Engineering Failure Analysis*, Vol. 135, Jan. 2022, p. 106137. doi: 10.1016/j.engfailanal.2022.106137.

[22] CSI Solar Co. Ltd., "Installation Manual of Photovoltaic Module v3.0" URL: https://static.csisolar.com/wp-content/uploads/sites/9/2025/08/04091415/CS_Installation-Manual_PV-Modules_EN-v3.0-EN.pdf

[23] Feldmann, M. et al. (2023): The New CEN/TS 19100: Design of Glass Structures. In: Glass Structures and Engineering.

[24] Vrouwenvelder, T. et al. (2024): Reliabilty background of the Eurocodes – Support to the implementation and further development of the Eurocodes. JRC139110

[25] Leicher, G.; Kasper, R. , Kasper, J. (2022): Tragwerkslehre in Beispielen und Zeichnungen. 5. Auflage. Reguvis Verlag

[26] https://www.mepla.net/

[27] EN 1990 (all parts) (2021) Eurocode: Basis of structural design.

[28] Reichart, H., Pander, M., Kasper, R., „Determining the strength of solar glass – test and evaluation methods" Progress in Photovoltaics: Research and Applications, in review process

[29] Jan Spelthahn (2025) Parametrische Betrachtung des Tragverhaltens von Solarmodulen in Abhängigkeit der Glaslagerung (unpublished). TH Köln.

[30] DIN 18008-2 (2020) Glass in Building – Design and construction rules - Part 2: Linearly supported glazings

3AV.2.42

Determination the reliability of solar modules in analogy to glass in buildings

R. Kasper, H. Reichart
TH Köln-University of Applied Sciences
IKI Institut für konstruktiver Ingenieurbau
Contact: ruth.kasper@th-koeln.de

Technology
Arts Sciences
TH Köln

MOTIVATION

In recent years, photovoltaic (PV) modules have doubled in size, introducing XXL modules around 3 m² that challenge mechanical load management. Simultaneously, glass thickness in glass-glass modules has reduced to below 2 mm, along with decreased frame stiffness, leading to increased breakage and earning them the moniker "big floppy modules". The current MQT 16 static load test according to IEC 61215 inadequately represents real-world damage scenarios as it doesn't take into account material strength variability, time and temperature depending behavior of the interlayer. Adopting the construction industry's design methods (EUROCODE), which use a partial safety concept accounting for load and material variations, could better ensure PV module structural reliability. Since decades, façade and roof elements made of the brittle material glass with individual shapes, boundary conditions and varying loading conditions are effectively used with a minimal breakage risk designed exclusively by calculation. First, this poster examines the load-bearing interaction of materials, mounting, and mechanics in glass-glass modules. Second, the established reliability methods of the construction industry is explained.

Material and geometrical factors influencing the stress state

GLASS AND INTERLAYER INTERACTION

The stress distribution across the thickness in a glass-glass-laminate is – besides the glass thickness - hardly influenced by the shear stiffness G of the encapsulation material. The shear stiffness itself depends on the load duration and the temperature. The real stress state lies in between of "no shear coupling" and "full coupling".

FRAMING AND CLAMPING

Frame stiffness EI (= E-Modulus · Area moment of inertia) hardly influences the stress distribution and the resulting maximal principal stresses in the glass. Stiffer frames induce clamping effects at the edges and lower stresses in the center.

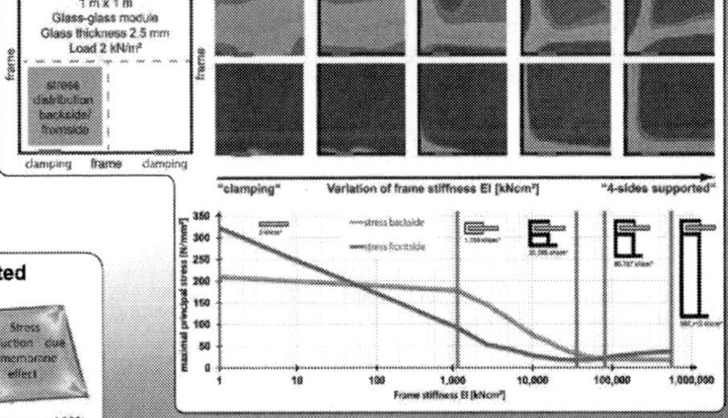

MECHANICAL SYSTEM, LOAD TRANSFER AND MECHANICAL CALCULATION THEORY

Stress distribution and deflection in the glass laminate depends highly on the load transfer and the calculation theory (linear plate theory or membrane theory).

CONCLUSION The stress distribution in a PV element due to external loading must be evaluated to estimate the stress state.

Material Strength Data

Test and material standards are the basis for a reliable structural design

EUROPEAN GLASS PRODUCT STANDARDS BASED ON EN 1288-3

Characteristic strength f_k = 5% quantile value at a 95% confidence level (glass thickness ≥ 3 mm)

Float glass (EN 572-1) $fk = 45$ N/mm²	Heat strengthened glass (EN 1863-1) $fk = 70$ N/mm²	Thermally toughened glass (EN 12150-1) $fk = 120$ N/mm²

SOLAR GLASS

Experimental tests and evaluation for solar glass shows material strength range from 119 to 198 N/mm² which results in a characteristic bending strength of 121 N/mm² (Glass producer GMB Germany). The large scattering is typical for the material glass.

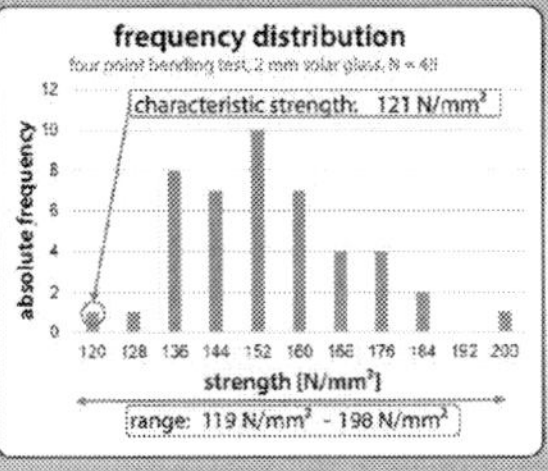

FRAME MATERIAL

For all constructive materials (steel or aluminum) reliable material data and product standards are available.

CONCLUSION A static load test according to IEC 61215 can not determine the strength scattering of the load bearing elements, so that the load bearing capacity of a PV element can not be evaluated by testing.

Safety concept according to EUROCODE

DESIGN VALUE OF EFFECTS

$$E_d < R_d$$

1. Wind and snow loads (EUROCODE 1) with climatic zones according to the national annex

2. Calculation of maximum stresses σ_{max} (characteristic effect) using a suitable calculation model

3. $E_d = \gamma_F \cdot \sigma_{max}$

DESIGN VALUE OF RESISTANCE

1. Reduction of the characteristic material strength f_k by individual material safety factor depending on the frequency distribution:
e.g. $\gamma_{M,Glass} = 1.5$, $\gamma_{M,Aluminum} = 1.1$
(Design according to e.g. EC9 for aluminum, EC10 for glass or EC3 for steel)

2. $R_d = f_k / \gamma_M$

CONCLUSION The global safety factor is the product of the partial safety factors $\gamma_{global} = \gamma_F \cdot \gamma_M$ and considers the variation of effects and material. Vice versa, a maximal design load respecting the variation of the material strength and of the effects can be determined.

Outlook

In combination with the load test according to IEC 61215 a theoretical assessment for the evaluation of the load bearing capacity is absolutely necessary. A roll model can be the safety concept according to the EUROCODES which has been used successfully in the construction industry to minimize the failure risk. The basis are proofed material data. Further research is necessary to evaluate the boundary effects with regard to the stress state (= "effects").

References

References, detailed information and further explanations can be found in the additional paper published in the Conference Proceeding.

Federal Ministry for Economic Affairs and Energy

This publication was funded by the Federal Ministry for Economic Affairs and Energy in the project Green Solar Modules under grant number 00EE1161A and 03EE1161B. The findings herein reflect the work, and are solely the responsibility, of the authors.

A VISUAL INSPECTION DATA COLLECTION TOOL FOR FLOATING PHOTOVOLTAIC SYSTEMS

Nathan Roosloot[1,2*], Harsha Walpita[2,1], Christoph Seiffert[1], Jean Thomas[3], Maarten Dörenkämper[4], Minne de Jong[4], Josefine H. Selj[1], Gaute Otnes[1]
[1]Institute for Energy Technology, Kjeller, Norway
[2]University of Oslo, Oslo, Norway
[3]Ciel et Terre, Lille, France
[4]TNO, Eindhoven, The Netherlands
*email: nathan.roosloot@ife.no

ABSTRACT: Floating photovoltaic (FPV) system reliability depends on the reliable performance of all system components, with degradation and/or failure of even a single element potentially leading to more extensive failure. Yet, most FPV reliability research to date has focused on the PV modules, leaving other components underexplored. To help address this gap, we here present a data collection tool for visual inspection of FPV systems. The tool complements existing tools for PV modules and enables the quantifiable assessment of visual defects on all non-module components in any FPV system. As such, it facilitates the evaluation of (long-term) visually observable degradation and/or failure in FPV systems and enables correlational analysis with system design and site-specific stressors, informing targeted system improvements and operations & maintenance (O&M) strategies. Lastly, if outputs are openly shared, large-scale use of the tool can provide statistics on FPV system degradation that can help derisk the sector as a whole.

KEYWORDS: Floating photovoltaics, reliability, visual inspection

1 INTRODUCTION

The floating photovoltaic (FPV) sector, where PV modules are mounted on floating structures on top of water bodies, is a relatively young but rapidly growing segment of the PV market. The global installed FPV capacity more than quadrupled between 2020 and 2024, reaching over 9 GW [1], with a further 20 GW of installations forecasted until 2030 [2]. The main driver behind the growth of FPV is the use of water bodies for electricity generation in cases where land area is unsuitable or too expensive for PV deployment. In addition, FPV can have several other benefits, such as installation close to areas of high electricity demand, dual use of water bodies, potential reduced evaporation of water and lower module operating temperatures [3], [4]. However, forecasted installations are still far from the global technical potential of FPV, which can for example be up to 7.6 TW for FPV systems on hydropower reservoirs alone, assuming a reservoir coverage of 20% [5].

The FPV market faces several obstacles to reaching its full technical potential, including legislative barriers, cost competitiveness with ground mounted PV (GPV), and uncertainties regarding environmental impacts, energy yield and reliability. Uncertainties regarding FPV system reliability primarily stem from expectations that these systems will be subjected to significantly different stress levels than GPV installations, while publicly available data on observed degradation or failures of FPV installations, which can be used as a basis for evaluating these expectations, are scarce. This is mainly caused by the fact that observations of degradation and/or failure on operational FPV systems are rarely openly shared. This can be attributed to fierce competition between the large number of FPV system suppliers [6], leading to confidentiality and limited data sharing. This ultimately reduces bankability as the sector lacks statistics on expected degradation rates, while research and development to improve system reliability, if needed, is slowed down. However, even if data were openly shared, mid- to end-of-life degradation and/or failure modes can typically not be evaluated, as most FPV systems are too young to have encountered these, with more than 75% of the global installed FPV capacity being less than 5 years old at the end of 2024 [1].

In addition to potential stress level differences, variations in system design can also affect FPV reliability compared to GPV. A FPV system, of which an example is sketched in Figure 1, typically consists of more components than a GPV one of similar size, with modules mounted on (interconnected) floats, which are held in place by mooring and anchoring systems, rather than on mounting systems that go straight into the ground. In addition, much of the electrical infrastructure might be placed on water too, requiring more floating parts. A comprehensive overview of FPV system components can be found in [7], [8].

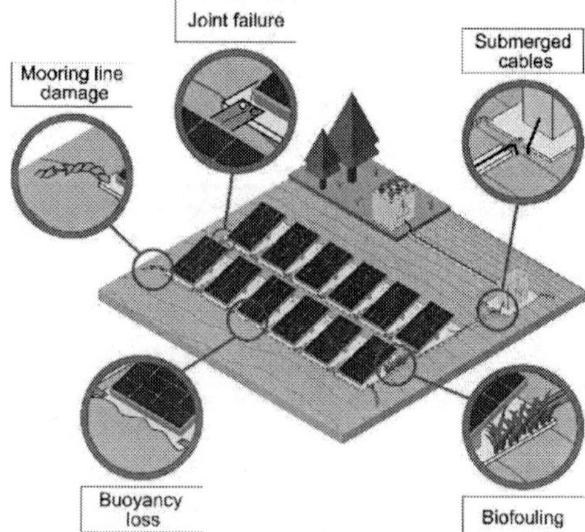

Figure 1: Sketch of an FPV system with examples of potential visually observable non-module defects.

In addition to having more components, the dynamic behavior of the FPV system on the water can increase the chance of parts failing, while the failure of even a single element, of which some examples are given in Figure 1, can potentially lead to wider system issues (for example due to sinking), something that is more rare for GPV cases. All in all, FPV system reliability is thus highly dependent on the reliable performance of all system components. In fact, several examples of FPV component and sometimes subsequent system degradation and/or failure have been observed in the field [7]. Yet, in FPV reliability literature, focus is typically on the module only.

A common way in which module health in the field is assessed is by visual inspection, which can be performed without the use of specialized equipment or in-depth PV knowledge. While visual inspection can give insights into the visually observable effects of degradation and/or failure, it does not necessarily reveal the underlying causes. However, it is complementary to more in-depth characterization techniques where the opposite might be true. As a result, visual inspection is typically a standard part of module health assessments.

When performing visual inspection, it is crucial that outputs are recorded in a consistent, user-independent and quantifiable manner, so that inspections of different systems or the same system over time can quantitatively be compared. For this reason, a standardized data collection tool for visual inspection of PV modules has been created at NREL [9], and adopted by Task 13 of the International Energy Agency's Photovoltaic Power Systems Programme (IEA PVPS) [10], with recommendations for use as an international standard for visual inspection in the field.

Due to the dependence of FPV system reliability on other components than the module, as mentioned before, a similar tool for the visual inspection of these components could be of great use, and is hence presented in this work. For individual FPV systems, the tool allows system conditions to be tracked over time, and visual observations of degradation and/or failure to be linked to system design and site-specific conditions, allowing for targeted system improvements and operations & maintenance (O&M) actions where necessary. Larger scale data collection allows for the statistical analysis of relationships between system degradation and/or failure and FPV system type, water body type and climate conditions. Additionally, large-scale statistics of FPV system degradation would give investors and insurers greater confidence in long-term performance, thereby facilitating financing and wider deployment.

In the next section, the tool and explanations for its use are given.

2 FPV VISUAL INSPECTION DATA COLLECTION TOOL

The FPV visual inspection data collection tool can be used to collect data on any component on the DC side of any FPV system except for the PV modules themselves, for which the tool from [10] can be used. The FPV tool was made in the same format as the tool from [10] to ensure complimentary between the two. The tool is based on a combination of published literature on FPV system reliability and first-hand experience from visual inspections of a wide range of FPV installations. In addition, it has been reviewed by international FPV experts from both industry and academia. To balance detail, ease of use, and the time required to complete, the tool combines multiple-choice items with open questions, the latter allowing respondents to provide additional information not captured by the fixed options. The tool is meant to be filled out once for an entire system and thus benefits from access to the full system for visual inspection. If this is not the case, relevant information can still be gained from filling out the tool for the accessible parts only. It is then recommended to indicate what parts

of the system were assessed in the tool.

In total, the tool focuses on four parts of the FPV system, each of which have their own section: (1) the floating system, (2) mooring and anchoring, (3) cables and inverters and (4) other relevant technologies. Due to the multitude of different FPV technologies in the market, the tool does not only include a description of damage to these parts, but also a more general description of the system components themselves. The description of the components are in part A of each section, while the damage description are in part B. An accurate description of the system can greatly aid in understanding what type of damage is seen and how it relates to the FPV design. However, such a description is not always necessary when the inspection is done on a known system with no plans to share the results beyond those that are familiar with it. In such cases, parts A of the checklist can be omitted for quicker inspection.

Section 1 of the tool focuses on the float technology. This includes all buoyant components and their interconnections, such as floats and float-to-float connectors, as well as the module mounting structures attached to them. The tool requires assessment of the entire floating system, which can be divided into two lower levels: interconnected floating islands/arrays and individual floats that make up the islands. An example of a floating system with two floating islands is given in Figure 2, while a single floating island with individually interconnected floats are shown in Figure 1. Note that this division does not apply to all FPV systems.

Figure 2: Example of a floating PV system that consists of two floating islands. Image courtesy of Ciel et Terre.

Section 2 of the tool looks at the mooring and anchoring system. Terminology for mooring and anchoring types are derived from [8].

Section 3 covers cables and inverters. As damage to module cables and interconnectors are already covered in [10], these are not included here. Instead, the tool considers placement and attachment of the cables and related components to the floating system. To keep the tool comprehensive, the AC side of the electrical system is not included.

Lastly, section 4 focuses on other technologies that might be present on FPV systems, including cooling and/or anti-soiling technologies and tracking systems. The questions in this section can also be used to provide information of other, rarer, technologies not included here, such as concentrator systems.

When filling out the inspection tool, the use of a measurement device and a camera are recommended to take measurements and images of relevant components and defects. To have images and the filled out inspection tool in the same location, digitalization of this tool can be of aid. The authors of this work also use a digitalized version of this tool for personal use. However, because of limitations in how easily this could be shared, this paper version is shared instead. In case of interest in use of the digital tool, please reach out to the corresponding author.

FPV system visual inspection data collection tool

Documentation of FPV system condition for field exposed systems

Date _________________ Name of recorder _________________________

System name____

Latitude _______________ Longitude ________________ Altitude _______________

1. Float technology

Floating system here refers to the entire FPV plant (of the same technology). The system can consist of several floating islands/arrays, which each can consist of several individually connected floats

1A – System description

1A.1 Floating system technology provider (Original Equipment Manufacturer) _______

____

1A.2 Floating system product name/model _________________________

1A.3 Is the system deployed? *Jump to question 1A.5 if answering 'Yes, on water' or 'No'* ☐ Yes, on water ☐ Yes, on land ☐ No (explain where system was surveyed): _______________

1A.4 Why is the system deployed on land? ☐ Intended amphibious operation ☐ Drought ☐ System not yet deployed on water ☐ Unknown ☐ Other _______________

1A.5 Approximate size of floating system *Either in m^2 or length x width (m x m)* ______________

1A.6 Number of modules on floating system *Capacity can be given also. Specify unit* _________

1A.7 Does the floating system consist of several floating islands/arrays? *Jump to question 1A.9 if answering 'No' or 'Unclear/Unknown'* ☐ Yes ☐ No ☐ Unclear/Unknown

1A.8 Number of floating islands/arrays on system _____________________

1A.9 Does the floating system consist of individually connected floats? *Jump to question 1A.15 if answering 'No' or 'Unclear/Unknown'* ☐ Yes ☐ No ☐ Unclear/Unknown

1A.10 Number of individual floats on system _____________________

1A.11 Do all individual floats contain modules? *Jump to question 1A.13 if answering 'Yes'* ☐ Yes ☐ No

1A.12 Describe location and rough fraction of all floats that do not contain modules *Add reason why no modules are present on these floats, if known* _____________________

____

1A.13 Amount of modules per individual float *Only for floats that contain modules* _________

1A.14 Are all individual floats of the same type? *Jump to question 1A.16 if answering 'Yes'* ☐ Yes ☐ No

1A.15 Describe how the individual floats differ and what part of the system consists of what float type *It is recommended to fill in the full tool once per float type* _______________

____

1A.16 Describe how the individual floats are connected *E.g. directly to each other, or by material in between (e.g. hinges). Describe connection points including location, number, dimensions and type of material if possible.* _____________________

____

1A.17 Float material(s) *Mark all that apply* ☐ Aluminium ☐ Steel ☐ Plastics (specify under 'other' if type is known) ☐ Cement ☐ Unknown ☐ Other _______________

1A.18 PV module mounting system materials *Mark all that apply* □ Same as float materials □ Aluminium □ Steel □ Plastics (specify under 'other' if type is known) □ Cement □ Unknown □ Other _________________

1A.19 Type of attachment of module to mounting system *Mark all that apply* □ Clamps □ Adhesive (glue/silicone/etc) □ Bolting □ Other _________________

1A.20 Location of attachment of module to mounting system *Mark all that apply* □ At edges □ In corners □ Across part of backside □ Across full backside □ Along full frame □ In middle □ Other _________________

1A.21 How does one move on the floating system? *Mark all that apply* □ Pathways to walk between modules □ Walking over modules □ Not possible to move □ Other _________________

1A.22 Are all modules accessible for visual inspection? *Jump to question 1A.24 if answering 'Yes' or 'Unknown/unclear'* □ Yes □ No □ Unknown/unclear

1A.23 If not all modules are accessible for visual inspection, explain why _________________
____

1A.24 Approximate inclination of the panels *0° = flat on water, 90° = vertical* _________________

1A.25 Direction panels are facing *Mark all that apply* □ North □ North-East □ East □ South-East □ South □ South-West □ West □ North-West □ Varying □ Single-axis zenith East-West tracking □ Single-axis zenith North-South tracking □ Single axis azimuth tracking □ Dual-axis tracking □ Directly up (0° tilt) □ Unknown

1A.26 If not all panels are facing in the same direction, describe what modules face in what direction ____

1A.27 Approximate height of panels above water (cm) *Use lowest panel-water distance according to design (in case of no damage)* _________________

1A.28 Does the floating system cover the water surface directly underneath the modules? *Jump to question 1A.30 if answering 'Yes'. Answer 'No' or 'Partly' if theoretically possible to touch the water at any location directly underneath the module.* □ Yes □ No □ Partly

1A.29 Describe the space and size of the floating system underneath the module, focusing on water coverage *E.g. 'rectangular gap in float approximately half the length of the module' or '30 cm wide beam across middle of module backside'. Add measurements if possible.* _________________

1A.30 Other relevant information for float description *Only focus on description of the floating system that is not covered by the questions above. Description of other components (mooring lines, anchors, cables) will come in the following sections.* ____

1B - System damage

The questions in this section refer to damage to the entire floating system, not of a single individual float.

1B.1 Float and/or PV supporting system damage *Jump to question 1B.6 if answering 'Not present/visible'. Damage of mooring lines, anchors and cables are discussed in coming sections and should not be included here* □ Not present/visible □ Small, localized □ Extensive

1B.2 Float damage type *Mark all that apply* □ Corrosion □ Parts fallen/broken off/disconnected □ Scratches/cracks □ Holes □ Fire/burn marks or damage □ Other _________________

1B.3 Float damage location (1) *Mark all that apply* □ Walkways □ Underneath modules □ Between modules □ Attachment between module and supporting system □ Attachment between smaller floats □ Underneath float □ Float edges □ Float corners □ Other _________________

1B.4 Float damage location (2) *If relevant, explain where on the overall system the damage is (e.g. towards N/E/S/W, incoming waves, land, etc)* ____

1B.5 Fraction of floating system affected by damage *If multiple types of damage exist, specify what accounts for what percentage in question 1B.16* ☐ <5% ☐ 5 - 25% ☐ 25 - 75% ☐ 75 - 100% (uniform)

1B.6 Float and/or PV supporting system soiling *Jump to question 1B.11 if answering 'Not present/visible* ☐ Not present/visible ☐ Small, localized ☐ Extensive

1B.7 Float soiling type *Mark all that apply* ☐ Biofouling ☐ Bird soiling ☐ Dust/dirt ☐ Pollen ☐ Bird nests ☐ Other ____________________

1B.8 Float soiling location *Mark all that apply* ☐ Walkways ☐ Underneath modules ☐ Between modules ☐ Attachment between module and supporting system ☐ Attachment between smaller floats ☐ Underneath float ☐ Float edges ☐ Float corners ☐ Other ______________________

1B.9 Float soiling location *If relevant, explain where on the overall system the soiling is (e.g. towards N/E/S/W, incoming waves, land, etc)* ____

1B.10 Fraction of floating system affected by soiling *If multiple types of soiling exist, specify what accounts for what percentage in question 1B.16* ☐ <5% ☐ 5 - 25% ☐ 25 - 75% ☐ 75 - 100% (uniform)

1B.11 Floating system buoyancy *Jump to question 1B.15 if answering 'Buoyant'* ☐ Buoyant ☐ Partially non-buoyant ☐ Completely non-buoyant

1B.12 Fraction of floating system under water ☐ <5% ☐ 5 - 25% ☐ 25 - 75% ☐ 75 - 100% (uniform)

1B.13 Locations of floating system that is under water *Mark all that apply* ☐ Edges ☐ Corners ☐ Walkways between modules ☐ Around/at modules ☐ Random/no pattern ☐ Complete system ☐ Other ____________________

1B.14 Suspected cause of loss of buoyancy ____

1B.15 Describe damage to attachment points *Can be module supporting system to floats and floats to floats.* ____

1B.16 Other relevant information on float damage *Only focus on description of damage to the floating system that is not covered by the other questions in Section 1B* ____

2. Mooring and anchoring

2A - System description

System description of the full mooring and anchoring system

2A.1 Mooring lines *Jump to question 2A.6 if answering 'Not present/visible'* ☐ Present and visible ☐ Not present/visible

2A.2 Amount of mooring lines *If uncertain, write how many are visible* ____

2A.3 Type of mooring lines *Mark all that apply* ☐ Compliant mooring ☐ Taut mooring ☐ Catenary mooring ☐ Rigid piles ☐ Unknown ☐ Other ____________________

2A.4 Mooring line materials *Mark all that apply* ☐ Steel ☐ Fiber (specify type under 'other' if known) ☐ Other ____________________

2A.5 Mooring line attachment *Describe attachment of mooring lines to the floating system and anchoring (including but not limited to used materials, location on system, attachment type)* ____________________

2A.6 Anchors **Jump to section 2A.9 if answering 'Not present/visible'* ☐ Present and visible ☐ Not present/visible

2A.7 Location of anchoring **Mark all that apply* ☐ Under water ☐ On land ☐ Unknown ☐ Other ________________

2A.8 Type of anchoring **Mark all that apply* ☐ Gravity anchor ☐ Pile/helical anchor ☐ Plate anchor ☐ Drag anchor ☐ Unknown ☐ Other ________________

2A.9 Other relevant information on mooring and anchoring **Only focus on description of mooring and anchoring that is not covered by the questions above.* ________________

2B – System damage

Damage description of the full mooring and anchoring system

2B.1 Mooring lines physical state **Jump to question 2B.5 if answering 'No visible issues'* ☐ No visible issues ☐ Damaged ☐ Missing

2B.2 Mooring lines damage type **Mark all that apply* ☐ Corrosion ☐ Biofouling ☐ Breakage ☐ Soiling ☐ Abrasion ☐ Entangled lines ☐ Other ________________

2B.3 Location of mooring line damage **Mark all that apply* ☐ Attachment with floats ☐ Middle of line (above water) ☐ Middle of line (under water) ☐ Attachment with anchors ☐ Other ________________

2B.4 Fraction of mooring lines affected **Fraction of all observable mooring lines. Specify how damage is distributed (e.g. even across all lines, one line with all damage) in question 2B.8 if relevant.* ☐ <5 % ☐ 5 - 25% ☐ 25 - 75% ☐ 75 - 100% (uniform)

2B.5 Anchoring physical state **Jump to question 2B.8 if answering 'No visible issues'* ☐ No visible issues ☐ Damaged ☐ Missing ☐ Not observable

2B.6 Anchoring damage type **Mark all that apply* ☐ Corrosion ☐ Biofouling ☐ Breakage ☐ Soiling ☐ Other ________________

2B.7 Fraction of anchors affected **Fraction of all observable anchors. Specify how damage is distributed (e.g. even across all anchors, one anchor with all damage) in last question of section if relevant.* ☐ <5 % ☐ 5 - 25% ☐ 25 - 75% ☐ 75 - 100% (uniform)

2B.8 Other relevant information on mooring and anchoring damage **Only focus on description of mooring and anchoring damage that is not covered by the questions above.* ________________

3. Cables and inverters

Only covers DC side of the system. For questions regarding wire and connector damage on module level, use the PV module visual inspection data collection tool

3A – System description

Description of the DC cabling and inverters

3A.1 Cables between modules in string **Jump to question 3A.3 if answering 'Not present/visible'* ☐ Present and visible ☐ Not present/visible

3A.2 Placement of cables between modules **Mark all that apply* ☐ Above water, and no contact with water ☐ Above water, but in contact with water ☐ Under water ☐ Other ________________

3A.3 Cable combiner boxes **These combine string cables into larger DC cables. Jump to question 3A.5 if answering 'Not present/visible'* ☐ Present and visible ☐ Not present/visible

3A.4 Placement of cable combiner boxes *Mark all that apply* □ Above water, and no contact with water □ Above water, but in contact with water □ Under water □ Other

____

3A.5 Cables from strings to inverter *Jump to question 3A.7 if answering 'Not present/visible'* □ Present and visible □ Not present/visible

3A.6 Placement of cables to inverter *Mark all that apply* □ Above water, and no contact with water □ Above water, but in contact with water □ Under water □ Other ________________

3A.7 Inverters *Jump to section 3A.10 if answering 'Not present/visible'* □ Present and visible □ Not present/visible

3A.8 Number of inverters _______________________

3A.9 Inverter locations *Mark all that apply* □ On land □ On water □ Unknown

3A.10 Other relevant information on cables and inverters *Only focus on description of cables and inverters that is not covered by the questions above.* __________________________________

3B - System damage
Damage description of the DC cabling and inverters

3B.1 Cable combiner box damage *Mark all that apply* □ No visible issues □ Burn marks/heat discoloration □ Damages/loose glands or cable entries □ Water ingress/condensation □ Corrosion/rust □ Other _______________

3B.2 Cables to inverter damage *Mark all that apply* □ No visible issues □ Pliable, but degraded □ Embrittled □ Cracked/disintegrated insulation □ Burnt □ Corroded □ Animal bites/marks □ Other _______________

3B.3 Attachment of cables/combiner boxes to floats □ No attachments □ No visible issues □ Damaged □ Missing in some locations □ Unknown

3B.4 Inverter physical state *Jump to question 3B.6 if answering 'No visible issues'* □ No visible issues □ Damaged

3B.5 Inverter damage *Mark all that apply* □ Cracks/dents/holes (impact damage) □ Burn marks/heat discoloration □ Damages/loose glands or cable entries □ Water ingress/condensation □ Corrosion/rust □ Labels/markings missing or illegible □ Other

3B.6 Other relevant information on cables and inverters damage *Only focus on description of cable and/or inverter damage that is not covered by the questions above.* ______________________________

4. Additional technologies
Potential additional technologies present on FPV systems: cooling/anti-soiling, tracking or others

4A – System description
Description of additional technologies

4A.1 Is a cooling and/or anti-soiling technology used? *Jump to question 4A.3 if answering 'No' or 'Unknown'* □ Yes □ No □ Unknown

4A.2 Describe the cooling and/or anti-soiling technology __________________________________

4A.3 Is a tracking technology used? *Jump to question 4A.7 if answering 'No' or 'Unknown'* □ Yes □ No □ Unknown

4A.4 Type of tracking technology *Jump to question 4A.6 if answering 'Dual-axis' or 'Unknown'* □ Single-axis □ Dual-axis □ Unknown

4A.5 What axis is tracked? □ Azimuth □ Zenith □ Other ________________

4A.6 Is the tracking technology functioning? ☐ Yes ☐ No ☐ Unknown

4A.7 Other relevant information on damage of other technologies *Only focus on description of cooling/anti-soiling, tracking or other relevant technologies that is not covered by the questions above.*

4B - System damage
Description of damage to additional technologies

4B.1 Cooling/anti-soiling technology damage *Jump to question 4B.4 if answering 'No damage'* ☐ No damage ☐ Small, localized ☐ Extensive

4B.2 Cooling/anti-soiling damage type *Mark all that apply. If cooling and anti-soiling are not the same system, specify which of the two is damaged in question 4B.7.* ☐ Corrosion ☐ Cracks/breakage ☐ Biofouling ☐ Soiling ☐ Other electrical failure (specify in question 4B.7) ☐ Other _______________

4B.3 Cooling/anti-soiling damage location *Mark all that apply* ☐ Connection with floater ☐ Connection with modules ☐ On technology itself ☐ Other _______________

4B.4 Tracker damage *Jump to question 4B.7 if answering 'Not present/visible' or 'Unknown'* ☐ Not present/visible ☐ Small, localized ☐ Extensive

4B.5 Tracker damage type *Mark all that apply* ☐ Corrosion ☐ Cracks/breakage ☐ Biofouling ☐ Soiling ☐ Electrical failure ☐ Abrasion ☐ Entangled lines ☐ Damage to propulsion system ☐ Other _______________

4B.6 Tracker damage location *Mark all that apply* ☐ Connection with floater ☐ Connection with module support ☐ On tracker itself ☐ Other _______________

4B.7 Other relevant information on tracker technology and damage *Only focus on description of damage to cooling/anti-soiling, tracking or other relevant technologies that is not covered by the questions above.* _______________

5. Other remarks

5.1 Other remarks *Further clarification or additional information not covered above. Include location/ID wherever relevant.* _______________

ACKNOWLEDGMENTS

This work was supported by the European Union's Horizon Europe research and innovation program through the project SuRE (grant agreement 101135567).

REFERENCES

[1] T. Reindl, "Overview, Status and Outlook of Floating PV," in *4th International Integrated PV Workshop*, 2025.

[2] International Energy Agency, "Trends In Photovoltaic Applications 2024," 2024.

[3] International Energy Agency, "Trends In Photovoltaic Applications 2023," 2023.

[4] SolarPower Europe, "Floating PV Best Practice Guidelines Version 1.0," 2023.

[5] N. Lee, U. Grunwald, E. Rosenlieb, H. Mirletz, A. Aznar, R. Spencer, and S. Cox, "Hybrid floating solar photovoltaics-hydropower systems: Benefits and global assessment of technical potential," *Renew Energy*, vol. 162, pp. 1415–1427, Dec. 2020, doi: 10.1016/j.renene.2020.08.080.

[6] C. D. Rodríguez-Gallegos, O. Gandhi, H. Sun, C. Paton, J. Zhang, J. Moideen Yacob Ali, M. S. Alvarez-Alvarado, W. Zhang, C. A. Rodríguez-Gallegos, L. H. C. Chua, and T. Reindl, "Global floating PV status and potential," *Progress in Energy*, vol. 7, no. 1, p. 015001, Jan. 2025, doi: 10.1088/2516-1083/ad9074.

[7] IEA PVPS Task 13, "Floating Photovoltaic Power Plants: A Review of Energy Yield, Reliability, and Maintenance," 2025.

[8] H. L. Walpita, N. Roosloot, G. Otnes, B. L. Aarseth, J. Selj, V. S. Nysted, and E. S. Marstein, "Operation and Maintenance of Floating PV Systems: A Review," *IEEE J Photovolt*, vol. 15, no. 3, pp. 400–415, May 2025, doi: 10.1109/JPHOTOV.2025.3548322.

[9] C. E. Packard, J. H. Wohlgemuth, and S. R. Kurtz, "Development of a Visual Inspection Data Collection Tool for Evaluation of Fielded PV Module Condition," in *PV Module Reliability Workshop*, 2012.

[10] M. Kontges *et al.*, "Review of failures of photovoltaic modules," 2014.

A visual inspection data collection tool for floating PV systems

Nathan Roosloot[1,2*]
Harsha Walpita[1,2]
Christoph Seiffert[1]
Jean Thomas[3]

Maarten Dörenkämper[4]
Minne de Jong[4]
Josefine Helene Selj[1]
Gaute Otnes[1]

[1]Institute for Energy Technology, Kjeller, Norway
[2]University of Oslo, Oslo, Norway
[3]Ciel et Terre, Lille, France
[4]TNO, Eindhoven, The Netherlands
*nathan.roosloot@ife.no

Visual inspection is a key tool for identification and assessment of field failures and degradation in PV systems. By using a standardized data collection tool, system conditions can be assessed consistently, allowing for longitudinal analysis and meaningful comparison of system conditions across sites. Due to these benefits, a harmonized collection tool has been developed for PV modules [1], [2]. For floating PV (FPV) systems, module reliability can be strongly affected by degradation and/or failure of other system components. Therefore, this work complements the existing PV module inspection tool with a similar tool to quantify the condition of all other components of an FPV system except for the PV modules. The tool has been developed based on reported (potential) system component degradation in FPV literature and on experience with visual inspections performed on different FPV systems. It has been reviewed by FPV experts both from industry and academia. The tool is shared with the aim of standardizing visual inspection outputs in the FPV sector, thereby contributing to improved system reliability.

Below are examples of potential FPV system component issues that are covered in the visual inspection tool. The full tool is published in the conference proceedings. In addition, it can be found using the QR-code on the right or the link below:
https://docs.google.com/document/d/14kV1Vi6dzO_1TiVqEx11RC1HVFZk9eXej1XA3Zvii8Q/edit

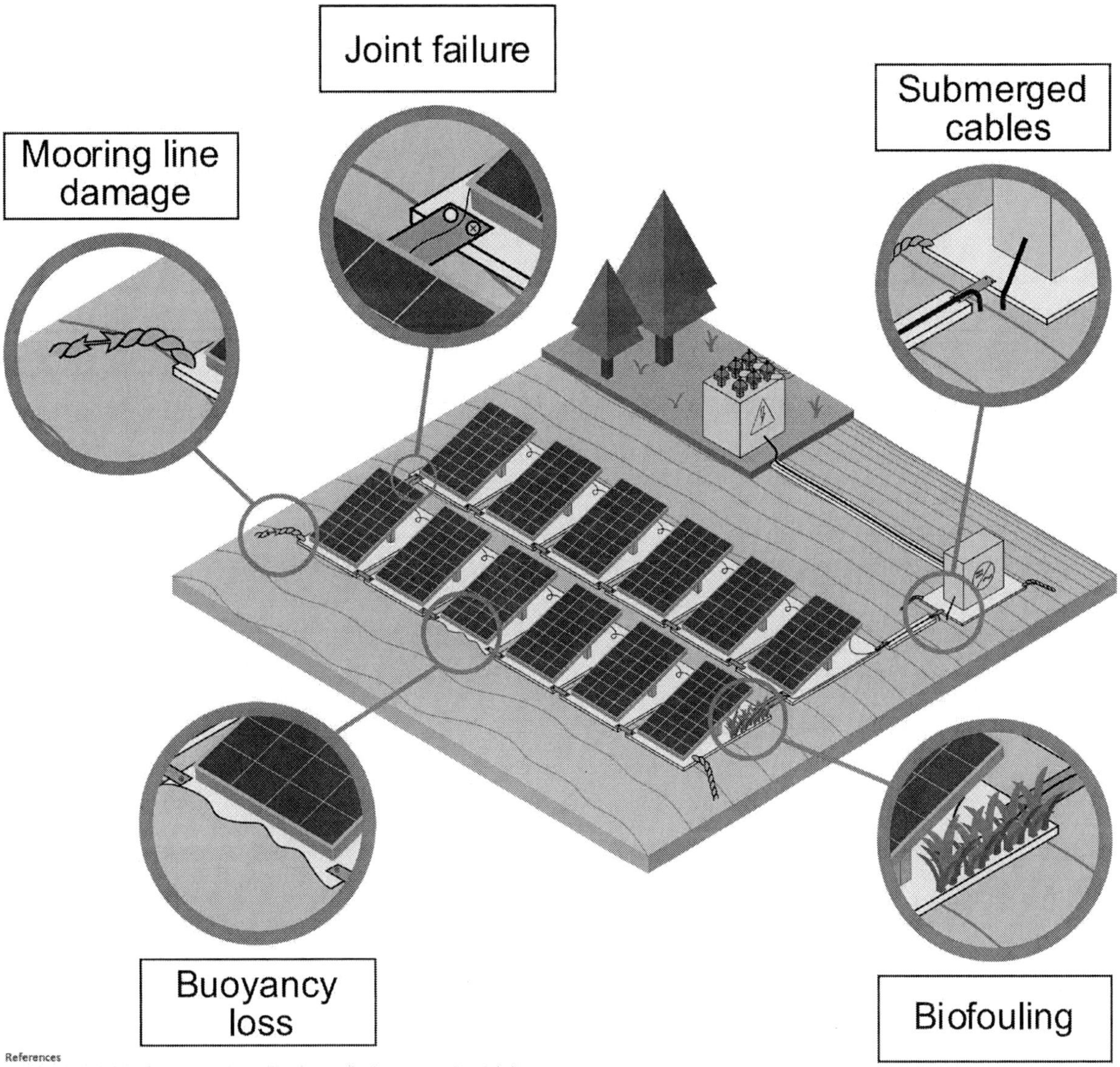

Joint failure

Submerged cables

Mooring line damage

Buoyancy loss

Biofouling

References
1. C. E. Packard, J. H. Wohlgemuth, and S. R. Kurtz, "Development of a Visual Inspection Data Collection Tool for Evaluation of Fielded PV Module Condition," in *PV Module Reliability Workshop*, 2012.
2. M. Köntges et al., "Review of failures of photovoltaic modules," 2014.

SUSTAINABLE, RELIABLE AND EFFICIENT FLOATING PHOTOVOLTAIC POWER PLANTS

THE SOLE RESPONSIBILITY FOR THE CONTENT OF THIS POSTER LIES ONLY WITH THE AUTHORS. IT DOES NOT NECESSARILY REFLECT THE OPINION OF THE EUROPEAN UNION. THE EUROPEAN COMMISSION IS NOT RESPONSIBLE FOR ANY USE THAT MAY BE MADE OF THE INFORMATION CONTAINED THEREIN.

 SuRE project has received funding from the European Union's Horizon Europe research and innovation program grant agreement No 101135567.

020170-001

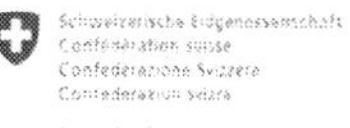 Schweizerische Eidgenossenschaft
Confédération suisse
Confederazione Svizzera
Confederaziun svizra
Swiss Confederation

Federal Department of Economic Affairs, Education and Research EAER
State Secretariat for Education, Research and Innovation SERI

A NEW METHOD FOR COMPREHENSIVE POWER RATING AND PERFORMANCE ANALYSIS OF PERC MODULES BASED ON HALF-CUT CELL TECHNOLOGY

Khadija El Ainaoui[a, b*], Mhammed Zaimi[a], Imane Flouchi[b], Said Elhamaoui[b], Yasmine El mrabet[b],

Abdellatif Ghennioui[b], El Mahdi Assaid[a]

*[a]Electronics and Optics of Semiconductor Nanostructures and Sustainable Energy Team,
Laboratory of Instrumentation of Measure and Control, Department of Physics,
Faculty of Sciences, Chouaïb Doukkali University, El Jadida, Morocco*
[b]Electrical Systems and Photovoltaics Department, Green Energy Park, Benguerir, Morocco

Corresponding author: elainaoui@greenenergypark.ma; elainaoui.k@ucd.ac.ma

ABSTRACT: Photovoltaic (PV) Solar energy plays a vital role in the transition to sustainable and renewable energy sources. The performance and durability of PV cells are significantly influenced by their operating conditions, particularly temperature and irradiance. Understanding these variables and their combined effects is critical for optimizing PV technology. In this context, this work evaluates the effect of temperature and irradiance on the performance of PERC (Passivated Emitter and Rear Cell) modules with half-cut cell technology using novel approach based on an analytical model. The model includes three shape parameters (A , M and N) and two PV metrics: open-circuit voltage (V_{OC}) and short-circuit current (I_{SC}). By developing explicit formulas for A and M in terms of PV metrics and employing an iterative method to determine N , the model accurately describe the module behavior under controlled power rating tests across a range of irradiances (100 to 1100 W/m²) and temperatures (15 to 75°C), as specified by IEC 61853-1, as well as real weather variations. The findings indicate that irradiance has a significant effect on PERC performance. As irradiance increases, the generation rate of electron-hole pairs rises significantly, leading to a substantial increase in I_{SC} and output power. On the other hand, temperature predominantly affects V_{OC} , with higher temperatures reducing it due to increased electron-hole recombination, leading to a decline in output power. In contrast, I_{SC} shows a slight increase as temperature rises, driven by enhanced material conductivity and a broader absorption spectrum. The reliability and accuracy of the approach are evidenced by an average Root Mean Square Error (RMSE) of under 0.053 A and a normalized Root Mean Square Error (NRMSE) of less than 1.76 %. These outcomes highlight the method's precision in modeling PV performance across different temperature and irradiance conditions.
Keywords: Photovoltaic; PERC; Effects of temperature and irradiance; Energy testing; IEC 61853-1.

1 INTRODUCTION

PERC technology has become a dominant choice due to its high efficiency and cost-effectiveness [1]. PERC leverages monocrystalline silicon cells with a rear surface passivation layer [2,3], enabling reduced surface recombination, enhanced light reflection, and improved energy conversion efficiency compared to conventional aluminum back surface field (Al-BSF) modules [4]. The integration of half-cut cells further minimizes resistive losses, improving output energy even under partial shading conditions [5]. Despite these advantages, the performance of PERC modules based on half-cut cells, like other PV technologies, is highly influenced by environmental factors, particularly solar irradiance and temperature [6,7]. The simultaneous variation of these factors introduces dynamics that necessitate a deeper understanding of their combined effects on module performance. To address this, the study proposes a novel approach to assess the impact of temperature and irradiance on the performance of PERC modules with half-cut cell technology. The approach is based on the

analytical model that incorporates two PV metrics (V_{OC} and I_{SC}), along with three shape parameters (A , M and N). By developing explicit formulas for A and M in terms of PV metrics and using an iterative method to determine N , the module's behavior under controlled power rating tests across a range of irradiance values (100 to 1100 W/m²) and temperature values (15 to 75°C), as specified by the IEC 61853-1 standard, as well as under real-world environmental variations, is investigated.

2 METHODOLOGY

2.1 PV modeling

Miceli et al. [8] introduced an analytical model to characterize the behavior of thin-film PV modules:

$$I = I_{SC} \frac{1 - (V/V_{OC})^{M}}{1 + A(V/V_{OC}) + (V/V_{OC})^{N}} \qquad (1)$$

Where A , M and N are model parameters. To determine these parameters, we introduce novel formulas in terms of key PV metrics. The model is then applied to mimic the behavior of PERC module based on half-cut cell technology.

At Maximum Power Point (MPP) (V_{MPP}, I_{MPP}) , Eq. (1) becomes:

$$I_{MPP} = I_{SC} \frac{1 - \left(V_{MPP}/V_{OC}\right)^{M}}{1 + A\left(V_{MPP}/V_{OC}\right) + \left(V_{MPP}/V_{OC}\right)^{N}} \qquad (2)$$

The MPP condition is expressed as:

$$\frac{d}{dV}\left(V \frac{I_{SC}\left(1 - \left(V/V_{OC}\right)^{M}\right)}{1 + A\left(V/V_{OC}\right) + \left(V/V_{OC}\right)^{N}} \right) = 0 \qquad (3)$$

At $V = V_{MPP}$, the condition for MPP is satisfied.

New formulas of A and M are derived by solving Eqs. (2) and (3):

$$A = -V_{OC} \frac{I_{MPP}\left(e^{\alpha N}\left(\beta + \alpha\left(1 - N\right)\right) + \beta + \alpha\right) - I_{SC}\beta}{\beta I_{MPP} V_{MPP}} \qquad (4)$$

$$M = \frac{\beta}{\alpha} \qquad (5)$$

Where:

$$\alpha = \ln\left(\frac{V_{MPP}}{V_{OC}}\right) \qquad (6)$$

$$\beta = LambertW\left(-\frac{\alpha I_{MPP}}{I_{SC}}\left(e^{\alpha N}\left(N - 1\right) - 1\right) \right) \qquad (7)$$

To determine the parameter N , an iterative method is used, as illustrated in the flowchart below.

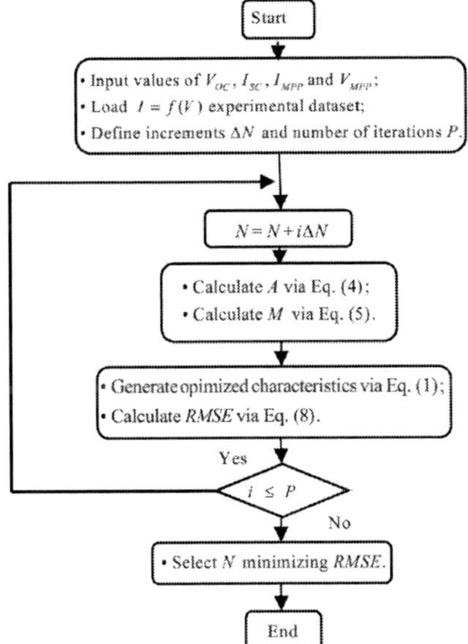

Fig. 1. Flowchart of the iterative method for determining the suitable value of parameter N .

2.2 Assessment of the method

The reliability of the proposed method, aiming to produce numerical values of PV metrics and analyze PV performance data, is evaluated using the RMSE and NRMSE statistical indicators [9]:

$$RMSE = \sqrt{\frac{1}{K}\sum_{i=1}^{K}\left(I^{i}_{Measured} - I^{i}_{Produced}\right)^{2}} \qquad (8)$$

$$NRMSE = \frac{\sqrt{\frac{1}{K}\sum_{i=1}^{K}\left(I^{i}_{Measured} - I^{i}_{Produced}\right)^{2}}}{\frac{1}{K}\sum_{i=1}^{K}I^{i}_{Measured}} \qquad (9)$$

3 RESULTS AND DISCUSSION

In order to validate the proposed method for analyzing the influence of temperature and irradiance on PV module performance, we selected a PERC module based on half-cut cell technology, recognized for its high efficiency and applicability across various PV systems. The module experienced a series of power rating tests designed to examine how solar irradiance and temperature affect its performance. Additionally, real weather testing was conducted to observe the module's behavior under natural environmental conditions.

3.1 Indoor testing

Indoor testing was conducted using an Eternal Sun pulse solar simulator, classified as class AAA and compliant with IEC 60904-9. Irradiance across the module plane was measured using a Fraunhofer WPVS-type reference cell and module temperature was monitored at six points using RTD sensors with measurements recorded across a temperature range from 15°C to 75°C. The irradiance levels were controlled to range between 200 and 1100 W/m² covering most of the required points specified by the IEC 61853-1 standard. However, the test at an irradiance level of 100 W/m² could not be performed due to equipment limitations.

Table 1. Test points for the performance matrix measurements required by IEC 61853-1.

Irradiance (W/m²)	Solar spectrum	Temperature (°C)			
		15	25	50	75
1100	AM1.5	☒	1	2	3
1000	AM1.5	4	5	6	7
800	AM1.5	8	9	10	11
600	AM1.5	12	13	14	15
400	AM1.5	16	17	18	☒
200	AM1.5	19	20	21	☒
100	AM1.5	22	23	☒	☒

Fig. 2.   Eternal Sun pulse solar simulator.

3.1.1 Irradiance effects

Table 2 summarizes the module's performance metrics across the irradiance range at a constant temperature of 25°C.

Table 2. Module performance across the irradiance range.

I_{POA} (W / m²)	I_{SC} (A)	V_{OC} (V)	I_{MPP} (A)	V_{MPP} (V)	P_{MPP} (W)
1100	13,12	53,3	12,40	42,3	524,86
1000	11,70	53,0	11,06	42,6	471,45
800	9,57	53,2	9,10	43,8	398,72
600	7,38	52,0	7,06	43,3	305,69
400	4,96	51,6	4,76	43,7	208,13
200	2,51	50,1	2,35	43,1	101,31

As depicted in Figs. 3 and 4, I-V and P-V curves measured across the irradiance range from 200 to 1100 W/m² at a constant temperature of 25°C closely match those produced by the proposed method. The results reveal that as irradiance increases, the absorption of photons intensifies, leading to a higher generation rate of electron-hole pairs within the material. This causes a substantial rise in output current and power, while voltage remains relatively stable due to the logarithmic relationship between voltage and irradiance, as dictated by the PN junction characteristics. The upward shift in MPP with increased irradiance highlights its direct impact on carrier generation and collection efficiency. The effects of irradiance are enhanced in PERC cells by rear surface passivation and dielectric layer displacing rear metal reflector, which reduces electron-hole recombination, improves photon absorption and reduces heat absorption, further enhancing performance.

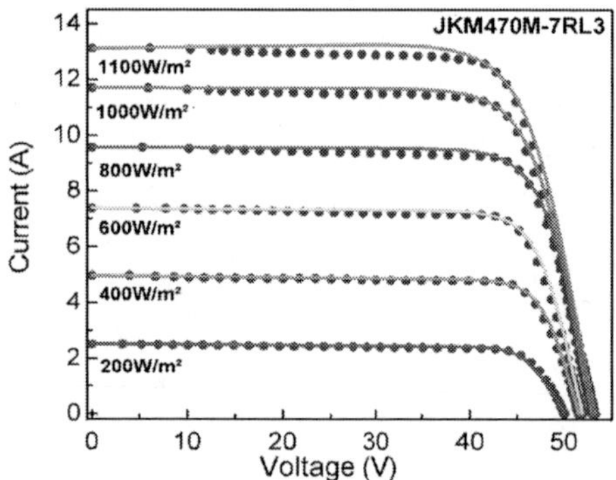

Fig. 3.   Measured (garnet dots) and produced (colored lines) I-V curves at 25°C, for irradiance values ranging from 200 to 1100 W/m².

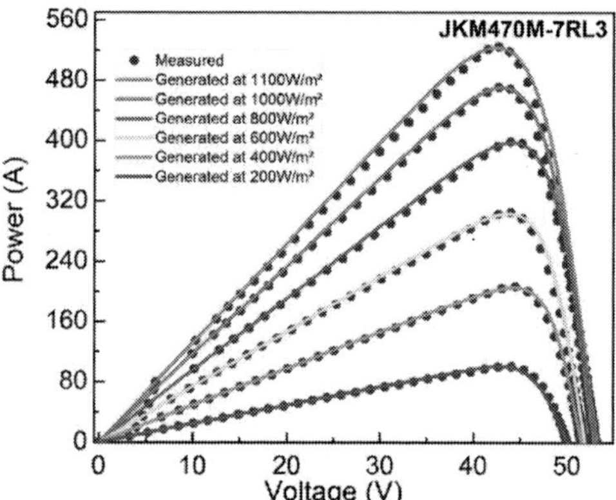

Fig. 4.   Measured (garnet dots) and produced (colored lines) P-V curves at 25°C, for irradiance values ranging from 200 to 1100 W/m².

3.1.2 Temperature effects

Table 3 summarizes the module's performance metrics across the temperature range at a constant irradiance of 1000 W/m².

Table 3. Module performance across the temperature range.

T_{MBS} (°C)	I_{SC} (A)	V_{OC} (V)	I_{MPP} (A)	V_{MPP} (V)	P_{MPP} (W)
15	11,22	54,4	10,70	44,7	478,4
25	11,70	53,0	11,06	42,6	471,4
50	11,70	48,3	11,06	37,3	412,9
75	11,85	46,8	11,21	36,0	404,1

Figs. 5 and 6 present I-V and P-V curves measured over a temperature range from 15°C to 75°C, under a constant irradiance of 1000 W/m². The experimental results align closely with the produced ones. As temperature rises, significant changes occur in the module's performance. The increase in temperature reduces the bandgap energy of PERC cells, causing a notable drop in open-circuit voltage, which contributes to the decrease in overall output power. While the current slightly increases due to enhanced material conductivity and a broader absorption spectrum with higher temperatures, this gain is insufficient to offset the voltage-related losses, resulting in a net reduction in output power.

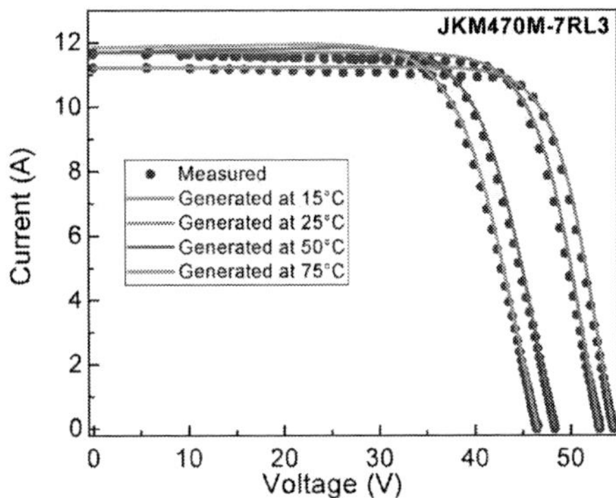

Fig. 5. Measured (garnet dots) and produced (colored lines) I-V curves at 1000 W/m², for temperature values ranging from 15 to 75 °C.

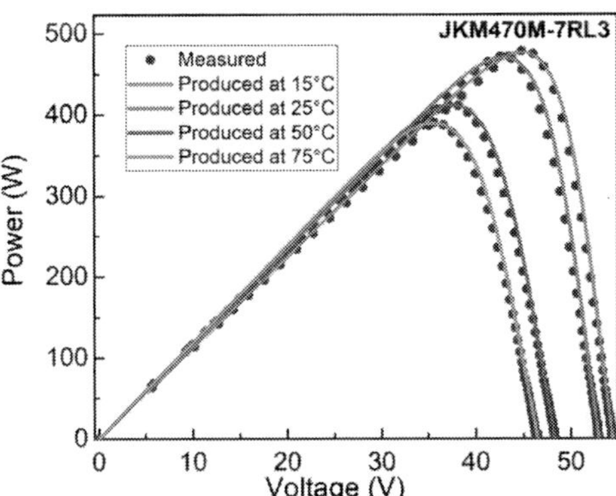

Fig. 6. Measured (garnet dots) and produced (colored lines) P-V curves at 1000 W/m², for temperature values ranging from 15 to 75 °C.

3.2 Outdoor testing

The module, initially subjected to performance matrix testing indoors, was then installed outdoors on a cloudy day to investigate the effects of real world irradiance and temperature. Data were collected using the PVPM1000X I-V curve tracer, along with its accessories: the PT1000 thermal sensor to monitor the module's back surface temperature and a reference cell to measure solar irradiance. Fig. 7 shows the PV module (a), reference cell (b), PT1000 sensor (c), and PVPM1000X I-V curve tracer (d).

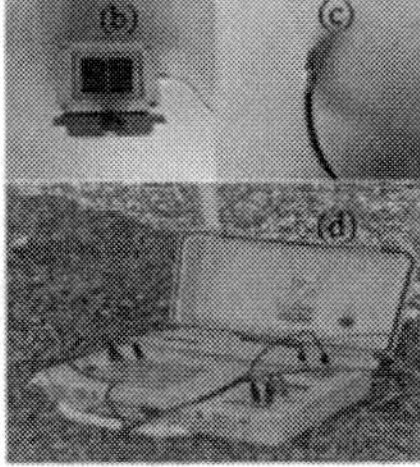

Fig. 7. The evaluated module (a), the reference cell (b), PT1000 thermal sensor (c) and PVPM1000X I-V curve tracer (d).

Figs. 8 to 10 show the measured and produced curves (I-V, P-V and peak power) for the evaluated module serving in Benguerir, Morocco, on May 8, 2024, under varying levels of temperature and irradiance. The produced curves, shown in colored lines show high agreement with the measured curves, represented by garnet dots, reflecting the precision of the method in generating performance data in real world conditions. The observed curves reveal how the combined effects of irradiance and temperature influence module performance. While increasing irradiance boosts current and power, higher temperatures lead to voltage reduction, which limits output power.

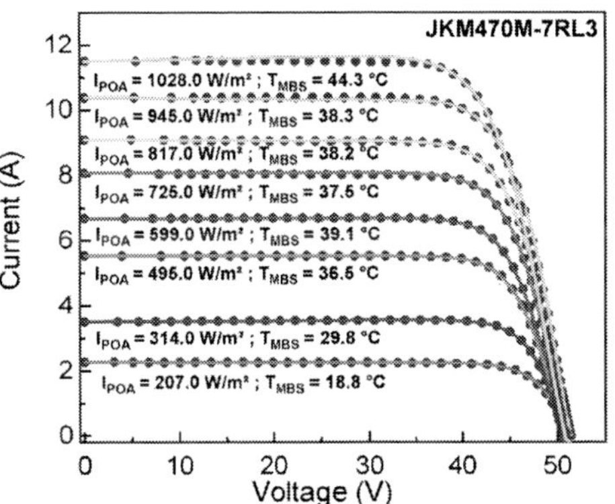

Fig. 8. Measured (garnet dots) and produced (colored lines) I-V curves under real weather conditions.

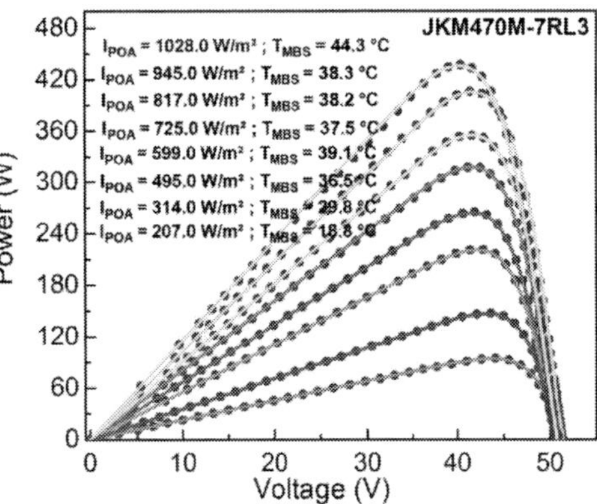

Fig. 9. Measured (garnet dots) and produced (colored lines) P-V curves under real weather conditions.

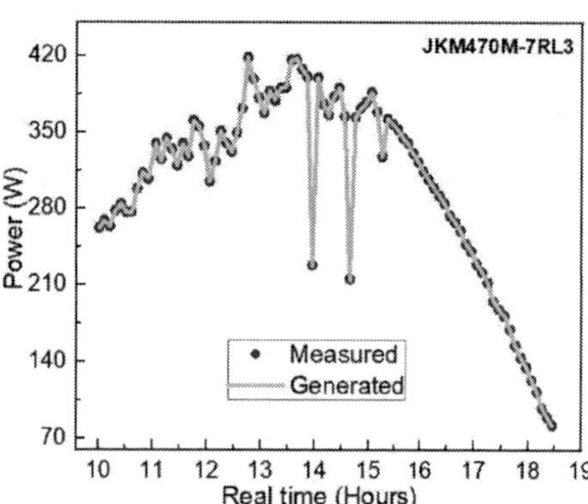

Fig. 10. Measured and produced peak power curves under real weather conditions.

The curves in Figs. 11 and 12 provide a clear visualization of the method's performance over time, as measured by RMSE and NRMSE. The RMSE curve (Fig. 11) exhibits fluctuations throughout the day due to varying conditions caused by cloud cover. However, the average RMSE remains low at 0.053 A.

Similarly, the NRMSE curve (Fig. 12) reflects these fluctuations, with the average normalized error remaining within 1.76 % over the entire observation period. This relatively low percentage of error compared to actual measurements underscores the method's accuracy and reliability, even under dynamically changing environmental conditions.

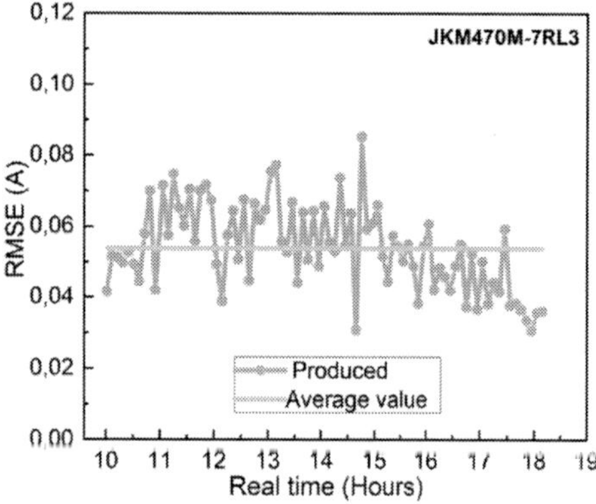

Fig. 11. RMSE for produced current corresponding to evaluated module operating under real weather conditions.

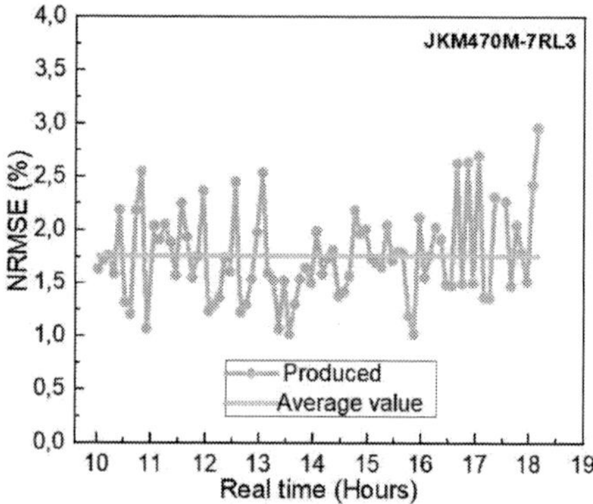

Fig. 12. NRMSE for produced current corresponding to evaluated module operating under real weather conditions.

4 CONCLUSION

This study highlights the significant effects of temperature and irradiance on the performance of PERC modules with half-cut cell technology. The results show that higher irradiance enhances the output power, while elevated temperatures lead to a reduction in voltage and power. The analytical model based method successfully captures these effects, providing an accurate representation of module performance under varying environmental conditions, with an average NRMSE of less than 1.76 %. This method offers a valuable tool for optimizing the design and power rating of PV systems, ensuring better performance forecasting and more reliable operation in diverse climatic settings.

ACKNOWLEDGMENT

The authors express their gratitude to Chouaib Doukkali University and Green Energy Park for their support.

REFERENCES

[1] Fazal MA, Rubaiee S. Progress of PV cell technology: Feasibility of building materials, cost, performance, and stability. Solar Energy 2023;258:203–19. https://doi.org/10.1016/j.solener.2023.04.066.

[2] Green MA. The Passivated Emitter and Rear Cell (PERC): From conception to mass production. Solar Energy Materials and Solar Cells 2015;143:190–7. https://doi.org/10.1016/j.solmat.2015.06.055.

[3] Blakers AW, Wang A, Milne AM, Zhao J, Green MA. 22.8% efficient silicon solar cell. Applied Physics Letters 1989;55:1363–5. https://doi.org/10.1063/1.101596.

[4] Danelli A, Brivio E, Girardi P, Baggio N, Libal J. Environmental Life Cycle Assessment of Passivated Emitter and Rear Contact (PERC) Photovoltaic Module Technology 2024.

[5] Cabrera-Tobar A, Dolara A, Leva S, Mazzeo D, Ogliari E. Comparative analysis of half-cell and full-cell PV commercial modules for sustainable mobility applications: Outdoor performance evaluation under partial shading conditions. Sustainable Energy Technologies and Assessments 2024;71:103981. https://doi.org/10.1016/j.seta.2024.103981.

[6] Zaimi M, El Achouby H, Ibral A, Assaid EM. Determining combined effects of solar radiation and panel junction temperature on all model-parameters to forecast peak power and photovoltaic yield of solar panel under non-standard conditions. Solar Energy 2019;191:341–59. https://doi.org/10.1016/j.solener.2019.09.007.

[7] El Ainaoui K, Zaimi M, Flouchi I, Elhamaoui S, El mrabet Y, Ibaararen K, et al. Novel optimized models to enhance

performance forecasting of grid-connected PERC PV string operating under semi-arid climate conditions. Solar Energy 2024;282:112976. https://doi.org/10.1016/j.solener.2024.112976.
[8] Miceli R, Orioli A, Di Gangi A. A procedure to calculate the $I - V$ characteristics of thin-film photovoltaic modules using an explicit rational form. Applied Energy 2015;155:613–28. https://doi.org/10.1016/j.apenergy.2015.06.037.
[9] El Ainaoui K, Zaimi M, Assaid EM. Innovative approaches to extract double-diode model physical parameters of a PV module serving outdoors under real-world conditions. Energy Conversion and Management 2023;292:117365. https://doi.org/10.1016/j.enconman.2023.117365.

A new method for comprehensive power rating and performance analysis of PERC modules based on half-cut cell technology

K. El Ainaoui, M. Zaimi, I. Flouchi, S. Elhamaoui, Y. El mrabet, A. Ghennioui, E. M. Assaid

Laboratory of Instrumentation of Measure and Control, Chouaïb Doukkali University, El Jadida, Morocco

Electrical Systems and Photovoltaics Department, Green Energy Park, Benguerir, Morocco

How do temperature and irradiance affect the performance of PERC modules with half-cut cells?

Key contributions

- Proposes a practical method to evaluate PERC module performance using key PV metrics;
- Performance assessed under controlled power rating tests conducted according to IEC 61853-1;
- Validated with real outdoor operational data, demonstrating accuracy and reliability;
- Quantifies and models the effects of irradiance and temperature on current, voltage, and power.

Methodology

Miceli et al. analytical model [1]:

$$I = I_{SC} \frac{1-(V/V_{OC})^M}{1+A(V/V_{OC})+(V/V_{OC})^N} \quad (1)$$

At Maximum Power Point (MPP):

$$I_{MPP} = I_{SC} \frac{1-(V_{MPP}/V_{OC})^M}{1+A(V_{MPP}/V_{OC})+(V_{MPP}/V_{OC})^N} \quad (2)$$

$$\frac{d}{dV}\left(V\frac{I_{SC}\left(1-(V/V_{OC})^M\right)}{1+A(V/V_{OC})+(V/V_{OC})^N}\right)=0 \quad (3)$$

New formulas of A and M are derived by solving Eqs. (2) and (3):

$$A = -V_{OC} \frac{I_{MPP}\left(e^{\alpha N}\left(\beta+\alpha(1-N)\right)+\beta+\alpha\right)-I_{SC}\beta}{\beta I_{MPP} V_{MPP}} \quad (4)$$

$$M = \frac{LambertW\left(-\alpha I_{MPP}/I_{SC}\left(e^{\alpha N}(N-1)-1\right)\right)}{\alpha = \ln(V_{MPP}/V_{OC})} \quad (5)$$

Flowchart for Parameter N Determination:

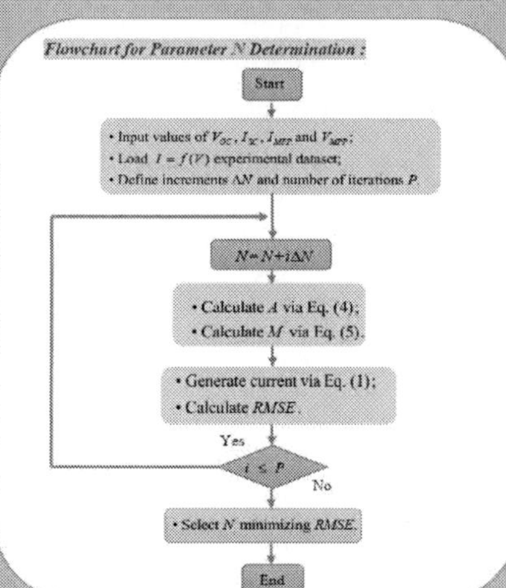

Results

Table 1: Test points for the performance matrix measurements required by IEC 61853-1 [2]

Irradiance (W/m²)	Solar spectrum	Temperature (°C)			
		15	25	50	75
1100	AM1.5	☒	1	2	3
1000	AM1.5	4	5	6	7
800	AM1.5	8	9	10	11
600	AM1.5	12	13	14	15
400	AM1.5	16	17	18	☒
200	AM1.5	19	20	21	☒
100	AM1.5	22	23	☒	☒

Table 2: Module performance across the irradiance range

I_{POA} (W/m²)	I_{SC} [A]	V_{OC} [V]	I_{MPP} [A]	V_{MPP} [V]	P_{MPP} [W]
1100	13,12	53,3	12,40	42,3	524,86
1000	11,70	53,0	11,06	42,6	471,45
800	9,57	53,2	9,10	43,8	398,72
600	7,38	52,0	7,06	43,3	305,69
400	4,96	51,6	4,76	43,7	208,13
200	2,51	50,1	2,35	43,1	101,31

Table 3: Module performance across the temperature range

T_{MOD} (°C)	I_{SC} [A]	V_{OC} [V]	I_{MPP} [A]	V_{MPP} [V]	P_{MPP} [W]
15	11,22	54,4	10,70	44,7	478,4
25	11,70	53,0	11,06	42,6	471,4
50	11,70	48,3	11,06	37,3	412,9
75	11,85	46,8	11,21	36,0	404,1

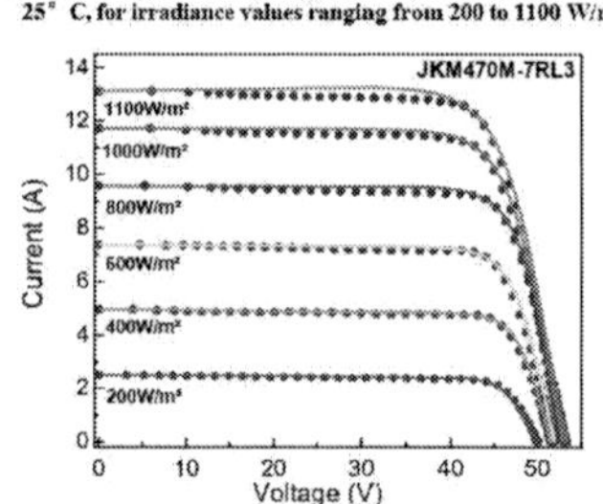

Fig. 1: Measured (garnet dots) and produced (colored lines) I-V curves at 25° C, for irradiance values ranging from 200 to 1100 W/m²

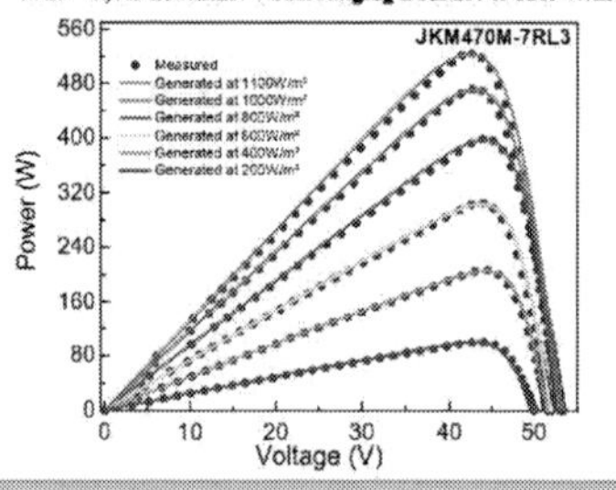

Fig. 2: Measured (garnet dots) and produced (colored lines) P-V curves at 25° C, for irradiance values ranging from 200 to 1100 W/m²

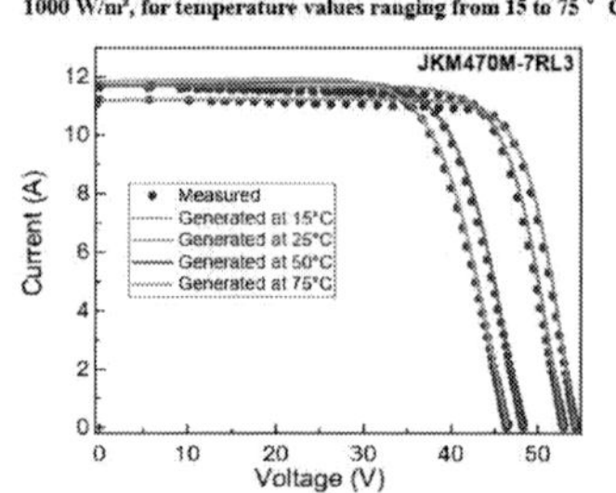

Fig. 3: Measured (garnet dots) and produced (colored lines) I-V curves at 1000 W/m², for temperature values ranging from 15 to 75 ° C

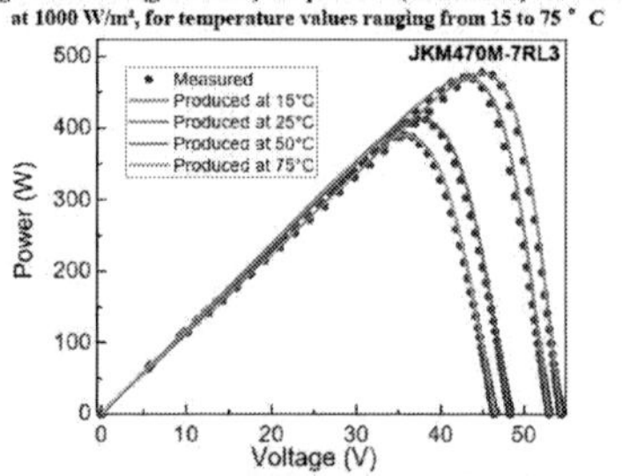

Fig. 4: Measured (garnet dots) and produced (colored lines) P-V curves at 1000 W/m², for temperature values ranging from 15 to 75 ° C

Fig. 5: Measured (garnet dots) and produced (colored lines) I-V curves (a), P-V curves (b) and peak power curve (c) under real weather conditions

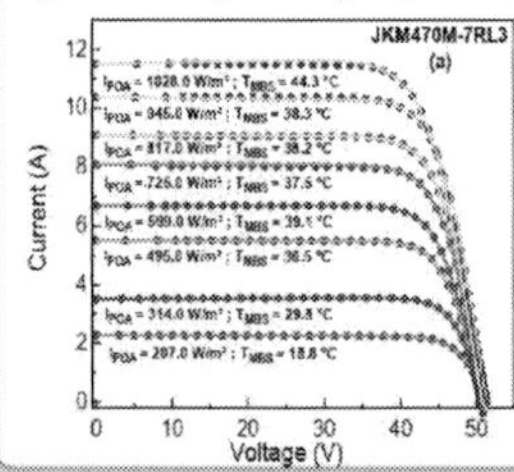

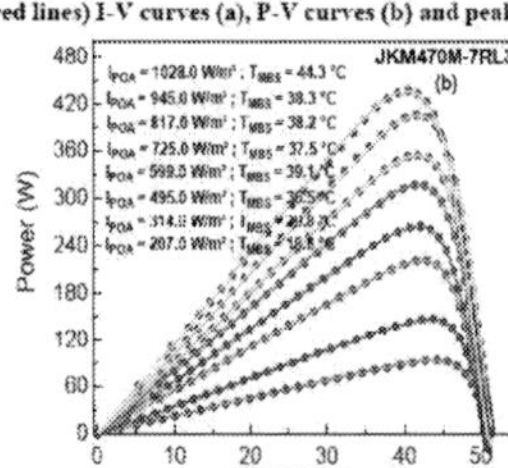

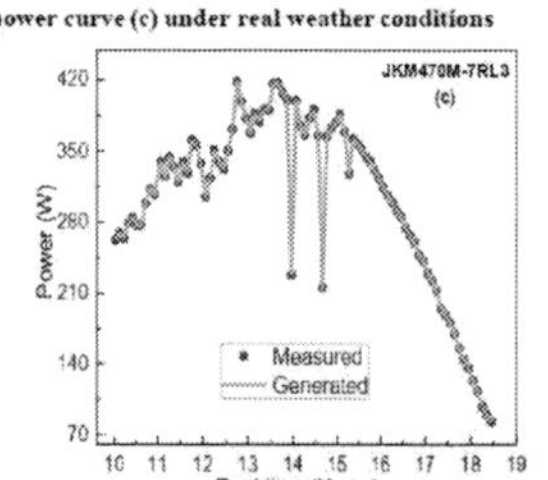

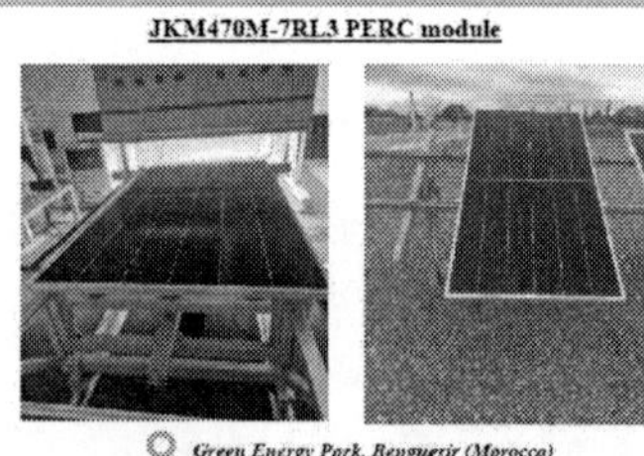

Fig. 6: RMSE for produced current corresponding to evaluated module operating under real weather conditions

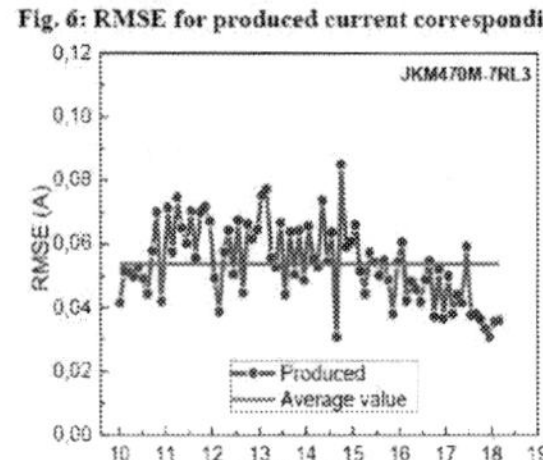

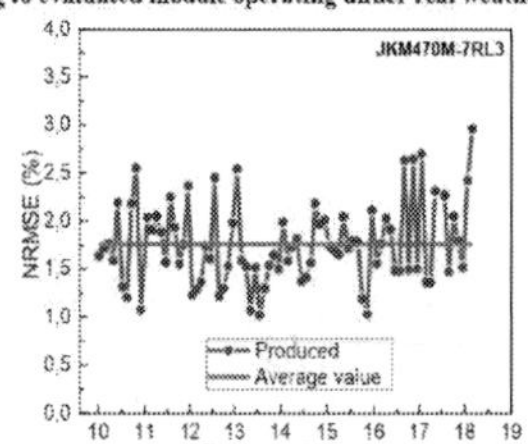

Conclusions

- The method accurately describes PERC module behavior under controlled power rating tests and real outdoor conditions;
- Irradiance strongly impacts performance: higher irradiance increases electron-hole pair generation, boosting current and output power;
- Temperature mainly reduces V_{OC}, decreasing output power, while I_{SC} slightly increases with temperature;
- The approach demonstrates high accuracy and reliability: RMSE < 0.053 A, NRMSE < 1.76 %.

References

[1] Miceli R, Orioli A, Di Gangi A. A procedure to calculate the I – V characteristics of thin-film photovoltaic modules using an explicit rational form. Applied Energy 2015;155:613–28. https://doi.org/10.1016/j.apenergy.2015.06.057

[2] Photovoltaic (PV) module performance testing and energy rating - Part 1: Irradiance and temperature performance measurements and power rating. https://webstore.iec.ch/en/publication/6035

ENERGY RATING ANALYSIS OF HETEROJUNCTION PV MODULES

Teodora S. Lyubenova, Ewan D. Dunlop
European Commission, Joint Research Centre (JRC), Ispra (VA), Italy
e-mail: Teodora.LYUBENOVA@ec.europa.eu

ABSTRACT: This work analyses the Climate Specific Energy Rating (CSER) of three heterojunction (HJT) PV devices from the same production batch, following the methodology outlined in IEC 61853-1 [1]. The objective is to assess the reliability and repeatability of the performance analysis and to determine if testing three modules is necessary, or whether fewer tests could provide equally reliable results, thus reducing measurement time and costs. This study is focused on HJT technology as one of the solar PV that has gained huge industrial popularity over the last decade. However, it presents challenges during characterization due to capacitive effects and temporal metastability, known as "dark ageing". Such effects require the use of non-routine instrumentation like steady-state solar simulators and complex measurement protocols. This study also investigates the influence of irradiance and temperature on module performance, as well as the electrical response of modules under different climatic profiles (IEC 61853-4 [2]), with a particular focus on CSER and annual energy yield.
Keywords: Energy rating; IEC 61853 standard; heterojunction PV modules

1 INTRODUCTION

Silicon heterojunction technology (HJT) has been gaining popularity over the last decade due to its rapid technological developments and cost-effectiveness. It is currently the solar industry's most effective process for increasing efficiency (>20%) and power output (720W) [3]. In terms of market outlook, the global HJT solar cell market is expected to reach $4.6 billion by 2031, rising at a market growth of 17.3% during the forecast period 2024-2031 [4]. The advanced manufacturing processes, premium raw materials, and specific cell design of these PV modules make them highly appealing to consumers, commercials and academic field, establishing HJT devices as a compelling option in the industry. However, this technology presents challenges for accurate characterization. The HJT cell architectures, made by passivating a-Si layers, exhibit high open circuit voltages (V_{oc}) that requires longer sweeps (>250ms) for accurate I-V measurements to avoid under or overestimated power output (P_{max}). Depending on the sweep time and sweep direction, the P_{max} could be inaccurately measured by over 20% [5] [6]. This technical requirement of sweep duration puts severe constraints for the flash simulators commonly used in industry to test PV devices. For these purposes, continuous or long-pulse solar simulators are recommended. However, these simulators are not universally adopted, nor routinely used by manufacturers or testing labs. Their temperature control can be problematic, although temperature correction can be applied with good results in terms of accuracy.

Additionally, the HJT devices suffer from "dark ageing" i.e. degradation during extended storage in low light or dark conditions and pre-conditioning treatments are needed to ensure that the performance measurements are representative of those in normal operation [5].

While a single I-V measurement at STC can be a challenging task for the HJT modules, energy rating analysis according to standard series IEC 61853 [1], [7], [8], [2] adds an extra layer of complexity, requiring multiple testing under specific conditions and algorithms that are time-consuming to implement. The IEC 61853-1 (point 3) outline, as a sampling requirement, the testing of three modules from a production batch. The goal of this investigation is to assess the reliability and repeatability of performance analysis and to determine whether testing

three modules is strictly necessary or if the number of tests can be reduced to simplify the procedure. The study investigates the impact of irradiance (G) and temperature (T) on module performance parameters, including open-circuit voltage (V_{oc}), short-circuit current (I_{sc}) and power output (P_{max}). Furthermore, we analyze the behavior of the devices under test (DUTs) for each climate profile, discussing the influence of ambient (T_{amb}), module temperature (T_{mod}) and irradiance (G) on maximum power (P_{max}), CSER and yearly energy yield (EY).

The present work is of relevance to the PV community and to manufacturers that may be required to estimate and provide the CSER values in their information sheets due the future Ecodesign [9] and Energy label [10] legislation. In addition, the PV experts involved in the revision of IEC 61853 standard series can be assisted of the results from this work as well.

2 RESUTLS AND DISCUSSION

The devices under test (DUTs) were pre-conditioned (light soaked) and characterized using a pulsed solar simulator with a multiflash approach (~300 ms). Extended power matrices with 28 operating points (irradiance: 100–1100 W/m²; module temperature: 15–75°C) were experimentally determined. The results show linear dependence of P_{max} and I_{sc} with irradiance (G) and temperature (T) and logarithmic growth of V_{oc}. All tested modules exhibit highly consistent electrical behavior, as expected from devices originated from the same production batch and class.

CSER values were calculated using an in-house developed algorithm in accordance with the requirements of IEC 61853. The behavior of the DUTs was analyzed under different standard climatic profiles, focusing on the effects of ambient temperature (T_{amb}), module temperature (T_{mod}), and irradiance (G) on P_{max}, CSER, and annual energy yield (EY). Notable differences were observed across climatic zones, particularly due to temperature and irradiance variations in the reference datasets. Consequently, the annual energy yield shows significant variation between climates.

These results highlight the added value of CSER

analysis, which provides more realistic performance predictions for specific climatic zones compared to the conventional power rating at Standard Test Conditions.

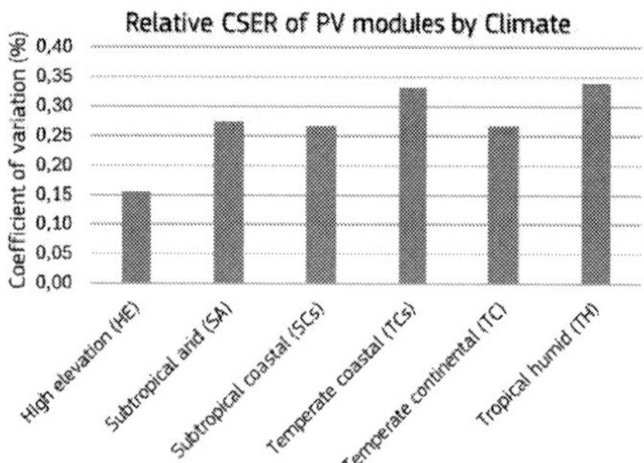

Figure.1: Coefficient of variation of for all modules and climates (CSER spread in % relative to the mean value).

The CSER values of the modules were close, though not identical. The coefficient of variation (CV) in Fig.1, defined as the ratio of standard deviation to the mean vales, ranged from ~0.15% (High elevation) to ~0.34% (Tropical humid). The values fall within the estimated measurement uncertainty of 2–4% and are therefore statistically insignificant. This indicates highly consistent PV behavior.

The findings suggest that fewer test samples may be sufficient for reliable CSER determination, and that reducing the number of devices tested would not compromise accuracy.

3 CONCLUSIONS

The analysis shows that CSER values of the three HJT devices are highly consistent across all climatic profiles, with coefficients of variation below 0.4%, well within measurement uncertainty. Repeating tests on three modules provides only marginal additional insight and could be reduced without significantly affecting reliability. Furthermore, the study confirms the effectiveness of CSER analysis in providing more accurate estimates of PV module energy yield in specific climates, revealing significant regional differences due to environmental conditions.

4 REFERENCES

[1] IEC61853-1: PV module performance testing and energy rating - Part 1: Irradiance and temperature performance measurements and power rating, 2011.

[2] IEC61853-4: PV module performance testing and energy rating - Part 4: Standard reference climatic profiles, 2018.

[3] T. S. M. TaiylanNews, "www.taiyangnews.info." TaiylanNews, January 2025. [Online]. Available: https://taiyangnews.info/topmodules. [Accessed 28/01/2025 January 2025].

[4] K. Research, "Heterojunction (HJT) Solar Cell Market," KBV Research, KBV-23512, 2024.

[5] N.Taylor, "Guidelines for PV Power Measurment in Idustry," Luxemburg, 2010.

[6] Mauro Pravettoni, Daren Poh, Jai Prakash Singh, Jian Wei Ho and Kenta Nakayashiki, "The effect of capacitance on high-efficiency photovoltaic modules: a review of testing methods and related uncertainties," Journal of Physics D: Applied Physics , vol. 54, p. 193001, 2021.

[7] IEC61853-2: PV module performance testing and energy rating - Part 2: Spectral responsivity, incidence angle and module operating temperature measurements, 2016.

[8] IEC61853-3: PV module performance testing and energy rating - Part 3: Energy rating of PV modules, 2018.

[9] "Directive 2009/125/EC of the European Parliament and of the Council establishing a framework for the setting of ecodesign requirements for energy-related products, OJ L285, 31.10.2009, p.10-35," 2009.

[10] "Regulation (EU)2017/1369 of the European Parliament and of the Council of 4 July 2017 setting a framework for energy labelling and repealing Directive 2010/30/EU, OJ L198, 28.7.2017, p.1–23." 2017.

ENERGY RATING ANALYSIS OF HETEROJUNCTION PV MODULES

Teodora S. Lyubenova, Ewan D. Dunlop

European Commission, Joint Research Centre, Ispra, Italy

This study evaluates the Climate Specific Energy Rating (CSER) of silicon heterojunction (HJT) photovoltaic modules, focusing on whether the IEC 61853-1 requirement of testing three devices is essential or if fewer measurements can ensure reliable results. The analysis examines the influence of irradiance and temperature on P_{max}, I_{SC} and V_{OC}, and assesses device performance under IEC 61853-4 climatic profiles. The findings provide guidance for PV manufacturers in CSER reporting and for testing laboratories seeking to improve measurement protocols.

Climatic Specific Energy Rating (CSER)

Tool for accurate comparison of PV module performance under real operating conditions worldwide (IEC 61853 series)

$$CSER = \frac{E_{year}/P_{STC}}{G_{year}/1000}$$

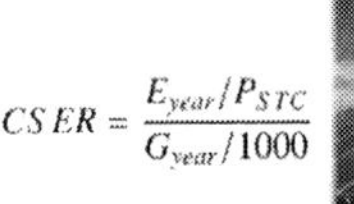

| Irradiance-Temperature (G-T) power matrix (IEC 61853-1) | Angular response, NMOT, Spectral responsivity (IEC 61853-2) | Climatic Specific Energy Rating (CSER) (IEC 61853-3) | Standard reference climatic profiles (IEC 61853-4) |

HJT module characterization

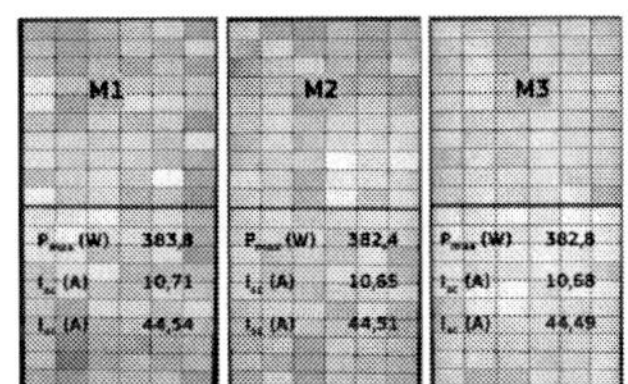

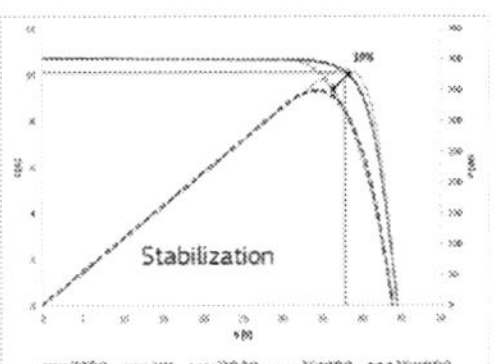

HJT annual energy yield

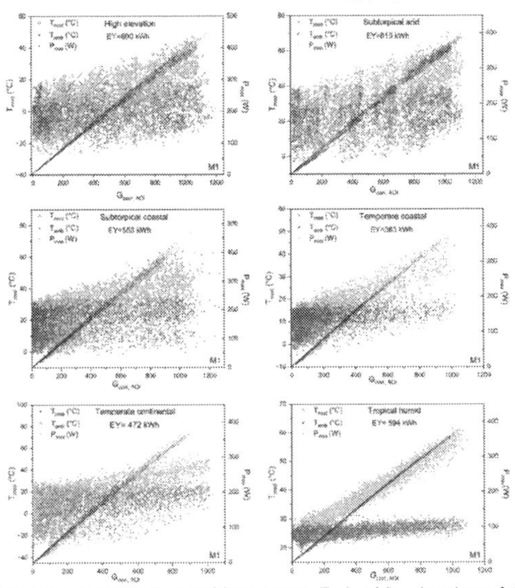

HJT electrical performance

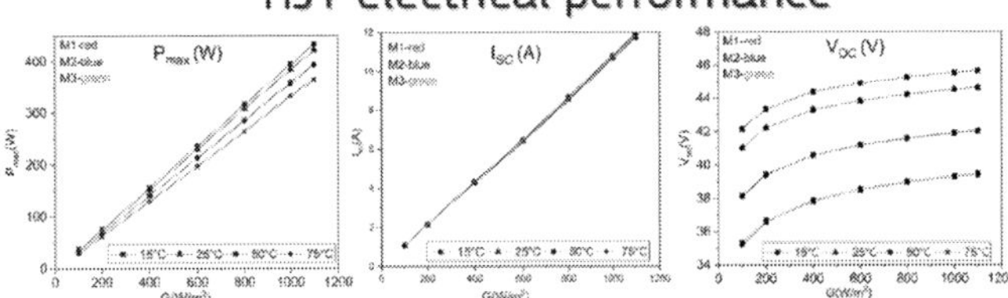

Extended power matrices with 28 data points were experimentally determined indoors. The results illustrate that P_{max} and I_{sc} exhibit linear dependence, with both irradiance (G) and temperature (T), while V_{oc} increases logarithmically. All tested modules are from the same production batch, which is reflected in their highly consistent electrical behavior.

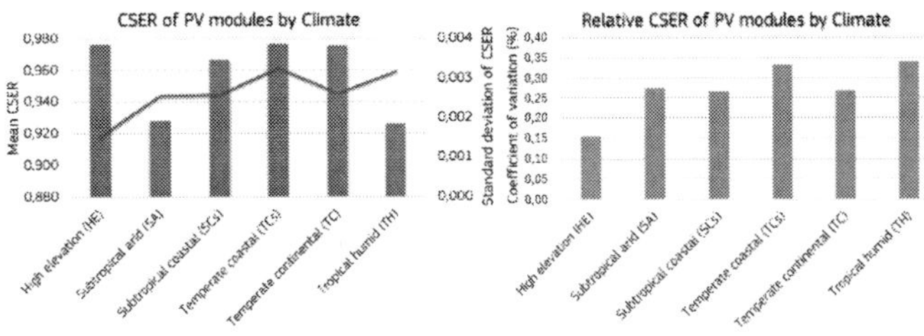

Mean CSER and Standard deviation for each climate.
- The lowest STD variation is in High elevation (HE).
- The highest SDV is in Temperate coastal (TCs) and Tropical humid (TH).

Coefficient of variation (%), CSER relative to the mean value.
- The lowest variation is in High elevation (HE) (~0.15%).
- The highest variation is in Tropical humid (TH) (~0.34%).

Scatter plots display an ambient (T_{amb}), module temperature (T_{mod}) and P_{max} dependence of the angle of incidence (AOI) corrected irradiance for each reference climatic profile. Inset, the estimated annual energy yield (EY, kWh) is shown. Difference PV module behavior is expected, driven by variations in irradiance and temperature profiles within the representative environmental dataset.

CSER values across the modules are close, but not identical. The lower standard deviation and coefficient variation values reveal consistent PV behaviour. The results suggest that fewer tests might be enough for reliable CSER determination. The results highlight the value of Climatic Specific Energy Rating analysis (CSER), as it enables realistic real-world performance energy generation prediction.

Climate		High elevation (HE)	Subtropical arid (SA)	Subtropical coastal (SCs)	Temperate coastal (TCs)	Temperate continental (TC)	Tropical humid (TH)
EY (kWh)	M1	799,8	815.3	553,5	363,2	472,4	594,3
	M2	798,6	812,9	552,6	363,4	472,1	593,2
	M3	800.1	817,4	555	364,7	473,7	596,7
Mean_EY		799,5	815,2	553,7	363,8	472,7	594,7
STD_EY		0,79	2,25	1,21	0,81	0,85	1,79
CV_EY (%)*		0,10	0,28	0,22	0,22	0,18	0,30

Climate	High elevation (HE)	Subtropical arid (SA)	Subtropical coastal (SCs)	Temperate coastal (TCs)	Temperate continental (TC)	Tropical humid (TH)
M1_CSER	0,974	0,926	0,964	0,973	0,972	0,923
M2_CSER	0,976	0,926	0,966	0,977	0,975	0,925
M3_CSER	0,977	0,930	0,969	0,979	0,978	0,929
Mean_CSER	0,9759	0,9273	0,9660	0,9763	0,9750	0,9256
STD_CSER	0,00151	0,00254	0,00257	0,00324	0,00261	0,00315
CV_CSER (%)*	0,1551	0,2735	0,2660	0,3321	0,2673	0,3401

* coefficient of variation CV = SD/mean × 100%

CONCLUSIONS

The analysis shows that the CSER values of the three HJT devices are highly consistent between climates, with coefficients of variation below 0.4% in all cases. The lowest variation occurs in High elevation (HE) (~0.15%), while the highest is observed in Tropical humid (TH) (~0.34%). These results, together with the highly consistent electrical behavior of the devices suggest that repeating tests on three modules may give only marginal additional insight. Moreover, the uncertainty estimation (UC) of the energy yield and CSER are in the order of 2 to 4% so such module to module variation is statistically insignificant. The study suggest that testing laboratories could potentially optimize their measurement protocols by reducing the number of devices tested without significantly affecting reliability. The CSER give a more consistent estimate of the energy yield of a PV module installed in a specific climatic region.

Teodora Stoyanova Lyubenova
Email: Teodora.LYUBENOVA@ec.europa.eu

Trend of temperature coefficients of c-Si Module technologies from the past 15 years

Bengt Jaeckel, Matthias Pander

Fraunhofer Center for Silicon Photovoltaics CSP, Otto-Eißfeldt-Str. 12, 06120 Halle (Saale), Germany
*Corresponding author: bengt.jaeckel@csp.fraunhofer.de

ABSTRACT: The temperature dependence of PV module power is a key parameter for energy yield calculations, especially for hot climates. Project yield assessments typically rely on datasheet values where temperature coefficients (TCs) are often reported optimistically and seldom verified. A representative selection of crystalline silicon (c-Si) modules with various cell technologies produced over the past 15 years was screened. The dataset covers Al-BSF, PERC, TOPCon, HJT and back contact (BC) designs with varying cell sizes (5", M0, M3, M6, M10), module circuitries (60 cells in series, 144 cells with 2x72cells as series-parallel interconnection) and module sizes (168x97cm² vs 228x114cm²).

A long-pulse flash method to determine TCs consistently across three irradiance levels was applied. A clear trend towards lower TCs for maximum power γ with newer cell technologies was observed. Additionally, module design and cell cutting quality can impact absolute values. The TC irradiance dependence for Isc α, Voc β and Pmpp γ showed similar patterns across all technologies. The presented data support industry trends and helps to further improve energy rating according to IEC 61853-series. The presented results can also serve as base for benchmarks where new concepts are checked versus older modules where long term field experience exists.

Keywords: temperature coefficient, PV module, crystalline silicon, irradiance dependence, energy yield

1 INTRODUCTION

Accurate temperature coefficients (TCs) for Isc α, Voc β and Pmpp γ are essential inputs for energy yield prediction and bankability for a PV project. While STC power is routinely verified, low-light behavior and temperature dependence are typically taken from manufacturer data-sheets and not systematically checked. Recent datasheet trends suggest improving (less negative) TCs for Pmpp γ and Voc β Resulting in higher yields especially in hot climates. This work evaluates whether such improvements are observed in practice across c-Si module generations and architectures, and quantifies the influence of irradiance, cell cutting and module circuitry. The data collection presented is essentially reproducing the module temperatures and irradiance matrix ($G–T$ matrix) which is the major contribution to the yield prediction.

The results can be integrated in energy yield calculations and energy rating per IEC 61853 and can support to overall improve climate-specific energy yield modelling [1–4].

2 EXPERIMENTAL

2.1 Test setup and procedure

Modules were characterized using a long-pulse A+A+A+ xenon flash tester (halm electronics cetis PV-Moduletest 4) with an extended pulse to mitigate capacitive effects, particularly for HJT and TOPCon cell technologies. The flash was set to three irradiance levels, namely 1000, 500, and 200 W/m² in a single very long flash. This approach was taken to measure all three intensities at exact the same PV module temperature during the cooling phase. The temperature range covered measurements from 30 to 75°C. Each individual measurement took approximately two hours and is in line with IEC 61215 best practice for 1000 W/m² TC measurements [1–4].

Pre- and post-tests with electroluminescence (EL) were performed to exclude any cell damage during heating and cooling of the PV module while determining the TCs. For HJT, TOPCon and BC a hysteresis check was conducted to qualify the extent of hysteresis and its temperature dependence. Based on test runs with a long pulse, approx. 140ms, 1000 W/m² with hysteresis measurement (Isc $\rightarrow$ Voc, Voc $\rightarrow$ Isc) it was determined that the impact on TC is negligible. Therefore, the measurements for such technologies were performed only in Isc $\rightarrow$ Voc direction, accepting a lower FF/Pmpp compared to hysteresis corrected values.

Temperature coefficients for Isc, Voc, and Pmpp were extracted by linear regression of each parameter versus temperature at each irradiance level.

2.2 Samples

We measured commercially produced modules and laboratory demonstrator's representative of the last 15 years, focusing on c-Si. The modules included:

- Aluminum back surface field (Al-BSF), Passivated Emitter and Rear Cell (PERC), Tunnel Oxide Passivated Contact (TOPCon), Heterojunction (HJT) and (interdigitated) Back contact ((I)BC)
- Cell formats: 5", 6" full cells and various half-cut generations (e.g., M3, M6, M10)
- Module circuitries: from smaller early-generation designs with 60 full cells in series to utility modules with 144 half-cut cells
- Module formats: from 168x97cm² (60 cell Al-BSF) to 228x114cm² PERC/TOPCon.
- (~2.28 × 1.14 m²).

This diversity enables technology- and design-dependent TC comparisons while maintaining a uniform measure-ment methodology.

The analysis focused on technology- and design-related trends using a single, repeatable indoor setup; developing detailed uncertainty budgets (e.g., per [12]) was not a primary objective. While indoor flash testing offers high repeatability, complementary outdoor validation remains valuable for capturing site-specific effects. This cross-validation between indoor and outdoor data enables further improvements.

3 EXPERIMENTAL RESULTS

All modules were measured with the procedure described in section 2. Exemplarily a suite of IV-curves is given in Figure 1.

From such curves the temperature coefficients for Isc α, Uoc β and Pmpp γ were determined. Exemplarily the three intensities (1000, 500, and 200 W/m²) for Pmpp are given in Figure 2. A linear regression was applied to determine the slope for each suite of measurements.

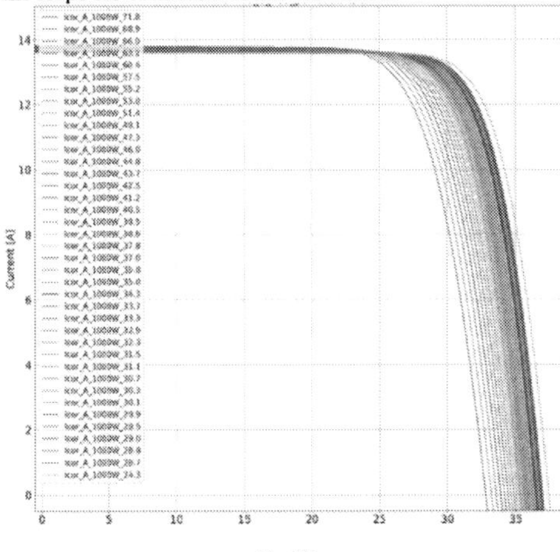

Figure 1: Selected set of IV-curves from a PERC PV module measured at 1000W/m² in the temperature range of ~25°C to 71°C.

The results from all measurements with respect to irradiance and sorted by cell type and number of cells is shown in Figure 3.

4 DISCUSSION

4.1 Overall trends

A trend towards lower absolute values of temperature coefficients for Pmpp is observed from Al-BSF, PERC to TOPCon, HJT and (I)BC cell types, meaning the cells are less temperature sensitive. This is consistent with manufacturers' more favorable TC claims and attributable to improvements in device physics and reduced series resistance.

Module level implementation is, however, critical. Cell cutting quality, interconnection layout, and number of cells influence TC. This is highlighted with the circle in

Figure 3 for a 108-half cell (HZ) module. Here the same cells were used as for the 54-full cell (VZ) module showing clear impact on the cutting process.

4.2 Irradiance dependence

Across cell technologies, TC β (Voc) and TC γ (Pmpp) become less negative as irradiance decreases, while TC α (Isc) shows a slight reduction in magnitude. These shifts are consistent with the differing irradiance sensitivities of recombination and resistive losses reported in indoor and outdoor studies [5–11]. The persistence of these trends across multiple module generations and the relatively small magnitude supports the use of simplified irradiance-dependent matrices within IEC 61853-1 energy rating workflows [3] CSER assessments, and supports tool enhancements (e.g., SmartCalc) within the GSM project.

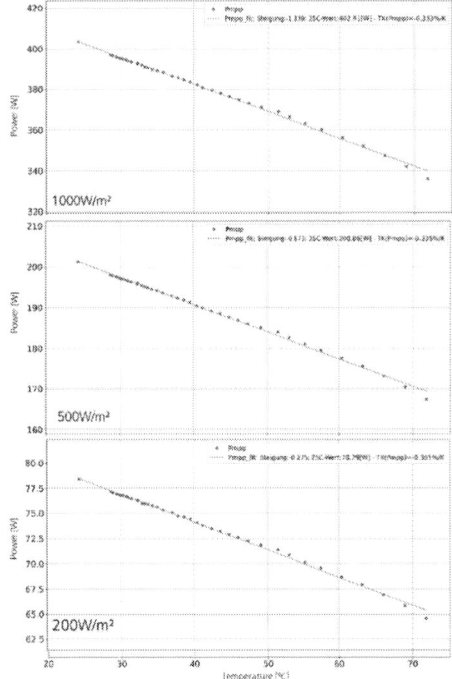

Figure 2: Pmpp results from a PERC module, measured at 1000, 500, and 200 W/m².

4.3 Implications for energy yield and rating

Using (too) optimistic datasheet temperature coefficients (TCs) can significantly bias energy-yield predictions, particularly in hot climates [4]. The measured and presented technology- and design-specific TC distributions enable more realistic project modeling and de-risk key assumptions.

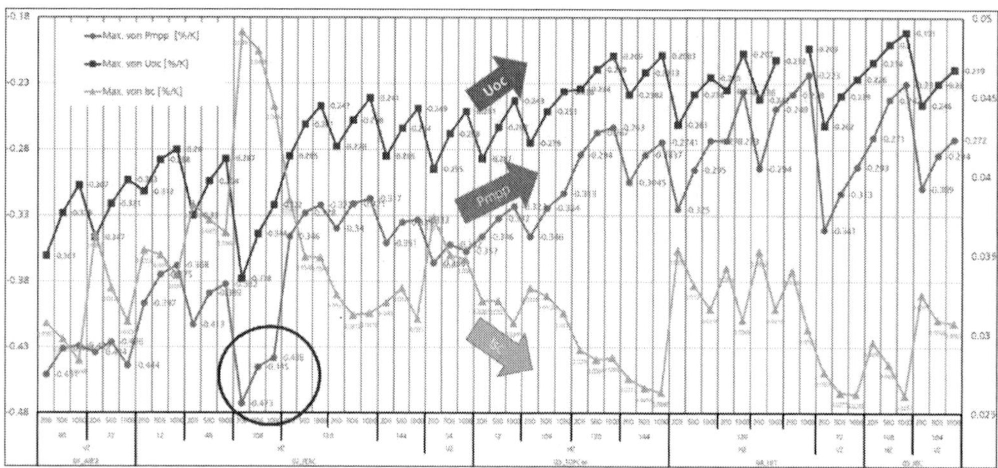

Figure 3 TC measurement results for Voc β, Isc α and Pmpp γ for various PV cell and module technologies, sorted by cell architecture and number of cells for intensities of 1000, 500, 200W/m². Each triple of numbers shows basically same trend to either higher (Uoc, Pmpp) or lower (Isc) TCs as a function of intensity. The PERC with 108 cells had bad cell cutting process impacting the TC negatively.

5 CONCLUSIONS AND OUTLOOK

We measured temperature coefficients for a broad set of c-Si modules spanning over the past 15 years. Multiple cell architectures under three irradiance levels using a long-pulse flash method were studied.

A pronounced improvement (reduction of temperature impact /lower number) in TC γ (Pmpp) with newer technologies was observed, while module design and cell cutting quality can offset intrinsic gains. Irradiance dependence shows consistent patterns across technologies, supporting standardized energy rating praxis.

Future work will include results from accelerated-aged and field-aged modules to quantify TC shifts over lifetime and their impact on climate-specific energy yield.

6 ACKNOWLEDGMENT

This publication was funded by the Federal Ministry for Economic Affairs and Climate Action in the project GreenSolarModules (GSM) under grant number 03EE1161A. The findings herein are solely the responsibility of the authors.

7 REFERENCES

[1] IEC 61215 series: Design qualification and type approval.

[2] IEC 61730 series: Photovoltaic (PV) module safety qualification.

[3] IEC 61853-1: Photovoltaic (PV) module performance testing and energy rating – Part 1: Irradiance and temperature performance measurements and power rating.

[4] W. Herrmann, "Uncertainty of Climate Specific Energy Rating (CSER) of PV Modules in Accordance With IEC 61853", Progress in Photovoltaics: Research and Applications (2025): 1–15, https://doi.org/10.1002/pip.70007

[5] D. Philipp, "Nominal Module Power vs. Measured Power," PV Symposium, Bad Staffelstein, 2024.

[6] K. Emery, "Temperature dependence of photovoltaic cells, modules and systems," Proc. 25th IEEE PVSC, 1996. https://doi.org/10.1109/PVSC.1996.564365

[7] D. L. King, "Temperature Coefficients for PV Modules and Arrays: Measurement Methods, Difficulties, and Results," 26th IEEE PVSC, 1997. [7] A. Virtuani, "Overview of Temperature Coefficients of Different Thin Film Photovoltaic Technologies," 25th EU PVSEC/5th WCPEC, 2010. [8] R. Dubey, "Measurement of Temperature Coefficient of Photovoltaic Modules in Field and Comparison with Laboratory Measurements," 41st IEEE PVSC, 2015. https://doi.org/10.1109/PVSC.2015.7355852

[8] H. Ibrahim, "Variations of PV module parameters with irradiance and temperature," Energy Procedia 134, 276–285, 2017. https://doi.org/10.1016/j.egypro.2017.09.617

[9] M. Piliougine, "Temperature coefficients of degraded crystalline silicon photovoltaic modules at outdoor conditions," Prog. Photovolt: Res. Appl. 25(5), 556–570, 2020. https://doi.org/10.1002/pip.3396

[10] B. R. Paudyal, "Investigation of temperature coefficients of PV modules through field measured data," Solar Energy 224, 425–439, 2021. https://doi.org/10.1016/j.solener.2021.06.013

[11] P. Kamkird, "Investigation on Temperature Coefficients of Three Types Photovoltaic Module Technologies under Thailand Operating Condition," Procedia Engineering 32, 376–383, 2012. https://doi.org/10.1016/j.proeng.2012.01.1282

[12] B. Mihaylov, "Uncertainty Estimation of Temperature Coefficient Measurements of PV Modules," 43rd IEEE PVSC, 2016.

Trend of Temperature Coefficients of c-Si Module Technologies from the past 15 Years

Fraunhofer CSP

Fraunhofer Center for Silicon Photovoltaics CSP

Bengt Jaeckel, Matthias Pander

3AV.3.3

Motivation

* Longevity and predictability are key parameters for the operation of PV assets. All projects start with a financial forecast.
* Energy production calculations typically are based on datasheet values and fixed numbers, assuming the given linear degradation rate
* Only maximum power and e.g. gel content are evaluated in quality assessment campaigns – temperature coefficients are taken for granted
* Irradiance dependence is normally not given

* Some older studies presented some irradiance dependence [1-6]
* PV module power increased in recent years while temperature coefficients decrease to enable higher energy yields – at least in the calculations
* Aim of the study: validate this trend and to check for outliers.
* Check for influence of cell cutting, solar cell dimensions and PV module circuitry and number of cells

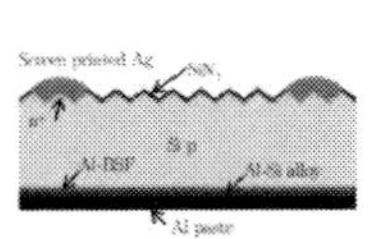
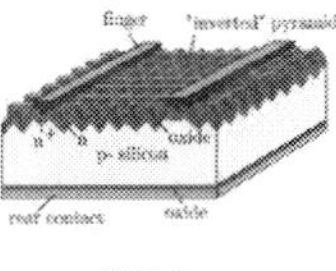
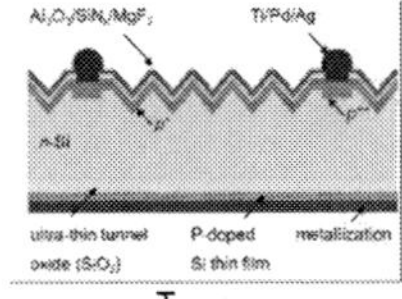
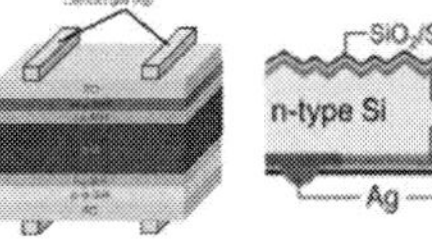
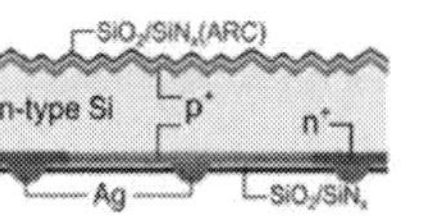

Figure 1: typical c-Si cell structures from the past 15+ years (images: Pbg ISE)

Test setup, procedure and samples

* Halm A+A+A+ solar simulator used for IV characterization
* Approach utilized a multi-intensity flash (1000 [7], 500 and 200W/m²) to simultaneously measure the IV curves at specific temperature (see Figure 2).
* heat-up and cool down procedure used to measure within temperature of ~75°C to ~30°C → time per module approx. 2h
* Dependent on cell technology, a hysteresis check was made.
* Modules are from all common cell technologies (Al-BSF, PERC, TOPCon, HJT, (I)BC) from the past 15 years
* Prior measurement modules were checked for major cell damages by EL
* Isc, Voc, Pmpp evaluation via linear regression (see Figure 3)

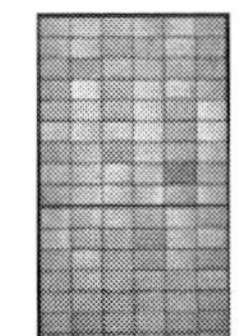

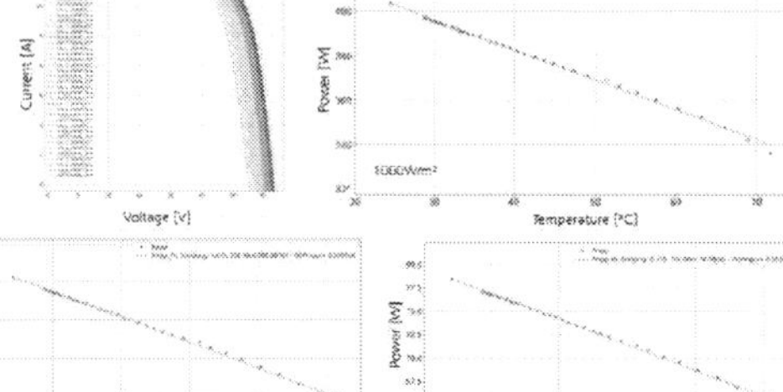

Figure 2: PERC 108 half cell module: No critical findings in EL, set of IV curves taken at 1000W/m². Corresponding power vs temperature plots for 1000, 500, and 200 W/m² to determine temperature coefficients for Pmpp.

Temperature coefficients (TC) overview

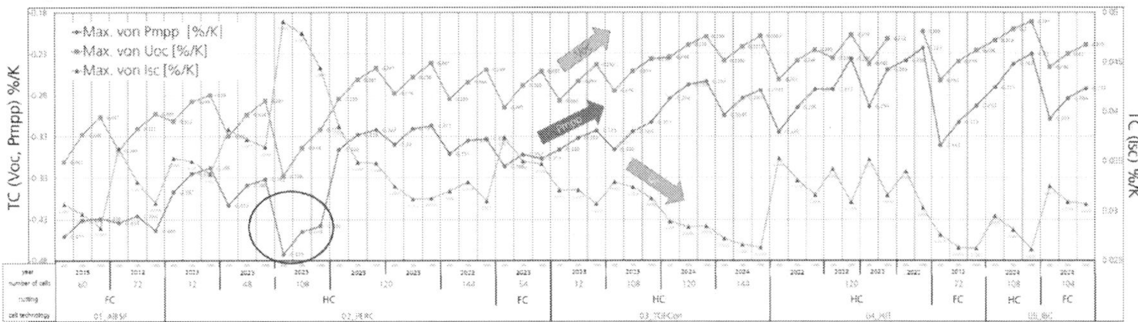

Figure 3: TC measurement results for Voc β, Isc α, and Pmpp γ for various PV cell and module technologies, sorted by cell architecture and number of cells for intensities of 1000, 500, 200W/m². Each triple of numbers show basically same trend to ether higher (Voc, Pmpp) or lower (Isc) TCs as a function of intensity. The PERC with 108 cells had bad cell cutting process impacting the TC negatively.

Take aways

* A trend to lower TC for Pmpps is clearly visible as a function of cell technology from Al-BSF to TOPCon/BC → agrees with "better" TC statements made by manufactures
* Module design and cell cutting play a role in the absolute number of PV-module TC
* The "old" 72 cell HJT-module (2012) is quite impressive keeping its age in mind showing how advanced the technology was compared to Al-BSF almost 15 years ago

* All measurements show a very similar trend of the TC change by irradiance. TC of Pmpp (γ) and Voc (β) increase with decreasing irradiance, vice versa does TC of Isc (α)

* Outlook: Not only does cell technology has an impact on the TC, but also module design and cell cutting. The data herein is the basis for a comparison between new and accelerated/field aged modules.

Contact

Dr. Bengt Jaeckel
PV Modules, Components and Manufacturing
Tel. +49 345 5589-5135
bengt.jaeckel@csp.fraunhofer.de

Fraunhofer CSP
Otto-Eißfeldt-Straße 12
06120 Halle (Saale)

[1] A. Virtuani, "Overview of Temperature Coefficients of Different Thin Film Photovoltaic Technologies", 25th EuPVSEC
[2] R. Dubey, "Measurement of Temperature Coefficient of Photovoltaic Modules in Field and comparison with Laboratory Measurements," 41st PVSC, 2015
[3] H. Ibrahim, "Variations of PV module parameters with irradiance and temperature", Energy Procedia, 134, 276-285, 2017
[4] M. Piliougine, "Temperature coefficients of degraded crystalline silicon photovoltaic modules at outdoor conditions", PiP, 25, 5, 556-570, 2020
[5] B. R. Paudyal, "Investigation of temperature coefficients of PV modules through field measured data", Solar Energy 224 (2021) 425-439
[6] P. Kamkird, "Investigation on Temperature Coefficients of Three Types Photovoltaic Module Technologies under Thailand Operating Condition", Procedia Engineering 32 (2012) 376-383
[7] IEC 61215 series: Design qualification and type approval

020176-001

This publication was funded by the Federal Ministry for Economic Affairs and Energy in the project GreenSolarModules GSM under grant number 03EE1161A.

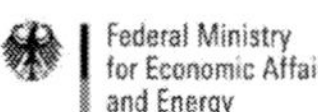

Federal Ministry for Economic Affairs and Energy

ANGLE OF INCIDENCE MEASUREMENTS ON BIFACIAL PV MODULES

Frank Weinrich[1*], Stefan Riechelmann[1] and Stefan Winter[1]

[1]*Physikalisch-Technische Bundesanstalt* (PTB), Braunschweig, Germany

*Corresponding author: frank.weinrich@ptb.de

ABSTRACT: The current international standard EN IEC 61853-2 presents an outdoor and an indoor measurement method for the determination of angular losses [1]. Both methods determine the short circuit current $I_{sc}(\theta)$ of the PV device in the angular range from -90° to +90° with a maximum step size of 10°. The results are used to calculate the incident angle modifier $IAM(\theta)$ and the angular response curve $AR(\theta)$ with fitting parameter a_r. Angle of Incidence (AOI) measurements are usually carried out with indoor solar simulators which lead to certain problems for commercial sized modules due to light field non-uniformity when tilting the PV devices. To overcome these problems the standard allows for testing smaller-size and optically equivalent modules, to isolate electrically one cell within the module (destructive method) or to partially shade one cell in the module (non-destructive method). We show measurement results conducted with an outdoor method, utilizing direct sunlight for AOI measurements while most of the diffuse light is shaded. The advantage of this outdoor measuring method is that full-sized modules can be measured without limiting them to a particular cell, getting the most realistic values for the full module. We performed measurements on the front and rear side of seven bifacial modules of different product designs and cell technology. During rear side-measurements we observed partial cell row shading from the module frame. Although this shading effect has no influence on the output of the short-circuit current $I_{sc}(\theta)$ it does have an influence on the output of the maximum power point $P_{mpp}(\theta)$. The fitting parameters a_r from our rear side measurements show a factor of approximately 2 to 3 between $a_{r\,rear\,Isc}$ and $a_{r\,rear\,Pmpp}$ resulting in significantly different energy yield calculations for the rear side. The traditionally used $a_{r\,rear\,Isc}$ gives the wrong result. This effect cannot be characterized by the methods given by the current standard EN IEC 61853-2, since all methods rely on I_{sc} for the calculation of $IAM(\theta)$ and using just a particular cell for those measurements only produces correct values if there is no self-shading of the module apparent. Our results lead to the conclusion that for rear side AOI measurements on bifacial modules with a frame, the self-shading effect must also be considered.

Keywords: PV Module, Energy Rating, Incidence Angle Modifier, Direct Sunlight Method (DSM)

1 INTRODUCTION

The angular losses of PV modules during non-optimal irradiance incident angles play an increasingly important role for yield prediction and energy rating. Our working group focuses on reducing measurement uncertainty along the photovoltaic value chain. For this purpose, we also participate in standardization work, including revising the current international standard, EN IEC 61853-2. For our current study, we conduct AOI measurements for seven bifacial PV modules based on the described outdoor measurement method in the standard. The device used for this is our outdoor test stand, the so-called solar module tube (SMT), an in-house construction by PTB whose concept was already presented in 2022 [2]. The SMT allows us to measure full-sized modules without limiting measurements to a particular cell. This way, we can see the influence of angular effects on the whole PV module and not only on a particular cell. In addition, we obtain the whole IV curve including I_{sc} and P_{mpp} and not only I_{sc}. In 2024 the SMT took part in an interlaboratory comparison of conducting frontside AOI-measurements for commercial-size modules. Therefore, we performed outdoor method 1 (absolute method). The results showed a very good agreement between the different measurement methods, which also prove the capabilities of our outdoor test stand [3]. Despite these conclusions, our current paper aims to show that certain limitations in other AOI measurement methods, such as limiting measurements to a particular cell, can lead to inaccurate rear side IAM results for bifacial PV modules.

2 SETUP

To conduct our AOI measurements, we are using the direct sunlight method on our outdoor test stand (SMT). Inside the SMT the module is mounted on an adjustable module holder while most of the diffuse light is shaded by the tube. A pyrheliometer, which monitors the direct component of the irradiance, is mounted on a separate two-axis solar tracker near the SMT. Five temperature sensors attached to the rear of the tested module are used to record the temperature. The measurements were taken on days with clear sky in August 2024 and March 2025 in the region of Northern Germany.

2.1 Modules

We decided to measure seven different bifacial full-sized PV-modules, which are listed in Table 1. They are built by different manufacturers and show a representative selection of product designs and technologies as well as a wide range of bifaciality factors. The factors shown for each module were previously determined by our LED-based solar simulator (SINUS-3000, Wavelabs). The modules M1 to M4, M6 and M7 are framed, while M5 is frameless. M5 will be used to cross-check our measurement results and verify the influence of rear side cell row shading caused by a module frame.

Table 1: List of measured bifacial PV modules with their technology and bifaciality factors.

Module	Technology	$\varphi Pmax,$ measured
M1	Heterojunction, n-Type	88 %
M2	TOPCon white	76 %
M3	TOPCon transparent	80 %
M4	TOPCon black	73 %
M5	PERC frameless	70 %
M6	IBC	41 %
M7	TOPCon transparent	77 %

2.2 Outdoor test stand

All seven PV modules were measured using the direct sunlight method on our outdoor test. The SMT, as shown in Figure 1, is a large rectangular tube with a size of 4.0 m x 4.0 m x 7.2 m capable of tracking the sun and limiting the field of view of a mounted PV module under test. The tube is lined with optical black fabric and equipped with a shutter to allow a well-defined start/end of the module's light exposure. The module under test is mounted on an adjustable module holder inside the tube. All seven bifacial PV modules were measured front and rear side with an angular range from -95° to +95° and a step size of 5°. At each step an IV curve is measured. The results were used to calculate the incident angle modifier $IAM(\theta)$ and the angular response curve $AR(\theta)$ with the fitting parameter a_r.

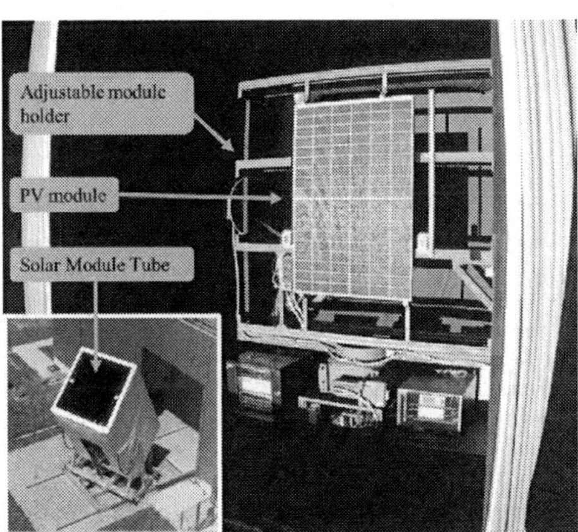

Figure 1: Photograph of the solar module tube during AOI measurements with a mounted PV module inside.

3   RESULTS

We perform AOI measurements for front and rear side of the PV modules shown in Table 1. The $I_\mathrm{sc}(\theta)$ and $P_\mathrm{mpp}(\theta)$ are derived from IV curves that are measured at every angle between -95° and +95° and calculated the $IAM(\theta)$ from both $I_\mathrm{sc}(\theta)$ and $P_\mathrm{mpp}(\theta)$ to check whether there is any difference when following an energy-based approach. Figure 2 shows all seven of these IAM curves for each module. For the front side IAM measurements, the difference between I_sc-based and P_mpp-based IAM is small for all examined modules. In case of the rear side measurements, we observe a substantial drop between I_sc-based and P_mpp-based IAM results for the framed modules, but as expected not for frameless module M5.

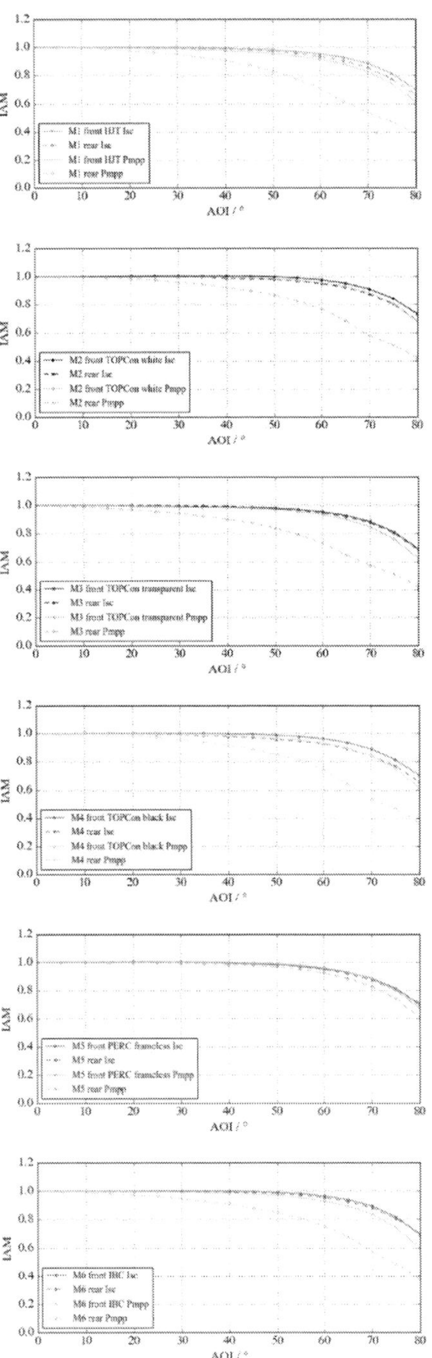

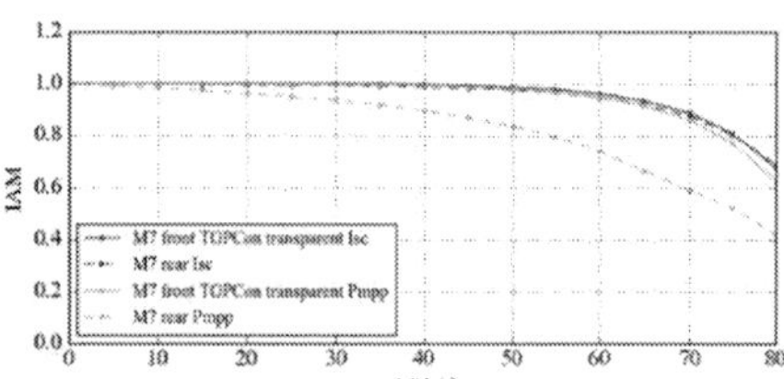

Figure 2: IAM curves based on I_{sc} and P_{mpp} for all seven examined bifacial PV modules.

The deviation of the rear side P_{mpp} -based IAM can be explained by a cell row shading effect as shown in Figure 3 and 4. This causes a reduced current flow in the shaded cells, which can also lead to a bypass of the entire string. This can only be seen by additionally determining the angle-dependent power output of the entire module. The results from the frameless module M5 also confirm this assessment, as the previously observed effects do not occur. Rather, all measured values are close to each other without the P_{mpp} -based IAM on the rear side deviating significantly.

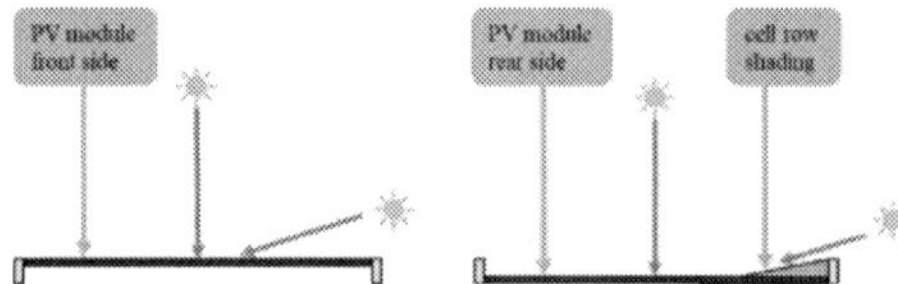

Figure 3: Picture of rear side cell row shading, caused by a PV module frame depending on the angle of irradiation.

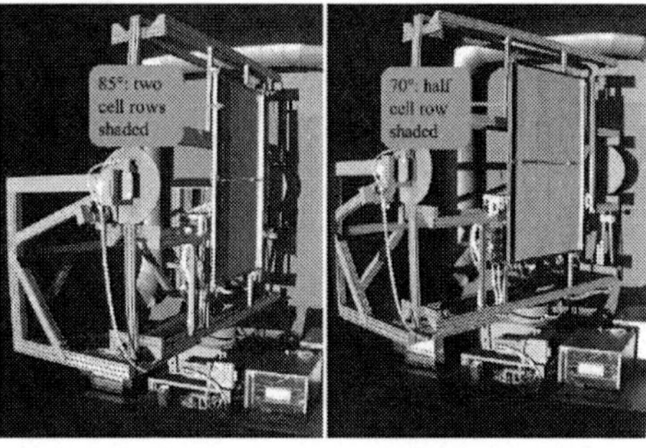

Figure 4: Photograph of cell row shading from PV module M2 at angle 85° (left) and 70° (right).

In addition, we calculate the fitting parameter a_r of the angular response curve for the I_{sc} -based front and rear side measurements and the P_{mpp} -based rear side measurements. The results can be seen in Table 2. The greater the a_r value, the higher the angular loss. The I_{sc} -based a_r range for PV modules is typically between 0.13 and 0.18, which was confirmed by our measurements. On the other hand, the P_{mpp} -based rear side a_r shows a much larger range due to the previously observed cell row shading effect caused by the module frame. The last column shows the difference between $a_{r\,rear\,Isc}$ and $a_{r\,rear\,Pmpp}$ as well as the mean value difference for all six framed PV modules. Module M1 has the largest difference with a value of 0.353 while the mean value difference for all six framed modules is 0.309. The difference between $a_{r\,rear\,Isc}$ and $a_{r\,rear\,Pmpp}$ for the frameless

M5 module is much smaller (0.031), due to the absence of cell row shading from the module frame. However, even if a frameless module does not cause self-shading on the rear side, the standard module mountings will instead cause shading in the application. For the frameless modules to benefit from their improved angle dependence, an appropriate module holder would need to be used or even developed.

Table 2: Calculated fitting parameter a_r of the angular response curve based on front side $I_{sc}(\theta)$, rear side $I_{sc}(\theta)$ and rear side $P_{mpp}(\theta)$.

Module	$a_{r\,front}$ I_{sc}	$a_{r\,rear}$ I_{sc}	$a_{r\,rear}$ P_{mpp}	Difference
M1 (HJT)	0.153	0.169	0.522	0.353
M2 (TOPCon white)	0.152	0.163	0.445	0.282
M3 (TOPCon transparent)	0.157	0.163	0.468	0.305
M4 (TOPCon black)	0.152	0.177	0.491	0.314
M6 (IBC)	0.153	0.154	0.466	0.312
M7 (TOPCon transparent)	0.154	0.154	0.443	0.289
Mean value:				**0.309**
M5 (PERC frameless)	0.155	0.159	0.190	0.031

4 CONCLUSION

The previously described shading effect cannot be characterized by the methods given by the current standard EN IEC 61853-2, since all methods are based on I_{sc} for the calculation of $IAM(\theta)$ or perform measurements on a particular cell of the PV module which also does not take P_{mpp} losses into account. Our results lead to the conclusion that for rear side AOI measurements on bifacial modules with a frame, the self-shading effect must also be considered. Since most laboratories use indoor methods to conduct AOI measurements, the determination of the $P_{mpp}(\theta)$ for a full-sized PV module cannot be realized due to light field non-uniformity of indoor solar simulators when a module is tilted. However, if the effect is to be considered, a constant offset could be added to $a_{r,rear}$ if a frame is present, according to the results of these measurements on a wide variety of bifacial PV modules. Based on our current research, we would suggest an offset within the range of 0.3 to 0.35 (see Table 2).

5 ACKNOWLEDGEMENT

This work is partly developed within the project „ MetroKomPV ", which is funded by the Federal Ministry for Economic Affairs and Energy (BMWE), Germany (funding reference number 03EE1024) and within ECOSTANPV.

6 REFERENCES

[1] IEC 61853-2, "Photovoltaic (PV) module performance testing and energy rating – Part 2: Spectral responsivity,

incidence angle and module operating temperature measurements" (2016).

[2] Riechelmann S, Friedrich D, Müller M et al. (2022) Primary Calibration of Solar Modules With Direct Sunlight. 39th European Photovoltaic Solar Energy Conference and Exhibition; 474 - 476

[3] Pravettoni M, Saw M, Bardizza G, Bellenda G, Couderc R, Friesen G, Herrmann W, Leow S, Riechelmann S, Valoti F, van der Heide A, Weinrich F, Winter S. (2024) Incidence Angle Effect: Results of an Interlaboratory Comparison of Measurements on Commercial-Size Modules. 41st European Photovoltaic Solar Energy Conference and Exhibition.

Physikalisch-Technische Bundesanstalt
National Metrology Institute

Frank Weinrich, Stefan Riechelmann, Stefan Winter

Angle of Incidence Measurements on Bifacial PV Modules

Are AOI measurements based on I_{sc} values representative of actual module performance?

- We conduct AOI measurements for seven different bifacial PV modules, built by various manufacturers who show a representative selection of product designs and technologies as well as a wide range of bifaciality factors. The modules were not purchased directly from the manufacturers.

- The modules are measured based on the described outdoor measurement method in the current international standard EN IEC 61853-2, utilizing direct sunlight. Therefore, we are using our outdoor test stand the so-called solar module tube (SMT).

- Inside the SMT an adjustable module holder is located that allows us to measure full-size modules with an angular range from -95° to +95° and a step size of 5°. At each step we obtain the IV curve of the module without limiting the measurements to a particular cell.

- All AOI measurements have been conducted for the front and rear side of all bifacial modules.

Solar Module Tube (SMT)

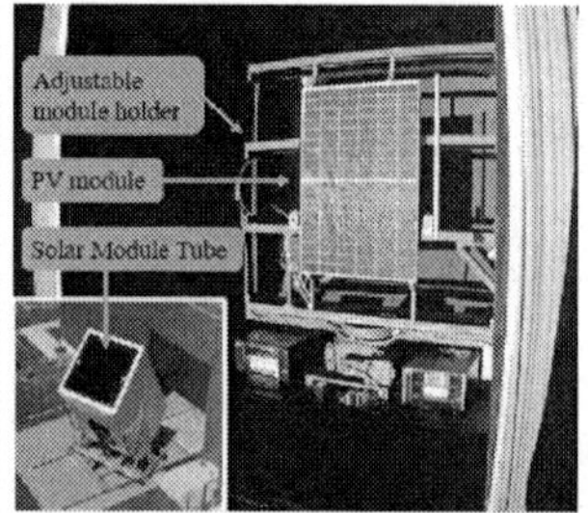

Fig. 1: Solar module tube (SMT) during AOI measurements with a mounted PV module inside.

Examined Bifacial PV Modules

Module	Technology	φ_{Pmax} measured
M1	Heterojunction	88 %
M2	TOPCon white	76 %
M3	TOPCon transparent	80 %
M4	TOPCon black	73 %
M5	PERC frameless	70 %
M6	IBC	41 %
M7	TOPCon transparent	77 %

Tab. 1: List of measured bifacial PV modules with their technology and bifaciality factors.

Angular Measurement Results

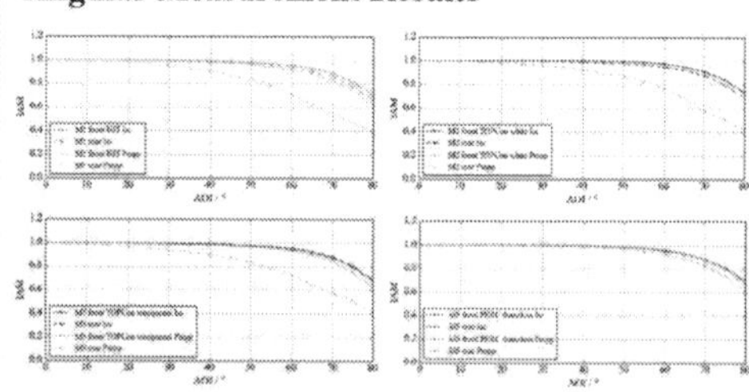

Fig. 2: IAM curves based on I_{sc} and P_{mpp} for four of the bifacial PV modules examined. While the front and rear side IAM is nearly identical when using I_{sc} as a measure, there is a substantial drop in Pmpp for higher angles on modules with frames. Calculating rear-side IAM based on Pmpp results in significantly worse performance.

Module Frame Shading Effect

- During rear-side measurements we observed partial cell row shading from the module frame which causes a reduced current flow in the shaded cells.

- While I_{sc} is unaffected, P_{mpp} of the module is significantly reduced by the shade.

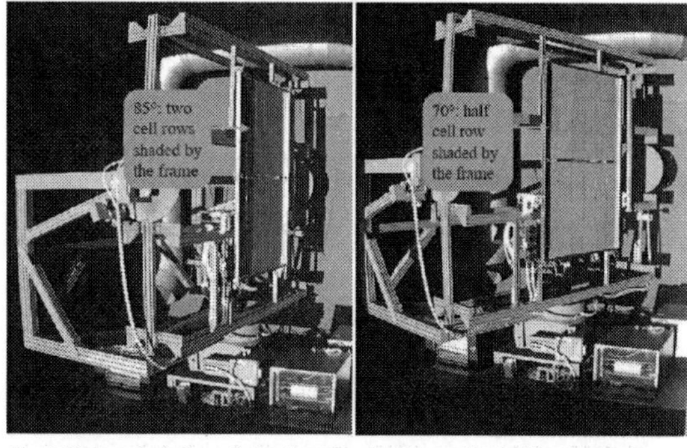

Fig. 3: Photograph of cell row shading from PV module M2 at angle 85° (left) and 70° (right).

Calculation of the Fitting Parameter a_r

- We calculate the front and rear side fitting parameter a_r of the angular response curve both on I_{sc} and P_{mpp}. The results can be seen in Table 2.

- The last column shows the difference between ar rear I_{sc} and a_r rear P_{mpp} as well as the mean value difference of 0.309 for all six framed PV modules, while the difference for the frameless M5 module is much smaller (0.031), due to the absence of cell row shading.

Module	$a_{r\ front\ Isc}$	$a_{r\ rear\ Isc}$	$a_{r\ rear\ Pmpp}$	Rear-side Difference
M1 (HJT)	0.153	0.169	0.522	0.353
M2 (TOPCon white)	0.152	0.163	0.445	0.282
M3 (TOPCon transparent)	0.157	0.163	0.468	0.305
M4 (TOPCon black)	0.152	0.177	0.491	0.314
M6 (IBC)	0.153	0.154	0.466	0.312
M7 (TOPCon transparent)	0.154	0.154	0.443	0.289
Mean value:				**0.309**
M5 (PERC frameless)	0.155	0.159	0.190	0.031

Tab. 2: Calculated fitting parameter a_r of the angular response curve based on front side $I_{sc}(\theta)$, rear side $I_{sc}(\theta)$ and rear side $P_{mpp}(\theta)$.

Conclusion: For rear-side AOI measurements on bifacial modules with a frame, I_{sc}-based IAM results might not be representative for the actual loss in performance due to steep incidence angles.

The study is supported by the European Climate, Infrastructure and Environment Executive Agency (CINEA)

Frank Weinrich

4.53 | Solar Modules
+49 531 592 4536
frank.weinrich@ptb.de

Physikalisch-Technische Bundesanstalt
Bundesallee 100, 38116 Braunschweig, Germany
www.ptb.de

Plug & Play IV Curve Tracer for PV Modules

EU PVSEC 2025, 22.-26. September 2025 Bilbao (Spain)
Adrian Jäggi[1], Christof Bucher[1], Matthias Burri[1]
[1]Bern University of Applied Sciences (BFH), School of Engineering and Computer Science (TI), Institute for Energy and Mobility Research (IEM),
Laboratory for Photovoltaic Systems (PV-Lab), Burgdorf (Switzerland) christof.bucher@bfh.ch

A newly developed current-voltage characteristic curve measuring device (IV Curve Tracer) for photovoltaic modules enables novel measurements. It can briefly disconnect photovoltaic modules from the inverter during operation and measure the current-voltage characteristic curve, including bypass diodes. It is small, lightweight and universally applicable thanks to wireless communication. The IV Curve Tracer has numerous connections for various external sensors, which can measure the module temperature or irradiation. Several IV Curve Tracers can be used in a measurement network with temporal synchronization and central data processing.

Concept

The IVCT is designed to automatically measure photovoltaic modules (PV modules) on a regular basis during operation. It measures the characteristic curve from no-load to short circuit, including bypass diode on request. The IVCT also records the module and ambient temperature, irradiation and other parameters from external sensors. Several IVCTs can be operated in a measurement network, which is controlled by a central host. This also processes and stores all measurement data. The user interface consists of a website that can be accessed via any device.

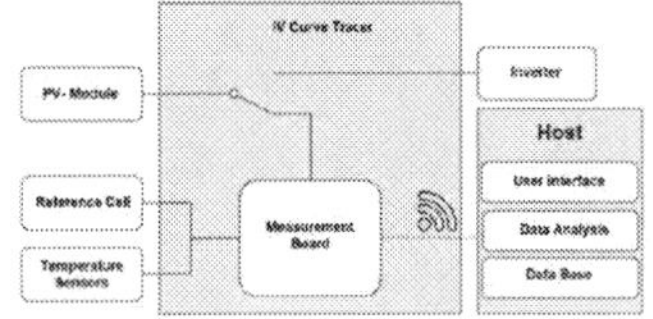

Figure 1: Concept of IV Curve Tracer

Measures

- The IVCT can record the following measurands:

- Current-voltage characteristic curve (IV curve) and power-voltage characteristic curve (PV curve)

- Current and voltage values during operation

- Irradiation on a reference cell

- Module backside and ambient temperature

- Irradiation by external pyranometer via Modbus

- Weather data by external weather station via Modbus

Figure 2: The characteristic curve measuring device IVCT developed in this work.

Evaluation and Data Export

In the user interface, the IV curve with various characteristic parameters is printed after the measurement. In addition, current, voltage and power are displayed in the point of maximum power (MPP), short-circuit current, open-circuit voltage, temperatures and irradiance values. All measurements are is stored in a database, which can be exported for further analysis. Additional parameters are calculated (e.g. the number of local maxima, fill factor, shunt and series resistance).

Measurements

Figure 3 shows an measurement of a TOPCon module in the solar simulator. Two different measurement time durations show an overshoot and undershoot of the characteristic curve in the capacitive module if the measurement is too fast. Thanks to the individually adjustable measurement time duration and support point distribution, characteristic curve measurements can be individually adapted to the PV module to be measured with the new IVCT.

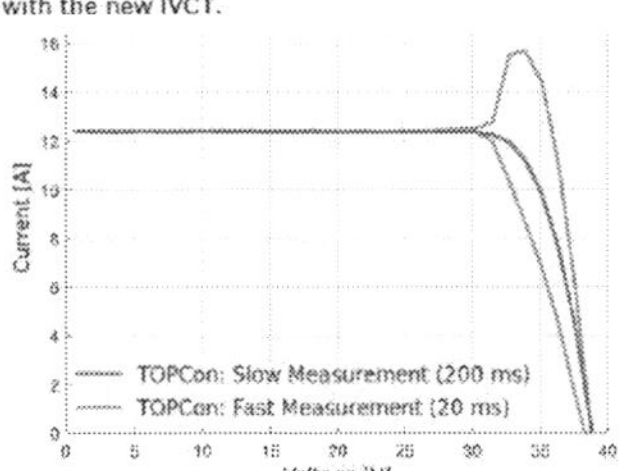

Figure 3: Measured IV curve of a TOPCon module. Measurement too fast (orange), slower, correct measurement (blue)

Validation

The measurement accuracy of the IVCT is validated in a defined environment in the laboratory. The temperature dependence of the measured variables is determined by tests in a climatic chamber. The results of the validation are presented in Table 1. The IVCT is tested for the applications in an installation of several PV modules and an inverter, as well as for different module technologies. Several IVCTs in a measurement network can measure in time synchronously, so that productive operation is not disrupted.

Table 1: Measurement accuracy and temperature dependence of the IVCT

Measurement	Measurement accuracy absolute	Measurement accuracy relative	Temperature dependence
Voltage	+/- 400 mV	+/- 0.4 %	- 0.02 % / K
Current	+/- 90 mA	+/- 0.6 %	+ 0.02 % / K

User interface

The IVCT is operated via the web browser of any device. In the user interface shown in Figure 4, the direction and duration of the characteristic curve measurement can be set, the measurement of the bypass diodes can be activated, and other configurations can be made. Furthermore, measurements can be started and the measurement database can be exported. Measurements of characteristic curves can be carried out individually or automatically at regular intervals. The IVCT can be calibrated and updated via the user interface.

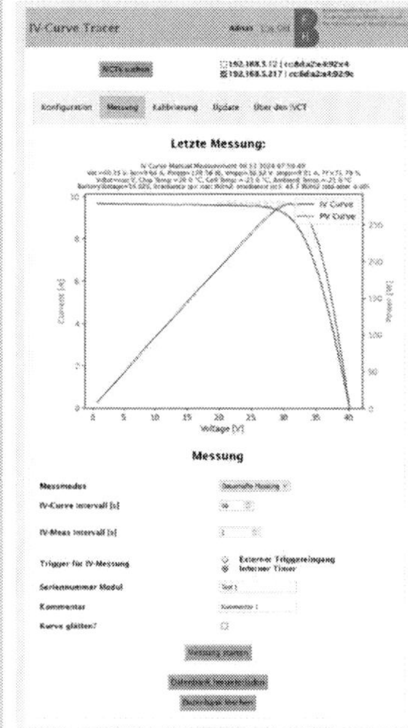

Figure 4: User interface of the IVCT in the web browser

References

[1] M. Müller, IV-Curve-Tracer, Bachelorarbeit, BFH, 2021
[2] J. Keta, D. Villiger, Firmware und Bedienungssoftware für ein Photovoltaik-Kennlinienmessgerät, Bachelorarbeit, BFH, 2023

Berner Fachhochschule
Haute école spécialisée bernoise
Bern University of Applied Sciences

» Departement Technik und Informatik (TI)
» Institut für Energie- und Mobilitätsforschung (IEM)

Labor für Photovoltaiksysteme
3400 Burgdorf | Jlcoweg 1
www.bfh.ch/pvlab | christof.bucher@bfh.ch

Kiwa PI Berlin

3AV.3.9 | SEASONAL AND LOCATION-DEPENDENT TEMPERATURE COEFFICIENTS FOR THIN-FILM PV MODULES: ENHANCING YIELD PREDICTION ACCURACY

Incorporate stabilization-dependent Tcoeff variations for a-Si/µc-Si & CdTe PV modules in laboratory testing, yield predictions, and warranty claims

Thomas Weber[1], Abdullah Abu Sayed[1,2], Benjamin Lippke[1], Steven Xuereb[1], Marcus Rennhofer[3], Bart E. Pieters[4]

[1]Kiwa PI Berlin AG
Wrangelstr. 100, 10997 Berlin, Germany
thomas.weber@kiwa.com, +49 30 314 52 64 -111

[2]Carl von Ossietzky University of Oldenburg, Germany
[3]AIT Austrian Institute of Technology GmbH, Austria
[4]IMD-3 Photovoltaics Forschungszentrum Jülich GmbH, Germany

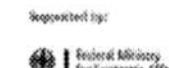

This research work has been carried out under the ReliaREN-Pro-D Project 03EI4052A (G202266) supported by the Federal Ministry for Economic Affairs and Climate Action.

Introduction

Background

- Thin-Film (TF) PV modules show often metastability behavior.
- Nominal power varies in TF equipped PV plants depending on the locations.
- Seasonal fluctuation are not considered when predicting the yield of a TF module, as datasheets provide only a constant (nominal, stabilized) power.
- Current warranties, testing standards and industry practice are insufficient to cover these TF-specific deviation properties.

Aim

Improve yield prediction by determining variable temperature coefficients (Tcoeff).

- Based on different stabilization states:
  - high power = summer and
  - low power = winter
- Considering the location impact on this new variable Tcoeff.

Methodology

Reference conventional scenario: One fixed Tcoeff (datasheet)
New: Tcoeff as a function of location and season

Stabilization	Experimental Determination of Tcoeff	Monte Carlo Environmental Simulation of Tcoeff	Yield analysis Simulation
a) Field exposure b) High & low power	Following MQT 04 by IEC 61215-2021	In: Varying weather conditions and locations Out: Random variable range of monthly possible Tcoeff	Capacity: 5 MW Type: FS-4110A-5 Tilt: 30° Yearly degradation: 0.4 % New average Tcoeff values

See Table 1, Investigated thin-film technologies:
a) a-Si/µc-Si (2010)
b) CdTe (2015, Serie 4)

Validation of Nominal Module Power / Tcoeff

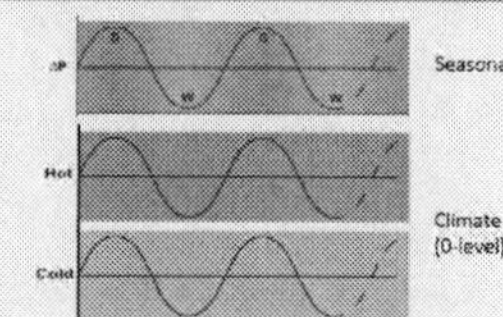

Figure 1: The mean temperature level of a specific site sets the 0-level. Therefore, power is a function of climate and location of the site. A climate dependent datasheet should be included in standard warranty procedures or contracts [1].

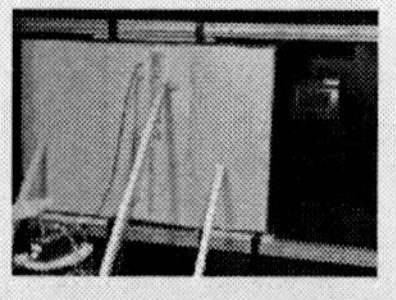

Figure 2: Experimental determination of Tcoeff following IEC 61215:2021, MQT 04. The Tcoeff values were determined on a module heated to 70°C during the cooling process of the solar simulator. The cooling process was delayed by insulation material.

Locations of the 4 Studied PV Plants

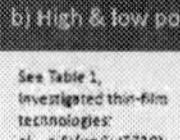

Figure 3: Four PV plant places have been selected: Berlin – DEU, Sicily – ITA, Cairo – EGY, Kuala Lumpur – MYS.

Climate Data Sets

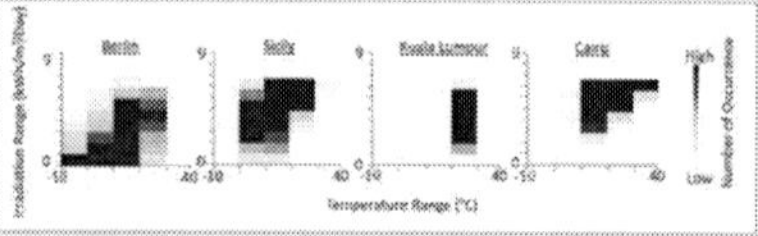

Figure 4: Heat-maps showing the 4 climate data sets. It shows a statistical analysis of the frequency distribution for the ranges of irradiation and temperature.

Precondition of Thin-Film Module

Technology	High power stabilization		Low power stabilization	
	Method	Parameter	Method	Parameter
a-Si/µc-Si (Sharp) [2]	Annealing	85°C, 2 days	Light soaking	66 kWh/m² (2 * Δ t)
CdTe [3]	Annealing	65°C, 24 h, 70 V	Dark storage	(25 ± 3)°C, two weeks

Table 1: Used methods for stabilization of a-Si/µc-Si and CdTe modules according to IEC standard, module manufacturer prescribed preconditioning, and dark storage. Field exposure (mpp) was stopped in Berlin after long-term exposure in January 2025 in order to determine the Tcoeff.

Results

Laboratory: P@STC & Tcoeff = f(stabilization)

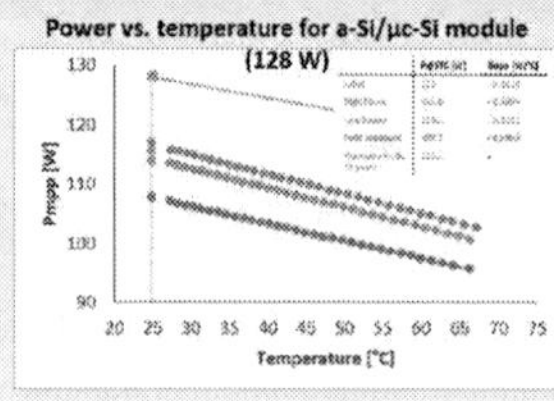

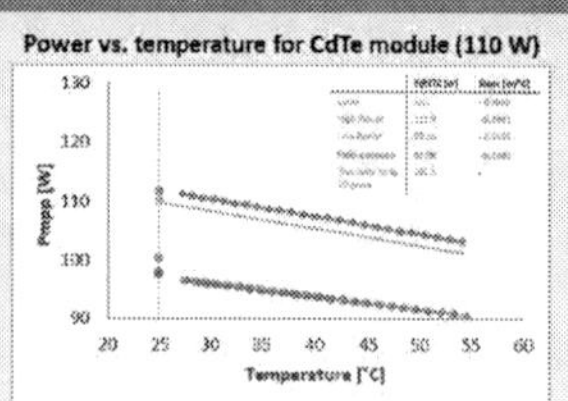

Figure 5: Measured power as function of temperature for a a-Si/µc-Si (left) and a CdTe (right) module (n = 1) for different stabilization scenarios. The datasheet provided Tcoeff and the nameplate power are marked in purple.
P@STC and Tcoeff deviate under the different stabilization from nameplate values. The field exposure (red) shows the lowest slope, the low-power stabilization (blue) shows a mid-slope, and the high-power stabilization (grey) shows the highest slope. A delta of 14 W is observed for both technologies at 25 °C, comparing low power to label. For CdTe, the high-power stabilization Tcoeff is even higher compared to nominal power.

Monte Carlo Simulation (CdTe): Monthly Tcoeff

Berlin

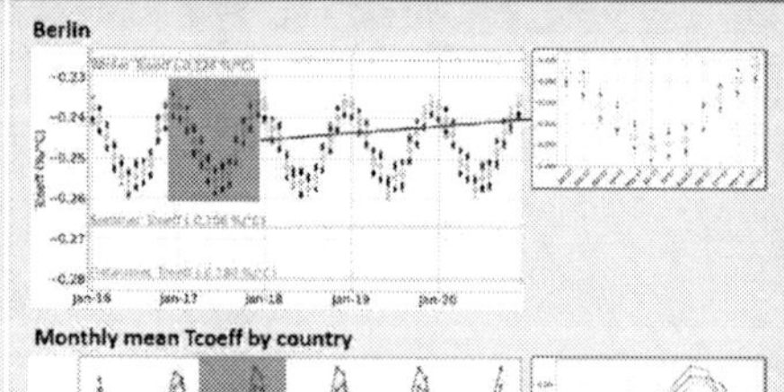

Monthly mean Tcoeff by country

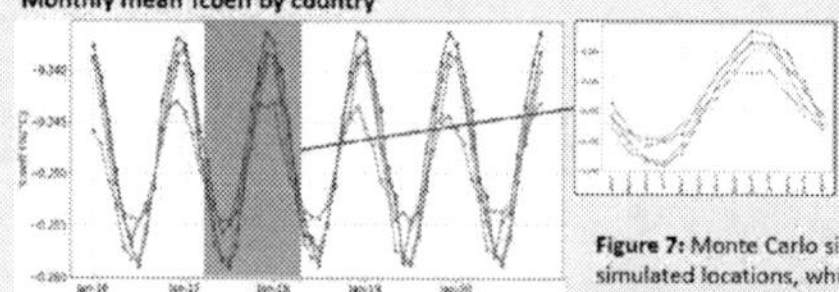

Figure 6: The graph show 5 years sinusoidal behavior in Berlin with the new simulated Tcoeff of the CdTe module. All the values are fluctuating in between the high-power stabilization Tcoeff and low-power stabilization Tcoeff determined in the laboratory (dashed lines). In summer, Tcoeff values reach to high-power stabilization Tcoeff value. In winter, Tcoeff values reach to low-power stabilization Tcoeff value.

Figure 7: Monte Carlo simulated monthly Tcoeff for all simulated locations, which reveal significant different results and deviation to nameplate.

Yield Analysis Comparison (CdTe)

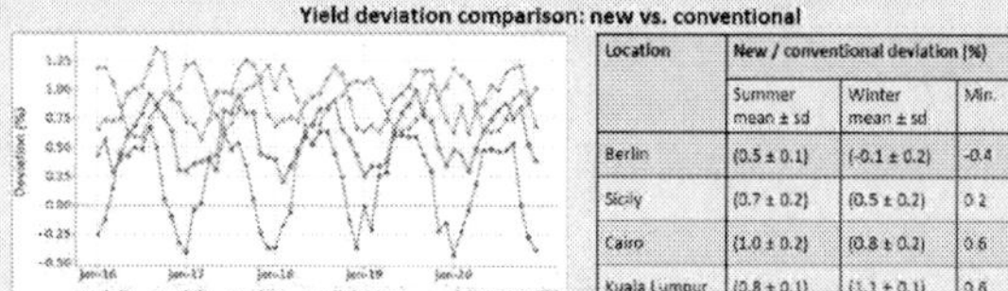

Location	New / conventional deviation (%)			
	Summer mean ± sd	Winter mean ± sd	Min.	Max.
Berlin	(0.5 ± 0.1)	(-0.1 ± 0.2)	-0.4	0.7
Sicily	(0.7 ± 0.2)	(0.5 ± 0.2)	0.2	1.0
Cairo	(1.0 ± 0.2)	(0.8 ± 0.2)	0.6	1.4
Kuala Lumpur	(0.8 ± 0.1)	(1.1 ± 0.1)	0.6	1.2

Figure 8: Simulation results are shown in 4 places over 5 years. The new simulation uses the modified set of Tcoeffs and the conventional simulation uses the datasheet Tcoeff. First, all monthly absolute yields were determined. **Left:** The graph shows the percentage deviation of yield compared to the conventional datasheet value-based approach (reference line). **Right:** Statistics showing summer (April to September) and winter (October to March) mean ± sd, minimum and maximum value.
Cairo shows the highest yield deviation (in max. value), which is 1.4 % higher and Berlin the lowest -0.4 % than the conventional approach. For a-Si/µc-Si the effects are much more pronounced but not shown here.

Conclusion

Results

- Tcoeff is not constant through the year.
- Tcoeffs change depending on module stabilization status, leading to
  - Seasonal variation of Tcoeff,
  - Location dependency of Tcoeff.
- Module manufactures should provide a set of high- and low-power Tcoeff, and the corresponding stabilization procedures.
- PVsyst and other simulation tools should allow at least two temperature coefficients for better output prediction.
- For CdTe, an installation closer to the equator is leading to higher module power and yields. In other words: the current industry standard for yield prediction leads to significant underestimations, especially in regions close to the equator.

Discussion

- Laboratory determined IV-curves on fielded modules are likely not able to determine the last actual field-stabilized power value. This make the current approach of warranty claims not working anymore.
- Will field-stabilized power determinations become the standard for warranty claims on all metastable technologies?
- IEC 61215 needs an update or creation of a new technical specification to cover variable Tcoeffs.
- Seasonal and location influence should be checked for all technologies. Different stabilizations influence the Tcoeff, if necessary, the stabilization procedures need to reflect that.

[1] Thomas Weber, Marcus Rennhofer, Benjamin Lippke, Lars Schmidt, Moslie Grass, Abdumenio Erbao; "One way correctly determine the power of thin-film modules", 38th European Photovoltaic Solar Energy Conference and Exhibition
[2] Energy CERANDATA/Sharp, "Maximum Power Measurement Subroutine for Shin-film PV modules"
[3] Paul Suresy, "First Solar Module Pre-conditioning for CdTe Modules", Reliability Group, 2016-07

STANDARDISATION METHODS FOR BIFACIAL ENERGY YIELD ESTIMATION AND PV MODULE LONG-TERM PERFORMANCE DEGRADATION ESTIMATION: POTENTIAL POLICY IMPLICATIONS

Jaione Bengoechea[1], Ana Maria Gracia[1]; Stefan Riechelmann[2], Stefan Winter[2]; Giorgio Bardizza[3]; Christos Monokroussos[4]; Davide Polverini[5]; Pablo Vicente-Laiglesia[6]; Maria Getsiou[7]
Spanish National Renewable Energy Center[1]; German National Metrology Institute[2]; TÜV Rheinland Italia SRL[3]; TÜV Rheinland Shanghai SRL[4]; Directorate General for Internal Market, Industry, Entrepreneurship and SMEs[5]; European Climate, Infrastructure and Environment Executive Agency[6]; Directorate General for Research and Innovation[7]
jbapezteguia@cener.com[1], agracia@cener.com[1]; stefan.riechelmann@ptb.de[2], stefan.winter@ptb.de[2];
giorgio.bardizza@tuv.com[3]; christos.monokroussos@tuv.com[4], davide.polverini@ec.europa.eu[5]; pablo.vicente-laiglesia@ec.europa.eu[6]; maria.getsiou@ec.europa.eu[7]

ABSTRACT: European policies like the Ecodesign Directive [1], the Energy Labelling Regulation [2] or the recently implemented Ecodesign for Sustainable Products Regulation [3] have improved the efficiency and sustainability of energy related products in the European market. In recent years, measures to incorporate PV products (modules and inverters) within the scope of these policies are being prepared [4]. In this regard, the EC's European Climate, Infrastructure and Environment Executive Agency (CINEA) is managing a three-year project aimed at developing standardized methods relevant for the implementation of the aforementioned policy measures to PV modules. The project has two distinctive objectives. Define a methodology to estimate the energy yield of bifacial PV modules, and develop a method and testing sequence to estimate the long-term degradation rate of the PV module's performance. The project is carried out by the consortium formed by the German National Metrology Institute (PTB), TÜV Rheinland Italia SRL and the Spanish National Renewable Energy Centre (CENER), and it is supported by the EC's Directorate General for Internal Market, Industry, Entrepreneurship and SMEs (DG GROW) and the Directorate General for Research and Innovation (DG RTD).
Keywords: energy yield, bifacial modules, long-term degradation rate.

1 INTRODUCTION

The European Commission (EC), through policies like the Ecodesign Directive [1], the Energy Labelling Regulation [2] or the recently implemented Ecodesign for Sustainable Products Regulation [3] has improved the efficiency and sustainability of the energy related products in the European market, providing consumers information and tools to make better informed decisions about the products available. Likewise, manufacturers have received means by which improve the characteristics of their products in terms of efficiency and sustainability, which in turn advances their position in the EU market and upgrades the overall quality of the products therein available.

Photovoltaic (PV) energy is one of the key players to achieve the EU's ambitious objectives for energy transition and security, which is reflected in the pace at which the installed PV capacity in the EU has grown in recent years. However, the deployment of this technology should not pose new burdens on the environment. With the aim of reducing and minimizing this impact, in recent years, measures to incorporate PV products (modules and inverters) within the scope of the aforementioned policies are being prepared [4].

In this regard, the EC's European Climate, Infrastructure and Environment Executive Agency (CINEA) is managing a project aimed at developing standardized methodologies relevant for the potential implementation of Ecodesign and Energy Label policy measures for PV modules. The project, which has a duration of three years starting in December 2023, has a twofold objective. On the one hand, define a methodology to estimate the energy yield of bifacial PV modules. And, on the other hand, develop a method and testing sequence to estimate the long-term degradation rate of the PV module's performance. The project is being developed by the contractor formed by the German National Metrology

Institute (PTB), TÜV Rheinland Italia SRL and the Spanish National Renewable Energy Centre (CENER). Furthermore, it is supported by the active participation of the EC's Directorate General for Internal Market, Industry, Entrepreneurship and SMEs (DG GROW) and the Directorate General for Research and Innovation (DG RTD).

This paper presents the current status of the project detailing the methodologies and testing sequences proposed to determine both parameters: the energy yield of bifacial PV modules and the long-term performance degradation rate. The project is divided in two tasks, each dedicated to one objective. Similarly, each objective has a dedicated section in the current paper, where information about the PV modules tested and results obtained so far are presented as well. For the project's development, the involvement of stakeholders is highly valuable and Section 4 is dedicated to the consultation activities performed to date. The paper finalizes with the conclusions drawn thus far, presented in Section 5.

More information about this project can be found at: https://ecodesign-pv-testing.eu/ or requested to the contractor at info@ecodesign-pv-testing.eu.

2 ENERGY YIELD OF BIFACIAL PV DEVICES

2.1 Introductory remarks

The first objective of this CINEA project is the development of a standardisation method for the calculation and testing of the energy yield of bifacial PV modules. The method should take into consideration the effect of the in-plane irradiance, the albedo, the module's temperature and the impact on the performance of the mounting configurations considering, primarily, those normally applied in bifacial PV modules installations in Europe.

Based on the potential implementation of this model in energy label measures to bifacial modules, the aim of the requested method is not a detailed energy yield assessment model but an estimation model for an energy rating application.

2.2 Methodology

The EC's proposal for an energy label for PV modules is based on the IEC 61853 Standard series which defines a method to estimate the energy yield from a monofacial device (Part 3) [5] based on input data retrieved from analysing the module under test (Part 1 [6] and 2 [7]) and predefined working conditions described as yearly datasets of hourly values of irradiance and climatological variables (Part 4) [8]. The thus estimated yield from monofacial devices is extended to bifacial ones assuming a fixed gain based on the device's bifaciality factor.

In opposition to this simplified approach, the method developed in this CINEA project follows the IEC's approach for monofacial devices based on hourly simulations. The new method estimates the rear side's contribution to the estimated energy yield in the hourly calculations by means of the effective irradiance received by the bifacial device (front side irradiance plus rear side irradiance multiplied by the bifaciality factor) and the temperature reached by the module, estimated from the received irradiance, ambient temperature and wind speed. Besides, the effective irradiance considers as well the spectral response of the device and the angle of incidence effects, like in [5], but in this case analysing both front and rear side of the bifacial device.

The IEC 61853 Standard series defined for monofacial devices, does not take into consideration the effect of albedo. However, in this project, in order to consider the effect of the ground-reflected irradiance on the estimated energy yield, different values of albedo will be analysed. These could be possibly linked to the three reference climates in [8] relevant for Europe, denoted Subtropical arid, Temperate coastal and Temperate continental.

Furthermore, different mounting configurations representative of bifacial installations will be considered. The current IEC 61853 Standard series assumes the monofacial module installed in an open-rack ground mounted configuration with a tilt angle of 20° and facing the Equator. In the proposed methodology three additional configurations will be analysed for bifacial devices, as shown in Fig. 1. In addition to the standard configuration (Top left), an equator facing building attached system (Top right), a vertical east/west oriented configuration (Bottom left), and a one-axis horizontal tacking system (Bottom right) will be studied.

For every mounting configuration, both the front and the rear side in-plane irradiance values have to be defined, for every reference climate in the form of new hourly values like in [8] to extend these reference climatic datasets.

Figure 1: Proposed new mounting configurations for bifacial PV modules.

2.3 Testing sequence

The testing activities described in IEC 61853 Part 1 [6] and 2 [7] for monofacial devices have been adapted where necessary for bifacial devices. For example, the performance matrix defined in [6] has been extended with more data points to complete a regular grid and reach higher irradiance values, up to 1300 W/m². While tests defined in [7] have been applied to both sides of the bifacial device to obtain the spectral responsivity (SR) and the angle of incidence parameter (a_r) or incidence angle modifier (AIM) for both sides. The thermal coefficients of the bifacial module (u_0 and u_1) used to estimate the temperature under working conditions have been obtained with a testing procedure equivalent to that applied to monofacial devices, following the method defined in the ongoing amendment to Part 2. However, further indoor testing is being carried out in this project to validate this approach for bifacial PV devices.

All the testing activities are being carried out by PTB.

2.4 Selected bifacial PV modules for the energy yield estimation task

Based on the project's specifications, the current European PV market and future market share projections, the stakeholders' opinions and the availability of bifacial PV modules in small quantities in the German PV retail market six different bifacial PV modules were selected from different manufacturers, who have been duly informed. As shown in Table I there are devices from the main PV technologies, with diverse characteristics and configurations (for example, spacing between cells) to analyse the effect on the performance. The selection contains one heterojunction (HJT) device, three TOPCon modules, one PERC module and one Interdigitated back contact (IBC) device. Glass/glass IBC modules could be considered bifacial devices since the rear side of the cell receive irradiance contributing to the performance of the module. All modules have frame except the PERC device.

Table I: Selection of bifacial PV devices for the energy yield estimation task.

	Technology	Bifaciality φ_{Pmax} (%)
1	HTJ	90 ± 5
2	TOPCon, white	80 ± 10
3	TOPCon, transparent	80 ± 5
4	TOPCon, black	80 ± 10
5	PERC	Not declared
6	IBC	Not applicable

2.5 Interim results

All bifacial PV devices have been characterized already and the parameters used as input for the energy yield method have been determined. One module of every PV module type has been used to obtain the performance matrix modifying the measurement conditions from 15°C to 75°C for the module's temperature and from 100 W/m² to 1300 W/m² for the in-plane irradiance. As an example, the results, in terms of efficiency, obtained for the HJT module and the IBC are shown in Fig. 2. From the selected devices, the IBC module shows higher efficiency values than the HJT device.

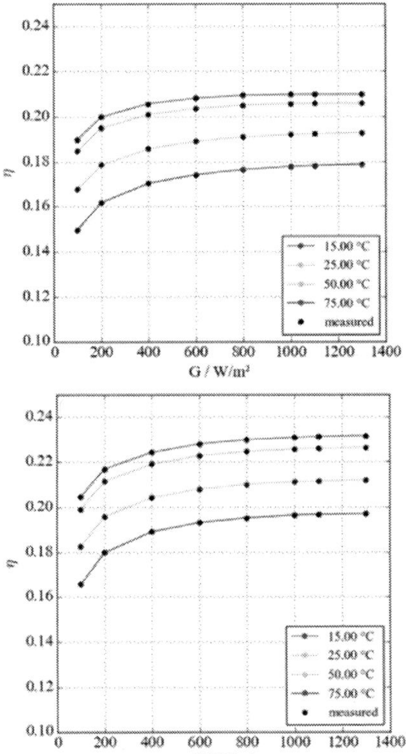

Figure 2: Performance matrix for the HJT (Top) and IBC (Bottom) selected PV bifacial devices.

The same PV module was then used to retrieve the *SR* and the *AIM* parameter for each side of the bifacial module, and the bifaciality factor, which is always within the declared tolerance. The bifaciality factor of the IBC module was determined as 41%.

In general, the rear side performs worse than the front side in relation to the *SR* (Fig. 3) and the *AIM* (Fig. 4) parameters.

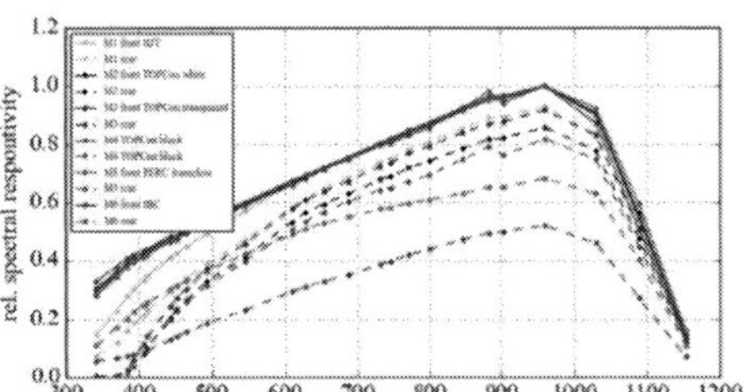

Figure 3: Relative spectral responsivity measured for the front and rear side of the selected bifacial devices.

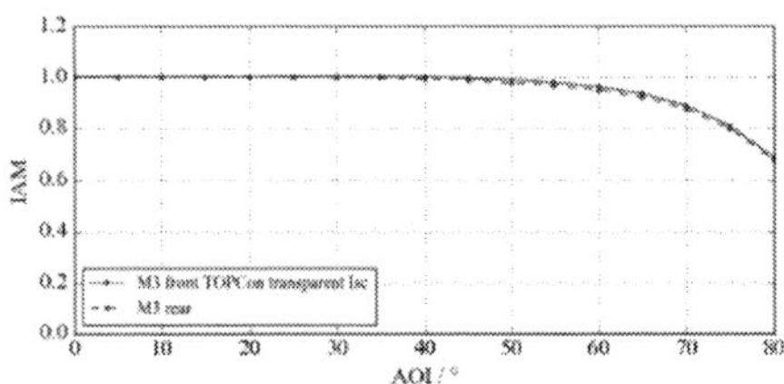

Figure 4: Relative internal angular transmittance values for one of the selected TOPCon device.

Considering the duration of the outdoor monitoring campaign to obtain the thermal coefficients (u_0 and u_1), a different PV module was used for this test. The monitoring campaign will be completed in forthcoming weeks.

3 LONG-TERM PV PERFORMANCE DEGRADATION

3.1 Introductory remarks

The second objective of the ongoing CINEA project is the development of a standardisation method for the measurement and testing of the long-term degradation of the PV modules' performance, including both monofacial and bifacial devices. The method shall take into consideration the effect of environmental stress factors like irradiance and temperature, and internal stress factors such as presence of non-suitable materials.

Based on the potential implementation of this model in ecodesign and energy label measures to PV modules, the complexity of the proposed method will be carefully assessed to balance duration and reliability of the results, since it should be easily implemented by Market Surveillance Authorities and PV testing laboratories.

3.2 Methodology

Due to the implications on the profitability of any PV installation on an underestimated degradation factor, the scientific community has tried with remarkable efforts to define this parameter. Furthermore, while there is significant evidence that PV installations perform mostly as expected, there are also cases of product recalls and observations of new (unexpected) failures. Therefore, the topic of degradation of the PV modules is still under open debate within the PV community and all the standardisation bodies.

Well-known performance (IEC 61215 series [9]-[14]) and safety (IEC 61730 [15]-[16]) qualification Standards are valuable for rapidly uncovering well-known early field failures, but they are insufficient to assess long-term degradation and its risk/impact. Recently, testing approaches for the long-term durability of PV modules are being explored within the preparatory work for the second edition of IEC TS 63209-1 Photovoltaic modules - Extended-stress testing - Part 1.

The proposed methodology focuses on the most common and impactful degradation mechanisms affecting the most representative PV technologies in the PV market, and includes a series of tests trying to trigger them on the devices analysed. These tests are based on others available in standardized protocols in order to minimize, when possible, the number of new tests assuming PV modules in the EU market comply with these standardized protocols.

The main degradation mechanisms considered include potential induced degradation (PID), moisture diffusion processes and UV induced degradation. These will be studied submitting the PV modules to severe conditions of temperature, humidity and UV irradiation. The results on the observed performance loss will be used in an extrapolation method, based on Arrhenius kinetics, to estimate the long-term degradation rate.

3.3 Testing sequence

The proposed testing sequence contains four main sections:

- PID testing sequence. Three temperatures of 65°C, 75°C and 85°C are applied with 85% relative humidity for 96 hours. Three separate PV modules are used, one per temperature. The applied voltage depends on the modules' specifications in terms of range and polarity.
- Damp heat testing sequence. Same conditions of temperatures and relative humidity as for the PID tests, no applied voltage and increased duration of 2000 hours per temperature. Three separate PV modules are used, one per temperature.
- UVID testing sequence. The main aim of this test is the analysis of the susceptibility of the PV material to the UV irradiation. Based on renown characterization protocols of various PV laboratories (TÜV and PVEL) which already include an independent UVID testing sequence and the lack of an standardized approach in this regard, the proposed UVID testing sequence includes a UV dose of 200 kWh/m^2 on the front side only of the device under test. One PV module is required for this test, whose temperature throughout the test shall be 60°C±5°C.
- Outdoor exposure. One year of outdoor exposure of one PV module which shall be electrically polarized at its maximum power point using an individual MPP tracker.

These testing activities will be performed by TÜV and CENER. While the damp heat and the UVID testing sequences are to be performed by both laboratories, the PID testing sequence and the outdoor exposure will be carried out by CENER.

The proposed testing sequence is completed by an initial characterization of the PV devices by means of IV curves at Standard Test Conditions (STC) and electroluminescence images, followed by outdoor exposure or Light Induced Degradation test (LID). Additionally, insulation test and wet leakage test are to be applied before the actual testing sequence. Similarly, at the end of every testing sequence, this characterization is to be performed again.

3.4 Selected PV modules for the long-term degradation rate estimation task

For this task a total of eight different module types have been selected based on the project's requirements, the current and projected European PV market share, the stakeholders' collaboration and the availability of PV modules in small quantities in the Spanish PV retail market.

The final selection, shown in Table II, includes two PERC devices, four TOPCon devices (two monofacial and two bifacial), one heterojunction (HJT) device and one Interdigitated Back Contact (IBC) device. They all belong to different manufacturers who have been informed about their products being used in this study. The power under STC, the efficiency and the layout are also indicated. This latter parameter indicates whether it is a monofacial (M) or bifacial (B) device, and the configuration glass/glass (G/G) or glass/backsheet (G/BS). Due to the characteristics of the climatic chambers used in this project, the size of the modules was limited to 2 m.

Table II: Selection of PV modules for the long-term degradation rate estimation task.

	Technology	$P_{max\ STC}$ (W)	Eff (%)	Layout
A	TOPCon, n-Type	450	22.5	M, G/BS
B	PERC, p-Type	450	20.8	M, G/BS
C	HJT, n-Type	450	21.6	M, G/BS
D	TOPCon, n-Type	475	21.9	B, G/G
E	TOPCon, n-Type	440	22.5	B, G/G
F	IBC, p-Type	460	22.5	M, G/BS
G	TOPCon, n-Type	500	22.2	M, G/BS
H	PERC, p-Type	460	21.2	M, G/BS

3.5 Interim results

The testing activities in this second task are not as advanced as in the energy yield estimation task. First results show significant deviations of the power output compared to nominal values. Figure 5 shows the differences, compared to the *Pmax* under STC declared by the manufacturer, of the obtained values in the initial characterization upon reception of the PV modules and after LID test.

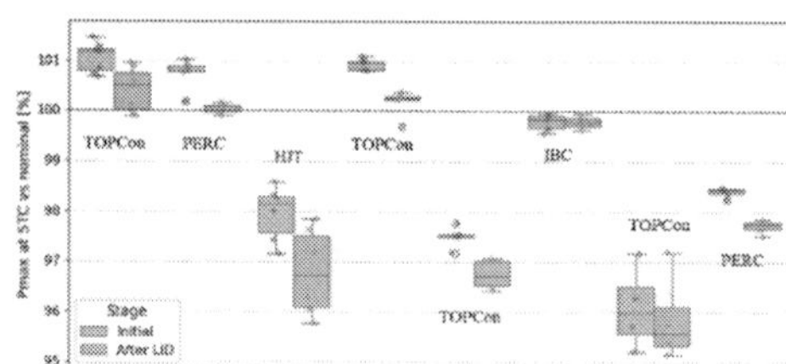

Figure 5: Comparison of *Pmax* at STC in the initial characterization and after LID test with regard to nominal values.

Two PV devices have already reached 100 kWh/m^2 of UV dose (half of the complete test) showing already 0.7% and 1.8% power loss respectively. Other results from PID testing are being analysed while testing continues.

4   STAKEHOLDERS CONSULTATION

Throughout the duration of the project, the consortium in charge of the project is committed to ensure that relevant stakeholders can provide input on the methodologies being developed. To that aim a dedicated website (https://ecodesign-pv-testing.eu/) was created were documentation and updates as well as invitations to consultation activities are announced. Furthermore, a functional mailbox was created to communicate directly with registered stakeholders (info@ecodesign-pv-testing.eu).

At present, more than 130 people have registered to the project including academia, research institutes and PV manufacturers. Two general stakeholder meeting have been organized so far, in months 3 and 19 to update stakeholders on the status of the project's development. Presentation and minutes are shortly after available on the website. After every meeting a period of various weeks is granted to provide feedback. Furthermore, an specific online questionnaire was launched after the first stakeholder meeting to get detailed feedback about the first approach to develop both standardized methodologies.

In addition, various meetings with experts have been organized for both tasks, particularly with the group of experts of IEC TC82 WG2 involved in the amendment of IEC 61853 Standard series and experts on the field of PV performance degradation.

So far, the project has benefited from the active participation and collaboration of stakeholders.

A third and last stakeholder meeting is planned for Autumn 2026 before the end of the project (November 2026). In this meeting the final methodologies and results will be presented.

5   CONCLUSIONS

In policy terms, the expected outcome from this study, which consists in the development of standardised (pre-normative) methods, could be highly relevant, inter alia, for environmental policies such as the potential implementation ecodesign and energy labelling measures to PV modules. This possibility implies that both methods and the corresponding testing activities should be easily implemented and validated by Market Surveillance Authorities. Furthermore, they should not become an excessive burden for manufacturers who shall comply with these testing requirements.

To facilitate the implementation of the proposed methodologies, the tests required are based on standardized ones, which are already applied by the PV industry. Furthermore, in the next stages of the project, a sensitivity analysis will be performed to study the impact of simplified testing and estimation methods in the final parameters' estimation. For example, by reducing the number of measurement points in the performance matrix, the new bifacial mounting configurations or the temperatures or UV dose applied in the testing activities for the degradation rate determination. If these simplifications were validated, the proposed testing activities could be also simplified.

With regard to the results obtained so far from the bifacial PV modules task, front and rear sides show significant differences. Therefore, it does not seem reasonable to assume the parameters of one side only for the estimation of the performance of both.

Despite the early stages in the testing activities of the long-term degradation rate task, it is important to highlight the value of the first initial characterization and stabilization (LID test) where significant differences between the modules of the same module type and between module types have been observed already. The final conclusions from the completed testing activities will be presented at the final stakeholder meeting. To register, please fill in the form in https://ecodesign-pv-testing.eu/meetings/.

6   REFERENCES

[1] Directive 2009/125/EC of the European Parliament and of the Council of 21 October 2009 Establishing a Framework for the Setting of Ecodesign Requirements for Energy-Related Products, OJ L285, 31.10.2009, p. 10–35, https://webstore.iec.ch/home.

[2] Regulation (EU) 2017/1369 of the European Parliament and of the Council of 4 July 2017 Setting a Framework for Energy Labelling and Repealing Directive 2010/30/EU, OJ L198, 28.7.2017, p. 1–23, https://webstore.iec.ch/home.

[3] Regulation (EU) 2024/1781 of the European Parliament and of the Council of 13 June 2024 establishing a Framework for the setting of ecodesign requirements for sustainable products, amending Directive (EU) 2020/1828 and Regulation (EU) 2023/1542 and repealing Directive 2009/125/EC Text with EEA relevance.

[4] Dodd N, Espinosa N et al. Preparatory study for solar photovoltaic modules, inverters and systems. https://publications.jrc.ec.europa.eu/repository/handle/JRC122431

[5] IEC 61853-3. Photovoltaic (PV) module performance testing and energy rating – Part 3: Energy rating of PV modules. Edition 1.0 International Electrotechnical Commission (2018).

[6] IEC 61853-1. Photovoltaic (PV) module performance testing and energy rating – Part 1: Irradiance and temperature performance measurements and power rating. Edition 1.0 International Electrotechnical Commission (2011).

[7] IEC 61853-2. Photovoltaic (PV) module performance testing and energy rating – Part 2: Spectral responsivity, incidence angle and module operating temperature measurements. Edition 1.0 International Electrotechnical Commission (2016).

[8] IEC 61853-4. Photovoltaic (PV) module performance testing and energy rating – Part 4: Standard reference climatic profiles. Edition 1.0 International Electrotechnical Commission (2018).

[9] IEC 61215-1 ED2. Terrestrial photovoltaic (PV) modules - Design qualification and type approval - Part 1: Test requirements. Edition 2.0 International Electrotechnical Commission (2021).

[10] IEC 61215-1-1 ED2 Terrestrial photovoltaic (PV) modules - Design qualification and type approval - Part 1-1: Special requirements for testing of crystalline silicon photovoltaic (PV) modules. Edition 2.0 International Electrotechnical Commission (2021).

[11] IEC 61215-1-2 ED2 - Terrestrial photovoltaic (PV) modules - Design qualification and type approval - Part 1-2: Special requirements for testing of thin-film Cadmium Telluride (CdTe) based photovoltaic (PV) modules. Edition 2.0 International Electrotechnical Commission (2022).

[12] IEC 61215-1-3 ED2 Terrestrial photovoltaic (PV) modules - Design qualification and type approval - Part 1-3: Special requirements for testing

of thin-film amorphous silicon based photovoltaic
(PV) modules. Edition 2.0 International
Electrotechnical Commission (2021).

[13]   IEC 61215-1-4 ED2 Terrestrial photovoltaic
(PV) modules - Design qualification and type
approval - Part 1-4: Special requirements for testing
of thin-film Cu(In,Ga)(S,Se)2 based photovoltaic
(PV) modules. Edition 2.0 International
Electrotechnical Commission (2021).

[14]   IEC 61215-2 ED2 Terrestrial photovoltaic (PV)
modules - Design qualification and type approval -
Part 2: Test procedures. Edition 2.0 International
Electrotechnical Commission (2021).

[15]   IEC 61730-1 ED3 Photovoltaic (PV) module
safety qualification – Part 1: Requirements for
construction. Edition 3.0 International
Electrotechnical Commission (2023).

[16]   IEC 61730-2:2023/COR1:2024 ED3
Corrigendum 1 - Photovoltaic (PV) module safety
qualification – Part 2: Requirements for testing.
Edition 3.0 International Electrotechnical
Commission (2023).

STANDARDISATION METHODS FOR BIFACIAL ENERGY YIELD ESTIMATION AND PV MODULE LONG-TERM PERFORMANCE DEGRADATION ESTIMATION: POTENTIAL POLICY IMPLICATIONS

Jaione Bengoechea[1], Ana María Gracia[1]; Stefan Riechelmann[2], Stefan Winter[2]; Giorgio Bardizza[3]; Christos Monokroussos[4]; Davide Polverini[5]; Pablo Vicente-Laiglesia[6]; Maria Getsiou[7]

Spanish National Renewable Energy Center[1]; German National Metrology Institute[2]; TÜV Rheinland Italia SRL[3]; TÜV Rheinland Shanghai SRL[4]; Directorate General for Internal Market, Industry, Entrepreneurship and SMEs[5]; European Climate, Infrastructure and Environment Executive Agency[6]; Directorate General for Research and Innovation[7]

jbapezteguia@cener.com[1]; agracia@cener.com[1]; stefan.riechelmann@ptb.de[2]; stefan.winter@ptb.de[2]; giorgio.bardizza@tuv.com[3]; christos.monokroussos@tuv.com[4]; davide.polverini@ec.europa.eu[5]; pablo.vicente-laiglesia@ec.europa.eu[6]; maria.getsiou@ec.europa.eu[7]

 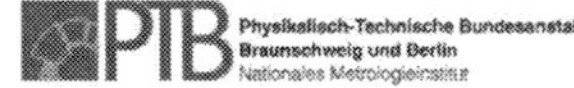  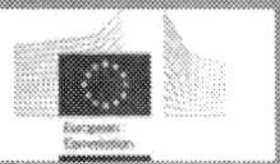 

ABSTRACT:

European policies like the **Energy Labelling Regulation**, the **Ecodesign Directive** and the recently implemented **Ecodesign for Sustainable Products Regulation** have successfully improved the efficiency and sustainability of energy related products in the European market. In recent years, measures to incorporate **photovoltaic (PV) modules** within the scope of these policy tools are being prepared. In this regard, the European Commission's European Climate, Infrastructure and Environment Executive Agency (CINEA) is managing the **ECODESIGN-PV-TESTING project** aimed at developing two standardized methodologies relevant for the implementation of these policy measures to PV modules. The project is supported by the EC's Directorate General for Internal Market, Industry, Entrepreneurship and SMEs (DG GROW) and the Directorate General for Research and Innovation (DG RTD).

Keywords: energy yield, bifacial PV modules, long-term degradation rate.

1. INTRODUCTION

The three-year project (December 2023 to November 2026) developed by the German National Metrology Institute (PTB), TÜV Rheinland Italia SRL and the Spanish National Renewable Energy Centre (CENER) has a twofold objective:

> ➤ Define a methodology to estimate the energy yield of bifacial PV modules.
> ➤ Develop a method and testing sequence to estimate the long-term degradation rate of the PV module's performance.

These standardised methods shall be easily implemented by **Market Surveillance Authorities**, PV laboratories and manufacturers.

2. ENERGY YIELD OF BIFACIAL PV MODULES

Methodology

❖ Energy yield method to **account for various effects** including:

- Irradiance
- Temperature
- Albedo
- PV module design
- Mounting configuration

❖ Based on IEC 61853 Standard series approach and extended for bifacial devices analysing in detail the **contribution from the rear side**.

IEC 61853 configuration (top left) and three relevant configurations for bifacial PV systems.

Testing activities and First results

❖ Bifacial PV module characterization:

- Spectral responsivity (SR) — Front & Rear side
- Incidence angle modifier (IAM)
- Performance matrix (G-T)
- Thermal coefficients (u_0 & u_1)
- Bifaciality (φ_{Pmax})

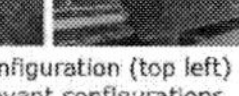

❖ Six bifacial PV module types from different manufacturers

- 1 HJT
- 3 TOPCon
- 1 PERC
- 1 IBC

❖ Declared φ_{Pmax} between 80% and 90%.

3. LONG-TERM PV PERFORMANCE DEGRADATION

Methodology

❖ **Accelerated stress tests**, based on standardised sequences, to activate the most severe and common degradation mechanisms.

❖ **Extrapolation model** to relate testing results to long-term evolution of the degradation modes based on Arrhenius kinetics.

Testing activities and First results

❖ Eight PV module types from different manufacturers

- 1 HJT
- 2 PERC
- 4 TOPCon
- 1 IBC

❖ 6 monofacial and 2 bifacial devices (TOPCon)

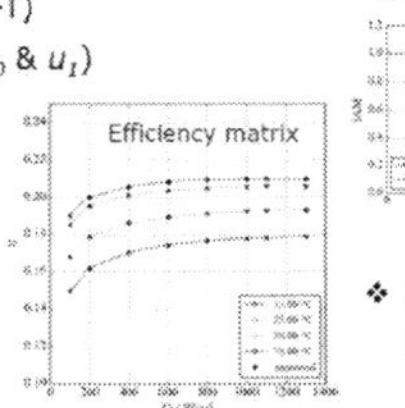

❖ 96 PV devices to be tested

Comparison of Pmax at STC in the initial characterization and after LID test with regard to nominal values.

4. STAKEHOLDERS CONSULTATION

- More than 130 people registered from **academia, research institutes and PV manufacturers**.
- **Two general stakeholder meetings** organized so far, in months 3 and 19 to update stakeholders on the status of the project's development. Feedback received at info@ecodesign-pv-testing.eu.
- **Presentation and minutes** are available on the website https://ecodesign-pv-testing.eu/.
- **Last stakeholder meeting in autumn 2026**. To register visit https://ecodesign-pv-testing.eu/meetings/.

Development of standardisation methods for eco-design and energy labelling of photovoltaic products

Home   The Study   Register   Meetings   Documents   Contact

5. CONCLUSIONS

- Both standardised methods, could be highly relevant for the **potential implementation ecodesign and energy labelling measures to PV modules**.
- **Duration and complexity** will be carefully assessed to guarantee an easy implementation by Market Surveillance Authorities, PV laboratories and manufacturers.
- Proposed testing activities are **based on available standard methods** already implemented by the PV industry.
- **First results show significant differences** between the tested PV devices.
- Final standardised methods and results will be presented in the **last stakeholder meeting** at the end of 2026.

SHAALKE: DEVELOPMENT OF A MATLAB SOFTWARE TOOL FOR ADVANCED STATISTICAL OUTDOOR DATA EVALUATION

Andreas Schneider[1] and Jorge Rabanal Arabach[2]
[1]University of Applied Sciences Gelsenkirchen, Neidenburger Str. 43,
45897 Gelsenkirchen, Germany
[2]Universidad de Antofagasta, Angamos Avenue 601, 1270300 Antofagasta, Chile

ABSTRACT: This paper introduces Shaalke, a novel analytical software tool developed for the high-accuracy evaluation of long-term photovoltaic module measurement data. Addressing the critical need for robust parameter extraction from field data, Shaalke integrates advanced filtering, linear regression, and algorithmic processing to overcome limitations of traditional evaluation methods. We demonstrate Shaalke's capability to accurately determine STC parameters and both static and dynamic temperature coefficients, showing excellent agreement with manufacturer specifications and independent laboratory measurements. A key finding is Shaalke's precise mapping of the irradiance dependence of module efficiency, filling a significant gap left by typical datasheet values which often only provide data at 1000 and 200 W/m². Furthermore, the tool enables reliable power degradation analysis, identifying modules that exceed manufacturer-tolerated limits. Shaalke provides a comprehensive, data-driven platform for understanding real-world module performance, offering invaluable insights for system design, operation, and quality assurance, thereby bridging the gap between laboratory specifications and field performance.
Keywords: Photovoltaic modules, Software tool, Data Evaluation, Field performance, STC parameters, Temperature coefficients, Power degradation

1 INTRODUCTION

Accurate determination of key performance parameters of photovoltaic (PV) modules - such as power at standard test conditions (STC), temperature coefficients, irradiance response, and long-term degradation behavior - is essential for both, scientific analysis and operational decision making in solar energy systems. While laboratory characterization provides controlled measurements, real-world performance often deviates due to environmental variability, non-standard operating conditions, and measurement noise. Over the past two decades, several approaches have been proposed to extract module parameters from field data, including linear regression methods, filtering of irradiance and temperature fluctuations, and statistical degradation analyses [1–3]. These studies highlight the value of long-term monitoring but also demonstrate the challenges of reducing uncertainty and ensuring reproducibility.

Despite these advances, the gap remains wide between raw monitoring data and actionable, accurate module parameters, particularly when effects of degradation and dynamic thermal behavior are to be captured simultaneously. Traditional evaluation pipelines often rely on restrictive filtering or simplified regression, potentially overlooking subtle but relevant effects in large datasets. There is, therefore, a strong need for analytical software that can process long-term high-resolution data efficiently, while integrating advanced signal processing and modeling algorithms for parameter extraction [4].

In response to this need, we introduce Shaalke, a dedicated software tool designed for analytical long-term evaluation of PV module performance. The program combines advanced filtering techniques, robust linear regression, and algorithmic post-processing to reliably determine STC performance, degradation rates, and static as well as dynamic temperature coefficients. This approach provides improved reproducibility and higher accuracy compared with standard methodologies, as shown by the initial analyses presented here.

In this paper, we first outline the methodological framework of Shaalke, followed by a demonstration of its application to long-term measurement datasets from solar modules under realistic outdoor conditions. We then present initial results highlighting the accuracy of extracted STC parameters and module temperature coefficients. The study concludes with a discussion of Shaalke's value for both research and industry practice, as well as its potential for enabling standardized, high-fidelity evaluation of long-term PV data.

2 SOFTWARE DEVELOPMENT

For the systematic evaluation of long-term field measurements, a dedicated software tool named Shaalke (Software for Harvested and at Ambient Acquired and Logged Key data for Evaluation) has been developed at the University of Applied Sciences, Gelsenkirchen. The program was implemented in the MATLAB environment, a platform well-suited for handling large numerical datasets and performing statistical analysis of time-series measurement data.

Shaalke is specifically designed to process data from PV module measurements collected in outdoor test facilities. It provides an intuitive graphical user interface (GUI) and supports the direct import of I–V parameters (current, voltage, operating power) and module rear-side temperature (T_{module}) on a one-minute timescale. These electrical and thermal data are automatically synchronized with local weather station records, including irradiance (G_{POA}), ambient temperature, relative humidity, and wind vectors. This design ensures that all relevant environmental and electrical parameters can be evaluated in a temporally consistent manner. With input capabilities for up to several years, the software can process datasets exceeding 500,000 rows (>5 million data points).

The main functions of Shaalke are (i) advanced filtering, allowing automated removal of outliers and erroneous entries caused by sensor drift or failures, and (ii) statistical parameter extraction by means of linear regression and correlation analysis. The software facilitates the determination of characteristic module coefficients such as temperature dependence of power,

10.4229/EUPVSEC2025/3AV.3.11

voltage, and current. In addition, Shaalke contains modules for yield simulation, enabling direct estimation of energy output under both, measured and synthetic climatic conditions. For synthetic inputs, the software provides seamless integration of Meteonorm datasets and other climate models, supporting comparative studies of climate variability and its influence on PV performance.

A distinctive feature of Shaalke is its ability to predict module operating temperature from purely meteorological inputs (irradiance, wind, ambient temperature) in combination with static module-specific parameters. This function enables two independent approaches for assessing electrical performance: one directly based on measured operating conditions, and another derived from reconstructed thermal behaviour. Such redundancy enhances model reliability and provides additional robustness in long-term degradation and climate impact studies.

By combining flexible data import, robust statistical analysis, and predictive functions, Shaalke establishes a unified platform for bridging experimental field measurements with theoretical yield simulations. The modular design allows further extension to additional performance metrics or future integration with machine-learning approaches for long-term PV performance prediction. Figure 1 shows exemplarily the temperature coefficient determination part of the GUI: Determination of the temperature coefficient of open circuit voltage close to 1000 W/m².

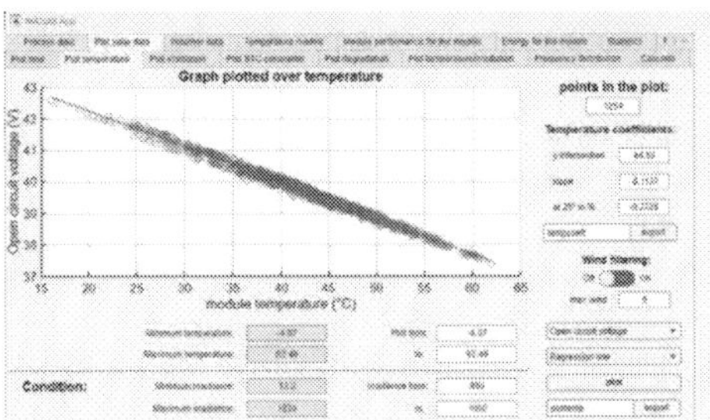

Figure 1: Example plot showing part of Shaalkes GUI

3 RESULTS AND DISCUSSION

3.1 Metrological and specimen information

A long-term outdoor monitoring campaign of photovoltaic (PV) modules was initiated in 2020 and is currently ongoing. The study focuses on commercially available crystalline silicon modules, the relevant datasheet specifications are provided in Table I. The modules are mounted under fixed-tilt conditions (module no 1-6), on a 2-axes tracker (module no 7) and on a single axis tracker (module 8 and 9) and continuously operated at their maximum power point (P_{mpp}), ensuring realistic field exposure and degradation assessment.

Current-voltage (I–V) characteristics are recorded at one-minute resolution using a calibrated Papendorf SOL.Connect® device. The system reports an accuracy better than 1% for I–V tracing, consistent with metrological standards. Module operating temperature is determined at the rear side with a Pt1000 resistance thermometer, while in-plane global irradiance is measured by an ISET sensor. Complementary environmental data, including ambient temperature, relative humidity, wind

speed, wind direction, and both, global horizontal and tilted plane irradiance, are obtained from a nearby Thies weather station at five-minute intervals.

Table I: Type of solar modules including specific data from the datasheets

Module type	No	Cell /module technology	P (W)
Panasonic VBHN 340 SJ53	1	HIT	340
Sunpower P3 325 BLK	2	PERC shingled	325
REC Alpha-Series	3	HJT SmartWire	365
Heckert NeMo 4.1 80M	4	PERC	400
Hyundai DG-Series, HiE-S420DG	5	G12 PERC shingled	420
Solarwatt Vision AM4	6	PERC	405
Trina-TSM-440NEG9R.25	7	N-Typ i-TOPCon	420
Aiko Neostar Series-A445-MAH54Mb Nebular 2P Serie	8	N-Type ABC	445
Aiko A-MCE54Db Neostar 3S+54	9	N-Type ABC	470

The measurement schedule is illustrated in Figure 2, showing the individual PV modules included in the campaign, their start times, and whether they are still under evaluation or have completed testing. This long-term dataset allows the temporal evolution of module performance to be correlated with environmental stress factors such as temperature fluctuations, irradiance dose, and seasonal variations. To validate field measurements, modules are periodically dismounted and characterized under STC using an A+A+A+ mbj solar simulator (solar flasher), following IEC 60904-9 guidelines.

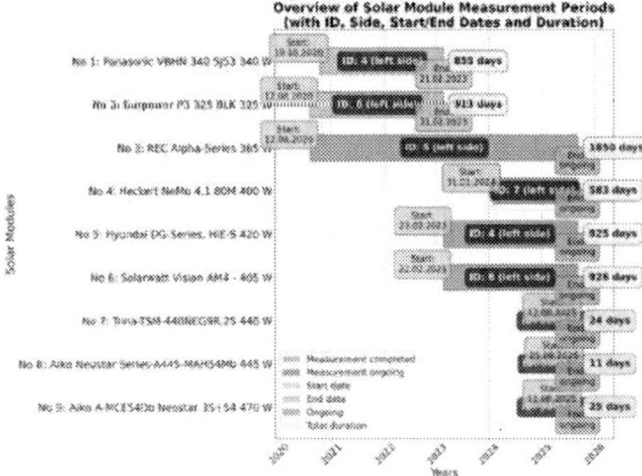

Figure 2: Measurement campaign schedule

Such continuous outdoor-to-laboratory correlation ensures that observed degradations are reliably attributed to environmental exposure rather than measurement artifacts. The combination of high temporal resolution, redundant temperature and irradiance sensing, and independent cross-validation through flasher tests provides a robust metrological framework. Similar approaches to long-term field monitoring have been described in literature on PV reliability studies [5].

3.2 Determination of STC parameters

Measurement data of the first six operation months were imported and subsequently filtered within the irradiance range of 1000 ± 50 W/m² (except for modules 7–9, which were just installed in August 2025 and hence less measurement data was available). Linear regression was then applied to the filtered dataset. Due to the large volume of available data points, sufficient coverage exists to accurately calculate I_{sc}, V_{oc}, and P_{mpp} at a reference temperature of $25°C \pm 0.5°C$. Table II lists the STC data for I_{sc}, V_{oc}, and P_{mpp} as specified by the supplier.

Table II: STC data given by the supplier (datasheet)

No	Datasheet (supplier)		
	I_{sc} (A)	V_{oc} (V)	P_{mpp} (W)
1	6.1	71.3	340
2	9.7	43.6	325
3	10.3	44.3	365
4	18.2	28.3	400
5	12.9	41.6	420
6	13.7	37.2	405
7	10.7	52.2	440
8	14.0	40.6	445
9	14.7	40.6	470

For reference, the modules had also been characterized using a calibrated mbj LED flasher immediately before the start of the measurement campaign. This provides an independent benchmark to which the results of Shaalke can be compared. Table III summarizes the corresponding results obtained through the mbj flasher (using a calibrated reference module) and through the Shaalke analysis tool.

Table III: STC results as obtained by the mbj LED flasher using a calibrated reference module and Shaalke

No	Flasher Data			Outdoor results (fitting)		
	I_{sc} (A)	V_{oc} (V)	P_{mpp} (W)	I_{sc} (A)	V_{oc} (V)	P_{mpp} (W)
1	6	70.9	320	6.1	70.1	326
2	9.4	43.5	321.1	9.6	43.1	322
3	10.1	43.6	337.1	10.2	43.3	335.3
4	17.9	27.8	390.5	17.9	27.3	385
5	12.5	42.2	407.6	12.7	41.4	394.1
6	13.6	37.5	400.9	13.8	36.7	400.9
7	10.7	52.8	445.4	10.5	52.9	431.3
8	13.3	40	425	13.6	39.7	435.0
9	15	40.3	479.7	14.9	40.1	477.9

The comparison clearly illustrates that Shaalke yields results in excellent agreement with the independent flasher measurements. Minor deviations can be attributed to differences in calibration schemes and slight module aging between flasher characterization and the onset of long-term data collection or any degradation occurring during the first 6 months of operation. Also, the

regression-based evaluation confirms the high validity of Shaalke for automated STC determination under field conditions. These findings underline the robustness of combining long-term datasets with advanced filtering and regression techniques, providing a reliable complement and potential alternative to laboratory-based STC verification.

Figure 3 shows a box plot of the differences of P_{mpp}, V_{oc} and I_{sc} determined by Shaalke and the calibrated flasher measurement.

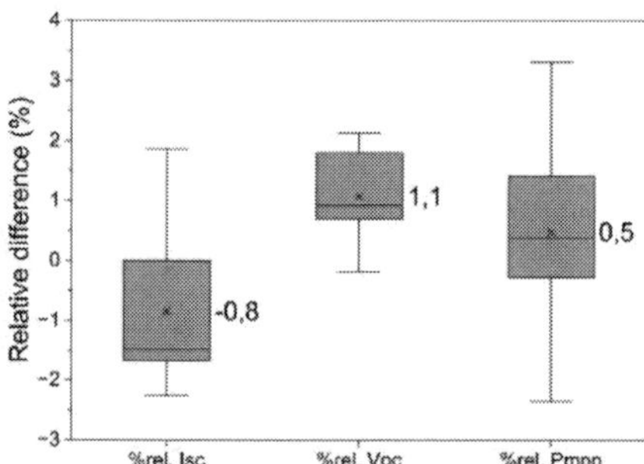

Figure 3: Relative difference of P_{mpp}, V_{oc} and I_{sc}

3.3 Determination of temperature coefficients

In the next step, the temperature coefficients for voltage, current, and power were determined for the same PV modules. As in the STC evaluation, the key requirement for extracting meaningful coefficients is to restrict the irradiance band as closely as possible to 1000 W/m², while still maintaining a sufficient number of datapoints after filtering to allow a stable linear regression fit. This ensures that variations in irradiance do not bias the slope determination and that the regression reflects only the temperature dependence of the electrical parameters.

Among the parameters considered, the temperature coefficient of voltage is typically the most straightforward to determine, as module voltage is measured with the highest accuracy and exhibits a clear and strong linear dependence on temperature. In contrast, the determination of the current coefficient is more difficult and is often affected by a higher degree of noise. This difficulty originates partly from the small intrinsic magnitude of the current-temperature dependence and partly from the nature of current measurement itself, which introduces larger measurement deviations compared with voltage.

Even under controlled laboratory environments, extracting reliable temperature coefficients of current is challenging because the small change of current with temperature is often comparable to the measurement uncertainty. As a result, significant scatter is commonly observed, and researchers typically mitigate this by employing wide temperature intervals, repeated measurements, and averaging procedures. In the present study, considerable improvement was achieved through the combination of long-term outdoor datasets and Shaalke's filtering and regression algorithms, which reduce noise levels and stabilize the regression slope. Figure 4 illustrates the filtered short-circuit current data used for determining the current temperature coefficient for one module. When compared to the supplier information, the values obtained through Shaalke show excellent agreement.

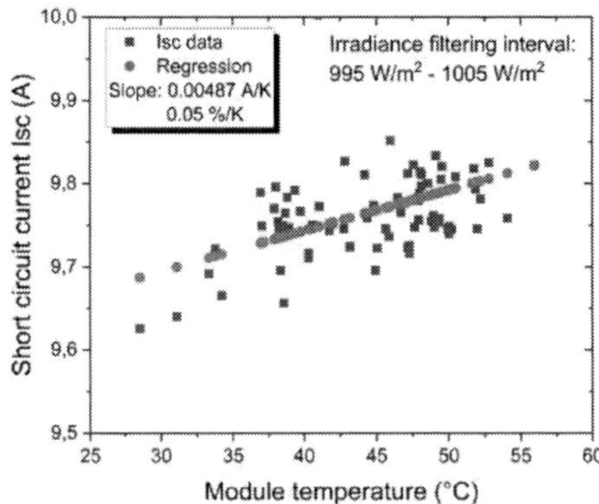

Figure 4: Example of filtered data for short circuit current to determine its temperature coefficient

Table IV lists the temperature coefficients provided by the manufacturer alongside results determined by Shaalke. The close match highlights the effectiveness of the method, particularly considering that values were obtained from field data under naturally varying conditions.

Table IV: Temperature coefficients as given by the module maker and determined by Shaalke

No	Datasheet			Outdoor results (fitting)		
	T_K for P_{mpp} (%/K)	T_K for V_{oc} (%/K)	T_K for I_{sc} (%/K)	T_K for P_{mpp} (%/K)	T_K for V_{oc} (%/K)	T_K for I_{sc} (%/K)
1	-0.26	-0.24	0.06	-0.30	-0.24	0.02
2	-0.36	-0.29	0.05	-0.37	-0.29	0.05
3	-0.26	-0.24	0.04	-0.35	-0.24	0.05
4	-0.34	-0.26	0.03	-0.36	-0.27	0.04
5	-0.34	-0.27	0.04	-0.34	-0.27	0.02
6	-0.33	-0.26	0.05	-0.39	-0.27	0.04
7	-0.29	-0.24	0.04	-0.31	-0.23	0.05
8	-0.26	-0.22	0.05	-0.25	-0.22	-
9	-0.26	-0.22	0.05	-0.24	-0.22	-

Small deviations are within typical uncertainty margins and can be attributed to measurement errors, environmental noise, and minor module variability. Importantly, Shaalke not only reproduces the voltage and power coefficients with good reliability but also yields a consistent estimate of the current coefficient—despite the known difficulties associated with its determination. This demonstrates that long-term outdoor monitoring, when combined with filtering and regression approaches, can yield results comparable to controlled laboratory testing.

Overall, these findings validate Shaalke as a powerful tool for automated determination of temperature coefficients directly from field data. Beyond the practical advantages of avoiding repeated laboratory flash tests, the methodology also reflects real operating conditions, which are highly relevant for long-term energy yield prediction and reliability assessment. The demonstrated accuracy of the results illustrates the potential for standardized, field-based module evaluation and quality assurance.

3.4 Irradiance dependence of efficiency

The dependence of module efficiency on irradiance was analyzed in detail for module 3 and compared with the reference data provided in the manufacturer's datasheet. Under standard test conditions (STC), both Shaalke and the datasheet predict the almost same efficiency value,

confirming the consistency of the initial calibration. When moving away from STC and assessing performance in lower or higher irradiance ranges, however, deviations in the efficiency curve become apparent. Specifically, Shaalke results reveal a relative deviation of approximately 2–3% compared with the supplier's curve.

Although this deviation may appear numerically large at first glance, it is important to emphasize that the value is a relative percentage difference. In terms of absolute efficiency, the divergence is comparatively small and does not significantly affect overall energy yield estimations. Still, such irradiance-dependent effects are technologically relevant, as they impact performance particularly under real operating conditions with frequent low-light levels (e.g., mornings, evenings, or cloudy conditions).

A critical problem is that most suppliers usually specify efficiency values only at 1000 W/m² and, in some cases, at 200 W/m² for so-called "low light" behavior. This leaves the important irradiance range between 200–1000 W/m² largely undocumented in datasheets, even though this interval is where modules spend a significant portion of their operating lifetime.

Figure 5 illustrates the irradiance dependence of module 3, plotting both the supplier's reported curve and the results derived with Shaalke.

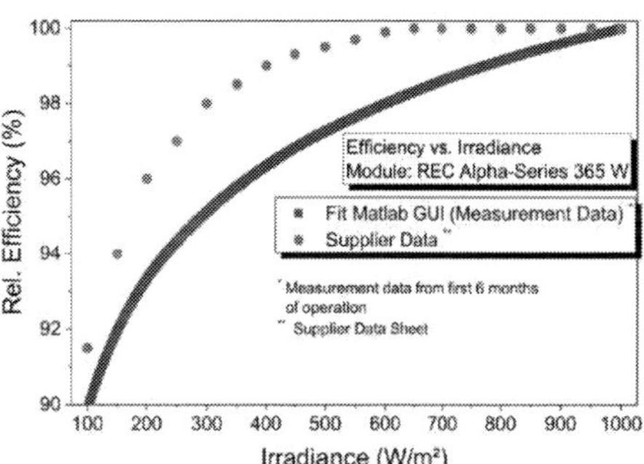

Figure 5: Irradiance dependence of module 3 as given by the supplier and determined by Shaalke

It can be observed that while the general shape and trend are in agreement, Shaalke provides a more data-driven representation that reflects actual long-term outdoor operation. This highlights the value of long-term datasets in capturing subtle performance deviations that are not always apparent from laboratory tests alone.

The observed difference may be attributed to several factors, including natural module degradation, variations in spectral distribution under real conditions, or the simplifications in measurement protocols used by the supplier. Importantly, the small but consistent deviations illustrate that Shaalke can serve not only as a validation tool for datasheet claims but also as a means to uncover real-world performance characteristics that are highly relevant for system energy yield predictions.

In summary, the assessment demonstrates that Shaalke reliably reproduces manufacturer-given efficiency curves while also capturing subtle irradiance-dependent effects that stem from outdoor operation. This ability to quantify low-light behavior and irradiance effects helps bridge the gap between laboratory specifications and field performance, thereby providing valuable input for module comparison, system modelling, and bankability assessments.

3.5 Determination of the power degradation

As shown in the measurement data set, many of the investigated modules have been in continuous operation at the location for several years, with some still active today. This provides an extensive long-term data pool that can be leveraged to assess the power degradation of the modules under real outdoor conditions. Since suppliers typically report only limited degradation values - such as the performance loss in the first year and a subsequent annual linear degradation rate, or, in some cases, only the total guaranteed degradation after 25 or 30 years, our evaluation focuses on the actual years of operation available for the tested modules.

This necessarily introduces some uncertainty because the degradation trajectory during the first years may not be perfectly linear, and measurement intervals differ from the assumptions underlying the datasheet values. On the other hand, the supplier's values are provided as maximum guaranteed limits, which means our results can be directly compared against them to verify whether observed degradation remains within the specified tolerance.

The Shaalke analysis, based on regression of long-term monitoring data, reveals that most modules remain within the acceptable limits of the manufacturer's degradation specifications. However, in the case of modules 3 and 4, significantly larger degradation rates were identified compared to the values tolerated by the datasheet. This suggests either early-onset degradation mechanisms (e.g., encapsulant browning, interconnect fatigue, or light-induced degradation) or module-specific issues related to production variability. Importantly, Shaalke's long-term analysis makes such deviations from expected performance visible at an early stage, supporting proactive quality control.

Table V summarizes the degradation results determined with Shaalke after several years of operation and compares them directly to the manufacturer's maximum degradation claims. The comparison demonstrates that while most modules are well within specification, individual modules exceed supplier guarantees, underscoring the importance of continuous monitoring with advanced analysis tools rather than relying solely on datasheet projections.

Table V: Degradation after several years of operation as determined by Shaalke and compared to the max. value as calculated by the supplier datasheet

No	Operation	Max. degradation Datasheet (supplier)	Determined Degrad-ation (fitting)
	Years	%	%
1	2	3.5	1.2
2	3	3	0.2
3	6	4.5	7.3
4	2	2	2.8
5	3	3.1	0.4
6	3	1.3	0.6

These findings highlight both, the practical relevance and the reliability of Shaalke for degradation monitoring. In contrast to manufacturer warranties, which often use conservative or averaged values, our approach provides real data tailored to module-specific conditions. This information is highly valuable for system operators, investors, and researchers alike, as it enables more accurate predictions of long-term energy yield, early detection of underperforming modules, and validation of warranty claims.

3.6 Dynamic temperature coefficient determination

If long-term measurement data are available, Shaalke enables straightforward determination of dynamic temperature coefficients, which describe the irradiance dependence of the individual temperature coefficients. In contrast to static values taken at nominal conditions, dynamic coefficients provide deeper insight into how voltage, current, and power responses evolve under varying irradiance and temperature combinations [6, 7].

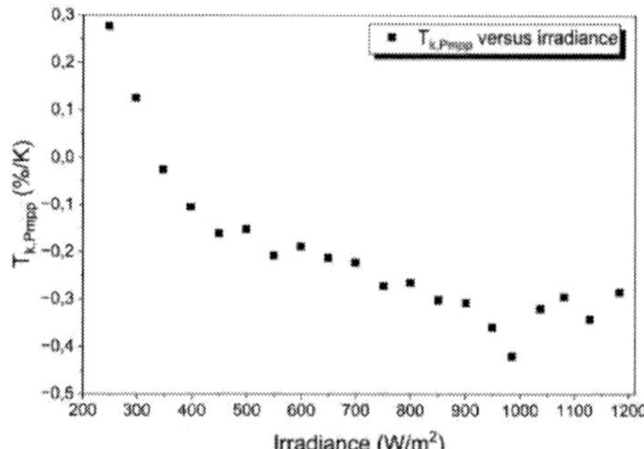

Figure 6: Dynamic P_{mpp} temperature coefficient

Shaalke incorporates a built-in function that automatically extracts these parameters once the dataset is imported, cleaned and filtered. This greatly simplifies the analysis, reducing a complex evaluation to a user-friendly process while retaining high accuracy. Figure 6 illustrates the determination of the dynamic P_{mpp} temperature coefficient as obtained with Shaalke.

The ability to derive dynamic coefficients from real, long-term data provides valuable information for modelling real-world module behavior, enabling more precise yield simulations and more reliable system design.

4 CONCLUSION

This paper presents Shaalke, an advanced analytical software tool designed for the high-accuracy evaluation of long-term PV module measurement data. Addressing the critical need for robust parameter extraction from field data, Shaalke integrates sophisticated filtering techniques, linear regression, and algorithmic processing to overcome the limitations of traditional evaluation methods and datasheet-only information.

Our results demonstrate Shaalke's capability to accurately determine key module parameters under real-world operating conditions. The analysis of STC parameters (I_{sc}, V_{oc}, P_{mpp}) showed excellent agreement with independent laboratory flasher measurements, thereby validating Shaalke's foundational accuracy. Furthermore, the software proved highly effective in determining temperature coefficients for voltage, current, and power. Notably, Shaalke successfully extracted the challenging current temperature coefficient from noisy field data, a task often difficult even in controlled laboratory environments.

A significant contribution of this work is the detailed

assessment of the irradiance dependence of module efficiency. While initial STC values matched supplier data, Shaalke revealed subtle yet important relative deviations of 2–3% in efficiency across varying irradiance levels. Crucially, our analysis highlighted a critical gap in manufacturer datasheets, which typically provide efficiency data only at 1000 W/m² and 200 W/m², leaving the vital operating range between 200–1000 W/m² largely undocumented. Shaalke effectively fills this gap by providing a data-driven, continuous efficiency curve, offering invaluable insights for accurate energy yield predictions and system modelling.

The long-term data pool also enabled a robust determination of power degradation. While most modules performed within supplier-specified maximum degradation limits, Shaalke identified two modules (modules 3 and 4) exhibiting significantly higher degradation than tolerated by their datasheets. This capability underscores Shaalke's role in early detection of underperforming modules and validation of warranty claims, moving beyond generalized manufacturer guarantees to module-specific performance insights. Finally, the software's ability to determine dynamic temperature coefficients, which account for the irradiance dependency of these parameters, further enhances the precision of real-world performance modelling.

In conclusion, Shaalke represents a significant advancement in PV module analysis. By leveraging long-term measurement data, it provides a comprehensive, accurate, and user-friendly platform for determining STC parameters, temperature coefficients, irradiance-dependent efficiency, and power degradation. This tool not only bridges the gap between laboratory specifications and field performance but also offers critical insights for researchers, system operators, and investors, ultimately contributing to more reliable PV system design, operation, and quality assurance.

5   ACKNOWLEDGEMENTS

The author wants to thank Mrs. Julia Chochollek for her long-term support with the development of Shaalke. This work was partly funded by the Federal Ministry for Economic Affairs and Energy inside the project BuKuMu under contract no. FKZ 03EE1225F.

6   REFERENCES

[1] Jordan, D.C. & Kurtz, S.R. (2013). Photovoltaic Degradation Rates - an Analytical Review. Prog. Photovolt: Res. Appl., 21(1), 12–29.
[2] Dirnberger, D. et. al. (2015). On the Impact of Solar Spectral Irradiance on the Yield of Different PV Technologies. Sol. Energy Mater. Sol. Cells, 132, 431–442.
[3] IEA PVPS Task 13 Reports (various years). Reliability and Performance of Photovoltaic Systems
[4] Köntges, M. et. al. (2014). Review of Failures of Photovoltaic Modules. NREL Report / IEA PVPS Task 13.
[5] Jordan, D. C. et. al (2016). Compendium of photovoltaic degradation rates. Progress in Photovoltaics. Volume 24, Issue 7, Pages 978-989
[6] Gasparin, F. P. et. al. (2022). Assessment on the variation of temperature coefficients of photovoltaic modules with solar irradiance. Solar Energy, Volume 244, Pages 126-133
[7] Schneider, A. et. al. (2024). Advanced Determination of Temperature Coefficients of Photovoltaic Modules by Field Measurements, SiliconPV Conference Proceedings. https://doi.org/10.52825/siliconpv.v1i.905

Westfälische Hochschule

Where Science Meets Practice.

SHAALKE: Development of a MatLab Software Tool for Advanced Statistical Outdoor Data Evaluation

Andreas Schneider[1] and Jorge Rabanal Arabach[2]

[1]University of Applied Sciences Gelsenkirchen, Neidenburger Str. 43, 45897 Gelsenkirchen, Germany
[2]Universidad de Antofagasta, Angamos Avenue 601, 1270300 Antofagasta, Chile
*Phone: + 49 (209) 9596-313, Fax: + 49 (209) 9596-544, Email: andreas.schneider@w-hs.de

Introduction

Shaalke (Software for Harvested and at Ambient Acquired and Logged Key data for Evaluation) is a Matlab-based tool developed over four years at the University of Applied Sciences, Gelsenkirchen, designed for comprehensive data evaluation and yield simulation of solar modules. It enables importing extensive time-series PV module measurement data collected at one-minute intervals for up to several years, combined with ambient weather data. Shaalke handles large datasets with several million data points, allowing advanced filtering and (linear) regression techniques to accurately extract key solar module parameters such as: temperature coefficients (static and dynamic) and STC data beside studying in detail irradiance and temperature dependencies and degradation behavior.

Sample testing overview

The following picture gives an overview on the long-term measurement plan

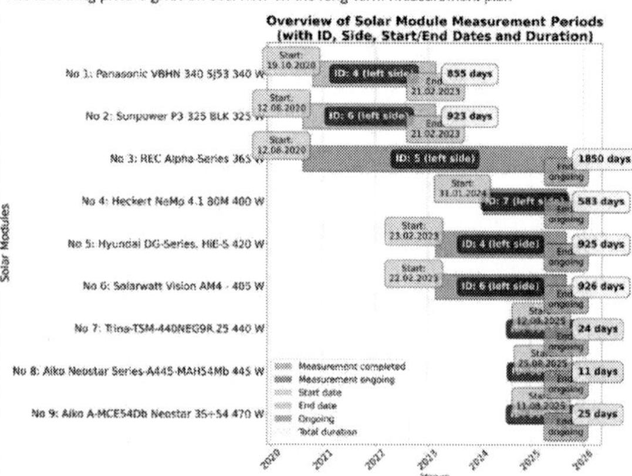

Shaalke – The Matlab GUI for advanced PV module data evaluation

The GUI allows fast access to several evaluation tools, including data import, export and data filtering. Even Meteonorm climatic data sets can be imported.

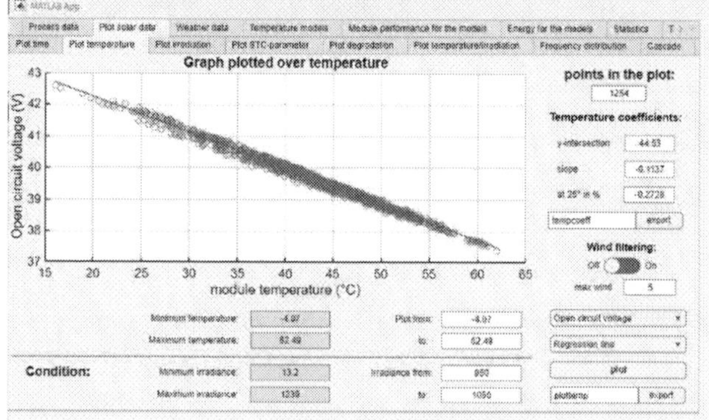

Determination of STC data

STC data as determined by Shaalke in comparison to the measurement data by an mbj-LED flasher and the supplier data as given in the datasheet.

No	Data sheet (supplier)			Flasher (mbj flasher)			Outdoor results (fitting)		
	I_{sc} (A)	V_{oc} (V)	P_{mpp} (W)	I_{sc} (A)	V_{oc} (V)	P_{mpp} (W)	I_{sc} (A)	V_{oc} (V)	P_{mpp} (W)
1	6.1	71.3	340	6	70.9	320	6.1	70.1	326
2	9.7	43.6	325	9.4	43.5	321.1	9.6	43.1	322
3	10.3	44.3	365	10.1	43.6	337.1	10.2	43.3	335.3
4	18.2	28.3	400	17.9	27.8	390.5	17.9	27.3	385
5	12.9	41.6	420	12.5	42.2	407.6	12.7	41.4	394.1
6	13.7	37.2	405	13.6	37.5	400.9	13.8	36.7	400.9
7	10.7	52.2	440	10.7	52.8	445.4	10.5	52.9	431.3
8	14.0	40.6	445	13.3	40	425	13.6	39.7	435.0
9	14.7	40.6	470	15	40.3	479.7	14.9	40.1	477.9

Boxplot showing the relative differences between flasher and Shaalke results

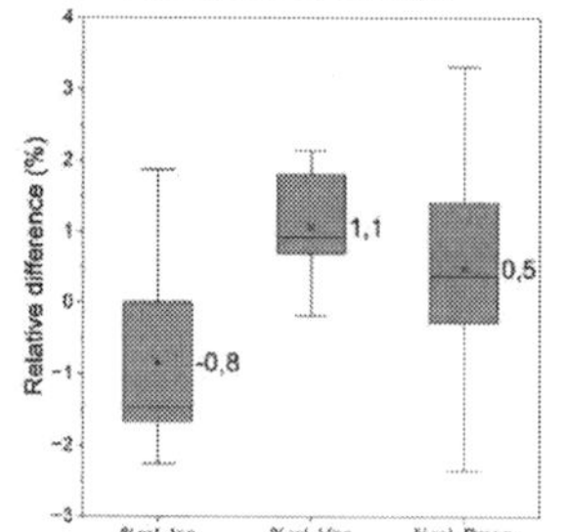

Determination of temperature coefficients

Temperature coefficients determined by Shaalke in comparison to supplier data as given in the datasheet.

No	Datasheet		Outdoor results (fitting)	
	T_{KPmpp} (%/K)	T_{KVoc} (%/K)	T_{KPmpp} (%/K)	T_{KVoc} (%/K)
1	-0.26	-0.24	-0.30	-0.24
2	-0.36	-0.29	-0.37	-0.29
3	-0.26	-0.24	-0.35	-0.24
4	-0.34	-0.26	-0.36	-0.27
5	-0.34	-0.27	-0.34	-0.27
6	-0.33	-0.26	-0.39	-0.27
7	-0.29	-0.24	-0.31	-0.23
8	-0.26	-0.22	-0.25	-0.22
9	-0.26	-0.22	-0.24	-0.22

Determination of power degradation

Power degradation as determined by Shaalke using several years of measurement data and compared to the maximum supplier degradation, as given in the datasheet.

No	Duration after inauguration	Max. degradation according to Data sheet (supplier)	Determined degradation according to outdoor results (fitting)
	Years	%	%
1	2	3.5	1.2
2	3	3	0.2
3	6	4.5	7.3
4	2	2	2.8
5	3	3.1	0.4
6	3	1.3	0.6

Irradiance dependency of module efficiency

Rel. module efficiency in dependency of irradiance for the REC alpha module (Shaalke data versus supplier data)

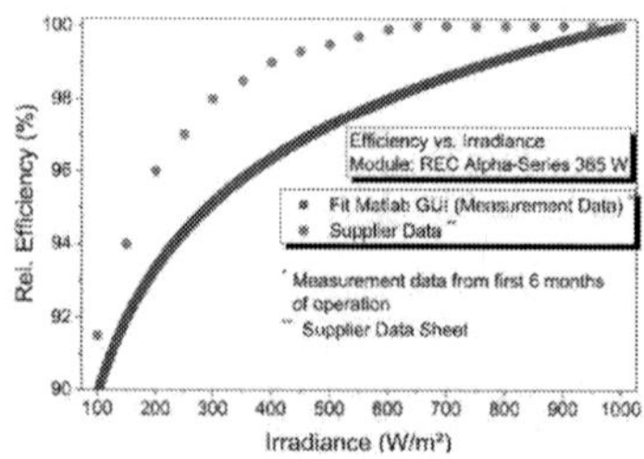

Summary

This paper presents Shaalke, an innovative software tool for long-term PV module measurement data evaluation. The presented results on the determination of STC data, temperature coefficients, power degradation and irradiance dependency of module efficiency proof nicely the strong and high-quality evaluation capabilities of Shaalke.

Supported by:

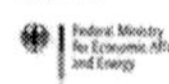

Federal Ministry for Economic Affairs and Energy

on the basis of a decision by the German Bundestag

This publication was partly funded by the Federal Ministry for Economic Affairs and Energy inside the project BuKuMu under contract no. FKZ 03EE1225F.)

DEGRADATION AND DEFECT CHARACTERISATION OF FIELD-DEPLOYED SILICON PV MODULES

RP Roodt[1], EE van Dyk[1], JL Crozier McCleland[1], M Vumbugwa[1], FJ Vorster[1], O Stroyuk[2], C Buerhop-Lutz[2]
[1]Department of Physics, Nelson Mandela University, Port Elizabeth, South Africa
[2]Forschungszentrum Jülich GmbH, Helmholtz-Institut Erlangen Nürnberg für Erneuerbare Energien
(HI ERN), 91058 Erlangen, Germany

E-Mail address: s217357709@mandela.ac.za

ABSTRACT: A sample of fifteen monocrystalline silicon-based PV modules was tested and characterised in this study. These modules have been deployed in the field for over a decade at the Outdoor Research Facility of Nelson Mandela University, South Africa. Various characterisation techniques were utilised, including visual inspection, electroluminescence (EL) imaging, and current-voltage (I-V) curves. A detailed analysis was done on the various PV modules in order to understand the observed defects or anomalies and associated performance degradation. When compared to historically acquired I-V curve measurements, the modules show substantial degradation in the performance for one type of module and the other module type does not show any power decrease compared to specification. Combining visual, UV Fluorescence (UV-F) imaging, and EL imaging provided deeper insight into hidden defects and material degradation not evident from visual inspection alone.
Keywords: Ultraviolet-fluorescence imaging, EL imaging, visual inspection, current-voltage curve

1 INTRODUCTION

Silicon PV modules have long been the leading technology for commercially available PV modules. With that being said, PV modules that have been exposed to real-world, long-term exposure are a source of valuable information to monitor performance and to observe how the different components of the PV modules last in these conditions. It has been observed that recording current-voltage (I-V) curves and visual inspection, various defects and performance results can be identified [1].

Cracks, snail trails, encapsulant browning and discolouration, delamination, metal corrosion and back sheet chalking are just a few of the features visible and can be noted using visual inspection [1]. So, utilising the characterisation techniques available to us, various PV modules were investigated. This was done to investigate the performance of the modules as they have been deployed for a substantial period, and to investigate if there were defects, what defects may be identified and to determine the root cause and impact on performance[3]. In addition, studies into long-term PV module performance using the characterisation tools employed here provide crucial insights for optimising maintenance schedules and enhancing overall operational PV power plant efficiency [2].

2 EXPERIMENTAL PROCEDURE

2.1 PV Modules

The investigation was conducted on fifteen monocrystalline Solar World Sunmodule PV modules deployed in two arrays at the Outdoor Research Facility of Nelson Mandela University. The modules were of two types: SW 175, which has been in operation for 16 years from 2009 until 2025, consisting of 9 modules, and SW235, which has been in operation for 9 years from June 2016 – July 2025, consisting of 6 modules.

The Standard Test Conditions (STC) parameters as specified are listed in Table I.

Table I: Manufacturer STC specification of modules investigated.

Module type	SW 235 mono	SW 175 mono
Maximum power (Pmax)	235 Wp	175 Wp
Maximum power point voltage (Vmpp)	30.3 V	35.8 V
Maximum power point current (Impp)	7.77 A	4.89 A
Open circuit voltage (Voc)	37.5 V	44.4 V
Short circuit current (Isc)	8.19 A	5.30 A

2.2 Measurement procedure

Module performance was evaluated using visual, electroluminescence (EL), and UV-fluorescence (UV-F) imaging, as well as I-V curves. These techniques were utilised as there is some overlap between the defects that can be observed, but they also show unique features. Visual and UV-F images were captured with a digital camera, while EL imaging and I-V curves were obtained using a MBJ 3.0 mobile laboratory an A+A+A+ LED solar simulator with integrated NIR-CMOS cameras. The analysis also incorporated historical I-V data from the two PV arrays. The focus was on the degradation of these two systems, as the older technology used in these modules makes their ageing particularly relevant compared to modern materials. Historical results include indoor I-V curves (from an Optosolar – AAA Xenon- flash solar), outdoor I-V curves (PVe and Solmetric I-V curve tracers), and indoor and outdoor EL images (from a Greateyes EL system).

3 RESULTS

The results for the two module types are discussed in the following sections.

3.1 SW 175 modules

Three modules were used to illustrate the performance of the SW 175 modules over the 16 years. The modules are referred to as Module A, B and C.

From the I-V curves shown in Figure 1, the following results are seen. In 2018, the I-V curves and Pmax values of all nine modules closely matched those of module A. In Module A, no defects were observed, and it was used for comparison with Modules B and C.

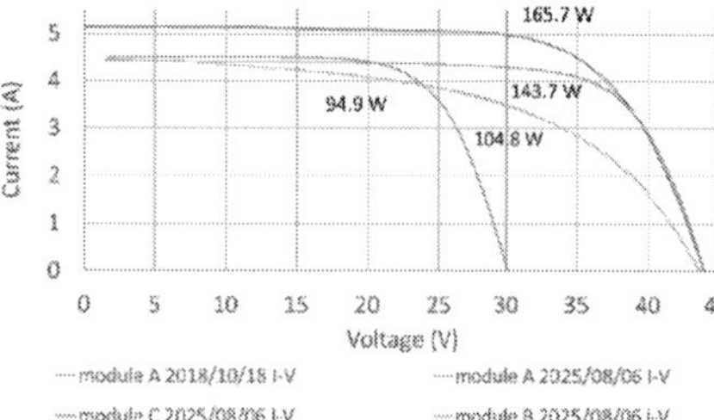

Figure 1: I-V curves obtained for 3 of the SW 175 modules. Module A's I-V curves obtained in 2018 and 2025, and module B and C's I-V curves for 2025.

The power decreased by 22.0 W since 2018. Module B has a bypassed substring, as the Voc value has decreased to 30.2 V in 2025, which severely affects the power output of the module, which only produces 94.9 W at STC.

Module C has a different shape I-V curve, while there is no change in the Isc or Voc of the module. This shape of the I-V curve shows that the module has an increased series resistance and decreased shunt resistance [4].

Considering the modules that do not show obvious visual or other defects, the average power in Aug 2025 was 140.4 W. This translates to an annual degradation rate of 1.12 % when taking the specified 3.00% degradation in the first year of operation of the module into account. This is more than the specified 0.7 % per annum [5].

3.2 Imaging Techniques results

The results obtained from the various imaging techniques for Modules A to C are shown in Figure 2. Visual, UV-F, and EL inspections reveal ageing effects and defects in the modules (2020–2025). Visual inspection shows a square browning pattern on cell interiors; modules B and C show additional square patterns on the interior of the cells. In the UV-F images, the brown patterns correspond to brighter fluorescence interiors, while the edges show quenching [6,7]. Module B shows extra inner features matching the visual image. Comparing the EL images obtained in 2020 to the ones obtained in 2025, Module A has signs of a bright brim/dark interior pattern, which is also seen in Module C. Conveyor belt tracks are also visible, and this is from non-uniform heating during manufacturing [2]. The luminescence intensity of module B decreased; likely, acetic acid formation between EVA and cells, which reacted with the fingers of the cells and increased series resistance [8]. Looking at cracks, we can see that active area and busbar cracks are visible in UV-F (quenching), and this is confirmed by the EL images. This is highlighted by cells with yellow squares around them. The UV-F image of Module C shows age-related crack growth [6]. In the 2020 EL image of module C, the top substring was bypassed, while in the 2025 EL image, a different substring was bypassed due to a burned bypass diode damaging the junction box. All modules show chalking, no backsheet cracks/damage. Future work: Verification Bill of Materials comprising Glass front, EVA, Tedlar backsheet [5].

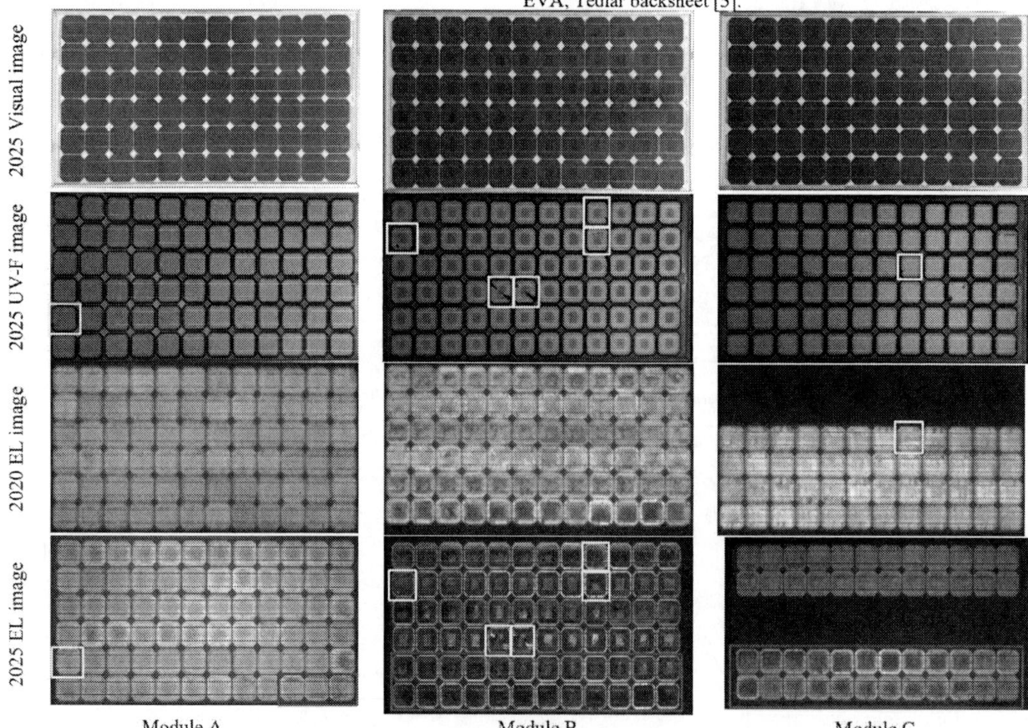

Figure 2: Visual, UV-F and EL images obtained for modules A, B and C in 2025 and EL images obtained in 2020. Features and changes in the intensity patterns in the EL images of the cells are highlighted with yellow squares and purple rectangles, respectively.

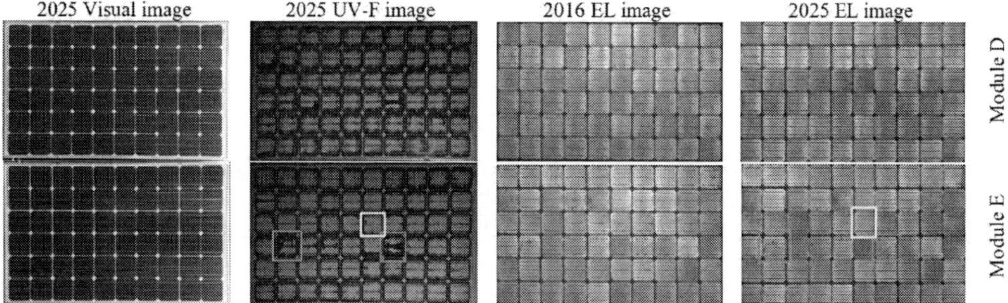

Figure 3: Visual, UV-F and EL images obtained for modules D and E. Cracks in the cells are highlighted by green (long) and red ("x"-shaped) squares.

3.2 SW 235 modules

These modules show no electrical degradation after a decade, likely due to initial underspecification, considering that the specifications have a +5.00 % tolerance [9]. Pre-installation measurements and more recent flash power measurements were acquired, but this was done using different measurement equipmentmaking it difficult to compare the results. Two modules were used to illustrate findings on the SW 235 modules over the period of investigation. The modules are referred to as Module D and E.

After further inspection, the following was observed. The modules have been deployed for nearly a decade with no visual signs of module degradation, encapsulant discolouration, or backsheet chalking. Looking at the backside of the module, some exhibit scratches or marks on the backsheet, likely due to grass cutting at the facility, but no chalking is visible. In module E, small "x"-shaped cracks are visible in the 2025 EL image and confirmed by a circular quenching pattern in the UV-F image, indicating it has been there for a few years. This is highlighted by a yellow square. Furthermore, diagonal cracks across cells are also visible in both EL and UV-F images, highlighted by green squares.

A pattern observed in the UV-F images of all six modules is the finger soaking pattern, which is may be caused by solder flux being drawn along cell fingers, extinguishing the UV-F [6]. Busbar cracks that ma have formed behind the busbars are also visible in the UV-F images of Modules D and E.

These findings indicate that while the modules are performing well electrically, they do show signs of internal material degradation that could potentially impact their future performance.

4. Conclusion

Two SolarWorld module types were investigated, both during and after deployment, for over a decade. The SW 175 mono modules showed a linear degradation rate of 1.12%/year, considering 3.00% degradation in the first year. Visual, UV-F, and EL imaging revealed several defects and material degradation, correlating directly with reduced performance. The SW 235 mono modules showed no clear decrease in power compared to the original specification. This performance stability may be linked to underspecification at manufacture. Visual inspection of the modules revealed no obvious degradation. UV-F and EL imaging showed cracks and identified material degradation. Combining visual, UV-F, and EL imaging provides deeper insight into hidden defects and materialdegradation not evident from visual inspection.

5 REFERENCES

[1] M. Köntges, S. Kurtz, U. Jahn, K.A. Berger, Review of Failures of Photovoltaic Modules, n.d. https://www.researchgate.net/publication/274717701.

[2] L. Koester, S. Lindig, A. Louwen, A. Astigarraga, G. Manzolini, D. Moser, Review of photovoltaic module degradation, field inspection techniques and techno-economic assessment, Renewable and Sustainable Energy Reviews 165 (2022). https://doi.org/10.1016/j.rser.2022.112616.

[3] B. Doll, J. Hepp, M. Hoffmann, R. Schuler, C. Buerhop-Lutz, I.M. Peters, J.A. Hauch, A. Maier, C.J. Brabec, Photoluminescence for Defect Detection on Full-Sized Photovoltaic Modules, IEEE J Photovolt 11 (2021) 1419–1429. https://doi.org/10.1109/JPHOTOV.2021.3099739.

[4] J.L. Crozier, F.J. Vorster, E.E. van Dyk, Evaluating the relationship between electroluminescence (EL) imaging and the power output of photovoltaic modules, in: 3rd South Afr. Sol. Energy Conf, 2015: pp. 24–28.

[5] SolarWord Sunmodule SW 155/165/175 mono specification sheet, https://shop.solardirect.com/pdf/solar-electric/modules/sunmodule-data-sheet.pdf.F.

[6] Vorster, E. Van Dyk, UV fluorescence imaging of photovoltaic modules, in: 6th South Afr. Sol. Energy Conf, 2019: pp. 1–5.

[7] C. Buerhop, E. Dyk, F. Vorster, O. Stroyuk, O. Mashkov, J. McCleland, M. Vumbugwa, J. Hauch, I. Peters, Advancing Photovoltaic Module Inspection: The Power of UV Imaging for Comprehensive Material Analysis and Quality Assurance, in: 2024: pp. 250–252. https://doi.org/10.1109/PVSC57443.2024.10749225.

[8] U. Weber, R. Eiden, C. Strubel, T. Soegding, M. Heiss, P. Zachmann, K. Nattermann, H. Engelmann, A. Dethlefsen, N. Lenck, Acetic acid production, migration and corrosion effects in ethylene-vinyl-acetate-(EVA-) based pv modules, in: 2012: pp. 2992-2995. https://doi.org/10.4229/27thEUPVSEC2012-4CO.9.4

[9] The SolarWorld Sunmodule Advantage, https://naturalsolar.com.au/wp-content/uploads/2015/11/solar-world-warranty.pdf.

Architecture for monitoring PV degradation in real time from EL images

Tohru Kohno*, Jun Tsunoda*
Hitachi, Ltd. Research & Development Group
1-280 Higashi-Koigakubo, Kokubunji, Tokyo 185-8601, Japan
E-mail: toru.kono.cw@hitachi.com

ABSTRACT: We developed an architecture to monitor the degradation rate of PV (Photovoltaic) in real time from EL(Electroluminance) images. In recent years, technology has been developed to measure EL images outdoors, but it has been difficult to accurately grasp performance degradation from EL images. First, we extracted the luminance distribution from the EL image of the PV module that underwent an accelerated test, and created an input layer for machine learning. Second, in the training of a neural network that isolates EL images of PV modules before and after the output drops rapidly, we found a high correlation between the output and degradation of the hidden layer, and created an approximate equation. By applying the luminance distribution of the measured EL image to the learned parameters and applying the output of the calculated hidden layer to an approximate formula, we succeeded in calculating the power generation performance instantaneously.
Keywords: EL images outdoors, Degradation rate, The hidden layer, Neural Network

1 INTRODUCTION

The reuse of PV modules and the promotion of recycling are being considered. Legislation is also being considered for reinvestment in existing equipment and repowering when small-scale equipment is consolidated. PV modules in the early stages of FIT (Feed-in Tariff) in Japan, which were expected to operate stably for more than 20 years, have also been in operation for 12~13 years as of 2025. It isn't be know how stably these PV modules can be used in the future, and the performance itself. However, there is no clear standard for reuse and repowering, and the secondary market for PV is stagnant.

On the otherhand, there have been some cases where the performance of PV power plants has declined sharply, and understanding the current soundness of PV modules will lead to a market for long-term stable business continuity using PV facilities. However, as of 2025, visual inspection of PV modules is the mainstay, and although it is possible to identify adhesion of foreign matter, broken glass, and scorching of the backsheet caused by lightning strikes, etc., the performance has not been grasped. Although it is used for drone inspections and IV measurements at exposure sites, there is a problem that accurate results cannot be obtained due to the time and cost.

We conducted many reliability tests and acceleration tests of PV modules in the early stages of FIT in Japan and accumulated data [1-2]. On top of that, PV modules installed in power generation equipment installed in 2005 and 2012 are regularly monitored once every few years to observe deterioration. From the results of the FY2023 survey, it was found that these PV modules are degraded called fake shunt [3], which is a type of degradation in which the output drops sharply from a certain point, that is, a type of degradation that reaches the end of its life. Furthermore, about this degradation mode, it is difficult to grasp without observing the busbar and fingers in EL (Electroluminance) images [4].

From the above, it is desirable to inspect power generation equipment without moving the PV modules from the installation site to the laboratory for measurement, and to be able to grasp the performance and quality ranking on the spot. In recent years, the acquisition of EL images at exposed sites has been put into practical use [5]. However, it has been difficult to accurately grasp the electrical performance from EL images. The purpose of this study is to construct an algorithm that can estimate the deterioration rate and determine the quality ranking of PV

modules only from the EL images measured in the room.

2 Architecture for estimating PV degradation rate in real time from EL images

2.1 Development concept

Fig. 1 shows the concept of the architecture. First, as shown in Fig. 1 (a), an EL camera acquires a current while applying a current from a current source to the PV array installed in exposure. First, as shown in Fig. 1(a), an image is acquired with an EL camera while applying a current from a current source to the PV array installed in exposure. Next, by applying the developed monitoring architecture to the acquired EL image of the PV module, the output ratio of the PV module, that is, the degradation, is calculated instantaneously as shown in Fig. 1 (b).

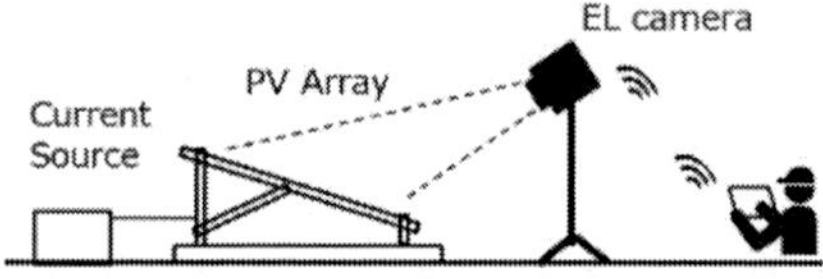

(a) Concepts in measurement

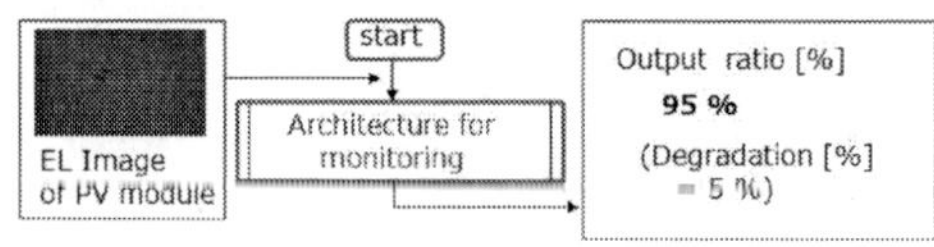

(b) Concepts on the software screen

Figure 1: The concept of developed algorithm

2.2 Learning with Neural Networks

Fig. 2 shows the procedure for obtaining the luminance distribution from an EL image of a PV module. For each of the A-F constituting the PV module, it is divided into 11 rows parallel to the busbar, and the luminance is acquired by image processing software. The luminance of the 11 lines of A-F is averaged and set as the luminance of 11 lines. The values shown in Fig. 2 are the average luminance of the 11 lines in areas A to F and the luminance of the whole PV module. These values are obtained by Image J [6-7].

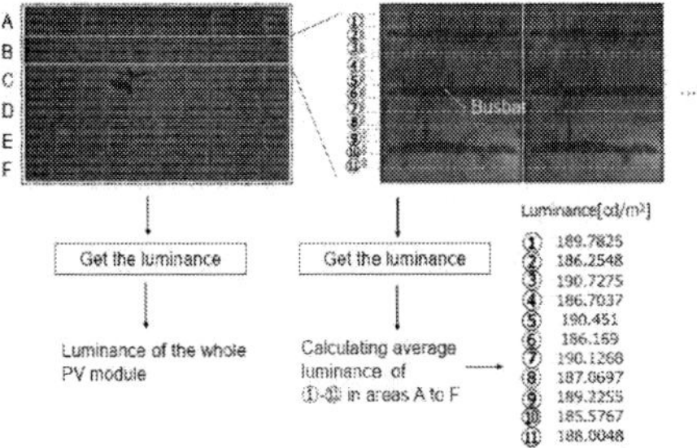

Figure 2: Procedure for determining the luminance distribution from the EL image of the PV module

Thereafter, as shown in Fig. 3, these 11 line's luminance values are normalized by the whole PV module brightness as 1 and are set in the input layer of machine learning. The difference between the average and deviation of these luminances is also set in the input layer. The "correct " is to set the PV module before the sudden change in the output ratio as 01 and the PV module after the sudden change as 10.

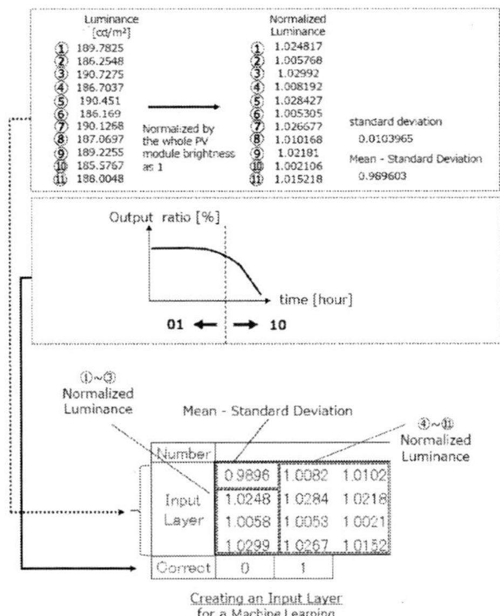

Figure 3: Setting the luminance distribution as an input layer for learning of neural network

Table 1 shows the output ratio of PV modules that underwent an accelerated dump heat test (temperature 85°C, humidity 85%). This PV module is a polycrystalline silicon PV module of the same type as the one evaluated in Ref. [3]. As a result of the dump heat using 4 PV modules, the output ratio of module No. 1 is 90.0% at the test time of 4500 hours, so for Number 1~6, 01 is set as the PV module before the power ratio changes suddenly. On the other hand, for modules No. 2, 3, and 4, the output ratios are 82.0%, 82.6%, and 79.0%, respectively, at 4500 hours, so for Number 7~9, the PV module is set to 10 after the output ratio drops sharply.

Table 1: PV module and performance in the dump heat test (85°C, 85%)

DH Test Time [hour]	Output rate [%]	Module No.	Number
0	100.0	1	1
3500	96.9	1	2
3500	94.4	2	3
4000	92.2	1	4
4000	90.4	2	5
4500	90.0	1	6
4500	82.0	2	7
4500	82.6	3	8
4500	79.0	4	9

Fig.4 is a schematic diagram showing the procedure for learning "10" and "01". In this study, we will use a learner built by a neural network to learn whether the EL image is before or after the sudden decrease in the output ratio. Here, the input layer receives the matrix constituted of the standard deviation and the normalized luminance as shown in Fig. 3. Fig. 4 shows the neural network in which the middle layer (hidden layer) is composed of three neurons and the output layer is composed of two neurons.

This neural network is built to classify whether the EL image is before or after the sudden drop in output ratio. As described in the Correct section above, if the output from the two neurons in the output layer is close to "0" and "1", it means that the PV module of the input EL image is before the sudden decrease in the output ratio. If it is close to "1" and "0", it means that the PV module of the input EL image is after the output ratio has dropped sharply.

Enter the matrix constituted of the standard deviation and the normalized luminance of Number 1 in Table 1 and the normalized values for the first neuron. In this example, the correct answer is before the output ratio drops sharply (output layer "0" and "1").

The first neuron in the hidden layer has a weight matrix consisting of 12 elements that multiply by each of the 12 elements of the matrix that described as the input sequence in Fig. 3. The result of multiplying both matrices is substituted into the sigmoid function represented by the first formula at the bottom of Fig. 4. The threshold for the first neuron in the hidden layer is defined as 1.00. By following the above steps, the output y of the first neuron in the hidden layer is obtained. The same is true for the second neuron in the hidden layer and the third neuron in the hidden layer.

Next, the output y of the first neuron of the hidden layer is input into the first neuron of the output layer. The first neuron in the output layer has a weight matrix composed of three elements that multiply by the output y of each neuron of the 1st~3rd neuron in the hidden layer. The result of multiplying the two matrices is substituted into the sigmoid function represented by the second formula at the bottom of Fig. 4. The threshold for the first neuron in the output layer is defined as 35.46. By following the above steps, the output z of the first neuron in the output layer is obtained. The same is true for the second neuron in the output layer.

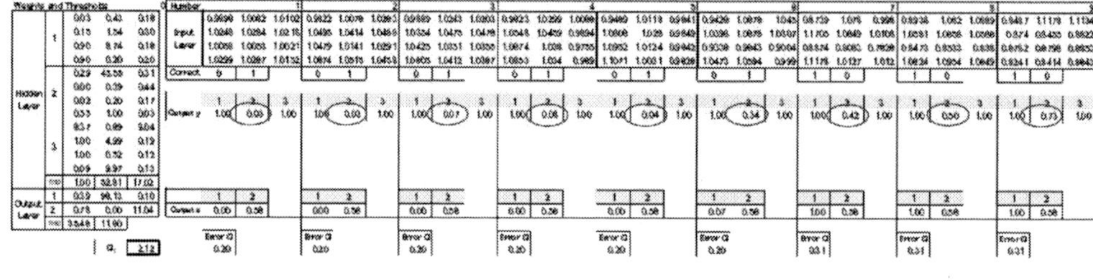

Sigmoid function

Output y_1 = 1/{1+ exp (- {0.03 * 0.9896 + 0.15 * 1.0248 + ⋯ + 0.20 * 1.0152} + 1.00)}

     Input layer × weight of hidden layer 1   Threshold of hidden Layer 1

Output z_1 = 1/{1+ exp (- {0.39 * 1.00 + 96.13 * 0.03 + ⋯ + 0.10 * 1.00} + 35.46)}

     Weight of output layer 1 × output y   Threshold of output layer 1

Error Q = $(0 - 0.00)^2 + (1 - 0.56)^2$

Figure 4: The learning of neural network for setting the "correct" to 01 for Number 1-6 and 10 for Number 7-9

Based on the above calculations, the output of the first neuron in the output layer is 0.00, and the output of the second neuron in the output layer is 0.56. On the other hand, since the correct answer of Number1 is "0" and "1", the error Q between the output from the output layer and the correct answer can be calculated as shown in the third calculation formula at the bottom of Fig. 4. The same is calculated for Numbaer2~9. The learning is completed by optimizing the matrix elements and thresholds of each layer so that the error Q is minimized.

2.3. Architecture for estimating PV degradation rate in real time from EL images

We focus on Output y (2) surrounded by a circle in Fig. 4. The values of Numbers 1 to 9 are 0.03, 0.03, 0.07, 0.08, 0.04, and 0.34, respectively. ,0.42,0.5 and 0.53. Fig. 5 shows the relationship between these values and the output ratios in Table 1. As shown in Fig. 5, there is a high correlation between Output y (2) and the output ratio, that is, the degradation rate.

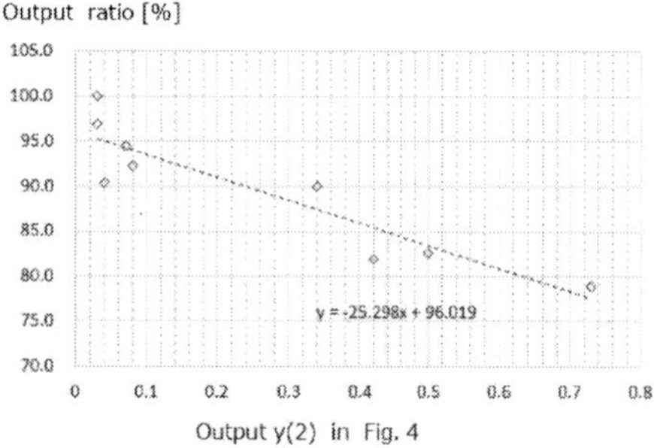

Output ratio [%]

y = -25.298x + 96.019

Output y(2) in Fig. 4

Figure 5: The relationship between output y (2) in Fig. 4 and the output ratio

We devised the architecture to calculate the output ratio from the EL image, as shown in Fig. 6. First, the input layer of the neural network is created from the brightness distribution calculated by the method shown in Fig. 2 and 3 from the EL image. Next, matrix calculations are performed using the parameters of the learned hidden layer and the output layer as shown in Fig. 4. Here, the hidden layer Output y (2) is extracted. Finally, the output ratio is calculated using the approximate formula y=-25.298x + 96.019 shown in Fig. 5.

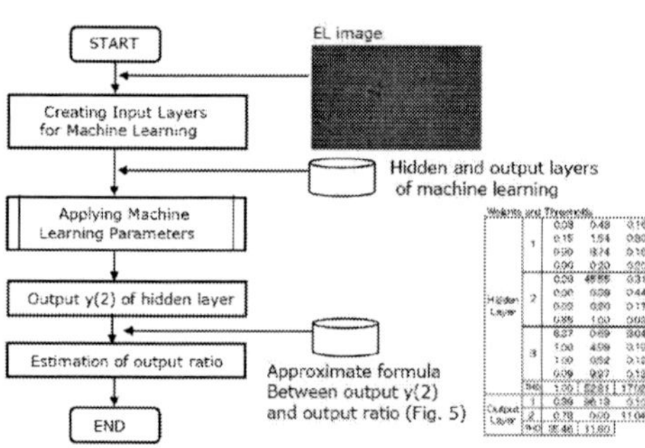

Figure 6: The architecture for calculating the output ratio from the EL image

3 EXPERIMENTAL RESULTS

The results of applying the PV module (the same type as the learning) extracted from the site for 11 years of exposure to the architecture in Fig. 6 are shown in Fig 7. The result of Output y (2) is 0.0478, which is 94.81% when applied to the approximate equation y = -25.298x + 96.019. In addition, since Output z becomes "0.00" and "0.56", it was judged that it was before the sudden drop in output.

Exposed PV module (11 years)

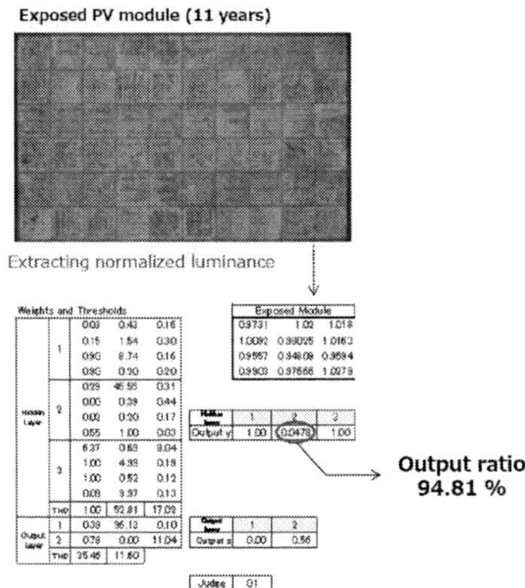

Extracting normalized luminance

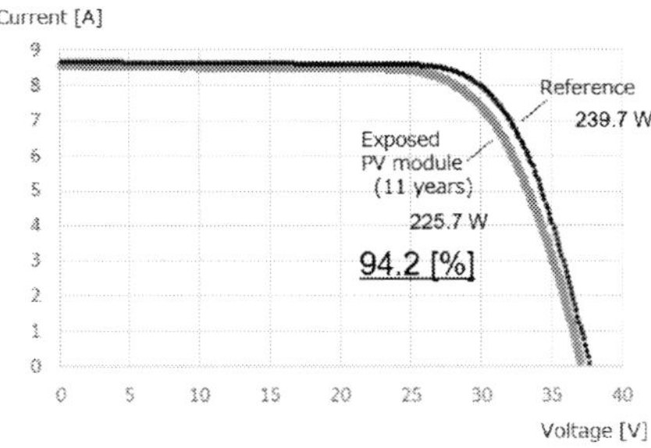

Output ratio
94.81 %

Figure 7: The results of applying developed the architecture to the exposed PV module (11 years)

The PV module for 11 years of exposure was compared with the reference PV module as shown in Fig. 8. The I-V characteristics were measured based on IEC60904-1 Edition 3.0 (2020-09) / IEC61215-2 Edition 1.0 (2016-03) at Standard Condition (solar radiation 1.0 kW/m^2 and temperature 298 K). It can be seen that the PV module after 11 years of exposure has deteriorated. Focusing on the maximum power point (MPP), the MPP of reference was 239.7 W, and the MPP of PV module after 11 years of exposure was 225.7 W. In other words, the output ratio was 94.2% (= 225.7/239.7*100), which showed a high correlation with 94.81% above.

Figure 8: I-V characteristics of the exposed PV module (11 years)

Next, the results of applying the PV module, which was subjected to a dump heat (DH: temperature 85°C, humidity 85%) for 4000 hours, to the architecture are shown in Fig. 9. The result of Output y (2) is 0.4141, which is 85.54 [%] when applied to the approximate formula y = -25.298x + 96.019. In addition, since Output z becomes "0.99" and "0.56", it was judged that it was after a sharp decrease in output.

PV module after 4000 hours of DH testing

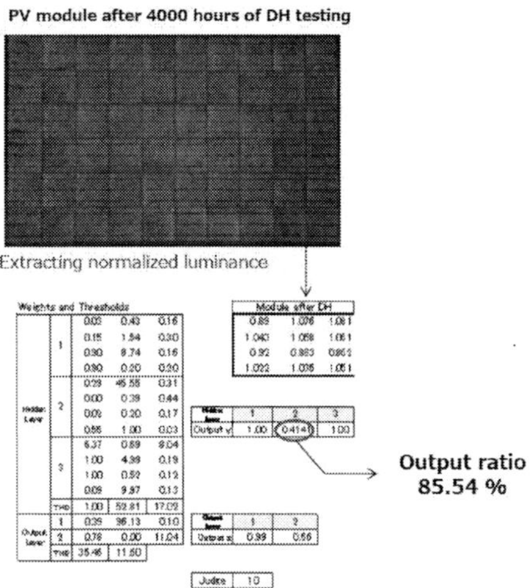

Extracting normalized luminance

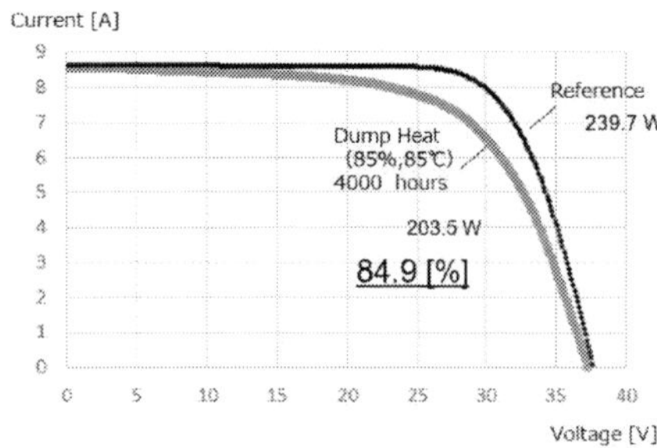

Output ratio
85.54 %

Figure 9: The results of applying developed the algorithm to the PV module after DH 4000 hours

Fig. 10 shows a comparison of the I-V curve of the PV module accelerated by the 4000-hour dump heat (DH: temperature 85°C, humidity 85%) with I-V curve of the reference PV module. It is clear that the accelerated test PV module is degraded. Focusing on the MPP, the MPP of the reference was 239.7 W, and the MPP of accelerated PV module was 203.5 W. In other words, the output ratio was 84.9% (=203.5/239.7*100), which showed a high correlation with 85.54 % above.

Figure 9: I-V characteristics of the PV module after DH 4000 hours

4 CONCLUSION

We have developed an architecture to monitor the degradation rate of PV in real time from EL images. Fake shunts, which are considered to be the main cause of deterioration due to exposure, are difficult to detect without the use of EL images. In recent years, technology has been developed to measure EL images outdoors, but it has been difficult to accurately grasp performance degradation from EL images. Therefore

1. The luminance distribution was extracted from the EL image of the PV module executed the dump heat acceleration test, and the input layer for machine learning was created.

2. In the acceleration test, we created an approximation of the output and degradation of the hidden layer in the training of a neural network that separates the EL image of the PV module before the power drops sharply and the EL image of the PV module after the drop.

3. By applying the luminance distribution of the measured EL image to the learned parameters, we succeeded in calculating the power generation performance instantly.

5   ACKNOWLEDGEMENT

The authors would like to thank Mr. K. Morita, and the members of PVSQ management, LLC for the evaluation of PV module and their valuable suggestions.

6   REFERENCES

[1] K. Morita et al., Proceedings European Photovoltaic Solar Energy Conference 2015 (2015) pp. 2515 - 2520.

[2] M. Fujimori et al., Proceedings European Photovoltaic Solar Energy Conference 2015 (2015) pp. 1911 - 1914.

[3] E. A. Gaulding et al., IEEE Journal of Photovoltaics, vol. 12, Issue. 3 (2022) pp. 690–695

[4] T. Kohno et al., Proceedings European Photovoltaic Solar Energy Conference 2024 (2024) pp. 020325-001 - 020325-005.

[5] Y. Ishikawa; JSAP Review Vol. 2022, pp. 2204 12-1–2204 12-5, April 2022

[6] Rasband, W.S., ImageJ, U. S. National Institutes of Health, Bethesda, Maryland, USA, http://imagej.nih.gov/ij/, 1997-2012.

[7] Schneider, C.A., Rasband, W.S., Eliceiri, K.W. "NIH Image to ImageJ: 25 years of image analysis". Nature Methods 9, 671-675, 2012.

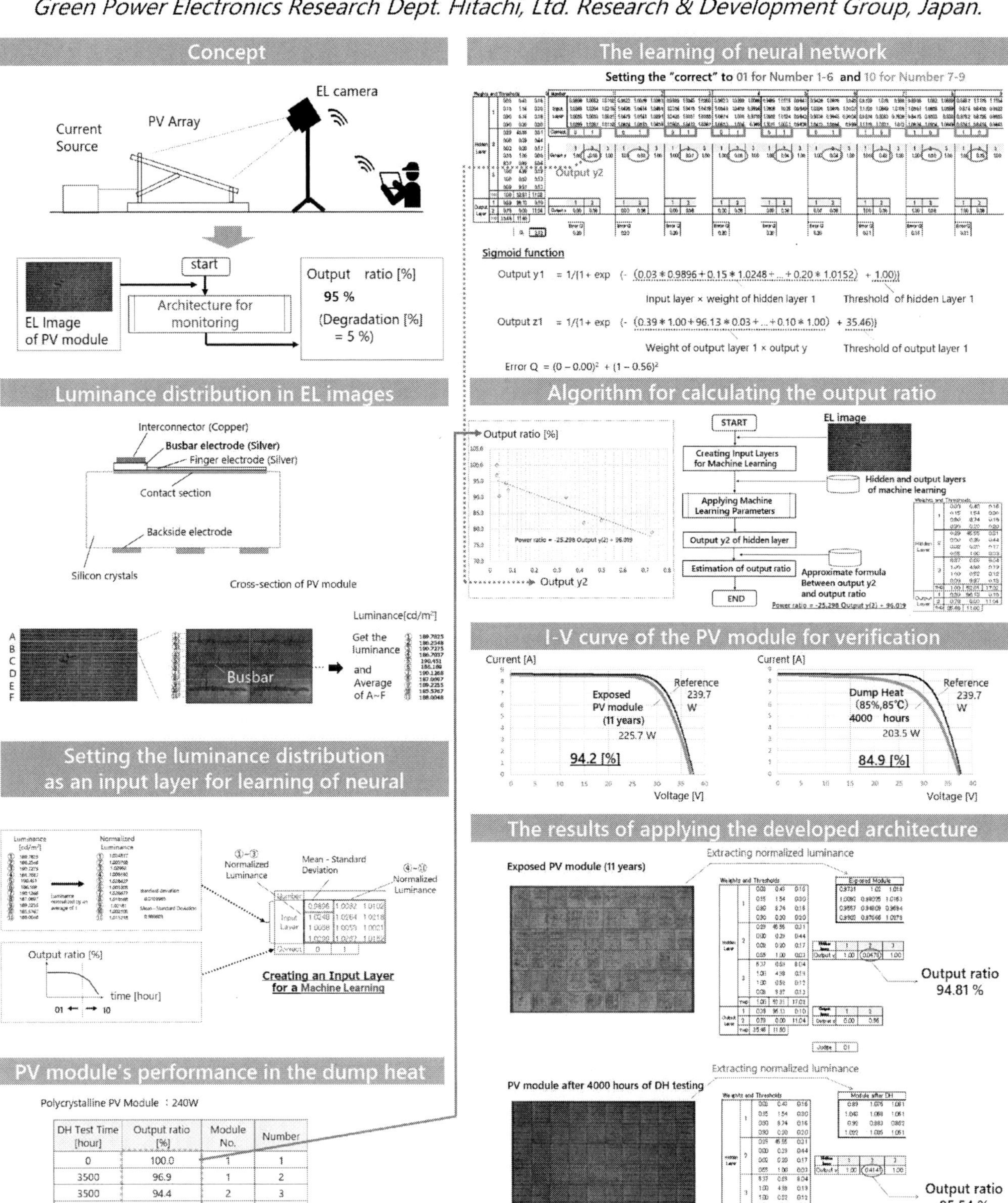

PV module's performance in the dump heat — Polycrystalline PV Module : 240W

DH Test Time [hour]	Output ratio [%]	Module No.	Number
0	100.0	1	1
3500	96.9	1	2
3500	94.4	2	3
4000	92.2	1	4
4000	90.4	2	5
4500	90.0	1	6
4500	82.0	2	7
4500	82.6	3	8
4500	79.0	4	9

SIMPLE CELL SEGMENTATION ROUTINE FOR QUANTITATIVE ELECTROLUMINESCENCE ANALYSIS OF C-SI MODULES

João Victor Oliveira Santos[1,3], Daniel Ory[2], Christine Abdel Nour[1], Damien Barakel[3], Olivier Palais[3], Julien Dupuis[1]
[1]EDF R&D, EDF Lab Les Renardières, Avenue des Renardières, 77250 Moret Loing et Orvanne, France
[2]EDF R&D – IPVF, 18 boulevard Thomas Gobert, 91190 Palaiseau, France
[3]Aix-Marseille Univ, Université de Toulon, CNRS, IM2NP, Marseille, France

ABSTRACT: Electroluminescence (EL) testing of photovoltaic modules is a crucial step for quality inspection. As forward current is biased into the module, it emits light, allowing clear differentiation between defective and healthy regions. Beyond fault detection, performance parameters can also be accessed through this imaging technique. Many quantitative methods have already been developed in the literature providing metrics to estimate series and shunt resistances, dark saturation currents, diode ideality factors, etc. Nonetheless, these methods do not precise which pixels were considered for their approach. A single method to distinct one cell from the other on the whole EL image was found, yet it was focused on full-cell modules and no mention to its application on quantitative EL has been verified. The present work aims to establish an easy to apply cell segmentation algorithm for rectangular-shaped half-cell modules along with an alternative algorithm for corner-cut full-cell module segmentation. The proposed routines were applied to full and half-cell modules, providing satisfactory visual results. From the segmentation, the quantitative estimation of series resistances and dark saturation current densities were performed for each cell on a module. For a single cell within this module, the EL estimated parameters enabled to simulate its I-V curve which was then compared to its experimental one. A good agreement between the curves was verified despite a relative error for the fill factor of 7% which originates mainly from the assumption of an ideality factor being equal to 1. Furthermore, the relative errors for $P_{mpp}, I_{mpp}, V_{mpp}$, and V_{oc} were all below 5%. Possible improvements are also presented, pointing out that this work is an initial step for more precise quantitative EL analysis.
Keywords: Electroluminescence, Quantitative, Segmentation, Solar, Si Modules.

1 INTRODUCTION

The importance of Electroluminescence (EL) testing for quality control of photovoltaic modules is well known. EL, nonetheless, also has the potential to provide quantitative metrics to compare the impacts of single cells on the whole module performance. Series and shunt resistances, dark saturation currents, diode ideality factors are among the parameters that have been investigated by different authors [1]. These methods take the measured intensity values within the EL image to compute the desired parameters. Nonetheless, no mention has been made on how determining which pixels must be considered and which must not before applying quantitative analysis. S. Deitsch et al. [2] developed a complete and performant method to extract single cell images from the EL of a whole module paying a close attention to lens distortion. This method divides the initial image into sub images of single cells from which the image of an "average cell" is computed. Local thresholds are defined all over this image to obtain a binary mask which is then submit to morphological operations to fill empty regions within the cell area. Extra geometries are then subtracted considering the median profile across rows and columns and Convex Hull transformation, resulting in a binary mask representing the cell geometry. However, this method is focused on full-cell modules, and, to the best of our knowledge, it was not applied to quantitative EL methods.

The present work aims at developing an easy-to-apply segmentation method that can be used to rectangular-shaped half-cell modules as well as an alternative strategy for segmenting corner-cut full-cell modules before estimating single-diode model (SDM) parameters. In figure 1, a representation of the expected result for the segmentation methods is shown. This article is, structured as follows: first, the segmentation methods will be illustrated; then, these methods will be applied to experimental data followed by a quantitative analysis of series resistances and dark saturation current densities based on the works of A. S. Rajput et al [3] and T. Potthoff et al. [4]; afterwards, these values will be used to simulate the I-V curve of a single cell and to compare to its experimental curve; finally, a conclusion will summarize the results and provide perspectives.

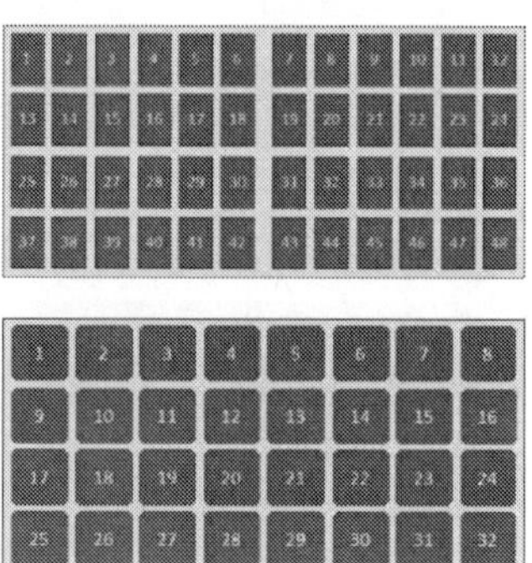

Figure 1: Labeled matrices for PV module with (top) rectangular-shaped and (bottom) corner-cut cells. An integer indexation increasing from top left to bottom right is obtained for each cell.

2 SEGMENTATION METHODS

2.1 Half-cell modules

In a first step, the EL image must be summed across both horizontal (columns) and vertical (lines) axis. This sum will provide a profile with plateaus and valleys which represents, respectively, the emitted signal and the background, that is, the gap between adjacent cells. Hence, by simply choosing a threshold, one can distinguish signal

10.4229/EUPVSEC2025/3AV.3.14
020188-001

from background, resulting in a binary line vector for the sum across lines and a binary column vector for the sum across columns. The outer product of these two binary vectors produces a binary mask that separates active areas (cells) from inactive areas (background). Finally, the label function from Python scikit-image library provides a different integer index for each closed region from this binary matrix [5], then each cell is labeled by a specific number.

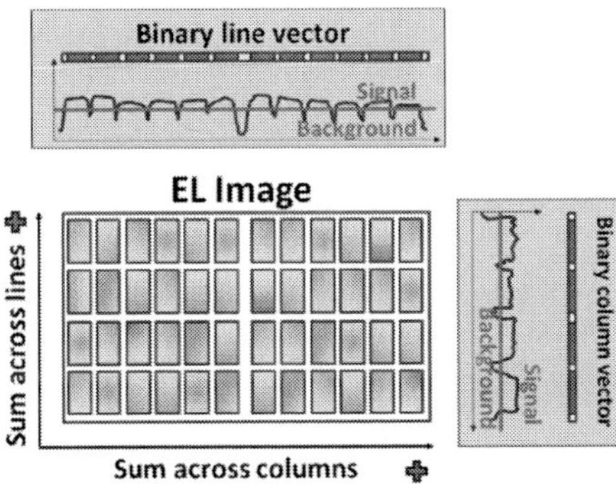

Figure 2: Schematic of half-cell module segmentation approach. By summing the image across its horizontal and vertical axis, then thresholding these sums, binary column and line vectors are obtained. The multiplication of these vectors results in a matrix which is a mask of active (cell) and inactive (background) regions within the image, which is used for labelling each cell.

2.2 Full-cell modules

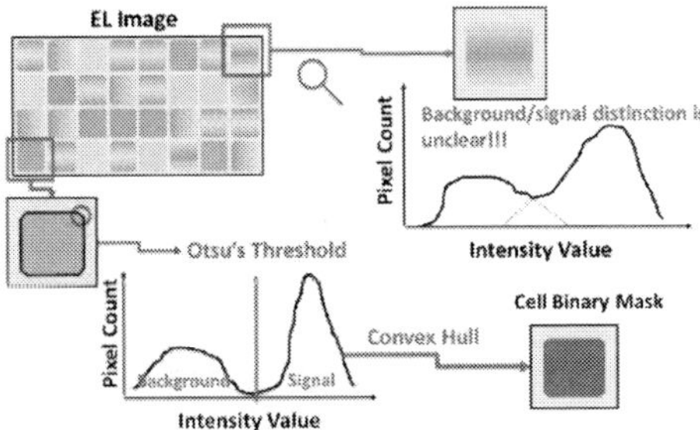

Figure 3: Schematic of full-cell module segmentation approach. The EL image is cropped into one sub image per cell. Then, a histogram analysis is performed on the sub images and a cell for which background/signal distinction is clear is chosen. Otsu's threshold along with a Convex Hull transform provides a binary mask with the chosen cell's geometry. This mask will be replicated to the whole image and used for labelling individual cells.

Considering a full-cell module whose cells are corner-cut, the horizontal and vertical sum is no longer a valid strategy since it would not provide the corner geometry. As it was said, S. Deitsch et al. [2] performed this segmentation by computing an average cell from the image. Here, we suggest an alternative method which consists of cropping the EL image based on the number of cells per line and column. Then, for each cell, the threshold that best divide its histogram into two regions is obtained

with Otsu's method, resulting in a binary mask. Following, a Convex Hull transform is applied on the mask to obtain its closed geometry. However, not all geometries faithfully represent that of the cells. Depending on their histograms, background/signal distinction might be unclear and, thus, Otsu's threshold followed by a Convex Hull transform will fail in representing the cell. Here, we consider that there might be a cell within the module for which a binary mask containing the cell geometry can be extracted. Thus, by performing this algorithm on every cell a visual analysis is enough to choose a correct binary mask with the cell's geometry. By systematically replicating this chosen mask across all cell positions, a complete binary mask is reconstructed, preserving the original image dimensions. Finaly, as it was done for half-cell modules, label function from Python scikit-image library can provide a different integer index for each cell from the binary matrix [5].

3 EXPERIMENTAL ANALYSIS

A Phase One 150 MP XT camera was adapted to detect the emitted EL signals from full-cell and half-cell modules. Three images were measured at 10% of the module's nominal short circuit current (low bias) and three others were taken at its short circuit current (high bias). These images were averaged, subtracted to background, and corrected for noise [6], vignetting [7], and perspective [8] prior to the segmentation and quantitative analysis.

3.1 Segmentation
The full and half-cell segmentation methods were applied to the processed high bias images. Figures 4 and 5 show, respectively the results obtained for a half-cell and a full-cell module.

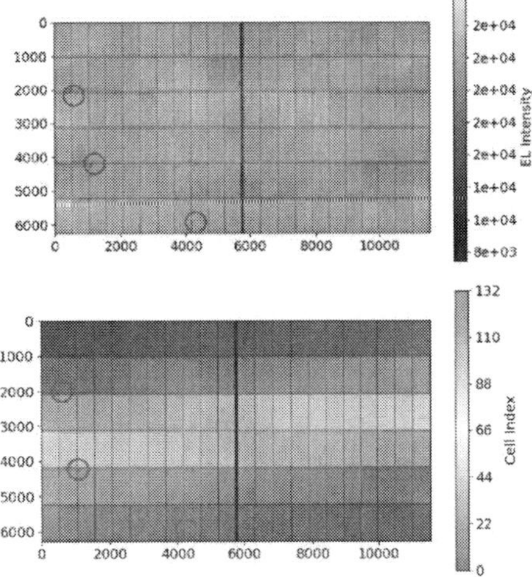

Figure 4: (top) High bias EL image of rectangular-shaped half-cell module. (bottom) Labeled mask superposed to EL image with a transparency degree of 50%. Red circles represent patterns that can be seen in both top and bottom images.

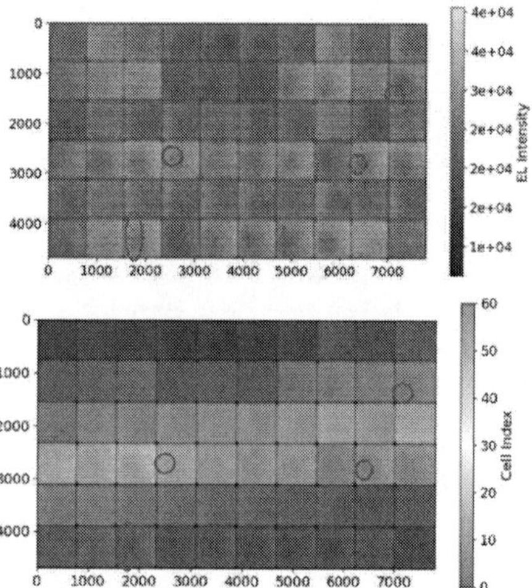

Figure 5: (top) High bias EL image of corner-cut full-cell module. (bottom) Labeled mask superposed to EL image with a transparency degree of 50%. Red circles represent patterns that can be seen in both top and bottom images.

On the top of each figure the EL image after the preprocessing steps described previously is presented and, on the bottom, the labeled mask providing a different integer index for the pixels that represent a given cell in the same order as the one represented in Figure 1 is shown. These masks are displayed with a certain degree of transparency as a manner to identify whether the segmentation routines were successful or not. For the full-cell module, the binary geometry mask was obtained with the 26th cell. Red circles represent features that can be seen in both the EL and the labeled figures. The results obtained indicate that the proposed methods are robust and yield satisfactory outcomes. Following, since the pixels that represent individual cells within an EL image of a whole module were determined, quantitative parameters that provide the performance of these cells can be extracted, which will be presented in the next subsection.

3.2 Quantitative EL

A simple method to represent the electrical circuit of a solar cell is the single-diode model (SDM) [1]. This model is represented in Figure 6 containing the photogenerated current (I_{ph}), the extracted current (I), the cell's terminal voltage (V), a diode representing the p-n junction, a series resistance (R_s) and a parallel shunt resistance (R_{sh}). The single diode is characterized by its dark saturation current density (J_0) and ideality factor (n).

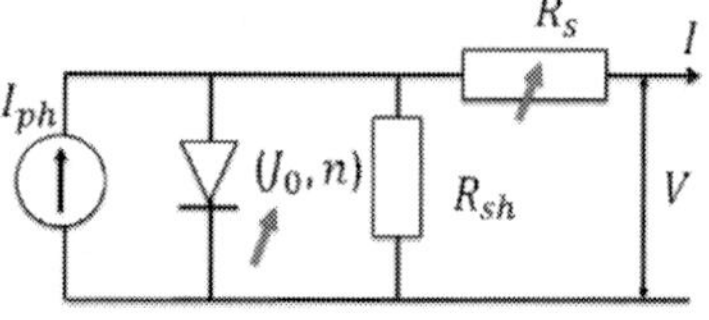

Figure 6: Single-diode model (SDM) electrical circuit representation. Red arrows indicate the parameters that estimated with quantitative EL: R_s and J_0.

When submit to a forward bias, a solar cell emits light.

Current injection induces radiative recombination within the bulk peaking at 1150 nm for *Si*-based cells [9], thus a camera sensible to the near infrared is necessary for detection. The EL signal emitted by the cell (ϕ_{EL}) is modeled as

$$\phi_{EL} = C \cdot \exp\left(\frac{V}{V_{th}}\right)$$

where C is a calibration factor, V is the local voltage, and V_{th} the thermal voltage [4].

Many methods to estimate parameters from EL signal have already been proposed on the literature. T. Fuyuki et al. [9] first proposed EL imaging as a source to investigate minority carrier diffusion length. Other authors followed Fuyuki in what was named "Fuyuki's linear approximation" which considers the calibration factor and the dark saturation current density to be inversely proportional. This method measures low and high bias emission, providing at the same time the dark saturation current density and the series resistance in the ideal scenario where shunts are neglected and ideality factors are assumed to be unitary [10], [3]. A similar approach was conducted by O. Breitenstein et al. [11] in an iterative manner.

Nonetheless this linear approximation has some limitations. The diffusion length linearity with the EL intensity is considered valid for diffusion lengths lower than 100 μm; nowadays technologies, on the other hand have diffusion lengths greater than the cell thickness [12], [13], [14]. P. Wurfel et al. [12], while studying this lack of linearity, developed an interesting analysis on diffusion length extraction from EL images which accounted for the emission coming from the front and rear part of the cell. G. Dost et al. [14] considered the series resistance after taking the nonlinearity of Fuyuki's approximation into consideration, yet it required the cell's global R_s extracted from I-V measurements.

Apart from Fuyuki's approximation, T. Potthoff et al. [4] considered computing a calibration factor to estimate local voltages and external series resistance. This method is the basis for the generalized quantitative electroluminescence (g-QUEL), which after a previous classification of EL images, provides not only SDM parameters, but also double-diode model (DDM) ones depending on the module degradation level [15]. This method, however, obtains the parameters at the cell level, not considering inhomogeneities within the cell itself and it requires imaging at a set of different biases. Acquisitions at varying injection currents were also investigated by other authors, but with a different approach. From the current injection, local voltages were estimated providing a Dark I-V curve which was then used to fit SDM parameters [16], [17]. Moreover, ratio between acquisitions was also suggested, but methods considering this approach would either compare a cell with another one that is chosen as reference [18] or present previous knowledge on the ideality factor from global module I-V measurements [19].

For the scope of the present work, the methods described by A. S. Rajput et al [3] and T. Potthoff et al. [4] were applied. The low and high bias EL acquisitions after the preprocessing steps described previously were used to estimate R_s and J_0. A. S. Rajput et al [3], which relies on "Fuyuki's linear approximation" [9], [10], proposes a strategy to measure the dark saturation current density and the internal series resistance (R_s^{int}). As said before the linear approximation considers the calibration factor and the dark saturation current density to be related by $C = f/J_0$, where f is a constant value. By assuming negligible shunt losses and unitary ideality factor, A. S. Rajput et al. [3] provided a formula to obtain the constant f based on the low bias applied current and terminal voltage as well as its EL intensity. Local voltage, calibration factor and J_0 were then estimated in this order.

For a high bias image, given that the calibration factor is known, local voltages are easily determined and so is the current density through the diode; with these terms, the internal R_s is then obtained.

Now, by comparing the sum of the cell's voltages to the module terminal voltage, one can determine the external series resistance following T. Potthoff et al. [4], which represents the cell-to-module connection resistance. It is important to know, nonetheless, that R_s^{ext} is constant for each cell within the module.

In Figure 7 are depicted the average internal resistances and dark saturation current densities obtained for the same full-cell module used for segmentation. Note that the pixels for which these parameters were measured correspond to the labeled ones, that is, only the pixels determined for each cell were used to perform this estimation. The external R_s obtained was $0.88\ \Omega \cdot \text{cm}^2$.

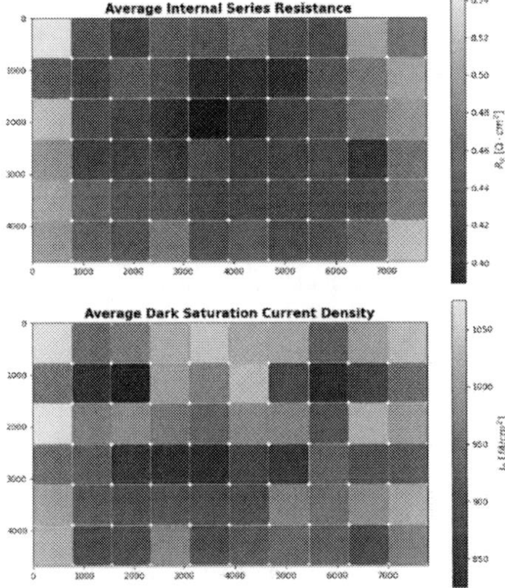

Figure 7: (top) Average internal R_s for corner-cut full-cell module. (bottom) Average J_0 for corner-cut full-cell module.

4   I-V CURVE SIMULATION

A further investigation consisted of verifying the accuracy of the values obtained for J_0 and R_s. The device under test was drilled on its backsheet and two connectors were placed on the middle of the 13th cell and 14th cell to not crack the cell edges as can be seen in Figure 8. The experimental I-V curve measured at the Standard Test Conditions (STC) on these connectors is represented in Figure 9. For the sake of simplicity, we consider that it represents the I-V curve of the 13th cell.

Regarding the EL estimated parameters, the idea was to simulate an I-V curve out of them to compare with the experimental one. From the SDM represented in Figure 6, one can obtain the equation that determines the I-V curve

$$I = I_{ph} - I_0 \left(\exp\left(\frac{V + I \cdot R_s}{n \cdot V_{th}} \right) - 1 \right) - \frac{V + I \cdot R_s}{R_{sh}}$$

This equation does not provide the current explicitly in terms of the voltage and vice-versa, yet this can be overcome by applying Lambert W function [20]. This function is such that

$$\omega = W(\omega \cdot \exp(\omega)), \quad \omega \in \mathbb{C}$$

Hence, the I-V curve can be rewritten by some algebraic manipulation with Lambert W function, providing the voltage in terms of the current as follows

$$V(I) = \left(I_{ph} + I_0 \right) R_{sh} - I(R_s + R_{sh})$$
$$- n\,V_{th}\,W \left[I_0 \frac{R_{sh}}{nV_{th}} exp\left(\frac{R_{sh}}{nV_{th}} \left(I_{ph} + I_0 - I \right) \right) \right]$$

Figure 8: (left) Full-cell PV module used for quantitative EL validation. (right) Backsheet of the module with connectors placed in the middle of 13th and 14th cell for measuring single-cell I-V curve, connectors are highlighted with a red rectangle and the region is zoomed.

Lambert W is the default solution method for pvlib built-in functions *pvsystem.i_from_v* and *pvsystem.singlediode* which, respectively, provide the current values for a set of voltages generating an I-V curve and estimate the operational points of this curve $(I_{sc}, V_{oc}, P_{mpp}, I_{mpp}, V_{mpp})$ [21]. These functions were used to simulate the I-V curve of the 13th cell simulation from its average dark saturation current (I_0) and its total series resistance obtained with the quantitative EL methods presented previously. Here, the total series resistance is the sum of the external and average internal series resistances. Besides that, the simulation was performed with $n = 1$ and taking an infinity value for R_{sh} so that shunts could be neglected to account for the assumptions of A. S. Rajput et al. [3], as well as considering the short-circuit current of the module provided on its datasheet being equal to the cell photocurrent [15]. This simulated curve is presented in Figure 9 along with the experimental curve.

One might note, in a first moment, that the datasheet short-circuit current is slightly smaller than the measured I_{sc} and that there was a small overestimation for P_{mpp}. Meanwhile, the simulated and experimental values for V_{oc} are alike. Table I summarizes the SDM parameters of the experimental curve extracted with pvlib function ivtools.sde.fit_sandia_simple [22] and those estimated with quantitative EL, while Table II presents the experimental and simulated values for V_{oc}, MPP, and FF as well as their relative errors, which are defined as

$$Relative\ error = \left(\frac{Simulated - Experimental}{Experimental}\right) \cdot 100\%$$

One might also note that, apart from the fill factor (FF), all relative errors are below 5%. Among the possible uncertainty sources the different assumptions must be recalled. First, the assumption of no shunt resistance, modeled by an infinite value, seems to not have impacted our analysis since it is mostly linked to the shape of the I-V curve close to I_{sc}. Further, the datasheet value for I_{sc} is 2.8% smaller than its experimental value, so assuming the datasheet I_{sc} as I_{ph} to simulate the I-V curve raises some uncertainties. However, a quick simulation taking the experimental I_{sc} as I_{ph} increased mostly the simulated I_{mpp} and P_{mpp}, not providing relevant changes to the FF. Besides that, since the connectors for experimental I-V extraction were placed in the middle of the 13th and 14th cell, there might be some mismatch between them. Also, "Fuyuki's linear approximation" not being representative to nowadays technologies is a limiting factor to the estimation of R_s^{int} and J_0 as mentioned previously and it might have an impact on our analysis. Nonetheless, A. S. Rajput at el. [3] claimed no relevant difference on their results when taking the nonlinearity into account.

Finally, the assumption of a uniform and unitary ideality factor is the one with the most important impact. Note that, instead of being equal to 1 as assumed, its experimental value is of 1.255. The ideality factor is within the denominator of an exponential term in the I-V curve equation, thus even small variations provide significant impacts. Due to that, the experimental and EL estimated dark saturation currents differ by 2 orders of magnitude. Another relevant side effect of this assumption is that this exponential term impacts the rate at which the current drops as the voltage increases and, hence, the shape of the curve around the maximum power point will not be faithfully reproduced. This is the main reason for the 7% relative error for the fill factor.

Table I: Comparison between experimental SDM values issued from the I-V flasher (experimental) and by performing quantitative analysis on EL images. R_s^{int} and R_s^{ext} indicates respectively the internal and external series resistances and their sum results in the total series resistance, R_s^{tot}.

	Experimental	Quantitative EL
R_s^{int} ($\Omega \cdot cm^2$)	-	0.45
R_s^{ext} ($\Omega \cdot cm^2$)	-	0.88
R_s^{tot} ($\Omega \cdot cm^2$)	1.80	1.33
R_{sh} ($\Omega \cdot cm^2$)	7993	∞ (assumed)
I_0 (pA)	27005	215.051
I_{sc} (A)	9.033	8.78 (datasheet)
n	1.255	1 (assumed)

Table II: Experimental and simulated values from I-V curve

	Experimental	Simulated	Relative Error (%)
P_{mpp} (W)	4.096	4.238	+3,5
I_{mpp} (A)	8.394	8.322	-0.9
V_{mpp} (V)	0.488	0.509	+4,3
V_{oc} (V)	0.632	0.628	-0.6
FF (%)	72	77	+7

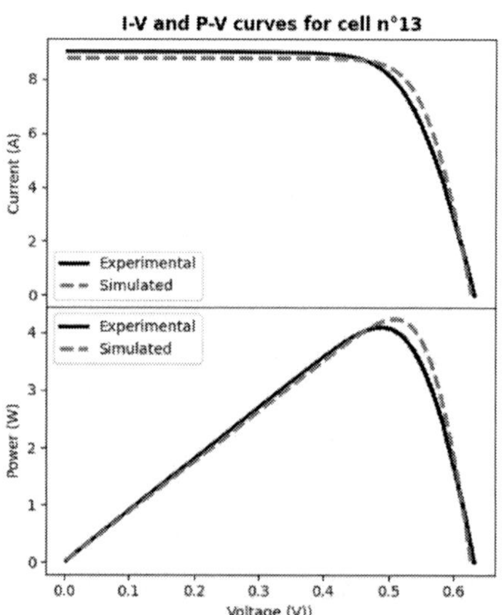

Figure 9: Experimental and simulated I-V and P-V curves for the 13th cell of the module presented on Figure 8. The simulation was performed with the results from the quantitative EL analysis.

5 CONCLUSION

The segmentation routine developed in this work provided two different methods to distinct which pixels belong to a single cell within an electroluminescent image. Modules containing rectangular-shaped half-cells were segmented by computing the sum across both lines and columns. Corner-cut full-cell modules, on the other hand, were segmented by analyzing and thresholding the histogram of sub images containing a different cell each. These methods were applied in two modules – one with full-cells and the other with half-cells – after noise, perspective and vignetting correction which are essential requisites for the algorithms developed. Both methods provided satisfactory results, nonetheless, there is still path for improvement such as accounting for shunted cells while applying the half-cell method since they might pose local drops on the column and line sum profiles making the threshold choice troublesome. Also, for the full-cell method, instead of applying the histogram on each cell and then choosing the cell that provided a sufficient cell geometry mask, computing the "average cell" as done by S. Deitsch et al. [2] to then apply Otsu's threshold followed by a Convex Hull might make this method simpler.

Moreover, the quantitative analysis that followed from the segmentation routine consisted on computing the internal series resistance and the dark saturation current density based on the method developed by A. S. Rajput et al. [3] as well as the external series resistance following the strategy of T. Potthoff et al. [4]. These parameters were used to simulate the single-diode I-V curve of a cell within a module following Lambert W function using a Python library developed for PV systems [21]. The simulated curve was compared to experimental I-V curve measured on the middle of this cell and of its neighbor (which was connected to it in series). For simplicity, this measurement was taken as the real I-V curve of this cell. Experimental and simulated I-V curves presented a remarkable agreement despite for their behavior around the MPP, which originates from the assumption of a unitary ideality factor. This resulted in a fill factor relative error of 7%. Besides that, values for $P_{mpp}, I_{mpp}, V_{mpp}$, and V_{oc} are within a relative error range of 5%.

A global analysis comparing simulated and experimental values for different cells is still necessary and so it is comparing the results with and without a segmented mask. For the moment, we can say that the methods investigated on the present work enable to determine which pixels must be considered before applying the quantitative algorithms on the literature. This represents the first step for an effective quantitative EL at the module scale, and it will be refined throughout the development of a global methodology.

6 REFERENCES

[1] V. E. Puranik, R. Kumar, and R. Gupta, "Progress in module level quantitative electroluminescence imaging of crystalline silicon PV module: A review," *Sol. Energy*, vol. 264, p. 111994, Nov. 2023, doi: 10.1016/j.solener.2023.111994.

[2] S. Deitsch *et al.*, "Segmentation of photovoltaic module cells in uncalibrated electroluminescence images," *Mach. Vis. Appl.*, vol. 32, no. 4, p. 84, May 2021, doi: 10.1007/s00138-021-01191-9.

[3] A. S. Rajput, J. W. Ho, Y. Zhang, S. Nalluri, and A. G. Aberle, "Quantitative estimation of electrical performance parameters of individual solar cells in silicon photovoltaic modules using electroluminescence imaging," *Sol. Energy*, vol. 173, pp. 201–208, Oct. 2018, doi: 10.1016/j.solener.2018.07.046.

[4] T. Potthoff, K. Bothe, U. Eitner, D. Hinken, and M. Köntges, "Detection of the voltage distribution in photovoltaic modules by electroluminescence imaging," *Prog. Photovolt. Res. Appl.*, vol. 18, no. 2, pp. 100–106, 2010, doi: 10.1002/pip.941.

[5] scikit-image, "skimage.measure." [Online]. Available: https://scikit-image.org/docs/stable/api/skimage.measure.html

[6] K. G. Bedrich, M. Bliss, T. R. Betts, and R. Gottschalg, "Electroluminescence imaging of PV devices: Camera calibration and image correction," in *2016 IEEE 43rd Photovoltaic Specialists Conference (PVSC)*, June 2016, pp. 1532–1537. doi: 10.1109/PVSC.2016.7749875.

[7] T. S. Ramsay, "Edge-based vignetting factor estimation and correction comparative analysis," *Imaging Sci. J.*, vol. 65, no. 5, pp. 299–307, July 2017, doi: 10.1080/13682199.2017.1337284.

[8] "OpenCV: Geometric Image Transformations." Accessed: Aug. 29, 2025. [Online]. Available: https://docs.opencv.org/4.x/da/d54/group__imgproc__transform.html#ga20f62aa3235d869c9956436c870893ae

[9] T. Fuyuki, H. Kondo, T. Yamazaki, Y. Takahashi, and Y. Uraoka, "Photographic surveying of minority carrier diffusion length in polycrystalline silicon solar cells by electroluminescence," *Appl. Phys. Lett.*, vol. 86, p. 262108, June 2005, doi: 10.1063/1.1978979.

[10] J. Haunschild, M. Glatthaar, M. Kasemann, S. Rein, and E. R. Weber, "Fast series resistance imaging for silicon solar cells using electroluminescence," *Phys. Status Solidi RRL – Rapid Res. Lett.*, vol. 3, no. 7–8, pp. 227–229, Oct. 2009, doi: 10.1002/pssr.200903175.

[11] O. Breitenstein, A. Khanna, Y. Augarten, J. Bauer, J. -M. Wagner, and K. Iwig, "Quantitative evaluation of electroluminescence images of solar cells," *Phys. Status Solidi RRL – Rapid Res. Lett.*, vol. 4, no. 1–2, pp. 7–9, Feb. 2010, doi: 10.1002/pssr.200903304.

[12] P. Würfel, T. Trupke, T. Puzzer, E. Schäffer, W. Warta, and S. W. Glunz, "Diffusion lengths of silicon solar cells from luminescence images," *J. Appl. Phys.*, vol. 101, no. 12, p. 123110, June 2007, doi: 10.1063/1.2749201.

[13] O. Breitenstein, F. Frühauf, D. Hinken, and K. Bothe, "Effective Diffusion Length and Bulk Saturation Current Density Imaging in Solar Cells by Spectrally Filtered Luminescence Imaging," *IEEE J. Photovolt.*, vol. 6, no. 5, pp. 1243–1254, Sept. 2016, doi: 10.1109/JPHOTOV.2016.2571621.

[14] G. Dost, H. Höffler, and J. M. Greulich, "Advanced Series Resistance Imaging for Silicon Solar Cells via Electroluminescence," *Phys. Status Solidi A*, vol. 218, no. 6, p. 2000546, Mar. 2021, doi: 10.1002/pssa.202000546.

[15] V. E. Puranik, R. Kumar, and R. Gupta, "Generalized quantitative electroluminescence method for the performance evaluation of defective and unevenly degraded crystalline silicon photovoltaic module," *Prog. Photovolt. Res. Appl.*, vol. 31, no. 3, pp. 269–282, 2023, doi: 10.1002/pip.3632.

[16] B. Li, A. Stokes, and D. M. J. Doble, "Evaluation of two-dimensional electrical properties of photovoltaic modules using bias-dependent electroluminescence," *Prog. Photovolt. Res. Appl.*, vol. 20, no. 8, pp. 936–944, Dec. 2012, doi: 10.1002/pip.1161.

[17] S. Guo, E. Schneller, K. O. Davis, and W. V. Schoenfeld, "Quantitative analysis of crystalline silicon wafer PV modules by electroluminescence imaging," in *2016 IEEE 43rd Photovoltaic Specialists Conference (PVSC)*, Portland, OR, USA: IEEE, June 2016, pp. 3688–3692. doi: 10.1109/PVSC.2016.7750365.

[18] T. Fuyuki, H. Kondo, Y. Kaji, A. Ogane, and Y. Takahashi, "Analytic findings in the electroluminescence characterization of crystalline silicon solar cells," *J. Appl. Phys.*, vol. 101, no. 2, p. 023711, Jan. 2007, doi: 10.1063/1.2431075.

[19] F. Fruehauf and M. Turek, "Quantification of Electroluminescence Measurements on Modules," *Energy Procedia*, vol. 77, pp. 63–68, Aug. 2015, doi: 10.1016/j.egypro.2015.07.010.

[20] "Lambert *W* function," *Wikipedia*. Aug. 22, 2025. Accessed: Sept. 01, 2025. [Online]. Available: https://en.wikipedia.org/w/index.php?title=Lambert_W_function&oldid=1307306923

[21] "pvlib.pvsystem.PVSystem — pvlib python 0.13.0 documentation." Accessed: Sept. 01, 2025. [Online]. Available: https://pvlib-python.readthedocs.io/en/stable/reference/generated/pvlib.pvsystem.PVSystem.html

[22] "Single diode models — pvlib python 0.13.0 documentation." Accessed: Sept. 12, 2025. [Online]. Available: https://pvlib-python.readthedocs.io/en/stable/reference/pv_modeling/sdm.html

Simple Cell Segmentation Routine for Quantitative EL Analysis of c-Si Solar Modules

João Victor Oliveira Santos[1,3], Julien Dupuis[1], Christine Abdel Nour[1], Daniel Ory[2], Damien Barakel[3], Olivier Palais[3]

[1]EDF R&D, EDF Lab Les Renardières, Avenue des Renardières, Moret Loing et Orvanne 77250, France
[2]EDF R&D – IPVF, 18 boulevard Thomas Gobert, 91190 Palaiseau, France
[3]Aix-Marseille Univ, Université de Toulon, CNRS, IM2NP, Marseille, France

Context and Objective

* Determining the pixels within each cell from EL images enables to obtain its local voltage, series resistance, and dark saturation current density [1];

* An automatic segmentation was developed focusing on full-cell modules and it considers computing an average cell from the EL image [2].

* The goal of this work is to provide an easy to apply segmentation algorithm for rectangular-shaped half-cell modules as well as a simple alternative algorithm for corner-cut full-cell module segmentation, resulting in a labeled mask with a different integer index for each cell.

Half-cell Modules

1. Sum the EL image across horizontal and vertical axis;

2. Chose a threshold for each sum, separating signal from background on binary vectors;

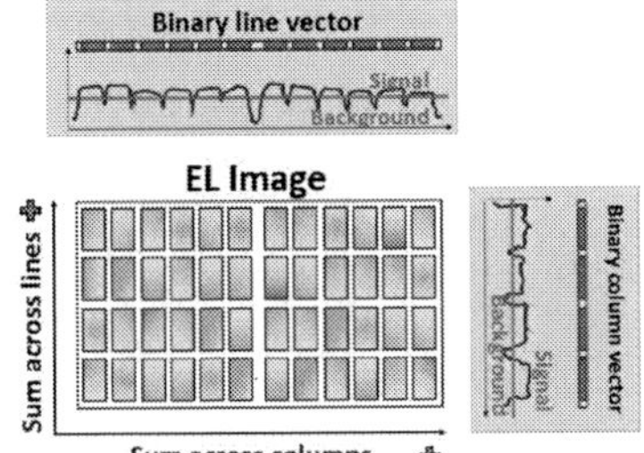

3. Multiply binary vectors, obtaining a binary matrix;

4. From binary matrix a labeled matrix can be obtained with a different index for each cell.

skimage.measure.label [3]

Full-cell Modules

1. Crop the EL image based on the number of cells per line and column;

2. For each cell, apply Otsu's threshold and a Convex Hull transform;

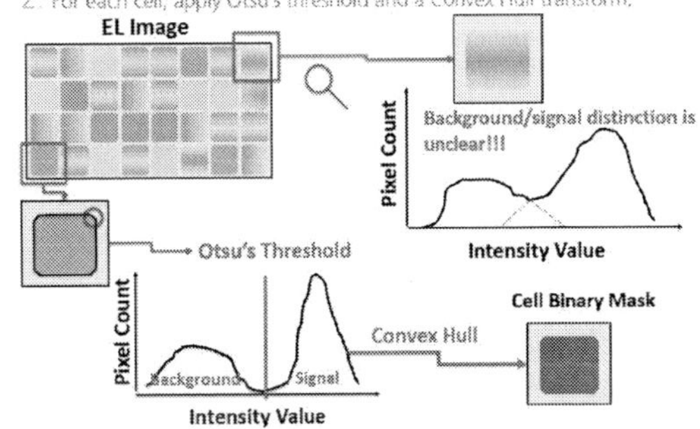

3. Select a cell mask for which geometry was accurately obtained and replicate it to the module dimension, obtaining a binary matrix;

4. From binary matrix a labeled matrix can be obtained with a different index for each cell.

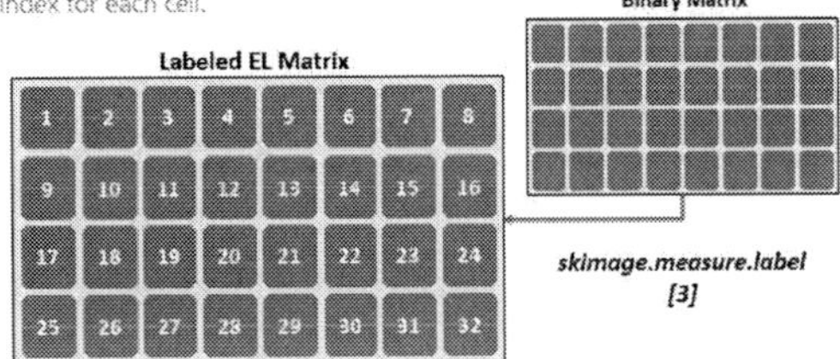

skimage.measure.label [3]

Quantitative EL Analysis

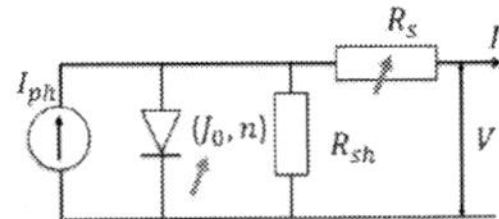

$$\emptyset_{EL} = C \cdot exp\left(\frac{V}{V_{th}}\right)$$

EL Intensity

* Computation of internal series resistance (R_s^{int}) and dark saturation current density (J_0) from low and high bias EL image, assuming n=1 and no shunts [1];

* Computation of external series resistance (R_s^{ext}), accounting for the cell-to-module connection resistance [4];

* I-V curve extraction of a single cell within a module;

* I-V curve simulation for the same cell inputting the quantitative EL parameters into PVLIB built-in functions with Lambert W solving method [5];

* Relative errors for power, current and voltage at the maximal power point as well as for the open circuit voltage below 5% comparing simulated and experimental values.

Conclusion and Perspectives

* The segmentation methods enables quantitative analysis;

* Good correspondence between experimental and EL simulated I-V curves;

* Possibility to estimate power production for each cell within module;

* This segmentation analysis represents the first step for an effective quantitative EL at the module scale, and the methodology will be refined throughout the development of the global methodology.

References:

NUMERICAL SIMULATION OF OUTPUT CHARACTERISTICS OF PHOTOVOLTAIC MODULE WITH SHORT AND OPEN CIRCUITED BYPASS DIODES

Ibuki Kitamura[1], Toshiyuki Hamada[1], Ikuo Nanno[2]
[1]Osaka Electro-communication University, Japan
[2]Nanno Energy Research Center, Japan
hamada@osakac.ac.jp

ABSTRACT: In recent years, decarbonization efforts have advanced rapidly, especially in developed countries, due to climate change and rising energy costs. Photovoltaic (PV) power generation is being widely adopted as an effective energy source, but increasing penetration brings operational problems such as failures. For example, bypass diode (BPD) failures in PV modules can cause heating, burning, fire, and electric shock risks. BPDs protect against electrical continuity problems and hot spots under partial shading, but failures are difficult to detect when modules are roof-mounted. Failed BPDs exhibit different electrical characteristics, ranging from short- to open-circuit failures, with varying heat generation. The authors previously clarified the correlation between resistance and heat generation using a single PV module, but verification for systems with multiple modules requires large-scale testing, making simulations desirable. We propose a model that simulates the output of a PV module string with a failed BPD at various fault resistances. The model reproduces the output when one BPD fails in a PV module with three cell strings and is validated against measured data from a failed BPD module. The study successfully reproduced outputs of PV modules with short-circuit failures (0.1–50 Ω) and open-circuit failures, and also situations with partial shading. The model is expected to support understanding failure mechanisms and diagnosing PV system faults.

1 INTRODUCTION

In recent years, efforts toward decarbonization have been accelerating worldwide, particularly in developed countries, driven by pressing issues such as global climate change, the depletion of fossil fuel resources, and the continuous rise in energy prices. Renewable energy technologies are regarded as indispensable solutions to these challenges, with photovoltaic (PV) power generation being one of the most rapidly expanding options [1].

As the penetration of PV power generation continues to rise, however, various operational and reliability issues are also becoming more prominent. Failures within PV systems not only reduce energy yield but also introduce serious safety concerns. A particularly critical problem arises from failures of bypass diodes (BPDs), which are embedded in PV modules to protect against electrical continuity problems and to mitigate hot spot formation when partial shading occurs. Under normal operation, BPDs ensure stable performance of the PV module. However, when a BPD fails, the component may generate significant heat, sometimes leading to burning. Such failures pose major risks of fire and electric shock, threatening both system safety and reliability [2].

The detection of failed BPDs presents an additional challenge. Because PV modules are often installed on rooftops or other inaccessible locations, visual inspection and maintenance are hindered, making early identification of failures difficult. Furthermore, the behavior of failed BPDs is not uniform: some exhibit short-circuits characteristics with resistance values as low as a fraction of an ohm, while others fail in an open-circuit mode. In some cases, failed BPDs generate excessive heat and burn, whereas in other cases little or no heating occurs. These diverse failure modes complicate failure diagnosis and reliability assessment.

In our previous work, we investigated the electrical and thermal characteristics of failed BPDs and clarified the correlation between their resistance values and heat generation [3]-[4]. While these results were validated using a single PV module, the behavior of an entire PV system—comprising strings of a dozen or more interconnected modules—remains insufficiently understood. Conducting large-scale field experiments to verify such system-level behaviors requires significant resources and repeated testing under controlled conditions, which is both costly and time-consuming. Consequently, the development of reliable simulation models is desirable for evaluating PV system performance under BPD failure scenarios.

In this study, we propose a simulation model that reproduces the output characteristics of a PV module string in the presence of a failed BPD. Specifically, the model considers fault resistances spanning from short- to open-circuit conditions and is designed for PV modules consisting of three cell strings. To validate the proposed approach, the simulated outputs are compared with measured data obtained from an actual PV module containing a failed BPD.

2 SIMULATION MODEL

Figure 1 shows a simulation model of a three-cell-string PV module with one failed BPD. Figure 1(a) shows models that reproduce the characteristics of a diode. These models were implemented in MATLAB/Simulink to represent the current characteristics of a diode given by equations (1) and (2), which provide the characteristic equation and photocurrent of a polarity-inverted diode [5].

$$I_d = I_{sat}\left\{exp\left(\frac{q_e\, v_r}{n\, k_b\, T}\right) - 1\right\} + I_{shunt} \qquad (1)$$

$$I_{shunt} = \frac{V_r}{R_p}\left\{1 + a\left(1 - \frac{V_r}{V_{br}}\right)^{-m}\right\} \qquad (2)$$

where I_{sat} is the reverse saturation current, V_r is the breakdown voltage, q_e is the electron charge, k_b is the Boltzmann constant, T is the temperature, and n is an ideal coefficient; these parameters were set to 3.8×10^{-7} A,

10.4229/EUPVSEC2025/3AV.3.22
020190-001

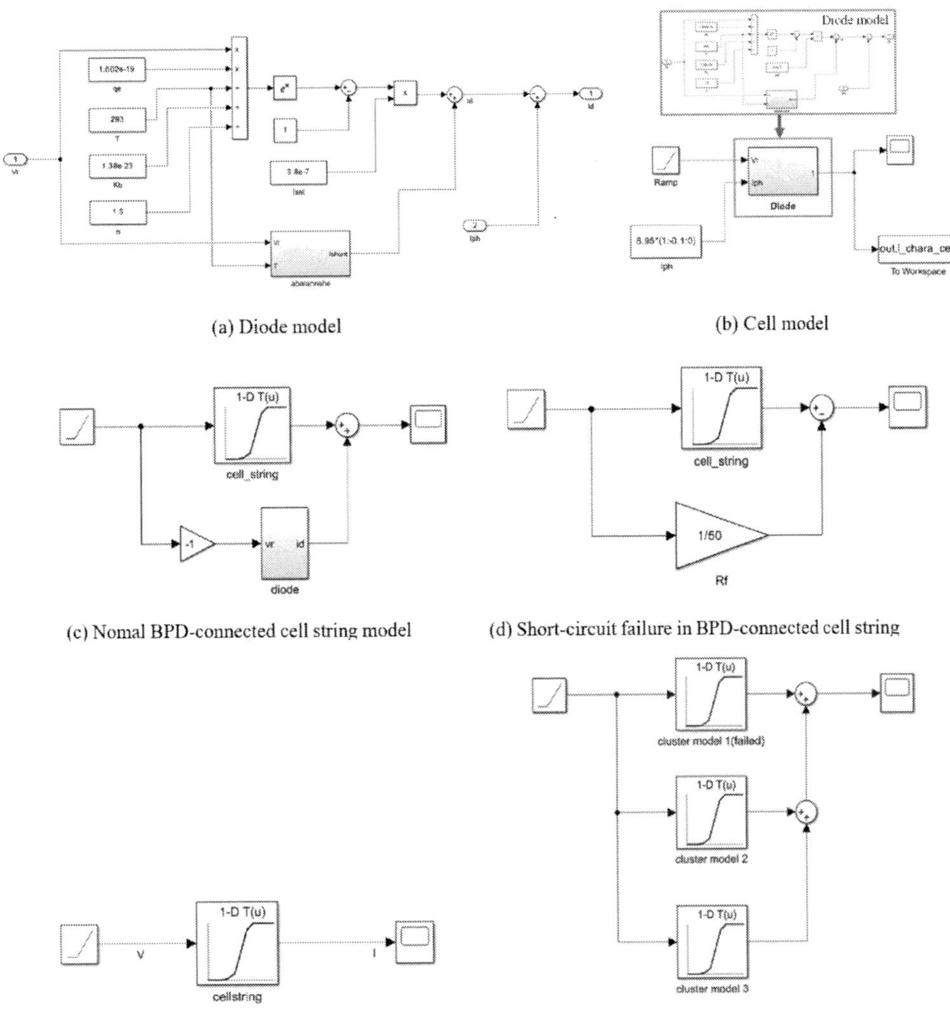

(a) Diode model

(b) Cell model

(c) Nomal BPD-connected cell string model

(d) Short-circuit failure in BPD-connected cell string

(e) Open-circuit failure in BPD-connected cell string model

(f) Three-cell-string PV module

Figure 1 Diagrams of three-cell-string PV module with BPD failures

-100 V, 1.6×10^{-19} C, 1.38×10^{-23} J/K, 293 K, and 1.5, respectively.

Figure 1(b) shows a solar cell model that corresponds to the diode model shown in Figure 1(a) with additional photocurrent I_{ph}. The characteristics of the PV module provided by Choshu Industry Co., Ltd. (CS-236B31) was selected for this study. As the solar cell output, open-circuit voltage V_{oc} was set to 0.64 V, and short-circuit current I_{sc} was set to 8.95 A.

Figure 1(c) shows a model of a cell string containing a BPD. The model replicates the cell model shown in Figure 1(b) to obtain a cell string structure composed of 18 solar cells connected in series. To reproduce a cell string including a BPD, a diode was connected in parallel.

Figure 1(d) shows a model of the cell string with a short-circuited BPD. In this case, the BPD loses its rectification characteristics and exhibits a resistor characteristic when operated under reverse bias. The short circuit is reproduced by replacing the BPD shown in Figure 1(c) with a resistor, R_F.

Figure 1(e) shows a cell string model with an open-circuited BPD. If a BPD is in open circuit, it cannot divert the current generated by other cell strings when the related cell string has conduction failure or is shaded. The output with an open-circuited BPD is reproduced using a cell string without BPD.

Figure 1(f) shows a model of a PV module with three cell strings and BPDs. This model adds three cell string models (Figure 1(e)), which deliver open-circuit voltage $V_{OC} = 10.9$ V and short-circuit current $I_{SC} = 8.95$ A, to reproduce a PV module with three cell strings connected in series.

3 RESULTS OF SIMULATION

Figure 2 shows the output characteristics of a PV module with three cell strings and BPDs, with one BPD having an open-circuit failure. In addition, the failure resistance of the short-circuited BPD varies between 0.1 and 50 Ω. Real measurements were acquired under a solar radiation intensity of 740–830 W/m² and air temperature of 8–13 °C. In Figure 2, when fault resistance R_F of the BPD decreases, the open-circuit voltage and operating voltage decrease. This is because the operating voltage of the cluster decreases with R_F. Due to the low solar radiation intensity, the measurement results show a lower current than the simulation results intended to reproduce the rated output, but the simulation can suitably reproduce the output of the PV module (CS-236B31).

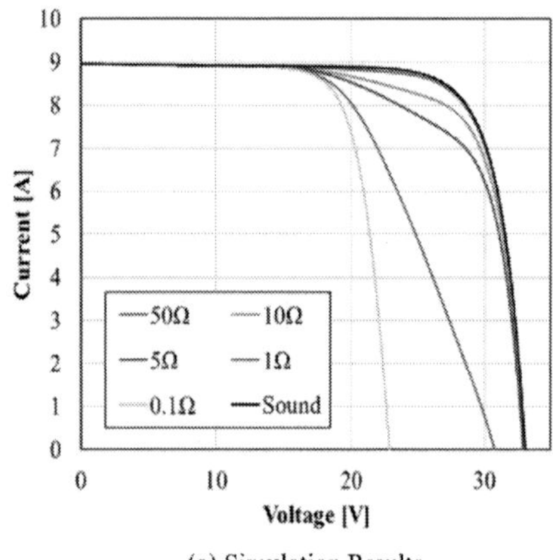

(a) Simulation Results

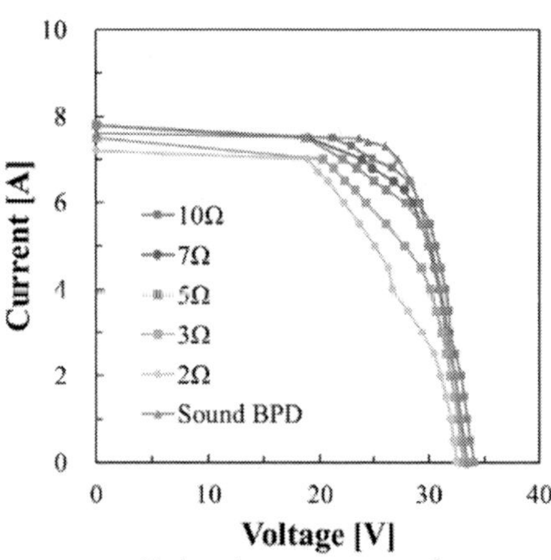

(b) Actual measurement results
Figure 2 Output characteristics of PV module containing three cell strings and BPDs with one short-circuited BPD.

Figure 3 shows the output characteristics of a PV module composed of three cell strings and BPDs, with one of the BPDs under open-circuit failure. Under normal

power generation conditions, no difference occurs in the output characteristics between a PV module with an open-circuited BPD and a normal module. We also evaluate the output characteristics when one cell in a string, which contains 18 solar cells connected in series, with an open-circuited failed BPD is gradually shaded. This scenario is reproduced by changing the shaded cell photocurrent, Iph, in the solar cell model. The percentages shown in Figure 3 indicate photocurrent Iph input to the cell to be shaded. A photocurrent of 100% represents a state of no shading, and the photocurrent is the same as that of the other cells in the cell string. A value of 50% reproduces a state in which photocurrent Iph of the shaded cell is halved, that is, a state in which half of the light-receiving surface of the cell is shaded. Figure 3 shows that in both the simulation and measurement results, the output of the entire PV module changes drastically with a short-circuited failed BPD and increasing shaded area. In addition, the solar cell operates with avalanche breakdown in the low-voltage region. Real measurements were acquired with a solar radiation intensity of 600–680 W/m² and temperature of 8–12 °C. Although the measured currents are lower than the corresponding simulation results, the simulation results agree with the output of the PV module (CS-236B31).

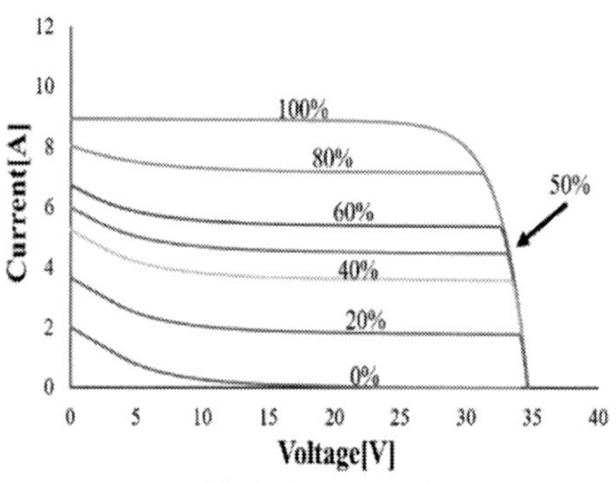

(a) Simulation Results

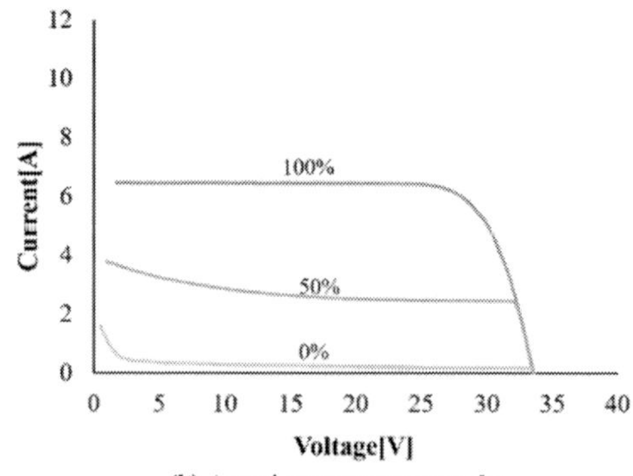

(b) Actual measurement results
Figure 3 Output characteristics of PV module containing three cell strings and BPDs with one open-circuited BPD and the solar cell in the cell string with the failed BPD being gradually shaded.

Figure 4 shows the output characteristics of a PV module that has three normal cell strings and normal BPDs when one solar cell is gradually shaded. When the shade on one solar cell in the cell string moves, the output current on the output-voltage side higher than 22 V changes. This region shows changes in the output voltage and current of the shaded cell string. Although the current is low due to the low amount of solar radiation in the real measurement, the simulation results suitably agree with the measurements.

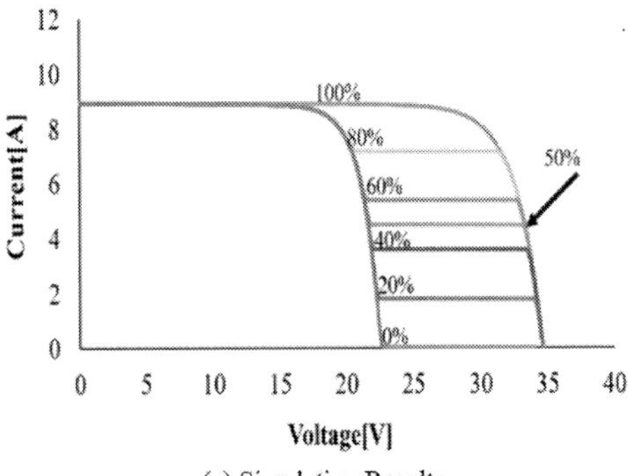

(a) Simulation Results

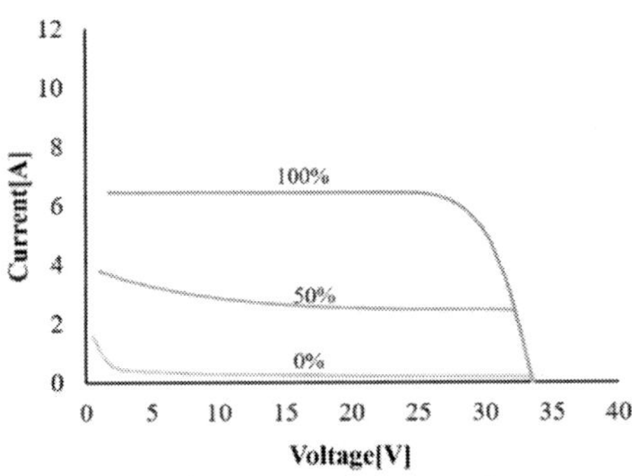

(b) Actual measurement results

Figure 4. Output characteristics of PV module containing three cell strings and BPDs with one solar cell being gradually shaded under no failure.

4 CONCLUSIONS

In this study, we proposed and validated a simulation model capable of reproducing the output characteristics of PV module strings under bypass diode (BPD) failure conditions. The model successfully reproduced the behavior of PV modules with BPDs exhibiting short-circuit failures with resistance values ranging from 0.1 to 50 Ω, as well as open-circuit failures. Furthermore, the model was also able to simulate partial shading effects in PV module strings. These results indicate that the proposed approach can serve as a useful tool for analyzing failure mechanisms and developing diagnostic methods for PV systems. Future applications of this model are expected to contribute to improving the safety, reliability, and maintainability of PV power generation systems.

Acknowledgements
This study was supported by JSPS KAKENHI (Grant No. JP21H01580).

References
[1] Ministry of Economy, Trade and Industry and Agency for Natural Resources and Energy, Japan's Energy 10 Questions for Understanding the Current Energy Situation, Tokyo, Japan, 2022.
[2] M. Koentges et al., Review of Failures of Photovoltaic Modules, Photovoltaic Power Systems Program, *Report IEA-PVPS T13-01*, 2014.
[3] T. Hamada, T. Azuma, I. Nanno, M. Fujii, N. Ishikura, S. Oke, Effect of Failure Characteristics of Bypass Diode in Photovoltaic Solar Module on Burnout, *J. Inst. Elect. Instal. Engnr. Jpn.*, 42, 2022, 16-17.
[4] T. Hamada, Tomoki Azuma, Ikuo Nanno, Norio Ishikura, Masayuki Fujii, Shinichiro Oke, Impact of Bypass Diode Fault Resistance Values on Burnout in Bypass Diode Failures in Simulated Photovoltaic Modules with Various Output Parameters, *Energies*, 16, 2023, 1-9.
[5] J.W. Bishop, Computer simulation of the effects of electrical mismatches in photovoltaic cell interconnection circuits, *Solar cells*, 25, 1988, 73-89.

EVALUATING THE EFFICACY OF NEUTRAL DENSITY FILTERS AND CAMERA LENS APERTURE FOR REDUCING SENSOR SATURATION AND INCREASE IMAGE QUALITY IN DAYLIGHT EL IMAGING

Kabir Paúl Sulca[1]*, Rodrigo del Prado Santamaria[2], Thøger Kari[2], Julian Anaya[1], Gisele Alves dos Reis Benatto[2], Sergiu Viorel Spataru[2], Oscar Martínez[1]

[1]GdS-Optronlab group, Dpto. Física de la Materia Condensada, Universidad de Valladolid, Edificio LUCIA, Paseo de Belén 19, 47011 Valladolid (Spain)

[2]DTU Electro, Technical University of Denmark (DTU), Frederiksborgvej 399, 4000 Roskilde, Denmark.

*kabirpaul.sulca@uva.es

Daylight electroluminescence (dEL) inspection using InGaAs cameras has proven to be a powerful technique for assessing the condition of photovoltaic (PV) modules in the field. Recent advancements have shown it suitable for quality control and evaluation tasks in large-scale solar installations. The quality of dEL images is crucial for accurately identifying potential defects. Therefore, it is important to determine which camera optical stack yields stronger signals in dEL imaging. Camera optical stacks typically include specialized short-wave infrared (SWIR) lenses and bandpass filters to reduce background sunlight. To further limit the light intensity reaching the sensor and prevent saturation, options include adjusting the lens iris, using neutral density (ND) filters, or reducing exposure time. The choice among these depends on system constraints. Even though reducing exposure time is the easiest way to accomplish no saturation, high exposure time reduces noise, so ND filters and the iris are interesting options independent of the camera's internal controller. This study compares the light intensity reduction methods between ND filters and iris providing higher EL and dEL image quality using signal-to-noise ratio (SNR) as metric. Two SNR metrics (SNR$_{kari}$ and SNR$_{(25)}$) are used to evaluate the configurations. We compare two setups: one using a C-RED 3 InGaAs camera with a SWIR lens (F-stop range 1.4–16) and a bandpass filter, and another using the same camera and lens fixed at F-stop 1.4 (fully open) combined with ND filters of varying transmittance (0.73 to 0.02). Indoor EL data is used to characterize light attenuation for each configuration. Subsequently, dEL images are captured under 600-800 W/m² irradiance for both setups. The results show that using the iris to reduce light intensity yields higher image quality. This is attributed to the increased depth of field resulting from a smaller optical aperture, which enhances the focus range and sharpness of the captured images. In conclusion, the study demonstrates that using a lens with an adjustable iris is more effective for dEL imaging with InGaAs cameras. This finding is valuable for optimizing optical setups to achieve high-SNR images in PV module inspections.

Keywords: Daylight Electroluminescence, InGaAs Camera, EL Signal-to-Noise Ratio, Photovoltaic Module Inspection.

1 INTRODUCTION

Photovoltaic (PV) module inspection is a critical task for ensuring the reliability and performance of PV solar energy systems [1,2]. Among the various diagnostic techniques available, daylight electroluminescence (dEL) imaging has emerged as a powerful method for detecting defects in PV modules under real-world operating conditions [3-8]. Unlike traditional electroluminescence (EL) imaging, which is typically performed indoors, dEL enables on-site inspection without the need for controlled lighting environments, making it highly suitable for large-scale solar installations.

The use of InGaAs cameras in dEL imaging has significantly enhanced the ability to capture high-quality images in the short-wave infrared (SWIR) spectrum [9-11]. However, achieving optimal image quality in daylight conditions remains a challenge, mainly due to the high noise caused by the ambient sunlight and the risk of sensor saturation, since sunlight intensity can be several orders of magnitude higher than EL intensity. Regarding the saturation problem, various optical components are employed to control the light intensity reaching the camera sensor, including neutral density (ND) filters, lens iris adjustments, and exposure time settings [10, 12].

Despite the reported use of these components, there is limited consensus on the most effective configuration for maximizing image quality while minimizing saturation. Reduced exposure time of the camera can solve directly this problem; however, using large exposure times can reduce certain types of CCD sensor noise [13]. In

particular, read out noise is not increased with exposure time [13]. For these reasons, studying the efficacy of ND filters versus lens iris adjustments in reducing light intensity and enhancing image quality is of interest for EL and dEL in PV inspections. This issue has not been thoroughly investigated, thats why this study addresses this gap by evaluating the performance of these two approaches using signal-to-noise ratio (SNR) metrics (SNR$_{(25)}$ and SNR$_{kari}$) as indicators of image quality [11].

We evaluate the efficacy of ND filters and iris through a series of controlled indoor and outdoor experiments using a C-RED 3 InGaAs camera equipped with a SWIR lens and a bandpass filter. We use the previously described asynchronous method [9,11] with a fixed frequency and injection current to have comparable images. We analyze the impact of varying F-stop and ND filter transmittance levels on image quality and defect visibility. While, in general, all results obtained show sufficiently visible details there are clear differences between both setups.

The data presented consists in indoor and outdoor EL. We then analyze the experimental intensity reduction based on the indoor EL data. Even though iris steps are measured in F-stops, we can approximate each F-stop to a transmittance value to compare the two in terms of transmittance. Then, we present how the intensity attenuation works for indoor EL. Next, we calculate SNR values for EL and dEL providing an experimental insight on the quality of the images. Finally, ray tracing simulations provide deeper insight into the quality of each setup, rather than offering only a qualitative assessment of both setups.

10.4229/EUPVSEC2025/3AV.3.23

020191-001

2 EXPERIMENTAL DESCRIPTION

This study aims to evaluate the effectiveness of two optical configurations — lens iris adjustment and ND filters — in reducing sensor saturation and improving image quality in dEL imaging of PV modules. The methodology consists of indoor EL and outdoor dEL experiments conducted with a controlled optical setup, followed by dEL image processing and quality assessment using two metrics: $SNR_{(25)}$ and SNR_{kari} [11].

2.1 Optical Setup

The experimental procedure began with the characterization of ND filters. A spectral measurement in the 900–1500 nm range was performed to determine the transmittance percentage of each ND filter.

ND filter transmittance values were obtained from manufacturer data, while equivalent transmittance values for the iris were calculated based on the F-stop formula. Since each F-stop increment halves the aperture area, it was assumed that the light intensity reaching the sensor is also halved. Two optical configurations were tested:

a) Iris-based setup: The lens aperture varied using F-stop values of 1.4, 2.0, 2.8, 4, 8, and 16. The corresponding equivalent transmittance values, calculated from the F-stop relationship, were 1.00 t, 0.50 t, 0.25 t, 0.13 t, 0.03 t, and 0.01 t, respectively. These values served as reference transmittances.

b) ND filter-based setup: A fixed F-stop of 1.4 (fully open) was used in combination with ND filters with transmittance values of 0.73, 0.51, 0.20, and 0.15. Although spectral characterization revealed slight deviations from these values, those provided by the manufacturer datasheets were used for consistency. To explore a broader range of attenuation, combinations of two filters were also tested, resulting in additional transmittance values of 0.37, 0.152, and 0.02.

EL and dEL measurements were carried out using a C-RED 3 InGaAs camera with a resolution of 640 × 512 pixels, a pixel pitch of 15 × 15 μm, 14-bit quantization, a 16-bit dynamic range, and a maximum frame rate of 600 fps. The camera was equipped with a Kowa LM25HC-SW 25 mm SWIR lens and a bandpass filter centered at 1150 nm with a 50 nm full width at half maximum (FWHM).

2.2 Indoor EL and dEL measurements

Indoor EL images were captured to characterize the light attenuation properties of each optical configuration, obtaining a low-noise reference image which has been used to establish a reference SNR value. Although obtaining high-signal EL images was not necessary, the data were processed using the asynchronous image processing method to ensure consistent noise treatment across indoor EL and outdoor dEL measurements. This approach is essential for obtaining the $SNR_{(25)}$ metric, which is defined within the asynchronous processing framework.

The modulation parameters included a modulated current forming a square wave with a frequency of 6.25 Hz and an amplitude of 9.85 A, with the camera operating at 50 fps. Three exposure times (1, 2 and 3 ms) were tested to ensure sufficient signal, particularly under high-attenuation conditions.

Daylight EL images were acquired under medium irradiance conditions (600–800 W/m²) using the same modulated dEL technique. Exposure times of 1, 2 and 3 ms were also used to assess the impact of light reduction on image quality.

2.3 Image Processing

Image processing was performed using the asynchronous dEL processing algorithm defined in [11]. This method is designed to suppress noise and obtain a denoised image. The number of sample images used to generate the final processed image was kept constant across all experiments to ensure comparability.

2.4 Image Quality Assessment

Image quality was quantified using two signal-to-noise ratio metrics: $SNR_{(25)}$ and SNR_{kari}.

a) as defined in [11], and $SNR_{(25)}$ value of above 10 is considered to be that of a high-quality image.

b) SNR_{kari}, described in [11], defines a good-quality image as one with an SNR value above 4.

Both metrics were applied to indoor and outdoor datasets to compare the performance of the iris-based and ND filter-based configurations.

2.5 Ray tracing simulations

Ray-tracing simulations were performed using the Optiland Python library. These simulations only model geometric optics and do not account for the wave nature of light or diffraction effects. The simulation uses the lens described in [14], with an initial F-stop of 2.0.

The ray-tracing model calculated the geometric light paths using ideal materials with refractive indices matching those of the actual lens. A 2D ray path was generated with y representing height and z the optical axis. Three-point light sources were simulated from an object plane located 2000 mm from the lens (z = −2000 mm). It was assumed the PV module to be parallel to the sensor, with (0, 0) corresponding to the center of both the panel and the sensor. The three source points were defined as follows:

- Point 1: (0, 0, −2000) mm.
- Point 2: (0, 550, −2000) mm.
- Point 3: (1100, 550, −2000) mm.

The x–y projection of the rays passing through the simulated lens onto the sensor plane was then plotted, and the number of rays reaching the sensor was quantified.

3 RESULTS AND DISCUSSION

3.1 Filter characterization

To ensure the quality and consistency of the intensity reduction provided by each ND filter, a spectral characterization was performed over the 900–1700 nm range. Ideally, the filters should exhibit approximately linear transmittance reduction behavior.

Figure 1 shows the measured counts across the spectral range and the corresponding relative transmittance (t), calculated relative to the "no filter" case.

We then compared the measured transmittance values with those provided by the manufacturer, as shown in Figure 2. Since the EL emission of the Si PV modules is centered around 1150 nm, particular attention was given to this wavelength. The measured transmittance values were found to be slightly lower than those reported in the manufacturer's datasheet.

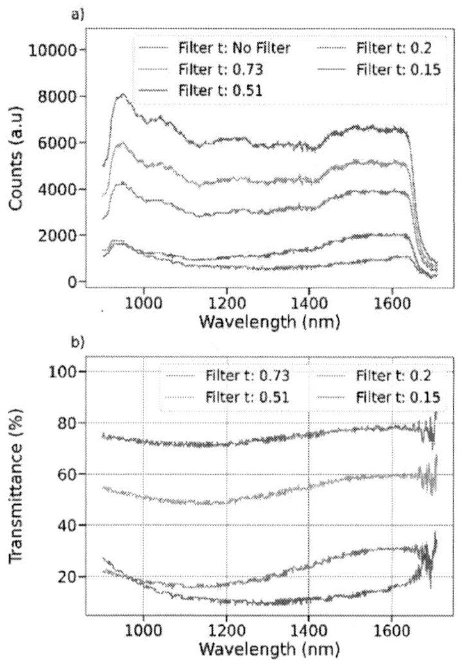

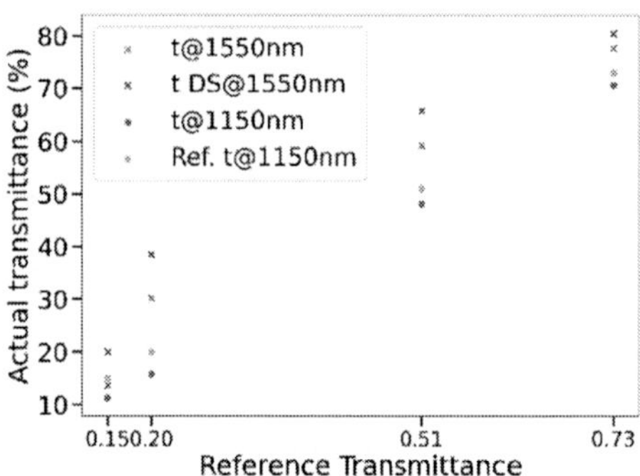

Figure 1: Filter transmittance in the 900-1700 nm range: a) counts (a.u), b) relative transmittance.

Figure 2: Reference transmittance vs measured transmittance percentage.

Since no significant differences were observed between the measured and reference transmittance values at 1150 nm, the reference values from the datasheet were used for subsequent analyses.

3.2 Indoor EL

An indoor dataset was acquired using both optical configurations: iris adjustment and ND filters. Figure 3 shows the EL images obtained under comparable conditions — 0.13 t (F-stop 4) for the iris and 0.15 t for the ND filter. The image captured with the iris shows uniform brightness and sharper detail, which improves visibility of small defects. The uniform brightness improvement can be attributed to reduced vignetting when the optical aperture is decreased. Vignetting is commonly caused by internal lens components. On the other hand, a sharper image can be attributed to an increase in depth of field and a reduction in optical artefacts due to the light's geometrical paths

within the lens's internal arrangement . These F-stop effects are explored further in the simulation section.

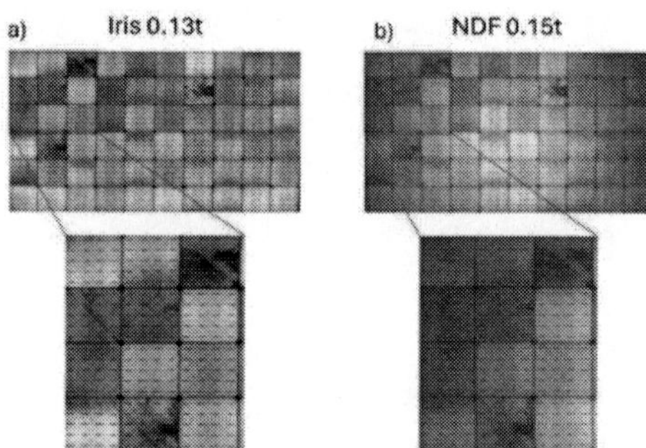

Figure 3: Indoor EL image at 1 ms exposure time for a) 0.13 t iris aperture and b) 0.15 t ND filter

To analyze the behavior of light intensity reduction, the average pixel intensity was plotted as a function of transmittance (Figure 4). Both the iris and ND filters were found to effectively reduce the signal received by the sensor. Tests were conducted with exposure times of 1, 2 and 3 ms. A linear relationship was observed in the case of the ND filter (Figure 4b), whereas the iris case (Figure 4a) deviated from linearity, likely due to the simplifications made when estimating the equivalent transmittance.

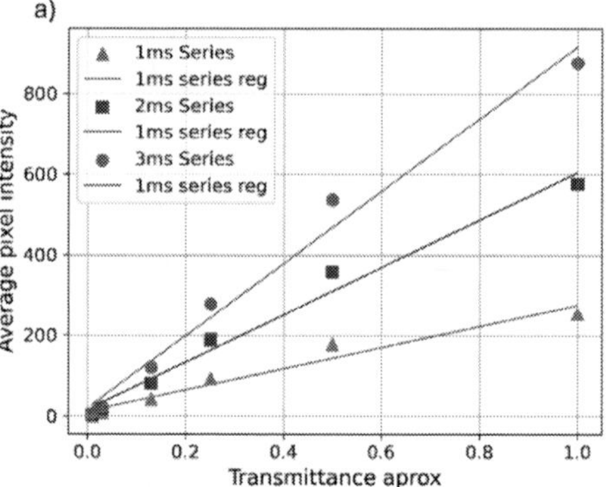

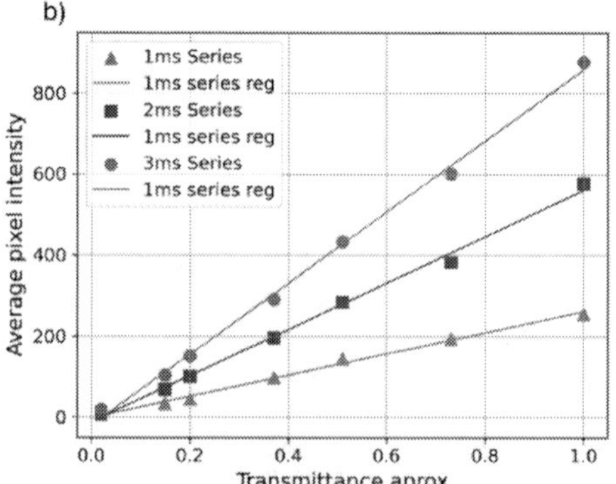

Figure 4: Average pixel intensity for a) iris aperture and b) ND filter, for 1, 2 and 3 ms exposure times

Next, we computed and plotted both SNR metrics for the indoor dataset (Figure 5). The iris configuration consistently produced higher SNR values than the ND filter configuration. Interestingly, Figure 5b shows that the $SNR_{(25)}$ is higher at 0.5 transmittance (F-stop 2.0) than at 1.0 transmittance (F-stop 1.4). This suggests that the noise introduced by optical artefacts at larger apertures exceeds the contribution expected from a 50% reduction in signal. Regarding SNR_{kari}, this metric is less informative at high signal levels, as it was designed to address low-signal noise behavior.

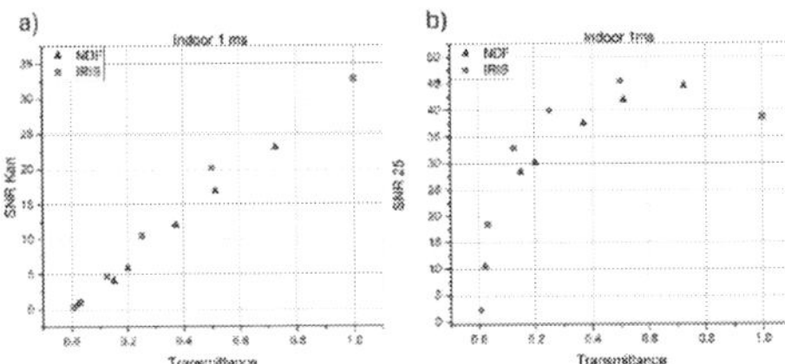

Figure 5: Indoor EL SNR for iris vs ND filter for 1 ms exposure time: a) SNR_{kari}, b) SNR_{25}.

3.2 dEL measurements

Daylight EL images were acquired and processed using the asynchronous method [11] under medium irradiance conditions (600–800 W/m²). Figure 6 shows the dEL images captured with a 1 ms exposure time for both configurations under similar conditions. While both images reveal most defects, the ND filter image exhibits vignetting, whereas the iris-based image shows sharper details and more uniform brightness, consistent with the indoor results.

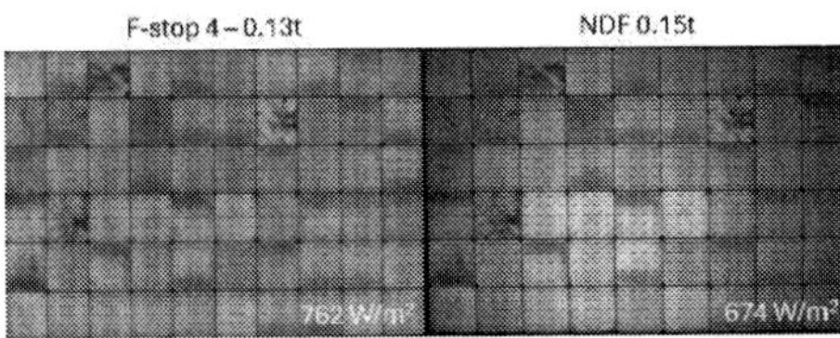

Figure 6: Daylight EL images obtained for similar intensity reductions using the iris (0.13 t) and the ND filter (0.15 t)

To quantitatively compare image quality, SNR metrics were computed for both setups (Figure 7). The iris configuration yielded higher SNR values, indicating stronger signals and better image quality. This can again be partially attributed to vignetting, as regions with lower intensity are interpreted as low-signal regions by the SNR metrics. Additionally, the same trend observed in the indoor experiments was reproduced: SNR values were higher at 0.5 transmittance (F-stop 2.0) and lower at 1.0 (F-stop 1.4). This supports the conclusion that, for the highest aperture, optical artefacts introduce more noise than signal is gained.

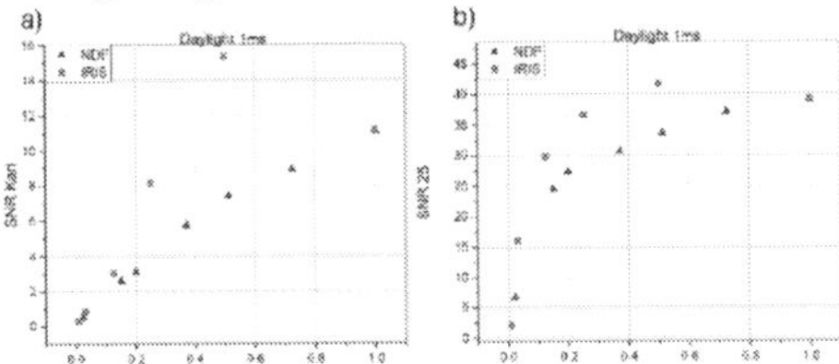

Figure 7: dEL SNR for iris vs ND filter for 1 ms exposure time: a) SNR_{kari}, b) SNR_{25}.

Overall, for both EL and dEL measurements, despite their methodological differences, both SNR metrics consistently indicate superior image quality when using the iris for all similar transmittance values. Higher SNR values indicate better data quality and more reliable signal detection from the images of the PV modules.

3.3 Ray tracing simulations

The simulation focused on three points of the PV module, as illustrated in Figure 8, with rays traced individually from each source point.

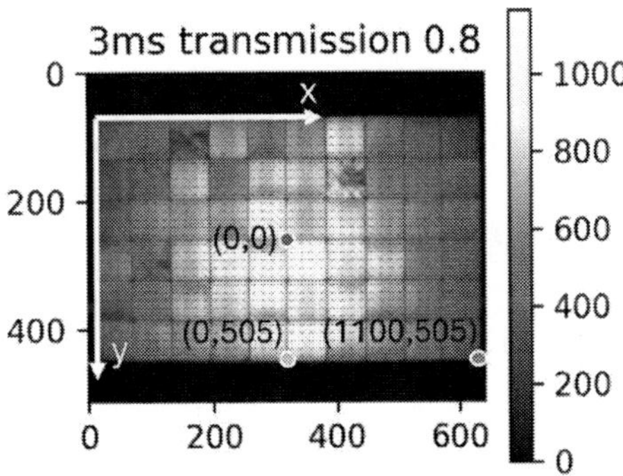

Figure 8: Ray tracing simulation source points scheme

We will study the rays reaching the final surface (sensor) only for the iris case because adding NDF to this kind of simulations will only linearly reduce the intensity without affecting the geometry of the setup. Figure 9 shows the (y,z) graph depicting the lens construction for a F-stop of 2.0 and the rays originating from the source points. We can observe the blue rays passing through the system from point (0,0), the orange rays from the point (0,550), and the green rays from the point (1100,550). We can also see the internal lens optic representation and sensor placement.

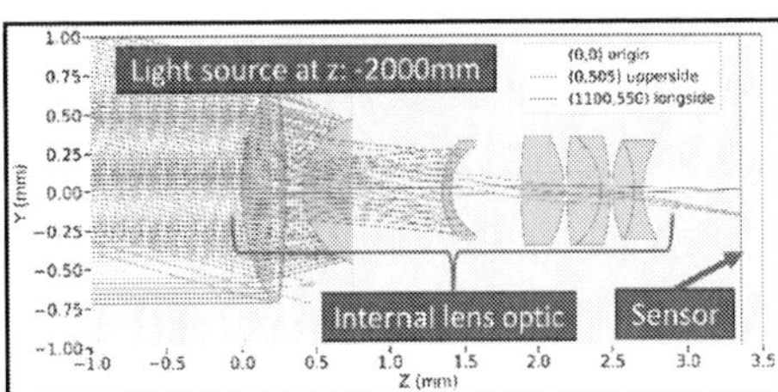

Figure 9: (y,z) internal optics and ray representations

An (x, y) projection of the sensor surface is shown in Figure 10, with normalized coordinates Hx and Hy. Normalization was performed relative to the longest sensor dimension.

We use the spot projection over the sensor to count the number of rays that reach the surface. We then make calculations for different F-stop values and plot the resultant rays that reach the sensor. Figure 11 shows the number of rays reaching the spot. The number of rays shows the expected tendency: a higher number of rays come from the origin, fewer from (0,550) and the fewest from the corner (1100,550). We can also observe that the difference between the sources is reduced when the aperture is closed; this is the same experimental pattern of reduced vignetting.

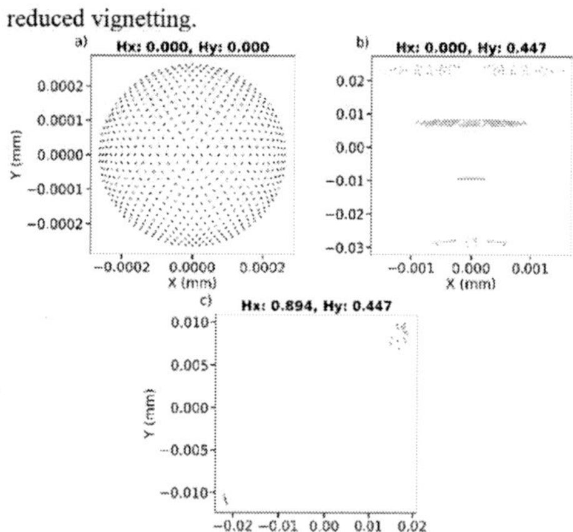

Figure 10: (x,y) ray tracing spot over sensor

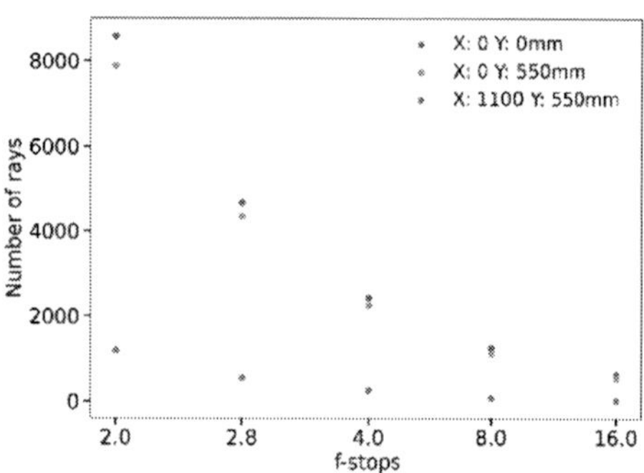

Figure 11: Number of rays for F-stops ranging from 2.0 to 16.0

To examine the vignetting effect further, a profile plot was generated along the x-direction from (0, 550) to (1100, 550) (Figure 12). The slope increases towards the sensor edges but decreases with smaller apertures.

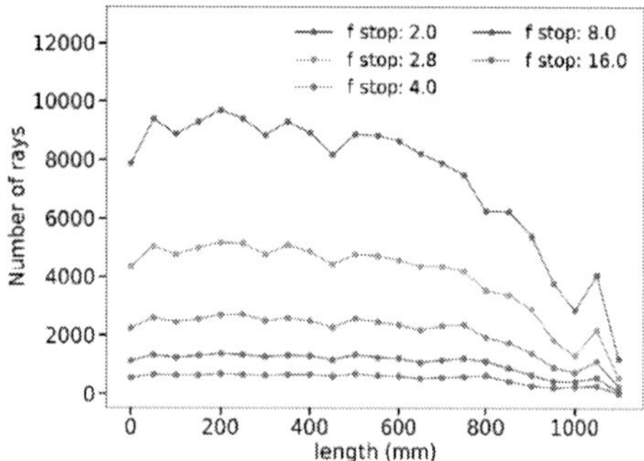

Figure 12: Profile plot for iris simulation

Lastly, we can observe the experimental profile plot in Figure 13. Half of the image is profiled, centered on the y-axis and along the x-axis. Notice how reducing the iris aperture flattens the reduction in intensity at the edges, whereas this does not happen as much with the neutral density filter.

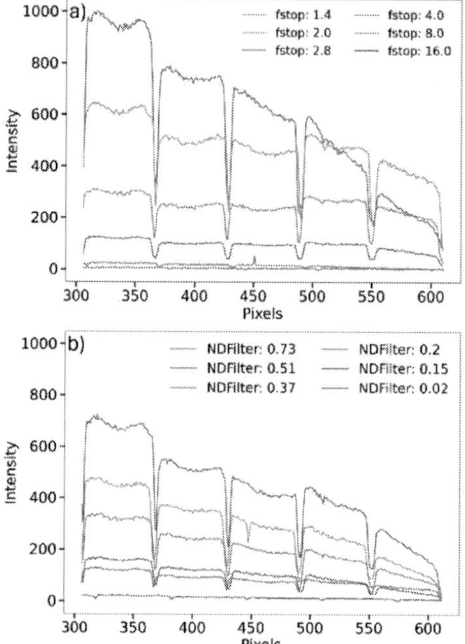

Figure 13: Experimental profile plot for F-stops (a) and ND filters (b)

4 CONCLUSIONS

This study systematically evaluated the effectiveness of neutral density (ND) filters versus lens iris adjustments in reducing sensor saturation and enhancing image quality in EL and dEL imaging of PV modules using InGaAs cameras. Through a combination of indoor EL characterization, outdoor dEL measurements, and ray tracing simulations, we demonstrated that adjusting the lens iris consistently yields superior image quality compared to using ND filters.

The comparative analysis revealed several important findings. First, adjusting the lens iris consistently produced higher SNR values across both SNR_{25} and SNR_{kari} metrics, indicating superior image quality and reduced noise. This improvement is attributed to the increased depth of field and reduced optical artefacts which can be related to the noise of the image and reduced vignetting associated with the signal. This results in enhanced image sharpness and uniformity. Second, ray tracing simulations supported these observations by showing that closing the iris leads to more evenly distributed light across the sensor, minimizing edge losses and optical artefacts. Third, the characterization of ND filters revealed discrepancies between manufacturer-stated and actual transmittance values, particularly at lower transmittance levels, which may introduce inconsistencies in image quality. Taken together, these findings demonstrate that iris-based light attenuation not only improves image clarity but also ensures more reliable and consistent imaging performance in both EL and dEL applications.

5 ACKNOWLEDGMENTS

This work has been funded by the Spanish Ministry of Science and Innovation, under project PID2023-148369OB-C43, financed by MICIU/AEI /10.13039/501100011033 and FEDER/UE, and by the Regional Government of Castilla y León (Junta de Castilla y León) and by the Ministry of Science and Innovation and the European Union NextGenerationEU / PRTR under the project "Programa Complementario de Materiales Avanzados". K. Sulca has been funded under the call for predoctoral contracts UVa 2022, co-financed by Banco Santander.

6 REFERENCES

[1] L. Koester, S. Lindig, A. Louwen, A. Astigarraga, G. Manzolini, D. Moser, Renew. Sustain. Energy Rev. 165 (2022) 112616.

[2] I. Høiaas, K. Grujic, A. Gerd, I. Burud, E. Olsen, N. Belbachir, Renew. Sustain. Energy Rev. 161 (2022) 112353.

[3] L. Stoicescu, M. Reuter, J.H. Werner, Proceedings 29th Eur. Photovolt. Sol. Energy Conf. Exhib., (2014) 2553.

[4] J. Adams, B. Doll, C. Buerhop, T. Pickel, J. Teubner, C. Camus, C.J. Brabec, Proceedings 32nd Eur. Photovolt. Sol. Energy Conf. Exhib., (2015) 1837.

[5] S. Koch, T. Weber, C. Sobottka, A. Fladung, P. Clemens, J. Berghold, Proceedings 32nd Eur. Photovolt. Sol. Energy Conf. Exhib., (2016) 1736.

[6] G.A. dos Reis Benatto, N. Riedel, S. Thorsteinsson, P.B. Poulsen, A. Thorseth, C. Dam-Hansen, C. Mantel, S. Forchhammer, K.H.B. Frederiksen, J. Vedde, M. Petersen, H. Voss, M. Messerschmidt, H. Parikh, S. Spataru, D. Sera, Proceedings 44th IEEE Photovolt. Specialist Conf., (2017) 2682.

[7] M. Guada, A. Moretón, S. Rodríguez-Conde, L.A. Sánchez, M. Martínez, M.A. González, J. Jiménez, L. Pérez, V. Parra, O. Martínez, Energy Science & Engineering 8 (2020) 3839.

[8] O. Kunz, J. Schlipf, A. Fladung, Y.S. Khoo, K. Bedrich, T. Trupke, Z. Hameiri, Prog. Energy 4 (2022) 042014.

[9] C. Terrados, D. G. Francés, J. Anaya, K.P. Sulca, V. Gómez-Alonso, M. A. González, O. Martínez, Daylight Photoluminescence of Silicon Solar Panels In Operation by Electrical Modulation, Proceedings of the 40th EUPVSEC, Vol I (2023) 258.

[10] Dhimish, M., & Tyrrell, A. M., Optical Filter Design for Daylight Outdoor Electroluminescence Imaging of PV Modules. In Photonics, Vol. 11, No. 1, p. 63 (2024). MDPI.

[11] G. A. dos Reis Benatto, T. Kari, R. del Prado Santamaría, S. V. Spataru, C. Terrados, D. G. Francés, J. Anaya, K. P. Sulca, V. Gómez-Alonso, M. A. González, O. Martínez, Daylight Electroluminescence Imaging Methodology Comparison, Proceedings of the the 40th EUPVSEC Vol I (2023) 374.

[12] G. A. dos Reis Benatto, T. Kari, R. del Prado Santamaría, A. Mahmood, L. Stoicescu, S. V. Spataru, Evaluation Of Daylight Filters For Electroluminescence Imaging Inspections Of C-Si Pv Modules, Proceedings of the 41st EUPVSEC, Vol I (2024) 2163

[13] Fellers, T. J., and M. W. Davidson. Concepts in Digital Imaging Technology, CCD Noise Sources and Signal-to-Noise Ratio. (2010).

[14] Laikin, M. Lens Design. Optical science and engineering series, 4th ed, (2007) 101.

DESIGN, MANUFACTURING AND ANALYSIS OF ALUMINIUM-BACKED BIPV FACADE MODULES: ELECTRICAL PERFORMANCE AND OUTDOOR TESTS

Sophia Jahreis, Bengt Jaeckel, Ringo Koepge, Jens Froebel, Paul Schenk, Matthias Pander
Fraunhofer-Center for Silicon-Photovoltaics (CSP), Halle (Saale), Germany
bengt.jaeckel@csp.fraunhofer.de

ABSTRACT: In driving the energy transition, the building sector plays a major role, with facades offering considerable but still underutilized potential for photovoltaic integration. Building-integrated photovoltaics (BIPV) enable a dual use of facades as energy generators and building envelopes, while aluminium as a backing material provides robustness and architectural flexibility. However, vertical installation exposes modules to non-standard operating conditions, including variable irradiance, partial shading, and diverse orientations, which directly affect their energy yield. In this work, aluminium-backed BIPV facade modules were evaluated through laboratory characterisation and one year of outdoor monitoring in a multi-oriented test setup, enabling direct comparison of north-, east-, south-, and west-facing facades under real operating conditions. A systematic data filtering procedure was applied to ensure reliable analysis of electrical parameters, irradiance, and module temperatures, providing a robust basis for performance analysis for performance analysis of the aluminium-backed BIPV facade modules and for validating simulation models. The results highlight pronounced orientation-dependent behaviour: the south-facing facade achieved the highest yields, peaking around the equinoxes, while east and west reached roughly three-quarters and north about one-third of the south-facing output. Seasonal trends reflect the solar geometry, with east and west peaking around the summer solstice. Slight but consistent east–west differences were linked to temperature effects, as confirmed by measured module temperatures. Combining multiple orientations potentially smooth generation across the day, reduce summer midday peaks, and align output more closely with building demand.

Keywords: Building-Integrated Photovoltaics (BIPV), Facade-Integrated Photovoltaics (FIPV), Aluminium-backed modules, Outdoor performance monitoring, Multi-orientation analysis

1 INTRODUCTION

Driving the energy transition requires contributions from the building sector, where the integration of photovoltaic systems into facades offers considerable potential. [1] In this context, building-integrated photovoltaics provide a dual function by generating renewable energy on-site while simultaneously serving the structural and aesthetic roles of conventional construction materials. Aluminium-backed BIPV modules combine robustness, durability, and architectural flexibility, which makes them attractive for facade applications. However, in contrast to conventional roof-mounted or ground-mounted PV systems, facade installations operate under non-standard conditions: the vertical arrangement results in diverse orientations, combined with variable irradiance, thermal stresses due to the installation situation and limited rear ventilation, and frequent partial shading, all of which strongly affect the energy yield. [2–7]

Accurate assessment of innovative BIPV module layouts requires not only laboratory characterisation but also outdoor measurements under real operating conditions. Such field data are essential to evaluate long-term performance, capture orientation-specific effects, and provide a reliable basis for validating simulation models. In particular, multi-orientation outdoor datasets enable a more realistic understanding of the energy contribution facades can provide and support the optimisation of system design and yield predictions.

2 MATERIAL AND METHODS

To assess the real-world performance of aluminium-backed BIPV facade modules, module samples were manufactured and installed on a multi-orientated outdoor test setup for long-term monitoring. The following section details the module layout, the configuration of the outdoor installation, and the methods used for data collection and processing applied in this work.

2.1 Module samples

The aluminium-backed BIPV facade modules consist of multiple functional layers, summarized in Table 1 and visualized in Figure 1. The base layer is a premanufactured coloured aluminium facade panel, which provides both mechanical rigidity and architectural flexibility.

Table 1: Layer structure of the aluminium-backed BIPV facade modules.

	Material
7	Low-iron, tempered glass, 3mm thickness
5	12 PERC M6 half-cells with electrically conductive adhesive interconnection
3	Insulation layer (MPE)
2,4,6	Encapsulant (POE)
1	Premanufactured, coloured aluminium facade panels

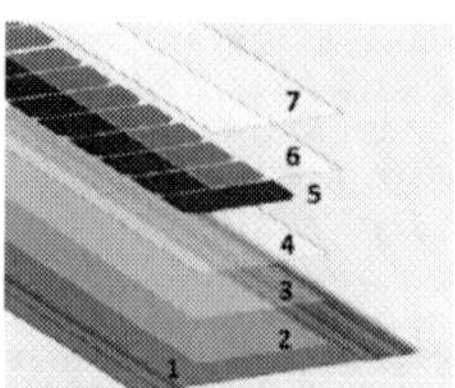

Figure 1: Schematic illustration of the layer structure of the modules.

To electrically isolate the solar cells from the conductive aluminium, a modified polyester (MPE) insulation layer was embedded between additional polyolefin elastomer (POE) encapsulant sheets. The photovoltaic part consists of 12 M6 PERC half-cells arranged with 2 mm cell spacing. A configuration with 9 busbars was combined with electrically conductive adhesive (ECA) for lead-free interconnection. The stack is completed with a low-iron tempered glass front, ensuring both mechanical protection and high optical transmission.

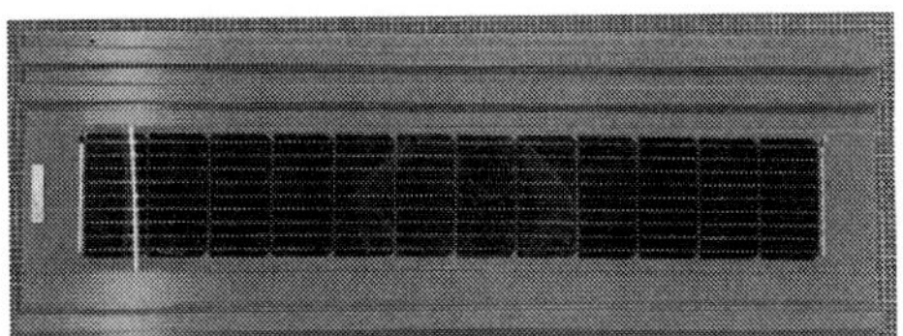

Figure 2: BIPV facade module with all electrical connections located on the rear side of the aluminium panel.

Electrical connections were positioned on the rear side of the aluminium panel to allow a flat facade integration without visible wiring (Fig. 2). Each module has a nominal power of $34.63 \pm 0.14\% \, Wp$ with dimensions of $1180 \times 420 \, mm$.

2.2 Outdoor test setup

The outdoor test setup represents a small-scale building with vertical PV facades oriented towards North, East, South, and West. Each wall comprises four aluminium-backed BIPV modules (Fig. 3), connected in series with four bypass diodes, resulting in an installed capacity of 135 Wp per orientation.

Figure 3: Outdoor test setup on the rooftop of the Fraunhofer CSP with minimal environmental shading.

Continuous monitoring covers key electrical parameters, orientation-specific in-plane irradiance, and both modules back-side and ambient temperatures. The modules are mounted on an aluminium profile substructure, while distribution boxes and measurement instrumentation are placed inside the setup (Fig. 4). This configuration enables simultaneous performance evaluation of all orientations under real outdoor conditions.

Figure 4: Outdoor test setup from the inside with module instrumentation (temperature and irradiance sensors) and distribution boxes for each orientation

2.3 Method

Based on this setup, long-term monitoring was carried out, recording electrical parameters ($I_{SC}, V_{OC}, I_{mpp}, V_{mpp}$), in-plane irradiance ($Irr$), and thermal behaviour (T_{mod}) every 10 seconds for each orientation. For data selection, only measurements with irradiance above 10 W/m^2 were considered, and it was verified that the module temperature remained below 60 °C throughout the monitoring period.

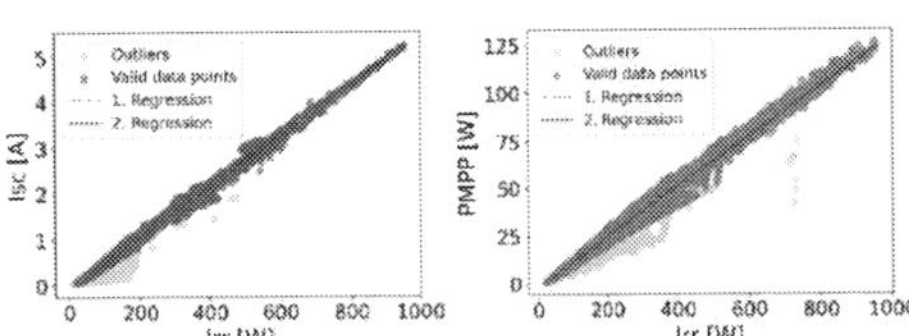

Figure 5: Filtering via linear regression (example: East facade, Aug 2024).

The selected data were further processed by orientation and aggregated on a monthly basis. A two-step linear regression filter was applied to Irr versus I_{SC} and Irr versus P_{mpp}, which is examplarily visualised in Fig. 5 for the East facade in August 2024. This procedure served to exclude inconsistent data points and improve the robustness of the dataset by identifying values that significantly deviated from the expected linear relationship under certain irradiance conditions. Since raw measurements can contain faulty entries, data were systematically checked to remove implausible records, for example cases where energy yield values were logged without corresponding irradiance data. [8]

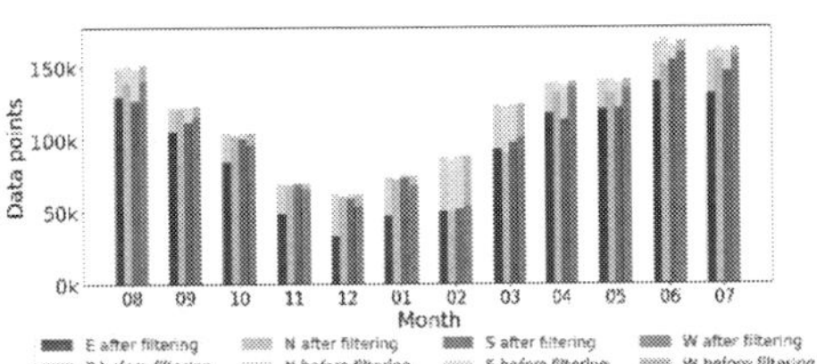

Figure 6: Number of data points above 10 W/m^2 irradiance before and after filtering.

To check the effect of the filtering procedure, the number of data points above 10 W/m^2 irradiance was compared before and after filtering for each orientation and month (Fig. 6). As expected, fewer data points are available during the winter months due to the shorter sunshine duration compared to summer.

In addition, the dataset was cleaned by removing data corresponding to system outages or scheduled maintenance periods, which mainly occurred on a few days in February, March, and May 2025. Measurement gaps were also excluded for the times when the modules were re-flashed under standard test conditions (STC) in the laboratory to verify that no performance degradation had occurred. These checks were conducted in February 2025 and September 2025, as illustrated in Figure 7.

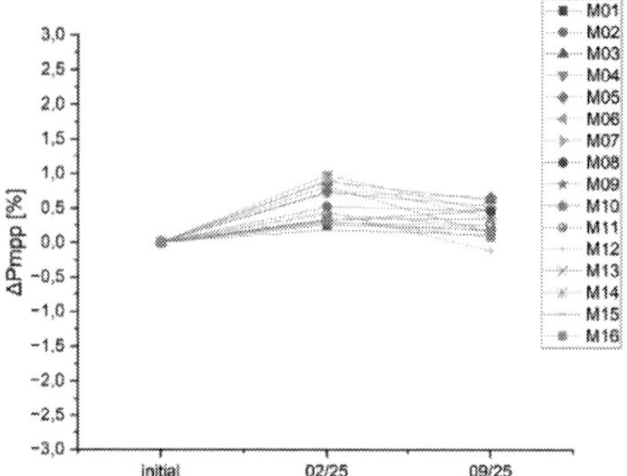

Figure 7: **Verification of stable STC performance of the 16 identical BIPV facade modules. ΔP_{mpp} shows no power degradation of the modules, with deviations remaining within measurement tolerance.**

Figure 6 also highlights the proportion of excluded data points, which varies with orientation and season. A noticeably higher fraction was removed for the East facade during autumn and winter. To verify that these outliers were not caused by systematic shading, the filtered data were further examined using heat maps, as exemplarily shown for the East facade in August 2024 (Fig. 8).

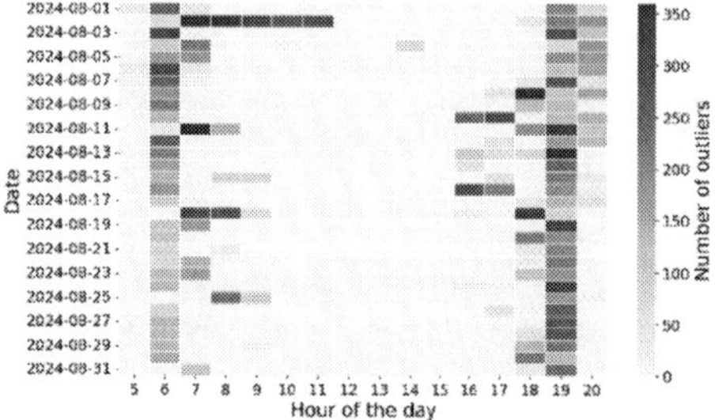

Figure 8: **Outlier heat map (example: East facade, Aug 2024).**

The analysis confirmed that no persistent shading occurred; most rejected points corresponded to low-irradiance conditions in the early morning, late evening, or on overcast days with diffuse light. For the East facade, data points were excluded due to locally induced reflections of the surrounding under diffuse conditions, which were shown to have only a negligible impact on the overall energy yield.

3 RESULTS

In the following, the results from the one-year measurement period (August 2024 to July 2025) are presented to illustrate the behaviour of the different orientations on daily, monthly, and annual scales.

3.1 Daily power profiles

The power profiles on selected days illustrate the seasonal behaviour of the different orientations (Fig. 9). Representative clear-sky days around the solstices and equinoxes reveal the seasonal variation of the facades. The east- and west-facing modules reach their highest overall power output around the summer solstice, while the south-facing facade shows its lowest seasonal contribution during this period. Towards the winter solstice, the output of the east and west facades decreases to its minimum, whereas the south-orientated modules provide the main share of the output. The north-facing facade contributes only marginally but measurable, mainly through diffuse irradiance and, during summer, direct irradiance in the early morning and late evening.

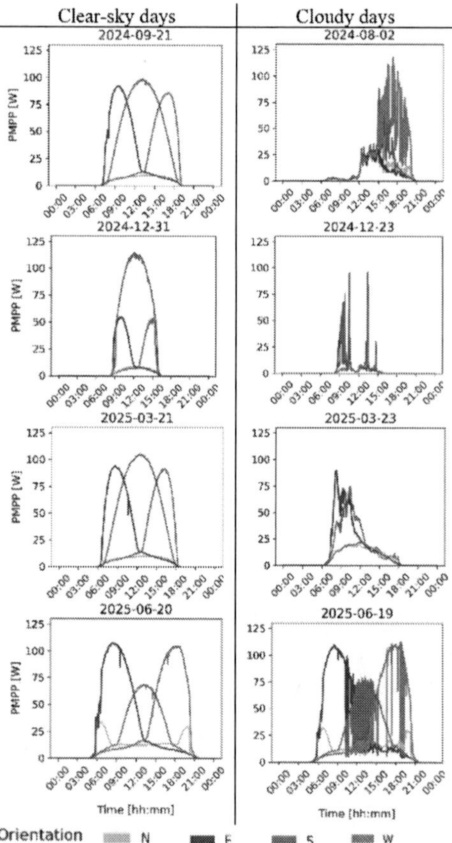

Figure 9: **P_{mpp} – Plot of the different orientations on selected days throughout the year.**

On 31 December, the south-facing modules exhibited higher power than predicted by clear-sky simulations [9], which are attributed to enhanced albedo from snow reflections and illustrates one of the possible factors causing deviations between simulations and real outdoor data. A slightly higher output is often observed for the east-facing modules compared to the west-facing ones. This effect is linked to temperature differences, as confirmed by the measured T_{mod}: modules remain cooler in the morning but heat up over the course of the day, resulting in higher afternoon operating temperatures and correspondingly reduced power output. Overall, compared to the STC rating of 135 Wp, the vertical facades still achieve substantial output under real outdoor conditions. On cloudy days, the profiles are less distinct and more irregular due to passing clouds, yet the orientation-dependent trends remain visible.

The different orientations of facades within a single building offer the potential to combine multiple BIPV surfaces, distributing power generation more evenly throughout the day and mitigating pronounced midday peaks, particularly in summer. When compared with representative household and industrial load profiles [10], such aggregated generation patterns indicate a closer alignment with demand, thereby enhancing the potential for self-consumption through multi-oriented BIPV facades.

3.2 Monthly specific energy yield analysis

The monthly specific energy yields reflect the behaviour observed in the daily power profiles, translating these into the seasonal trends of energy yield for the different orientations. (Fig. 10). The east- and west-facing facades follow a similar trend, with maximum yields around the summer solstice. The north-facing facade shows the same seasonal behaviour but with substantially lower values, reflecting its limited irradiance capture.

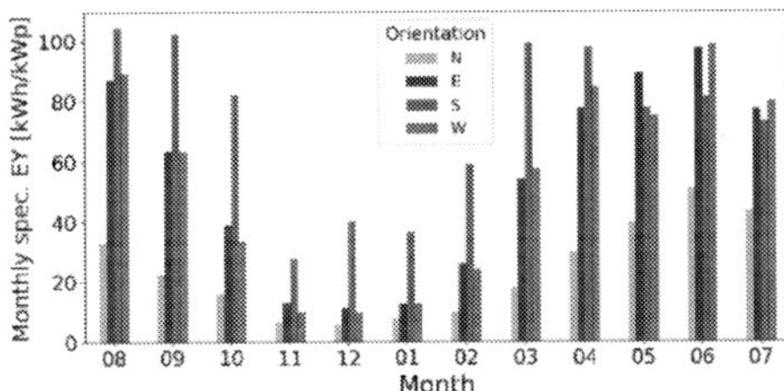

Figure 10: Monthly specific energy yield (EY) per orientation.

The south-facing facade exhibits distinct seasonal pattern: yields rise in autumn, peak around the equinoxes, decrease during winter, increase again in spring, and decline towards the summer solstice. Compared to the east and west facades, the south-facing facade shows a smaller amplitude between maximum and minimum monthly yields, resulting in a more consistent seasonal profile. This behaviour reflects the irradiance distribution across the year, with the equinoxes providing the most favourable solar geometry for vertical south-facing modules.

3.3 Yearly specific energy yield analysis

The annual comparison of specific energy yields reflects the share of the different orientations accumulated over one year (Fig. 11). As expected, the south facade provides the highest output and is set as the reference with 100%. The east- and west-facing facades achieve 74% and 72% of this value, respectively, showing that they contribute a substantial share of the annual yield despite their less favourable orientation. The north facade reaches 32% of the south reference, reflecting its limited irradiance but still adding a measurable share to the overall building-integrated generation.

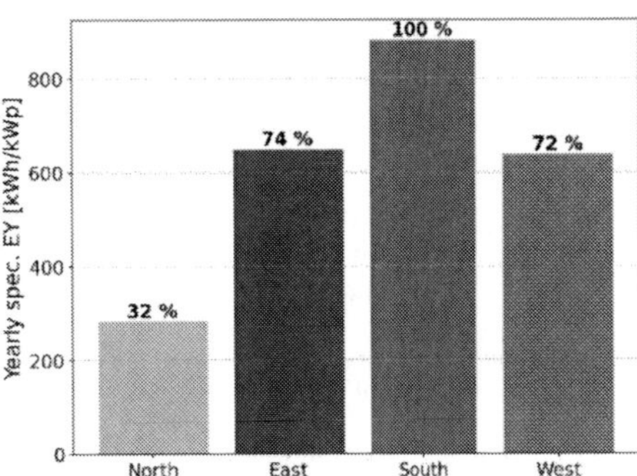

Figure 11: Annual yields, normalized to South facade (100%), Aug 2024 – Jul 2025.

4   SUMMARY AND OUTLOOK

Aluminium-backed BIPV facade modules were designed, manufactured, and evaluated under long-term monitoring in an outdoor test setup with four orientations. The resulting outdoor data provide a solid basis for validating simulation models, as they reflect the real-world performance of the modules and allow more reliable assessment of their behaviour under operating conditions. The applied data filtering ensured reliable input for performance analysis by excluding inconsistent or faulty measurements. The results from one year of monitoring highlight pronounced orientation-dependent behaviour across daily and seasonal, and scales.

The south-facing modules achieves its highest energy yields around the equinoxes, while the east- and west facades peak around the summer solstice. The north-facing modules shows a similar seasonal course to the east and west facades, but at significantly lower yield levels. Over the full year, the south-facing modules provided the highest output, with east and west reaching roughly three quarters and the north about one third of the south-facing yield. The small but consistent differences between east and west are mainly attributable to temperature effects, as confirmed by measured T_{mod}.

By combining modules of different orientations, the resulting generation profile would be more evenly spread across the day, mitigating pronounced midday peaks and thus potentially supporting grid stability. Alternatively, such a configuration could better match building load profiles, enhancing opportunities for self-consumption.

5   ACKNOWLEDGEMENT

Financial support by the Federal Ministry for Economic Affairs and Energy funded project "AluPV" (FKZ: 03EN1069B) is gratefully acknowledged.

6   REFERENCES

[1]   Behnisch M. Electricity from the house wall – the great potential of building facades to capture solar energy: Leibnitz Institute of Ecological Urban and Regional Development, 2021. https://www.ioer.de/en/press/news/electricity-from-the-house-wall-the-great-potential-of-building-facades-to-capture-solar-energy, accessed [08/25]

[2]   Biyik E. et al., "A key review of building integrated photovoltaic (BIPV) systems", Engineering Science and

Technology, Vol. 20 ,3, pp. 833–58, 2017,
https://doi.org/10.1016/j.jestch.2017.01.009

[3]   Martín-Chivelet N. et al., "Building-Integrated
Photovoltaic (BIPV) products and systems: A review of
energy-related behavior" Energy and Buildings, Vol. 262,
111998, 2022,
https://doi.org/10.1016/j.enbuild.2022.111998

[4]   Kuhn T. E. et al., "Review of technological design options
for building integrated photovoltaics (BIPV)", Energy and
Buildings, Vol. 231, 110381, 2021,
https://doi.org/10.1016/j.enbuild.2020.110381

[5]   Köhl M. et al., "Effect of thermal insulation of the back
side of PV modules in the module temperature", Progress
in Photovoltaics, Vol. 24, 9, pp. 1194–1199, 2016,
https://doi.org/10.1002/pip.2773

[6]   Quest H. et al., "Towards a quantification of thermal and
thermomechanical stress for modules in building-
integrated photovoltaics configurations", Progress in
Photovoltaics, Vol. 33, 1, pp.64-75, 2023
https://doi.org/10.1002/pip.3762

[7]   Calcabrini A. et al., "Simulation study of the electrical
yield of various PV module topologies in partially shaded
urban scenarios", Solar Energy, Vol. 225, pp. 726–733,
2021, https://doi.org/10.1016/j.solener.2021.07.061

[8]   Jaeckel B. et al., "Utilizing System Efficiency Evaluations
to Determine DC Output of PV Systems", 8th WCPEC,
2022,
10.4229/WCPEC-82022-4BV.5.37

[9]   Jahreis S. et al., "Design, manufacturing, and performance
of innovative aluminium-backed BIPV facade modules: a
case-study in Germany", Energy and Buildings, Vol. 344,
2025, https://doi.org/10.1016/j.enbuild.2025.116047

[10]   Open Power System Data, "Household Data (version
2020-04-15)", Open Power System Data platform,
https://data.open-power-system-
data.org/household_data/2020-04-15/, accessed [08/25]

ANALYSIS OF THE EFFECTS OF PARTIAL SHADING ON CELL PERFORMANCE IN A HALF-CUT CELL PHOTOVOLTAIC MODULE

Poland Michael[1,2], Monphias Vumbugwa[1], E. Ernest van Dyk[1], Frederik J. Vorster[1], Petja Dobreva[2]
[1]Department of Physics, Nelson Mandela University, Port Elizabeth, South Africa
[2]Department of Physics, Chemistry & Material Science, University of Namibia, Windhoek, Namibia
E-mail address: s227745558@mandela.ac.za

ABSTRACT: Half-cut cell photovoltaic (PV) modules have become increasingly popular in today's solar market, offering improved efficiency and reduced power losses compared to standard full-cell modules. These modules aim to reduce electrical losses and improve performance under real-world conditions. The unique structure and configuration of these modules introduce complexities when operating under real-world conditions, especially under partial shading conditions. This study investigates the effects of partial shading on the electrical and thermal characteristics of individual cells in a half-cut cell PV module. Measurements of individual cell voltages, substring currents, and module currents were taken under various shading conditions using a custom-made set-up. Partial shading caused a current mismatch and reduced the voltage across the shaded cell causing an increase in the operational voltages and temperatures of the unshaded cells connected in series with the shaded cell, and a decrease in the voltage of the shaded cell. Fully shading a single cell causes the parallel unshaded substring pair to operate at the same voltage under near short-circuit conditions, resulting in reverse biasing of some cells in the unshaded substring. The results also show that the thermal characteristics of the unshaded cells in the parallel substring may be affected by the partially shaded cell. These findings aid in understanding the effects that partial shading has on the electrical and thermal characteristics of half-cut cell modules and in the interpretation of their thermal images. It was noted that, if substrings were optimized to operate at their individual MPPs, a shaded cell would not become reverse-biased, even with significant shading. It is important to note that module-level optimization doesn't always translate to optimal substring operation.

Keywords: Individual cells, Half-cut cell module, Partial shading, Thermal image, Performance

1 INTRODUCTION

Half-cut cell PV modules are a newer design of PV modules, considered to be an improvement in the performance and partial shading tolerance of the conventional full-cell PV modules [1][2]. Half-cut cell modules typically have between 120 and 144 solar cells, divided into 6 substrings of 20 - 24 cells per substring connected in parallel pairs, with each pair sharing a bypass diode in parallel.

When some cells are shaded, depending on the level of shading, instead of producing power, they act as resistors, consuming power, resulting in them heating up more than the unshaded cells. Since half-cut cells are smaller than the standard full-cells, the substring currents are lower in half-cut cell modules than in full cell modules. This leads to reduced resistive losses in partially shaded half-cut cell modules compared to full cell modules, hence better performance of half-cut modules under partial shading conditions [3]. The reduced current per substring in a half-cut cell PV module also means that the temperature of hotspots is reduced. A hotspot is a localized high-temperature region in a PV module. Hotspot formation compromises the integrity of cells, making them prone to cracking, acceleration of material degradation, and burn marks [2].

Simulation results by Qian et al [4] found that the maximum hotspot cell temperature of a partially shaded half-cut cell module was 28°C lower than that of full cell module. Further simulation on the electrical characteristics revealed that when one of the parallel pairs of substrings is partially shaded enough to activate the bypass diode, a rounded knee was observed, and the current clipping is not nearly as sharp. This is because the unshaded pair compensates for the current loss in the shaded pair, and hence a larger shade area is required to activate the bypass diode.

Experimental results obtained by Chiodetti et al [5] have shown a low efficiency of half-cut cell modules under low irradiance compared to full cell modules for several cell technologies. This behaviour is attributed to the increased number of cell interconnects/soldering points, which leads to high series resistance, whose effect gets more pronounced at low irradiance. The benefits of half-cut cell modules are more pronounced at high irradiance levels, where reduced resistive losses lead to improved efficiency, indicating suitability for high irradiance regions and tracking systems.

Most prior studies focused on simulations or measurements at the module level. This work experimentally analyses the effect of partial shading on the thermal and electrical characteristics of individual cells.

2 METHODOLOGY

2.1 Experimental equipment

The Experiment was performed on a 540 Wp monocrystalline half-cut cell PV module. The module has a 3S2P configuration, with 6 substrings of 24 series-connected cells each. Every two substrings are connected in parallel, and the resulting three pairs are connected in series, totalling 144 cells. Each parallel pair is connected in parallel with a bypass diode, resulting in 3 bypass diodes in the module.

The structure of the experimental module is shown in Figure 1, showing the naming conventions used for substrings (SSs) and cell numbers. Also shown is the placement of shunt resistors (10 mΩ ± 5%) used for the measurement of currents in the different branches of the module. Small incisions were made in the back sheet between the cells to expose the cell interconnects and allow electrical connections to the cells to allow for the measurement of cell voltages.

Due to the datalogger limitation on the number of available channels, only 84 cells were monitored: All cells in SS1 - SS3, and only 4 cells in each of the substrings, SS4 - SS6.

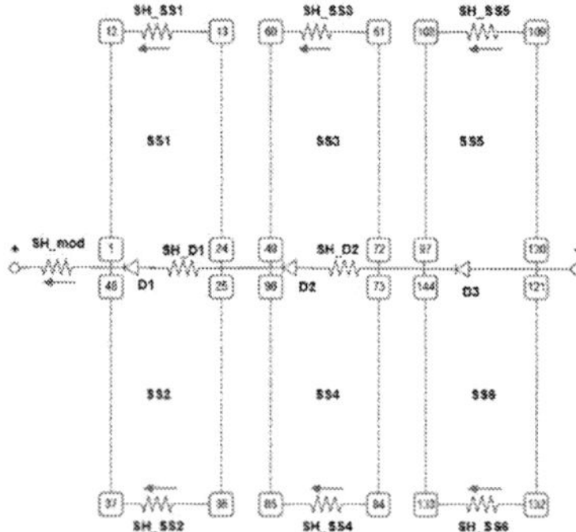

Figure 1: The Half-cut cell module layout. Shown is the position of the shunt resistors used for the measurement of current.

The measurements were taken with the following equipment: A Solmetric I-V tracer, which comes with an irradiance sensor and back-of-module temperature sensors. Agilent 34972A LXI data acquisition unit for measuring the voltage of individual cells, module, bypass diodes, and shunts. A Chroma programmable DC electronic load for sweeping the module I-V while at the same time communicating via LabView software with the Agilent data acquisition unit to take measurements at every step (0.5V) that the Chroma takes the I-V measurements. A manual variable resistor (load). FLIR Thermal camera for taking thermal images of the module. The experiment was set-up as shown in Figure 2:

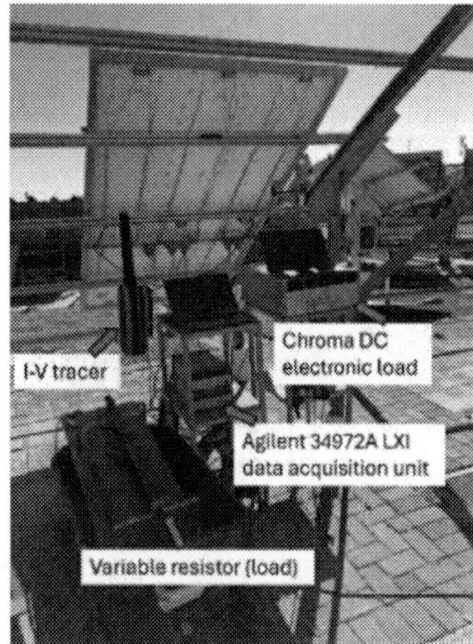

Figure 2: Experimental set up

2.3 Procedure

The experiment was performed in two parts; part 1 was performed at noon, and part 2 was performed in the afternoon when the power of the module dropped below 500W (the maximum power that the Chroma can support).

Part 1:

a) The thermal image and individual cell voltages were measured under open circuit.

b) The I-V curve of the unshaded module was measured using the I-V tracer under uniform illumination. From the I-V curve data, the maximum power point voltage (Vmpp) was identified.

c) The module was connected to the variable resistor and operated at the identified Vmpp.

d) The individual cell voltages were immediately measured using the Agilent data acquisition unit.

e) A waiting period of 5 minutes was considered before the thermal image of the module was captured.

f) Steps (b) to (e) were repeated while shading cell 37 using boards, covering 12.5 %, 25%, 50%, 62.5%, 75%, and 100% of the cell area, respectively.

Part 2:

a) The I-V of the unshaded module was measured using the I-V tracer.

b) The module was connected to the Chroma.

c) The Chroma was programmed to measure the module voltage and current, then communicate via LabView software with the Agilent data acquisition unit to take measurements of cell voltages. The chroma was set to take the I-V at an increment of 0.5 Volts.

d) The steps (a) to (c) were repeated while shading cell 37 using boards, covering 12.5%, 25%, 50%, 62.5%, 75%, and 100% of the cell area, respectively.

3 RESULTS

3.1 Module power output (Part 1 results)

The measured I-V curves and the corresponding maximum power points of the module while shading a single cell (cell 37) from 0% to 100% are shown in Figure 3. As the cell is shaded from 0% to 75%, the maximum power point (MPP) of the module shifts towards higher voltage (towards Voc), and at 100% the MPP shifts towards low voltage (towards short circuit). The jump in the MPP from high voltage to low voltage signifies the activation of the bypass diode at 100% cell shading.

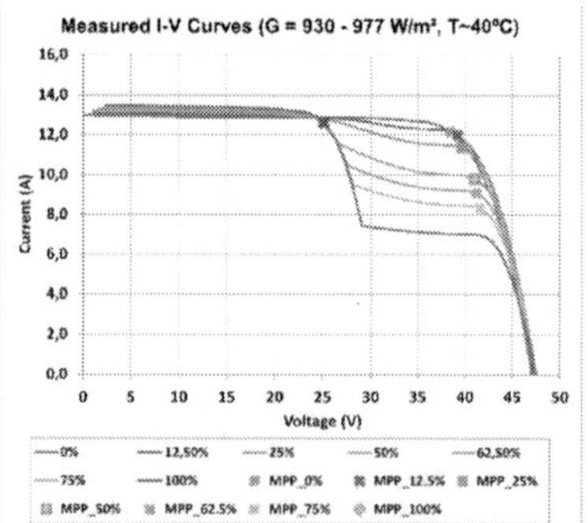

Figure 3: The measured I-V curves and corresponding MPPs of a half-cut cell module while shading a single cell from 0% to 100%.

The impact of cell shading on the module's MPP output is illustrated in Figure 4. As shown, shading a single cell can drastically reduce the power output, with losses reaching up to 1/3 of the module's capacity. Specifically, the unshaded module's MPP output of 480 W dropped to about 325 W when a single cell was fully shaded.

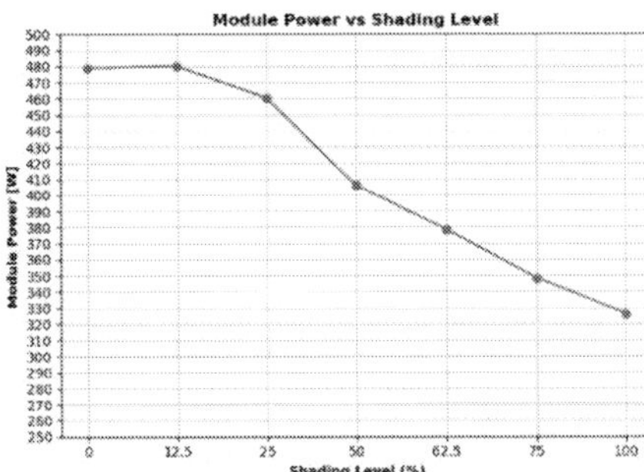

Figure 4: MPP output of a half-cut cell module as a function of single cell shading level.

3.2 Thermal and electrical characteristics of individual cells (Part 1 results)

Figure 5 shows the thermal images of the module under open circuit, and under operation at MPP while not shaded and while shaded by 75%, and 100%. Under open circuit, the module was found to heat up more compared to when it's under operation. This is because under open circuit, the absorbed photons cannot be converted into current and carried away to an external load, hence the energy is dissipated as heat in the cells.

Under Voc and under operation with no shading, the module showed nearly all cells having a uniform temperature distribution, except for two cells in SS6 that appeared abnormally hot. It was found that the two cells are cracked. Additionally, the lower part of the module looks slightly warmer due to the angle at which the thermal image was taken. As the module is shaded from 12.5% to 75% it was found that the shaded cell and the

unshaded cells in the shaded substring heat the most. The unshaded pairs heat up the second most, and the substring parallel to the shaded one was the coolest.

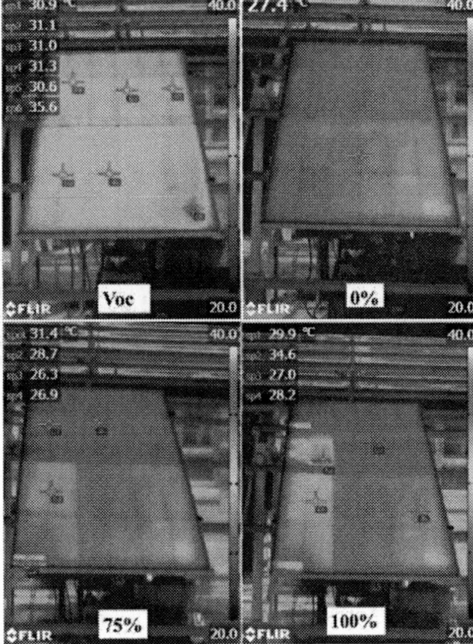

Figure 5: Thermal images of the half-cut cell module under open circuit, and while shading a single cell by 0%, 75%, and 100% shading.

Figure 6 shows the individual cell voltages of the cells while the module is operating at MPP with no shading: all cells are operating nearly at the same voltage of Vmpp ≈ 0.55V.

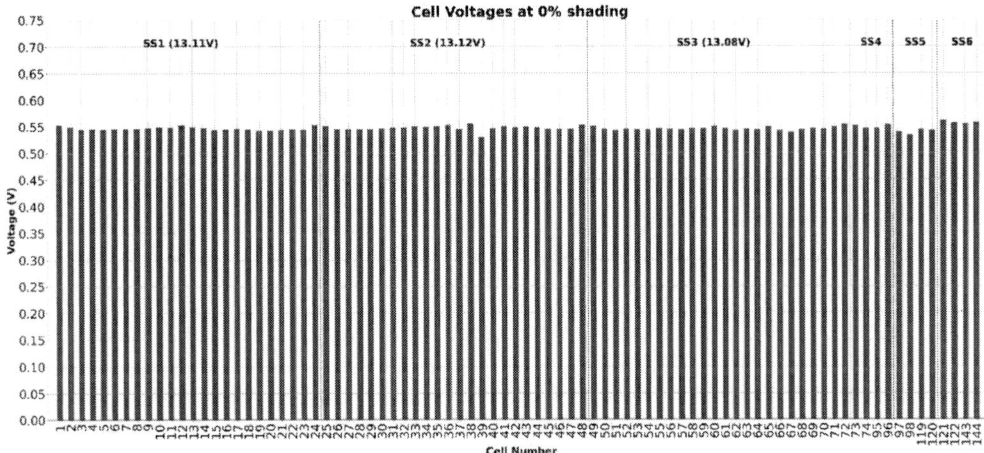

Figure 6: Individual cell voltages, module operating at MPP with no shading.

Shading cell 37 between 12.5% and 75% resulted in a difference in cell voltages between substrings, with a pattern as the shading level is increased. Figure 7 shows the cell voltages at 75% shading. The observed pattern showed that as the voltage of the shaded cell decreases, as

shown on the far right of the figure, the voltages of the unshaded cells in the same substring increase. The voltages of cells in SS1 decrease with an increase in cell shading level while the voltages of cells in the unshaded pairs increase with the increase in cell shading level up to

75%. At 75% shading, the cells in SS1 operate at Vmpp ≈ 0.50V, SS2 cells operate at about Vmpp ≈ 0.65V, and the cells in the rest of the substrings at Vmpp ≈ 0.60V.

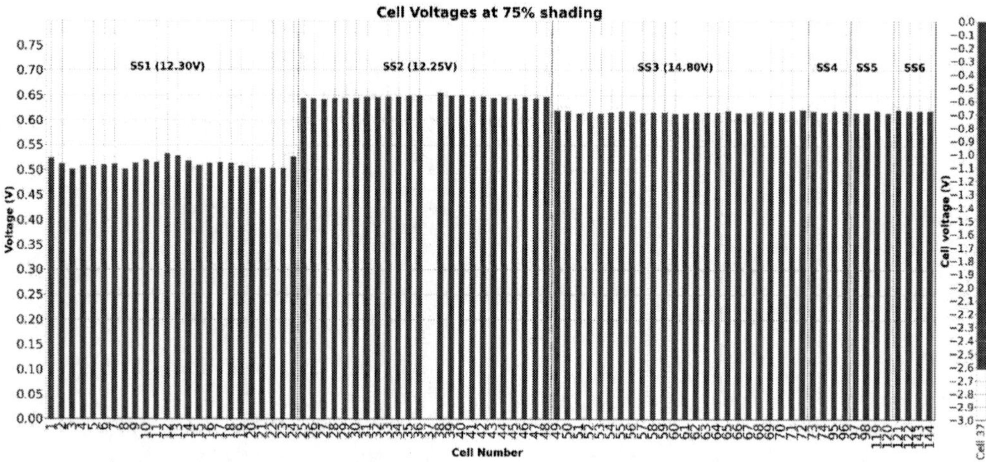

Figure 7: Individual cell voltages at 75% cell shading level. The negative voltage across the shaded cell (cell 37) is shown separately on the insert on the right.

Shading 100% of cell 37 reduces its voltage to about -15.5V, activating the bypass diode parallel to the shaded pair and resulting in the shaded pairs operating near short circuit. This forces some of the cells in the unshaded substring (SS1) to be reverse-biased and dissipate power although they are not shaded as shown in Figure 8. This is because both SS1 and SS2 must operate at the same voltage, because they are connected in parallel. Since at 100% shading the bypass diode is activated, the bypassed substrings (SS1 & SS2) do not produce power, while the rest of the cells in unshaded pairs operate at or close to their MPP, with cells operating at Vmpp ≈ 0.55V.

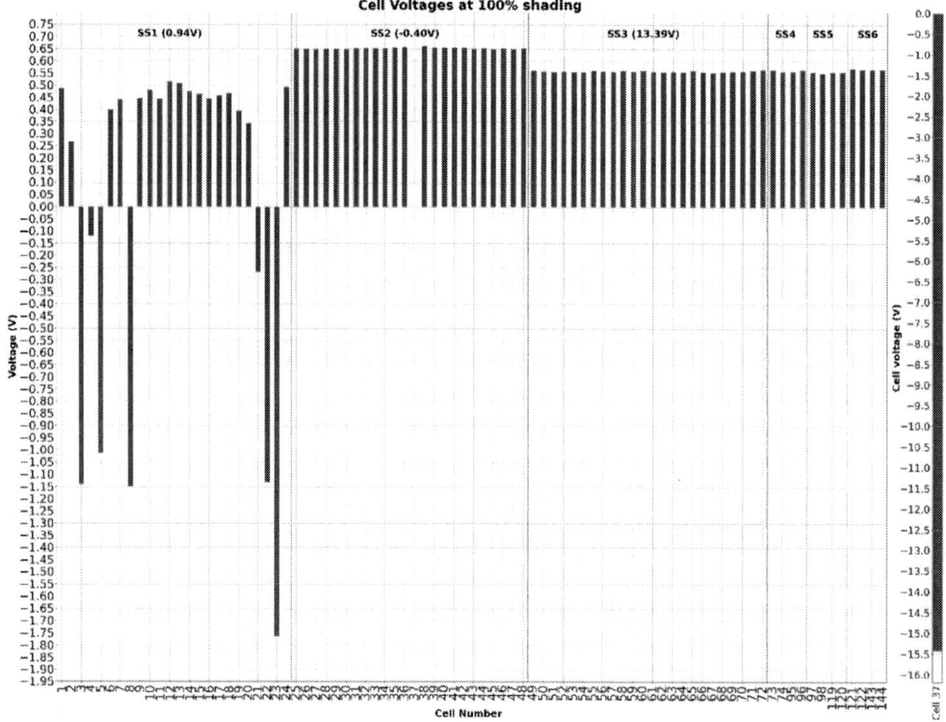

Figure 8: Individual cell voltages at 100% cell shading level. The negative voltage across the shaded cell (cell 37) is shown separately on the insert on the right.

3.3 Module and substring currents (Part 1 results)

Figure 9 illustrates the module and substring currents. It shows that the current in SS2 decreases with shading from 0 - 100% shading level, while the current in SS1 increases. On the other hand, the current in the unshaded substrings, SS3 - SS6 decreases until 75% shading, and increases at 100% when the bypass diode of SS1/SS2 pair is conducting. The results show that, before the bypass diode is activated, the module current is limited by the shaded substring pair. After the bypass diode of the shaded pair is activated, the module current is determined by the unshaded pairs.

We observed that, as the shading level increased from 12.5% to 75%, the substring currents were inversely proportional to cell temperatures, meaning cells operating below their maximum power point or under reverse bias appeared hotter.

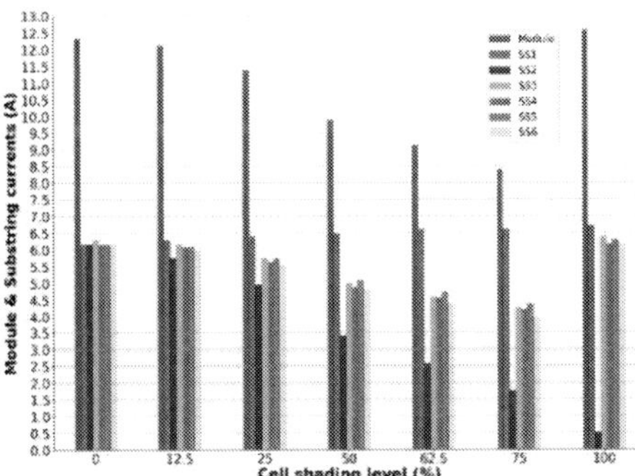

Figure 9:Module and substring currents while shading a single cell from 0 - 100%.

3.4 Module I-V characteristics with Chroma (Part 2 results)

The I-V curves of the module at low irradiance (G = 773 – 627 W/m², T~ 40 °C), with corresponding MPPs as obtained from Chroma, are shown in Figure 10. Showing the same behaviour as the I-Vs obtained at higher irradiance; a shift of the Vmpp towards Voc with increasing shading until the point where the bypass diode is activated, after which the Vmpp shifts towards short circuit.

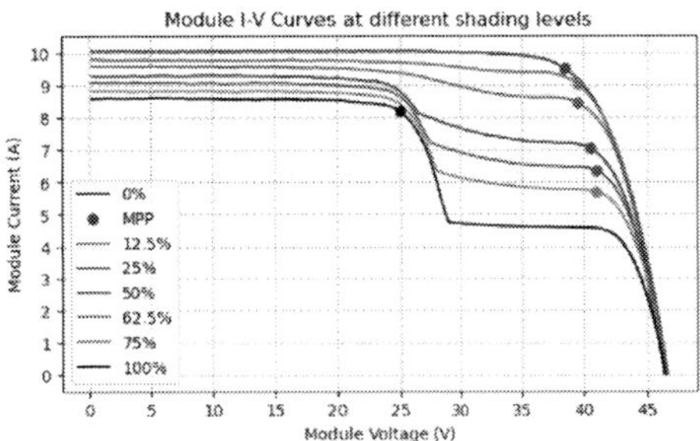

Figure 10: Module I-V as measured by Chroma at G = 773 - 627 W/m², T~ 40 °C

3.5 Substring I-V characteristics (Part 2 results)

The I-V curves of the individual substrings are shown in Figure 11, indicating the MPP of each substring and the operational points (OPs) of the substrings. With no shading, all substrings operate near or at their MPPs. However, with the increase in partial shading, there is a difference in operational points between the shaded pair and the unshaded pairs. The unshaded pairs operate towards Voc up to 75% shading and return to operate at or close to their MPP once the bypass diode is activated. The shaded substring operates towards short circuit, with a greater drop in operational current while the current in the parallel unshaded substring increases towards short circuit current (Isc).

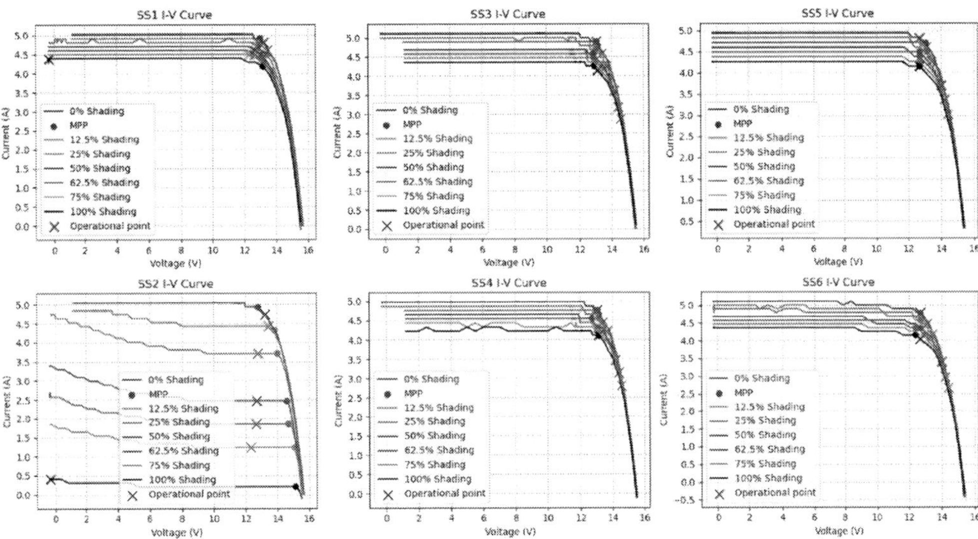

Figure 11: Measured I-V curves of individual substrings at different cell shading levels.

3.6 I-V characteristics of the shaded cell (Part 2 results)

The I-V curves of the shaded cell are shown in Figure 12. It shows that at low irradiance, the shaded cell becomes reverse biased at a much larger shading level, 25%, in this case, compared to 12.5% at a higher irradiance obtained in part 1 of the results. The analysis of the cells in SS1 and SS2 shows that, with shading, if the individual substrings operate at their individual substring MPPs, the shaded cell does not become reverse biased. It can be seen from the I-V of the shaded cell in Figure 12 that if the substring is to operate at its MPP, and the shaded cell is operating at its MPP, then it doesn't become reverse biased.

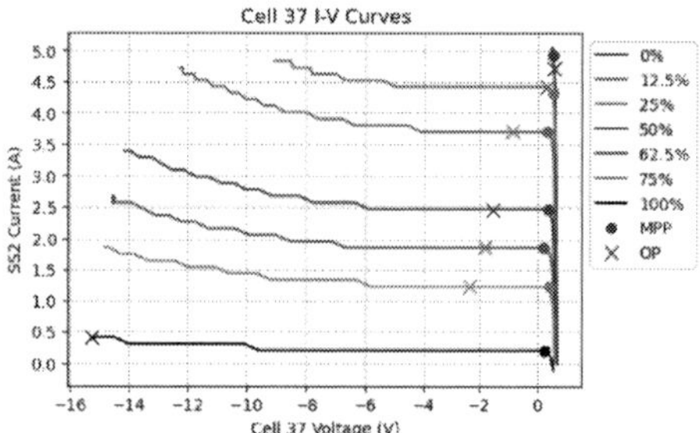

Figure 12: The measured I-V curves and respective MPP and OP of the shaded cell at different shading levels.

4 CONCLUSIONS

This study demonstrates that partial shading of a single cell in a half-cut cell PV module significantly affects the currents produced by all substrings. When the shading level is insufficient to activate the bypass diode, the module current is limited by the substring containing the shaded cell. Notably, the module current only increases when the bypass diode is activated, allowing the unshaded substrings to operate near their MPPs. However, operating the module at its MPP does not guarantee that individual substrings are producing maximum power, highlighting a potential mismatch between module-level and substring-level optimization.

The module's design, featuring parallel-connected cell pairs, minimizes current flow through the bypass diode when a single cell is fully shaded, thereby reducing the likelihood of bypass diode failures. However, simultaneous shading of both parallel pairs would force all module current through the bypass diode, potentially leading to overheating and failure. Therefore, careful consideration of installation orientation is crucial, particularly in scenarios where partial shading is unavoidable.

Given the smaller size of half-cut cells, the likelihood of full shading is increased, which can lead to non-optimal behaviour in the parallel-connected counterparts.

These findings have significant implications for the interpretation of thermal images, as hotspots may not necessarily indicate a defective cell in the affected area but rather a defective cell elsewhere in the module. To mitigate these issues and maximize power extraction, we propose incorporating substring optimizers in half-cut cell modules. This approach would prevent reverse biasing of cells under partial shading conditions, enhancing overall module efficiency and reliability.

5 REFERENCES

[1] Bosco N 2022 Turn Your Half-Cut Cells for a Stronger Module *IEEE J Photovolt* **12** 1149–53

[2] Waqar Akram M, Li G, Jin Y, Zhu C, Javaid A, Zuhaib Akram M and Usman Khan M 2020 Study of manufacturing and hotspot formation in cut cell and full cell PV modules *Solar Energy* **203** 247–59

[3] Huyeng J D, Lohmüller E, Shabanzadeh B, Reichel C, Rößler T, Weber J, Hofmann M, von Kutzleben D, Abdel Latif N, Kraft A, Neuhaus H, Clement F and Preu R 2024 Challenges and advantages of cut solar cells for shingling and half-cell modules *EPJ Photovoltaics* **15** 22

[4] Qian J, Thomson A, Blakers A and Ernst M 2018 Comparison of Half-Cell and Full-Cell Module Hotspot-Induced Temperature by Simulation *IEEE J Photovolt* **8** 834–9

[5] Chiodetti M, Dupuis J, Boublil D, Radouane K and Dupeyrat P 2019 HALF-CELL MODULE BEHAVIOUR AND ITS IMPACT ON THE YIELD OF A PV PLANT *36th European PV Solar Energy Conference and Exhibition* 1444–8

DEPENDENCE OF PHOTOVOLTAIC MODULE PERFORMANCE INDICATORS ON OPERATING TEMPERATURE AND IRRADIANCE

Heidi Kalliojärvi, Kari Lappalainen
Tampere University, Electrical Engineering Unit, P. O. Box 692, FI-33101 Tampere, Finland
heidi.kalliojarvi@tuni.fi, kari.lappalainen@tuni.fi

ABSTRACT: Condition of photovoltaic (PV) modules can be monitored by using measured current–voltage curves. The curves can be used to calculate numerical indicators that jointly can reveal possible changes in the condition of the PV modules. Such indicators are tied to the shape of the current–voltage curve. However, the changes in operating irradiance and temperature are known to affect the shape of the curve as well. Thus, also the operating conditions have an impact on the numerical values of the performance indicators. As a consequence, any such impact reflects on the diagnostical results. For this reason, it is important to investigate the dependence of the performance indicators on the operating conditions. This study addresses this issue by investigating four performance indicators in terms of their temperature and irradiance dependencies. The results assist in developing condition monitoring strategies of PV systems.
Keywords: condition monitoring, current–voltage curve, performance indicator, operating conditions

1 INTRODUCTION

Condition monitoring of photovoltaic (PV) power systems by using measured current–voltage (I–V) curves is an attractive way to obtain information of the state of the health of the PV modules. The measured I–V curves can provide information of ageing and other degradation phenomena occurring within the PV modules [1]. The curves can be subjected to identification of the parameters of the mathematical single-diode model that describes the operation of a PV cell, a PV module or a larger unit. Then, the identified model parameters can be used for the diagnosis.

The diagnostical usability of the I–V curves stems from the fact that the shape of the curve as well as its location in the I–V coordinate plane is affected by changes in the condition of the PV module. Leaning on this fact, several indicators characterizing the performance of the PV modules can be calculated. A commonly known indicator is the fill factor (FF) that expresses the area of the largest possible rectangle between the I–V curve and the coordinate axes [2]. In other words, FF measures the roundness of the I–V curve. The parasitic series (R_s) and shunt resistances (R_h) of the single-diode model are also known to be related to the condition of the PV modules. Series resistance is an indicator specific to PV module ageing; identified R_s values typically increase with the progression of ageing [3]. In turn, decreasing R_h is related to different shunting-type defects such as potential-induced degradation [4]. As R_s and R_h affect the slopes of the I–V curve in its high-voltage and high-current regions, respectively, [5] significant changes in them also contribute to the FF value [6]. The slopes of the I–V curve can be separately characterized by calculating ratios $\gamma_V = V_{\mathrm{MPP}}/V_{\mathrm{OC}}$ and $\gamma_I = I_{\mathrm{MPP}}/I_{\mathrm{SC}}$, where V_{MPP} and I_{MPP} are the voltage and current at the maximum power point (MPP), V_{OC} is the open-circuit (OC) voltage, and I_{SC} is the short-circuit (SC) current. The indicators γ_V and γ_I can be further utilized to calculate the series–parallel ratio (SPR) of the PV module. The SPR value determines which one of the two parasitic resistances is dominant [7]. If $SPR > 1$, then R_s dominates, and R_h can be neglected in the single-diode model parameter identification process. Conversely, the condition $SPR < 1$ implies the dominance of R_h, whence R_s can be neglected [7]. Such reduction in the number of identified parameters simplifies calculations

and reduces the computational costs [7]. These aspects are important in practical online condition monitoring applications.

When drawing conclusions based on the I–V curve-based performance indicators, it is mandatory to consider their dependence on the operating irradiance (G) and temperature (T) as the shape of the I–V curve changes not only with PV module degradation but also with operating conditions. Thus, also the values of the previously mentioned performance indicators vary with the operating irradiance and temperature. Some indicators are either very fundamental, such as FF, or have otherwise gained wide attention in literature, like R_s and R_h. The fill factor reduces with temperature [2], and this fact has been further employed e.g. in [8], the authors of which found a formula for the temperature gradient of the fill factor. There seems to be no clear consensus regarding the temperature dependence of series resistance [9]. Some studies have attributed positive temperature dependence to series resistance of crystalline silicon PV cells [10, 11]. In [12], series resistance of crystalline silicon PV modules was reported to increase with decreasing irradiance. When investigating the temperature dependence of shunt resistance, various results have been obtained. For instance, the authors of [12] reported the shunt resistance of silicon PV cells to decrease with temperature. However, it was observed in [13] that there was only weak temperature dependence, if any. Shunt resistance is generally considered to increase with decreasing irradiance as shown in [12]. As a remark, the single-diode model parameters should be identified from I–V curves measured under high irradiance conditions since then the model is known to perform best [14].

In contrast to these indicators, there exist unfortunately only a few studies in which such dependences have been investigated for the other, less common indicators like γ_V, γ_I and SPR. Indeed, their dependence on the operating conditions has gained relatively little attention despite their usefulness in condition monitoring. To the best of our knowledge, there is only one published study [15] that is related to the behavior of these indicators under varying operating conditions. It was observed in [15] that γ_V and γ_I decreased with increasing irradiance, and their overall level as well as their behavior as a function of the irradiance was tied to the severity of the ageing of the PV module. In addition, it was reported in [15] that SPR

10.4229/EUPVSEC2025/3AV.3.30

changed as a function of the irradiance. For a PV module in its actual condition, the change seemed to follow a linearly increasing trend, but when the ageing became more severe, the behavior of SPR turned both nonlinear and nonmonotonic. However, the temperature dependences of these three performance indicators were not considered in [15]. In fact, there are no published studies reporting the effect of operating temperature on γ_V, γ_I or SPR. However, the irradiance and temperature effects should be simultaneously considered to obtain a comprehensive understanding of the behavior of these indicators with changing operating conditions.

The present study fills in this research gap by investigating the effects of operating irradiance and temperature on γ_V, γ_I, R_s and SPR. The single-diode model parameter identification procedure used in this study is suitable for practical applications due to its capability to repeat the operating conditions mathematically jointly with the identification of the actual single-diode model parameters. The impact of the PV module ageing stage on the dependence of the investigated performance indicators on the temperature and irradiance has been also studied. The importance of the present study lies in providing guidelines for the exploitation of these indicators in diagnostical analyses in practical PV applications.

The remainder of the paper is organized as follows. Section 2 is dedicated to describing the single-diode model and the used parameter identification procedure, the calculation of the investigated performance indicators as well as the measurement data used in the present study. Section 3 is devoted to presenting and discussing the experimental results. Finally, Section 4 closes the paper.

2 METHODS AND DATA

2.1 Single-diode model

The PV module is modeled by using the widely known single-diode model [16]

$$I = I_{\text{ph}} - I_{\text{o}}\left(e^{\frac{V+IR_s}{AV_T}} - 1\right) - \frac{V+IR_s}{R_{\text{h}}}, \tag{1}$$

where I and V are the PV output current and voltage, I_{ph} is the photogenerated current accounting for the electron–hole pairs, I_{o} is the dark saturation current and A is the diode ideality factor. $V_T = N_s k_B T/q$ is the PV module thermal voltage, where N_s is the number of series-connected PV cells within the module, k_B is the Boltzmann constant, T is the operating temperature, and q is the electron charge.

2.2 Parameter identification procedure

The parameter identification procedure used in this paper was initially presented in [17]. It produces the set $\{G, T, R_s, R_{\text{h}}\}$ as its immediate output. From the indirect outputs that are adjusted during the parameter identification, I_{ph} is calculated as in [18] via

$$I_{\text{ph}} = \frac{G}{G_{\text{STC}}}(I_{\text{ph, STC}} + \alpha_I(T - T_{\text{STC}})), \tag{2}$$

where G_{STC} and T_{STC} are the irradiance and temperature in Standard Test Conditions (STC), α_I is the temperature coefficient of the SC current in STC, and $I_{\text{ph, STC}}$ is the photogenerated current in STC, which is calculated by solving I_{ph} as a function of I_{SC} in STC via

$$I_{\text{ph, STC}} = I_{\text{SC, STC}}\left(\frac{R_s + R_{\text{h}}}{R_{\text{h}}}\right). \tag{3}$$

As in [19], the ideality factor is fixed at its STC value A_{STC} calculated as in [20] via

$$A_{\text{STC}} = \frac{\alpha_V - \frac{V_{\text{OC, STC}}}{T_{\text{STC}}}}{V_{T,\text{STC}}\left(\frac{\alpha_I}{I_{\text{ph, STC}}} - \frac{3}{T_{\text{STC}}} - \frac{E_{\text{g, STC}}}{k_B T_{\text{STC}}^2}\right)}, \tag{4}$$

where, $V_{\text{OC, STC}}$ is the OC voltage in STC, α_V its temperature coefficient, and $V_{T,\text{STC}}$ and $E_{\text{g, STC}}$ are the thermal voltage and the energy band gap in STC. The dark saturation current I_{o} is calculated as in [21] via

$$I_{\text{o}} = C_{\text{STC}} T^{\frac{3}{A_{\text{STC}}}} e^{-\frac{E_{\text{g}}(T)}{A_{\text{STC}} k_B T}}, \tag{5}$$

where the coefficient C_{STC} is calculated as in [21] via

$$C_{\text{STC}} = \frac{I_{\text{ph, STC}}\, e^{\gamma_{\text{STC}}}}{T_{\text{STC}}^{\frac{3}{A_{\text{STC}}}}} \tag{6}$$

with

$$\gamma_{\text{STC}} = -\frac{V_{\text{OC, STC}}}{A_{\text{STC}} V_{T,\text{STC}}} + \frac{E_{\text{g, STC}}}{A_{\text{STC}} k_B T_{\text{STC}}}. \tag{7}$$

The energy band gap $E_{\text{g}}(T)$ in (5) is calculated as in [19] via

$$E_{\text{g}}(T) = E_{\text{g, STC}}(1 + \alpha_{E_{\text{g}}}(T - T_{\text{STC}})), \tag{8}$$

where $E_{\text{g, 0}}$ is the energy band gap at absolute zero temperature, and $\alpha_{E_{\text{g}}}$ is a thermal coefficient [19]. The parameter identification itself is performed by using the fit.m algorithm in Matlab. The maximum number of iterations and objective function evaluations has been set to 1e4. The tolerances both for the identified parameters and the objective function values between two consecutive iterations have been set to 1e-11. To reduce the computational cost, current is explicitly expressed as a function of voltage via

$$I = \frac{R_{\text{h}}(I_{\text{ph}} + I_{\text{o}}) - V}{R_{\text{h}} + R_s} - \frac{AV_T}{R_s} W(\theta_I), \tag{9}$$

where $W(\cdot)$ denotes the Lambert W function [16], and θ_I is obtained via

$$\theta_I = \frac{R_s R_{\text{h}} I_{\text{o}}\, e^{\frac{R_s R_{\text{h}}(I_{\text{ph}} + I_{\text{o}}) + R_{\text{h}} V}{AV_T(R_s + R_{\text{h}})}}}{AV_T(R_s + R_{\text{h}})}. \tag{10}$$

The initial guesses for the identified parameters are determined as follows. For the first I–V curve in each dataset, the initial guess is $\{G_{\text{STC}}, T_{\text{STC}}, R_{s,\text{STC}}, R_{\text{h, STC}}\}$, where the STC values for the parasitic resistances $R_{s,\text{STC}}$ and $R_{\text{h, STC}}$ are calculated as in [17] via the procedure presented in [16] utilizing the Lambert W function so that

$$R_{s,\text{STC}} = \frac{x A_{\text{STC}} V_{T,\text{STC}} - V_{\text{MPP, STC}}}{I_{\text{MPP, STC}}} \tag{11}$$

and

$$R_{\text{h, STC}} = \frac{x A_{\text{STC}} V_{T,\text{STC}}}{I_{\text{ph, STC}} - I_{\text{MPP, STC}} - I_{\text{o, STC}}(e^x - 1)}, \tag{12}$$

where $I_{\text{MPP, STC}}$, $V_{\text{MPP, STC}}$ and $I_{\text{o, STC}}$ are the MPP current, MPP voltage and the dark saturation current at STC, and the auxiliary variable x is obtained via

$$x = W\left(\frac{V_{\text{MPP, STC}}(2I_{\text{MPP, STC}} - I_{\text{ph, STC}})e^{\frac{V_{\text{MPP, STC}}(V_{\text{MPP, STC}} - 2A_{\text{STC}}V_{T,\text{STC}})}{(A_{\text{STC}}V_{T,\text{STC}})^2}}}{A_{\text{STC}}I_{\text{o, STC}}V_{T,\text{STC}}} \right) + 2\frac{V_{\text{MPP, STC}}}{A_{\text{STC}}V_{T,\text{STC}}} - \left(\frac{V_{\text{MPP, STC}}}{A_{\text{STC}}V_{T,\text{STC}}}\right)^2. \tag{13}$$

For the remainder of the I–V curves, the parameter values identified from the previous curve serve as the initial guess for the following curve. The lower and upper limits for the identified parameters are reported in Table I.

Table I: Lower and upper limits for the identified parameters

Parameter	Lower limit	Upper limit
G (W/m^2)	0	1300
T (K)	273.15	343.15
R_s (Ω)	0.1	5
R_h (Ω)	20	1000

2.3 Measurement data

The measurement data used in the present study was gathered from an individual PV module of the solar PV power research plant of Tampere University, Tampere, Finland [22]. The PV power plant is located on the rooftop of a campus building and consists of 69 PV modules (NAPS NP190GK) fabricated from multi-crystalline silicon. The irradiance received by the PV module and the PV module backplate temperature were respectively registered by a SPLite2 photodiode and a Pt100 thermocouple. The I–V curves were measured by using an I–V curve tracer utilizing IGBTs as an electronic load with a 1 Hz sampling frequency.

The measured I–V curves initially consisted of 4000 measurement points spaced evenly in terms of time. As such an operating principle of the I–V curve tracer causes an uneven distribution of the measurement points along the I–V curve in terms of voltage and current [23], the curves were preprocessed before the actual parameter identification as follows. At first, the clearly abnormal measurement points were removed by using a statistical interquartile range method [23]. Thereafter, those remaining points that had redundant voltage values were replaced by an individual point by averaging their currents as in [24]. Such preprocessing made the I–V curve measurement data less discrepant and mitigated the effects of uneven weighting of the measurement points.

The calculation of γ_V and γ_I require decent estimates for V_{OC} and I_{SC}. To address this issue, V_{OC} was calculated by fitting a second-order polynomial to those points of the I–V curve that had current values smaller than 25% of the MPP current. Correspondingly, I_{SC} has been calculated by fitting a line to the points with a voltage value smaller than 25% of the MPP voltage. In either case, this percentage of the MPP value was lifted to 50% if there existed less than 40 points below the described 25% limit.

It was previously observed in [25] that the electrical characteristics of the PV module in STC slightly differed from their values reported in the manufacturer's datasheet.

Hence, the values re-determined in [25] were used in the present study, and they are reported in Table II jointly with the other relevant electrical characteristics of the PV module.

Table II: Electrical characteristics of the studied PV module in STC

Parameter	Value
$I_{\text{SC, STC}}$	8.86 A
$I_{\text{MPP, STC}}$	8.06 A
$V_{\text{OC, STC}}$	32.8 V
$V_{\text{MPP, STC}}$	22.5 V
N_s	54
α_I	0.0047 A/K
α_V	-0.124 V/K
$R_{s, \text{STC}}$	0.7511 Ω
$R_{h, \text{STC}}$	95.5013 Ω
A_{STC}	1.0654

In this study, three 10-hour datasets, each one consisting of 36000 consecutive I–V curves measured during one day, were investigated. Each dataset described a certain stage of PV module ageing. The ageing was modeled by connecting additional series resistances ($R_{s, \text{add}}$) in series with the investigated PV module. The datasets were measured on 26, 9 and 23 August 2023, and the corresponding ageing stages described a PV module in its actual condition ($R_{s, \text{add}} = 0.00$ Ω), a mildly aged ($R_{s, \text{add}} = 0.22$ Ω) PV module and a severely aged ($R_{s, \text{add}} = 1.47$ Ω) PV module. Since all the investigated datasets were measured within a narrow time window of a few weeks, real ageing phenomena affecting the results could not practically have occurred between the measurements.

2.4 Investigated performance indicators

Among the four performance indicators investigated in the present study, the single-diode model parameter identification is needed only for R_s. The other three indicators are calculated by utilizing the three key points of the I–V curve. Indeed, γ_V is calculated based on the MPP and OC points. Correspondingly, γ_I is calculated based only on the MPP and SC points. The series–parallel ratio SPR is calculated by using the γ_V and γ_I values as in [7] via

$$SPR = \frac{1-\gamma_I}{e^{-r}}, \tag{14}$$

where

$$r = \frac{\gamma_I(1-\gamma_V)}{\gamma_V(1-\gamma_I)}. \tag{15}$$

3 RESULTS AND DISCUSSION

The joint effect of operating irradiance and temperature on the four performance indicators is presented in this section. Each indicator was plotted against irradiance and temperature measured during the 10-hour measurement period. The experimentally calculated values for each indicator were plotted with circular markers, whose colors varied with the range of the indicator values. Since not each irradiance–temperature combination was covered by a data point, linear interpolation was used to find the overall behavior of each investigated indicator. The interpolated values were shown as regions with different colors.

3.1 Ratio γ_V

Fig. 1 shows γ_V as a function of irradiance and temperature for the investigated ageing stages ($R_{s,\,add}$ = 0.00, 0.22 and 1.47 Ω). It was observed that the overall level of γ_V decreased with the progression of ageing. For the PV module in its actual condition, γ_V was within a range of 0.66–0.84. The corresponding ranges for the mildly aged and the severely aged PV module were 0.60–0.82 and 0.50–0.80, respectively. In particular, the γ_V range was the largest for the severely aged PV module. An interesting finding was the variation of γ_V magnitude with ageing under high irradiance conditions as such conditions form the basis for diagnostics. Indeed, when the irradiance was high (> 800 W/m^2), the overall γ_V level decreased with the progression of ageing. For the additional resistances $R_{s,\,add}$ = 0.00, 0.22 and 1.47 Ω, the respective maximum γ_V values were at most around 0.7, 0.65 and 0.57 or so. In turn, low irradiance levels yielded γ_V values which were at most around 0.8. These results were in accord with previous study [15].

All the subplots of Fig. 1 consisted of regions (indicated by different colors) obtained by linear interpolation that illustrated particular ranges of γ_V values. The orientation of these regions was close to vertical, indicating a clear irradiance dependence of γ_V in each investigated ageing stage. Larger irradiance levels produced smaller γ_V values. The regions were also slightly tilted to left, referring to a minor negative temperature dependence of γ_V.

3.2 Ratio γ_I

Fig. 2 exhibits the ratio γ_I as a function of the irradiance and temperature for the investigated ageing stages. It was observed that the overall γ_I level decreased with the progression of ageing. The respective γ_I ranges for $R_{s,\,add}$ = 0.00, 0.22 and 1.47 Ω were 0.87–0.94, 0.84–0.93 and 0.60–0.90, respectively. These findings were in line with the previous study [15].

The subplots of Fig. 2 differed quite strongly by the formation of the regions describing the γ_I sub-ranges. Roughly speaking, Fig. 2 (a) describing the PV module in its actual condition consisted of larger, horizontally oriented regions at low and medium irradiance levels and vertically oriented regions at high irradiance levels. The orientation of these regions referred to the existence of negative temperature dependence of γ_I at low and medium irradiance levels and negative irradiance dependence of γ_I at high irradiance levels. Moreover, there were smaller, island-like, regions within the vertically oriented regions. Such findings referred to somewhat unpredictable behavior of γ_I as a function of the operating conditions. For the mildly aged PV module, the irregular-shaped regions seemed to become more arranged, especially in vertical direction. This revealed the existence of negative irradiance dependence of γ_I. There also seemed to appear a slight negative temperature dependence.

In turn, the severely aged PV module produced nearly

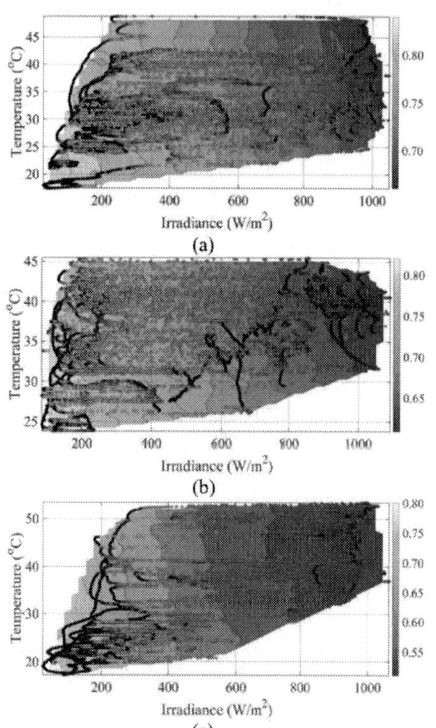

Figure 1: Ratio γ_V as a function of the measured irradiance and temperature for the PV module in its actual condition ($R_{s,\,add}$ = 0.00 Ω) (a) and with mild ageing ($R_{s,\,add}$ = 0.22 Ω) (b) and severe ageing ($R_{s,\,add}$ = 1.47 Ω) (c)

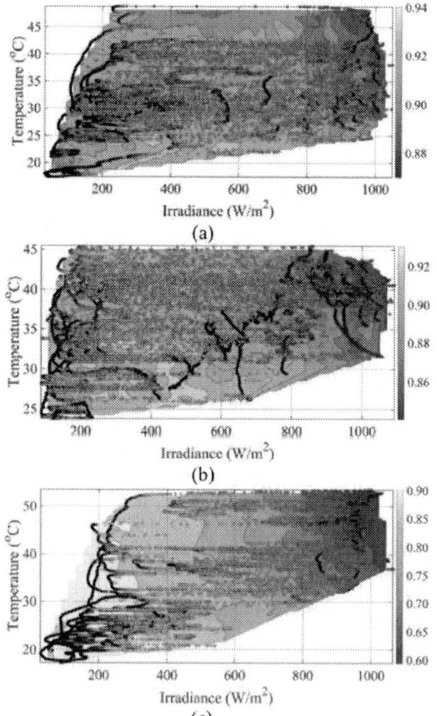

Figure 2: Ratio γ_I as a function of the measured irradiance and temperature for the PV module in its actual condition ($R_{s,\,add}$ = 0.00 Ω) (a) and with mild ageing ($R_{s,\,add}$ = 0.22 Ω) (b) and severe ageing ($R_{s,\,add}$ = 1.47 Ω) (c)

vertical regions slightly tilted to left that were more clearly separated than in the two other stages of ageing. Now, the clear negative irradiance dependence and slight negative temperature dependence were obvious.

In conclusion, these findings indicated the irradiance dependence to become more obvious with the progression of ageing, which was in line with the results of [15]. In addition, there appeared a slight but clear negative temperature dependence of γ_I.

3.3 Series resistance R_s

Fig. 3 illustrates the identified series resistance as a function of the irradiance and temperature for the three investigated ageing stages ($R_{s,\,add}$ = 0.00, 0.22 and 1.47 Ω). It was observed that the PV module in its actual condition yielded rather stable R_s values around 0.8 Ω from high irradiance down to low irradiance levels of around 300 W/m² or so. Such stability of the series resistance identification even under rather low irradiance conditions is a clear advantage in practical applications. When irradiance became lower than approximately 200 W/m², the identified R_s values increased abruptly. Such findings were in line with the results of [12]. The series resistance seemed to depend mostly on irradiance. The rightward tilted boundary between the dark blue and medium blue regions referred to slight positive temperature dependence of R_s at low irradiance conditions. In contrast, no significant temperature dependence appeared under high and medium irradiance conditions. These results were in accord with [12].

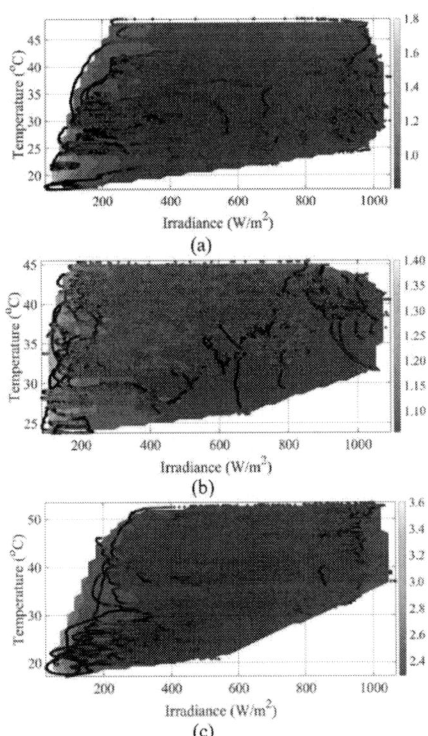

Figure 3: Series resistance (Ω) as a function of the measured irradiance and temperature for the PV module in its actual condition ($R_{s,\,add}$ = 0.00 Ω) (a) and with mild ageing ($R_{s,\,add}$ = 0.22 Ω) (b) and severe ageing ($R_{s,\,add}$ = 1.47 Ω) (c)

For $R_{s,\,add}$ = 0.22 Ω, stable R_s values around 1.05 Ω appeared from high irradiance levels down to irradiance levels somewhere between 400–600 W/m². The stable R_s range was followed by a region of R_s levels around 1.15 Ω when irradiance went down to approximately 200 W/m². Below 200 W/m², the series resistance continued to increase with decreasing irradiance. Now there seemed to be slight positive temperature dependence, being in line with the previous studies [10, 11].

For $R_{s,\,add}$ = 1.47 Ω, the identified R_s had stable values around 2.3 Ω for irradiance levels that were higher than 200–300 W/m². There seemed to appear a slight positive temperature dependence at low irradiance levels, which was in line with [10, 11].

In conclusion, the used parameter identification procedure produced stable R_s values down to rather low irradiance levels regardless of the ageing stage. The rapid increase in R_s values with very low irradiance suggested nonlinear negative irradiance dependence that was negligible at high and medium irradiance but become significant under low irradiance conditions. Such finding is in accord with the improper performance of the single-diode model at low irradiances [26]. Moreover, the current of crystalline silicon PV cells changes approximately linearly with irradiance, but voltage decreases rapidly with low irradiances affecting the shape of the I–V curve [27]. The temperature dependence was either negligible or slight in all investigated ageing stages.

3.4 Series–parallel ratio SPR

The calculated SPR values for the investigated ageing stages varied within the ranges 0.40–179.03 ($R_{s,\,add}$ = 0.00 Ω), 0.43–112.75 ($R_{s,\,add}$ = 0.22 Ω) and 0.42–44.37 ($R_{s,\,add}$ = 1.47 Ω). Fig. 4 illustrates the calculated SPR as a function of the irradiance and temperature for the investigated ageing stages. Remarkably, the condition $SPR < 1$ held true under low irradiance conditions, indicating the predominance of shunt resistance. This is in accord with the fact that shunt resistance becomes significant when irradiance decreases to a low level [28].

In the case of the PV module in its actual condition, there seemed to be a trend of positive irradiance dependence of SPR, being in line with the results of [15]. The rightward tilted boundary between the dark and medium blue regions around 500–700 W/m² might refer to the possible existence of negative temperature dependence of SPR at least in medium irradiance conditions. However, the island-like dark blue regions appearing under high irradiance conditions pointed against clear temperature dependence. It should be noted that these findings require more investigation before drawing conclusions.

The behavior of SPR as a function of irradiance and temperature for the mildly aged ($R_{s,\,add}$ = 0.22 Ω) PV module resembled closely that of the PV module in its actual condition. The irradiance dependence seemed to be positive also in this case, being in line with [15].

In contrast to the PV module in its actual condition and the mildly aged PV modules, the severely aged PV module ($R_{s,\,add}$ = 1.47 Ω) had a clearly different behavior as a function of irradiance. Indeed, low SPR values occurred both under low and high irradiance conditions, while the medium irradiance conditions provided higher SPR values. Such a finding is in accord with the previous study [15]. The dependence of SPR on temperature was a more involved question also in this case since SPR did not seem to behave regularly with respect to temperature. Indeed, the presented example is not sufficient for drawing

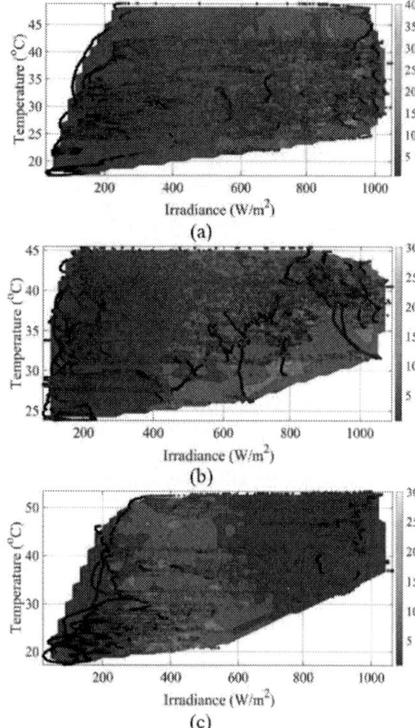

(a)

(b)

(c)

Figure 4: Series–parallel ratio as a function of the measured irradiance and temperature for the PV module in its actual condition ($R_{s,\ add} = 0.00\ \Omega$) (a) and with mild ageing ($R_{s,\ add} = 0.22\ \Omega$) (b) and severe ageing ($R_{s,\ add} = 1.47\ \Omega$) (c)

strict conclusions but more investigation is needed.

4 CONCLUSIONS

This study focused on investigating the irradiance and temperature dependence of four PV module performance indicators calculated based on measured current–voltage curves. The investigated indicators were the ratio of the maximum power point and open-circuit voltages, the ratio of the maximum power point and short-circuit currents, the series resistance and the series–parallel ratio. The series resistance was obtained via a single-diode model parameter identification procedure that identifies the operating irradiance and temperature jointly with the actual single-diode model parameters. The other three performance indicators were calculated based on the three key points of current–voltage curves.

The effects of operating conditions on the investigated performance indicators were separately studied for a PV module with three different ageing stages: a PV module in its actual condition, a mildly aged and a severely aged PV module. The ageing was emulated by connecting different-sized resistors in series with the PV module. For each ageing stage, a 10-hour dataset consisting of consecutive current–voltage curves was analyzed.

The ratio of the maximum power point and open-circuit voltages showed clear negative dependence on irradiance and slight negative dependence on temperature.

More severe ageing led to smaller levels of the ratio.

The ratio of the maximum power point and short-circuit currents seemed to depend mainly on temperature for the PV module in its actual condition, but severe ageing seemed to turn the irradiance dependence to be clearly more dominant. The mentioned dependences on temperature and irradiance were both negative.

The series resistance was stably identified from a wide irradiance range for all the stages of ageing. Within that range, there seemed to be no significant dependence on the operating conditions. However, very low irradiance levels resulted in rapidly increasing series resistance values. A slight positive temperature dependence was observed.

The behavior of the series–parallel ratio in terms of irradiance seemed to depend on the ageing stage of the PV module. Indeed, the PV module in its actual condition and the mildly aged PV module exhibited an increasing trend, while the severely aged PV module seemed to have the highest series–parallel ratios at medium irradiance. In turn, there did not appear an obvious dependence of series–parallel ratio on temperature.

As the investigated PV module performance indicators clearly varied with the operating conditions and ageing stage, the results of the present study serve as practical guidelines in their usage in PV module condition monitoring and assist in the interpretation of the diagnostical results based on these indicators.

REFERENCES

[1] J. Ahmad, A. Ciocia, S. Fichera, A.F. Murtaza, F. Spertino, Energies 12 (2019) 4547.

[2] M.A. Green, Solid-State Electronics 24(8) (1981) 788.

[3] E. Kaplani, Journal of Engineering Science and Technology 5(4) (2012) 18.

[4] S. Pingel, O. Frank, M. Winkler, S. Daryan, T. Geipel, H. Hoehne, J. Berghold, Proceedings 35th IEEE Photovoltaic Specialists Conference (2010) 002817.

[5] E.L. Meyer, E.E. Van Dyk, Conference Record of the Thirty-first IEEE Photovoltaic Specialists Conference (2005) 1331.

[6] W. Zhou, H. Yang, Z. Fang, Applied Energy 84(12) (2007) 1187.

[7] S. Cannizzaro, M.C. Di Piazza, M. Luna, G. Vitale, Proceedings IEEE 23rd International Symposium on Industrial Electronics (2014) 2266.

[8] H. Qu, X. Li, Journal of Mechanical Science and Technology 33 (2019) 1981.

[9] S. Bounouar, R. Bendaoud, H. Amiry, B. Zohal, F. Chanaa, E. Baghaz, C. Hajjaj, S. Yadir, A. El Rhassouli, M. Benhmida, International Journal of Renewable Energy Research 10(4) (2020) 1555.

[10] S. Bensalem, M. Chegaar, Journal of Renewable Energies 16(1) (2013) 171.

[11] M. Piliougine, G. Spagnuolo, M. Sidrach-de-Cardona, Renewable Energy 162 (2020) 677.

[12] C.S. Ruschel, F.P. Gasparin, A. Krenzinger, Solar Energy 217 (2021) 134.

[13] P. Singh, S.N. Singh, M. Lal, N. Husain, Solar Energy Materials and Solar Cells 92(12) (2008) 1611.

[14] S. Bana, R.P. Saini, Energy Reports 2 (2016) 171.

[15] G. Spagnuolo, K. Lappalainen, S. Valkealahti, P. Manganiello, Proceedings IEEE International Conference on Clean Electric Power (2019) 302.

[16] G. Petrone, C.A. Ramos-Paja, G. Spagnuolo, John Wiley & Sons (2017).

[17] K. Lappalainen, M. Piliougine, G. Spagnuolo, Energy Conversion and Management 258 (2022) 115526.

[18] U. Eicker, John Wiley & Sons (2003).

[19] W. De Soto, S.A. Klein, W.A. Beckman, Solar Energy 80(1) (2006) 78.

[20] N. Femia, G. Petrone, G. Spagnuolo, M. Vitelli, Taylor & Francis Group (2013).

[21] J.R. Wilcox, A.W. Haas, J.L. Gray, R.J. Schwartz, AIP Conference Proceedings 1407(1) (2011) 30.

[22] D. Torres Lobera, A. Mäki, J. Huusari, K. Lappalainen, T. Suntio, S. Valkealahti, International Journal of Photoenergy 2013(1) (2013) 837310.

[23] H. Kalliojärvi–Viljakainen, K. Lappalainen, S. Valkealahti, Proceedings 47th IEEE Photovoltaic Specialists Conference (2020) 0117.

[24] K. Lappalainen, S. Valkealahti, Applied Energy 301 (2021) 117436.

[25] H. Kalliojärvi–Viljakainen, K. Lappalainen, S. Valkealahti, Energy Reports 8 (2022) 4633.

[26] K. Ishaque, Z. Salam, H. Taheri, Syafaruddin, Simulation modelling Practice and Theory 19(7) (2011) 1613.

[27] J.A. Kratochvil, W.E. Boyson, D.L. King, Sandia National Laboratories (2004).

[28] A.D. Dhass, E. Natarajan, L. Ponnusamy, Proceedings 2012 IEEE International Conference on Emerging Trends in Electrical Engineering and Energy Management (2012) 382.

EVALUATING THE IMPACT OF SOILING ON AGRIVOLTAIC SYSTEMS

Paul Gebhardt, Tannaz Katouli, Thomas Kaltenbach, Tamara Bretzel, Lisa-Marie Bieber, Ingrid Haedrich
Fraunhofer Institute for Solar Energy Systems ISE
Heidenhofstr. 2, 79110 Freiburg, Germany

ABSTRACT: This study investigates the impact of soiling on the performance of agrivoltaic systems (AVS) through transmission measurements of glass plates exposed in four AVS, next to the actual PV modules. The research quantifies light transmission loss due to agricultural dust, soil, pesticide, and fertilizer residues, correlating these losses with solar spectrum intensity and solar cell response. Several AVS in Germany are analyzed to establish the relationship between soiling and energy output, as well as its effect on light availability for plants. Preliminary results indicate a significant light transmission reduction of up to ~40 %, depending on the kind of agricultural activity and installation type, with the highest losses observed above hop fields. In contrast, a vertical installation with winter wheat shows minimal soiling losses. This research contributes to the agrivoltaics field by addressing challenges of the unique environments in AVS, providing a practical method for analyzing soiling and a first empirical dataset for estimating the effects on electricity yield.

1 INTRODUCTION

The double-use of land by photovoltaics (PV) and agriculture, i.e. agrivoltaics (AV) is an increasingly applied approach with significant potential [1]. While the current literature focuses mostly on the integration of photovoltaics into the agricultural complex, i.e. the effect of photovoltaics on crop yield, and regulatory issues [2], long-term technical challenges concerning the PV system itself such as reliability issues and soiling losses, i.e. the effect of the agri-chemicals on the PV are barely researched [3].

This study specifically addresses optical losses in PV performance due soiling, being a combination of various depositions on the PV modules. We conduct transmission measurements on glass plates that have been exposed in various agricultural environments in Germany. The primary objective is to quantify the extent of light transmission loss caused by the depositions, e.g., different types of agricultural dust, soil, and debris, as well as residues from pesticides and fertilizers. The results are also compared to power measurements of modules that are affected by soiling.

2 METHODS

We have selected several AVS representing diverse conditions, including various crops and different orientations of the PV installation, based in Germany. 20 x 20 cm glass slides without antireflective coating were installed next to the PV modules in the same inclination angle.

Tab. 1: PV installations investigated in this study

Site	Crop	Installation	Exposure
1	Apple (Gala)	Over-head (W/E)	February – September
2	Apple (Freya)	Over-head (W/E) Or tracker	February – September
3	Hop	Over-head (S)	June–November
4	Winter Wheat	Vertical	March – August

After the exposure time, the transmission of the samples was measured with a spectrophotometer averaging the transmission over an area of ~5 cm in diameter. The resulting transmission spectra were weighted with the intensity of the sun spectrum (AM 1.5) and a spectral response of a TOPCon solar cell in order to weight the losses in different wavelength ranges according to their relevance in the PV application.

The transmission measurements on the glass slides were conducted using a Fourier-transform spectrometer (Bruker Vertex 70) equipped with a PTFE-coated integrating sphere, allowing for the measurement of both directly reflected and transmitted light, as well as scattered radiation. We first analyzed full-sized PV modules from two sites in their soiled state using photographs, followed by power- and electroluminescence measurements to assess their actual performance or any potential damage. Subsequently, the transmission properties were measured in the intercellular spaces (between the cells) using a mobile spectral hemispherical transmittance device that was specifically developed for this project. It is based on a spectrometer by Ocean Optics, (STS-VIS, 350 to 800 nm), an LED light source (Euro Lighting, Natural Spectrum Series SOL) and a 50 mm diameter Ulbricht sphere with an opening diameter of 10 mm. The two sides of the device, containing light source and detector unit, respectively, can be fixed on opposite sides of the PV module using magnetic rings and can thus measure the

Fig. 1: Inhouse-developed mobile spectrometer during measurement of a glass-glass PV module. Light source and detector are fixed on opposite sides of the PV module by a magnetic ring. The device is connected to a laptop for data acquisition and power source via a USB cable.

transmission in the intercellular space (measuring point approx. 5 mm diameter).

Finally, the influence of soiling on module performance was measured by taking STC-performance measurements on the same modules after cleaning.

3 RESULTS

Results from our measurements after an exposure time of 6-8 months in the field (Tab. 1) indicate that the reduction in light transmission due to soiling can be substantial, but strongly depends on the local conditions with losses reaching up to ~40 %. The strongest soiling loss was observed in installations above hop fields (Fig. 2, Fig. 3). A cleaning of the rear side and subsequent re-measuring the transmission revealed that around half of the soiling effect could be attributed to each glass side. This aspect can be relevant for distinguishing between the soiling losses for crop- and electricity yield, because the electricity yield is naturally mostly diminished by soiling on the module's front side, while the crops react to transmission losses on both module sides.

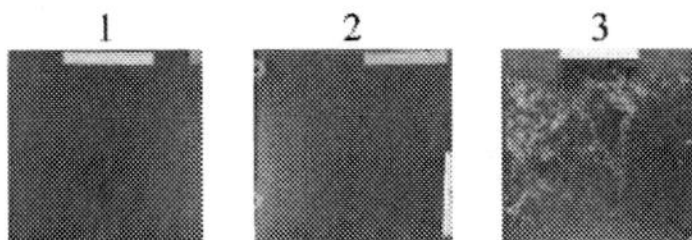

Fig. 2: Photographs of glass slides after exposure at Sites 1-3.

The lowest soiling effects were observed in an installation of winter wheat, where modules and glass plates were installed vertically, do show very little soiling losses. It seems plausible that the vertical installation reduces soiling by facilitating the removal of deposits during rain; however, other factors may also contribute, warranting further investigations, e.g. comparison of tilted and vertical glasses or vertical glasses from different crops, to better understand the reason for the low soiling in this instance.

Nevertheless, these findings illustrate the benefits of integrating effective cleaning strategies for AVS.

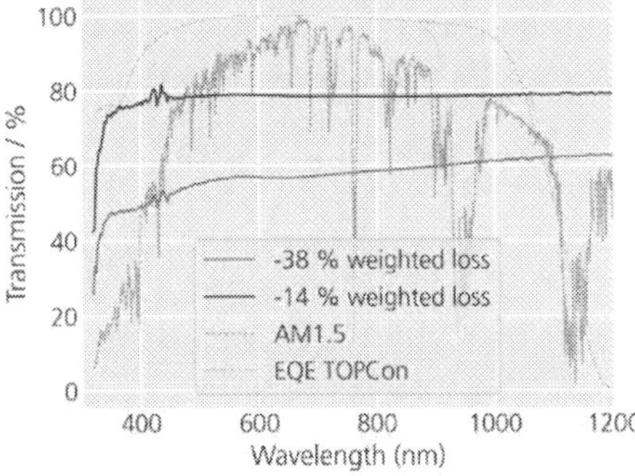

Figure 1: Transmission spectra of two glass samples from Site 3 (green, blue). The plot contains normalized AM1.5 spectrum and TOPCon EQE used as weighting factors resulting in weighted transmission losses of -38 and -14 %, respectively.

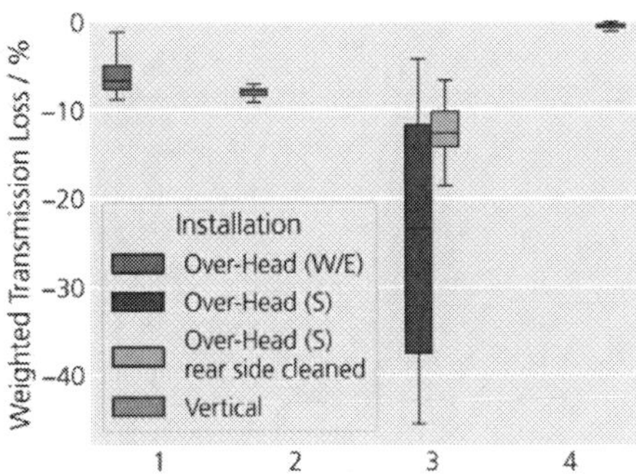

Fig. 3: Weighted transmission loss of glass slides exposed on AVS

To investigate the soiling effect on full-size modules, PV modules were dismantled from AVS in June 2025, after approximately 15 months of exposure, and evaluated in the laboratory. It is noteworthy that estimating the impact of deposits on module performance quantitatively is challenging because the deposits are typically unevenly distributed across the module, often exhibiting gradients from top to bottom or right to left (Fig. 4). This means that, depending on the module topology, i.e. the internal interconnection of the cells in the module, mismatch losses of varying severity reduce the overall module performance. Measurement points need to be chosen very carefully in order to allow a meaningful comparison between modules.

The soiling loss, calculated from of the difference between performance measurements before and after cleaning the modules (Fig. 5, bars) quantitatively deviates from the transmittance measurement at individual spots (Fig. 5, dots) but correlating with the general visual impression. The contamination primarily affects the performance on the front side of the modules, which is the more critical side regarding energy yield, as performance losses on the rear side were generally lower, remaining below 1%.

Another interesting finding from full-sized modules from Site 2 is that modules M03 and M04, which were mounted on trackers, show significantly less soiling compared to modules M05 and M06, which were mounted

Fig. 4: Photographs of PV modules after exposure in agrivoltaics System 1 (left) and 2 (right), before cleaning show inhomogeneous distribution of soiling.

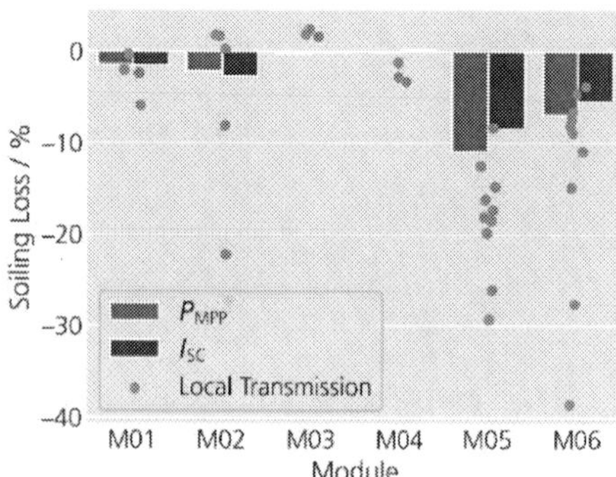

Fig. 5: Loss in module performance and weighted transmission of full size PV modules due to soiling. The modules originated from Site1 (M01, M02), Site 2 (Tracker, M03, M04) and Site 2 (fixed tilt, M05, M06).

at a fixed tilt. Similar to the results of the vertically installed modules on Site 4, this finding suggests that the module orientation has a strong effect on the observed soiling.

The results of the transmission measurements (Fig. 5, dots) tend to loosely correspond to the power loss of the module, whereby the measurement points were not selected systematically but according to the visual impression. However, as expected, the transmission decreases more significantly in heavily soiled areas of the module than the overall module performance. There is also a clear trend of stronger performance loss due to soiling for modules that showed higher transmission losses.

4   CONCLUSION

This study presents, to the best of our knowledge, the first investigation of soiling effects on AVS, addressing a critical knowledge gap in the field. Through transmission measurements using glass slides and full-size PV modules exposed in various agricultural environments across Germany, our initial findings demonstrate that agricultural soiling can significantly impact PV and crop performance, with light transmission losses ranging from 0 to approximately 40 %, depending on crop type and installation configuration.

The mobile spectrometer technique developed for this research proves suitable for in-field measurements and provides a practical tool for monitoring soiling effects in operational AVS.

This provides an initial empirical dataset for the agrivoltaics community. However, several questions require further investigation through systematic studies with larger datasets. For instance, the remarkably low soiling observed in vertical installations needs confirmation through controlled comparisons with tilted configurations under identical agricultural conditions to determine whether orientation or crop-specific factors drive this effect.

Future research should focus on expanding the dataset across diverse crop types and installation geometries to identify the main drivers for soiling losses for both crop and electricity yield.

5   ACKNOWLEDGMENT

This work was funded by the Federal Ministry for Economic Affairs and Energy (03EE1147, „VAckerPower"), the Ministry of Food, Rural Areas and Consumer Protection of the state Baden-Württemberg (27-8216, „StaMoMo") and the Federal Ministry of Agriculture, Food and Regional Identity (28CD405B22, „HoPVen").

6   REFERENCES

[1]   Fraunhofer-Institut für Solare Energiesysteme ISE, *Flächenpotenzial für Agri-Photovoltaik in Deutschland übertrifft Ausbauziele für Klimaschutz*. Freiburg, Germany, 2025. Accessed: Aug. 28 2025. [Online]. Available: https://www.ise.fraunhofer.de/de/presse-und-medien/presseinformationen/2025/fraunhofer-ise-ausgruendung-flaechenpotenzial-fuer-agri-photovoltaik-in-deutschland-uebertrifft-ausbauziele-fuer-klimaschutz.html

[2]   D. Soto-Gómez, "Integration of Crops, Livestock, and Solar Panels: A Review of Agrivoltaic Systems," *Agronomy*, vol. 14, no. 8, p. 1824, 2024, doi: 10.3390/agronomy14081824.

[3]   T. Katouli, P. Gebhardt, J. Markert, and I. Hädrich, "Developing Tests for PV Module Durability Against Pesticides and Fertilizers," in *AgriVoltaics World Conference*, Freiburg, Germany, 2025.

A GENERAL APPROACH TO MODEL HIGH-PERFORMANCE PV MODULES FOR ACCURATE ENERGY YIELD SIMULATIONS

Luca Antognini, Michele Oliosi, Auriane Canesse, Robin Vincent, André Mermoud, Bruno Wittmer
PVsyst SA
Route de la Maison-Carrée 30, CH 1242 Satigny - Switzerland

ABSTRACT: One of the challenges in PV module performance modeling is to obtain a good description of the I-V curves at various temperatures and illuminations, based solely on limited available data. Currently in PVsyst, this is done by calculating the parameters for the one-diode model (1DM) from datasheet information and common assumptions on low-light performance. However, this fails to reproduce high fill factors (FF), typically compromising V_{oc} accuracy. To address this, we use an evolutionary algorithm (EA) which improves parameter determination for the 1DM, extends to more sophisticated models and can use measurement variability as input. This method necessitates solely datasheet information and common low-light assumptions to reproduce IEC 61853-1 measurements. We demonstrate its benefits on both measured PERC modules and synthetic high-FF scenarios. On measured data from a low-FF module, the EA lowers the mean efficiency error in reproducing IEC 61853-1 data compared to the current method. To test the EA on high-FF devices, we generate synthetic data from a reference recombination model informed by solar-cell literature. In this case too, the EA reduces power error and greatly improves V_{oc} reproduction, which is further enhanced when switching from 1DM to the reference model itself.
Keywords: PV Module Modeling, PVsyst

1 INTRODUCTION

Accurate modelling of PV module I–V curves is essential for reliable energy yield simulations. The one-diode model (1DM), as implemented in PVsyst, remains an industry standard due to its simplicity and accuracy to represent PERC PV modules. PVsyst uses an analytical method to determine the model parameters based solely on the information available in datasheet, completed by observed technological trends for low-light performance.

However, for modern high-performance devices with elevated fill factors (FF), this approach often compromises open-circuit voltage accuracy, limiting its predictive power. Moreover, the origin of those high FF within crystalline silicon (c-Si) technology is well understood through more sophisticated models incorporating several recombination mechanisms impacting in parallel the I–V behaviour. These developments call for parameter evaluation methods that go beyond fixed assumptions and can flexibly adapt to new device characteristics.

To overcome the limitations arising at high FFs, we explore two approaches: 1) Change the determination method for the model parameters evaluation from datasheet information. 2) Investigate the potential benefit of a different I–V-parametrization that is established in literature and known to be able to describe high FF.

In particular, we propose an evolutionary algorithm (EA) framework that can adapt to both the conventional 1DM and recombination-based models. This method necessitates solely datasheet data and common low-light assumptions to reproduce IEC 61853-1 measurements. We demonstrate its benefits on both measured PERC modules and synthetic high-FF scenarios.

2 METHOD

We first summarize the current PVsyst I–V parameterization and a reference recombination-based model from the solar cell literature state-of-the-art. This model is commonly accepted to describe the origin of high FF in record efficiency device [1] and we will therefore use it to generate synthetic data in the next sections.

Then, we describe the current calculation procedure of PVsyst and the EA optimization approach.

2.1 Current PVsyst I-V Parametrization

We describe here the parametrization of the 1DM as it is implemented in the current version of PVsyst (8.0). As in any 1DM parametrization, the external current I is a balance between the photogenerated current and the current losses in the first diode and shunt resistor,

$$I = I_{ph} - I_0 \left(e^{\frac{q(V+IR_s)}{\gamma k_B T}} - 1 \right) - \frac{V + IR_s}{R_{sh}}$$

where the term $V_{int} = V + IR_s$ is the internal voltage of the solar cells prior to the voltage drop across the series resistance R_s. The equivalent circuit of this equation can be seen in Figure 1 (a).

The photogenerated current I_{ph} is assumed to depend linearly on the temperature and irradiance

$$I_{ph}(G,T) = \frac{G}{G_{ref}} I_{ph,ref} [1 + \mu_{I_{sc}}(T - T_{c,ref})]$$

where $I_{ph,ref}$ is the photogenerated current under the standard test conditions (STC) temperature $T_{c,ref} = 25\ °C$ and irradiance $G_{Ref} = 1000\ W/m^2$. $\mu_{I_{sc}}$ is the short-circuit current temperature coefficient. Similarly, the saturation current of the diode I_0 depends on the temperature as

$$I_0(T) = I_{0,ref} \left(\frac{T}{T_{ref}} \right)^3 \exp\left(\frac{qE_g}{\gamma k_B} \left(\frac{1}{T_{ref}} - \frac{1}{T} \right) \right),$$

where for crystalline silicon (c-Si) the bandgap E_g is set to a fixed value of 1.12 eV.

Next, based on experimental observations [2], PVsyst assumes an exponential behaviour of the shunt resistance with irradiance

$$R_{sh}(G) = R_{sh,Base} + \left[R_{sh}(0) - R_{sh,Base} \right] \times \exp\left(-R_{sh,exp}\left(\frac{G}{G_{ref}} \right) \right)$$

with

$$R_{sh,Base} = \frac{R_{sh}(\text{STC}) - R_{sh}(0)\exp\left(-R_{sh,exp} \right)}{1 - \exp\left(-R_{sh,exp} \right)}$$

Based on the measurement campaign led in [2], the two additional degrees of freedom $R_{sh,exp}$ and $R_{sh}(0)/R_{sh}(STC)$ ratio takes remarkably fixed values for a given PV technology, leaving only the shunt resistance at 1000 W/m², $R_{sh}(STC)$, as unknown parameter.

Finaly, PVsyst assumes a linear dependence on temperature of the diode ideality factor γ

$$\gamma(T) = \gamma_{ref} + \mu_\gamma(T - T_{ref}),$$

where μ_γ is an additional unknown parameter.

In summary, PVsyst 1DM has 9 parameters:

$$I_{ph,ref}, \ \mu_{I_{sc}}, I_0, \gamma, \mu_\gamma, R_s, R_{sh}(STC), R_{sh,exp}, \text{and } R_{sh}(0).$$

We additionally assume $R_{sh,exp} = 5.5$ and $R_{sh}(0) = 4\,R_{sh}(STC)$ for c-Si, which reduces the number of unknown parameters to 7.

2.2 Reference recombination model for high-FF

We explicitate here the reference parametrization of the I-V curve informed by solar cell literature on electron/hole recombination mechanisms. As for the 1DM, the model is still described as a current balance equation

$$I = I_{ph} - I_{aug} - I_{rad} - I_{SRH} - I_{sh},$$

where the different terms are defined below and the equivalent circuit diagram is shown in Figure 2 (a).

For the description of the intrinsic recombination, we follow the latest parametrization proposed in [3] [4]. In this formalism the Auger recombination current

$$I_{aug} = qW(g_{ehh}C_{p0}(p^2 n - p_0^2 n_0) + g_{eeh}C_{n0}(pn^2 - p_0 n_0^2))$$

and the radiative recombination current

$$I_{rad} = qW(1 - f_{PR})B_{low}B_{rel}(np - n_0 p_0)$$

depend explicitly on the electron and hole carrier concentration n and p, respectively, and the c-Si wafer thickness W. Those quantities are related to the equilibrium concentration n_0 and p_0 by

$$n = n_0 + \Delta n \text{ and } p = p_0 + \Delta n$$

where Δn is the excess charge concentration created by the excitation (voltage and illumination), related to the intrinsic carrier concentration n_i by

$$n_0 p_0 = n_i^2.$$

Finaly, in the case of n-type wafer, we have the approximation $n_0 = N$ (and $p_0 = N$ for p-type), where N is the base doping concentration of the wafer. We follow [4] for the value of the coefficients C_{p0}, C_{n0}, B_{low} and the remaining terms are defined in the same publication.

Note that the carrier concentrations are directly related to the internal voltage by

$$n_i^2 \exp\left(\frac{qV_{int}}{k_b T}\right) = pn \approx (\frac{n_i^2}{N} + \Delta n)(N + \Delta n).$$

Therefore, an increase in Δn results directly in an increase of V_{int}.

Within the description of [3] [4], n_i depends both on temperature and carrier concentrations. A commonly accepted parametrization is [5] [6]

$$n_i(T, n, p) = 9.653 \times 10^9$$
$$\times \left(\frac{T[°K]}{300}\right)^{1.706} \exp\left(-\frac{E_G(T, n, p)}{2 k_B T}\right)$$

where the function $E_G(T, n, p)$ represents the effect of the bandgap narrowing effect at increased carrier concentration. Note the resemblance with the 1DM's I_0 temperature dependance.

(a)

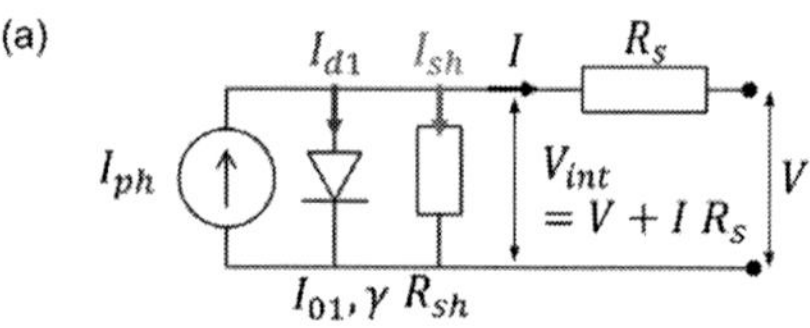

(b)
Breakdown of Current losses

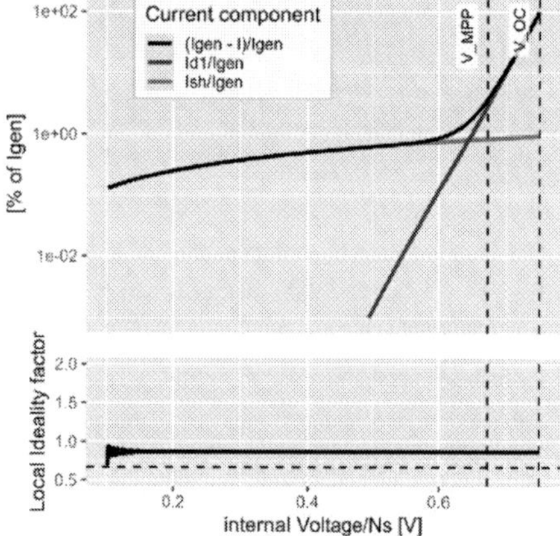

(a)

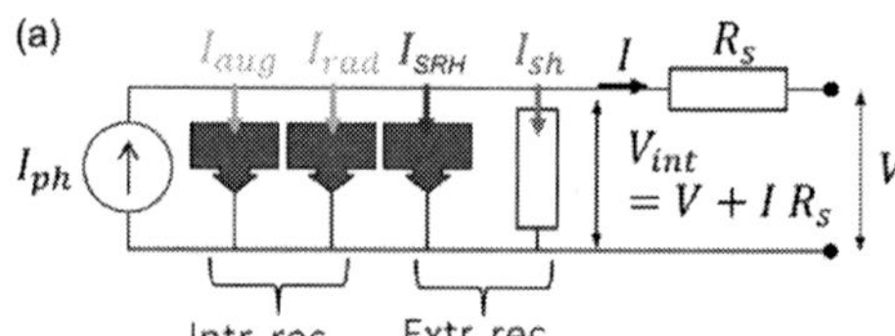

(b)
Breakdown of Current losses

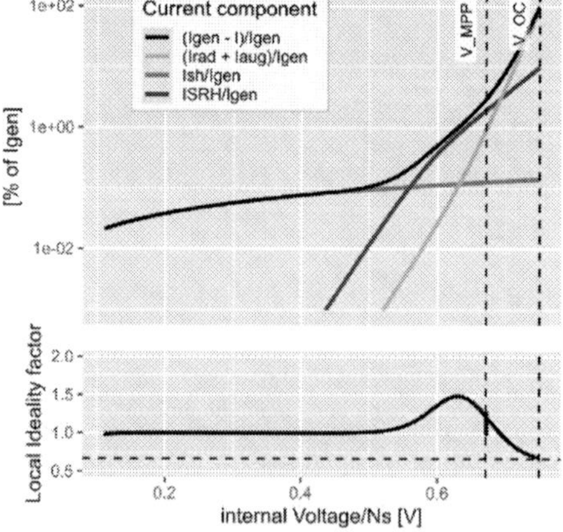

Figure 1: (a) Equivalent circuit diagram of the one diode model. (b) Breakdown of current losses for typical model parameters on logarithmic scale and local ideality factor derived from the slope of the top black curve.

Figure 2: (a) Equivalent circuit diagram of the recombination model. (b) Current losses breakdown for typical model parameters and local ideality factor derived from the slope of the top black curve.

For the description of the extrinsic recombination, we replace the single diode term with the Shockley-Read-Hall equation which uses the same formalism as presented in this section and, in the assumption of single defect level close to mid-gap [1], can be approximated as

$$I_{SRH} = q\,W\,\frac{pn - n_i^2}{\tau_{SRH}(n + p)}$$

where τ_{SRH} is the effective lifetime of the excess charge created by the excitation (voltage and illumination) and W the thickness of c-Si wafer.

The shunt current is still given by

$$I_{sh} = \frac{V + IR_s}{R_{sh}}$$

and we keep the same assumptions for the irradiance and temperature dependance of R_{sh} and I_{ph}. This also sums up to 9 unknown parameters

$$I_{ph,ref}, \mu_{I_{sc}}, \tau_{SRH}, W, N, R_s, R_{sh}(STC), R_{sh,exp}, \text{ and } R_{sh}(0)$$

where the same assumptions can be made on $R_{sh,exp}$ and $R_{sh}(0)$, which reduces the number of unknown parameters to 7 again.

The motivation to use this model is now described. It is a well-known fact that the STC efficiency of an ideal c-Si solar cell (i.e. with no extrinsic recombination nor shunt or series resistance) is limited by radiative and Auger recombination to a value of 29.4% while the FF is limited to 89.26%. Note that those numbers remained unchanged up to the second digit in the last decades [7] [8] [4]. The FF limit is explained by the strong increase of the Auger recombination at higher carrier concentrations (p^2n and pn^2 terms), and therefore at higher voltages, increasing gradually the intrinsic recombination current from the maximal power point (MPP) until the open-circuit conditions (OC). This is shown in Figure 2 (b). Another way to understand this, is that if one were to approximate by an effective single diode model representing the intrinsic recombination mechanisms, it would be required to introduce a voltage dependent diode ideality factor which decreases towards a value of 2/3 as the voltage increases, making the I-V curve's shape more squared and increase the FF.

2.3 Current PVsyst Parameter Calculation

In the current PVsyst implementation (8.0), the direct calculation method of the 1DM parameters requires at least 9 independent input data to be well defined. The 6 first are (almost always) specified in the PV module datasheet.

First, I-V curve is constrained to pass by three points defined by the STC values: (V_{mpp}, I_{mpp}), $(V_{oc}, 0)$, and $(0, I_{sc})$. Note that it is not specified that the first point is the maximum power point, and therefore the P_{mpp} value obtained by the model can be slightly different than the one of the input data.

Second, $\mu_{I_{sc}}$ is used directly as input parameter and the power temperature coefficient μ_{Pmpp} needs to be reproduced (mainly by adjusting the parameter μ_γ). Note that the temperature coefficient of the open circuit voltage $\mu_{V_{oc}}$ is not used in this calculation (its usage is restricted to compute in a separate way the V_{oc} at low temperature for system sizing and norm safety purpose).

Third, as mentioned above, two additional constraints can be set by fixing $R_{sh,exp} = 5.5$ and $R_{sh}(0) = 4\,R_{sh}(STC)$, validated for c-Si technology.

The final constraint is the relative efficiency loss under low-light conditions (200 W/m^2, 25 °C) compared to STC

$$\text{Rel. eff.} = 1 - \eta_{low}/\eta_{STC}.$$

This strongly helps to determine R_s since the power loss goes as $P_{loss} \sim I^2R_s$. Unfortunately, this information is almost never present in product datasheets and PVsyst assumes by default a value of -3% when no information is available based on previous experimental campaigns [2]. Since then, with the constant reduction in series resistance in PV manufacturing, driven by improvements in contact layer resistance, metallic grid conductivity and increased number of busbars, this relative efficiency has been decreasing consistently on average to values below -5% [9]. A lower bound of about -6.8% for this value can be estimated based on the measured series resistance of some best state-of-the-art c-Si solar cell [1]. Therefore, in the present study, recognizing the relative low light efficiency value of -3% as optimistic with currently available PV modules, we use a value of -4.5% when no other information can be assumed.

The first set of constraints defines 1DM parameters with a degree of freedom, leaving the series resistance free up to a maximum value $R_{s,max}$. The additional constraint imposed by the relative low-light efficiency fixes this value. However, in the case of high FF, not all values of relative low-light efficiency can be achieved while respecting the other constraints [10]. In these cases, PVsyst will artificially increase the V_{oc} value until it is possible to respect all the constraints, such as the MPP which is the first relevant information to preserve for accurate energy yield simulations. Such an example is presented in Figure 3, where we choose the extreme example of the above-mentioned certified record solar cell [1], leading to an inaccurate reproduction of the V_{oc}. In comparison, fitting those data using either the reference recombination model of section 2.2 or a two-diode model allows an accurate reproduction of the V_{oc}. This will be discussed further in the next sections.

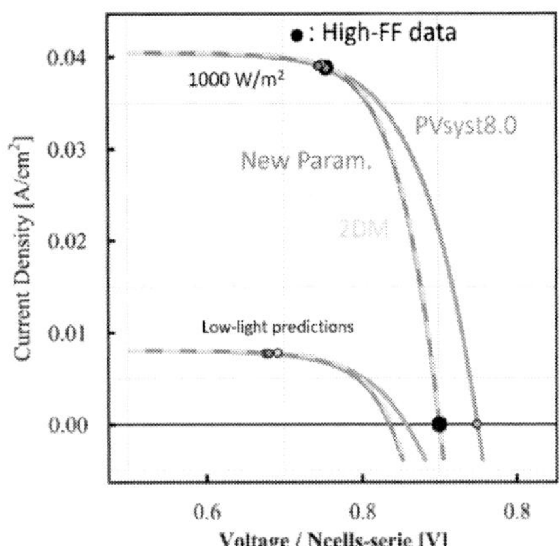

Figure 3: High FF solar cell certified data from *[1]* and corresponding I-V curve estimation from PVsyst 8.0 1DM, a two-diode model and the intrinsic recombination model ("New Param").

2.4 Alternative Parameter Evaluation

To circumvent the limitations of the current 1DM parameters calculation of PVsyst, we propose a fitting method based on an Evolutionary Algorithm (EA). EA are popular to handle non-linear optimization problems and easily adaptable to various problem formulations. They are notably used by some PV module characterization centers in order to produce .PAN files reproducing as closely as possible IEC 61853-1 measured data. In this work, we use a penalty-based differential evolution algorithm which was shown to beat other evolutionary algorithms in reproducing the original two-diode model parameters of synthetically generated data [11].

Our EA fit works by optimizing the set of model parameters of the 1DM. Note that it can also be adapted to find the parameters of the recombination model of section 2.2. Based on the typical available information in product datasheet and low-light performance assumption to reproduce, we write a fitting objective function that needs to be minimized by an optimal set of parameters. This function is written as

$$F_{obj}(Params) = \frac{1}{\sigma_{P_{mpp}}}\left(P_{mpp} - P_{mpp,fit}\right)/P_{mpp}$$
$$+ \frac{1}{\sigma_{V_{mpp}}}\left(V_{mpp} - V_{mpp,fit}\right)/V_{mpp}$$
$$+ \frac{1}{\sigma_{V_{oc}}}\left(V_{oc} - V_{oc,fit}\right)/V_{oc}$$
$$+ \frac{1}{\sigma_{I_{sc}}}\left(I_{sc} - I_{sc,fit}\right)/I_{sc}$$
$$+ \frac{1}{\sigma_{\mu_{P_{mpp}}}}\left(\mu_{P_{mpp}} - \mu_{P_{mpp,fit}}\right)/\mu_{P_{mpp}}$$
$$+ \frac{1}{\sigma_{\mu_{I_{sc}}}}\left(\mu_{I_{sc}} - \mu_{I_{sc,fit}}\right)/\mu_{I_{sc}}$$
$$+ \frac{1}{\sigma_{\mu_{V_{oc}}}}\left(\mu_{V_{oc}} - \mu_{V_{oc,fit}}\right)/\mu_{V_{oc}}$$
$$+ \frac{1}{\sigma_{Rel.eff}}(Rel.\,eff - Rel.\,eff_{fit})/Rel.\,eff$$

where the subscript "fit" indicate the respective values computed by the chosen I-V model for a given set of parameters, the elements without subscripts are the measured values and the σ's represent their respective standard deviation.

The latter is of importance because some input data have much stronger experimental variations. For example, in the case of data obtained from IEC 61853-1 reports, three similar modules are measured. By analyzing reports from several test centers, we observed that while the STC values variation is well below 1% among the three modules, the variation in $\mu_{I_{sc}}$ is of the order of 10%. Likewise, when the low-light efficiency is unknown, we can more generally assume a value of $-4.5\% \pm 2\%$, covering widely all the observable values reported in the literature [9]. Another advantage of this method is that it allows for the use of the $\mu_{V_{oc}}$ information. Note that any other available information that can be computed from an I-V model could be used in this objective function and it could therefore be adapted to reproduce all the measured elements of an IEC 61853-1 report.

3   TEST SCENARIOS

In this section, two case studies are used to compare the parameter evaluation method of the current PVsyst model and the EA fit. In the first case, we focus on reproducing IEC 61853-1 certified data from a real PERC PV module, with a conventional FF value of 78.4%, based solely on the above-cited available information.
In the second case, we repeat the operation with data synthetically generated from the reference recombination model of section 2.2. This emulates a PV module with very high FF (85.7%) and very low relative low-light efficiency (−6.8%), which represents closely the best performance we could expect one day from c-Si PV module and serves as an extreme case to test the presented methods.

3.1 Evolutionary Algorithm Fit for One Diode Model and Standard Fill Factor

Figure 4 shows how the 1DM EA fit reproduces the measured data of the PERC device at all temperatures and irradiances available in its IEC 61853-1 report. The efficiency and the V_{oc} are well fitted at 1000 W/m², but a small discrepancy at low-light level can be seen. This is explained by the fact that the real measured relative low light efficiency for this device ($-6.2\% \pm 1.2\%$) was assumed unavailable and the default value of $-4.5\% \pm 2\%$ was used instead according to our hypothesis on commonly available data.

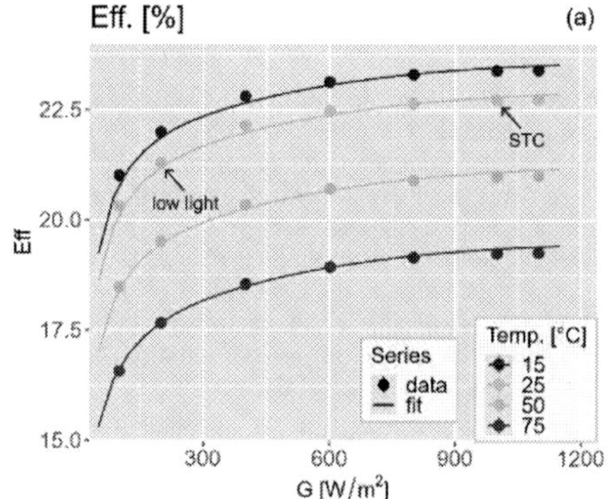

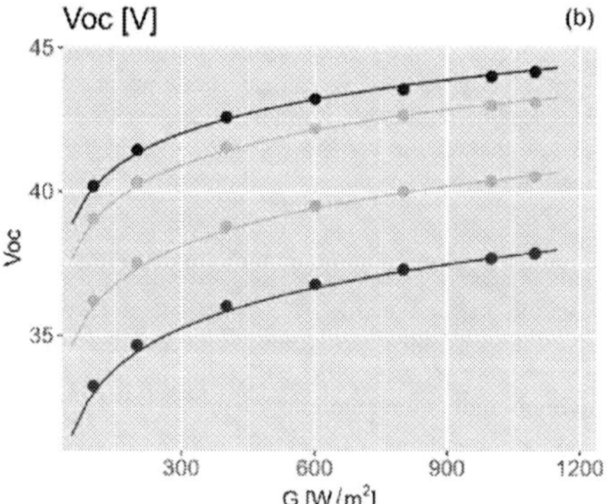

Figure 4: Reproduction of measured IEC 61853-1 data from the EA fit for a conventional FF (78.4%, PERC) based only on limited input ($P_{mpp}, V_{mpp}, V_{oc}, I_{sc}, \mu_{Isc}, \mu_{Voc}, \mu_{Pmpp}$) and conventional assumption on low light efficiency (-4.5% +/- 2%) [9].

Figure 5 shows how the measured parameters are reproduced by (a) the current PVsyst method and (b) the EA fit with the 1DM. Both methods are in good agreement and reproduce the IEC MPP data within 2.5%. The EA fit reduces the error further, close to the tolerated standard deviation of each PV module characteristic. It provides better reproduction of the MPP and V_{oc} data, their temperature coefficients, and reduces error across all temperature and irradiance conditions. This is due to the advantages of the EA fit, which leverages $\mu_{V_{oc}}$ information, variations in $\mu_{I_{sc}}$, and (often unknown) low-light efficiency, whereas PVsyst discards the first and assumes a fixed value for the others.

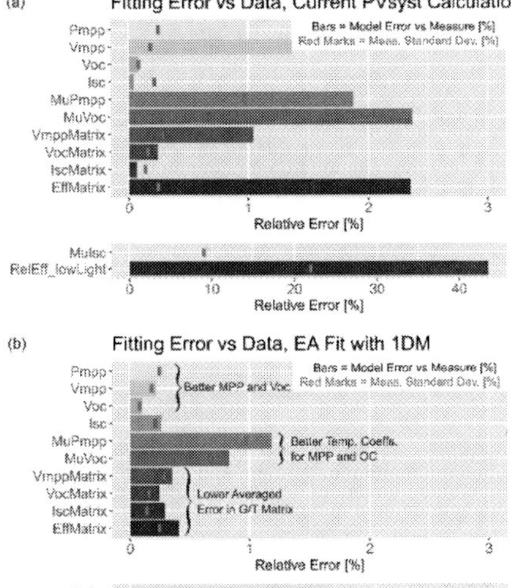

Figure 5: Error from (a) the PVsyst calculated model and (b) the EA fit model in reproducing the IEC 61853-1 data. Pmpp, Vmpp, Voc and Isc refer to the STC conditions, MuPmpp, MuVoc and MuIsc to the temperature coefficients calculated at 1000 W/m² from the data at the different temperatures, VmppMatrix, VocMatrix, IscMatrix and EffMatrix to the corresponding average error in reproducing the data over all the temperatures and illumination, and RelEff_lowLight is the ratio of the efficiency at 1000 W/m² and 200 W/m² (at 25 °C).

3.2 Fitting Synthetic Data for Hypothetical High Fill Factor

Synthetic data for STC values, temperature coefficients and relative low-light efficiency were generated using the recombination model of section 2.2, using input parameters reproducing closely the certified measured data of [1]. Random errors on the temperature and irradiance were added to emulate measurement errors. This scenario raises a caveat, since we are attempting to fit data with a relative low-light efficiency of -6.8% while assuming 4.5% for a modern PV module.

Figure 6 shows the relative error in reproducing P_{mpp} and V_{oc} at temperatures and irradiances relevant to PV system simulations for three approaches. The errors in reproducing P_{mpp} are small for each approach and mainly driven by the low light assumptions. The EA Fit improves even further the results as it does not impose a strict value for the low light efficiency. As expected for this test scenario, the error on V_{oc} by the PVsyst calculation is large, up to 4%. Very interestingly, the EA fit manages to

reduce this error below 0.5%, allowing a very good reproduction of both P_{mpp} and V_{oc} while keeping the same 1DM parametrization as PVsyst. Using the same model parametrization as the reference one used for generating data yields even lower error on the V_{oc}. However, the error on the P_{mpp} becomes larger. We explained this by the fact that this parametrization is less flexible and cannot allow a relative low light efficiency too far from the requested -4.5% without creating discrepancies on the other parameters. Therefore, in the case of unknown low light efficiency, the 1DM parametrization seems the most adapted to reproduce well high FF PV module behavior over all conditions of interest.

4 SUMMARY AND OUTLOOK

Accurately modelling PV module I–V curves across operating conditions remains a key challenge for yield simulations, especially for high-performance devices with high fill factors. The current PVsyst approach, based on direct parameter calculation for the one-diode model, provides reliable estimates but compromises open-circuit voltage reproduction when faced with high-FF technologies.

In this work, we introduced an evolutionary algorithm to improve parameter evaluation for the one-diode model. On measured data from a standard PERC module, the EA fit reduced errors in maximum power point, open-circuit voltage, and temperature coefficients compared to the current method, while robustly handling measurement variability and unavailable low-light performance. For a synthetic high-FF case, the EA successfully lowered V_{oc} reproduction errors from several percent to below 0.5%, demonstrating its ability to capture the voltage-dependent recombination mechanisms characteristic of state-of-the-art c-Si devices.

The results show that evolutionary algorithm provides a flexible framework that can estimate accurately PV performance at all relevant temperature and irradiance conditions based solely on available datasheet information and common low-light assumptions. It does so with greater accuracy than the current PVsyst deterministic calculation especially when low-light efficiency is unknown (leveraging μVoc and typical low-light trends). Importantly, even though the EA method already increases significantly the accuracy of the 1DM evaluation, it enables a straightforward extension to more advanced parametrizations.

This general framework lays the groundwork for more accurate PVsyst .PAN files, ensuring robust energy yield simulations for the next generation of PV technologies. Future work will focus on validating the approach with high-FF commercial modules. The possible exploitation of the full IEC matrix also offers promising prospects. The sensitivity to missing or inconsistent data (e.g. product datasheet v.s. certified IEC report) should be studied in more details. Finally, this case study focused exclusively on PV modules of a single power class. Other power classes could not be evaluated due to the lack of certified measurements; however, it would be valuable to investigate them once manufacturers provide standardized data.

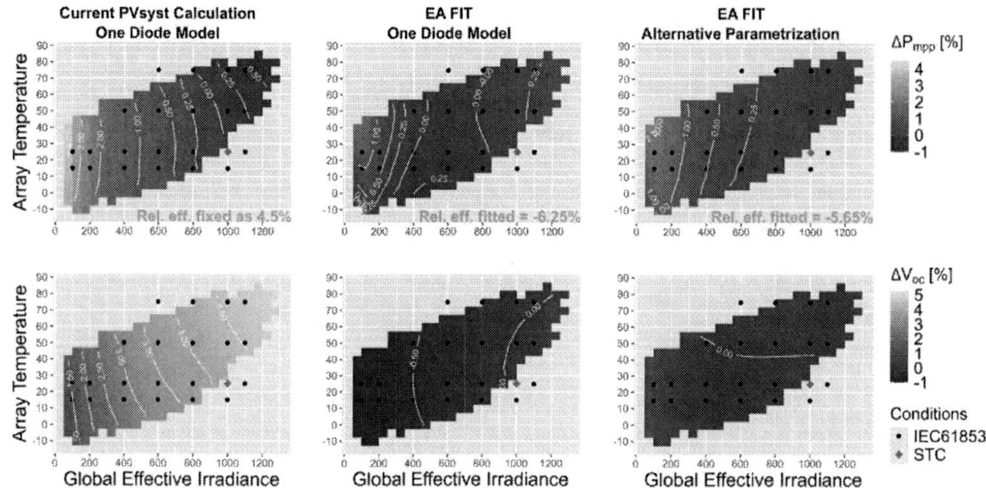

Figure 6: Relative error on Voc and Pmpp in reproducing the synthetic data for relevant temperatures and irradiances, either using the current PVsyt calculation with the 1DM, the EA fit with the 1DM, or the EA fit with the reference model parametrization (same as the one used for generating the synthetic data, denoted as "alternative parametrization"). The black dots references represent the mandatory measurement conditions within the IEC 61853-1 norm and the STC are marked by a red square.

5 ACKNOWLEDGEMENTS

We acknowledge Sandia National laboratories, KIWA PVEL, Groundwork Renewables, Supsi PVLAB, and EPFL PV-LAB, for fruitful discussion and guidance on the topic.

REFERENCES

[1] H. Lin, G. Wang, Q. Su, C. Han, C. Xue, S. Yin, L. Fang, X. Xu and P. Gao, "Unveiling the mechanism of attaining high fill factor in silicon solar cells," *Progress in Photovoltaics: Research and Applications*, vol. 32, p. 359–371, June 2024.

[2] A. Mermoud and T. Lejeune, "Performance assessment of a simulation model for PV modules of any available technology," 2010.

[3] L. E. Black e D. H. Macdonald, «On the quantification of Auger recombination in crystalline silicon,» *Solar Energy Materials and Solar Cells*, vol. 234, p. 111428, January 2022.

[4] T. Niewelt, B. Steinhauser, A. Richter, B. Veith-Wolf, A. Fell, B. Hammann, N. E. Grant, L. Black, J. Tan, A. Youssef, J. D. Murphy, J. Schmidt, M. C. Schubert and S. W. Glunz, "Reassessment of the intrinsic bulk recombination in crystalline silicon," *Solar Energy Materials and Solar Cells*, vol. 235, p. 111467, January 2022.

[5] P. P. Altermatt, "Models for numerical device simulations of crystalline silicon solar cells—a review," *Journal of Computational Electronics*, vol. 10, p. 314–330, September 2011.

[6] A. Schenk, "Finite-temperature full random-phase approximation model of band gap narrowing for silicon device simulation," *Journal of Applied Physics*, vol. 84, p. 3684–3695, October 1998.

[7] A. Richter, M. Hermle e S. W. Glunz, «Reassessment of the Limiting Efficiency for Crystalline Silicon Solar Cells,» *IEEE Journal of Photovoltaics*, vol. 3, p. 1184–1191, October 2013.

[8] S. Schafer and R. Brendel, "Accurate Calculation of the Absorptance Enhances Efficiency Limit of Crystalline Silicon Solar Cells With Lambertian Light Trapping," *IEEE Journal of Photovoltaics*, vol. 8, p. 1156–1158, July 2018.

[9] U. Kräling, P. Gebhardt, M. Kaiser and D. Philipp, "PV module performance measurements – statistical analysis of technological trends," 2022.

[10] A. Bridel-Bertomeu, M. Oliosi, A. Mermoud and B. Wittmer, "Limits of the single diode model in view of its application to the latest PV cell technologies," 2023.

[11] K. Ishaque, Z. Salam, H. Taheri and A. Shamsudin, "A critical evaluation of EA computational methods for Photovoltaic cell parameter extraction based on two diode model," *Solar Energy*, vol. 85, p. 1768–1779, September 2011.

A photovoltaic performance dataset for benchmarking of failure detection and diagnosis algorithms

J.D. Santos [a] (jose.santos@tecnalia.com), S. Riaño [a], A. Lucea [a], M. Jankovec [b], A. Del Pozo [a], R. Alonso [a], A. Sanz [a]

[a] TECNALIA, Parque Científico y Tecnológico de Bizkaia, Astondo Bidea, Edificio 700. E-48160 Derio (Bizkaia), Spain
[b] UNIVERSITY OF LJUBLJANA, Faculty of Electrical Engineering, Tržaška cesta 25, 1000 Ljubljana, Slovenia

EU PVSEC — 3AV.3.36

INTRODUCTION

- The development of algorithms for remote identification of failures from SCADA data requires PV datasets with known degradation modes. However, publicly available PV datasets often present a lack of information on existing failures. Synthetic datasets with software simulated degradation, while useful, do not reflect the complexity of real PV systems.
- To address this gap, this work present a new dataset based on the continuous monitoring of a set of PV modules with well-characterized failure modes. Designed for O&M applications, this PV performance dataset is shared open-access with the PV community within the SERENDIPV and CACTUS projects.

EXPERIMENTAL SETUP

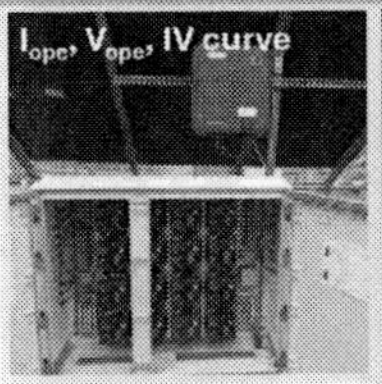

PV Monitoring System

- LPVO-MS1X16 system continuously monitored the performance of each PV module.
- Operating voltage and current (V_{OPE} & I_{OPE}) measured by MPPTs with 1-min frequency.
- Entire IV curve of each module characterized by an IV tracer with 5-min frequency.
- Plane-of-array irradiance (G_{POA}) measured synchronously with a combination of pyranometer and calibrated solar cell.
- PV module temperature (T_{MOD}) measured at the center and corner of each device.
- Environmental conditions such as global horizontal irradiance (GHI), air temperature, relative humidity, and wind speed (WS) recorded simultaneously.

PV modules and Failure modes

- The PV modules set included four different manufacturers and three solar cell technologies.
- JASolar modules were new and showed no defects. JASolar1 was used as the reference for benchmarking.
- JASolar2 and JASolar3 were used to simulate, through fabricated resistance boxes, the impact that some failure modes have on increasing series resistance (R_{SERIE}) and decreasing shunt resistance (R_{SHUNT}).
- Ningbo, Trinasolar and Photowatt exhibited combinations of failure modes caused by long-term exposure to harsh operation conditions in Spanish PV plants. Atersa showed defects associated with improper handling.
- Failure modes were identified by combining indoor IV curve, visual inspection and electroluminescence.

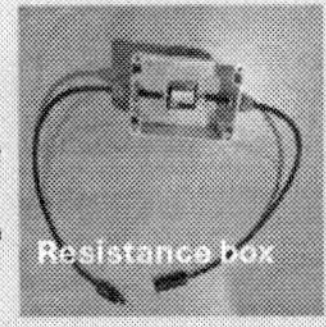

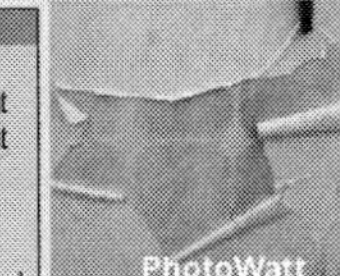

Manufacturer	Cell technology	Label Pmax	State	Main failure modes
JA Solar	Mono / PERC / 5 busbars	315 W	As new	None - Reference
JA Solar	Mono / PERC / 5 busbars	315 W	As new	Artificially higher Rserie or lower Rshunt
JA Solar	Mono / PERC / 5 busbars	315 W	As new	Artificially higher Rserie or lower Rshunt
Ningbo Solar	Mono / Al-BSF / 2 busbars	210 W	Degraded	Yellowing / Interconnect ribbon break
Trina Solar	Mono / Al-BSF / 2 busbars	185 W	Degraded	Internal circuitry corrosion
Atersa	Mono / PERC / 5 busbars	330 W	Degraded	MicroCracks / Shorted solar cells
PhotoWatt	Poly / Al-BSF / 2 busbars	160 W	Degraded	Solar cell cracks / Interconnect ribbon break

RESULTS

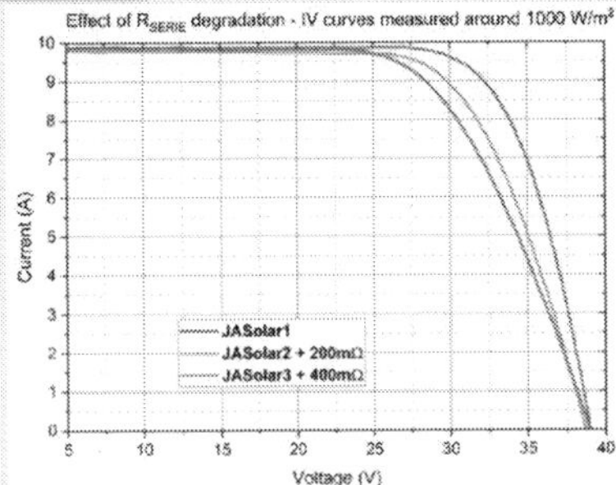

R_{SERIE} impact on IV curve

- Failure modes like internal circuitry corrosion cause an increase in the R_{SERIE} of the PV module.
- Impact of R_{SERIE} degradation on PV performance was investigated by connecting resistance boxes of 200 mΩ and 400 mΩ in series with JASolar2 and JASolar3.
- IV curves measured in outdoor conditions at $G_{POA} \approx 1000$ W/m² were filtered to show how R_{SERIE} degradation altered the shape of the IV curve, affecting MPP voltage or fill factor (FF) among other parameters

R_{SERIE} impact on irradiance dependence of FF

- Continuous monitoring enabled the study of how different failures affect the dependence of PV performance on operation conditions.
- Impact of R_{SERIE} increase on the FF was investigated as function of G_{POA}.
- R_{SERIE} degradation caused significant differences with reference FF (JASolar1) for $G_{POA} > 300$ W/m².
- At 1000 W/m², FF values ≈75% and ≈65% were measured for JASolar1 and JASolar3 respectively.

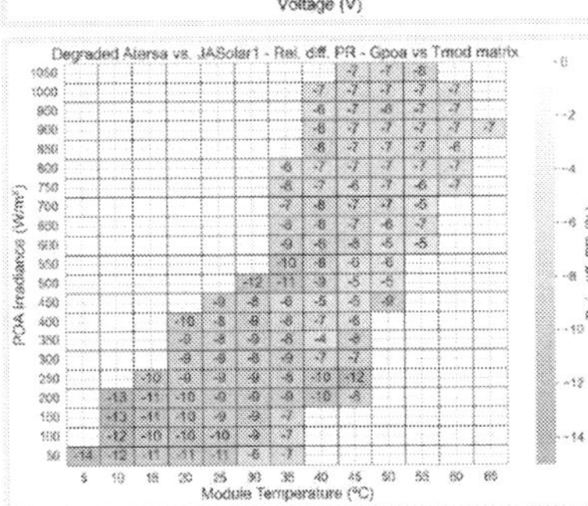

G_{POA} & T_{MOD} dependence of PR – Atersa vs. JASolar1

- Relative difference in performance ratio (PR) between Atersa and JASolar1 was plotted as G_{POA} vs. T_{MOD} matrix analogous to IEC 61853-1.
- Atersa showed a PR a 6-7% lower than JASolar1 for $G_{POA} > 800$ W/m².
- Rel. diff. PR between Atersa and JASolar1 was sensitive to changes in operating conditions, reaching -14% at $G_{POA} = 50$ W/m² and $T_{MOD} = 5$ºC.
- For $G_{POA} < 600$ W/m², rel. diff PR seemed to become more negative as T_{MOD} decreased.

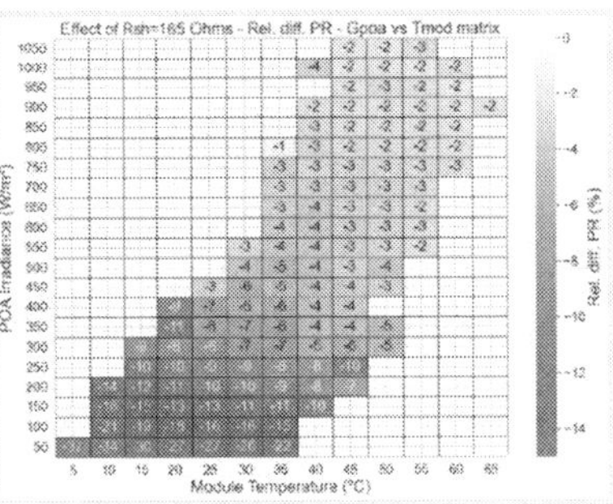

G_{POA} & T_{MOD} dependence of PR - Lower R_{SHUNT} + JASolar3 vs. JASolar1

- Failure modes such as potential induced degradation cause a reduction in R_{SHUNT} of the PV module.
- Impact of R_{SHUNT} degradation was investigated by connecting a 165 Ω resistance box in parallel to JASolar3.
- JASolar3 showed a 2-3% lower PR than JASolar1 for $G_{POA} > 800$ W/m². JASolar3 presented a 20-30% lower PR than JASolar1 for $G_{POA} < 100$ W/m².
- For a given POA irradiance interval, the R_{SHUNT} degradation also led to lower PR values as T_{MOD} decreased.

Funded by the European Union

This project has received funding from the European Union's Horizon Europe research and innovation programme under grant agreement No. 953016 and No. 101132182.

SERENDIPV — CACTUS

Reliability of quantitative analysis of lock-in electroluminescence images of PV modules based on histogram statistical parameters

3AV.3.37

J.D. Santos [a] (jose.santos@tecnalia.com), E. Setien [a], A. Del Pozo [a], L. Stoicescu [b], A. Villodas [a], A. Lucea [a], A. Pereda [a], R. Alonso [a]

[a] TECNALIA, Parque Científico y Tecnológico de Bizkaia, Astondo Bidea, Edificio 700. E-48160 Derio (Bizkaia), Spain
[b] SOLARZENTRUM STUTTGART GMBH, Rotebühlstr. 145 70197 Stuttgart, Germany

INTRODUCTION

- Electroluminescence (EL) imaging is a standard for quality control during the manufacturing process of photovoltaic (PV) modules, offering the broadest catalogue of detectable failure modes. In recent years, the PV community has increased efforts to extend its use for the operation and maintenance (O&M) of PV systems.
- One example is the research on lock-in EL, which has noticeably increased the range of operation of this tool, providing high quality images under daylight conditions. Another example is the IEC TS 60904-13:2018, putting the basis to obtain high-quality and reproducible EL images, opening the possibility for their later quantitative analysis.
- This last topic is particularly relevant for the PV O&M sector since it enables the assessment of the PV module/array performance from EL image analysis. However, studies on how measurement conditions affect the quantitative information from EL images remain limited.
- This work provides insights into how measurements conditions affect the histogram-based statistical parameters proposed in IEC TS 60904-13 for the quantitative analysis of EL images.

EXPERIMENTAL SETUP

- A DaySy Pro 1000 developed by SolarZentrum Stuttgart was used as the lock-in EL characterization system.
- The reference PV module was a JA Solar model JAP60S09/280SC composed of 60 pc-Si solar cells with Al-BSF technology.
- A mobile metallic structure was developed to easily modify the camera-module relative position and the module orientation.
- A monitoring system was developed to continuously record GTI irradiance, module temperature, current, and voltage during EL characterization.
- EL images were corrected in compliance with IEC TS 60904-13 (vignetting effect, barrel distortion, and perspective) using the PVScan software developed by Tecnalia.
- The module and individual solar cell areas were automatically detected by using an algorithm developed for this purpose.
- From the associated histogram, different statistical parameters like mean or standard deviation were calculated and used as state-of-health indicators of solar cells/module.

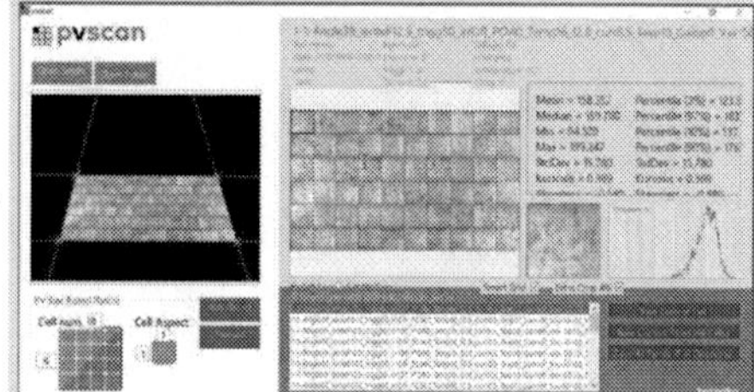

CHARACTERIZATION

Indoor vs. Outdoor

EL images were captured at different irradiance level to test its effect on quantitative analysis. The influence of exposure time on the response of the lock-in EL system was also studied. Qualitative analysis showed that EL image quality was comparable both indoors and outdoors.

Perspective vs. distance

EL images were captured at different relative module-camera angles and distances. Thus, the study provides information about the influence of perspective correction and limited pixel size on the results of the quantitative analysis of EL images.

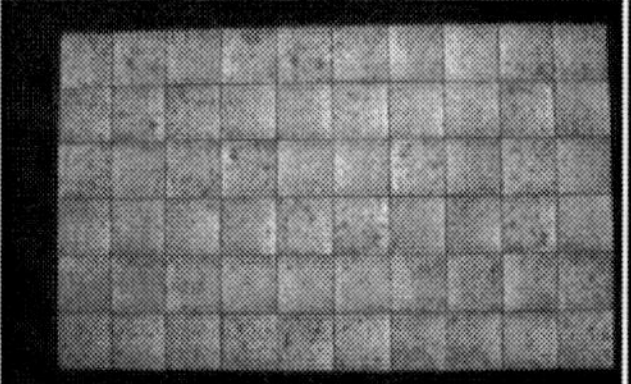

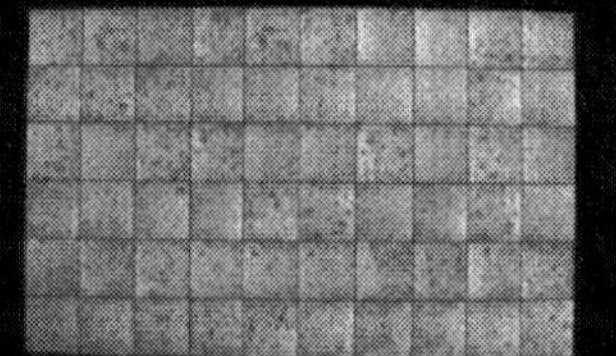

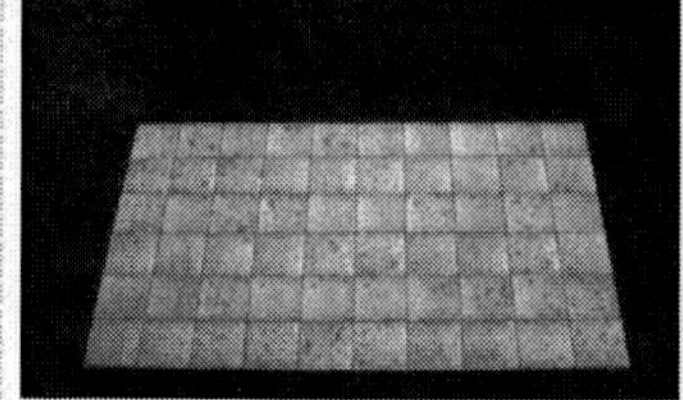

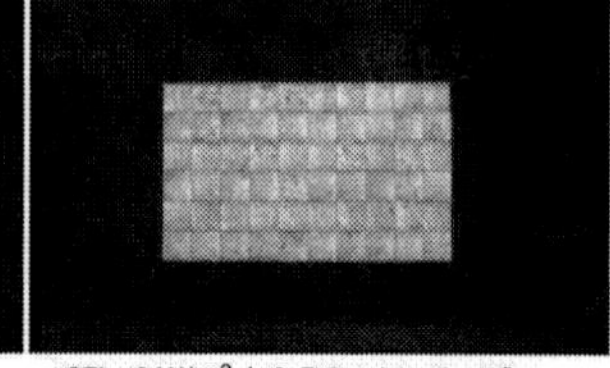

GTI = 0 W/m² / f1.4 / texp = 10 ms

GTI = 850 W/m² / f2.8 / texp= 10 ms

GTI = 0 W/m² / d = 2.6 m / angle=37°

GTI = 0 W/m² / d=5.2m / angle=0°

RESULTS

Indoor vs. Outdoor – EL intensity distribution

The normalized mean at cell level is plotted for EL images captured indoors and outdoors. The same pattern was observed for the normalized mean at 0 and 850 W/m². Cell (X8,Y1) shows the highest intensity, and cell (X1,Y6) the lowest. However, discrepancies in the absolute values indicate that environmental light may introduce some uncertainty.

Perspective

The increase in the relative camera-module angle causes a progressive decrease in measured mean intensity. A 5% reduction is obtained by increasing the relative angle from 0° to 37°. Additionally, the normalized StdDev decreased by 10%, suggesting that information about heterogeneity in the PV intensity distribution is lost.

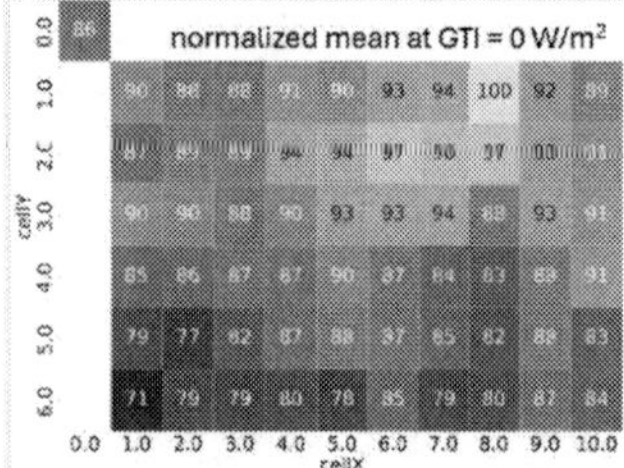

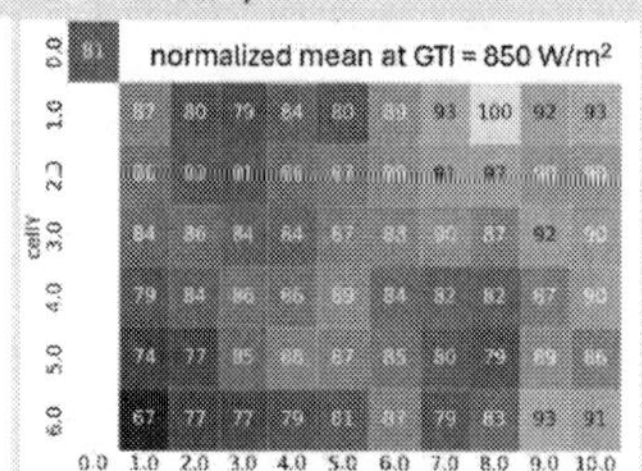

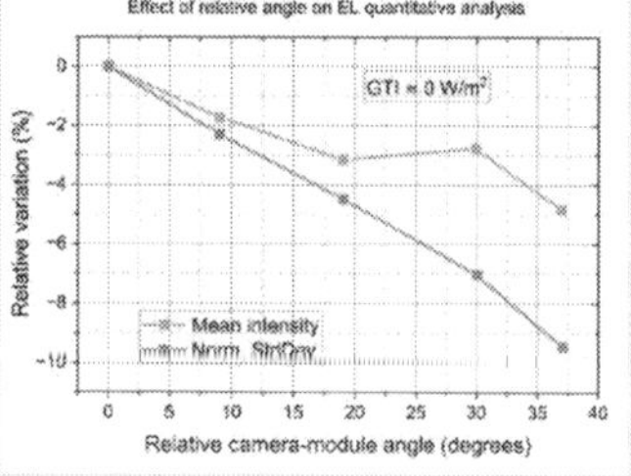

Indoor vs. Outdoor - Linearity

Exposure time (texp) must be adjusted to maximize image intensity. A linear response of the lock-in EL system allows the quantitative analysis of EL images captured at different texp. An excellent linearity is observed indoors and outdoors with R²=0.999. At GTI=500 W/m², the first signs of sensor saturation are observed at 15 ms.

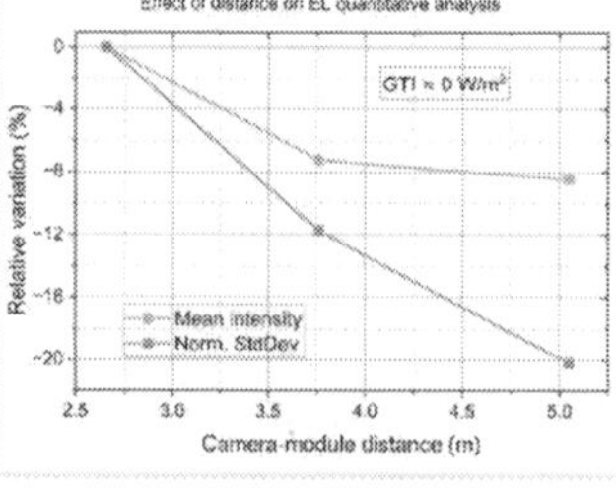

Distance

The increase in camera-module distance leads to a reduction of the captured EL mean intensity. An 8% decrease is obtained when increasing the camera-module distance from 2.6 to 5.2 m. The normalized StdDev is noticeably affected by distance increase. A relative decreased of 20% from 2.6 to 5.2 m due to limited camera resolution.

Funded by Department of Economic Development, Sustainability and Environment of the Basque Government under ref. KK2022/0067

Co-funded by the European Union

This project is co-funded by the European Union under Grant Agreement n° 101146883.

DEVELOPMENT OF A ROOFTOP MOCK-UP COVERED WITH PV PANELS FOR TEMPERATURE FLUX MEASUREMENTS

Michael Schrempf[1]* and Stefan Riechelmann[1]

[1]*Physikalisch-Technische Bundesanstalt* (PTB), Braunschweig, Germany

*Corresponding author: michael.schrempf@ptb.de

ABSTRACT:

This work describes a realistic small-scale rooftop setup of an urban house that was built at the Physikalisch-Technische Bundesanstalt (PTB) in Braunschweig, Germany. The setup consists of two identical chambers, where one side of the roof is covered with installed PV panels while the other side is uncovered. Temperature sensors are placed at various positions and different depths of the roof to measure the temperature flux between the inside and outside of the setup. Combined with auxiliary measurements, including the erection of a 17-meter-high measuring mast, results of these measurements will be used to validate a new PV parameterization of the Large-Eddy Simulation (LES) model PALM.

Keywords: PV Module, temperature flux, Palm

1 INTRODUCTION

Model simulations are a key tool to understand the effect of area-wide PV deployment in urban areas on the outdoor and indoor urban microclimate in terms of thermal comfort of residents and air quality. For this purpose, project partners from the Leibniz University Hannover and Technical University of Dresden plan to implement a new parameterization for rooftop PV panels in the LES model PALM [1] to calculate heat transport by convection or thermal radiation. Its application for simulating and analyzing the effects of the widespread installation of PV panels under realistic atmospheric conditions is intended to resolve previous contradictory results. These include, for example, whether comprehensive PV installations in cities lead to a cooling or warming of the urban atmosphere during the day [2]. Furthermore, the complex flow around the buildings has not been resolved in previous studies.

To validate the new parameterization for rooftop PV panels in the LES model PALM a small-scale outdoor setup simulating a city-like rooftop was built. The setup is placed on top of a 12 m high building at PTB to ensure similar wind conditions to city housings. The advantage of developing and building a small-scale, realistic new roof, instead of using already existing roofs, is that both situations having PV and having a bare roof are realized in a very well-defined way. Multiple temperature sensors can easily be integrated at different locations and levels within the roof during construction based on the needs of the experiment. Furthermore, the dimensions and coefficients of the materials used are known in detail, which is crucial as input data for the simulation model.

2 SETUP

The rooftop setup is based on a realistic rooftop of an urban house. To investigate the differences in temperature flux for a rooftop with and without PV panels, the interior of the setup is divided into two separately insolated chambers. One side of the roof being covered with installed PV panels and the other exposed to sunlight.

Figure 1: Small-scale rooftop installation with PV panels on one side of the roof.

2.1 Construction details

The basic structure consists of wooden beams, which are clad on the outside with oriented strand board (OSB) panels. The setup has a length of approx. 6 m, a width of 2 m and a height of about 2 m. The interior walls, the floor and the roof are insulated with wood fiber insulation materials from the brand Steico which has a declared thermal conductivity of 0.036 W/(m*K). The roof was insulated with 10 cm of insulation to represent typical existing houses, whereas newly built houses have thicker insulation. In addition to the insulation, the roof consists of an airtight barrier. The tiles used in this rooftop setup were concrete tiles from the brand Braas and the type "Frankfurter Pfanne" which are widespread in Germany. A cross section of the roof construction and its used elements is shown in Fig. 2.

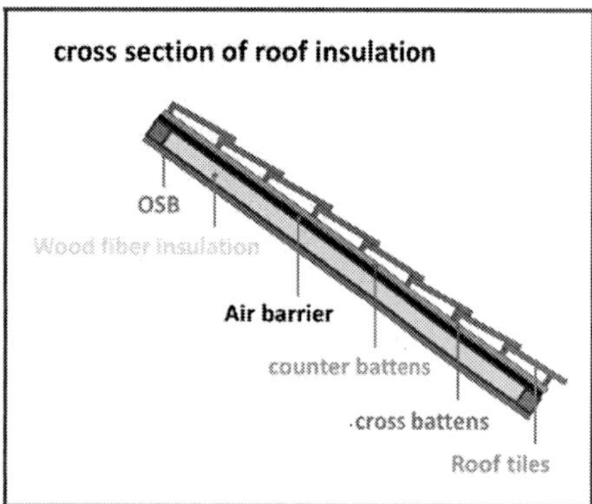

Figure 2: Extracts from the construction plan for the roof.

The walls and floor, on the other hand, were insulated much more heavily to reduce heat transfer to a minimum, so observed effects can be attributed to front-side irradiance.

The insulation of the wall consists of a 10 cm flexible wood fiber and 6 cm wood fiber boards. The bottom consists of a 16 cm wood fiber bottom insulation. This kind of insulation is walkable, so the chambers can therefore be entered for installation and inspection purposes. Since the setup consists of two separately insolated chambers, each chamber has a hatch for accessibility. A cross section of the wall and bottom insulation is shown in Fig. 3.

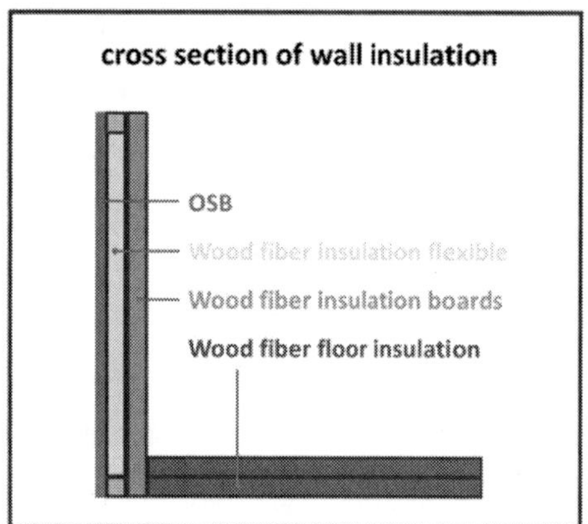

Figure 3: Extracts from the construction plan for the wall.

To measure the heat transfer between the inside and outside of the setup, 65 PT-100 temperature sensors were placed at 10 different positions that are illustrated in Fig. 4. For each position temperature sensors are placed at different levels in the roof during construction (e.g. bottom and center of roof tile as shown in Fig. 5 or on the inside wall of the rooftop setup as shown in Fig. 6. Table 1 lists all levels of the temperature sensors for both chambers. Four additional temperature sensors (two for each side of the setup) were placed on the surface of the air barrier and another four additional sensors were placed between the air barrier and the roof tiles.

Table 1: List of levels in which temperature sensors are placed in the rooftop setup for the sides with and without PV panels.

Level	Description of placing	PV	No PV
	Indoor room	x	x
1	Indoor wall	x	x
2	Interior side of insulation	x	x
3	Bottom of roof tile	x	x
4	Center of roof tile	x	x
5	Surface of roof tile	x	
6	Between roof and module	x	
7	Backside of solar module	x	
	Additional sensors on the surface of air barrier	x	x
	Additional sensors between air barrier & roof tile	x	x

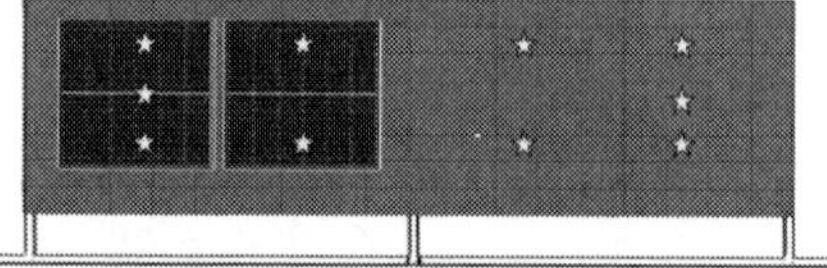

Figure 4: Different positions of the temperature sensors on the rooftop setup.

Figure 5 shows the wiring and placing of the temperature sensors between the air barrier and the roof tiles during construction.

The finished roof structure was painted with white weather protection paint to reduce the heating of the walls due to solar radiation and to protect the structure from weather conditions (see Fig 1).

Figure 5: Placement of the temperature sensors on the roof during construction.

Figure 6: Interior view of one of the chambers of the roof structure, with temperature sensors placed on the inside wall of the roof.

2.2 Data Acquisition and auxiliary Measurements

All PT-100 temperature sensors are connected to a datalogger via a 3-wire connection. In addition to the temperature measurements, incoming solar radiation is measured with two pyranometers. One pyranometer measures the global horizontal irradiance and the second pyranometer measures the irradiance in-plane of the PV panels of the setup. General weather parameters such as ambient air temperature, humidity and air pressure are measured with a weather station near the setup. The wind speed and wind direction is measured with three ultrasonic anemometers, installed at different positions near the setup. Two of the wind sensors are placed in front of the setup and one is placed on the side next to the setup. In addition, a vane anemometer is used to assess the wind speed in the air gap between the roof tiles and the PV panels. These various auxiliary measurements are recorded to obtain a picture of the temperature flux as complete as possible.

Both the data logger and all other devices are connected to a PC via different interfaces. All these electronics are installed in a weatherproof and climatized outdoor enclosure outside of the setup to avoid bringing an additional heat source into the rooftop setup. To capture the power production of the PV panels, the connected micro-inverter is read out via a Data Transfer Unit (DTU).

In addition to the above-mentioned parameters, the prevailing wind field is needed to model the rooftop setup with the model PALM. To determine the direction and speed of the prevailing wind field, a 17-meter-high measuring mast was erected a short distance from the building on which the rooftop setup was built (see Fig. 7). Three-dimensional measuring Ultrasonic wind sensors are mounted at three different heights (5,10 and 16m) to determine these parameters.

The Measurements are recorded every second for all instruments mentioned above.

Figure 7: Measuring mast with a total height of 17m and wind sensors at different heights to measure the prevailing wind field.

3   RESULTS

For a first analysis of the data of temperature sensors we averaged all data points of the 5 sensors of each level of one day for the left and right chamber respectively. As a result, the diurnal temperature variation of a sunny day from July 1st 2025 is shown in Figure 3 and Figure 4. As a next step the measurement data for all months will be analyzed for variations between different positions and different days and seasons.

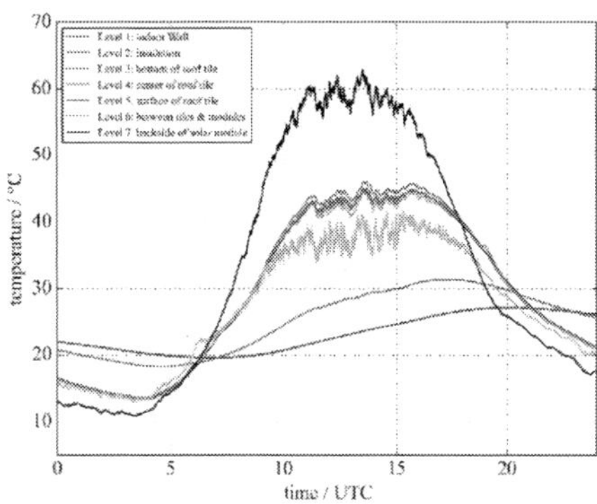

Figure 3: Diurnal temperature variation of a clear sky day of the chamber with installed PV panels.

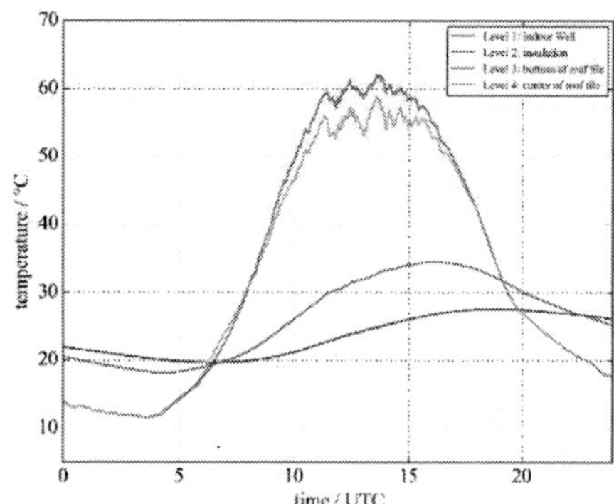

Figure 4: Diurnal temperature variation of a clear sky day of the chamber without PV panels,

4 CONCLUSION

We presented a description of the construction of a realistic rooftop of an urban house. The interior of the setup is divided into two separately insolated chambers in which 65 temperature sensors were integrated to investigate the differences in temperature flux for a rooftop with and without PV panels. One side of the roof being covered with installed PV panels and the other exposed to sunlight. This way, we can accurately distinguish the effect of the panels on this setup. Various auxiliary measurements have been set up and are recorded to obtain a picture of the temperature flux as complete as possible. This data will be used as necessary input data for the LES model PALM to validate its new PV parametrization.

5 ACKNOWLEDGEMENT

This work was funded within the project „EUPHORIC“ by the German Research Foundation (DFG), Germany (funding reference number 515096414).

Special thanks to Laura Stenzig[1] und Jörn Hauffe[1] for their help in the construction of the rooftop setup.

6 REFERENCES

[1] Maronga, B., G. Gross, S. Raasch, S. Banzhaf, R. Forkel, W. Heldens, F. Kanani-Sühring, A. Matzarakis, M. Mauder, D. Pavlik, J. Pfafferott, S. Schubert, G. Seckmeyer, H. Sieker, and K. Winderlich, 2019: "Development of a new urban climate model based on the model PALM - Project overview, planned work, and first achievements", Meteorol. Z., 28, 105–119.

[2] Sailor, D. J., J. Anand, and R. R. King, 2021: "Photovoltaics in the built environment: A critical review", *Energy & Buildings*, 253, 111479. DOI: 10.1016/j.enbuild.2021.111479.

Physikalisch-Technische Bundesanstalt
National Metrology Institute

Michael Schrempf, Stefan Riechelmann

Development of a rooftop mock-up covered with PV panels for temperature flux measurements

Realistic small-scale rooftop for validation of model parameterization

- Model simulations are a key tool to understand the effect of area-wide PV deployment in urban areas on the outdoor and indoor urban microclimate in terms of thermal comfort of residents and air quality.

- To validate a new parameterization for rooftop PV panels in the LES model PALM, we built a realistic small-scale rooftop typical for German cities at the Physikalisch-Technische Bundesanstalt (PTB) in Braunschweig.

- The rooftop consists of two identical chambers with one side of the roof being covered with installed PV panels and the other exposed to sunlight.

- Multiple temperature sensors are integrated in this rooftop setup that are placed at various positions and different layers of the roof to measure the temperature flux between the inside and outside of the rooftop.

Fig. 1: Location of the setup on top of a building.   *Fig. 2: small scale city-like rooftop*

Setup & construction of the small-scale rooftop

The setup is placed on top of a 12 m high building at PTB to ensure similar wind conditions to city housing. The structure consists of wooden beams, which are cladded on the outside with oriented strand board (OSB) panels.

- Dimensions are approx. 6 m x 2 m x 2 m (L x W x H).

- Roof insulation is 10 cm to represent typical existing houses.

- Walls and floor, were insulated much more heavily to reduce heat transfer to a minimum

- A white weather protection paint was used to reduce the heating of the walls due to solar radiation and to protect the structure from the weather (Fig. 2).

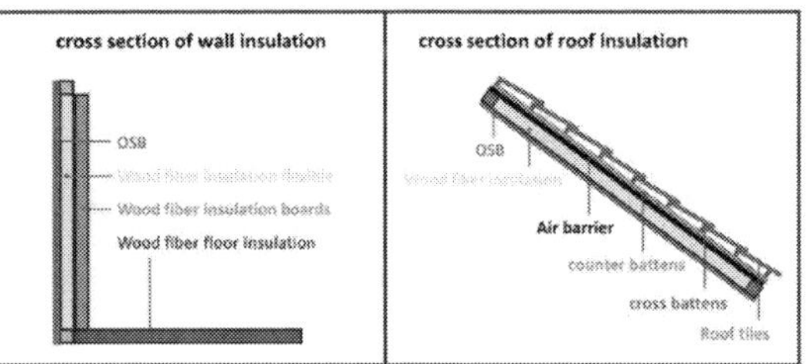

Fig. 3: Extracts from the construction plan for the walls and the roof

Instrumentation and sensors

To measure the temperature flux between the inside and outside of the setup, over 60 temperature sensors were placed at different positions and at different levels.(e.g. indoor room temperature, inside wall of setup, inside of insulation, air gap under roof tiles, inside of roof tiles, back side of PV modules).

Further instrumentation to provide atmospheric input data for the model:

- pyranometers for horizontal and in-plane irradiance.

- weather station (ambient temperature, humidity, …).

- several ultra sonic wind sensors around the setup.

- wind measurements between module and roof tiles.

- 17m high measuring mast for prevailing wind field measurements at different heights.

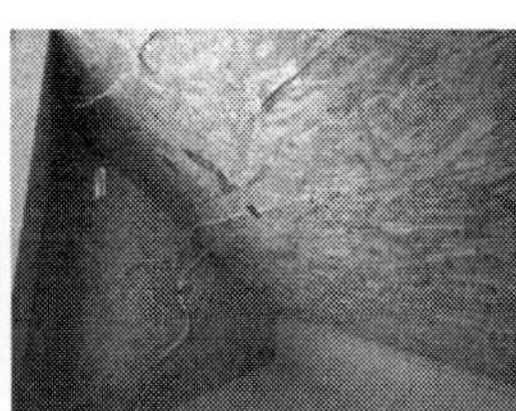

Fig. 4: Temperature sensors are being placed   *Fig. 5: Indoor View of the setup with sensors at the inside of the roof*   *Fig. 6: 17 m high measuring mast for prevailing wind field measurements*

Measurements of diurnal temperature variation

Data Acquisition

- Measurements are recorded for all instruments every second.

- Data logger, Interfaces and PC are placed in a weatherproof outdoor enclosure outside of the setup to avoid bringing extra heat in the setup.

First Results:

- Figure 7 shows the diurnal temperature variation of different temperature sensors of a clear sky day for the chamber with installed PV panels and the chamber without.

- For this day in the afternoon, the chamber with installed PV panels has an approx. 1°C lower indoor temperature.

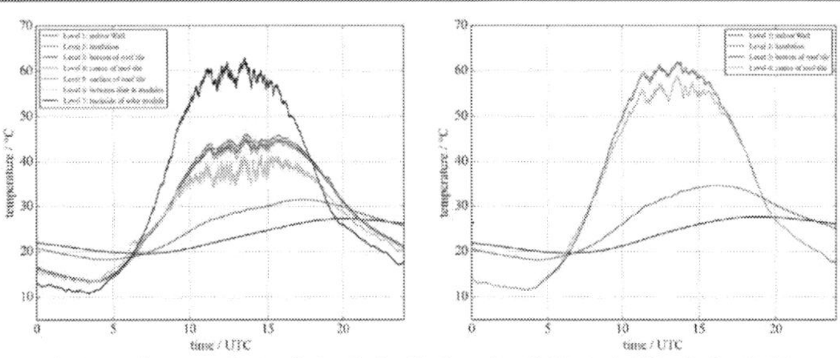

Fig. 7: Diurnal temperate variation of a clear sky day. Chamber with installed PV panels (left) and without (right)

The project „EUPHORIC" was funded by the German Research Foundation (DFG), Germany

Physikalisch-Technische Bundesanstalt
National Metrology Institute

Bundesallee 100
38116 Braunschweig, Germany
www.ptb.de

Michael Schrempf
Working Group 4.53
Solar Modules
phone: +49 531 592-4533
e-mail: michael.schrempf@ptb.de

INVESTIGATING THE IMPACT OF CELL CRACKS ON POWER LOSS AND ITS CORRELATION WITH THE MODELLING PARAMETERS.

Ahmad Hashem[1,2], Zonghan Jiang[1], Guido Willers[2], Leila Mortazavifar[1], Bengt Jaeckel [1,2] and Ralph Gottschalg[1,2]

[1]Hochschule Anhalt - Anhalt University of Applied Sciences, Bernburger Str. 55, 06366, Köthen, Germany
[2]Fraunhofer Center for Silicon Photovoltaics CSP, Otto-Eissfeldt-Str. 12, 06120 Halle (Saale), Germany
Email: ahmad.hashem@hs-anhalt.de

ABSTRACT: Assessing the reliability of photovoltaic (PV) cells—the fundamental units of any solar installation—is essential for ensuring optimal system performance. Cell cracking in PV modules is an inevitable outcome of lifecycle mechanical and thermal stresses, yet its implications for performance and safety continue to complicate module valuation. This study proposes a rigorous framework to quantify the relationships among crack extent, power loss, and equivalent-circuit parameters. Paired electroluminescence (EL) images and I–V curves were acquired on PERC modules with varying busbar (BB) counts under solar-simulator conditions. EL images were processed to detect busbars and to measure aggregate crack length, while I–V data collected across multiple irradiance levels were fitted using single-diode models to extract key parameters. A statistical correlation analysis was then performed to link crack metrics with the extracted parameters and measured power loss. For large crack lengths, crack extent shows a weak negative correlation with shunt resistance and a slight positive correlation with series resistance; power loss is weakly inversely related to shunt resistance and increases modestly with crack length under the same conditions. The proposed framework delivers a quantitative basis for evaluating cracked modules and informing performance and safety judgments.
Keywords: PV Modelling, Electroluminescence, Crack Detection, Power Loss, Shunt Resistance

1 INTRODUCTIION

Cracks in PV cells may originate at multiple stages—silicon ingot slicing, cell fabrication, module lamination, improper transport or installation, and environmental loading such as snow, wind, or hail [1–2]. For performance assessment, the primary focus is on cracks that arise from module production through end-of-life, as these most directly affect energy yield. Numerous taxonomies exist, differentiating cracks by physical extent, orientation relative to the metallization grid, and penetration depth. For example, they are often classified by extent as complete—spanning continuously from one cell edge to the opposite—or incomplete—terminating within the cell interior [3]. Further distinctions separate single from multiple cracks, with subtypes including double, dendritic, and small X- or V-shaped fissures. Orientation-based schemes categorize cracks relative to busbars [4–6], identifying parallel, perpendicular, and ±45° (diagonal) orientations, as well as dendritic and multidirectional patterns.

Cracks degrade module performance by interrupting current pathways and elevating resistive losses; consequently, affected cells may dissipate power instead of generating it, lowering overall efficiency. Several studies report a direct relationship among crack count, crack length, and power loss [7–10], as illustrated in Figure 1. However, this assumption is contestable for several reasons: (i) narrow line cracks typically exert far less influence than inactive cell areas; (ii) severity depends on wafer and metallization design, since increasing busbar count reduces worst-case crackable area and improves current collection [11]; and (iii) system topology matters—multiple cracks within the same module substring can produce an effect equivalent to a single dominant crack.

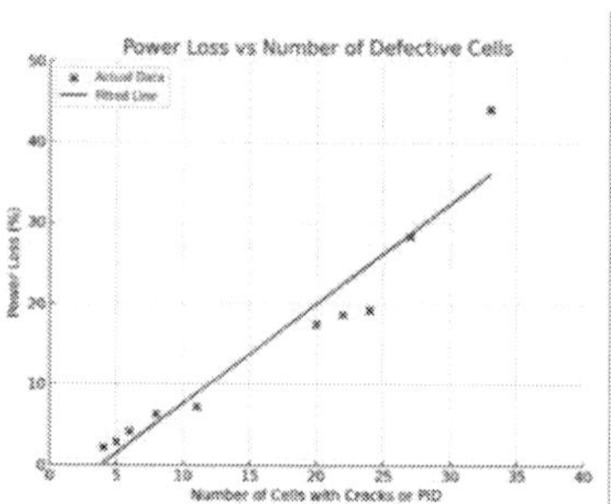

Figure 1: Correlation between the number of cracked cell and corresponding power loss (%) [9]

2 METHODOLOGY

2.1 Image Processing

OpenCV-based pipeline was developed to quantify crack length from EL images, comprising four stages: perspective correction, cell detection, busbar removal, and crack detection/measurement. A perspective transform based on the module outline and known physical dimensions ensures metric accuracy. Detected cell contours are arranged into a regular matrix to derive per-cell pixel dimensions and establish a pixel-to-length conversion factor. To prevent structural interference, busbars are identified via their vertical, linear signature using columnwise intensity sums and then removed. Each cell image is brightness-normalized; because busbar removal can truncate crack segments, a feature-restoration step reconnects discontinuities. Crack candidates are extracted with adaptive thresholding and refined with morphological filtering to suppress false positives. Confirmed cracks are skeletonized to single-pixel centerlines, and lengths are computed using the established scale, yielding physically meaningful totals per cell and module. Figure 2 summarizes the workflow and provides a representative detection example.

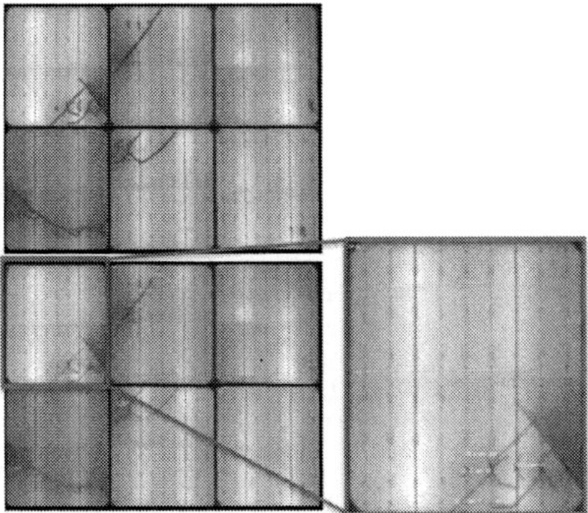

Figure 2: Example of Crack Detection with Length Calculation

2.2 Fitting and Parameter Extraction

Accurate PV modeling hinges on precise identification of the five single-diode model (SDM) parameters (I_L, I_o, R_s, R_{sh}, n). In practice, however, manufacturers' datasheets typically report only a few STC operating points from the I–V curve (I_{sc}, V_{oc}, I_{mp}, V_{mp}). This paper conducts a comparative analysis of four parameter-extraction techniques, one that relies on analytical equations (PVLib), two that integrates analytical equations with an iterative algorithm (Cubas,Villalva), one is purely iterative algorithm (Particle Swarm Optimization). Table 1 show the summary of these techniques

Table 1: Summary of the Parameter Extraction Techniques

Technique	Input	Free Parameters	Extracted Parameters
Cubas [12]	(I_{sc}, V_{oc}, I_{mp}, V_{mp}).	n	(I_L, I_o, R_s, R_{sh}).
Villalva [13]		n, $I_L = I_{sc}$	(I_o, R_s, R_{sh}).
PVLib [14]	(I-V curve, I_{sc}, V_{oc}, I_{mp}, V_{mp}).	-	(I_L, I_o, R_s, R_{sh}, n).
PSO [15]	SDM Equation	-	(I_L, I_o, R_s, R_{sh}, n).

2.3 Data Acquisition

The proposed framework was tested and validated on monocrystalline silicon PERC modules (M6 wafers) spanning 2–9 busbars, totaling ~111 samples. PERC mini modules comprise six full-size cells. Electrical and physical characterization combined I–V curves and EL imaging obtained with a Halm A+A+A+ flasher at a controlled module temperature of 25 °C. All measurements were performed at Fraunhofer CSP under laboratory conditions. The range of busbar configurations enabled a comprehensive assessment of how microcracks and broader cell-crack phenomena influence overall module performance.

3 RESULTS

3.1 Models' Accuracy

Figure 3 compares the absolute P_{mpp} difference (%) for four parameter-fitting techniques applied to PERC modules. All methods perform robustly, with absolute deviations generally at or below ~1%, indicating reliable parameter extraction. Cubas and PVLib achieve the lowest P_{mpp} differences with minimal variability, reflecting high precision and stability. PSO and Villalva show slightly larger deviations and wider spread, with PSO exhibiting a few notable outliers. Despite calibration differences, all four methods reproduce the same crack–parameter trends. Building on these results, Cubas and PVLib deliver the best accuracy on PERC modules; among them, Cubas aligns most closely with the reference R_s values for 5BB at STC [16]. Accordingly, Cubas is selected for the subsequent correlation analysis.

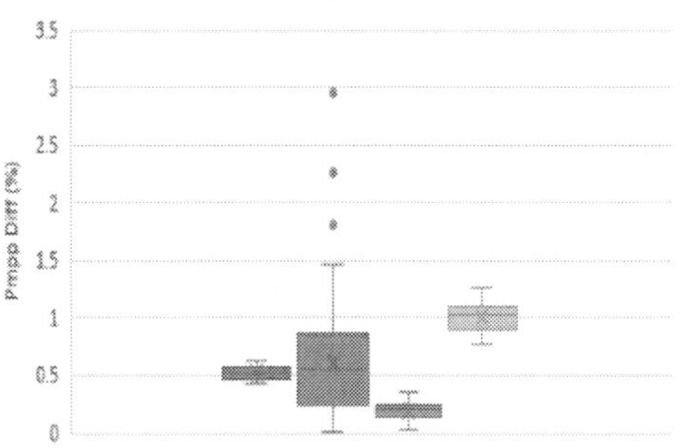

Figure 3: Comparison of Pmpp Diff (%) across different Techniques

3.2 R_s, R_{sh} Corrlation with Crack Length

At 200 W/m², intensity- and temperature-corrected I–V data were evaluated with a focus on R_s and R_{sh}, the parameters most diagnostic of conductive and leakage losses. The crack-free baseline (0 mm) is evident in Figure 4.

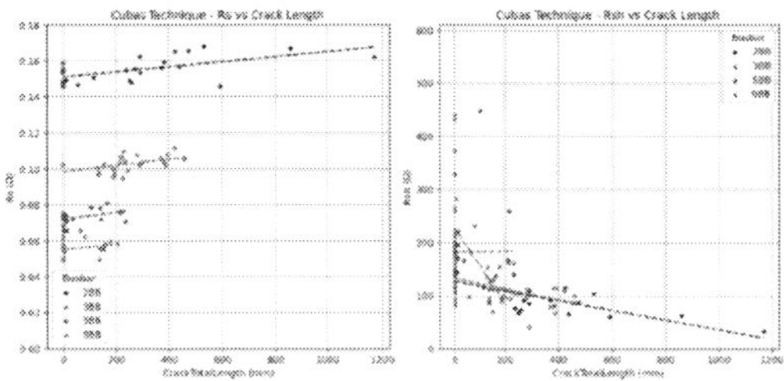

Figure 4: Rs and Rsh correlation with Crack Length

The results are unambiguous. Modules with fewer busbars exhibit substantially higher R_s than those with more busbars, confirming the strong inverse dependence on busbar count. Beyond this design effect, R_s shows a modest but consistent uptick with increasing crack length across all configurations, indicating progressively impaired current collection along fractured pathways. Conversely, R_{sh} declines with crack length, reflecting the growth of leakage channels initiated by the cracks. Taken together, the rise in R_s and the drop in R_{sh} at 200 W/m² establish a clear, crack-driven degradation signature that is robust across busbar designs and anchored by the crack-free reference. Quantitatively, the correlation coefficients are +0.54 for R_s and −0.50 for R_{sh}.

3.4 Pmpp Correlation with Crack Length

This observation is further supported by the correlation of P_{mpp} with the crack length in Figure 5 . It was observed that the pwer remains essentially unchanged for crack lengths up to ~400 mm across all busbar configurations, contradicting the direct crack–power relationship previously reported for multicrystalline modules. Beyond this threshold, P_{mpp} declines noticeably with increasing crack length, indicating that only extensive cracking produces measurable power loss. These results underscore that the crack–performance relationship is not strictly linear and is modulated by design factors such as cell architecture and busbar count. Quantitatively, the correlation coefficient between the power and crack length is -0.56.

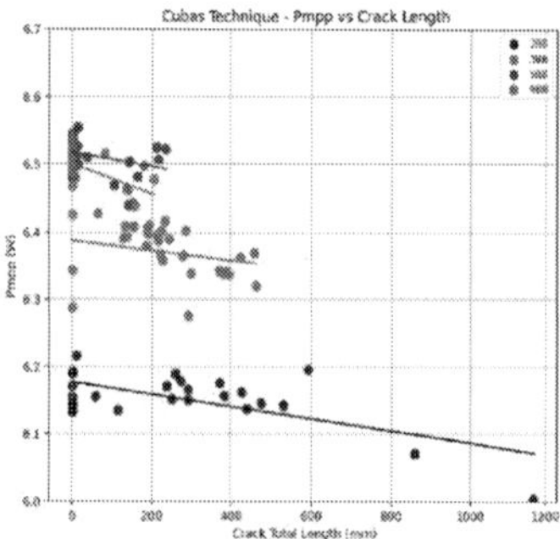

Figure 5: P_{mpp} correlation with Crack Length

4   CONCLUSION

This work establishes a quantitative, image-to-model framework that links EL-derived crack length to single-diode parameters and power loss in PERC modules. Using an OpenCV pipeline for crack metrology and a comparative evaluation of parameter-extraction methods, Cubas was selected for correlation analysis based on its accuracy and stability. The results at 200 W/m² show a consistent degradation signature: R_s rises with crack length and is systematically higher for lower busbar counts, while R_{sh} declines, evidencing enhanced leakage; correspondingly, P_{mpp} remains effectively unchanged up to ~400 mm of total crack length and then decreases with further cracking. These findings challenge simple crack-count/length heuristics and demonstrate that performance impact depends on both crack extent and design choices such as busbar number, providing a defensible basis for screening, valuation, and design optimization of cracked modules. Future work should extend this approach beyond controlled laboratory conditions to fielded systems and additional cell architectures to test generality and refine decision thresholds.

5   REFERENCES

[1] S.-T. Hsu, Y.-S. Long og Y.-T. Li, "Characterization of solar cells in transportation," in 2014 IEEE 40th Photovoltaic Specialist Conference (PVSC), Denver, CO, USA, 2014, s. 2592–2594.

[2] X. Gou, X. Li, S. Wang, H. Zhuang, X. Huang og L. Jiang, "The Effect of Microcrack Length in Silicon Cells on the Potential Induced Degradation Behavior," International Journal of Photoenergy, vol. 2018, s. 1–6, 2018. [Online] Hentet fra: doi:10.1155/2018/4381579.

[3] B. Jaeckel, M. Pander, P. Schenk, A. Linsenmeyer og J. Kirch, "Nomenclature and description of Electro-Luminescence (EL) observations: cell cracks and other observations," EPJ Photovolt., vol. 15, s. 44, 2024. [Online] Hentet fra: doi:10.1051/epjpv/2024039.

[4] S. Kajari-Schröder, I. Kunze, U. Eitner og M. Köntges, "Spatial and orientational distribution of cracks in crystalline photovoltaic modules generated by mechanical load tests," Solar Energy Materials and Solar Cells, vol. 95, nr. 11, s. 3054–3059, 2011. [Online] Hentet fra: doi:10.1016/j.solmat.2011.06.032.

[5] M. Köntges, S. Kajari-Schröder, I. Kunze, U. Jahn, "CRACK STATISTIC OF CRYSTALLINE SILICON PHOTOVOLTAIC MODULE," Solar Energy Materials and Solar Cells, vol. 95, nr. 11, s. 3054–3059, 2011. [Online] Hentet fra: doi:10.1016/j.solmat.2011.06.032.

[6] M. Sander, S. Dietrich, M. Pander, M. Ebert og J. Bagdahn, "Systematic investigation of cracks in encapsulated solar cells after mechanical loading," Solar Energy Materials and Solar Cells, vol. 111, s. 82–89, 2013. [Online] Hentet fra: doi:10.1016/j.solmat.2012.12.031.

[7] M. Köntges, I. Kunze, S. Kajari-Schröder, X. Breitenmoser og B. Bjørneklett, "The risk of power loss in crystalline silicon based photovoltaic modules due to micro-cracks," Solar Energy Materials and Solar Cells, vol. 95, nr. 4, s. 1131–1137, 2011. [Online] Hentet fra: doi:10.1016/j.solmat.2010.10.034.

[8] M. Köntges, I. Kunze, S.Kajari-Schröder, X. Breitenmoser, B. Bjørneklett, "Quantifying the risk of power loss in PV modules due to micro cracks," 2010.

[9] S. Hassan og M. Dhimish, "Broad-scale Electroluminescence analysis of 5 million+ photovoltaic cells for defect detection and degradation assessment," Renewable Energy, vol. 237, s. 121868, 2024. [Online] Hentet fra: doi:10.1016/j.renene.2024.121868.

[10] A. Morlier, F. Haase og M. Kontges, "Impact of cracks in multicrystalline silicon solar cells on PV module power - A simulation study based on field data," in 2015 IEEE 42nd Photovoltaic Specialist Conference (PVSC), New Orleans, LA, 2015, s. 1–3.

[11] A. Hashem, S. Mortazavifar og R. Gottschalg, "Impact of Modern Cell Photovoltaic Geometries on Power and Energy Loss due to Cell Cracks," (på en), 41st European Photovoltaic Solar Energy Conference and Exhibition, 2024. [Online] Hentet fra: doi:10.4229/EUPVSEC2024/3AV.2.5.

[12]   J. Cubas, S. Pindado og M. Victoria, "On the analytical approach for modeling photovoltaic systems behavior," Journal of Power Sources, vol. 247, s. 467–474,

2014. [Online] Hentet fra: doi:10.1016/j.jpowsour.2013.09.008.

[13] M. G. Villalva, J. R. Gazoli og E. R. Filho, "Comprehensive Approach to Modeling and Simulation of Photovoltaic Arrays," IEEE Trans. Power Electron., vol. 24, nr. 5, s. 1198–1208, 2009. [Online] Hentet fra: doi:10.1109/TPEL.2009.2013862.

[14] C. Birk Jones Clifford W. Hansen, "Single Diode Parameter Extraction from In-Field Photovoltaic I-V Curves on a Single Board Computer," 2019.

[15] J. Kennedy og R. Eberhart, "Particle swarm optimization," in Proceedings of ICNN'95 - International Conference on Neural Networks, Perth, WA, Australia, 1995, s. 1942–1948.

[16] T, Dullweber, C. Kranz, R. Peibst, U. Baumann, H. Hannebauer, M.Kutzer, M. Müller, G. Fischer, P. Palinginis & H. Neuhaus, "The PERC+ cell: More output power for less aluminium paste,"

|Ahmad Hashem

Fraunhofer CSP

HOCHSCHULE ANHALT University of Applied Sciences

Investigating the Impact of Cell Cracks on Power Loss and its Correlation with the Modelling Parameters

Ahmad Hashem[1,2], Zonghan Jiang[1] , Guido Willers[2] , Leila Mortazavifar[1,2] , Bengt Jaeckel [1,2] Ralph Gottschalg[1,2]

[1] Hochschule Anhalt University of Applied Sciences

[2] Fraunhofer Center for Crystalline Silicon Photovoltaics CSP

E-mail: ahmad.hashem@hs-anhalt.de
ahmad.hashem@imws.Fraunhofer.de

020202-001

|Ahmad Hashem

Motivation

- Can cell cracks be mitigated ?

- Do cracks always cause power loss?

- Correlation between line cracks & Performance

- Cell Tech Matters !

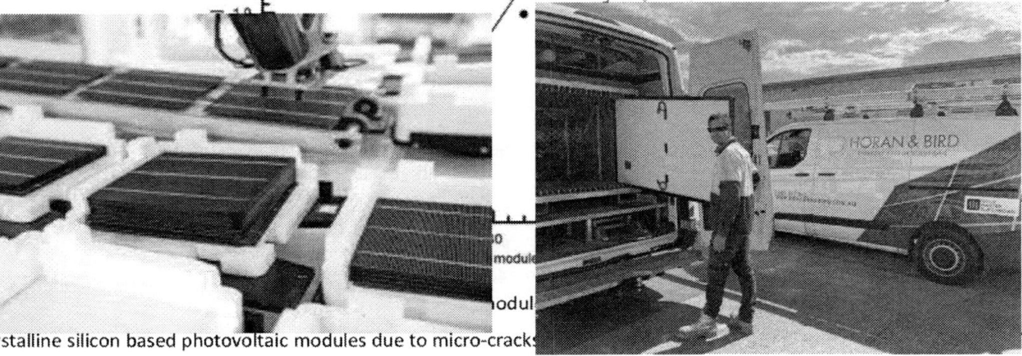

Dhimish, M., Holmes, V., Dales, M., Mather, P., Sibley, M., Chong, B., & Zhang, L. (20

Köntges, M., Kunze, I., Kajari-Schröder, S., Breitenmoser, X., (2011). The risk of power loss in crystalline silicon based photovoltaic modules due to micro-cracks.

Hassan, S., & Dhimish, M. (2024). Broad-scale Electroluminescence analysis of 5 million+ photovoltaic cells for defect detection and degradation assessment. *Renewable Energy, 237*, 121868.

020202-002

|Ahmad Hashem

Motivation

- By 2034, only 10% of the market share is expected to be covered by 12 busbar or less

- The Shift will be towards M10 & G12 Wafers !

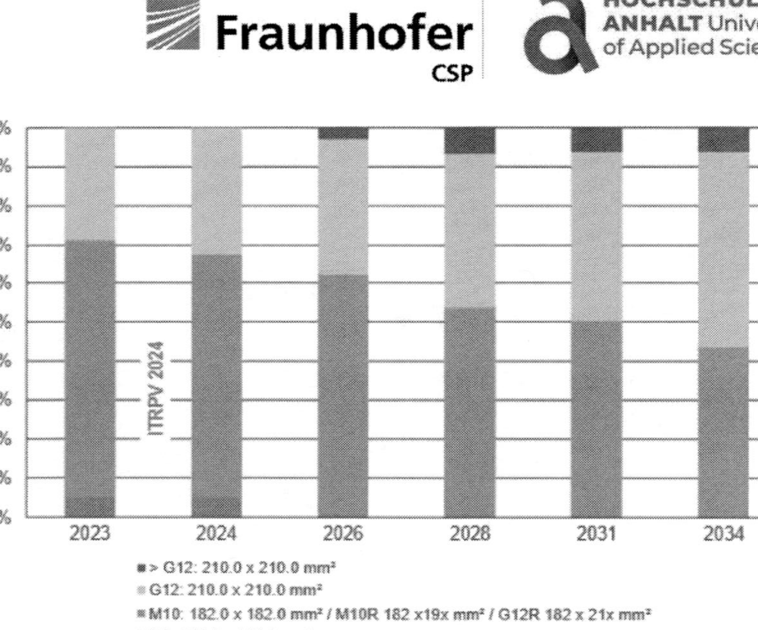

* International Technology Roadmap for Photovoltaics (ITRPV) 2023 Results

|Ahmad Hashem

Study Aim

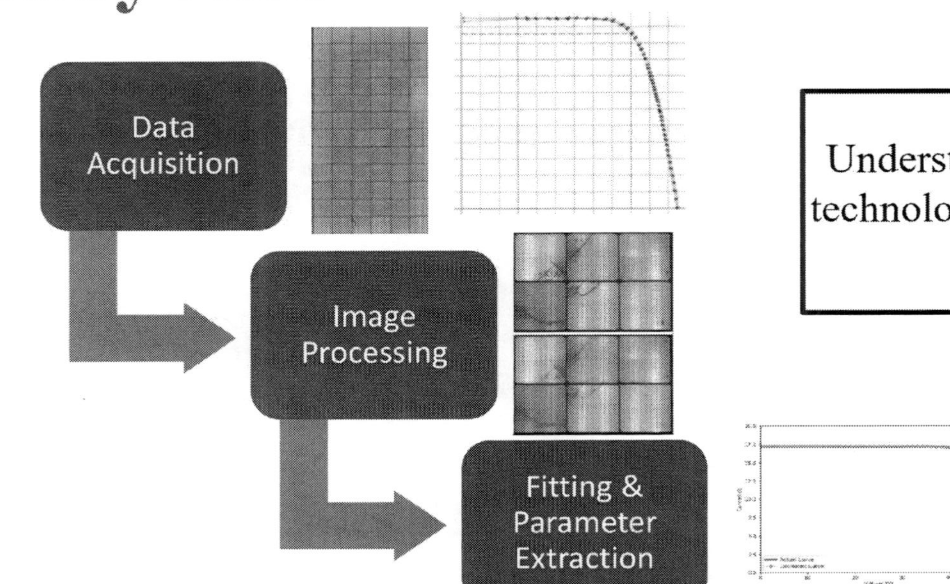

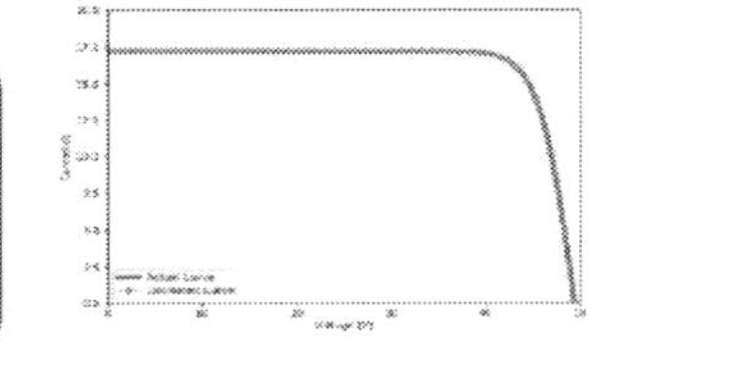

Understand the impact of cracks on different cell technologies and its correlation with the modelling parameters and power loss

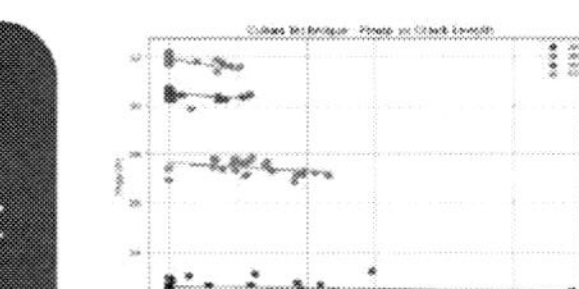

020202-004

|Ahmad Hashem

Data Acquisition

- A Halm A+A+A+ flasher system was employed.

- Flash test were performed at 1000 & 200 W/m² & Constant Temp of 25°C

- M6 Mono-Si PERC & TopCon Modules → Total ~230 Sample

- PERC Modules covered 2-9 BB count.

- TopCon Modules covered 2-12 BB count.

020202-005

|Ahmad Hashem

Image Processing

- OpenCV- based algorithm were used.

- Perspective transformation is applied using the module's outer contour and user-provided real-world dimension.

- Standard cell matrix is constructed to determine the pixel dimensions of each cell.

- Busbars are located and removed to reduce noise.

- Cracks are detected and skeletonized to single-pixel paths; lengths are converted from pixels to real units (mm).

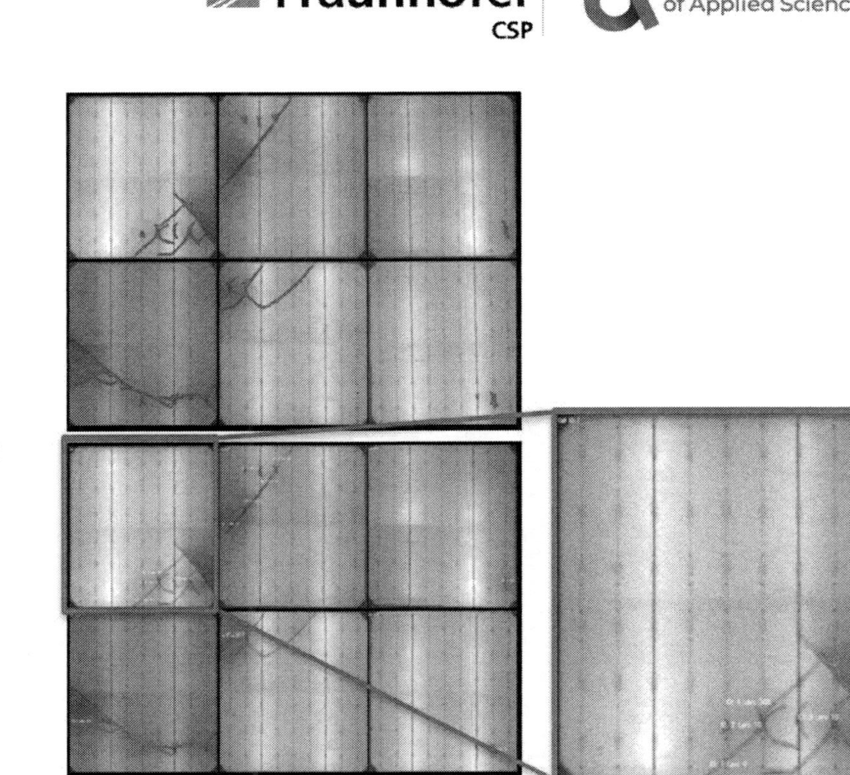

020202-006

|Ahmad Hashem

Fitting & Parameters Extraction

- Single Diode Model is widely used for PV modelling due to its accuracy and simplicity.

- The focus will be on the P_{mpp}, R_s, R_{sh}

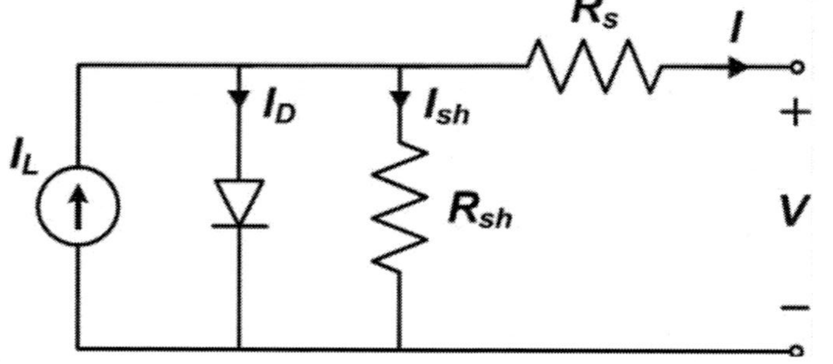

Single Diode Model Equivalent Circuit

$$I = I_L - I_o \left[\exp\left[\frac{V + IR_s}{nN_sV_t} \right] - 1 \right] - \frac{V + IR_s}{R_{sh}}$$

Fit → Extract → Replot → P_{mpp} Calculation

020202-007

|Ahmad Hashem

Fitting & Parameters Extraction

- **<u>PVLib (Analytical)</u>**

→ The linear region of the curve is fitted using a linear regression model (β_0, β_1)

→ Linear fit is removed from the current to isolate the pure exponential behavior of the diode

→ Residual is then linearized by taking its natural logarithm, and a simple least-squares regression of the log-transformed data against voltage and current returns two new coefficients (β_3, β_4).

→ Goodness-of-fit criterion : R^2 (0.99)

* C. Birk Jones Clifford W. Hansen, "Single Diode Parameter Extraction from In-Field Photovoltaic I-V Curves on a Single Board Computer," 2019.

020202-008

|Ahmad Hashem

 **Fraunhofer** CSP

 **HOCHSCHULE ANHALT** University of Applied Sciences

Fitting & Parameters Extraction

<u>Cubas Technique (Analytical + Iterative)</u> → Ideality Factor 'n' is set Free

→ Goodness-of-fit criterion : R^2 (0.98-0.99)

$$R_{start} = 0$$

$$\frac{aV_T V_{mp}(2I_{mp} - I_{sc})}{(V_{mp}I_{sc} + V_{oc}(I_{mp} - I_{sc}))(V_{mp} - I_{mp}R_s) - aV_T(V_{mp}I_{sc} - V_{oc}I_{mp})} = \exp\left(\frac{V_{mp} + I_{mp}R_s - V_{oc}}{aV_T}\right).$$

$$R_{sh} = \frac{(V_{mp} - I_{mp}R_s)(V_{mp} - R_s(I_{sc} - I_{mp}) - aV_T)}{(V_{mp} - I_{mp}R_s)(I_{sc} - I_{mp}) - aV_T I_{mp}}.$$

$$I_{pv} = \frac{R_{sh} + R_s}{R_{sh}} I_{sc}.$$

$$I_0 = \frac{(R_{sh} + R_s)I_{sc} - V_{oc}}{R_{sh} \exp\left(\frac{V_{oc}}{aV_T}\right)}$$

* J. Cubas, S. Pindado og M. Victoria, "On the analytical approach for modeling photovoltaic systems behavior," Journal of Power Sources, vol. 247, s. 467–474, 2014. [Online] Hentet fra: doi:10.1016/j.jpowsour.2013.09.008.

020202-009

|Ahmad Hashem

 **Fraunhofer** CSP

HOCHSCHULE
ANHALT University
of Applied Sciences

Fitting & Parameters Extraction

Villalva Technique (Analytical + Iterative)

→ Ideality Factor 'n' is set Free

→ $I_{ph} \approx I_{sc}$

$$I_o = \frac{I_{sc}}{exp(\frac{V_{oc}}{aV_t})} - 1$$

a=n*Ns

→ Iteratively tune R_s start from 0 → 1 (step 0.0025) then compute R_{sh} until the model's P–V peak

equals the measured

→ Goodness-of-fit criterion : R^2 (0.91)

$$R_{sh} = \frac{V_{mp}(V_{mp} + I_{mp}\,R_s)}{V_{mp}I_{ph} - V_{mp}I_o \exp\left(\frac{(V_{mp}+I_{mp}R_s)}{N_s a V_t}\right) + V_{mp}I_o - P_{max,m}}$$

* M. G. Villalva, J. R. Gazoli og E. R. Filho, "Comprehensive Approach to Modeling and Simulation of Photovoltaic Arrays," IEEE Trans. Power Electron., vol. 24, nr. 5, s. 1198–1208, 2009. [Online] Hentet fra: doi:10.1109/TPEL.2009.2013862.

020202-010

|Ahmad Hashem

Fraunhofer CSP

HOCHSCHULE ANHALT University of Applied Sciences

Fitting & Parameters Extraction

Particle Swarm Optimization (Iterative)

→The single-diode model equation is used as the PSO objective

→ A current for a given voltage is to be calculated I(V) !

→ Goodness-of-fit criterion : Root-Mean-Square error →5e-3

→ Stopping Criteria: Objective change less than 10e-12

Parameter	Lower-Bound	Upper-Bound
I_{ph} (A)	0	$2* I_{sc}$
I_o(A)	10e-4	10e-15
R_s(Ω)	0	1
R_{sh}(Ω)	10	1000
n	1	2

* J. Kennedy og R. Eberhart, "Particle swarm optimization," in Proceedings of ICNN'95 - International Conference on Neural Networks, Perth, WA, Australia, 1995, s. 1942–1948.

020202-011

|Ahmad Hashem

Cracks Scenario

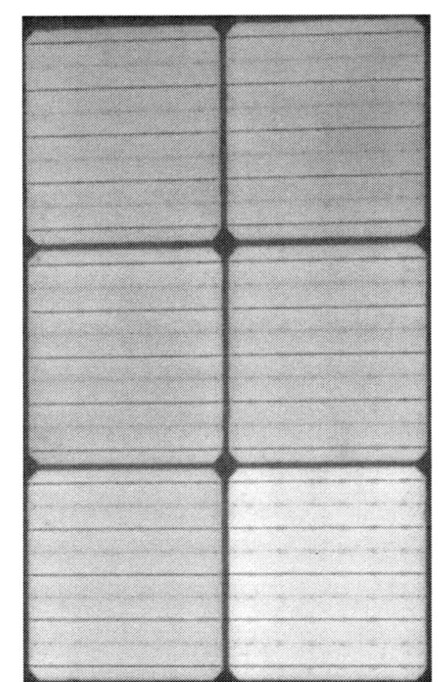

Crack-Free Module

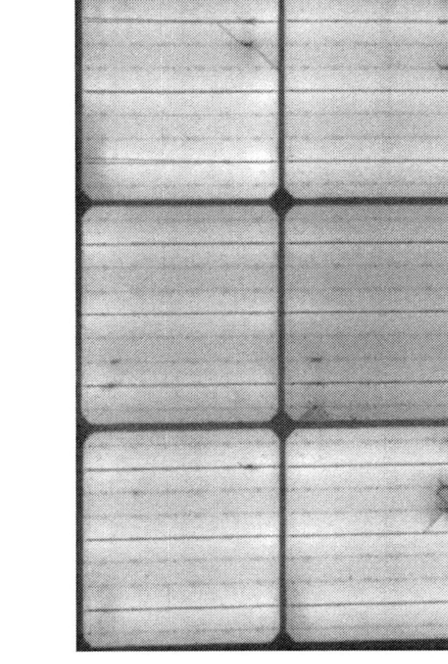

Module with 1-cell crack

Module with multi-cell cracks

020202-012

|Ahmad Hashem

Models' Accuracy

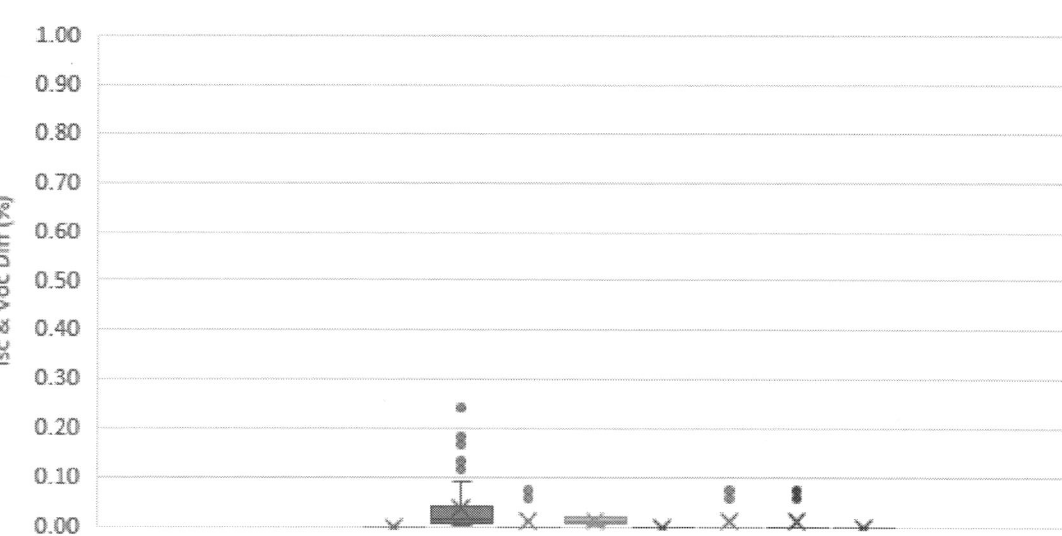

020202-013

|Ahmad Hashem

Models' Accuracy

- Cubas & PVLib achieves the best accuracy %.

- Cubas has closer agreement to $R_{s,ref}$

- R_{sh} is strongly dependent on R_s in PVLib model.

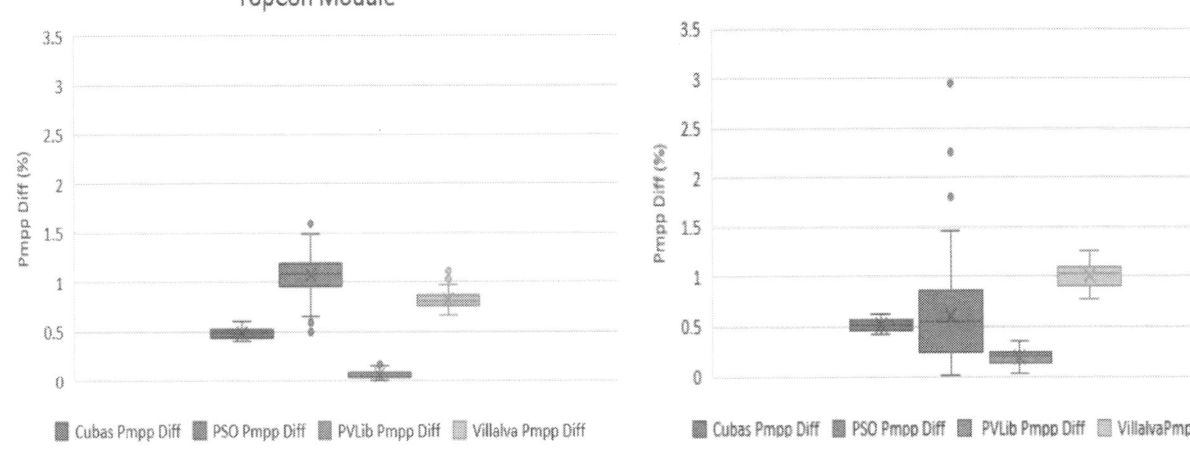

Comparison of Absolute Pmpp Estimation using Different Models

All Models Have the same trend for P_{mpp} , R_s , R_{sh} !!

020202-014

|Ahmad Hashem

PERC Simulations

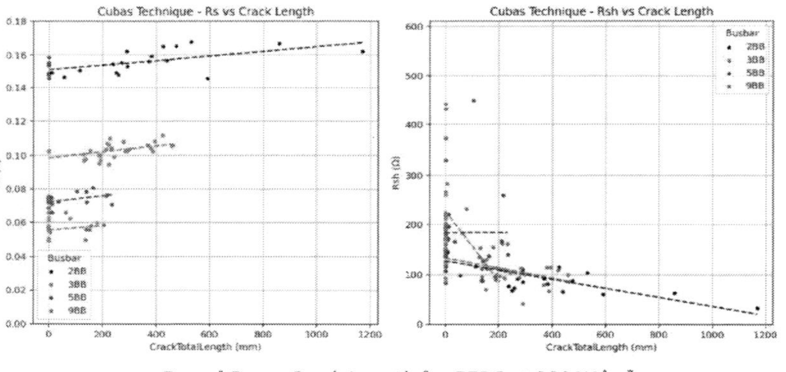

R_s and R_{sh} vs Crack Length for PERC at 200 W/m²

	Correlation Coefficient
R_{sh}	-0.5
R_s	0.54

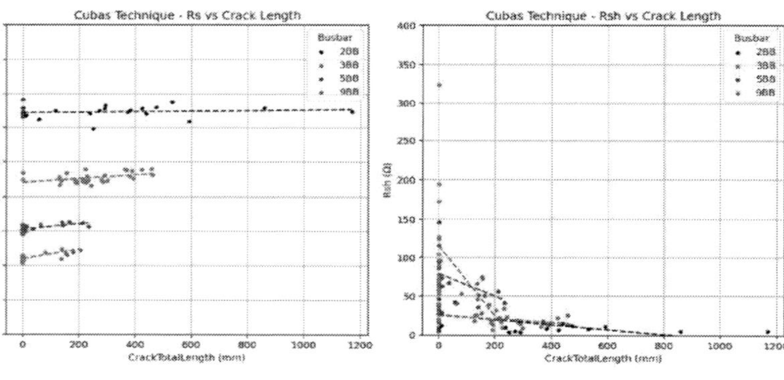

R_s and R_{sh} vs Crack Length for PERC at 1000 W/m²

	Correlation Coefficient
R_{sh}	-0.31
R_s	0.43

020202-015

|Ahmad Hashem

PERC Simulations

Cracks ≤ 400 mm show no measurable impact on P_{mpp} under the tested conditions

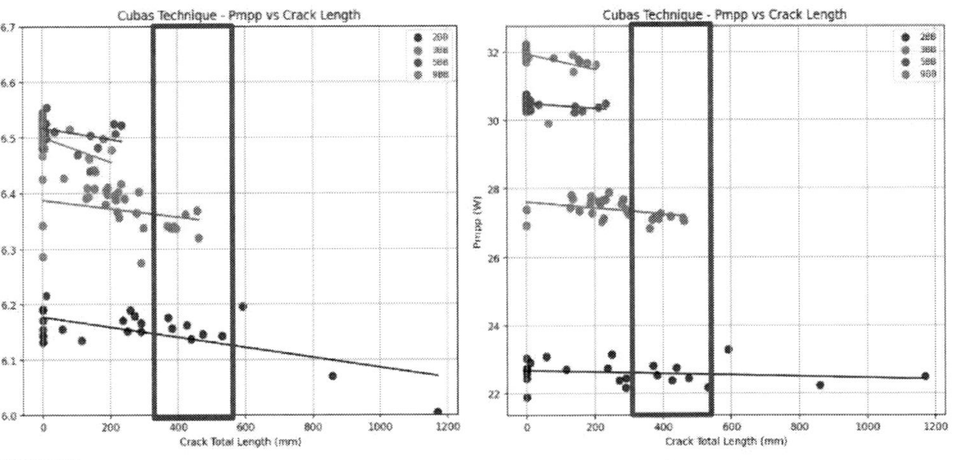

	Correlation Coefficient
P_{mpp} (200 W/m2)	-0.56
P_{mpp} (1000 W/m2)	-0.43

020202-016

|Ahmad Hashem

Fraunhofer CSP

HOCHSCHULE ANHALT University of Applied Sciences

TopCon Simulations

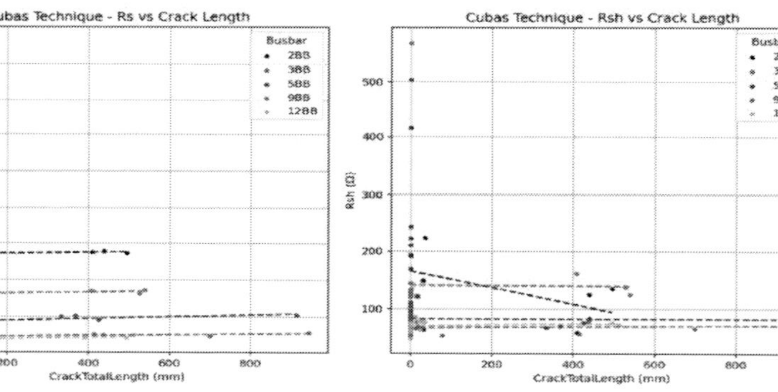

R_s and R_{sh} vs Crack Length for TopCon at 200 W/m²

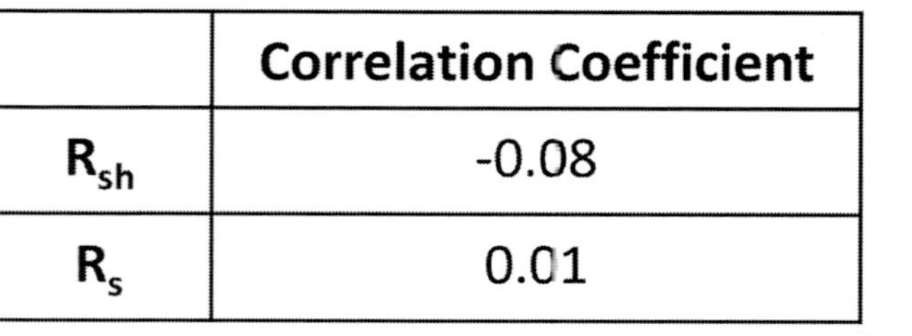

R_s and R_{sh} vs Crack Length for TopCon at 1000 W/m²

	Correlation Coefficient
R_{sh}	-0.08
R_s	0.01

	Correlation Coefficient
R_{sh}	-0.07
R_s	0.01

020202-017

|Ahmad Hashem

TopCon Simulations

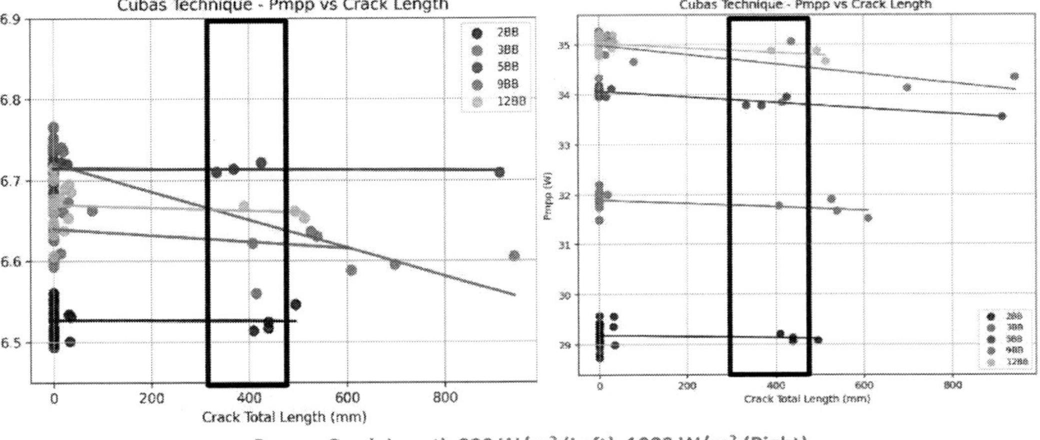

P_{mpp} vs Crack Length 200 W/m² (Left), 1000 W/m² (Right)

Shorter crack coverage (~800 vs ~1200 mm) + TopCon design gains ⇒ no Pmpp–crack correlation.

	Correlation Coefficient
P_{mpp} (200 W/m2)	-0.12
P_{mpp} (1000 W/m2)	-0.02

Crack length ≠ Power Loss !!

020202-018

|Ahmad Hashem

Key Takeaways

- Framework for analysing the correlation between crack , modelling parameters & Power Loss.

- Crack length alone is a poor predictor of power loss.

- There is no clear correlation between crack length , modelling parameters & Power loss

  └──────→ **Cell Tech, BB, crack location, Irradiance Level**

- Negligible P_{loss} for TopCon Modules compared to PERC for the same crack ranges (up to 800mm).

- Cracks ≤ 400 mm show no measurable impact on P_{mpp} under all tested conditions.

- **<u>Future Work</u> →** Comparison of cracks impact on modules with larger wafers & longer crack lengths.

020202-019

|Ahmad Hashem

Acknowledgment

The authors gratefully acknowledge the financial support by the German Federal Ministry for Economic Affairs and Climate Action (BMWK)of the project **"PV-Riss"** with grant #03TN0033A.

Gefördert durch:

aufgrund eines Beschlusses
des Deutschen Bundestages

020202-020

|Ahmad Hashem

 Fraunhofer CSP

 HOCHSCHULE ANHALT University of Applied Sciences

Thank you for your attention ☺

Photovoltaic Researcher/ PhD Candidate:
Email: Ahmad.Hashem@hs-anhalt.de
Tel: +4915560074802

020202-021

|Ahmad Hashem

PVLib Implementation

$$I = \frac{I_L}{1 + G_p R_s} - \frac{G_p V}{1 + G_p R_s} - \frac{I_0}{1 + G_p R_s}\left(\exp\left(\frac{V + IR_s}{nN_sV_{th}}\right) - 1\right)$$

- Linear portion is defined $V \leq vlim * Voc$

- Fit the Linear Portion with a line

$$I \approx \frac{I_L}{1 + G_p R_s} - \frac{G_p}{1 + G_p R_s}V$$
$$= \beta_0 + \beta_1 V$$

The exponential portion of the IV curve is defined by $\beta_0 + \beta_1 \times V - I > ilim \times i_{sc}$. Over this portion of the curve, $\exp((V + IR_s)/nN_sV_{th}) \gg 1$ so that

Fit the exponential portion of the IV curve.

$$\log(\beta_0 - \beta_1 V - I) \approx \log\left(\frac{I_0}{1 + G_p R_s}\right) + \frac{V}{nN_sV_{th}} + \frac{IR_s}{nN_sV_{th}}$$
$$= \beta_2 + \beta_3 V + \beta_4 I$$

020202-022

|Ahmad Hashem

n-Value

- Optimization to calculate the Ideality factor 'n'.

- n-Value < 1 for improved fitting !

- Associated reduction in goodness-of-fit for these n values was negligible.

Module Type & Irradiance	Cubas	Villalva
PERC (200 W/m²)	1	0.94
PERC (1000 W/m²)	1.3	0.9
TopCon (200 W/m²)	1	1.05
TopCon (1000 W/m²)	1.38	1

020202-023

|Ahmad Hashem

PVLib vs Cubas (TopCon)

200 W/m2

1000 W/m2

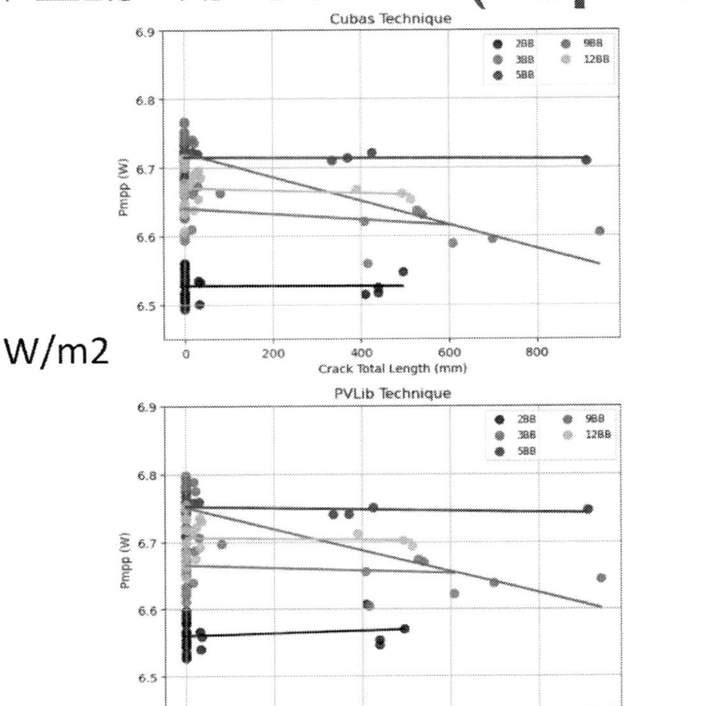

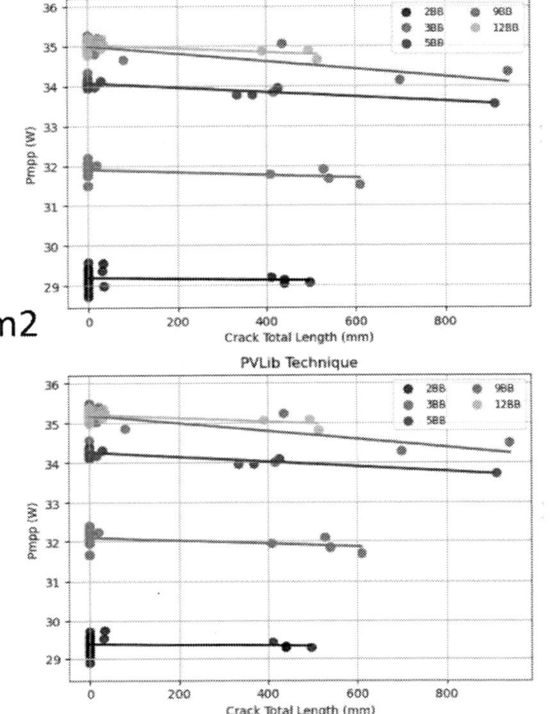

020202-024

|Ahmad Hashem

PVLib vs Cubas (PERC)

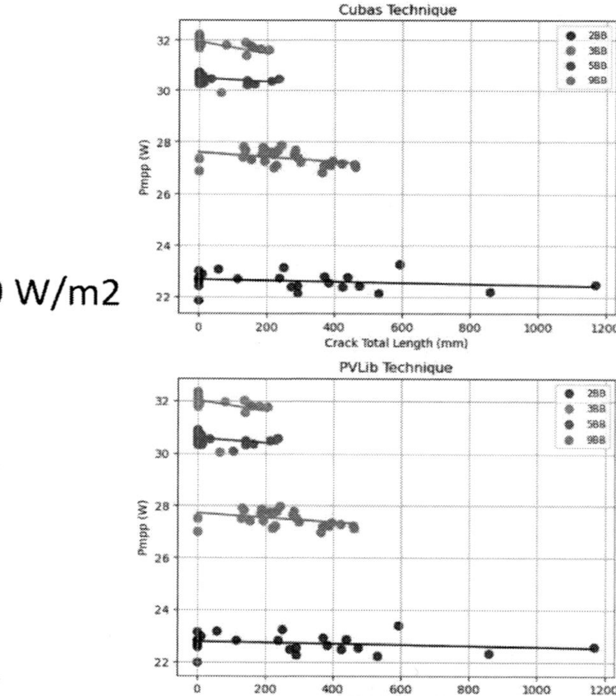

200 W/m2

1000 W/m2

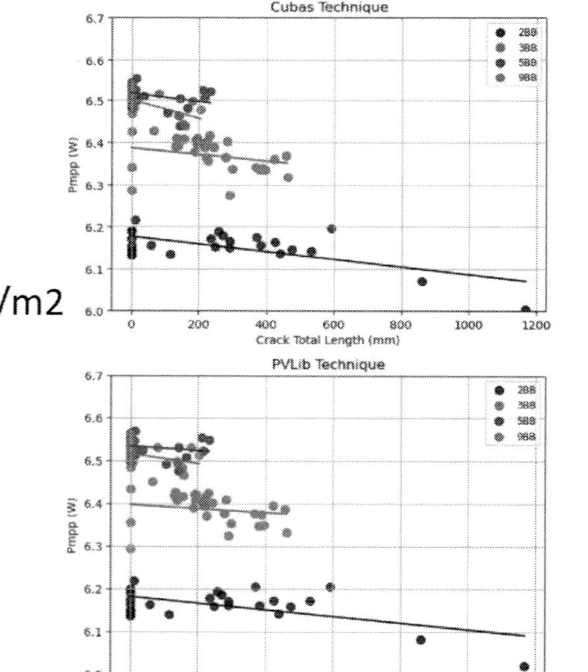

020202-025

|Ahmad Hashem

PSO Examples

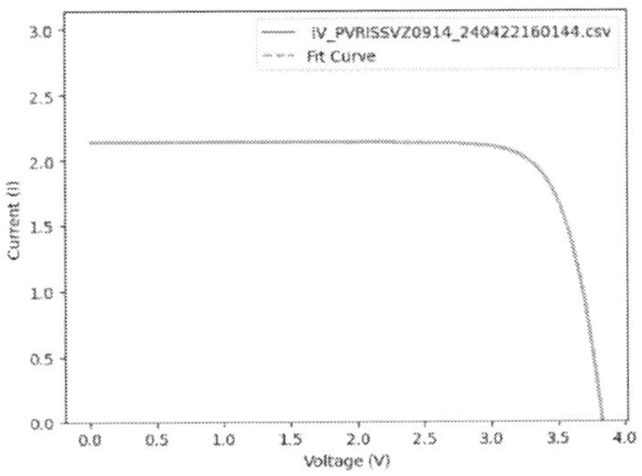

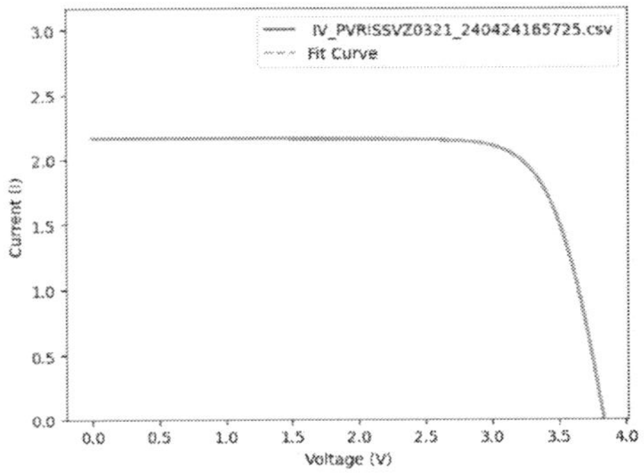

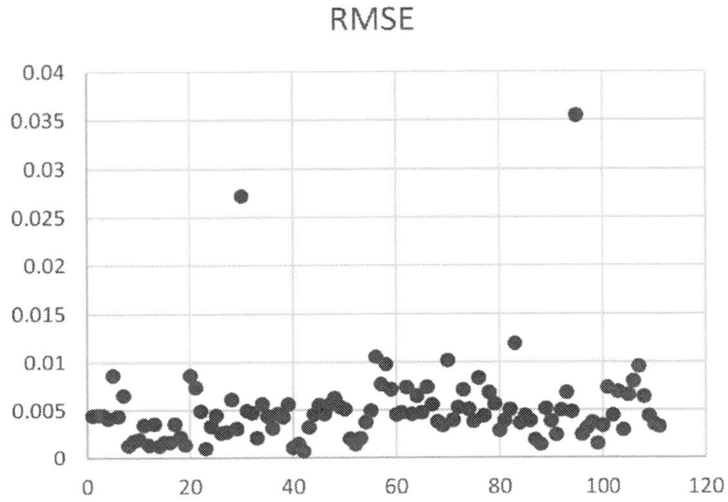

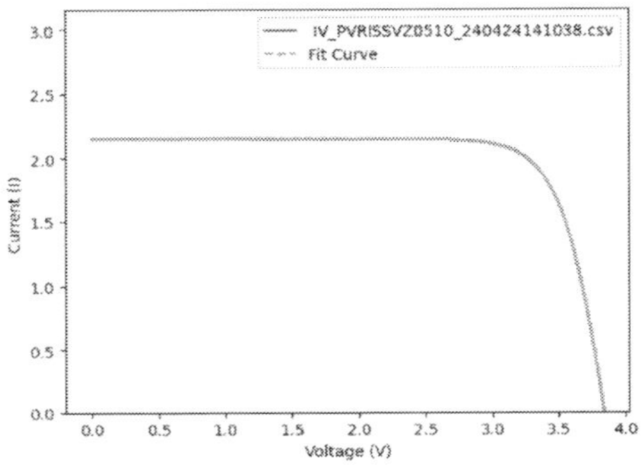

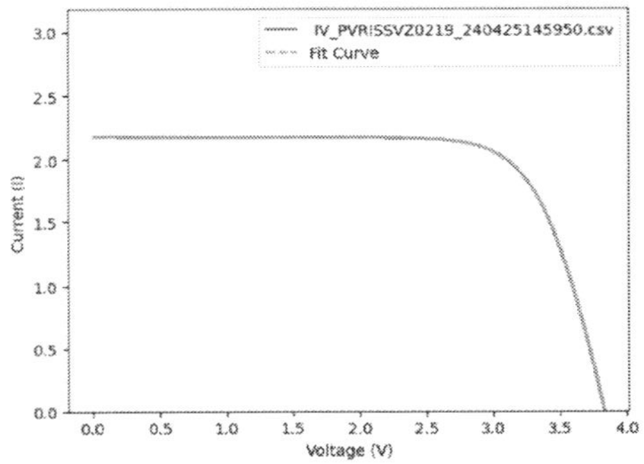

020202-026

|Ahmad Hashem

Fitting Examples

Fraunhofer
CSP

HOCHSCHULE
ANHALT University
of Applied Sciences

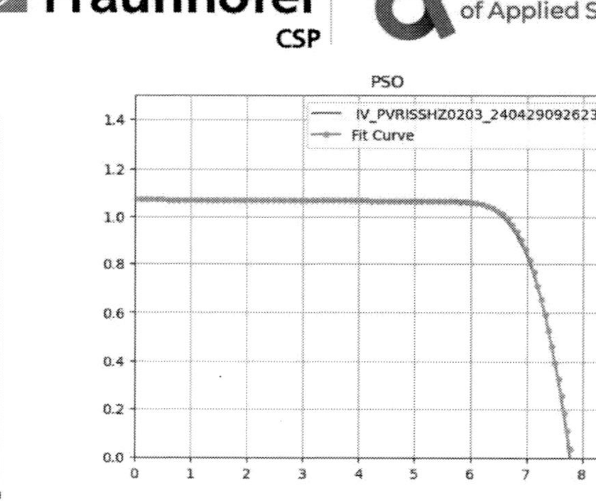

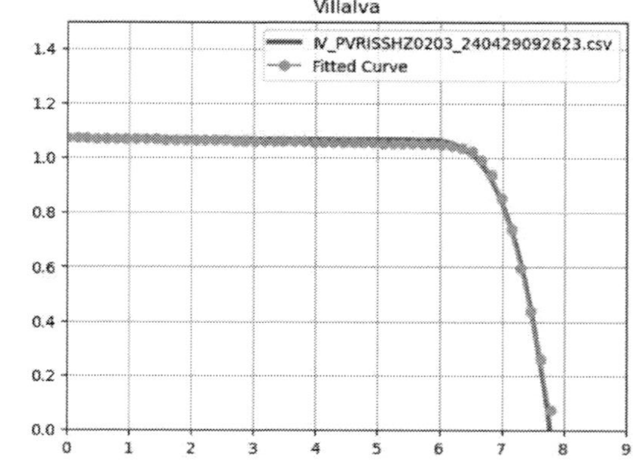

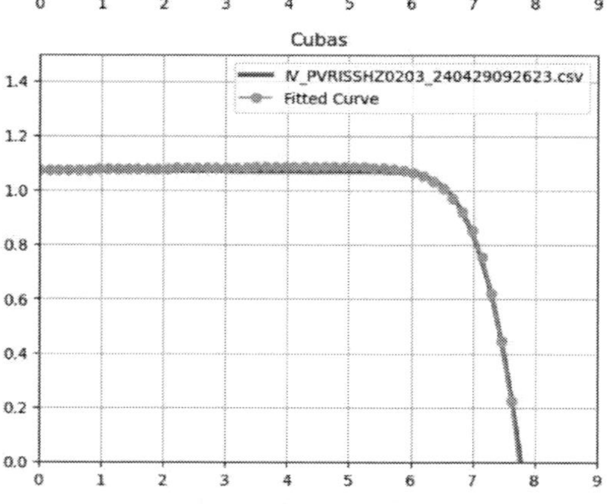

020202-027

|Ahmad Hashem

2-Curves Method

- Series resistance (R_s) from the Voc-region slopes:

$$R_s = \frac{R_1^s\, G_1 \; - \; R_2^s\, G_2}{G_1 - G_2}.$$

- Shunt resistance (R_{sh}) from the Isc-region slopes:

$$R_{sh} = \frac{R_1^{sh}\, G_1 \; - \; R_2^{sh}\, G_2}{G_1 - G_2}.$$

020202-028

|Ahmad Hashem

Series Resistance Rs by Bus-bar Count (PERC 200W/m2)

020202-029

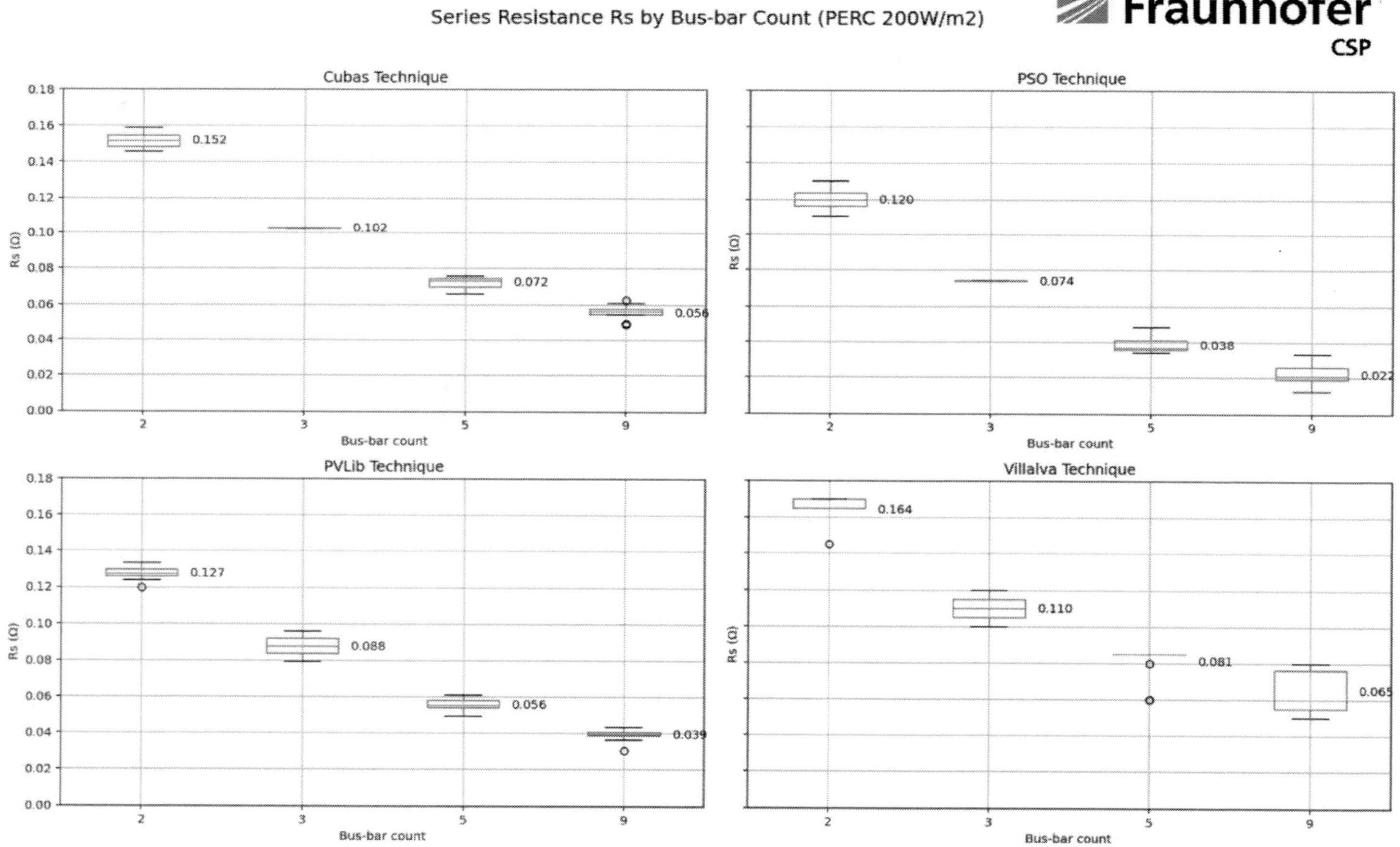

|Ahmad Hashem

Shunt Resistance Rsh by Bus-bar Count (PERC 200W/m2)

Fraunhofer CSP

HOCHSCHULE ANHALT University of Applied Sciences

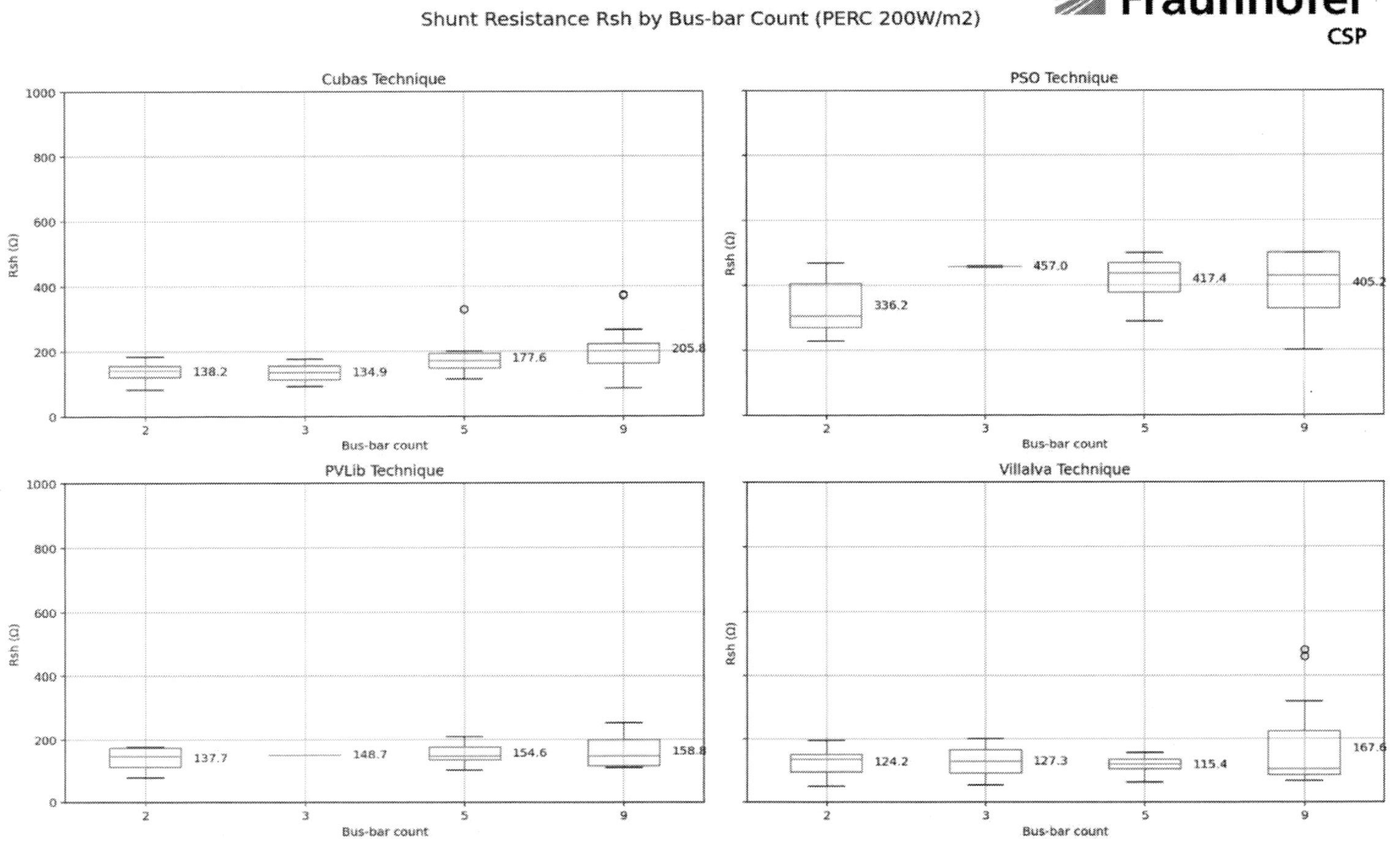

020202-030

|Ahmad Hashem

Series Resistance Rs by Bus-bar Count (PERC 1000W/m2)

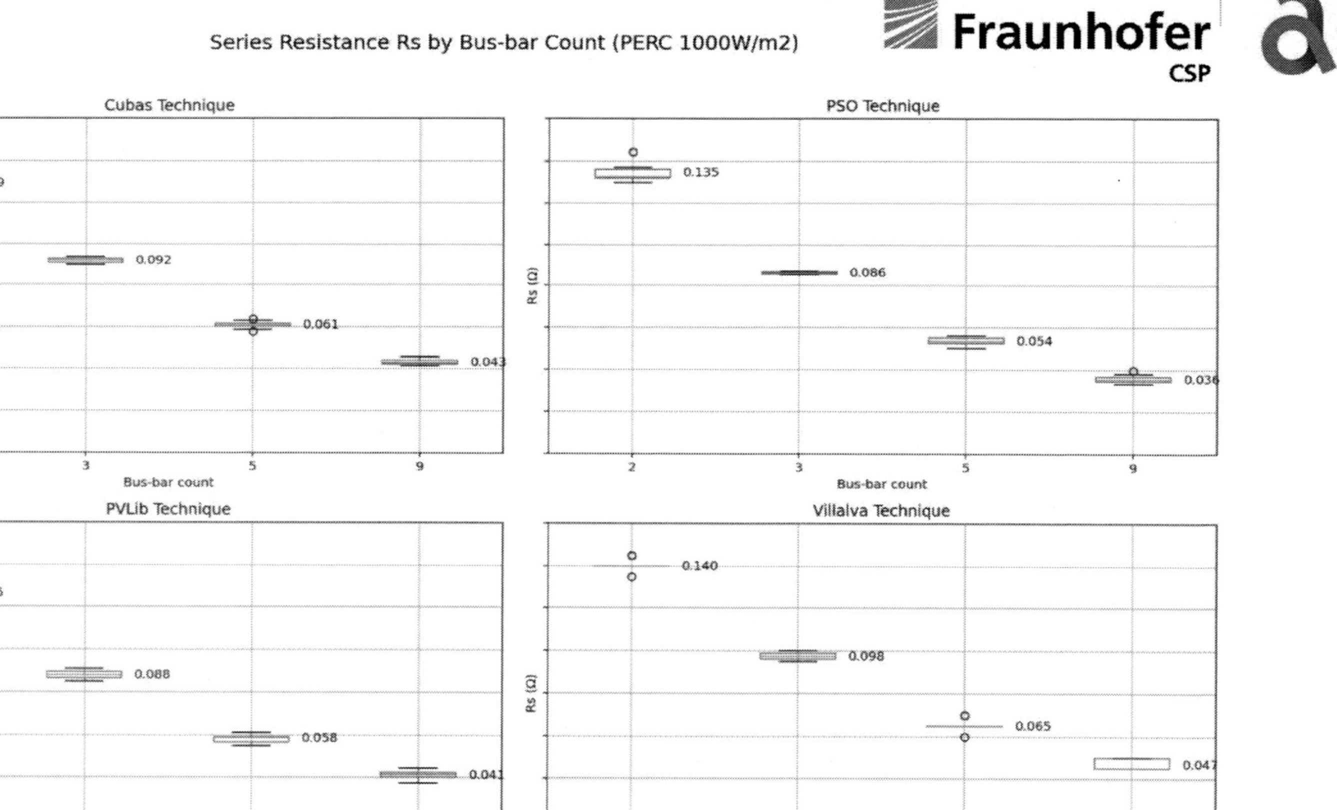

020202-031

|Ahmad Hashem

Shunt Resistance Rsh by Bus-bar Count (PERC 1000W/m2)

Fraunhofer CSP

HOCHSCHULE ANHALT University of Applied Sciences

020202-032

|Ahmad Hashem

2 Curves (PERC)

Fraunhofer CSP

HOCHSCHULE ANHALT University of Applied Sciences

2 Curves Method (PERC)

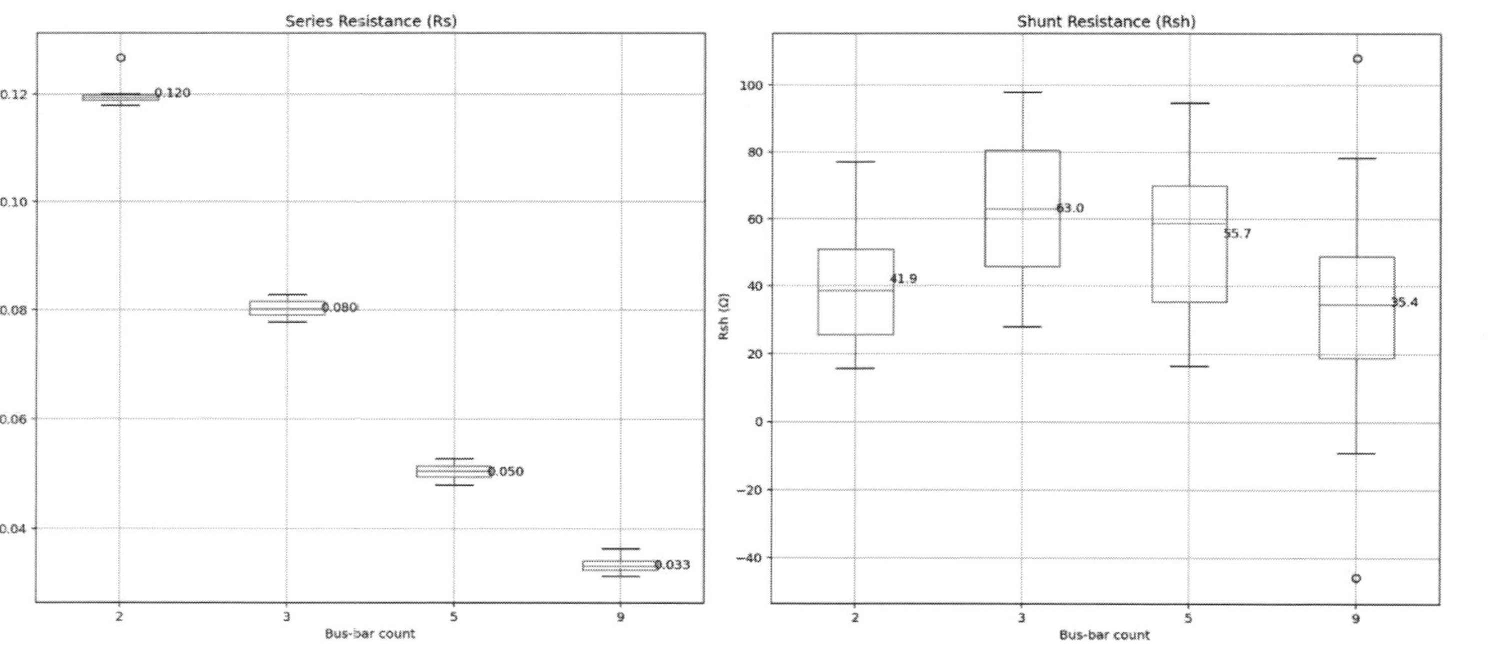

eurac research

ROBO&M

EL-VQA: An Electroluminescence Dataset for Visual Reasoning and Detection

Mohanad Diab, Lukas Koester, Jordi Veirman, Atse Louwen, David Moser, Luis Fialho

ROBO&M

1. Autonomous image acquisition from self-driving robots
2. Inclusion of advanced asset management platform for decision making, task definition, robot initiation
3. Autonomous image analysis – anomaly detection and failure identification

ERDF funded

Visual PV Components & Defect Detection

Credits: Eurac Research

Credits: Fraunhofer Italia

Infrared PV Hot-Cell Detection

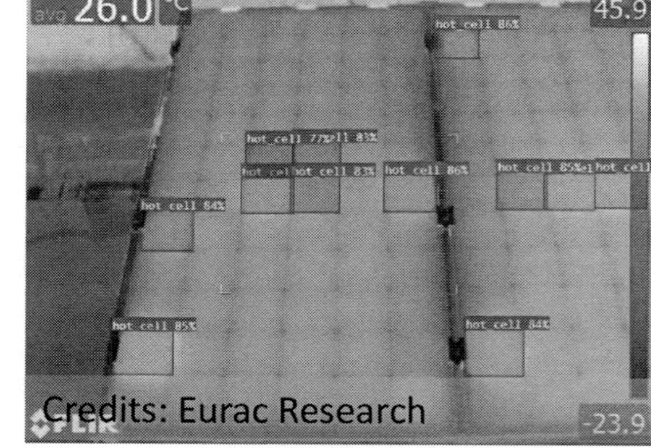

Credits: Eurac Research

020203-002

What is EL-VQA

ElectroLuminescence Visual Questin Answering: A dataset consisting of

- ~3000 images.
- ~ 65,000 bounding boxes across 14 classes.
- ~30,000 Q&A pairs + captions.
- Mono-crystalline only.
- Classes inspired by IEC60904-13
- VQA → simplified understanding of PV module status for non-experienced users.

020203-003

What is EL-VQA

Acquisition

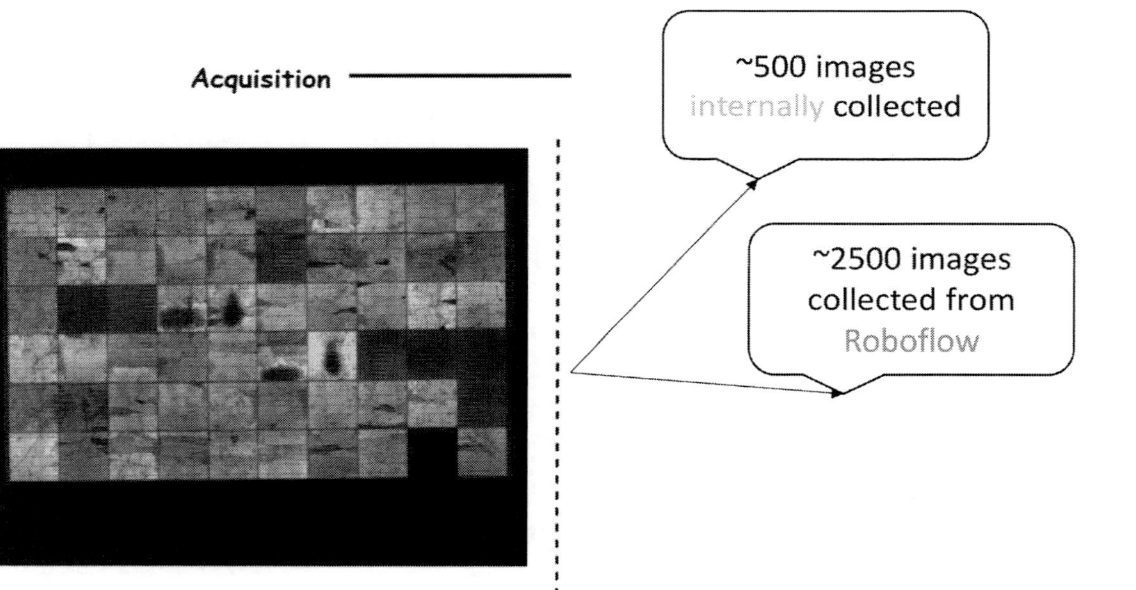

Original Image

What is EL-VQA

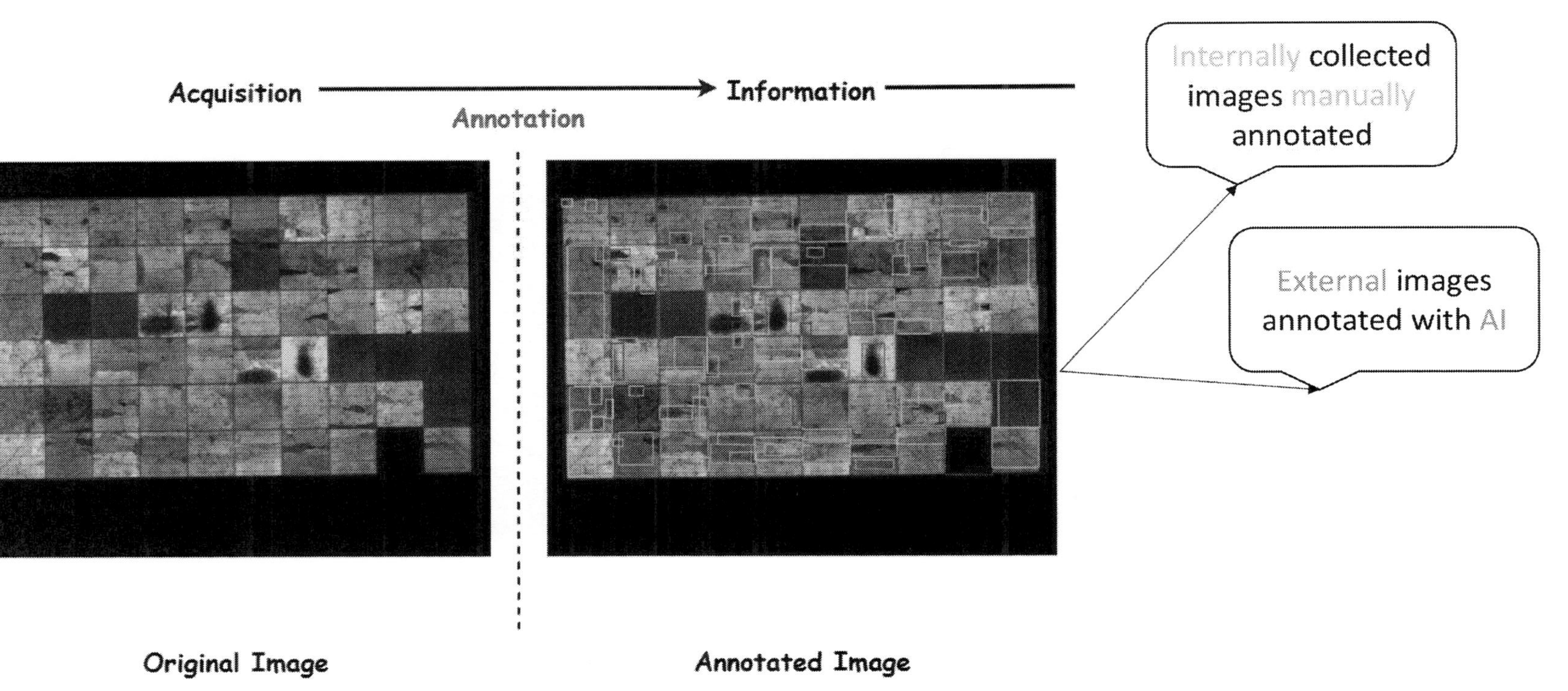

020203-005

What is EL-VQA

Acquisition → Information → Knowledge

Annotation   Reasoning

Original Image

Annotated Image

Metadata
Q: What is the cell technology of this module?
A: mono-crystaline.

Quantitative
Q: How many defects are in this module?
A: There are 97 defects in total.

Quantitative
Q: How many cells have defects in this module?
A: Based on the defect detection output, all cells have defects, so, all 60 cells have defects!

Qualitative
Q: Out of 10, how good is this module?
A: Not very good, 3 on a good day.

Q&As

020203-006

Annotation

Process
Annotate
~5% of dataset
Un-Annotated
~95% of dataset
Add to Training Dataset
Split
Training set
Validation set
Test set
Train
MoE
YOLO + DINO + Faster RCNN
Object Detection Models
Inference
Back to Dataset
Predictions
Low Confidence Pseudo labels
High Confidence Pseudo labels
Filter
Confidence
Human Annotator

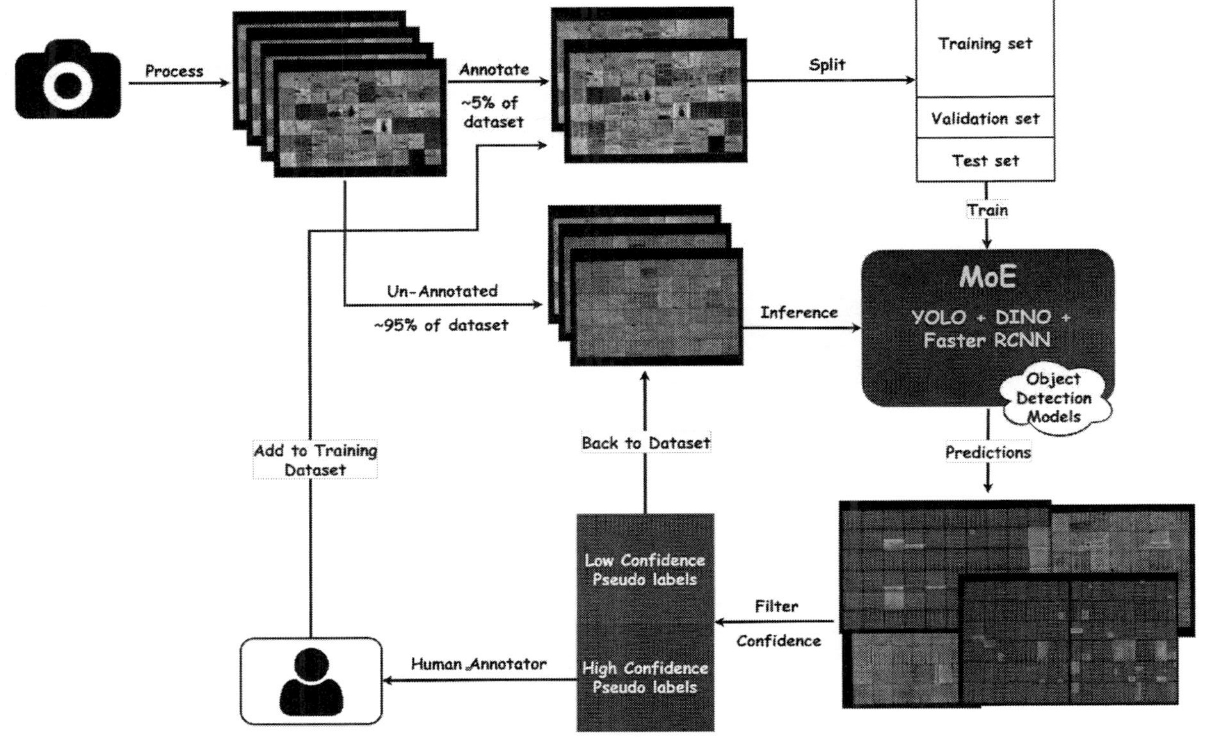

Annotation

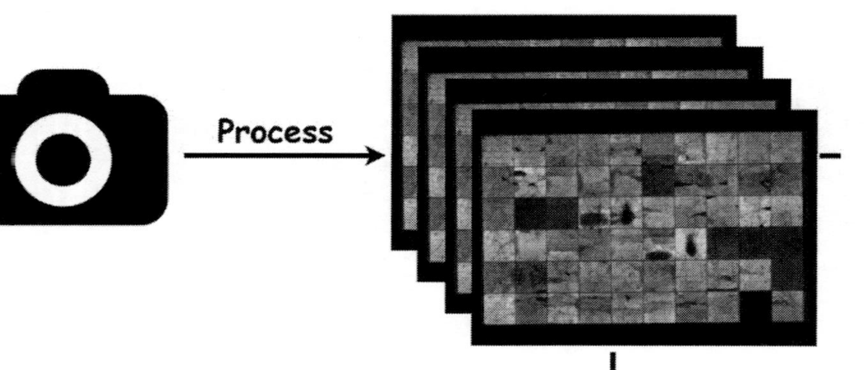

020203-008

Annotation

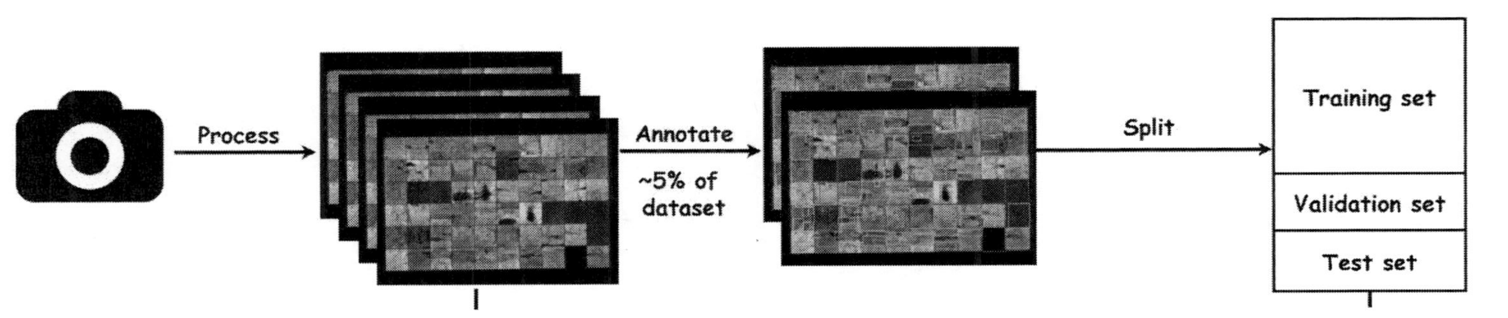

020203-009

Annotation

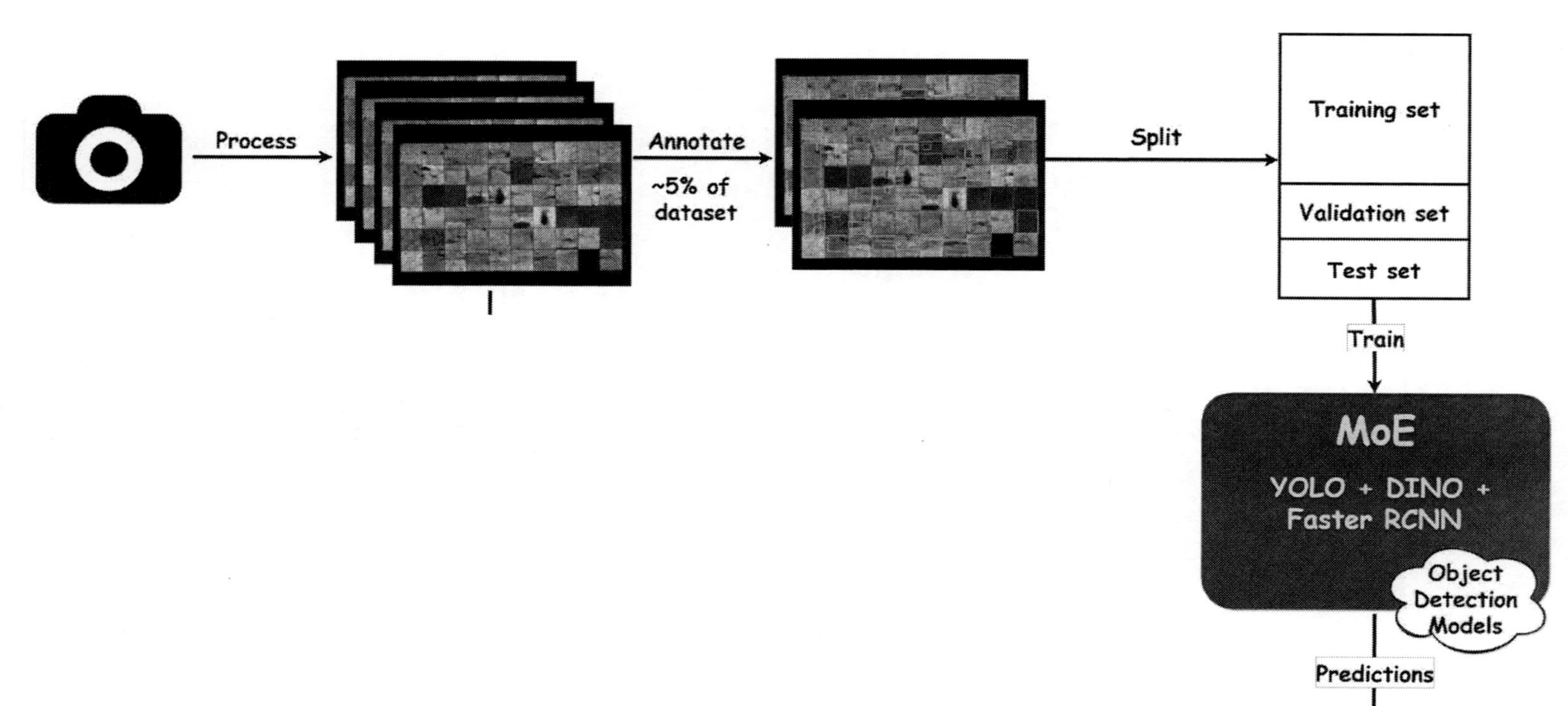

020203-010

Annotation

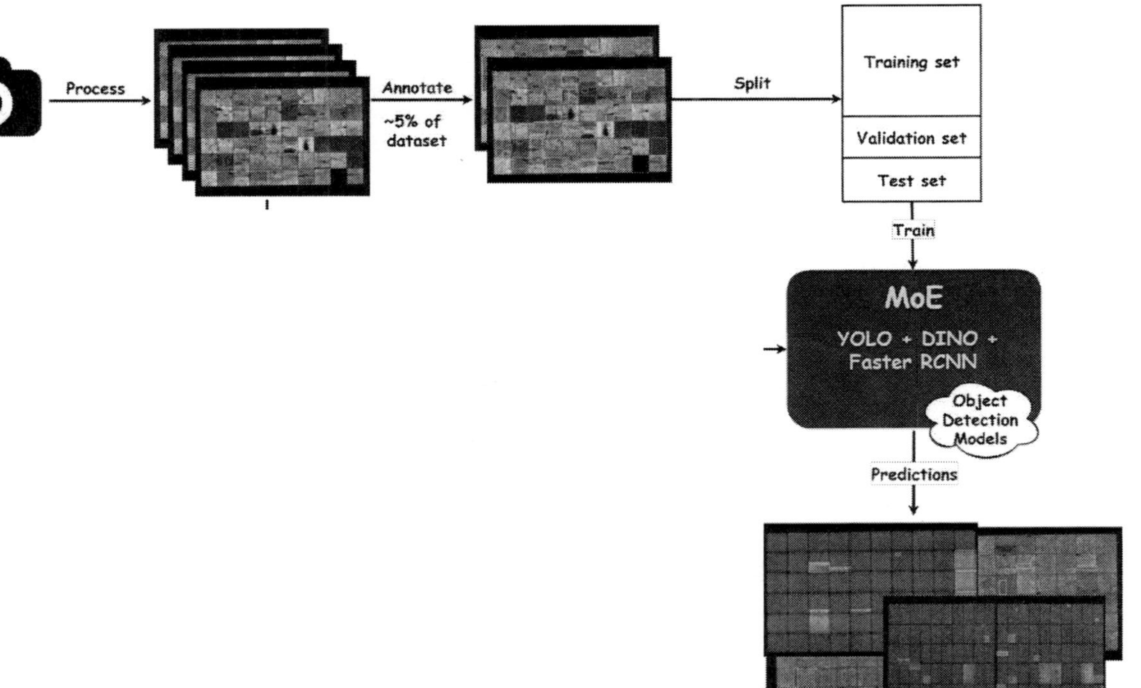

020203-011

Annotation

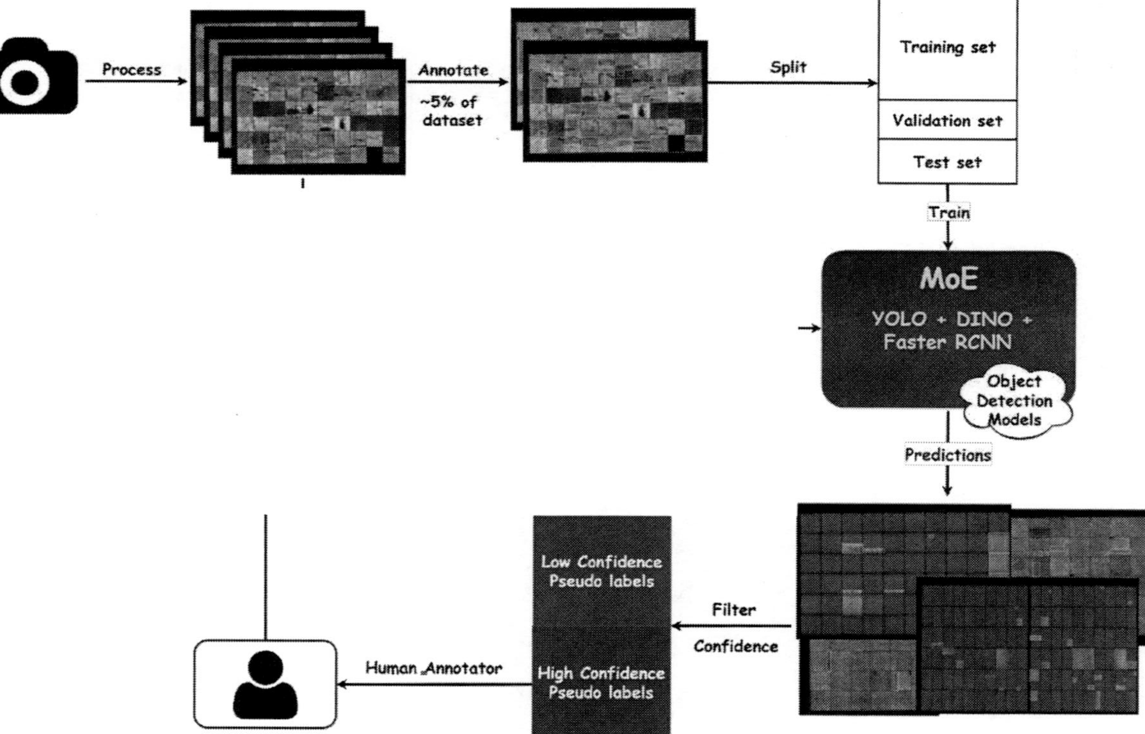

020203-012

Annotation

Process
Annotate
~5% of dataset
Split
Training set
Validation set
Test set
Train
MoE
YOLO + DINO + Faster RCNN
Object Detection Models
Un-Annotated
~95% of dataset
Inference
Predictions
Add to Training Dataset
Back to Dataset
Low Confidence Pseudo labels
High Confidence Pseudo labels
Filter
Confidence
Human Annotator

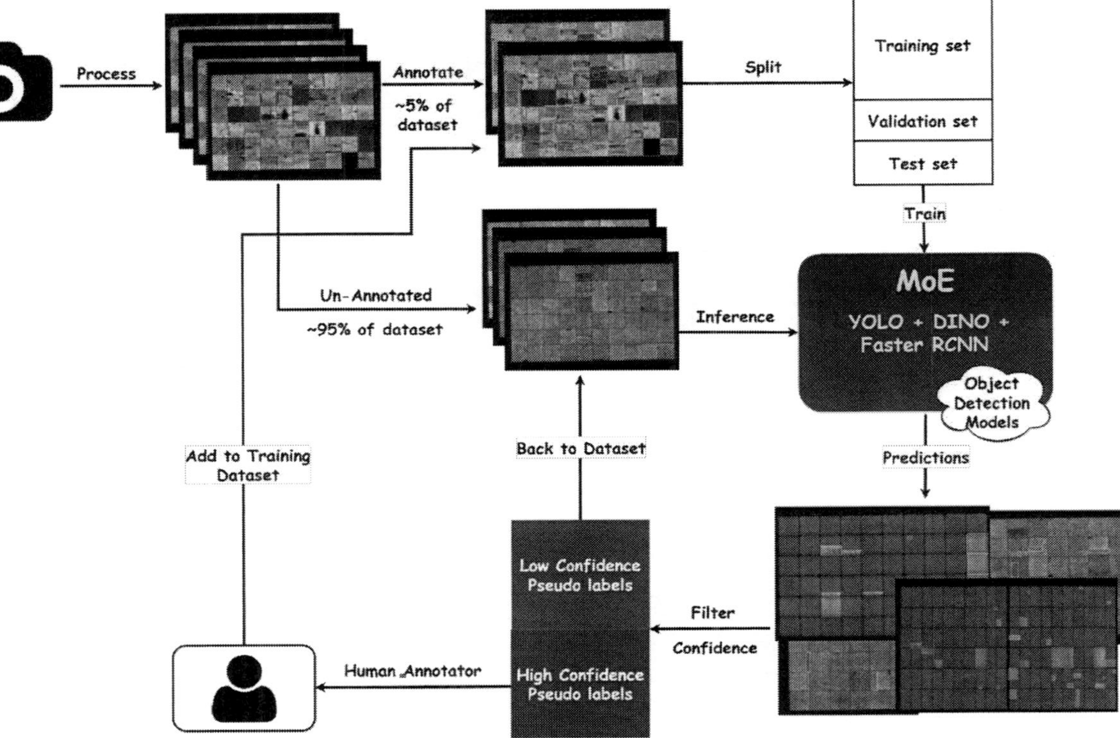

Annotation

Total: ~65,000 annotations

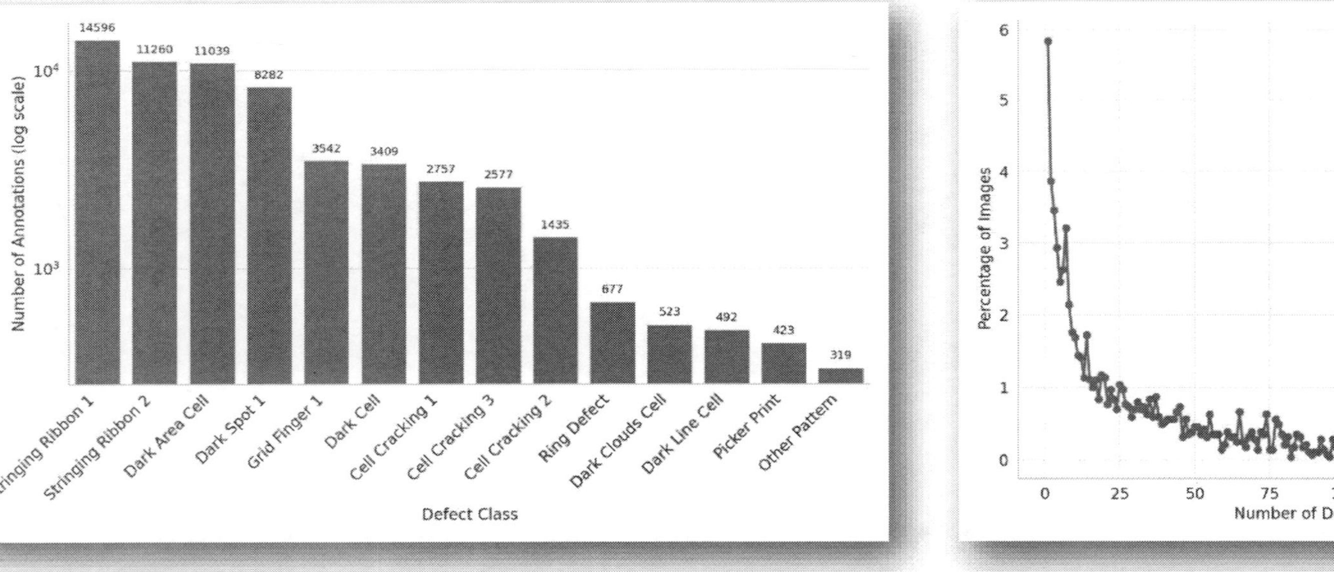

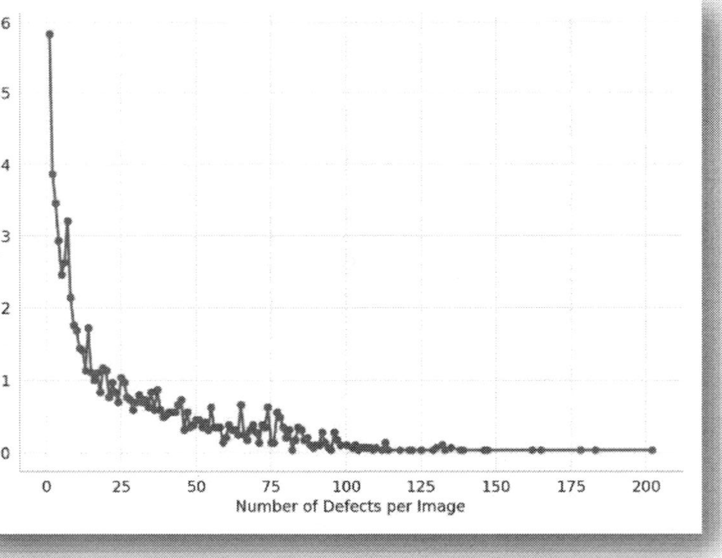

Annotation

Total: ~65,000 annotations

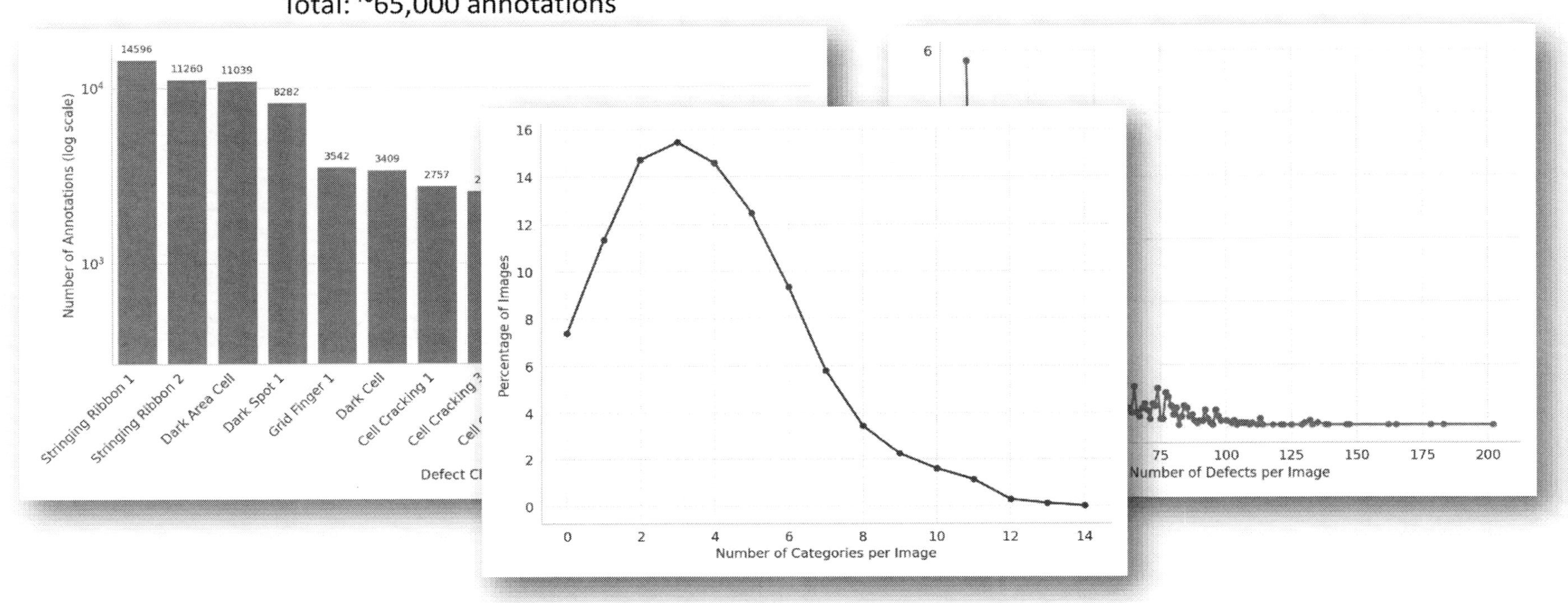

020203-015

Q&A

- **Manual + Automated Generation:** Combined human-written prompts with programmatically generated Q&A to cover both descriptive and analytical aspects.

- **Domain Knowledge Integration:** Used predefined expert knowledge about defect types (causes, severity, safety implications) to generate analytical and heuristic answers.

- **Cell-Level Detection Support:** A YOLO-based cell detector provided structural information (e.g., cell counts, defect positions) that fed into factual Q&A.

- **Image Quality Features:** Automated scripts extracted brightness, sharpness, and saturation to create Q&A pairs on imaging conditions.

- **Multi-Layer Reasoning Coverage:** Each image received ~10–12 Q&A pairs spanning factual (counts, types), analytical (causes/effects), heuristic (safety/condition rating), and descriptive (one-sentence summaries).

Conclusion

- Introduced **EL-VQA**, the first large-scale EL dataset with detection **and** reasoning tasks.
- Provides ~**3,000 images**, **65k+ bounding boxes**, and **30k Q&A pairs** across **14 defect classes**.
- Enables research in **object detection, captioning, and Visual Question Answering** for PV modules.
- Built with **semi-supervised annotation pipeline** (MoE + WBF + manual review).
- To be openly released under **MIT license** to accelerate AI solutions for PV inspection and O&M (within 2025, with publication of work in *Progress in Photovoltaics*)

Contact us

lukas.koester@eurac.edu

Eurac Research

Drususallee/Viale Druso 1

39100 Bozen/Bolzano

T +39 0471 055 055

info@eurac.edu

www.eurac.edu

Progetto cofinanziato dal programma FESR 2021 – 2027 della Provincia Autonoma di Bolzano tramite convenzione nr. EFRE 1027.

020203-018

eurac
research

Unlocking PV Performance: AI-Driven Defect Detection with Multi-Spectral Imaging

SUPSI PVLab

Ebrar Özkalay
Mauro Caccivio

FFHS

Danuta Paraficz
Ralf Jandl
Natasa Sarafijanovic-Djukic

The Challenge: Ensuring PV Reliability

- Growing number of PV systems means reliability is paramount.
- Degradation and defects lead to reduced energy production.
- To achieve lifespans, fast detection of defects in solar panels is critical.
- Ensure appropriate mitigation actions.

FFHS

The Challenge: Ensuring PV Reliability

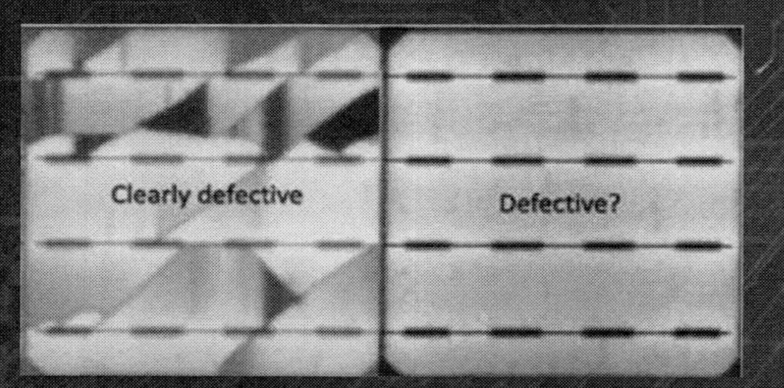

- Current monitoring methods are often inefficient.
- Manual analysis of the images, usually done by experts: slow and expensive.
- Subjective: different experts assign different labels.

FFHS

Mission 1: Automatic identification of defects

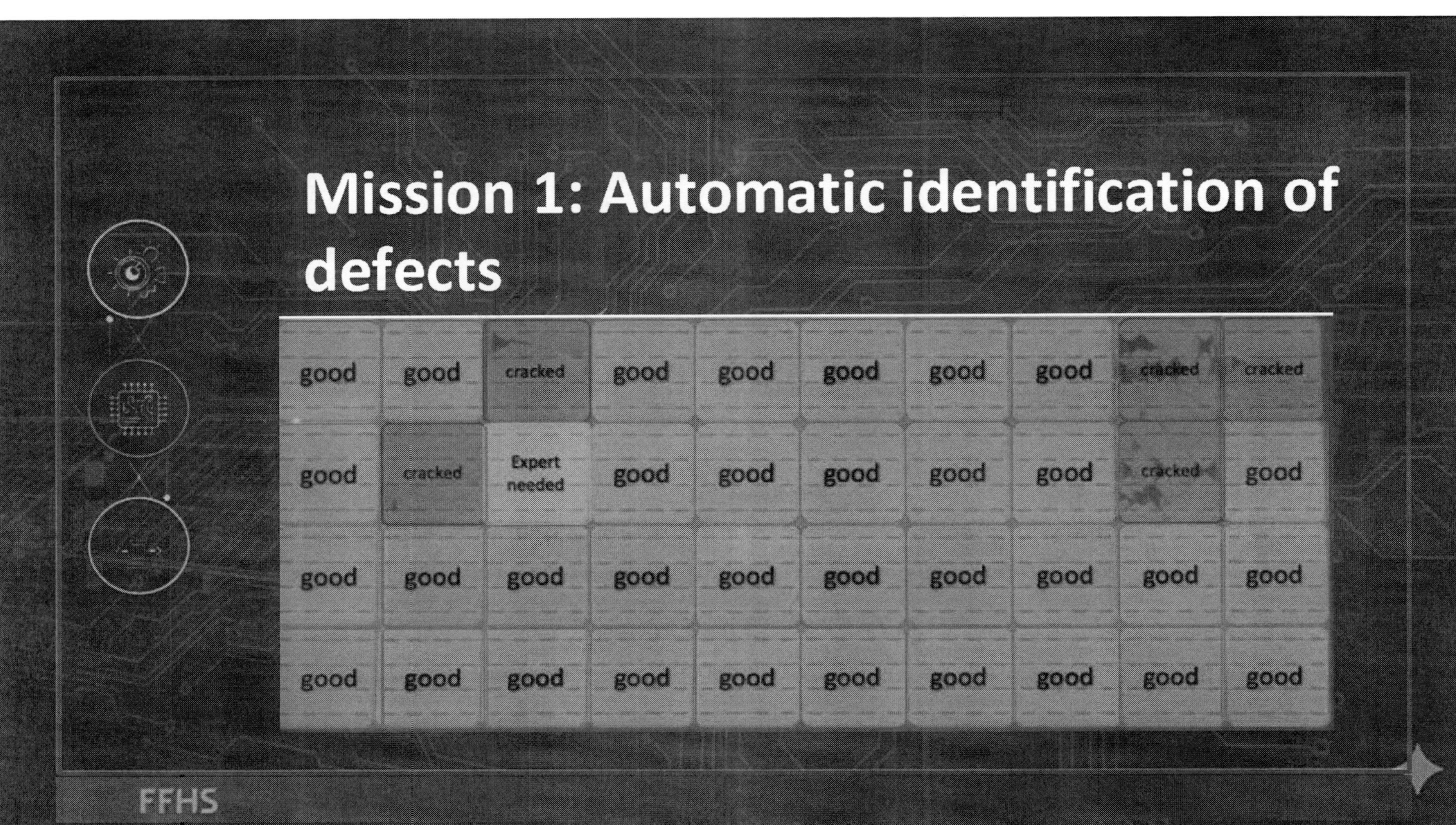

Mission 2: Correlate it with performance

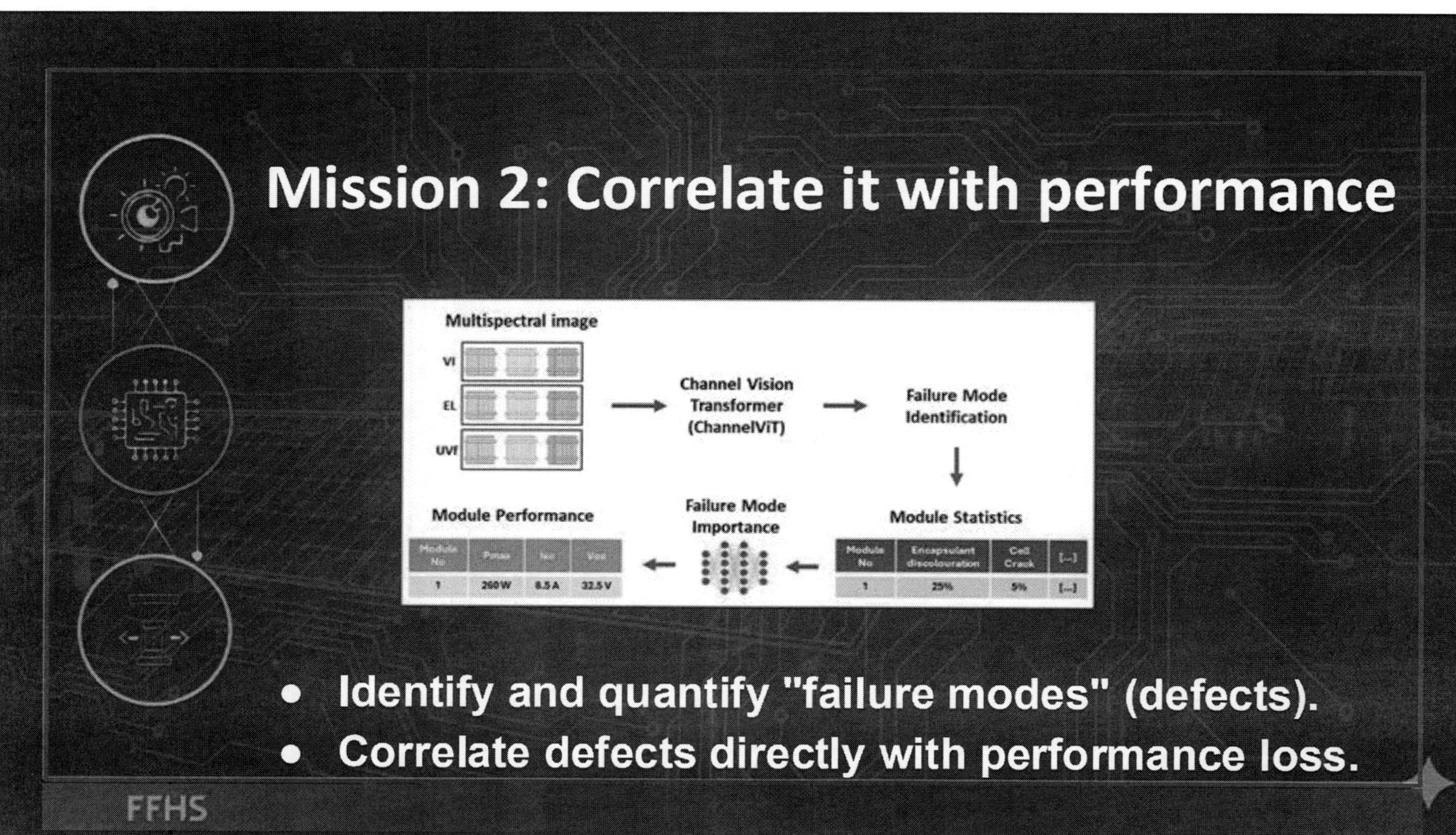

- Identify and quantify "failure modes" (defects).
- Correlate defects directly with performance loss.

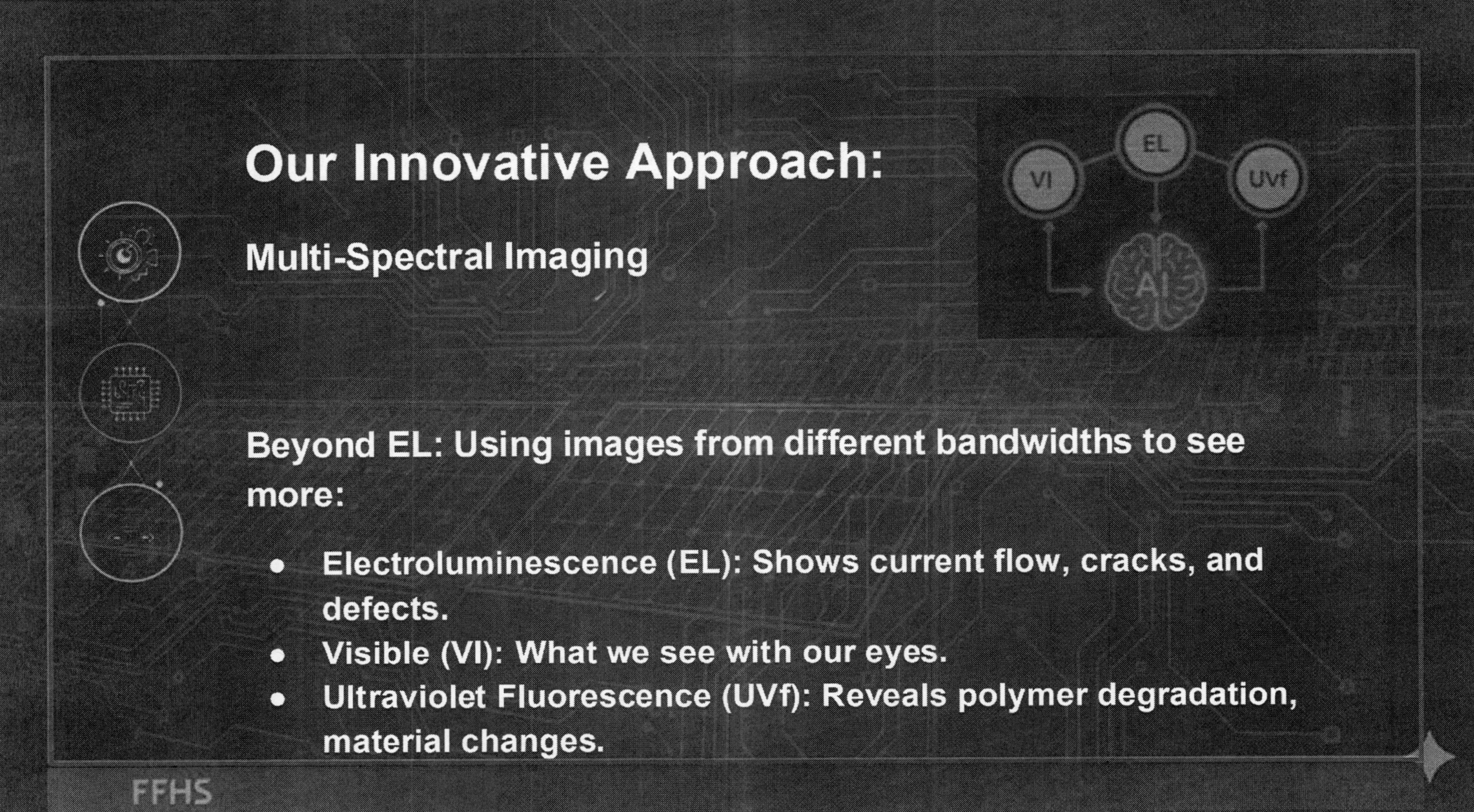
Our Innovative Approach:

Multi-Spectral Imaging

VI
EL
Uvf
AI

Beyond EL: Using images from different bandwidths to see more:

- Electroluminescence (EL): Shows current flow, cracks, and defects.
- Visible (VI): What we see with our eyes.
- Ultraviolet Fluorescence (UVf): Reveals polymer degradation, material changes.

FFHS

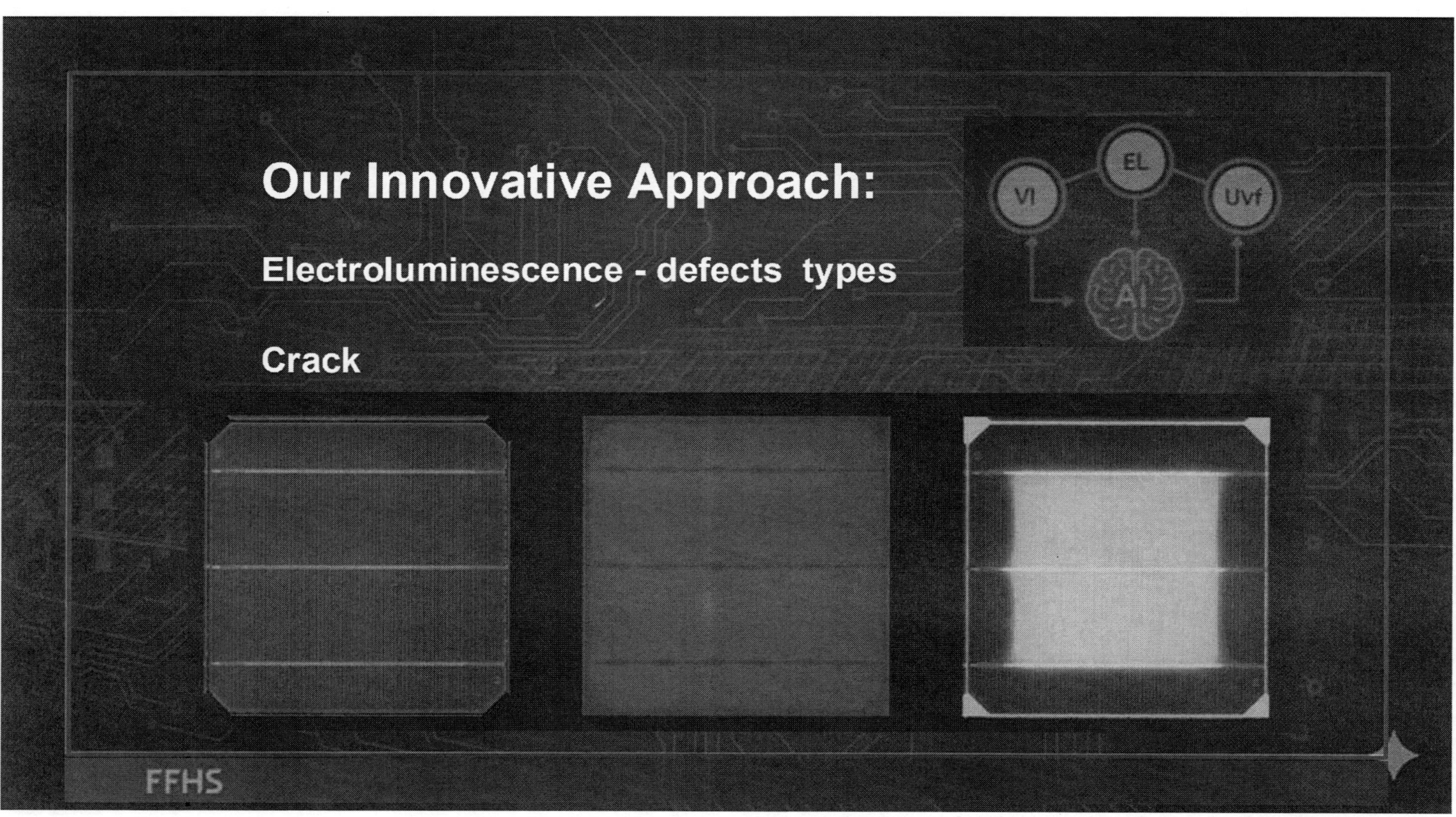
Our Innovative Approach:
Electroluminescence - defects types
Crack
VI
EL
Uvf
AI
FFHS

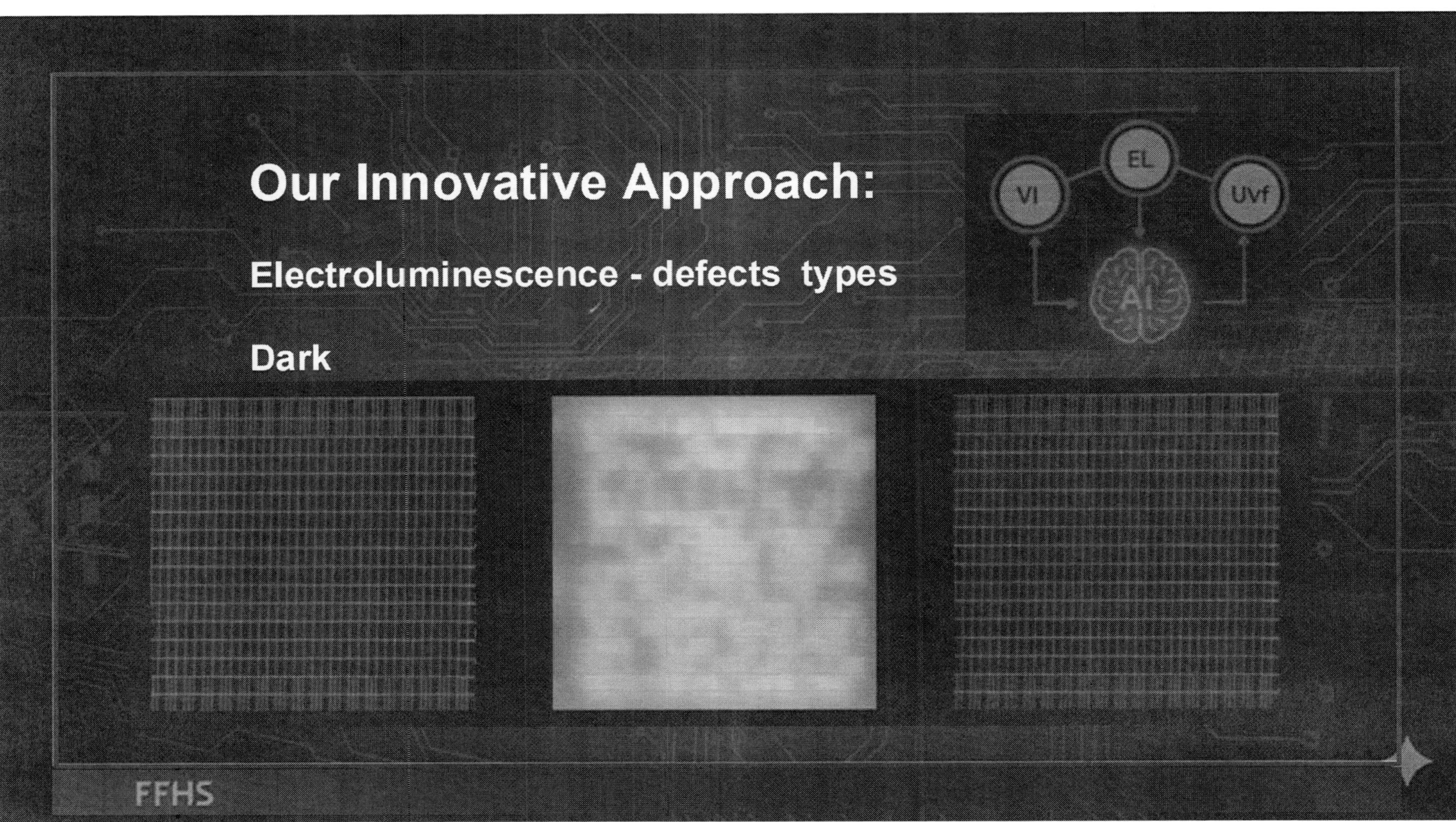

Our Innovative Approach:
Electroluminescence - defects types
Dark
VI
EL
UVf
AI
FFHS

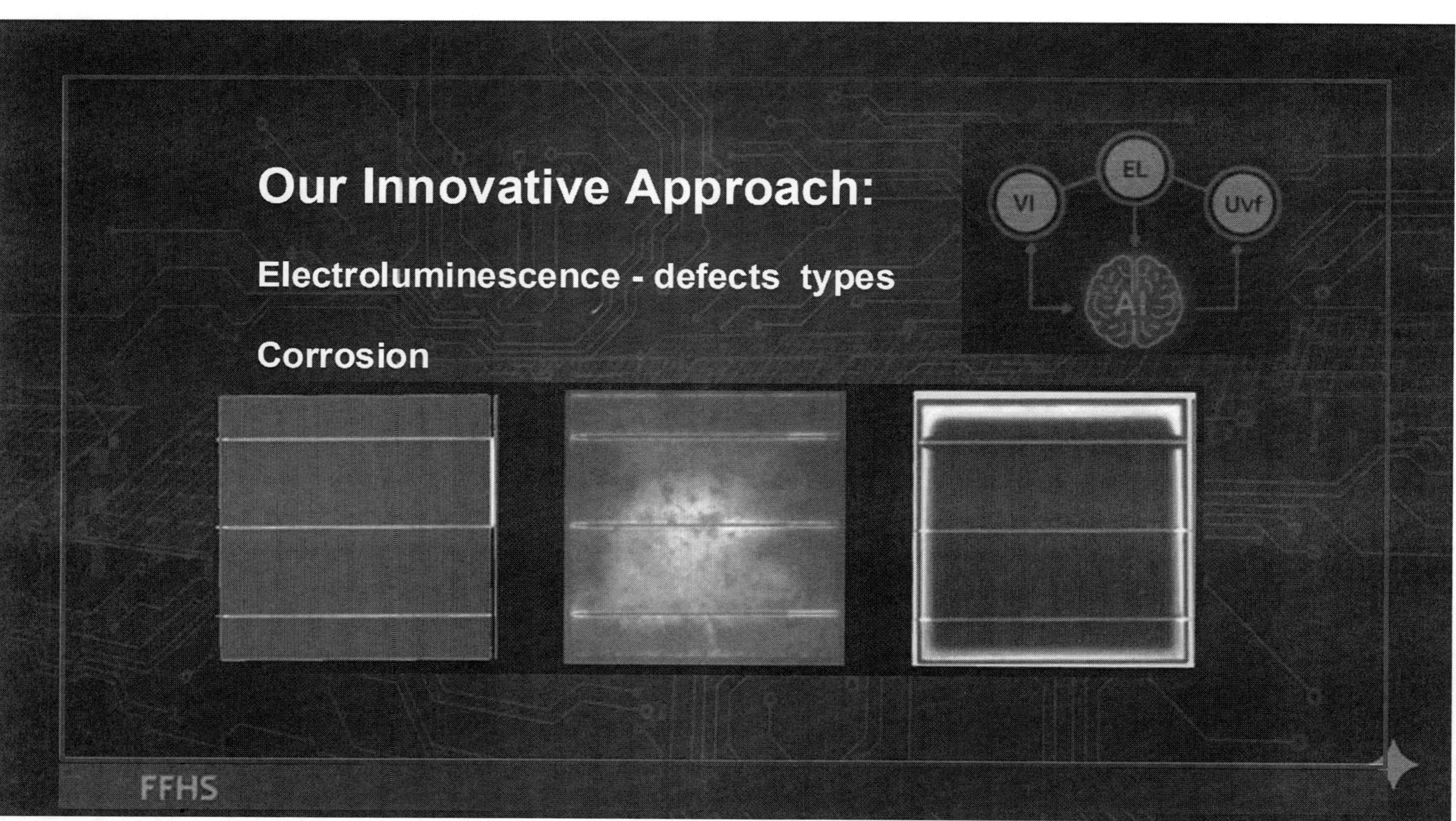

Our Innovative Approach:
Electroluminescence - defects types
Corrosion
VI
EL
Uvf
AI
FFHS

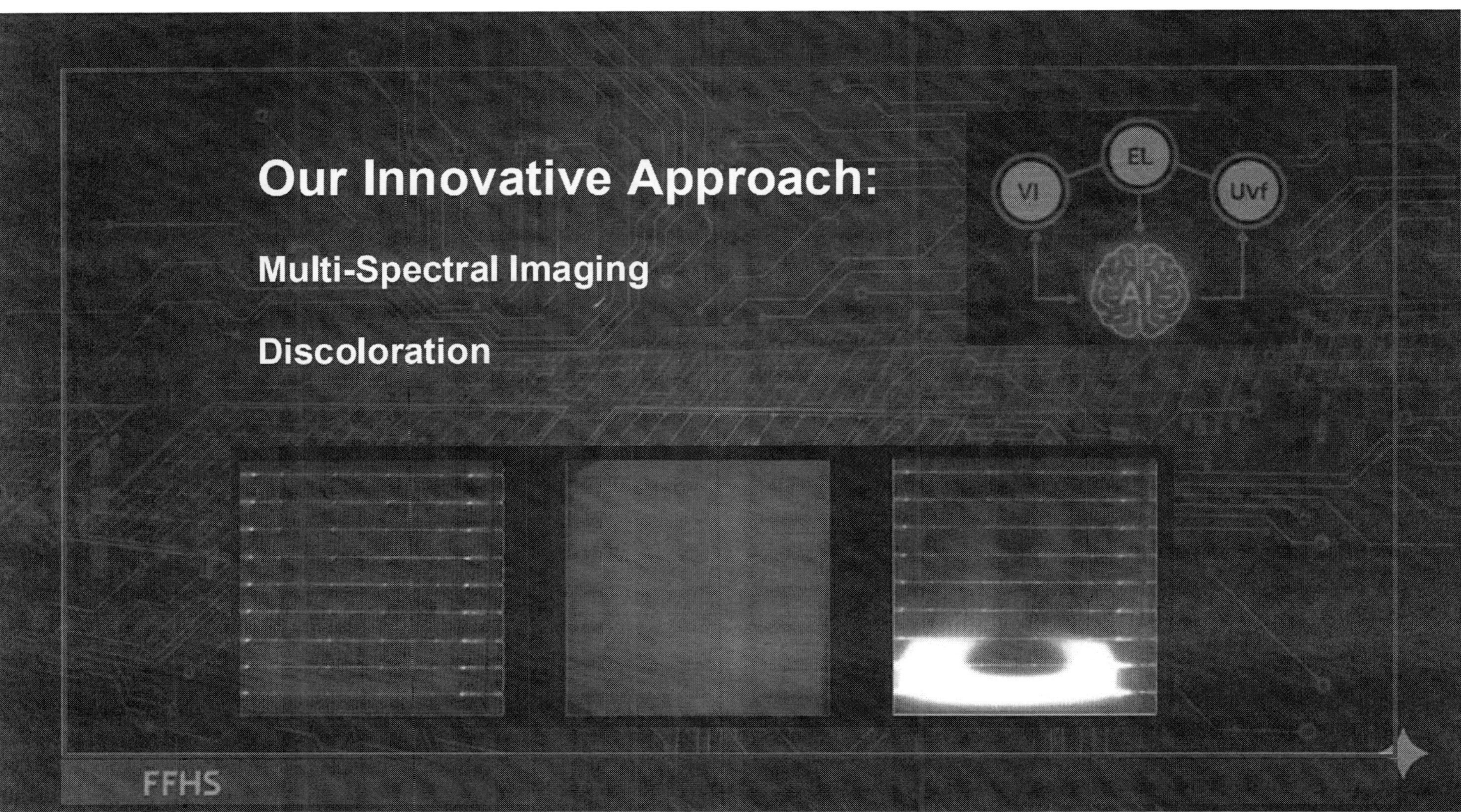
Our Innovative Approach:
Multi-Spectral Imaging
Discoloration
VI
EL
Uvf
AI
FFHS

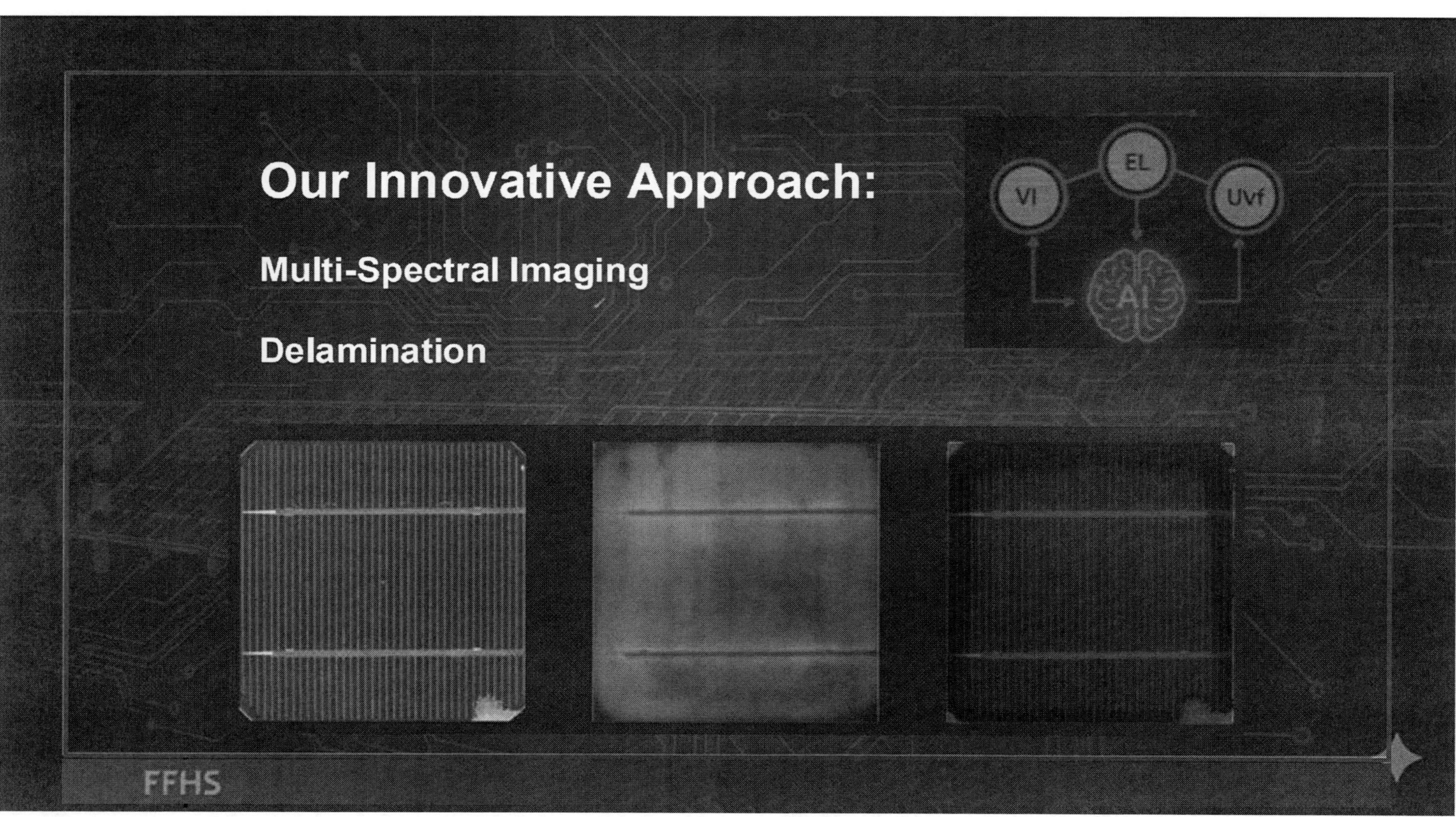

Our Innovative Approach:
Multi-Spectral Imaging
Delamination
VI
EL
UVf
AI
FFHS

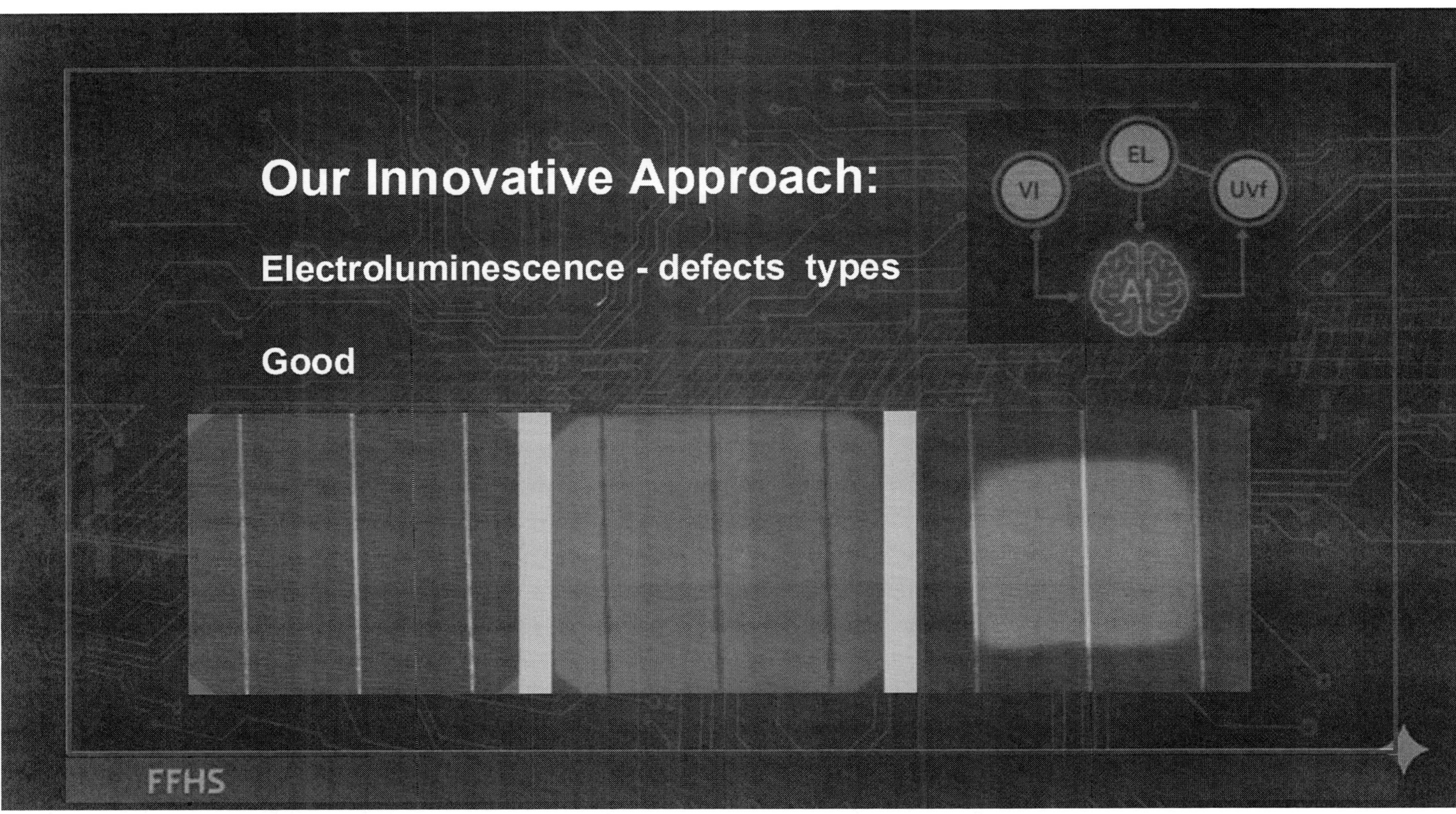

Our Innovative Approach:
Electroluminescence - defects types
Good
VI
EL
Uvf
AI
FFHS

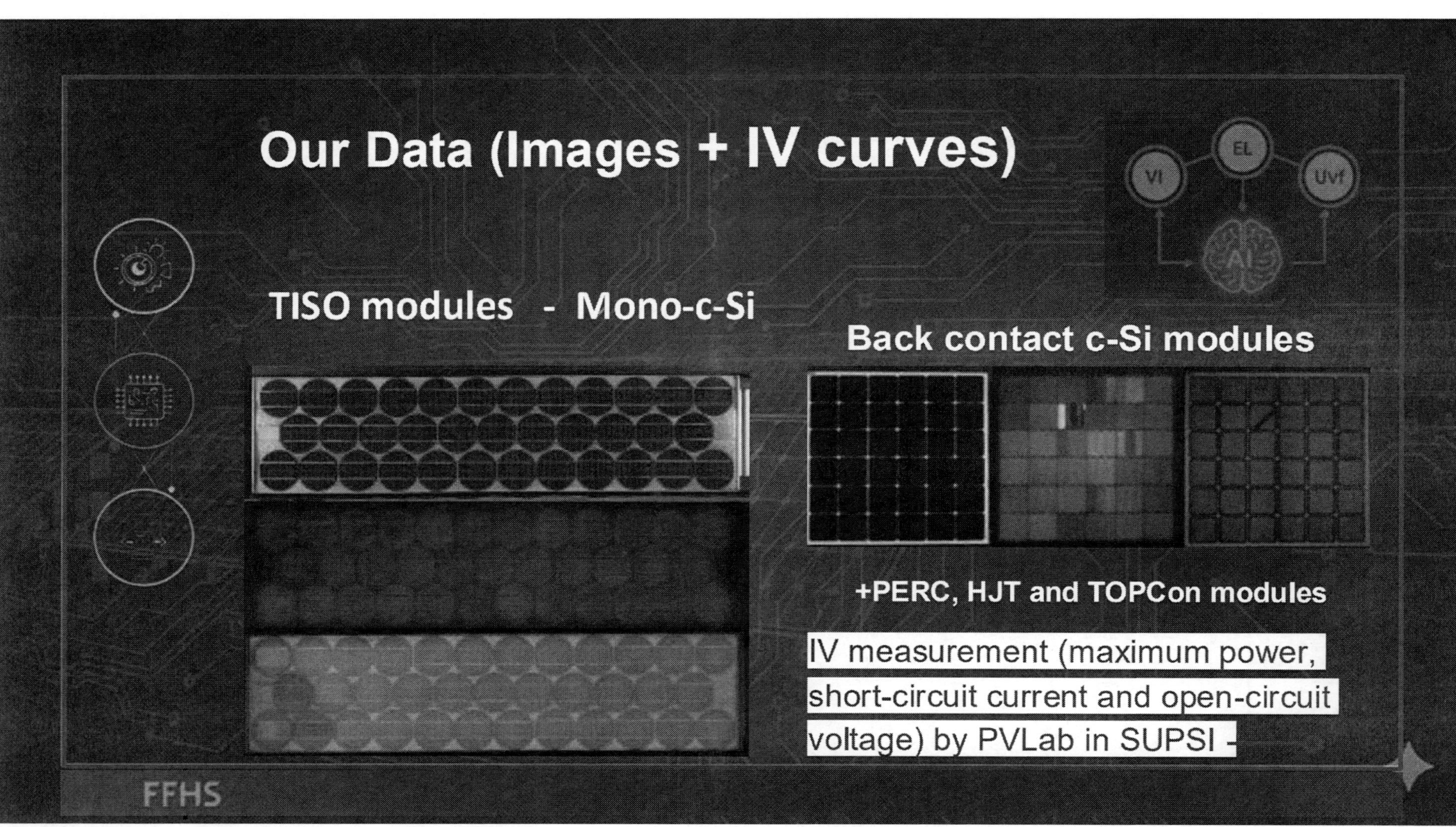

Our Data (Images + IV curves)
VI
EL
Uvf
AI
TISO modules - Mono-c-Si
Back contact c-Si modules
+PERC, HJT and TOPCon modules
IV measurement (maximum power, short-circuit current and open-circuit voltage) by PVLab in SUPSI -
FFHS

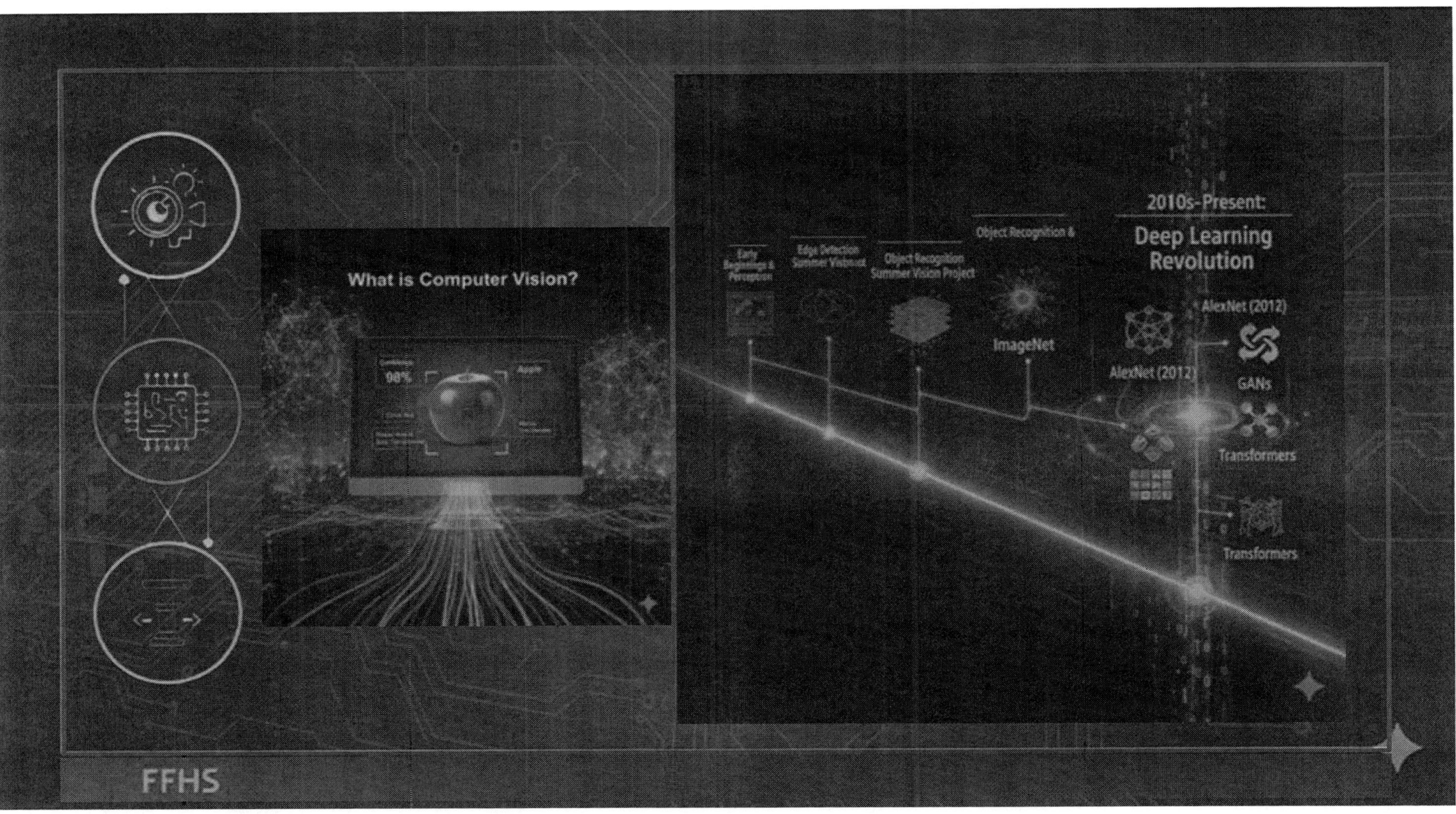
FFHS
What is Computer Vision?
98%
Apple
2010s-Present:
Deep Learning
Revolution
Object Recognition &
Early
Beginnings &
Perceptron
Edge Detection
Summer Vislonot
Object Recognition
Summer Vision Project
ImageNet
AlexNet (2012)
AlexNet (2012)
GANs
Transformers
Transformers

ViT vs CNN

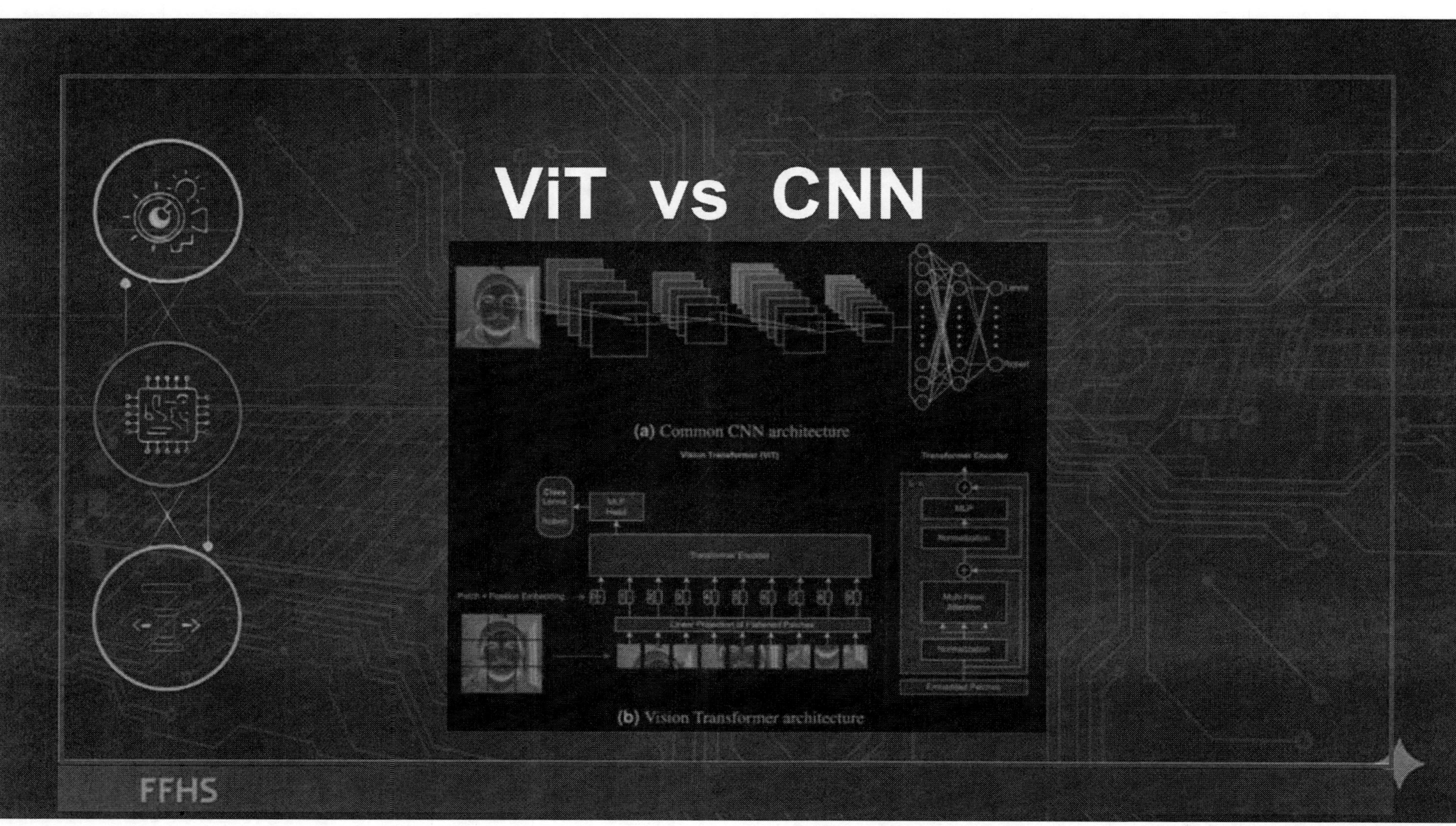

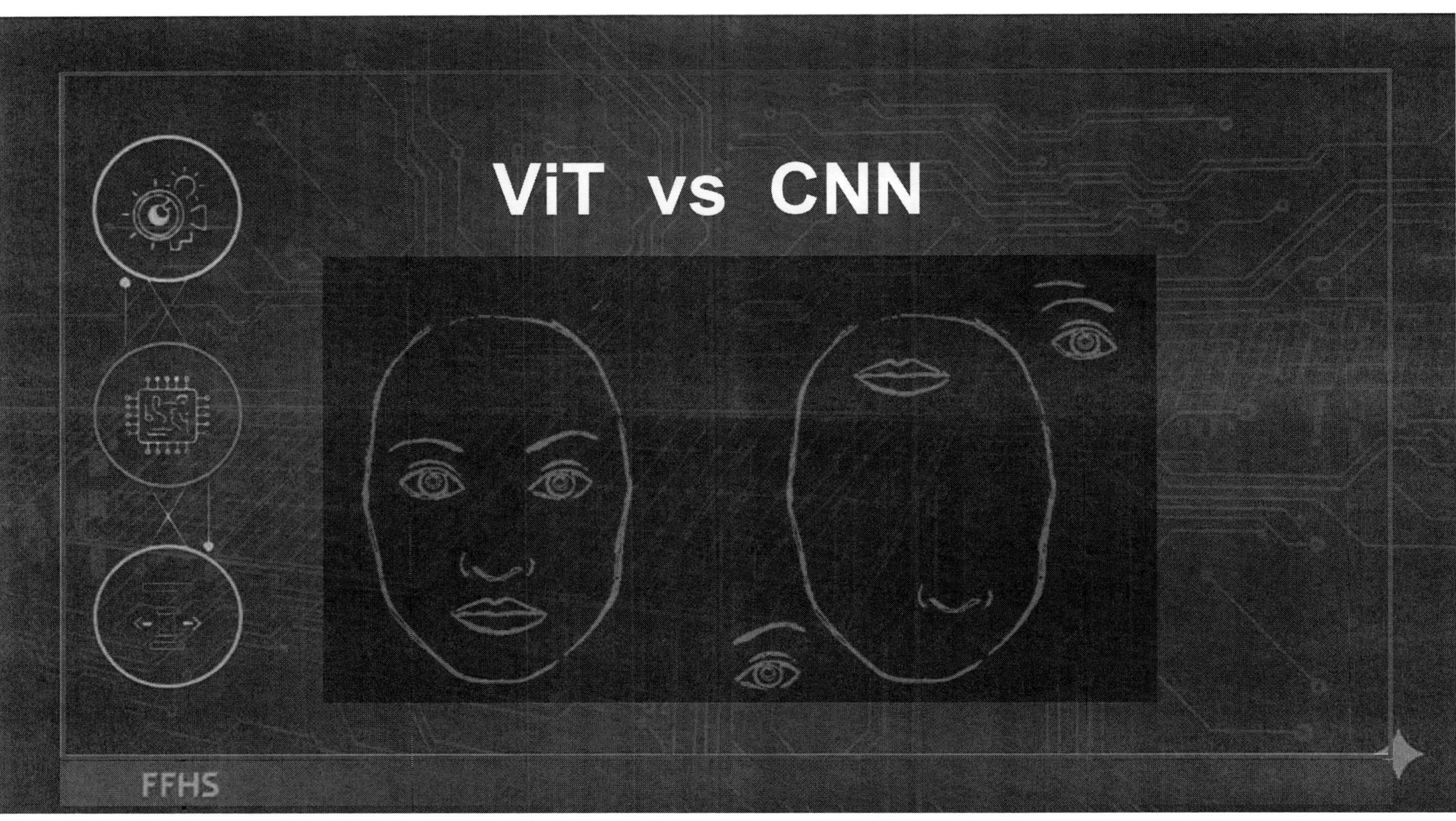

ViT vs CNN
FFHS

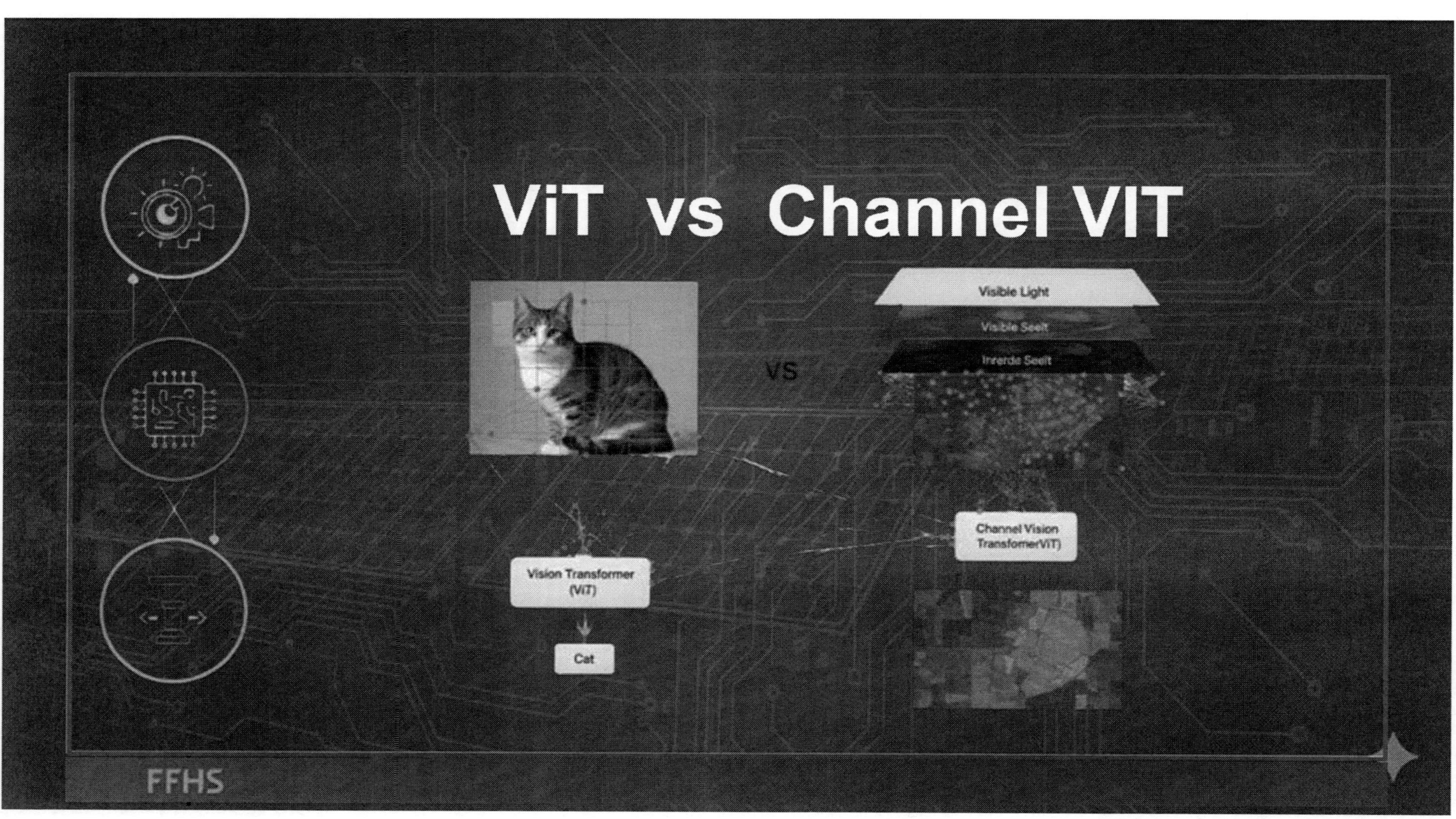
ViT vs Channel VIT
Visible Light
Visible SeeIt
Inrerda SeeIt
vs
Vision Transformer
(ViT)
Cat
Channel Vision
TransfomerViT)
FFHS

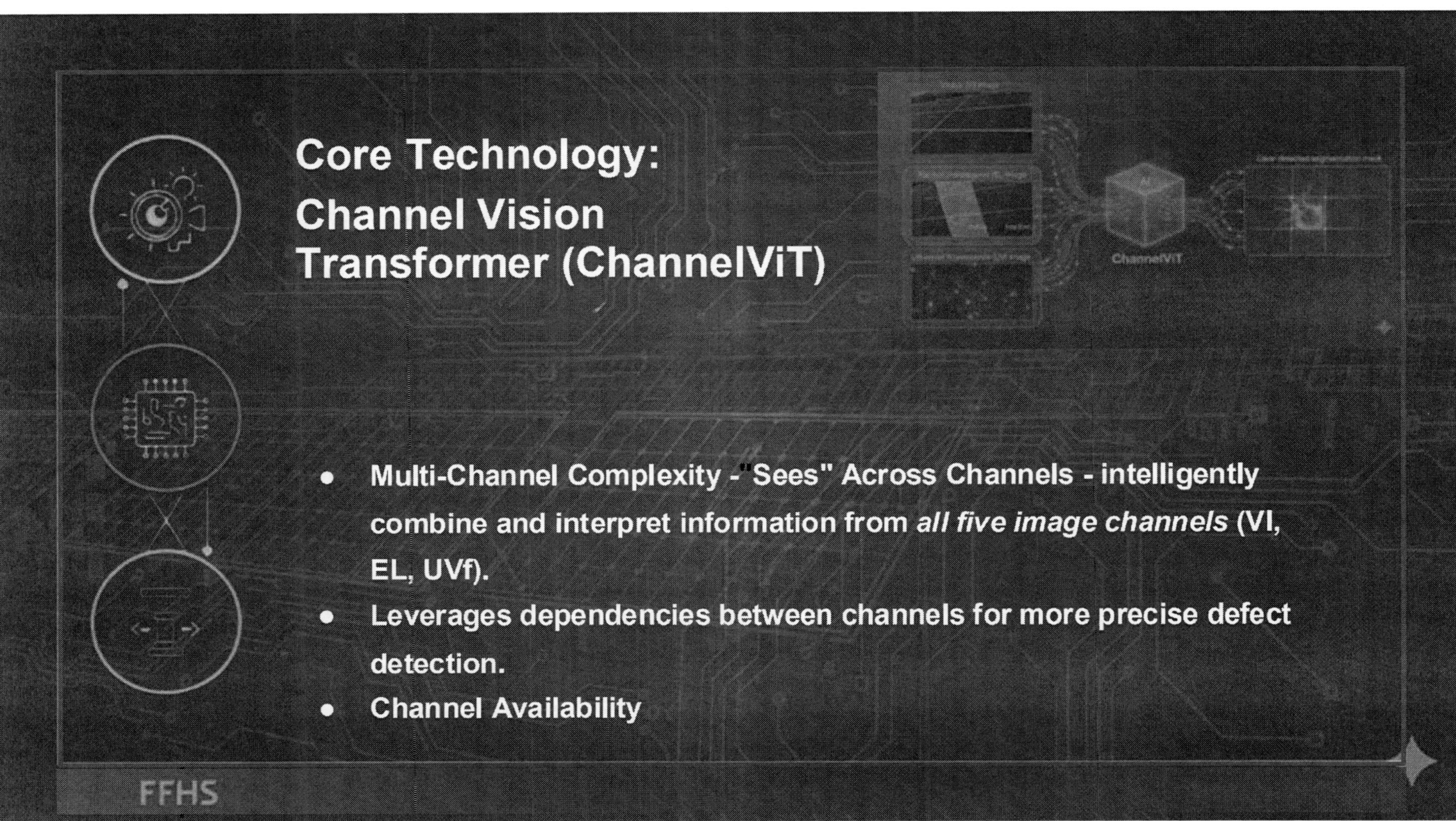

Core Technology: Channel Vision Transformer (ChannelViT)

- **Multi-Channel Complexity - "Sees" Across Channels - intelligently combine and interpret information from *all five image channels* (VI, EL, UVf).**
- **Leverages dependencies between channels for more precise defect detection.**
- **Channel Availability**

FFHS

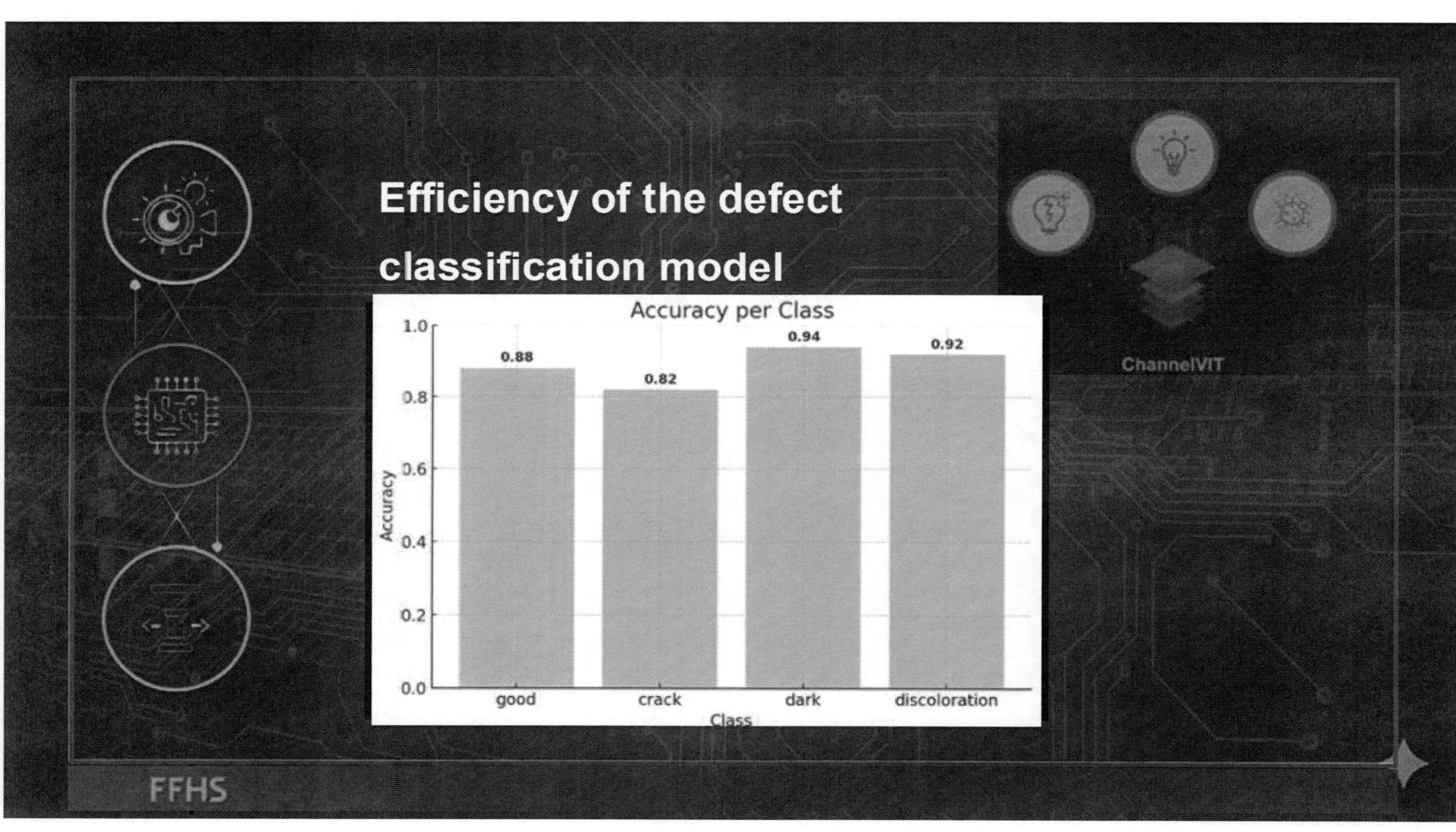
Efficiency of the defect classification model
ChannelVIT
Accuracy per Class
0.88
0.82
0.94
0.92
Accuracy
1.0
0.8
0.6
0.4
0.2
0.0
good
crack
dark
discoloration
Class
FFHS

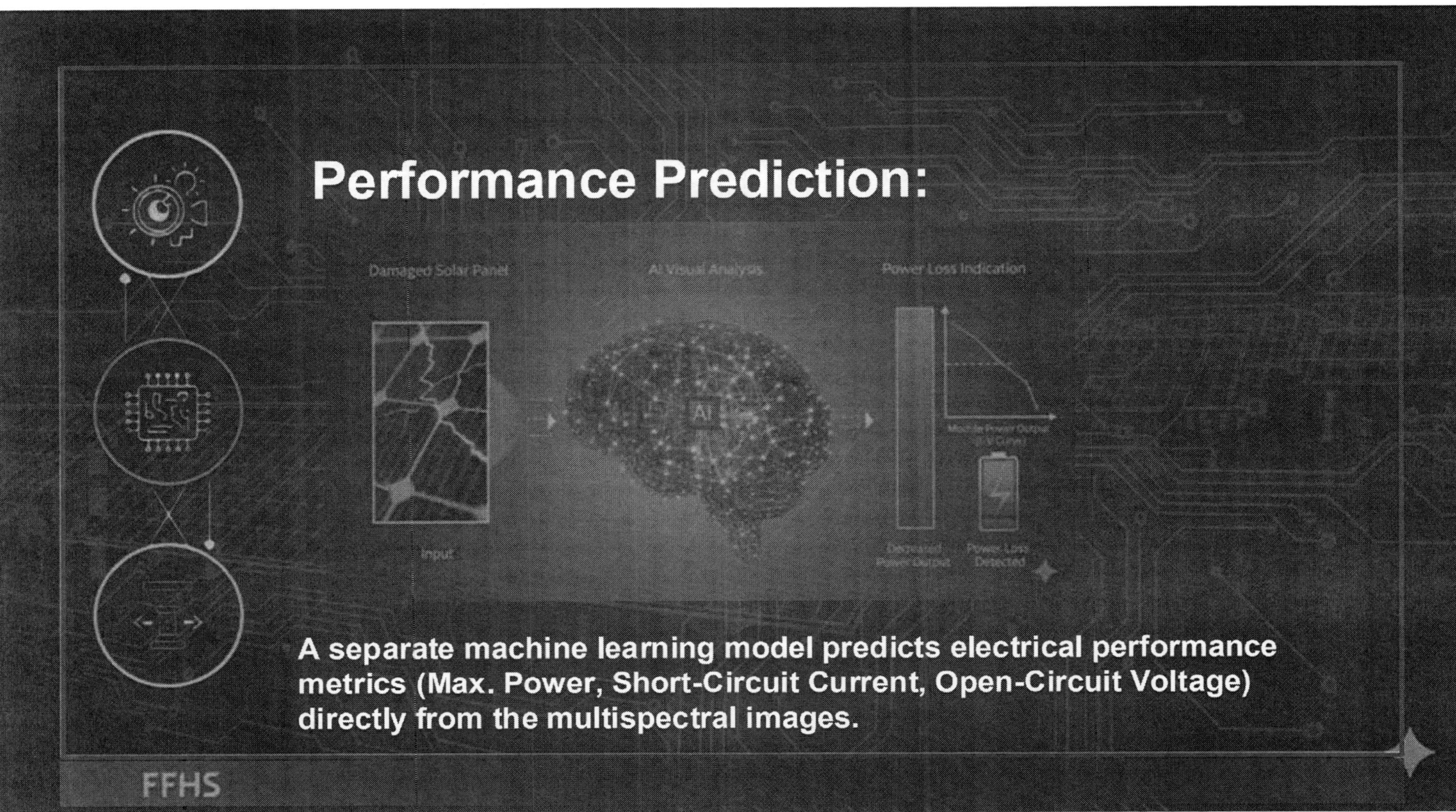

Performance Prediction:
Damaged Solar Panel
AI Visual Analysis
Power Loss Indication
AI
Input
Decreased Power Output
Power Loss Detected
A separate machine learning model predicts electrical performance metrics (Max. Power, Short-Circuit Current, Open-Circuit Voltage) directly from the multispectral images.
FFHS

Performance Prediction:

Multispectral

Metric	ResNet-18
MAE	4.35
MedAE	3.38
MSE	32.79
R^2 Score	0.47

Only EL

Metric	ResNet-18
MAE	5.67
MedAE	4.72
MSE	50.61
R^2 Score	0.18

A separate machine learning model predicts electrical performance metrics (Max. Power, Short-Circuit Current, Open-Circuit Voltage) directly from the multispectral images.

FFHS

Performance Prediction:

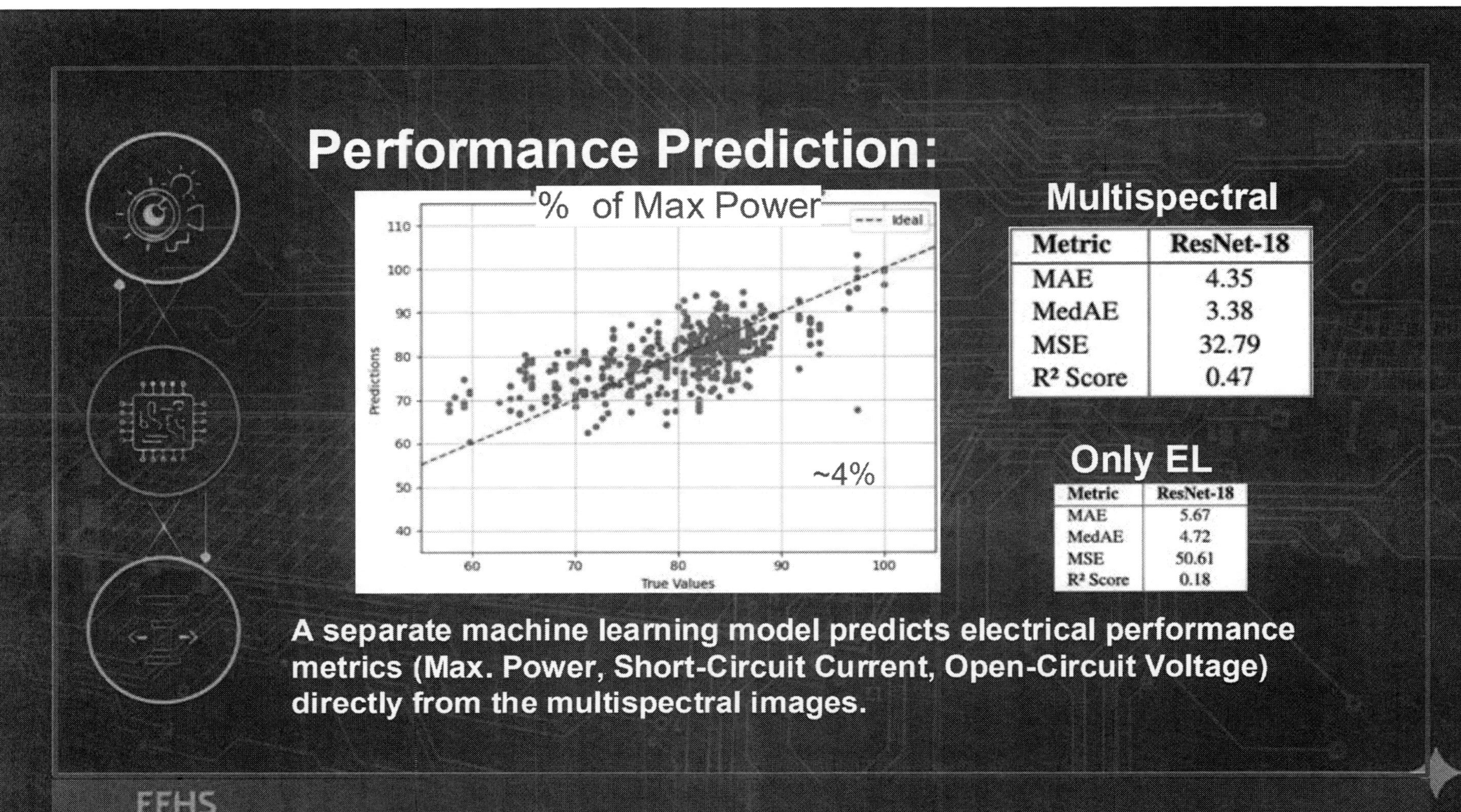

Multispectral

Metric	ResNet-18
MAE	4.35
MedAE	3.38
MSE	32.79
R² Score	0.47

Only EL

Metric	ResNet-18
MAE	5.67
MedAE	4.72
MSE	50.61
R² Score	0.18

A separate machine learning model predicts electrical performance metrics (Max. Power, Short-Circuit Current, Open-Circuit Voltage) directly from the multispectral images.

FFHS

Future Expansion:

- Validating in controlled environment, future - on-site drone analysis.

- Other type of measurements

  - Thermography
  - Daylight electroluminescence integration

- Digital twins

- Power to Image correlation – for colored PV panels

Thank you for your attention!

FFHS
Fernfachhochschule
Schweiz
Mitglied der SUPSI

The EAGLE research Project is being financed by the Swiss Federal Office of Energy and is a collaboration between the Laboratory for Web Science of the FFHS and the SUPSI PVLab.

FFHS

Danuta Paraficz
Ralf Jandl
Natasa Sarafijanovic-Djukic

SUPSI PVLab

Ebrar Özkalay
Mauro Caccivio

ebrar.oezkalay@supsi.ch

dr Danuta Paraficz
Researcher at Swiss Distance
University of Applied Sciences

danuta.paraficz@ffhs.ch

ASYNCHRONOUS DAYLIGHT LUMINESCENCE OBTAINED WITHOUT PROGRAMMABLE POWER SOURCES

Cristian Terrados[1,2], Eva de la Viuda[1], Kabir Paul Sulca[1], Julian Anaya[1], Miguel Ángel González[1], Oscar Martínez[1*]
[1] GdS-Optronlab group, Dpto. Física de la Materia Condensada. Universidad de Valladolid. Edificio LUCIA. Paseo de Belén, 11. Valladolid (Spain)
[2] Solar and Wind Feasibility Technologies (SWIFT). Escuela Politécnica Superior, Universidad de Burgos. Avda. Cantabria s/n 09006 Burgos (Spain)
*oscar.martinez@uva.es

ABSTRACT: Daylight Electroluminescence and Photoluminescence techniques (dEL/dPL) have rapidly advanced in recent years and are now well-established tools for the characterization of photovoltaic (PV) Si solar modules in the field. Performing dEL/dPL requires cameras capable of working in the near IR region of the light spectrum (such as InGaAs cameras) and sophisticated filtering procedures to distinguish the weak luminescence emission coming from the PV module from the more intense ambient light. Effective filtering of the weak luminescence requires specific acquisition schemes, both synchronous and asynchronous methods can be used for this purpose. Asynchronous schemes are more convenient, but they usually rely in expensive programmable power sources that produce high quality square or sinusoidal waveforms for the controlled current injection into the PV modules. When paired with fast InGaAs cameras (600 fps), dEL images can be obtained using very short (sub-second) acquisition times. However, the requirement for these programmable power sources may be a significant barrier to rapid in-field deployment of the technique. In this work we show the results of using asynchronous daylight luminescence inspections obtained without programmable power sources, using external control to modulate a DC signal from any power source, including the neighbor panels, or even without the use of a power source but using the Sun as the light source, in the dPL case. We specifically study the shape of the generated current and voltage signals, comparing the external control case with the case of using a programable power source. We also study the impact of varying the modulation frequency and camera speed on image quality and how these acquisition parameters influence performance. This approach broadens the applicability of the dEL technique, enabling effective filtering and identification of panel defects under self-powered or sunlight-driven conditions.
Keywords: daylight luminescence, module inspection, signal modulation, electroluminescence, photoluminescence

1 INTRODUCTION

Luminescence imaging techniques (EL/PL) are very well-established techniques for inspecting the condition of Si PV panels, providing complementary, and often more comprehensive information, compared to infrared thermography (IRT) and I-V characterization techniques [1, 2]. Given the large number of solar modules in a PV plant, the industry increasingly demands fast inspection techniques. For this reason, it is highly beneficial to perform on-site inspections at the solar plant without disassembling the modules, and preferably during the day. This allows for a rapid inspection of the modules and reduces the risk of damage during assembly and disassembly [3, 4]. In this context, daylight imaging techniques, such as dEL and dPL, have recently emerged and advanced rapidly [5-12]. However, it is still challenging to deploy these techniques effectively in a PV plant with a large number of modules. In this work we show a procedure that holds the potential to enable massive inspection of Si solar plants using these powerful techniques. For characterization we use the asynchronous mode, in which a modulated "on" and "off" signal allows for the filtration of the ambient light and allows to obtain the luminescence coming from the PV panels [13, 14]. In our asynchronous approach [14], we have previously used a large (15 kW) programable power source allowing for the high-quality modulated injection of current for a whole solar PV string. In the present work, we use instead an external and compact device to modulate the signal that can arise from any power source, including small and large DC power sources, but also the neighbor panels (self-powering configuration [15]), or even without the use of a power source but using the Sun as the light source, in the

dPL case [9, 10, 16]. Combining fast InGaAs cameras, with maximum acquisition speeds of up to 600 fps, adequate optical filters to block as much ambient light as possible, and advanced filtering of the acquired light, allows dEL/dPL images to be recorded in very short times. This process, which eliminates the need for high-quality external programmable power sources to be connected to each string, has therefore the potential to provide a fast and cost-effective inspection of solar modules condition – a growing necessity for the operation and maintenance of medium-to-large solar plants.

To make a comparison with the case of using programmable power sources, we examine the shape of the generated current and voltage signals, as well as the quality of the final dEL image, for modulated signals obtained using a programable power source or those obtained by means of our external control device. We also examine how varying the modulation frequency and camera speed impacts image quality and the effect of these acquisition parameters on performance.

2 EXPERIMENTAL DETAILS

2.1 External device for signal modulation

A compact external device (ED) for square-wave signal modulation has been designed by means of an Arduino-based switching device, incorporating an XBee module for wireless control. The time periods of the "on" and "off" domains are defined and communicated remotely to an IGBT capable of switching up to 1500 V and 15 A. In this way, by connecting the ED to a DC power supply, current is injected into a PV module or string in a square wave scheme, where the frequency of the wave can be easily adjusted. For instance, we have tested frequencies values of 6.25, 12.5, 25.0 and 50.0 Hz. One important advantage of this method is that square-wave signal modulation is generated independently of the power source, including the self-powering configuration of a PV string [15], and can be also applied for the dPL configuration, without the use of a power source, but just using the Sun for excitation and modifying (modulating) the position on the I-V curve to obtain two points with a large difference in currents drawn from the modules [16]. In this way, we can generate square "on" and "off" signals from any power source, also for the dPL case, eliminating the need for expensive, programmable power supplies, and simplifying in-field deployment of the dEL/dPL techniques.

2.1 Asynchronous scheme and experimental set-up

The acquisition of the dEL/dPL images is performed in an asynchronous scheme with the use of a high-speed camera, First Ligh C-RED 2 Lite, 640x512 – ~0.33 Mpixel – and pixel pitch of 15 x 15 μm, with 14-bit quantization and 16-bit dynamical range, with maximum speed of 600 fps. For these measurements, we have used 200 and 400 fps for the InGaAs camera speed. We have fixed the exposition time to 2.5 ms for all the measurements. We use a Kowa short wave infrared (SWIR) optical system with 16 mm focal length for image acquisition. A SWIR bandpass filter, centered around 1160 nm with a bandwidth of 150 nm and a transmittance close to 90%, is used in order to suppress as much ambient light as possible.

Multi-crystalline Si Al-BSF modules (Sharp, ND-AR330H 330 W, V_{oc}=45.5 V, I_{sc}=9.40 A) were used for the dEL/dPL tests. For the dEL case, we performed the signal modulation for just one module, using both a small power source (600 W, labelled as SPS) and the ED, as well as a large programmable power source (EA-PS 91500-30 3U 19" 3U 15000W model, labelled LPPS), which allows us to compare the signal modulation obtained from the programmable power source itself with the one obtained with the ED acting on a DC signal from this LPPS. We also performed dEL measurements exciting a string of 8 modules, also comparing the signal modulation obtained from the LPPS itself with the one obtained with the use of the ED acting on a DC signal from the LPPS. In both cases the injected current was fixed to the I_{sc} value of the modules. We also performed dEL measurements in the self-powering configuration [15], with two modules powering the inspected one, using the ED for signal modulation. We have also performed dPL measurements, using the Sun as the excitation source [10, 16] (that without the need of a power source), using also the ED for signal modulation. In all cases we have recorded both the current intensity and voltage waveforms at the entrance of one inspected module, using Fluke 80i-110s and Fluke 80K-40 probes, respectively.

The obtained whole stack of images is subsequently analyzed in the frequency domain using robust methods previously described [14] to obtain the final luminescence image from the PV panels. The quality of these images can be influenced by the noise and characteristics of the modulated signals. Therefore, the final images are thoroughly analyzed for various acquisition parameters using our previously proposed SNR_{25} metric [14].

3 RESULTS

3.1 dEL inspection of one module by acting on the SPS

The use of non-programmable DC power sources for injecting current into the modules is the standard procedure for EL image inspections on the dark. In particular, the EL inspection of just one Si module can be performed by a small DC power source, able to inject a current close to their I_{sc} value. On the other hand, for the case of dEL inspections, a signal modulation is needed. In this case, an external device to produce the signal modulation is thus required. We have already used in the past our developed ED for signal modulation of a DC signal, but in the synchronous mode, where the signal frequency is highly coupled to the camera speed [10, 16]. Here we have performed the dEL inspection of just one module by acting on a SPS, but in the asynchronous configuration, using different cameras velocities and signal frequencies, which in this case are decoupled.

Fig.1 (a, d) shows the measured current intensities and voltages at the entrance of the inspected module, reflecting the signal modulation performed by means of the ED acting on the SPS. The figure shows the case of two frequencies (25.0 Hz and 50.0 Hz). It can be observed that a non-perfect square wave form was obtained, with transients at the beginning of the "on" periods, with a duration of approx. 8-9 ms, independently of the used frequency. The figure also shows the pixel intensity captured by the InGaAs camera vs the number of images, for camera's acquisition velocities of 200 and 400 fps for each frequency.

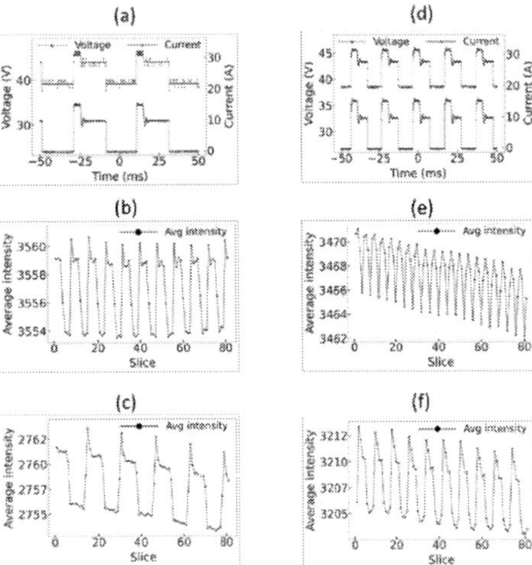

Figure 1: (a, d) Current intensities and voltages at the entrance of the inspected module, generated with the ED acting on a SPS, for ν=25.0 Hz (a) and ν=50.0 Hz (d). (b-f) Pixel intensity variations measured with the InGaAs camera vs number of images, corresponding to situation (a) (ν=25.0 Hz) for cameras' velocities of 200 fps (b) and 400 fps (c), and to situation (d) (ν=50 Hz) for cameras' velocities of 200 fps (e) and 400 fps (f), respectively

Thus, the use of the ED acting on the SPS for signal modulation produces a significative transient in both current intensity and voltage signals, with a large extension in time and a significative increase in the current intensity values at the beginning of each cycle. Moreover, the transient in the signal modulation is clearly reflected in the measured pixel intensity. The final dEL images obtained applying the post-processing procedure to different sub-stacks of images are shown in Fig. 2 for frequencies of 12.5 and 25.0 Hz, and a camera speed of 400 fps (G=830 W/m²). The obtained SNR₂₅ marker is good enough (see the following comments), for the case of processing 400 images (Fig. (2b, d)), although the images have some minor errors for the case ν=12.5 Hz. Incorrect processing (with many errors) is observed for the case of processing a lower number of images for a frequency of 12.5 Hz (Fig. 2a); on the other hand, a good image quality is observed for a frequency of 25.0 Hz even processing only a sub-stack of 100 images (Fig. 2c).

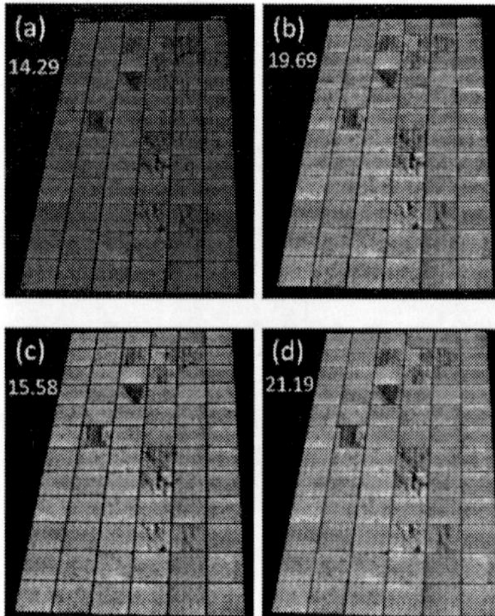

Figure 2: dEL images obtained after post-processing different sub-stacks of images, corresponding to the case of using a SPS, using the ED for square signal modulation. (a, b) ν=12.5 Hz, camera speed 400 fps; (a: post-processing of the first 250 images, b: post-processing of the whole 400 images of the stack). (c, d) ν=25.0 Hz, camera speed 400 fps; (c: post-processing of the first 100 images, d: post-processing of the whole 400 images of the stack) (in all cases G=830 W/m²) (The SNR₂₅ value is indicated on the right upper part of the images)

In this way, the transients do not seem to have a significant impact on the final quality of the dEL images. However, it would be preferable to avoid this type of transients, in order to prevent any effect on the power supply itself.

3.2 dEL inspection of one module by acting on the LPPS

The use of the LPPS allows us to directly compare the signal modulation produced by the power source itself with the modulation produced by means of our ED acting on a DC signal from the LPPS; in this section we show the case of exciting just only one module. Figure 3 shows the current intensities and voltages measured at the entrance of the module for both situations (for ν=50.0 Hz). It can be observed that the LPPS itself produces a perfect square signal (Fig. 3a). On the other hand, the ED acting on the LPPS (DC signal) produces a quite good square signal, except for the introduction, again, of a transient at the beginning of the cycles (Fig. 3d). This transient is now

very sharp, with an insignificant time duration; however, there is a large increase in current intensity. Fig. 3 (b-f) also shows the pixel intensity variations vs number of images measured with the InGaAs camera, at speeds of 200 and 400 fps. It can be observed now that the transient in current intensities produced by the ED is not reflected in the pixel intensities (Fig. 3(e, f)), which is ascribed to the very fast transient. In this case, the post-processing of the stack of images is completely similar for both situations. For instance, Figure 4 shows the obtained dEL images after processing a sub-stack of 200 images for a frequency of 50.0 Hz and camera speed of 400 fps, for both the signal modulation produced by the LPPS itself or by means of the ED acting on the LPPS.

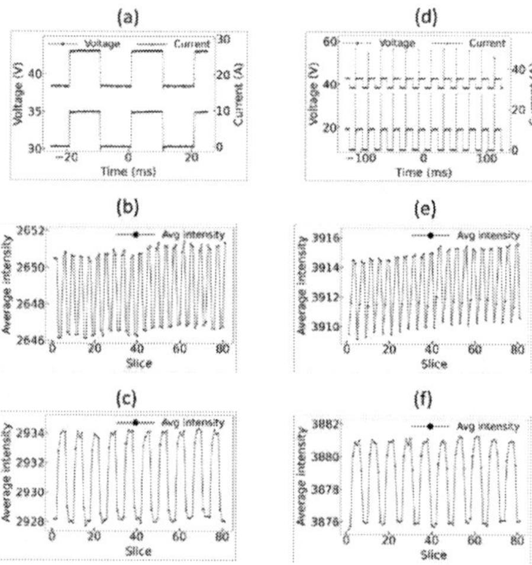

Figure 3: (a, d) Current intensities and voltages at the entrance of the inspected module, generated with the use of the LPPS by means of the power source itself (a) or by means of the ED acting on a DC signal from the LPPS (d), for ν=50.0 Hz. (b-f) Pixel intensity variations measured with the InGaAs camera vs number of captured images corresponding to (a) for camera's velocities of 200 fps (b) and 400 fps (c), and corresponding to (d) for camera's velocities of 200 fps (e) and 400 fps (f), respectively

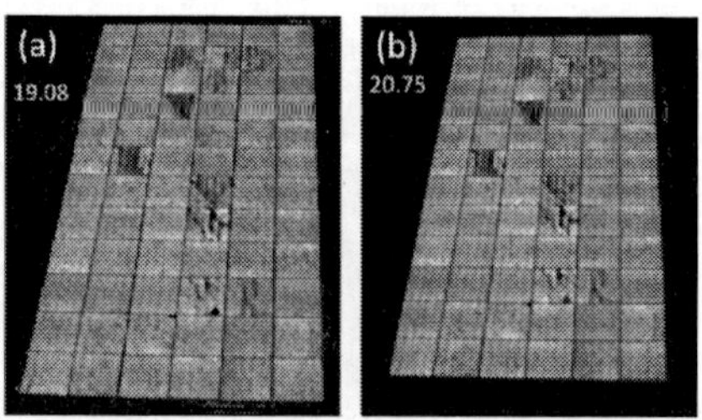

Figure 4: dEL images obtained after the post-processing of a sub-stack of 200 images, for both the signal modulation produced by the LPPS itself (a) or by means of the ED acting on a DC signal from the LPPS (b), for the case ν=50.0 Hz and camera speed of 400 fps (G=500 W/m² in (a), while G=840 W/m² in (b)). (The SNR₂₅ value is indicated on the right upper part of the images)

3.3 dEL inspection of a string of 8 modules by acting on the LPPS

We have also checked the signal modulation produced by the ED for a larger number of excited modules. In particular, in this section we show the case of using the LPPS for exciting 8 modules, comparing again the signal modulation when using the LPPS itself to produce it, respect to the situation of producing the modulation by the ED acting on a DC signal from the LPPS. Figure 5 (a-c) show the current intensities and voltages measured at one module, the one which is inspected with the InGaAs camera. The square wave produced by the LPPS itself is nearly perfect (with some round corners at the beginning of the "on" and "off" periods), whereas the ED produces again transients at the beginning of the cycles. In this case, there is a double transient effect, with a first large and sharp increase in current intensity, followed by a more persistent transient of approx. 7 ms. Figure 5(d-f) shows again the pixel intensities vs the number of images measured with the InGaAs camera. It can be observed that for the case of the modulation produced by the ED acting on the LPPS, the large and sharp transient at the beginning of the cycle is not reflected on the pixel intensities, but the more persistent transient is.

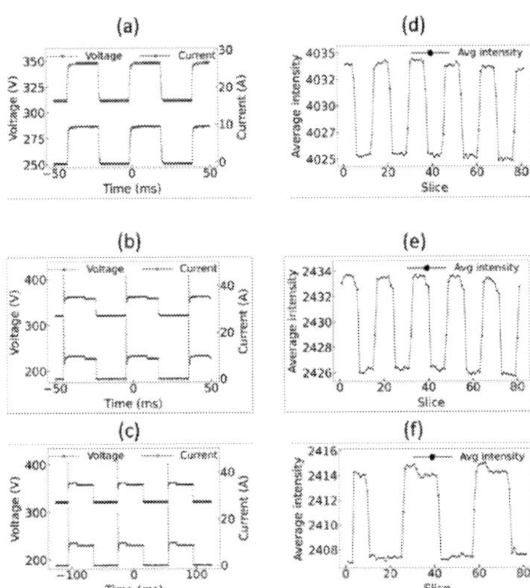

Figure 5: (a – c) Current intensities and voltages at the entrance of the inspected module (8 modules were powered in this case), for both the signal modulation produced by the LPPS itself for v=25.0 Hz (a) or by means of the ED acting on the LPPS for v=25.0 Hz (b) and v=12.5 Hz (c). (d – f) Pixel intensity variations measured with the InGaAs camera vs number of captured images, for a camera velocity of 400 fps, corresponding to (a), (b) and (c), respectively

Figure 6 shows the obtained dEL images for both the signal modulation produced by the LPPS itself or by means of the ED acting on the LPPS, for v=25.0 Hz and a camera speed of 200 fps. The quality of the dEL images are completely similar, not being affected by the transients. In any case, it is not likely very convenient the generation of these kind of transients for the power source itself. We are at present studying the way to eliminate such transients generated with the use of our ED.

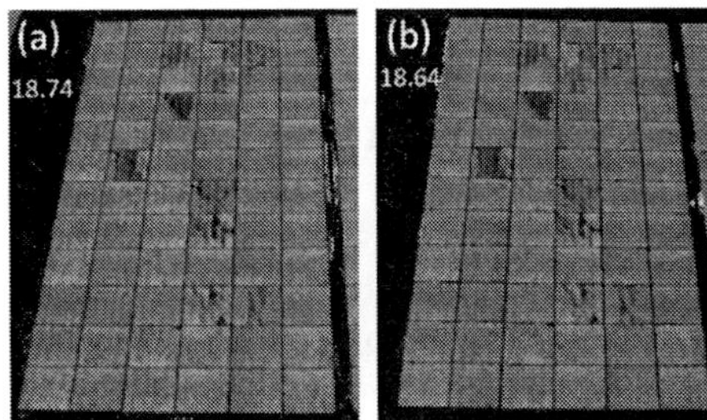

Figure 6: dEL images obtained after the post-processing of the stack of images (first 250 images), for both the signal modulation produced by the LPPS itself (a) or by means of the ED acting on the LPPS (b), for the case v=25.0 Hz and a camera speed of 200 fps (G=840 W/m^2 in (a), while G=500 W/m^2 in (b)). (The SNR$_{25}$ value is indicated on the right upper part of the images)

3.4 Other arrangements: dEL inspection of one module in the self-powering configuration

The advantage of the ED for signal modulation is to made it independently of the power source. In this section we show the results for the case of an individual module inspected in the self-powering configuration [15], with two other identical modules powering it. Figure 7(a, b) show the current intensities and the voltages measured at the inspected module, for frequencies of 12.5 Hz and 50.0 Hz. In this case, some sharp transients are observed both at the beginning or the end of the cycles, but not for all of them. These transients are not reflected on the pixel intensities captured by the InGaAs camera, Figure 7(c, d).

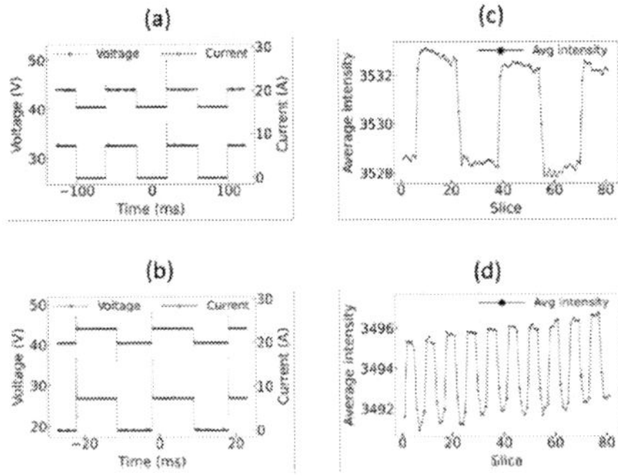

Figure 7: (a, b) Current intensities and voltages at the entrance of the inspected module, for the case of signal modulation produced by the ED acting on 2 modules (self-powering configuration), for v=12.5 Hz (a) and v=50.0 Hz (b). (c, d) Pixel intensity variations measured with the InGaAs camera vs number of captured images, for a camera velocity of 400 fps, corresponding to (a) and (b), respectively

Figure 8 shows the post-processed dEL images for a frequency of 12.5 Hz and a camera speed of 400 Hz, for sub-stacks of 300 and 600 images. In this case the quality is not very high due to the lower current injection (approx. 7.5 A instead of I$_{sc}$) into the inspected panel.

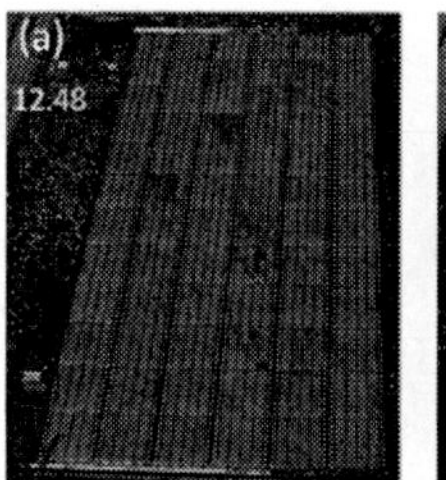
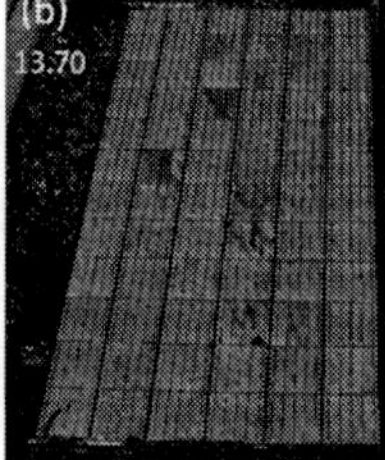

Figure 8: dEL image obtained after the post-processing of the obtained stack of images, for the case of using the ED acting on two other modules, in a self-powering configuration, for the case v=12.5 Hz and a camera speed of 400 fps (G=840 W/m^2) (a: post-processing of the first 300 images, b: post-processing of the whole 600 images of the stack). (The SNR$_{25}$ value is indicated on the right upper part of the images)

3.5 Analysis of the influence of frequency modulation and camera speed on image quality

We have previously shown the effect on the dEL image quality of processing sub-stacks of different number of images. In this section we will show more details of this dependence, and will analyze also the influence of the acquisition parameters (modulation frequency and camera speed) on the image quality. We have used a complete set of measurements, in particular for the case of the signal modulation produced by the LPPS itself, inspecting just one module (see section 3.2).

The previously mentioned tendency of the SNR$_{25}$ value to decrease with the diminution of the number of processed images is shown in Figure 9, for different frequencies and camera speeds. On the other hand, it is observed that the SNR$_{25}$ marker increases as the frequency of the modulated signal increases from 6.25 Hz to 50.0 Hz, for a camera velocity of 400 fps. Moreover, for a fixed frequency of 12.5 Hz, the SNR$_{25}$ marker increases for a camera velocity of 200 fps respect to the case of 400 fps.

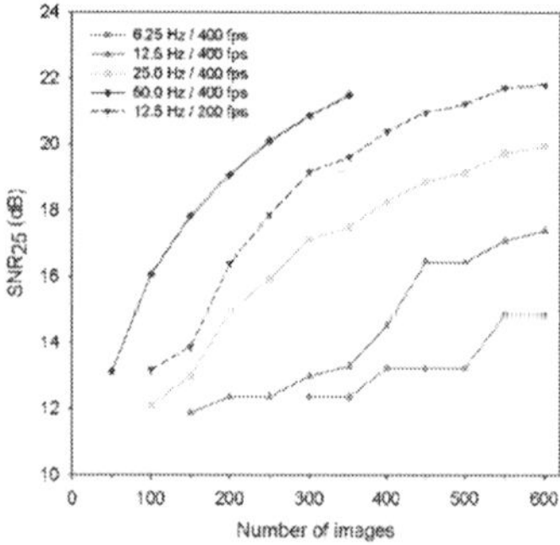

Figure 9: SNR$_{25}$ values obtained after the post-processing of the acquired stacks of images vs number of images of the sub-stack. The data have been obtained for the case of using a programmable source with the signal generated by the power source itself. Different frequencies were used (6.25, 12.5, 25.0 and 50.0 Hz) for a camera velocity of 400 fps. For v=12.5 Hz, two cameras velocities of 200 and 400 fps were used

This behavior is well understood when we observe the trend of the SNR$_{25}$ marker vs the number of captured cycles for the different sets of data, Figure 10. Clearly, the SNR$_{25}$ value depends nearly linearly with the number of cycles, varying in a minor way with the specific values of frequency and camera speed.

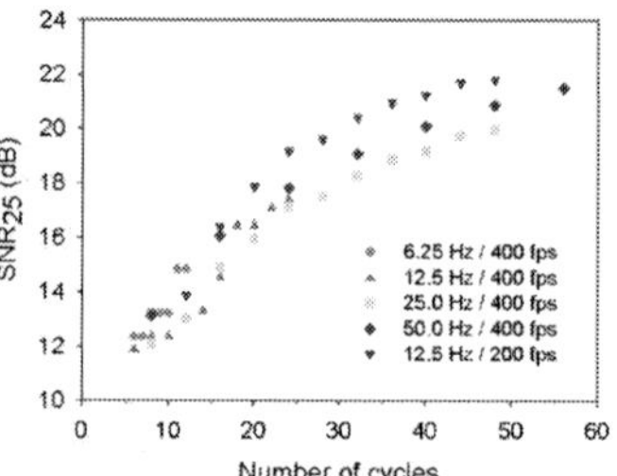

Figure 10: SNR$_{25}$ values vs number of cycles, for the set of data of Fig. 9

We have previously observed that SNR$_{25}$ values of around 16 are enough for a good image quality [14]. This value can be obtained, for instance, for the case of v=50.0 Hz and a camera speed of 400 fps, for just 16 cycles (100 images), which means inspection times of 250 ms per module. Figure 11 shows, for instance, the obtained dEL images for this especific situation, for sub-stacks of 50, 100, 150 and 200 images.

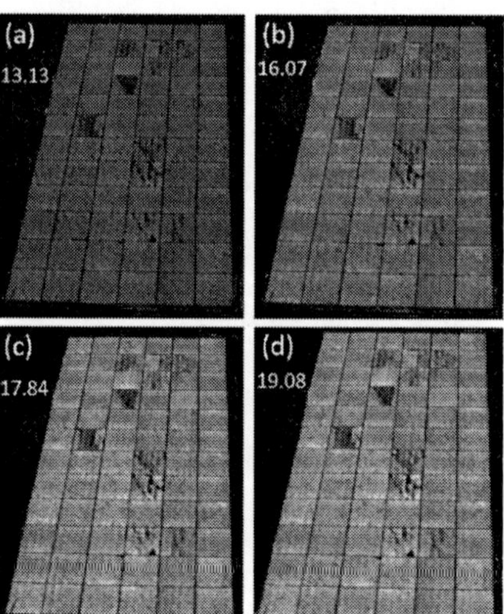

Figure 11: dEL images obtained after the post-processing of the obtained stack of images for the case of signal modulation produced by the LPPS itself, injecting current in only one panel, for the case v=50.0 Hz and a camera speed of 400 fps (G=500 W/m^2). (a) 50 images; (b) 100 images; (c) 150 images; (d) 200 images. (The SNR$_{25}$ value is indicated on the right upper part of the images)

Good image quality could be obtained in even shorter times when working with higher camera speeds (up to 600 fps). The combination of very short inspections times per module and the possibility to perform the modulation for every kind of power sources, even in the self-powering configuration or in the dPL mode, has therefore the potential to provide a fast and cost-effective inspection of solar modules condition.

4 CONCLUSIONS

In this study, we present a novel approach to asynchronous daylight luminescence inspection that eliminates the need for expensive programmable power sources. This simplifies and accelerates the deployment of these powerful techniques in the field. Our compact external device successfully modulates DC signals from various sources, including small and large power sources, as well as neighboring modules, in a self-powered configuration. dPL measurements can also be obtained.

We have demonstrated that, although the external device may introduce signal transients, this does not affect the quality of the final dEL images. Thorough analysis using the SNR_{25} metric revealed that high modulation frequencies and camera speeds enable very short acquisition times of as little as 250 ms per module without compromising image quality.

This methodology offers a cost-effective and scalable solution for inspecting large-scale solar plants. By leveraging readily available — or even self-generated — power, our approach enables high-quality luminescence imaging to be used more widely. This addresses the growing need for rapid and efficient operation and maintenance in the solar PV industry. Further work is underway to eliminate the signal transients observed with our device.

5 ACKNOWLEDGMENTS

This work has been funded by the Spanish Ministry of Science and Innovation, under project PID2023-148369OB-C43, financed by MICIU/AEI /10.13039/501100011033 and FEDER/UE, and by the Regional Government of Castilla y León (Junta de Castilla y León) and by the Ministry of Science and Innovation and the European Union NextGenerationEU / PRTR under the project "Programa Complementario de Materiales Avanzados". K. Sulca has been funded under the call for predoctoral contracts UVa 2022, co-financed by Banco Santander. C. Terrados is also grateful for the financial support received under project PDC2022-133419-I00, funded by MCIN/AEI/10.13039/ 501100011033 and NextGenerationEU/PRTR.

6 REFERENCES

[1] L. Koester, S. Lindig, A. Louwen, A. Astigarraga, G. Manzolini, D. Moser, Renew. Sustain. Energy Rev. 165 (2022) 112616.

[2] S. Gallardo-Saavedra, L. Hernández-Callejo, M.C. Alonso-García, J.D. Santos, J.I. Morales-Aragones, V. Alonso-Gómez, A.M. Moretón-Fernández, M.A. González-Rebollo, O. Martínez, Energy 205 (2020) 117930.

[3] I. Høiaas, K. Grujic, A. Gerd, I. Burud, E. Olsen, N. Belbachir, Renew. Sustain. Energy Rev. 161 (2022) 112353.

[4] O. Kunz, J. Schlipf, A. Fladung, Y.S. Khoo, K. Bedrich, T. Trupke, Z. Hameiri, Prog. Energy 4 (2022) 042014.

[5] L. Stoicescu, M. Reuter, J.H. Werner, Proceedings 29th Eur. Photovolt. Sol. Energy Conf. Exhib., (2014) 2553.

[6] J. Adams, B. Doll, C. Buerhop, T. Pickel, J. Teubner, C. Camus, C.J. Brabec, Proceedings 32nd Eur. Photovolt. Sol. Energy Conf. Exhib., (2015) 1837.

[7] S. Koch, T. Weber, C. Sobottka, A. Fladung, P. Clemens, J. Berghold, Proceedings 32nd Eur. Photovolt. Sol. Energy Conf. Exhib., (2016) 1736.

[8] G.A. dos Reis Benatto, N. Riedel, S. Thorsteinsson, P.B. Poulsen, A. Thorseth, C. Dam-Hansen, C. Mantel, S. Forchhammer, K.H.B. Frederiksen, J. Vedde, M. Petersen, H. Voss, M. Messerschmidt, H. Parikh, S. Spataru, D. Sera, Proceedings 44th IEEE Photovolt. Specialist Conf., (2017) 2682.

[9] R. Bhoopathy, O. Kunz, M. Juhl, T. Trupke, Z. Hameiri, Prog. Photovoltaics Res. Appl. 26 (2018) 69.

[10] M. Guada, A. Moretón, S. Rodríguez-Conde, L.A. Sánchez, M. Martínez, M.A. González, J. Jiménez, L. Pérez, V. Parra, O. Martínez, Energy Science & Engineering 8 (2020) 3839.

[11] L. Koester, A. Louwen, S. Lindig, G. Manzolini, D. Moser, Solar RRL 8 (2014) 2300676.

[12] M . Vuković, M.S. Wiig, G.A. dos Reis Benatto, E. Olsen, I. Burud, Prog. Energy 6 (2024) 032001.

[13] G. A. dos Reis Benatto, R. Del Prado, T. Kari, M. Bartholomäus, L. Morino, P.B. Poulsen, S.V. Spataru, Proceedings 8th World Conference on Photovoltaic Energy Conversion, (2022) 735.

[14] C. Terrados, D. González-Francés, J. Anaya, K.P. Sulca, V. Gómez-Alonso, M.A. González, O. Martínez, Proceedings 40th Eur. Photovolt. Sol. Energy Conf. Exhib. (2023) 3DO.16.5.

[15] L.A. Carpintero, M.A. González, C. Terrados, O. Martínez, D. González-Francés, K.P. Sulca, V. Alonso, Solar Energy 301 (2025) 113913.

[16] C. Terrados, D. González-Francés, K.P. Sulca, C. de Castro, M.A. González, O. Martínez, Progress in Photovoltaics (2025) doi.org/10.1002/pip.70004.

LUMINESCENCE MEASUREMENTS OF PV MODULES WITH A COST-EFFECTIVE AND SMALL-SIZED HOOD-BASED TOOL UNDER DAYLIGHT CONDITIONS

Marc Köntges[1], Michael Siebert[1], D. Lorenz[2], B. Kuhrmann[2], Michael Fuß[2]
[1]Institute for Solar Energy Research Hamelin, [2]MBJ Solutions GmbH

ABSTRACT: We developed a small sized luminescence tool for photovoltaic (PV)-systems that can measure luminescence of a small part of a PV module. The tool measures the luminescence signal under maximum power point (mpp) conditions. For excitation of the solar cells 850 nm LEDs are used and the luminescence is measured with a small sized industry InGaAs camera. Furthermore, the tool detects a unique luminescence patter caused by the reverse current if the module substring has an electrically disconnected bypass diode. To the best of our knowledge, no other luminescence tool can detect this failure without changing the circuits of the PV system. The physical cause of this luminescence pattern is discussed in the paper. As the measurement procedure does not need any opening of electrical contacts it can be operated by any person with a short safety instruction. The paper describes the basic working principle of the measurement technique and simulations of the electrical circuit of the module are show. A 1.5 times higher excitation level in the hood relative to a 1000 W/m² sun irradiation stabilizes the working point to get reproducible luminescence images. During the measurement the inverter can work in normal mpp tracking mode and no access to the inverter is needed. The system is capable of performing measurements under daylight conditions and is sufficiently compact to be transported conveniently during travel. However, you need physical access to the modules to be tested.
Keywords: electroluminescence, luminescence, reliability, inspection, PV modules

1 Introduction

Electroluminescence (EL) imaging methods give very detailed results for assessing the quality of a PV module. The EL method allows to detect most relevant failure modes (potential induced degradation, cell cracking, light induced degradation, electrical not connected cell interconnect ribbons, not connected modules, and short circuit bypass diodes, etc.) in a PV system [1]. Even measuring EL during day light and using a drone is possible [2]. However, to take EL images the electrical circuit of the module string has to be modified and a large powerful generator is needed on site to provide the needed power for the measurement [3]. Recently developed methods allow luminescence measurements during day light without changes in the electrical circuit [4]. However, for most existing outdoor luminescence methods, you need extra light modulation units on the modules or experimental and expensive filtering technique for blocking the unwanted reflected sunlight [3][4]. A new technique uses inverter based working point switching of the PV generator to extract the wanted luminescence signal from the day light background [5] by dark field subtraction. In this case one needs full access to the inverter. A new light induced electroluminescence method [6] does not need to change electrical circuits and does not need access to the inverter but it is only applicable to half-cell modules with internal parallel connected substrings. A drawback, common to all daylight luminescence technologies is, that they are not able to detect the important failure where the bypass diode of a substring is not connected (lost bypass diode). Therefore, we developed a new method combining all advantages of luminescence imaging in a small measurement tool to assess the quality of solar modules including the detection of lost bypass diodes. In the following we evaluate a small sized hood with switchable LED excitation light and an InGaAs camera to measure the luminescence of parts of PV modules in a PV array. The hood is simply moved onto a PV module bank in a PV system. We discuss how to bring the PV-module into the required working points for defect analysation and test its applicability under realistic conditions.

2 SETUPS

2.1 Prototype equipment

To demonstrate the new method, we setup two versions of a luminescence hood. We built one prototype to test the feasibility of the method presented in this chapter and one so called Quickcheck system presented in chapter 2.2 for realistic tests in the large PV systems. For image capturing in the prototype setup a SenS 1280V-ST camera from New Imaging Technologies is used with a resolution of 1280 x 1024 and a 14-bit dynamic range. However, the presented images have a resolution of about 290 x 445 pixel as the useful field of view (~32 cm x 50 cm) is limited. The camera is included in a hood shading the module part of interest which minimizes image artifacts from reflected sun light. The cameras optical axis is orthogonal to the module surface. The distance between camera and module is about 100 cm.

To eliminate background light all outdoor luminescence images presented here are difference images by combining an image taken without and an image taken with artificial illumination using infrared LEDs. The centre wave length of the used LEDs is 850 nm. A bandpass filter with a centre wavelength of 1150 nm and a bandwidth of ±25 nm is mounted onto the camera. It enables only the Si-luminescence spectrum to pass to the camera sensor while blocking the visible light spectrum and the LED peak spectrum. A typical exposure time for one image is 20 ms.

Figure 1: Basic setup of the luminescence tool with LED light, camera and camera filter on top of a half-cell PV module.

2.2 Professional equipment

The Quickcheck (Qcheck) tool is a small hood including some high intensity infrared LED flash light injecting a charge carrier density in the solar cells higher than the sun irradiation at 1000 W/m². A cost effective InGaAs camera with a resolution of 640 x 512 pixel is used to take luminescence images. The hood (~80 cm x 60 cm and 60 cm height) can be used on a part of a PV module to take luminescence images of a selected region. A typical exposure time for one image is 10 ms.

2.3 Measuring method

Images are taken under the following conditions.

1. While the LED flash is off, the cells under test are shaded and in reverse voltage. Not connected cell parts are at 0 V. There is no luminescence from cells at 0 V and from cells in reverse voltage. The bypass diode of the module passes the current close to the maximum power point I_{mpp} in parallel to the shaded PV module substring.

2. While the LED flash is on, the inverter still keeps the PV module string at the previous voltage of the LED OFF state as it is not able to react fast enough. There is enough light on the cells that the cell works also in I_{mpp} and the bypass diodes are not active any more. Therefore, I_{mpp} current is flowing through the solar cells.

The pixelwise subtraction of the images taken at condition 2 minus 1 allows to measure luminescence of cells under I_{mpp} current. All unwanted light is eliminated by this subtraction.

To increase the image quality multiple image pairs can be taken and averaged.

As the exposure time is very short in comparison to the dark time the electrical working point of the module is mainly in the shaded condition. Consequently, the inverter moves the PV module string into the voltage working point where the module substring under test is shaded.

2.4 PV modules under test

We use two types of test setups to assess the feasibility of the luminescent hood system.

The first test setup is a PV system consisting of nine solar modules with full M6 monocrystalline PERC cells (6 x 10) which are serially connected and regulated by an inverter of type Sunny Boy 3.6 from SMA Solar Technology AG. The solar modules are mechanically installed on a 38° inclined test roof top facing south. This system is used for measurements with the prototype equipment. Strings are measured in 3 situations:

1. Inverter OFF, no extra shading

2. Inverter ON, 100% shade on two cells of the substring under test

3. Inverter ON, no extra shading

The second test setup is a PV system consisting of M10 TOPCON half-cell modules (6 x 24 cells) within a string of 27 modules attached to a string inverter in a large PV system. Two module strings are attached to one maximum power point tracker. One module with a lost bypass diode in the middle substring is measured with the Qcheck equipment. The string is measured only under Inverter ON with no extra shading.

3 Simulation of electrical working points

3.1 Spice model

For the working point simulation of the half-cell PV module and of the cell voltage under the hood, a LTSPICE XVII [11] simulation is used. The solar cells are modeled by a two-diode model per half-cell. Each solar cell is represented by two parallel connected diodes, a parallel current source, a parallel resistance, and a series connected resistance. The schematic for the numerical simulation of the cell voltage for the LED OFF and LED ON situation under the hood is shown in Figure 2. The simulation parameters of the two-diode model are summarized in Table I. 10 solar cells are under the test hood and all the other cells of the module are irradiated by sun light at 1000 W/m².

We set up two simulation scenarios, listed in Table II. In the scenario "LED intensity" we vary the intensity of the LED light. In the scenario "Resistance" we simulate the cell voltage of an active cell part (75% of the cell area) and an inactive cell part (25% of the cell area) while the inactive cell part is contacted to the cell busbar by a very high ohmic resistance. This cell is one cell under the hood.

The models simulate the IV curve of the module when the Luminescence tool is on the module with LEDs OFF and shading 10 half-cells as shown in Figure 1 and LEDs ON. The voltage drop of a cell under the hood is used for evaluating the expected luminescence of the cells under the hood.

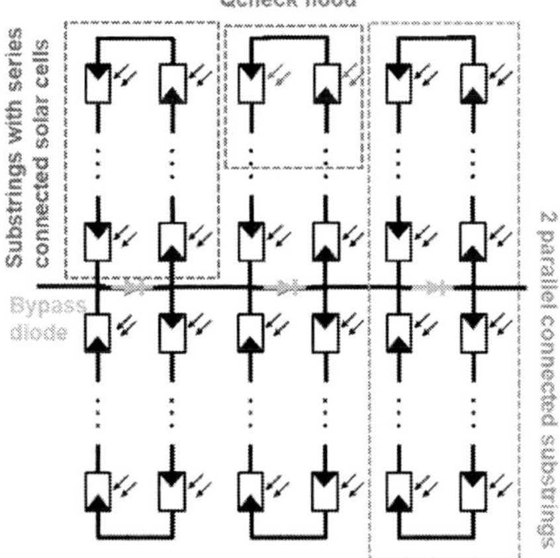

Figure 2: LTSpice circuit used for electric simulation.

Table I: Simulation basis parameter for an arbitrary half-cell PV module with 20 cell per substring, 6 substring (120 cells in total) and a STC power of ~345 Wp.

Parameter	Units	Value
A	cm²	136.0
j_{01}	fA/cm²	96.4
j_{02}	fA/cm²	3686.2
j_{sc}	mA/cm²	38.3
R_s	Ωcm²	0.7077
R_{sh}	Ωcm²	10000

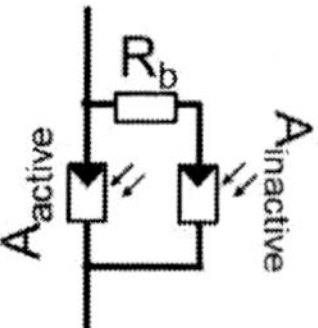

Figure 3: Circuit diagram of the active and the broken cell parts connected by the break resistance R_b. A_{active} and $A_{inactive}$ are, respectively, the areas of the connected part and the disconnected part of a cell and are represented by the same electrical model.

Table II: Description of the frame conditions of the LT Spice simulation and description of the parameter variation in Scenario LED Intensity and Resistance.

Scenario	Explanation	Range
all	Irradiance on cells outside the hood	1000 W/m²
LED Intensity	10 cells under the hood with various excitation levels	0 W/m² - 1500 W/m² in steps of 100 W/m²
Resistance	One cell under the hood with	25% of one cell area connected with 100 kOhm to busbar and 1500 W/m² Irradiance on cells inside the hood

4 RESULTS

4.1 Simulation results LED intensity

The simulation results for the half-cell PV module, based on the parameters listed in Table I, are presented in Figure 4Figure 6. Figure 4Figure 6 shows the simulated IV curve of the PV module (black lines) and a cell under the hood (red lines) when the measurement hood shades 10 cells of one substring. While the measurement the module outside the hood is exposed to a simulated AM1.5 excitation at 1000 W/m² in the module plane. The simulation corresponds to the hood position illustrated in Figure 1 and the corresponding electrical circuit sketched in Figure 2. The simulated IV curves are parametrized for an AM1.5 spectrum equivalent LED excitation of 0 W/m² (straight lines), 1000 W/m² (dashed lines), 1500 W/m² (doted lines) to the cells under the hood. Furthermore, the cell voltage of one half-cell under the hood is shown for the same LED irradiation variation.

The blue dot in Figure 4 shows the maximum power working point of the PV module without illumination under the hood. As the LED lights of the hood are off most of the time we assume that the inverter moves the working point of the PV module string into the blue dot. Due to its slow response to the very short light on phases (10 ms) the inverter should not move to the light on working point. The black dotted line is a guide to the eye to find the corresponding voltage of a shaded cell in the hood. At that working point the cells under the hood have a voltage below 0 V. At 0 W/m² the cells in the hood work at negative voltage and does not luminesce. At 1000 W/m² the cell voltage is at about 373 mV and the luminescent emission is very weak. At 1500 W/m² the cell voltage is at

about 639 mV and the luminescent emission is strong.

Even if the inverter will regulate the voltage a bit during 1500 W/m² of LED excitation the cell voltage under the hood will stay constant (less than 1% change) over a large range from 0 V to 35 V of PV module voltage. This guaranties reproducible results under unwanted inverter voltage regulation. Even if the inverter will regulate the voltage at 1500 W/m² into the new V_{mpp} at 34.5 V the voltage of the cell under test stays almost constant (639 mV to 640 mV).

As the LED intensity has also a significant influence on the cell under test voltage and its stability Figure 5 shows the voltage of a cell under the hood as a function of the LED intensity equivalent to an AM1.5 irradiation. Up to 1000 W/m² the cell voltage range, shown with the error bars, has a great dependence on the actual working point of the inverter. Starting with 1100 W/m² the dependence on the working point of the inverter vanishes. So, it is important to work with the hood some W/m² above the current out door irradiation to have stable conditions during luminescence measurement.

Remember even if the inverter shifts its working point the module and the cells under the hood work still under a current close to I_{mpp} during LED ON. So, we still see luminescence pattern influenced by lateral varying resistances on the cell.

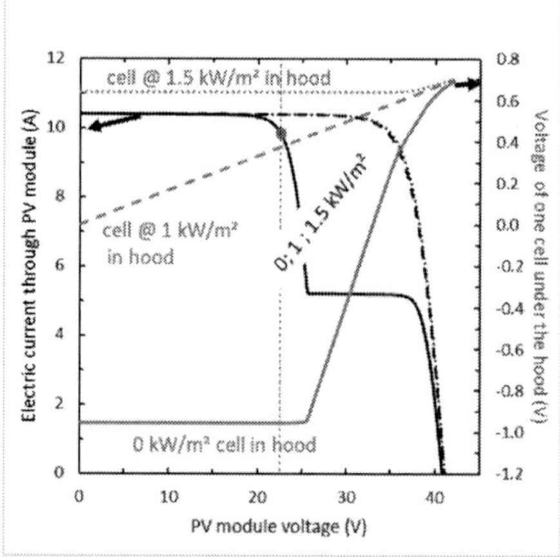

Figure 4: Current voltage curves (black) of the entire half-cell PV module under test and voltage of a cell under the hood (red). The cell voltage and the IV curves for the PV module are shown for 1000 W/m² irradiation outside the hood and 0 W/m², 1000 W/m², and 1500 W/m² AM1.5 irradiation equivalent LED irradiation under the hood. Exemplary it is assumed that 10 half-cells are under the hood.

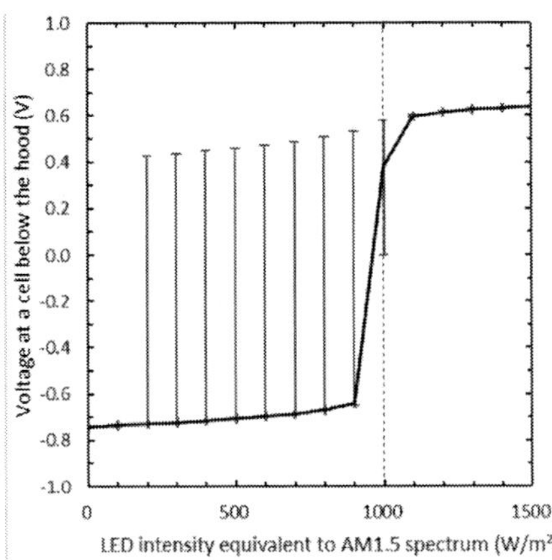

Figure 5: Voltage at a solar cell under the hood as a function of the LED intensity equivalent to an AM1.5 irradiation. The error bars show the range of voltage working point if the inverter is regulating the module voltage between 0 V and V_{mpp} in the LED ON case.

4.2 Simulation results resistance

To assess the influence of cell defects which are caused by serial resistances on a cell we simulate the electrical circuit of a PV module with one defect cell having a 75% active and a 25% inactive cell area as shown in Figure 3. This defective cell is located under the measurement hood.

Figure 6 a) shows the simulated IV curve of the PV module while LEDs are OFF in the measurement hood. Furthermore, the voltage of the active and inactive cell part is shown. As the active cell part is in the main circuit and shaded it is driven into reverse voltage when the module is in the Impp working point where the bypass diode carries the main current. The inactive cell part carries no current because of the high series resistance and therefore no voltage is applied to the inactive part of the cell. In this case both cell parts do not emit luminescence radiation.

Figure 6 b) shows the simulated IV curve of the PV module when the LEDs in the measurement hood irradiate the 10 cells below the hood at an equivalent AM 1.5 irradiation of 1500 W/m². Again, the black dotted line represents the PV module working voltage under LED OFF conditions. At this voltage and from 0 V to V_{mpp} the voltage of both cell parts is positive and both parts irradiate luminescence. However, the active part irradiates less luminescence compared to the inactive cell part.

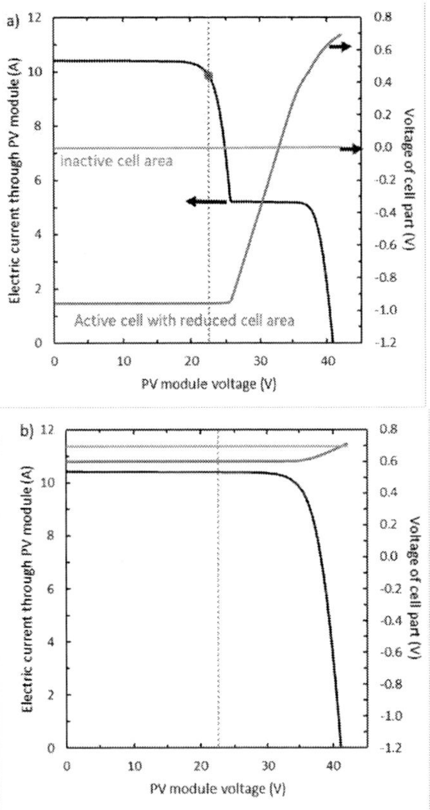

Figure 6: Current/voltage curves (black) of the entire half-cell PV module under test and voltage of a broken cell with its active (red) and inactive (grey) cell part under the hood. a) shows the conditions during dark conditions in the hood and b) shows the conditions while the cells under the hood are under LED irradiation (assuming an equivalent of 1500 W/m² AM1.5). Exemplary it is assumed that 10 half-cells are under the hood. Outside the hood 1000 W/m² AM1.5 excitites the rest of the PV module.

This enables us to identify inactive or resistive coupled cell parts. Inactive or resistive coupled cell parts are always brighter in luminescence then active cell parts.

Figure 7: Hood based outdoor luminescence image of a test module made while the module is in V_{oc} conditions.

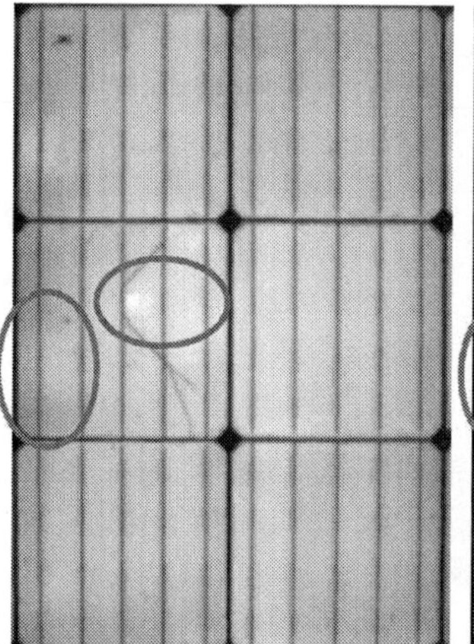

Figure 8: Luminescence image of same test module as in Fig. 2 made during mpp tracking of the inverter with 5.0 A module current at 645 W/m² sun irradiation in module plane.

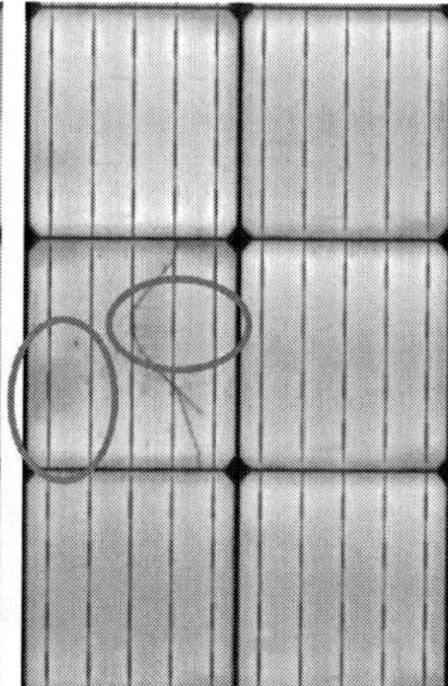

Figure 9: Lab based electroluminescence image of same test module as in Figure 7 and Figure 8 at 9.3 A module current.

4.1 Results for prototype equipment

Figure 7 shows a luminescence image of a part of a full cell module while the inverter is in OFF state. We see very bright solar cells with very little contrast. We see two cells with a cell crack (top left and middle left). An almost identical image (here not shown) is measured when the inverter is in ON state but we fully shade cells of the substring under test.

Figure 8 shows a luminescence image of a part of a full cell module while the inverter in ON state of the same module part as shown in Figure 7. We see much more contrast. Some red marked areas of the middle left cell are brighter than other areas.

Figure 9 shows an electroluminescence image of the same module part as shown in Figure 7 and Figure 8. Some red marked areas of the middle left cell are darker than other areas. These are areas with an additional resistance to the darker cell areas. This areas anticorrelate to the bright cell areas in the luminescence image in Figure 8.

5.2 Lost bypass diode with Qcheck equipment

In Figure 10 a luminescence image taken with the Qcheck system of a PV module with a lost bypass diode in a string with inverter on is shown. In this case the Qcheck system shades only four cells of one of two parallel connected substrings. Except for not equal luminescent cells no special pattern can be seen.

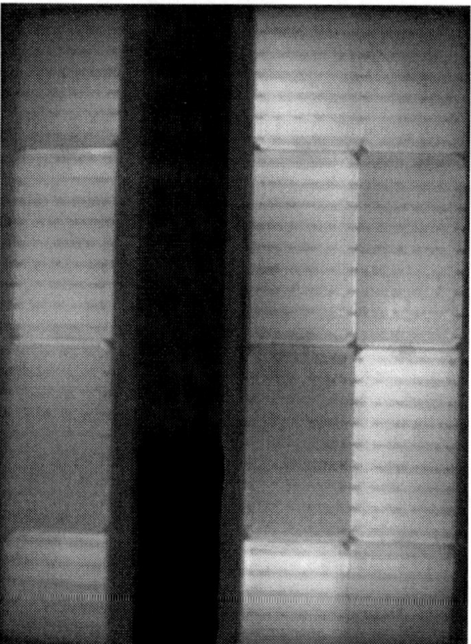

Figure 10: Qcheck luminescence image of the left side of solar cells of the middle substring of a half cell module with lost bypass diode. The image is taken while the module is in a string with 27 modules with an active string inverter during day time.

In Figure 11, a luminescence image of the same PV module shown in Figure 10 is presented. In this case the Qcheck system is positioned on the PV module that four cells of both parallel connected substrings with a lost bypass diode are shaded. A characteristic pattern is to be seen. It is similar to dark occurring striation rings in electroluminescence images [8], but the rings appear bright in the luminescence image.

Figure 11: Qcheck luminescence image of the middle solar cells of the middle substring of a half cell module with lost bypass diode. The image is taken while the module is in a string with 27 modules with an active string inverter during day time.

Figure 12 shows the same luminescence image like Figure 11 except an thermographic image taken after shading the cells (like it is done with the Qcheck system). By comparing Figure 11 and Figure 12 the bright luminescence correlates with the pattern seen in the thermographic image.

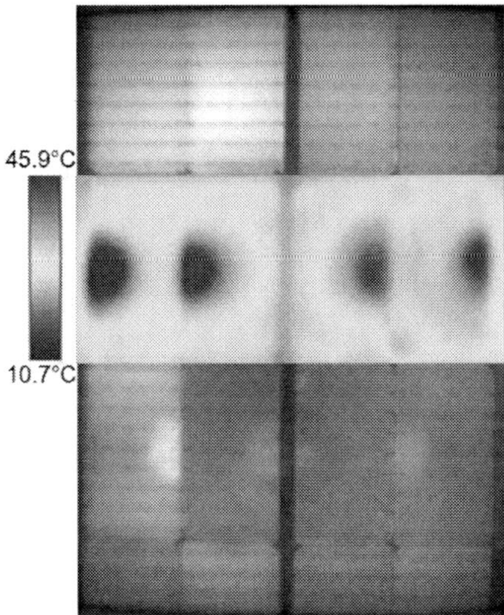

Figure 12: Qcheck luminescence image of middle substring of a half cell module with lost bypass diode with a thermographic image overlay. The temperature profile is measured directly after shading the four solar cells during daylight. Other conditions as described in Figure 5.

6 DISCUSSION

Figure 5 shows that an excitation level from the hood LEDs exceeding that of ambient sunlight stabilises the luminescence image against inverter operating point fluctuations. Furthermore, as long as the LEDs excitation level is higher than the sun outside we can measure a luminescence image. If the LEDs excitation level gets less than outside than the cells working point gets into reverse voltage and no luminescence image can be taken. We therefore recommend an LED intensity corresponding to an AM1.5 excitation level of at least 1300 W m^{-2} to ensure stable luminescence imaging, even under cloud-enhancement conditions where local solar irradiance may rise to 1200–1300 W m^{-2} depending on location.

6.1 Anticorrelation luminescence to electroluminescence

As found in the simulation show in Figure 6 the voltage of cell parts with an increased series resistance to the bus bar is higher than the voltage of the same cell with no additional resistance to the busbar when the module works in P_{mpp} conditions. Figure 8 shows this brighter luminescence signal for some broken cell metallisation fingers in actual test measurements. The broken cell metallisation fingers with increased bus resistance to the busbar are confirmed by a lab electroluminescence image of Figure 9.

6.2 How to use different working points for practical assessment

In Figure 7 we showed that a not connected module part is very bright in the luminescence and shows no current related pattern on the cells. Whereas the luminescence of a PV module with current flowing through the cells shows less luminescence compared to the not connected module. We also found that an additional shading (outside the Qcheck) on the substring under test shows the same luminescence intensity and pattern as a not connected substring. This fact can be used to identify not connected module substrings or not connected whole module strings in a PV system in day light while the inverter is on.

The suggested procedure is if one finds an extraordinary bright substring with Qcheck one must shade (two full cells) this substring additionally to the shading of the Qcheck system. When the luminescence image does not change during the additional shading procedure than this substring is not connected to the inverter. This is a very easy to use method to find not connected modules/module-substrings.

6.3 Luminescence pattern

Furthermore, the Qcheck method delivers basically the same luminescence images like an electroluminescence image for defects like shunt resistances due to potential induces degradation by shunts (PID-s), increased recombination due to light-induced degradation (LID) or cell cracks (but not if the cell crack isolates a cell part, see chapter 6.1).

6.4 Lost bypass diode

In Figure 12 a clear correlation between the luminescence pattern of cells of a module substring with a lost bypass diode and the temperature pattern of the PV module glass is found. The luminescence patter looks like inverse striation rings which are sometimes found electroluminescence pattern of monocrystalline solar cells.

In Figure 10 some cells of the same substring of the module with the lost bypass diode is shown. However, no striation ring like luminescence pattern can be found and no heating of the cells can be detected. Chill et al. [8] showed that a shaded solar cell can carry less current at the same reverse voltage compared to a not shaded solar cell (PERC, TOPCON and HJT). This means that if only one part of a half cell module is shaded, like for the measurement of the luminescence image in Figure 10 and no bypass diode is in parallel most current flows along the unshaded parallel substring. Therefore, no heating and no ring pattern can be seen in this case.

However, it is unclear why we see a bright striation ring like pattern. In a very well passivated silicon solar cell, the temperature dependence of luminescence is primarily determined by the narrowing of the silicon band gap, the increase in intrinsic carrier density, and the higher phonon occupancy for the indirect transition. This leads to a red shift of the luminescence spectrum and typically to a decreasing luminescence intensity with increasing temperature [10,11].

The wavelength of the luminescence radiation shifts as a function of the silicon band gap and the peak width of the luminescence is also a function of the temperature. The dissipating heat during the dark image phase may shift and broaden the luminescence peak in a way that the emitted luminescence can more effectively transmit trough bandwidth of the used filter. However, typically the luminescence intensity of silicon solar cells decreases with increasing temperature.

The temperature dependence of the intensity of band to band luminescence can be very complex. For example, Johnston et al. have found increasing band to band luminescence intensity with increasing temperature for crystal areas with few defects in multi crystalline solar cells [12].

A further alternative to explain the ring patter luminescence signal may be that the localized current and heating heals some defects in the wafer and increases the effective minority carrier life time. However, this should be an effect changing with time. But we could not find a change in luminescence intensity during repetitive measurements.

We also might get luminescence emission caused by the breakdown current in voltage reverse bias of the cell through into the camera in the dark image as described by Breitenstein et al. [7] for multi crystalline solar cells and Jia et al. for mono crystalline silicon solar cells [13]. This light should be seen in the dark image. We can exclude this root cause as if the dark image is bright along the areas with increased breakdown current the difference image should be dark in these areas.

We switch from extreme reverse voltage biased cells at I_{mpp} current to $\sim V_{mpp}$ conditions under illumination and take luminescence images immediately. To our knowledge such kind of luminescence measurement has not been reported before. Therefore, the seen luminescence might be a new effect. We speculate that during reverse bias conditions free charge carriers might be trapped. These trapped charge carriers might be reemitted and cause additional luminescence along areas with high trapping density.

This speculation will be checked in future work by changing the delay time between start of the LED OFF time and the start of the camera acquisition. The longer the delay, the less intense the luminescence should be in the striation ring like luminescence pattern as the reemitted free charge carrier should vanish with time.

7 CONCLUSIONS

Although the hood luminescence method is very simple and close to existing measurement ideas, this small hood-based luminescence method during daylight has never been reported before. Unfortunately, the proposed method can not be used by drones but it can be coupled to cleaning robots or ground based automated units.

This system is able to detect more PV module failure (not connected string, not connected PV module substring, lost bypass diode, all failures detectable with electroluminescence) within one method than all the other published methods listed in the introduction. Furthermore, the tool needs no change in the electrical circuit, no access to the inverter, it is used during daylight and it can be used by people without electrician training. The tool is applicable for an easy and quick spot checking of a PV system in the field. This combination of features is unique compared to existing methods in the literature and simplifies randomised acceptance procedures or failure analysis.

8 ACKNOWLEDGEMENTS

This work was funded by the state of Lower Saxony and the Federal Ministry for Economic Affairs and Energy (BMWE) under grant number ZIM KK5291103SY2 PVDETECTS. We thank Enerparc AG for supporting us evaluating our measurement tools in relevant PV systems.

9   References

[1] U. Jahn et al., "Review on Infrared and Electroluminescence Imaging for PV Field Applications," Report IEA-PVPS T13-10:2018, 2018.

[2] G. Alves dos Reis Benatto et al., "Drone-Based Daylight Electroluminescence Imaging of PV Modules," IEEE J. Photovoltaics, vol. 10, no. 3, pp. 872–877, May 2020.

[3] O. Kunz et al., "Outdoor luminescence imaging of field-deployed PV modules," Prog. Energy, vol. 4, no. 4, p. 042014, Oct. 2022.

[4] M. Vuković, M. S. Wiig, G. A. dos Reis Benatto, E. Olsen, and I. Burud, "A review of imaging methods for detection of photoluminescence in field-installed photovoltaic modules," Prog. Energy, vol. 6, no. 3, 2024.

[5] J. W. Weber et al., "Daylight photoluminescence imaging of photovoltaic systems using inverter-based switching," Prog. Photovoltaics Res. Appl., vol. 32, no. 9, pp. 643–651, 2024.

[6] M. Köntges, M. Siebert, A. Fladung, and J. Schlipf, "Evaluation of Light-Induced Electroluminescence in Photovoltaic Field Applications," in PV-Symposium Proceedings, 2024, vol. 1.

[7] O. Breitenstein et al., "Understanding junction breakdown in multicrystalline solar cells," J. Appl. Phys., vol. 109, no. 7, p. 071101, Apr. 2011.

[8] M. Köntges *et al.*, "Review of Failures of Photovoltaic Modules," Report IEA-PVPS T13-01:2014, 2014, p. 43 [Online]. Available: http://iea-pvps.org/index.php?id=275 [Accessed 18-Sep-2014]

[9] C. Reichel *et al.*, "Design aspects in consideration of hotspot phenomena in high-performance photovoltaic modules featuring different silicon solar cell architectures," *Sol. Energy Mater. Sol. Cells*, vol. 276, no. July, p. 113058, 2024, doi: 10.1016/j.solmat.2024.113058.

[10] T. Trupke *et al.*, "Temperature dependence of the radiative recombination coefficient of intrinsic crystalline silicon," *J. Appl. Phys.*, vol. 94, no. 8, pp. 4930–4937, Oct. 2003, doi: 10.1063/1.1610231.

[11] H. Schlangenotto, H. Maeder, and W. Gerlach, "Temperature dependence of the radiative recombination coefficient in silicon," *Phys. Status Solidi*, vol. 21, no. 1, pp. 357–367, Jan. 1974, doi: 10.1002/pssa.2210210140.

[12] S. Johnston *et al.*, "Temperature-dependent Photoluminescence imaging and characterization of a multi-crystalline silicon solar cell defect area," in *2011 37th IEEE Photovoltaic Specialists Conference*, IEEE, Jun. 2011, pp. 000069–000074. doi: 10.1109/PVSC.2011.6185848.

[13] Y. Jia *et al.*, "Diagnosing breakdown mechanisms in monocrystalline silicon solar cells via electroluminescence imaging," *Sol. Energy*, vol. 225, pp. 463–470, Sep. 2021, doi: 10.1016/j.solener.2021.07.052.

EU PVSEC 2025
Bilbao, Spain, 23rd September 2025

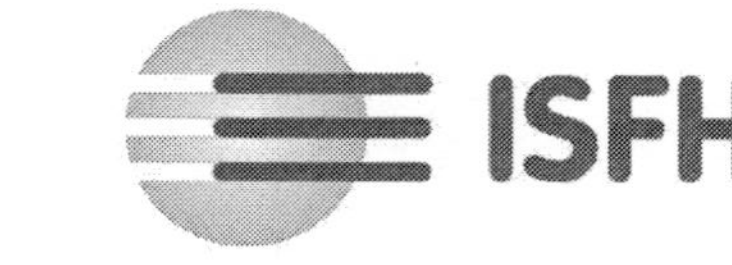

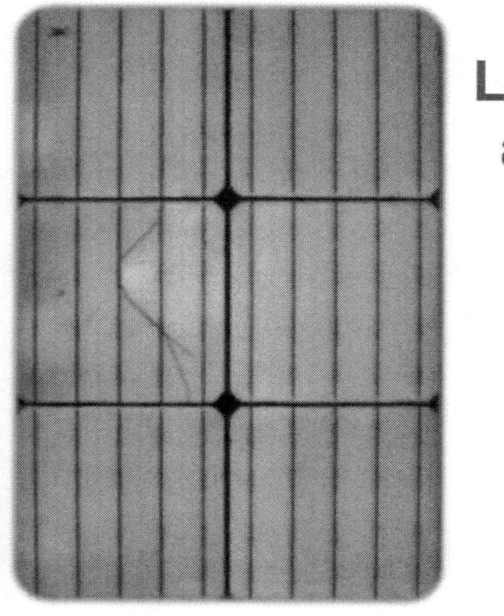

Luminescence measurement with a cost-effective and small-sized hood-based tool under daylight condition

M. Köntges[1], M. Siebert[1], D. Lorenz[2], B. Kuhrmann[2], M. Fuß[2]

[1]Institute for Solar Energy Research Hamelin, Germany
[2]MBJ Solutions GmbH

Introduction

Electroluminescence[1] (EL) or day light photoluminescence[2] (DPL) imaging

- is an effective method to detect defects and failure in PV modules

- but it requires night work & rewiring of modules (electrician) or lot of equipment or inverter access

We present a new luminescence setup with a small hood: Quickcheck

- A small hood tool, with camera and LED light is moved on the modules

- Detects all EL features

[1] U. Jahn et al., Report IEA-PVPS T13-10:2018, 2018
[2] M. Vuković, et al., Prog. Energy, vol. 6, no. 3, 2024

Leibniz Universität Hannover

020207-002

How does it work? Quickcheck dark image

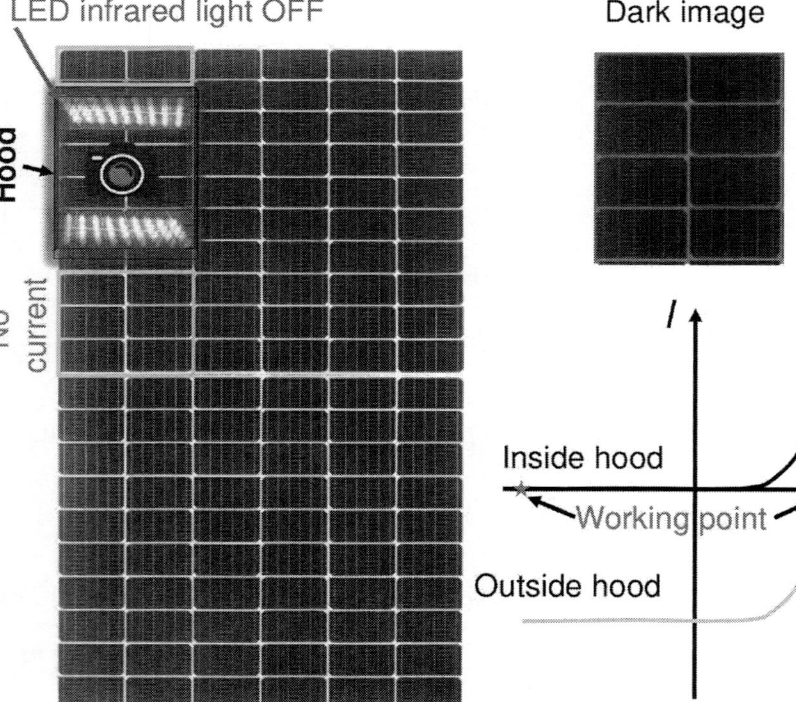

Components:

- Industry InGaAs camera with 512 x 640 pixel + band-pass filter 1150 ± 25 nm

- Exposure time per image in the range of 5 ms to 30 ms

- LED light source @850 nm

How does it work:

- Cell working point at LED OFF in the hood is in reverse bias voltage

- No luminescence from cell but background radiation is captured

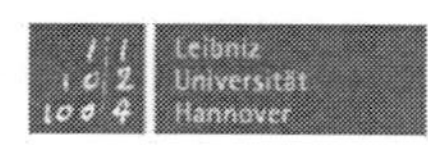

020207-003

How does it work? Quickcheck luminescence image

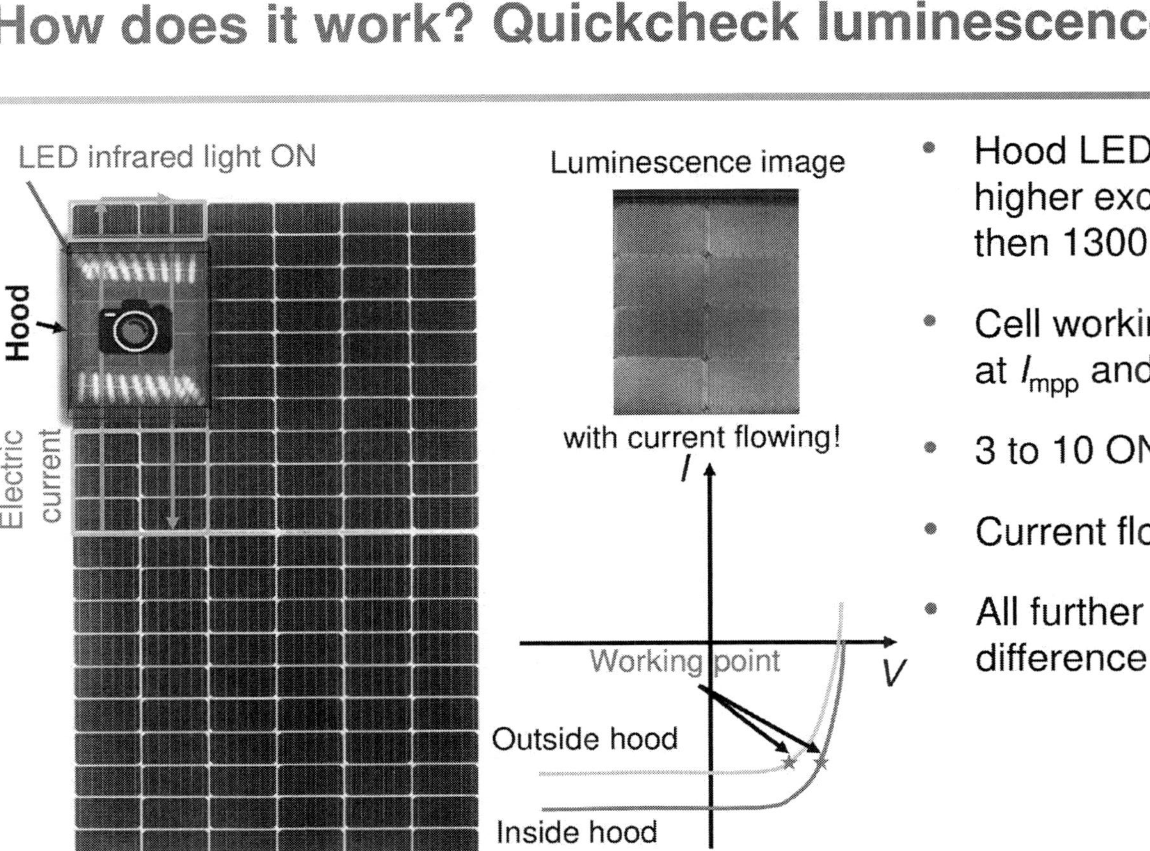

- Hood LED light source @850 nm generates higher excitation level in silicon solar cell then 1300 W/m² AM1.5g sun light

- Cell working point in the hood at LED ON is at I_{mpp} and is higher than V_{mpp}!

- 3 to 10 ON/OFF images are taken

- Current flow features are visible at actual I_{mpp}

- All further luminescence images show difference images

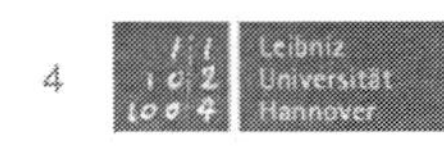

020207-004

How to read Quickcheck difference images

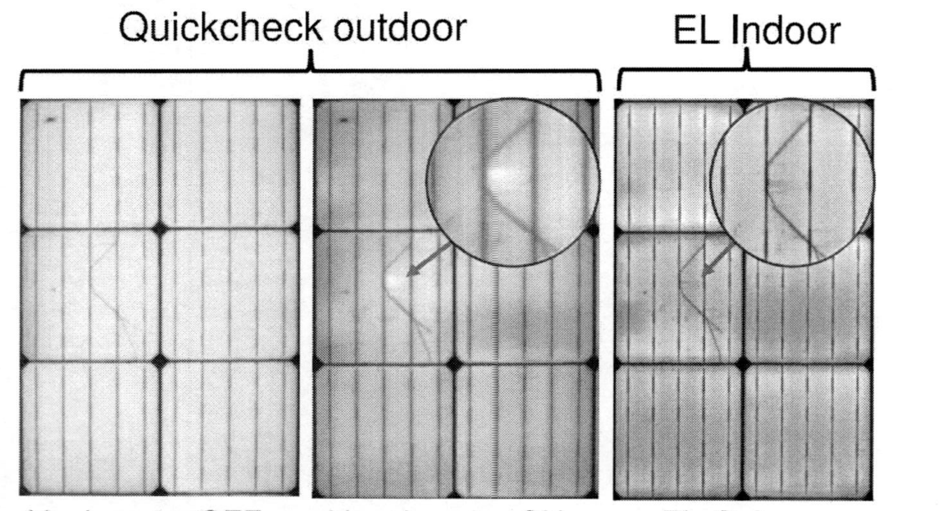

645 W/m² sun irradiation on module level
off the string under test

Quickcheck outdoor

- V_{oc} images
  → no resistive pattern in cells visible
  → string not connected

- V_{mpp} images
  Resistively coupled cell parts are brighter
  → less current = higher voltage
  → higher luminescence

In contrast EL image

- Resistively coupled cell parts are dimmed
  → less current = lower voltage
  → dimmed luminescence

Identify disconnected PV module part/strings

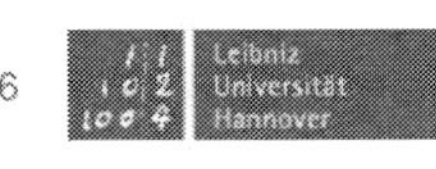

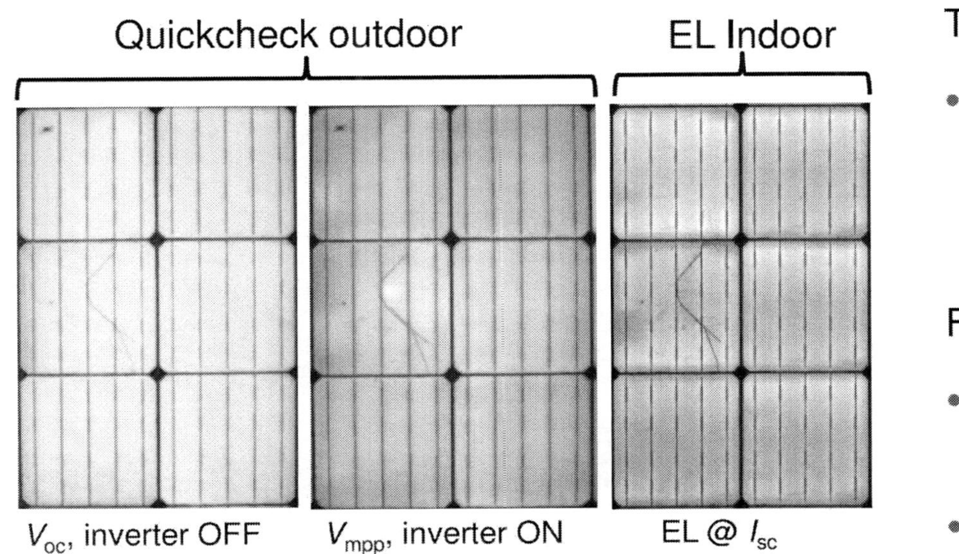

645 W/m² sun irradiation on module level
off the string under test

To check if you see V_{oc} image:

- Shade two or more full cells of current substring outside the hood.
  If intensity does not change you see V_{oc} image.

Finding a V_{oc} image means:

- Current cells are not connected (Substring, or PV module string)

- Inverter is OFF

- Images are taken under low light or in the dark

020207-006

Lost bypass diodes

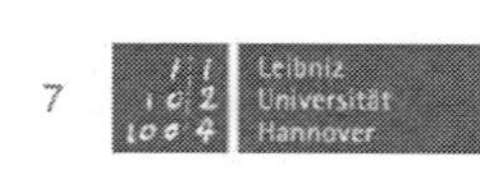

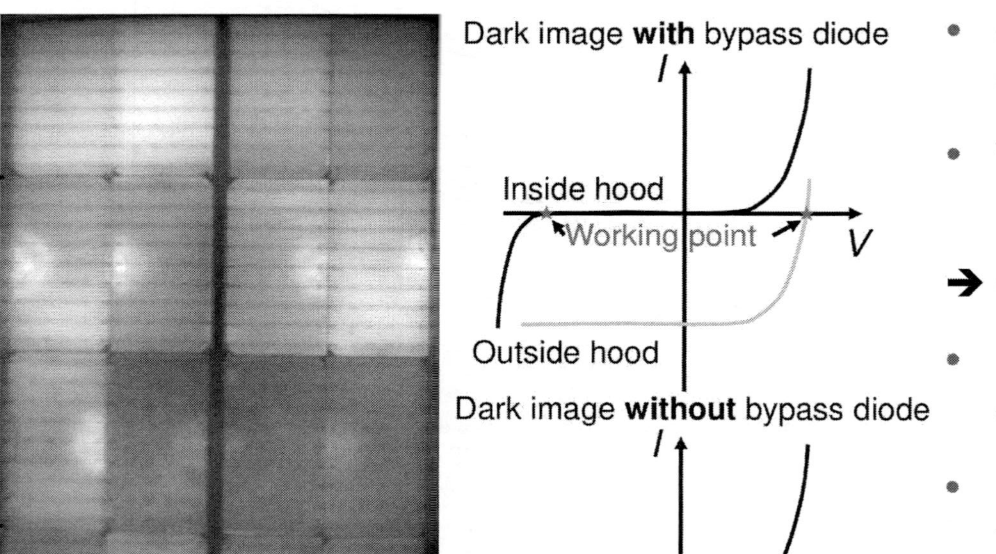

- Quickcheck in the module middle results in symmetric current distribution

- With lost bypass diode the cells work at high reverse bias voltage at I_{mpp} current

→ Cells heat up during dark image phase

- Heat dissipates typically along striation rings or other defects

- During LED ON luminescence imaging the heat pattern remains

- Reason for bright pattern is not clear but allows differentiation to striation rings (dark pattern)

020207-007

Lost bypass diodes

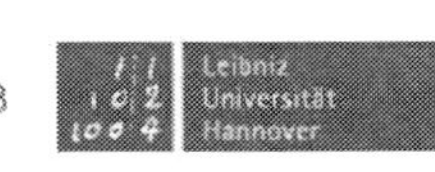

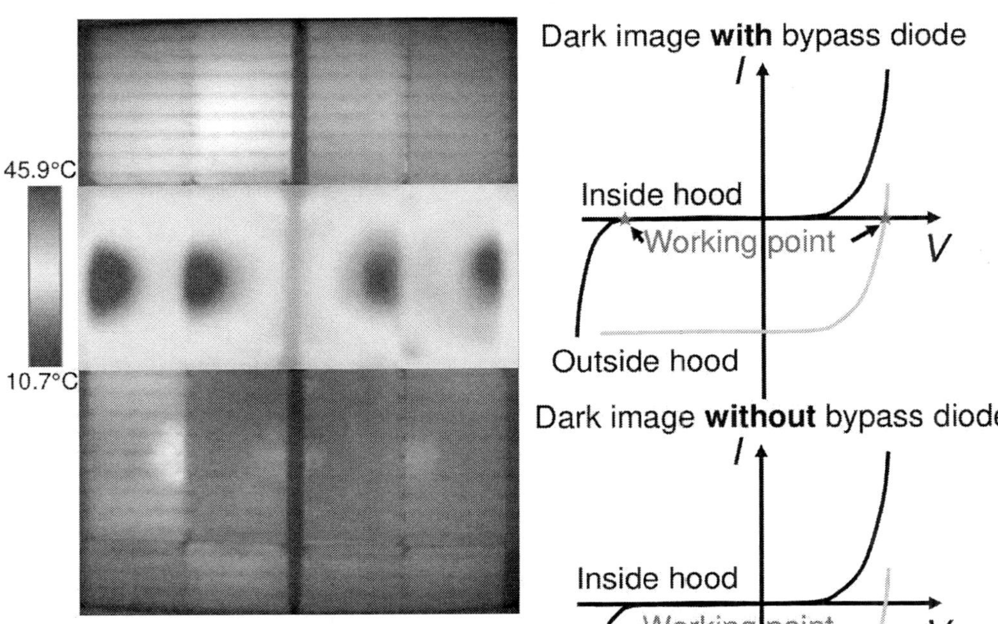

- Quickcheck in the module middle results in symmetric current distribution

- With lost bypass diode the cells work at high reverse bias voltage at I_{mpp} current

➔ Cells heat up during dark image phase

- Heat dissipates typically along striation rings or other defects

- During LED ON luminescence imaging the heat pattern remains

- Reason for bright pattern is not clear but allows differentiation to striation rings (dark pattern)

020207-008

Lost bypass diodes

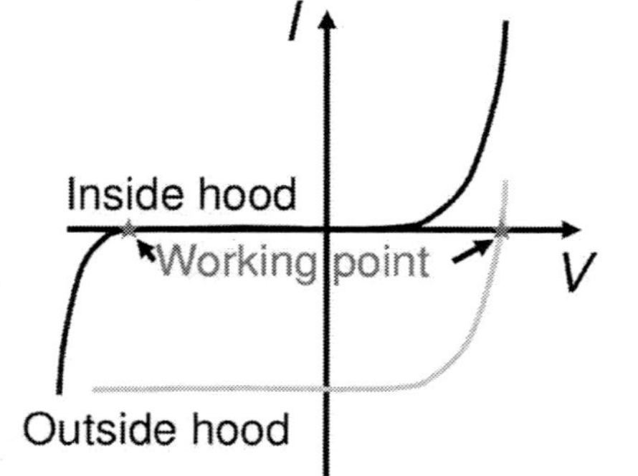

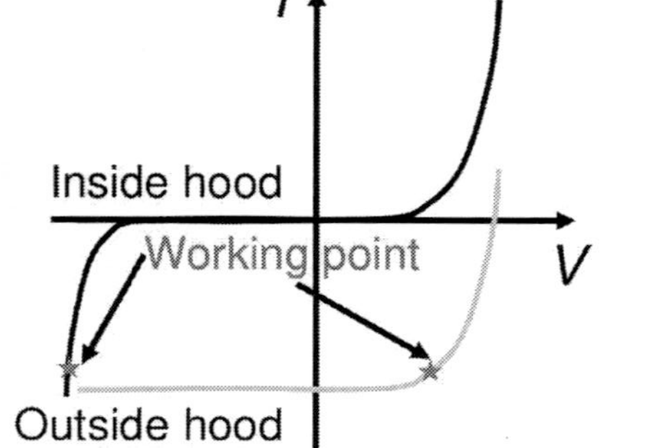

Facts:

- Striation ring like lum. pattern appears instant, while TG pattern need some 10 s

- Radiative recombination coefficient B decrease with increasing temperatures[1]

- Breakdown lum. in reverse voltage[2] is not the cause as image subtraction inverts lum. in dark

Speculation:

- Emission peak spectrum may shift into filter window & increases detected lum.

- In extreme reverse bias charge carriers may be trapped and flood the cell during switching to forward voltage

[1] T. Trupke *et al.*, *J. Appl. Phys.*, vol. 94, no. 8, pp. 4930–4937, Oct. 2003, doi: 10.1063/1.1610231.
[2] Y. Jia *et al.*, *Sol. Energy*, vol. 225, pp. 463–470, Sep. 2021, doi: 10.1016/j.solener.2021.07.052.

Conclusion

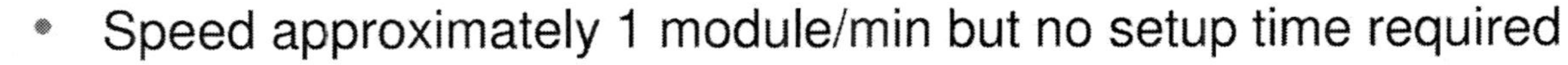

- Luminescence imaging at actual I_{mpp} of the system, that's what we really need!

- Can detect everything what EL can detect

- Additionally: can detect lost bypass diodes, not connected strings

- New luminescence effect found
while switching fast (some ms) from extreme reverse ➜ forward voltage

- Speed approximately 1 module/min but no setup time required

- Small hood can reach upper module row of PV rack (7 m)

- Instant imaging, no rewiring

- **Everyone can operate the Quickcheck system, no electrician needed!**

020207-010

Acknowledgments

This work was funded by the state of Lower Saxony and the Federal Ministry for Economic Affairs and Energy (BMWE) under grant number ZIM KK5291103SY2 PVDETECTS.

Supported by:

Federal Ministry
for Economic Affairs
and Energy

on the basis of a decision
by the German Bundestag

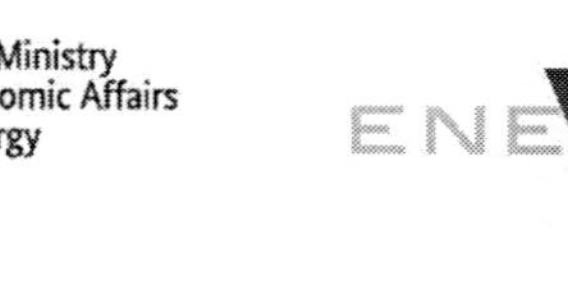

We thank Enerparc AG for supporting us evaluating our measurement tools in relevant PV systems.

020207-011

Come and learn about how to characterize your PV system

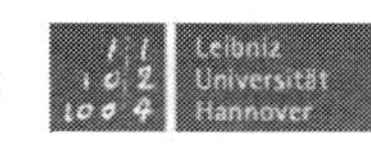

WEBINAR

IEA PVPS Task 13

Characterisation of Photovoltaic Systems

International Energy Agency
Photovoltaic Power Systems Programme

🕐 **Thursday, 23 October 2025**
08:15 - 11:00 (CEST)

🖥 **Virtual**

Registration:
https://t1p.de/8ofkn

Leibniz Universität Hannover

020207-012

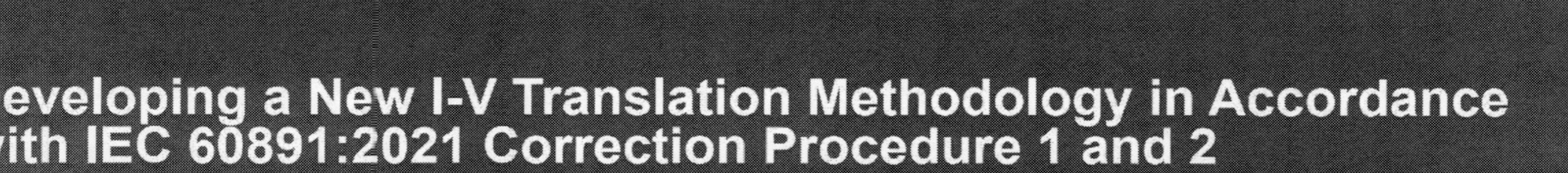

Developing a New I-V Translation Methodology in Accordance with IEC 60891:2021 Correction Procedure 1 and 2

Wenhao Xu, Yating Zhang, Mengdi Liu, Christos Monokroussos, Werner Herrmann, Giorgio Bardizza, Harald Müllejans

[2025.09.24] | [EUPVSEC 2025, Bilbao, Spain]

Agenda

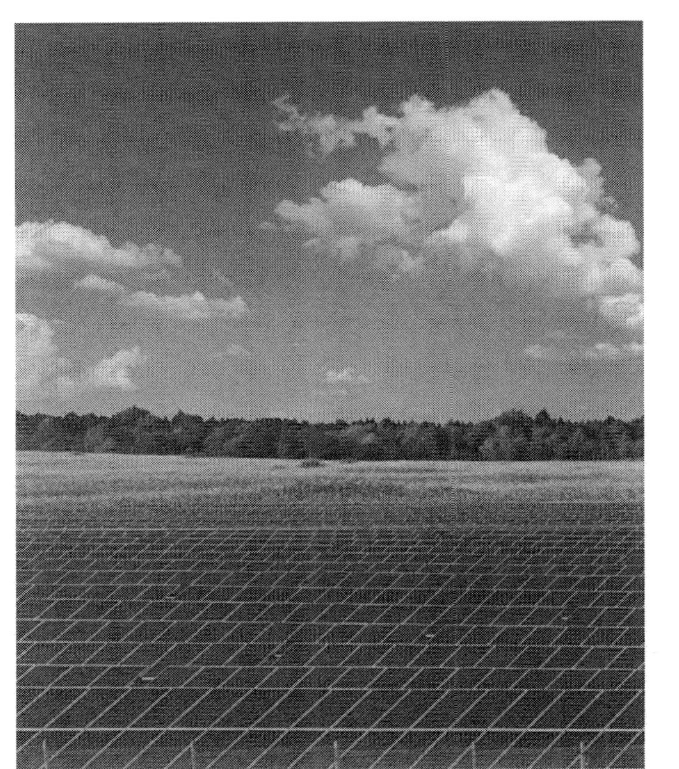

Introduction and Motivation

Concept of New Correction Procedure

Design of Experiments

Results

Conclusion

TÜVRheinland®
Precisely Right.

020208-002

Introduction and Motivation

IV correction

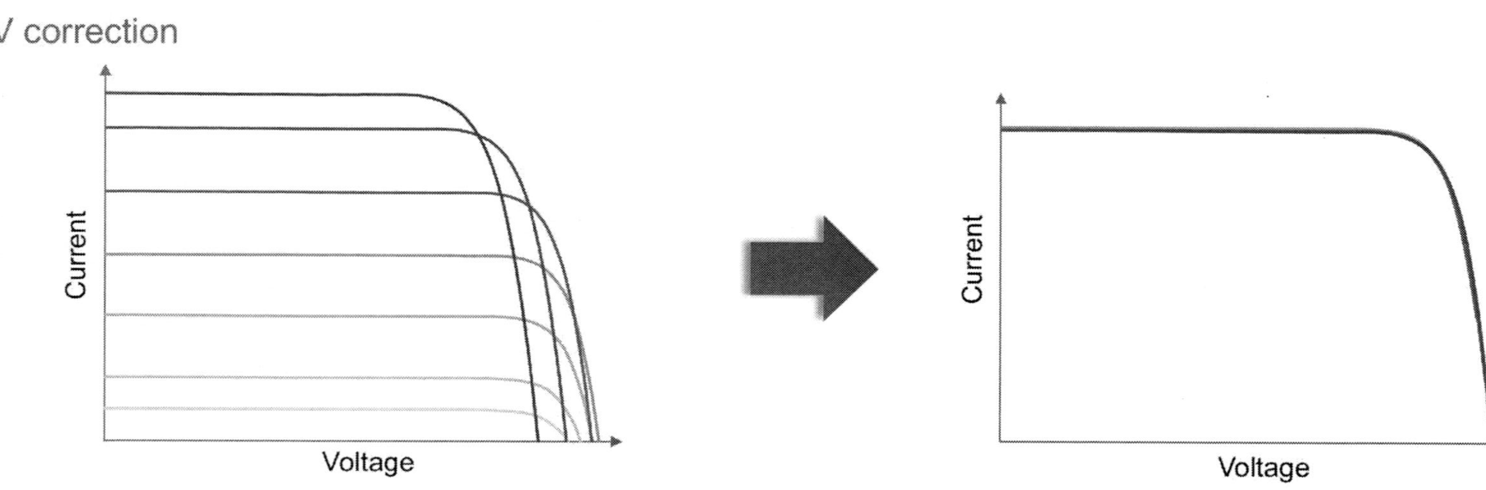

- The irradiance and temperature of I-V measurement always deviate from the target condition, especially for field test.
- IV correction aims to correct the I-V curve to the target irradiance and temperature condition

020208-003

Introduction and Motivation

IEC 60891 Correction Procedure

1987
- The 1st edition of IEC 60891 was published with the correction procedure 1 (CP1)

2009
- The 2nd edition of IEC 60891 with CP2 and CP3 published

2021
- The 3rd edition of IEC 60891 with revised CP2 and CP4

- CP1 and 2 are most commonly used in the industry.

TÜVRheinland®
Precisely Right.

020208-004

Introduction and Motivation

Correction Procedure 1 (CP1)

- **Advantage:**
  - Accurate in P_{MAX} and I_{SC}
- **Disadvantages:**
  - CP1: Incomplete I-V curve from low irradiance translated to high irradiance.
    - Results inaccurate V_{OC}
    - Need to measure negative current regime adequately but is not practical.

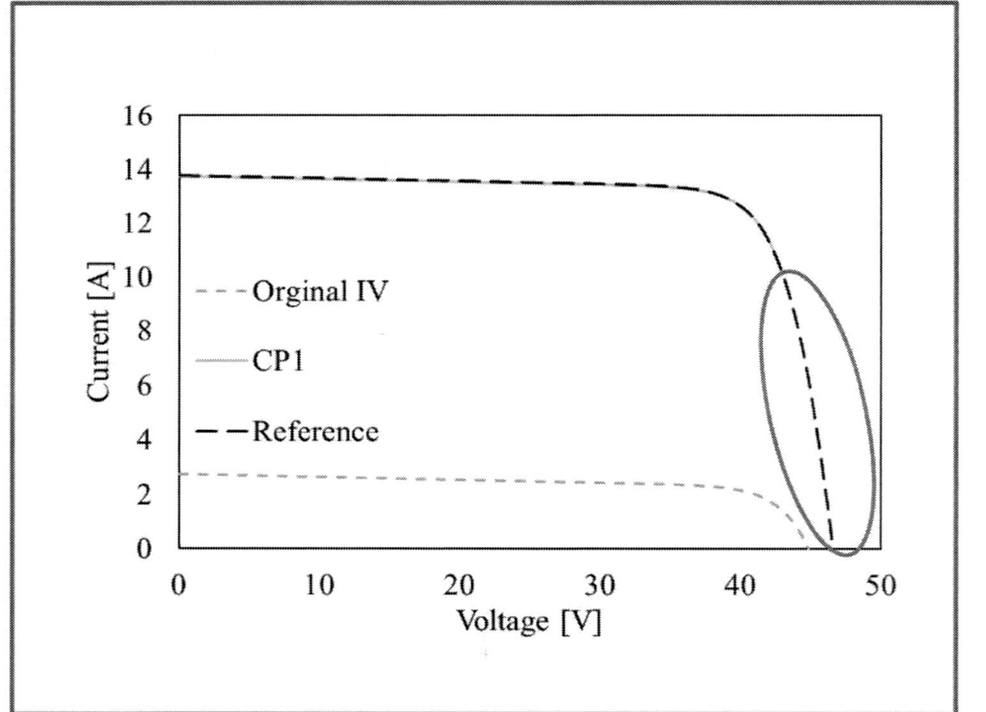

TÜVRheinland®
Precisely Right.

020208-005

Introduction and Motivation

Correction Procedure 2 (CP2)

- **Advantage:**
  - Highly accurate, except for low Rsh modules
  - Most precise in V_{OC} correction:
  - ❖ Introduce a non-linear scaling of V_{OC} against logarithmic irradiance
  - ❖ And introduce an irradiance-dependent temperature coefficient (TC) of V_{OC}
- **Disadvantages:**
  - CP2: Poor accuracy for low Rsh device.

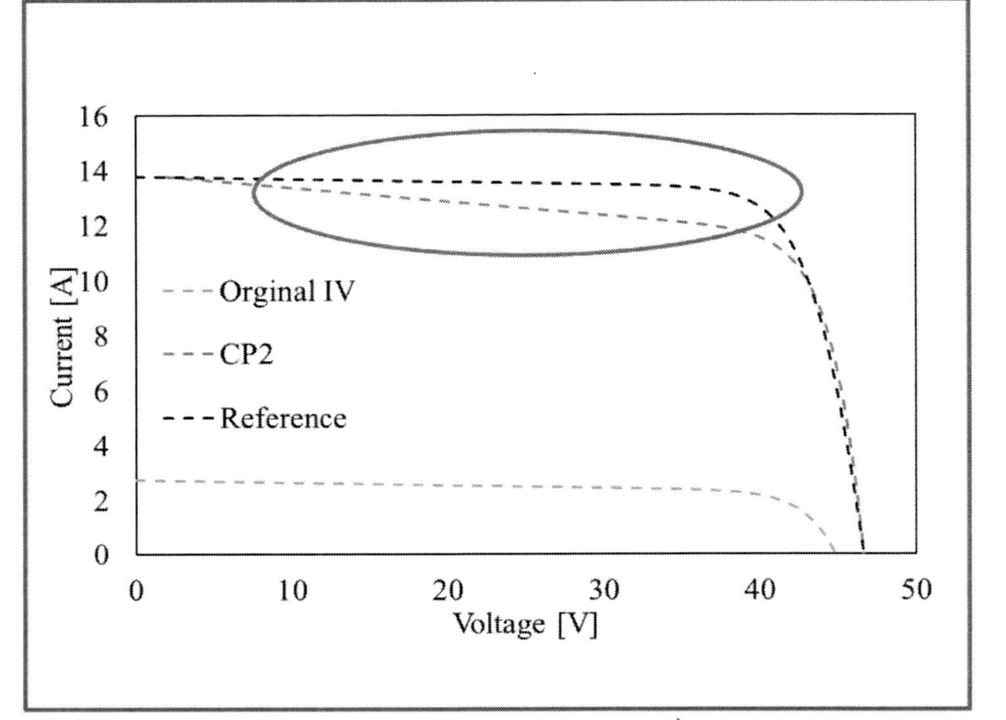

TÜVRheinland®
Precisely Right.

020208-006

Concept of New Correction Procedure (NCP)

NCP = CP1 + CP2

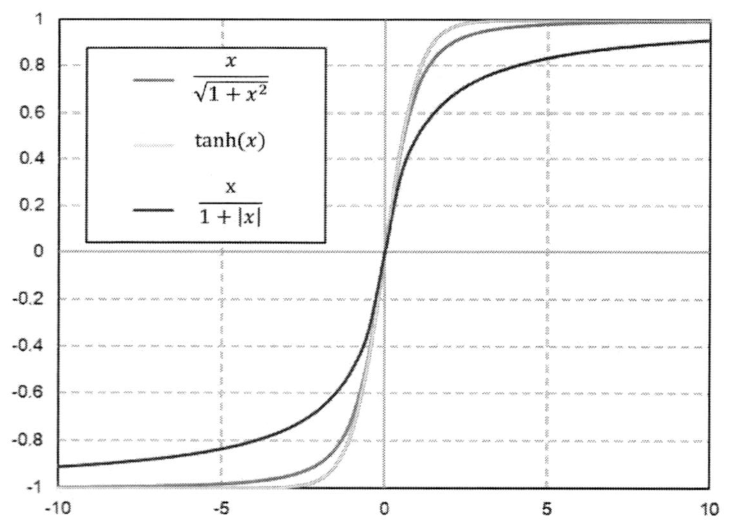

Examples of Sigmoid function

- ■ **Concept:**
- • To develop a new method that integrates CP1 and CP2, compensating for each's respective disadvantages.

- ■ **Combination of 2 methods:**
- • Introduce the suitable Sigmoid function
- • $NCP = w1(x) \cdot CP1 + w2(x) \cdot CP2$
- • $w1(x)$ and $w2(x)$ are two Sigmoid functions;

TÜVRheinland®
Precisely Right.

Concept of New Correction Procedure (NCP)

Gompertz Curve

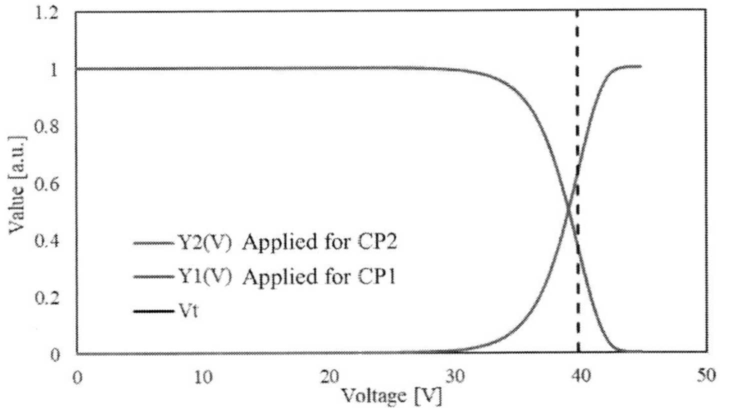

Example of Gompertz Curves introduced in NCP

- A type of S-shaped growth curve used to model growth processes across disciplines, including biology and economics.
- By adjusting parameters **A** and **B**, the curve varies from **0 to 1** along the **positive X-axis**.

- Four-parameters Gompertz Curve:

$$Y(V) = A + Bexp(-\exp(k(V - V_t)))$$

- Modified Gompertz Curve to:

$$Y1(V) = exp(-\exp(k(V - V_t)))$$
$$Y2(V) = -1 + exp(-\exp(k(V - V_t)))$$

k determine the increasing/decreasing rate, which is always 0.5 in this work;

V_t determine where the curve start increasing/decreasing.

NCP formula:

$$I_c = Y1 \times I_{CP1} + Y2 \times I_{CP2}$$
$$V_c = V_{CP2}$$

Concept of New Correction Procedure (NCP)

Determination of V_t

- Small V_t : Corrected IV curve trends towards **CP2** corrected IV.

- Large V_t: Current behavior approaches **CP1's result**.

- V_t Determination formula:

$$V_t = V_{MPP1} \times i$$

V_{MPP1} is the Vmpp of the original IV curve.

- i is determined semi-empirically.

- Determined by the difference of P_{max} between CP1 and CP2

Diff. of P_{MAX} in CP1&CP2	i
Diff. ≤ 0.5%	0.92
0.5% < Diff. ≤ 2%	0.97
2% < Diff. ≤ 5%	1
5% < Diff. ≤ 10%	1.025
10% < Diff. ≤ 20%	1.05
20% < Diff. ≤ 35%	1.07
35% < Diff. ≤ 50%	1.08
>50%	1.2

020208-009

Design of Experiments

Test Samples

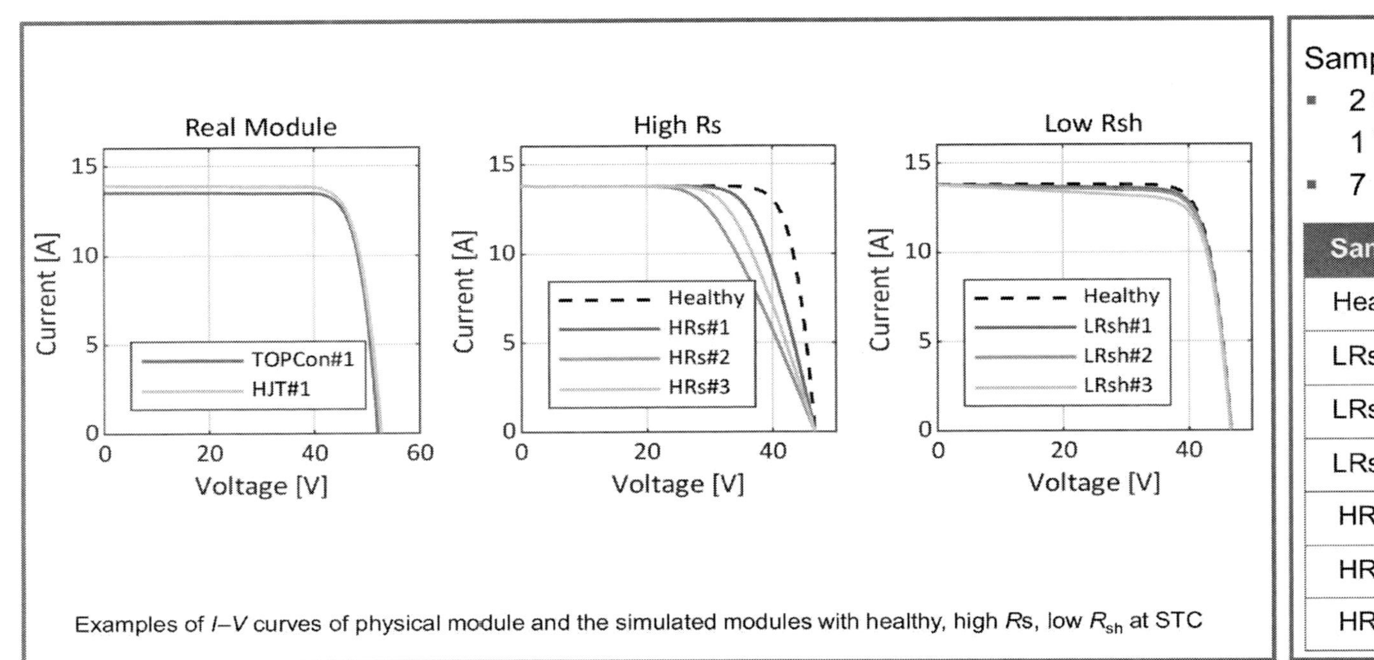

Examples of I–V curves of physical module and the simulated modules with healthy, high Rs, low R_{sh} at STC

Samples:
- 2 Commercial Modules: 1 TOPCon and 1 HJT
- 7 Simulated Modules

Sample	Rsh (Ω)	Rs (Ω)
Healthy	1500	0.1
LRsh#1	150	0.1
LRsh#2	100	0.1
LRsh#3	50	0.1
HRs#1	1500	0.5
HRs#2	1500	0.75
HRs#3	1500	1

TÜVRheinland®
Precisely Right.

020208-010

Design of Experiments

Evaluation Method

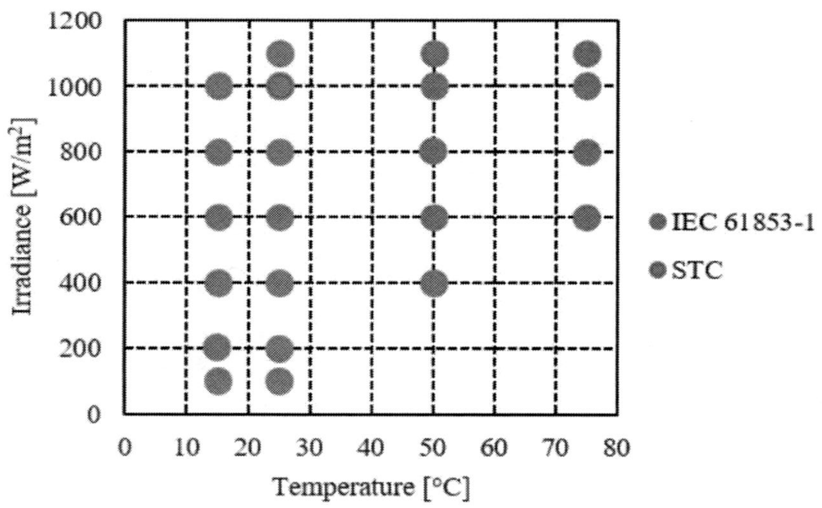

- Modules are tested/simulated under 22 different conditions, including STC.
- I-V curves are corrected to STC for comparison.
- Deviations in key electrical parameters are analyzed.
- RMSE of parameter deviations is evaluated across 21 test conditions.

020208-011

Results

Commercial Modules

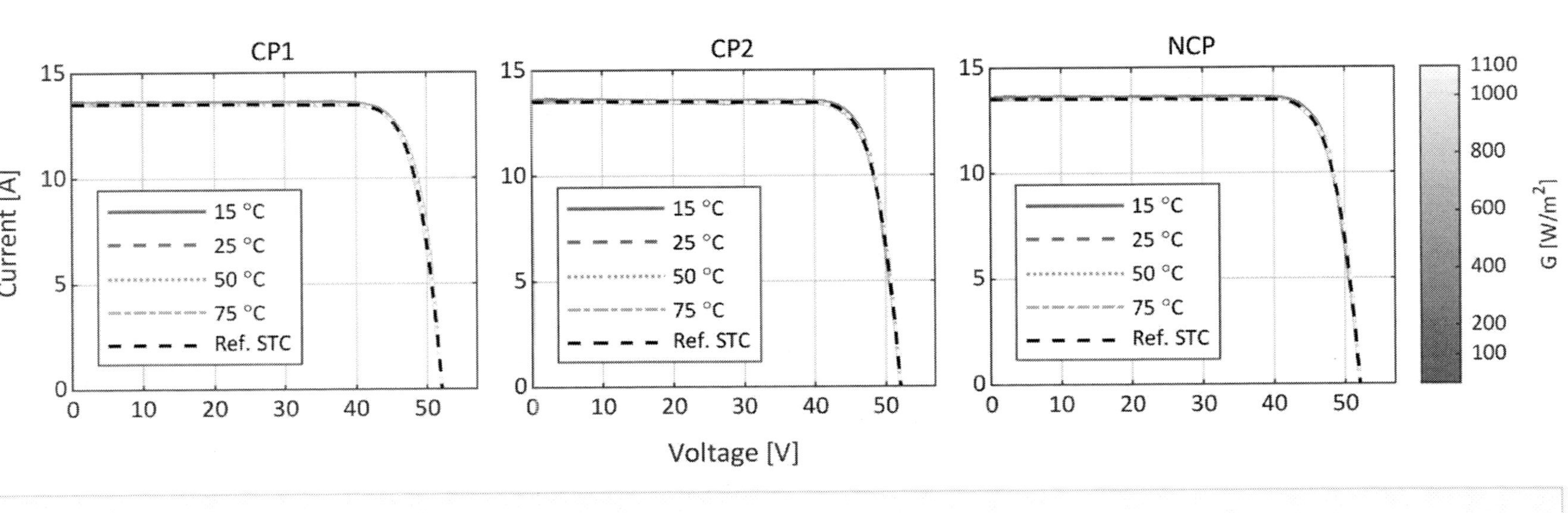

- I-V curves corrected by all three CPs align closely with the reference STC I-V curve.

TÜVRheinland®
Precisely Right.

020208-012

Results

Commercial Modules

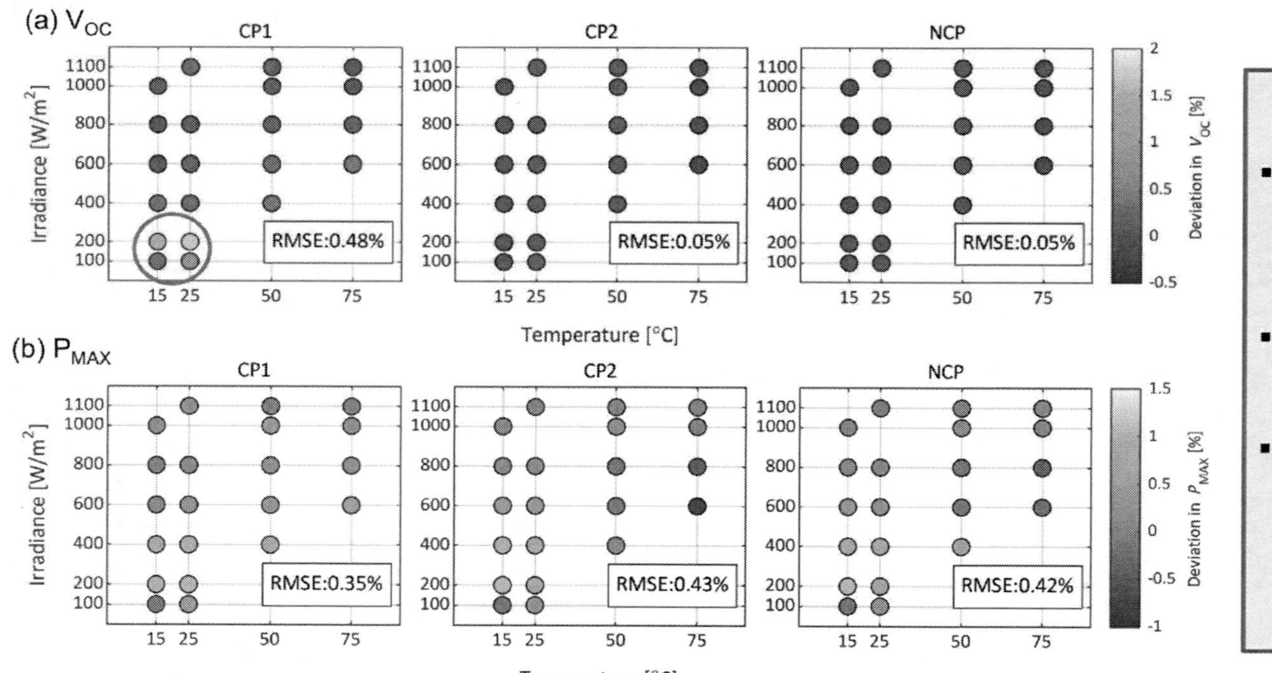

TOPCon#1 The deviation of translated I-V curves to STC using the three different CP

(a) V_{OC} (b) P_{MAX}

TÜVRheinland®
Precisely Right.

Results

Simulated Modules with Low R_{sh}

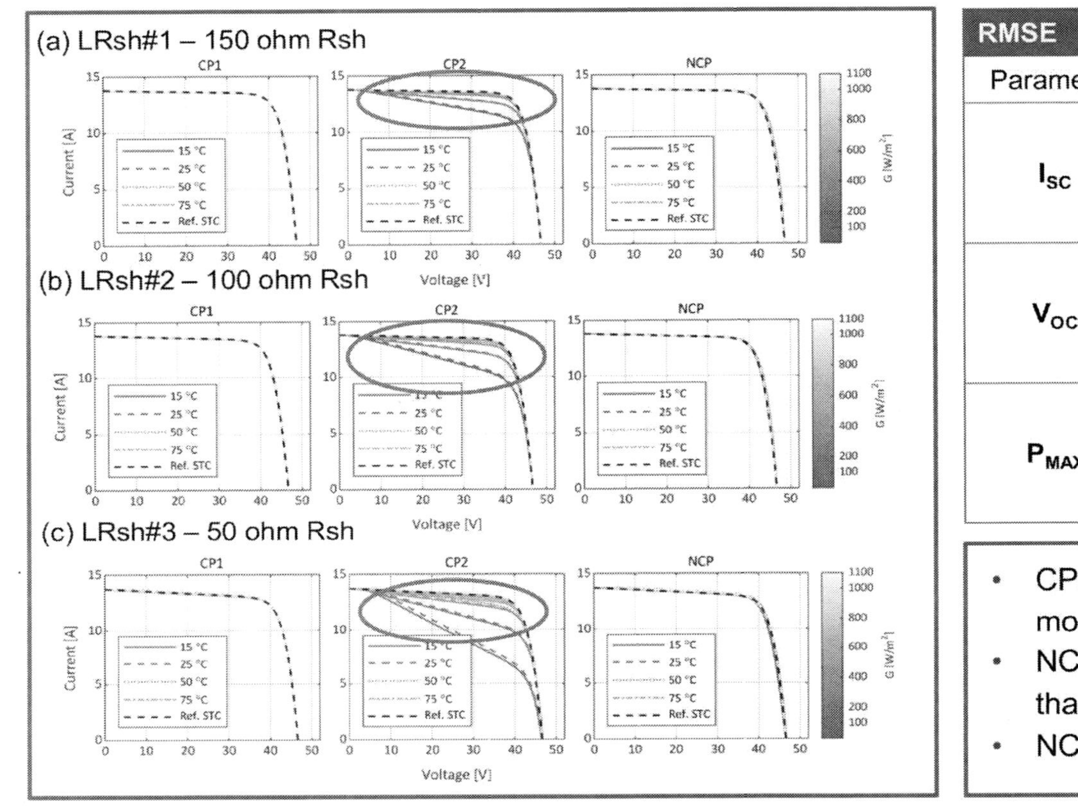

RMSE				
Parameter	Method	LRsh#1	LRsh#2	LRsh#3
I_{SC}	CP1	0.19%	0.28%	0.54%
	CP2	0.56%	0.92%	2.48%
	NCP	0.21%	0.31%	0.62%
V_{OC}	CP1	1.55%	1.86%	3.48%
	CP2	0.04%	0.06%	0.17%
	NCP	0.04%	0.06%	0.16%
P_{MAX}	CP1	0.02%	0.02%	0.01%
	CP2	4.99%	7.70%	15.41%
	NCP	0.16%	0.23%	0.45%

- CP2 produces distorted I-V curves for low R_{sh} modules.
- NCP produces significantly more accurate P_{MAX} than CP2.
- NCP produces more accurate V_{OC} than CP1.

Conclusion: Advancing I-V Correction with a New Procedure (NCP)

NCP presents a more reliable path forward for PV performance analysis.

- **I-V Correction is Vital** for accurate, standardized PV module characterization.

- Industry Standards CP1 & CP2 (IEC 60891) have known **inherent limitations**.

- **Objective Achieved**: A **New Correction Procedure** (**NCP**) was developed to combine the strengths of CP1 and CP2.

- **Key Finding**: The proposed **NCP outperforms both CP1 and CP2** in accuracy for most cases.

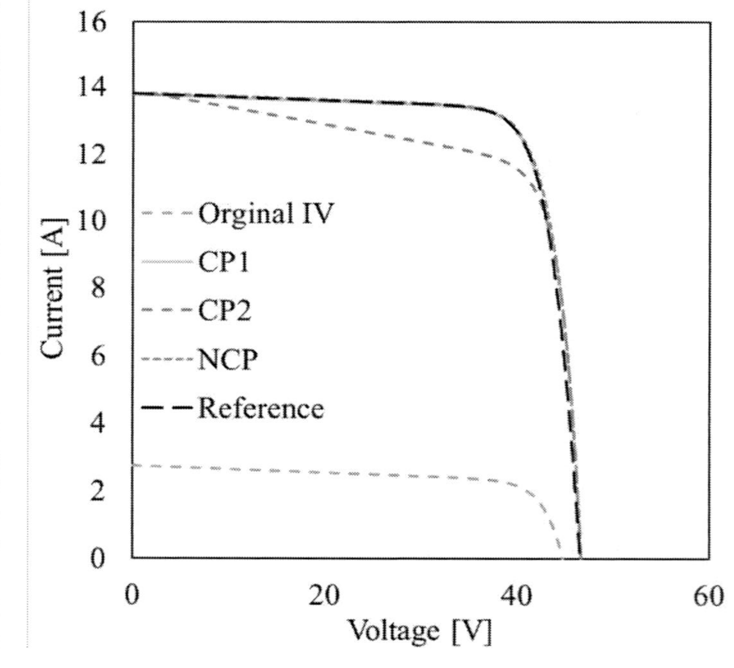

TÜVRheinland®
Precisely Right.

020208-015

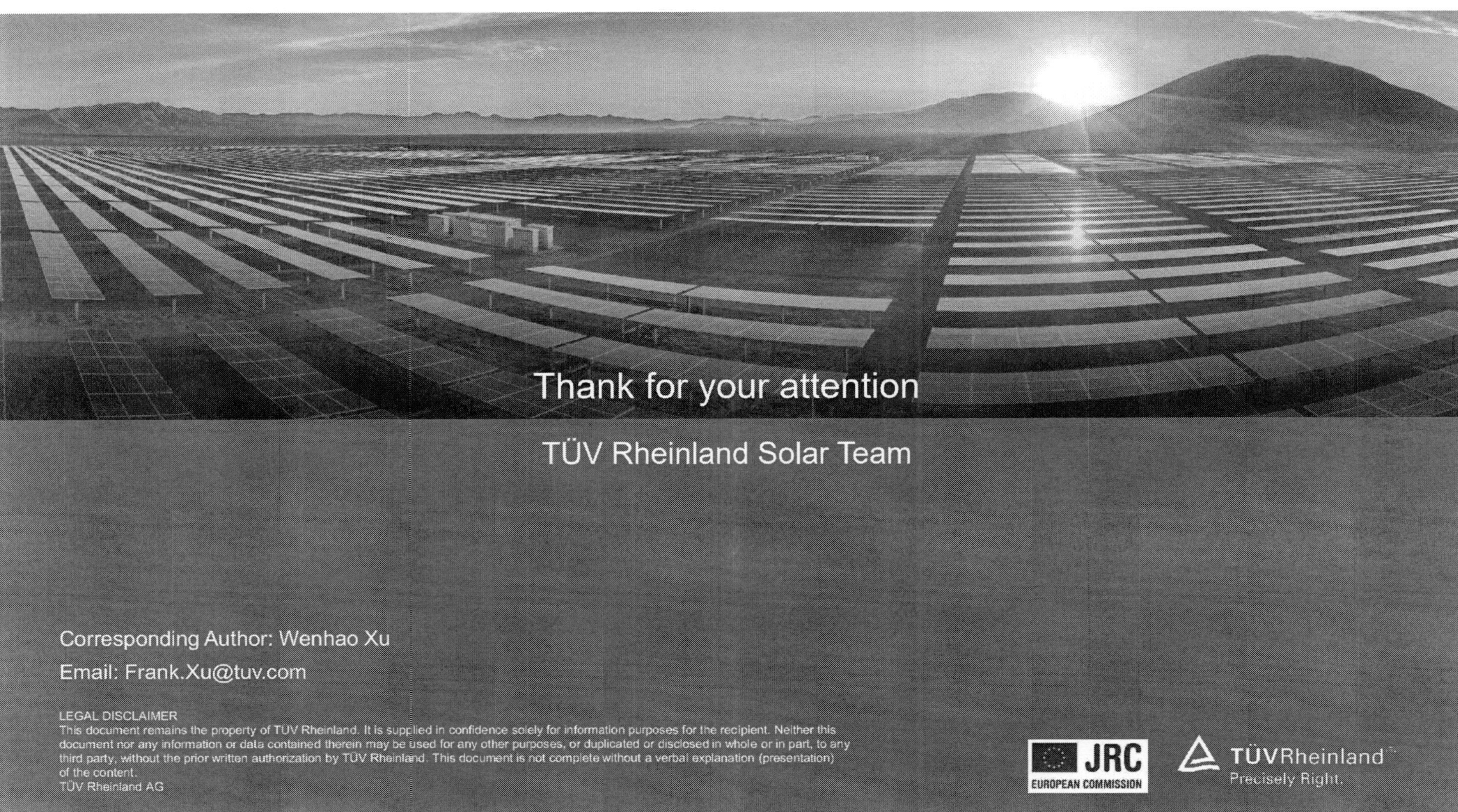

Corresponding Author: Wenhao Xu
Email: Frank.Xu@tuv.com

JRC EUROPEAN COMMISSION

TÜVRheinland
Precisely Right.

EUPVSEC, 2025

Characterization of Vehicle Integrated Photovoltaic Modules

Ricardo Moruno[1], Francisco Martín[1,2], Juan Manuel Redondo[1], Javier Malo[3], Luis J. San José[1], Guido Vallerotto[1], Steve Askins[1], Rubén Núñez[1], César Domínguez[1], Ignacio Antón[1], Rebeca Herrero

[1]Instituto de Energía Solar-Universidad Politécnica de Madrid (IES-UPM), Madrid, Spain

[2]Solar Added Value (SAV), Madrid, Spain

[3]E.T.S. de Ingeniería Y Sistemas de Telecomunicación, UPM, Madrid, Spain

Introduction

VIPV specific features

- Curvature: complex 3D shapes

  – Inherent non uniform irradiance

- Operating conditions

  – Wide range of angles of incidence and

  directionalities

Curvature and cell interconnection affect the module's
angular response, which is critical on VIPV

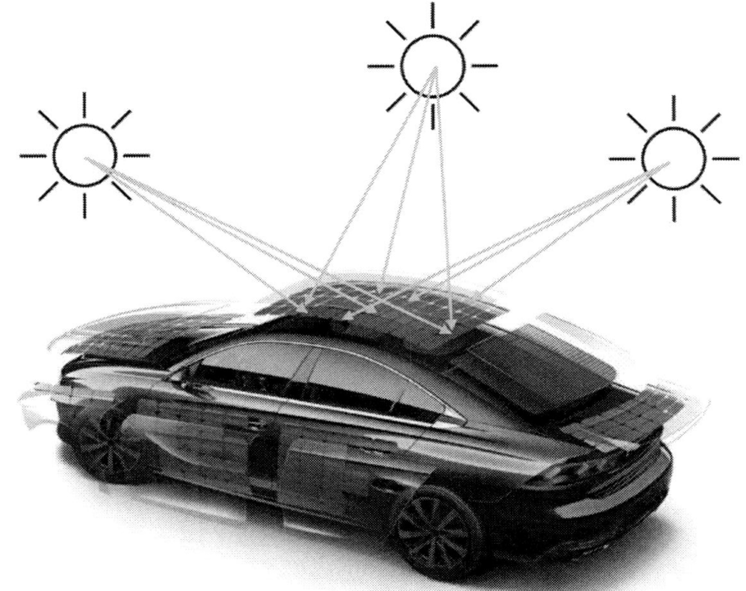

020209-002

Motivation

- To advance in VIPV, we need to be able to determine module properties so we can:

  - **COMPARE** TECHNOLOGIES
  - **MODEL** PV PERFORMANCE

- Characterization

  - IV curve on STC
  - Angular response tests

Current procedures and gear are not suited for VIPV

We are going to share the lessons learned on VIPV characterization

- What is being done about it?

  - IEC series for flat modules:
    - PT600 (TC 82 IEC) Project Leader K. Araki
  - International Round Robin:
    - To compare Power Rating
    - To define instrumentation, procedures and metrics for VIPV

(cannot disclose IV curves values)

Outline

- Methodology
  - INDOORS: Solar simulator of collimated light
  - OUTDOORS: Two-axis tracker
- Results
  - IV curve at STC
  - Angular response
- Conclusions

020209-004

Methodology: Collimated light solar simulator

- Conventional solar simulator

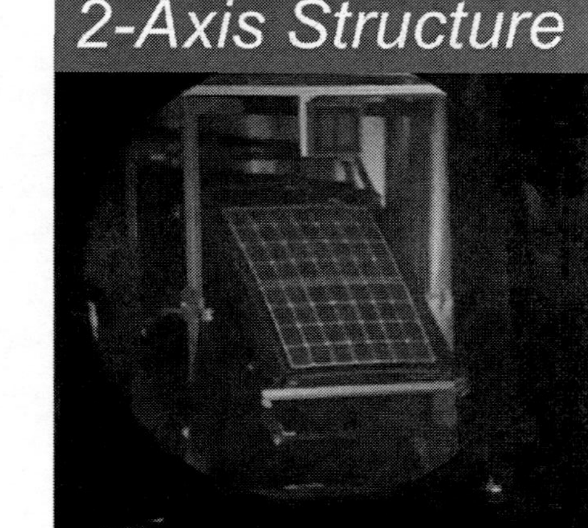

Increased error in replicating solar illumination.
Aoi depends on distance to source AND curvature.

- Collimated light solar simulator

Reasonable solar illumination replication:
Aoi depends ONLY on curvature

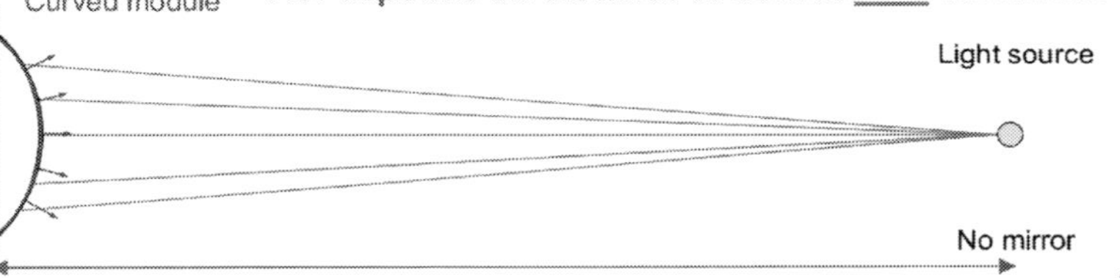

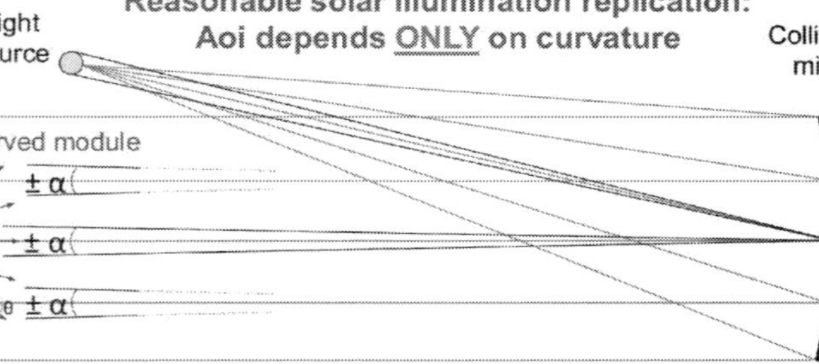

[1] G. Vallerotto, et Al., "Collimated solar simulator for curved PV modules characterization", Solar Energy Materials and Solar Cells 258 (2023) 112418, doi: 10.1016/j.solmat.2023.112418

Methodology: 2-axis tracker

- STC at normal incidence – 2 axis tracker is mandatory

- Angular response – Programmed tracker control for different angles of incidence [2]

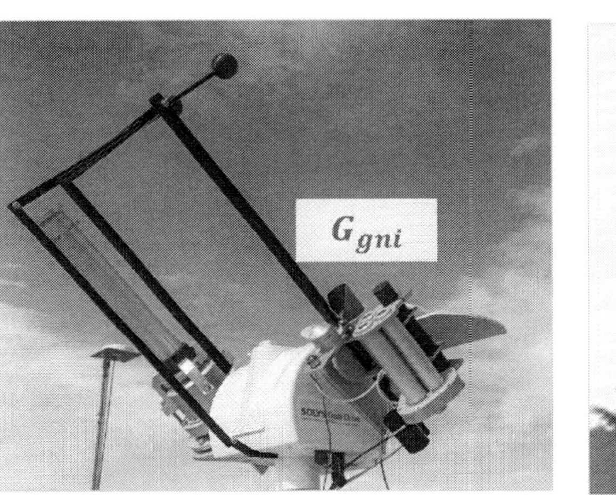

[2] Riley, D. et al. ,ASME. J. Sol. Energy Eng.; 137(3): 031008, (2015)

020209-006

Results: IV curve at STC

INSTITUTO
DE ENERGÍA
SOLAR

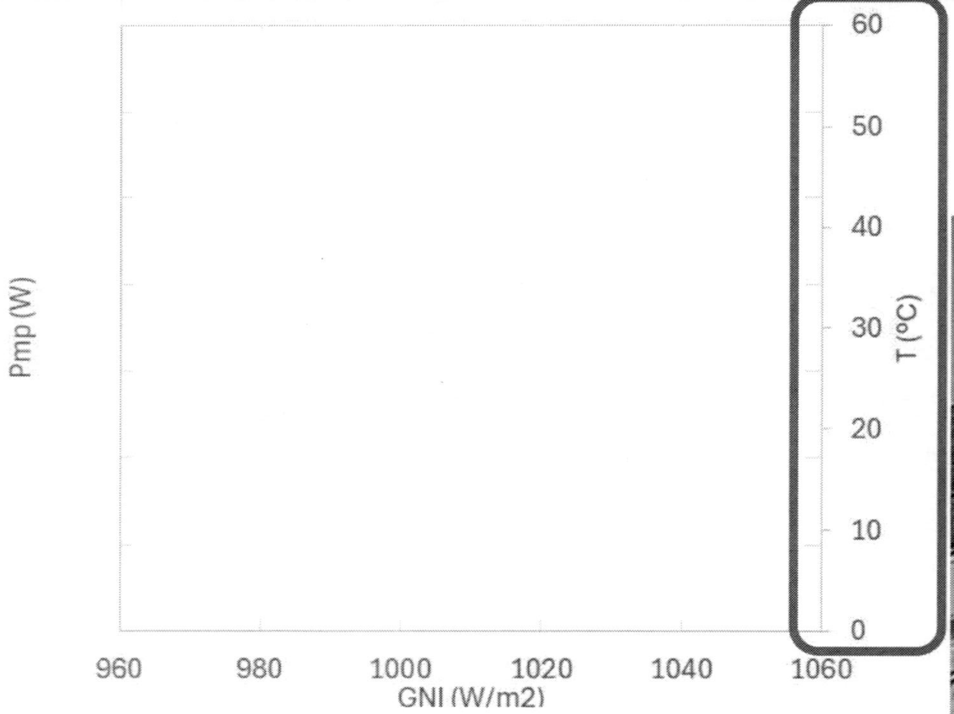

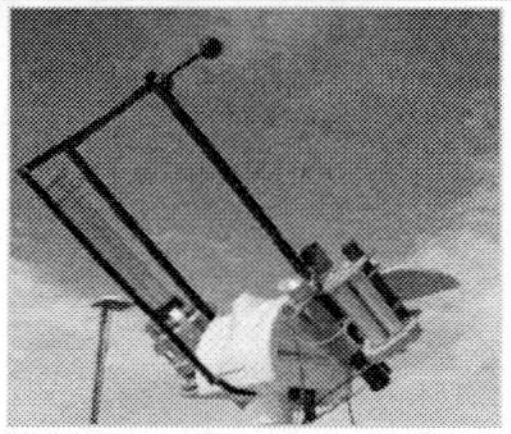

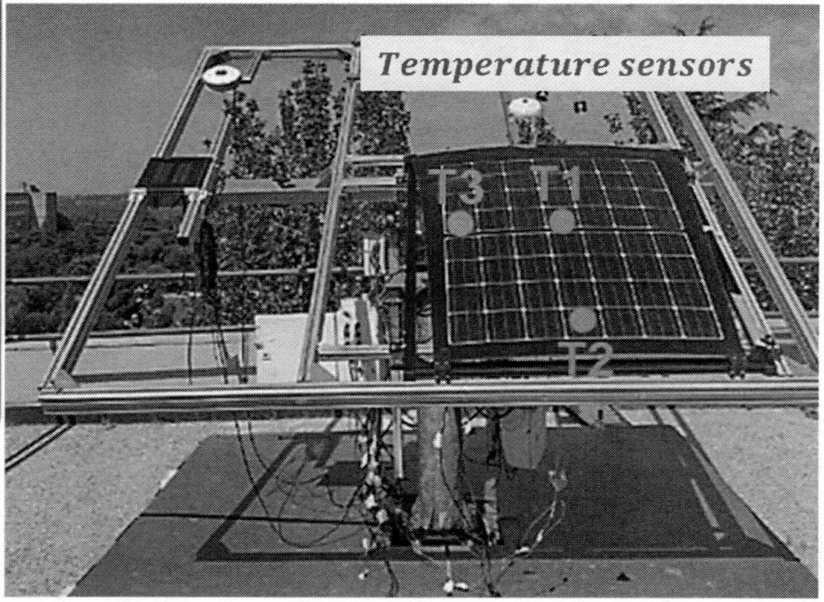

020209-007

Results: IV curve at STC

INSTITUTO DE ENERGÍA SOLAR

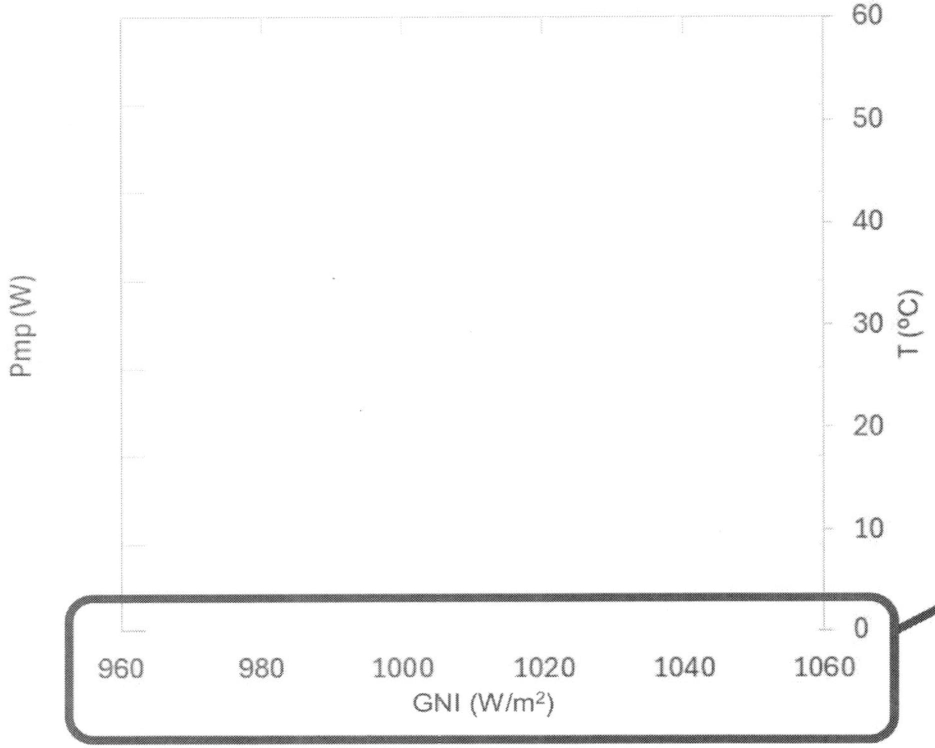

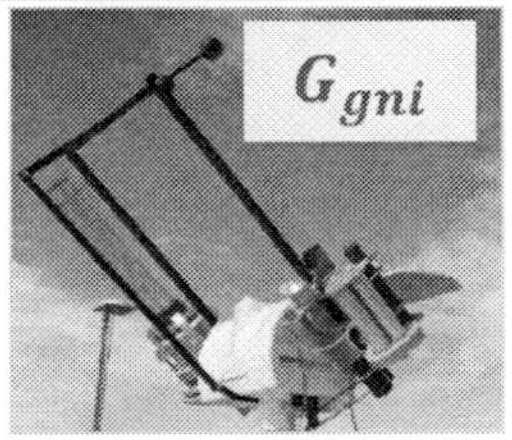

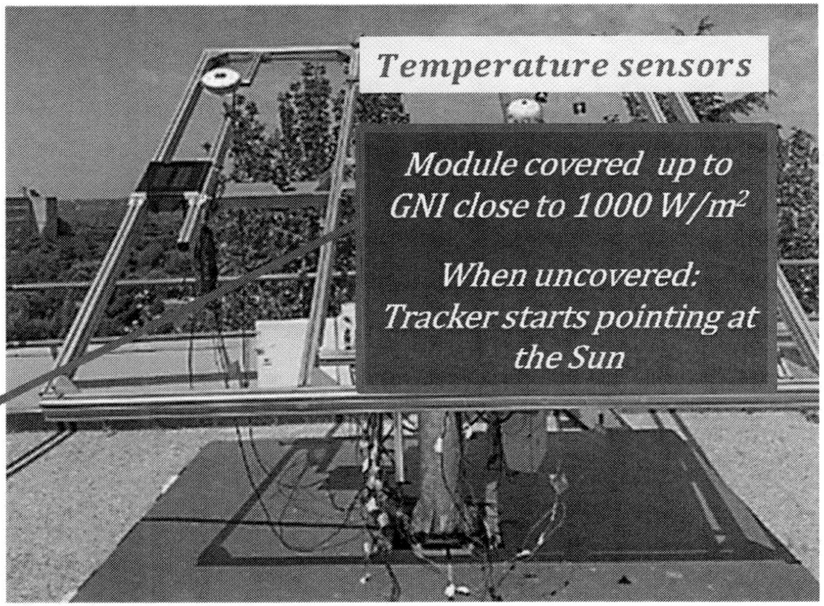

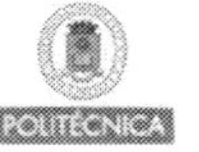

Results: IV curve at STC

INSTITUTO
DE ENERGÍA
SOLAR

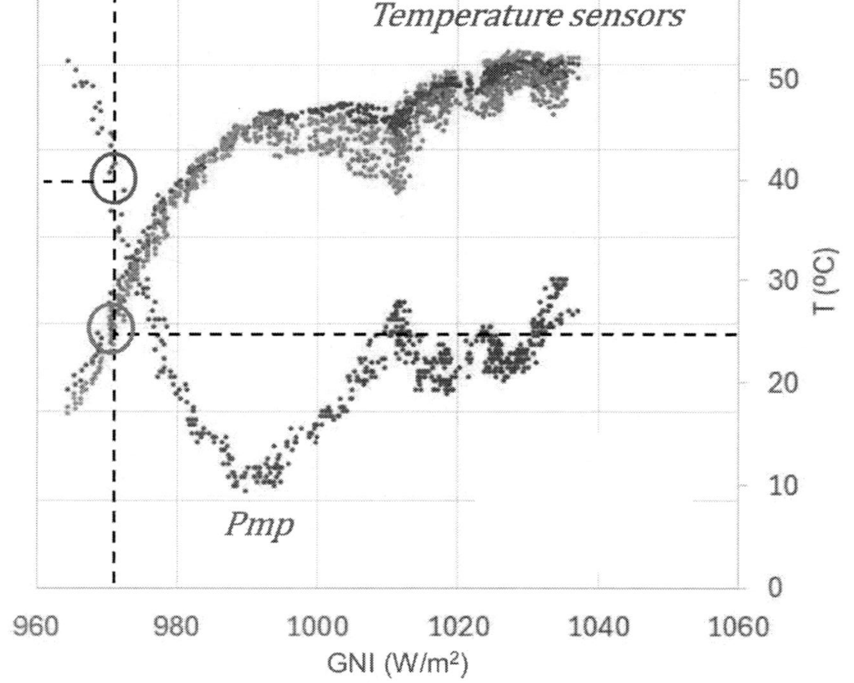

- Outdoor vs. indoor:

  - 0.93 % relative error on Pmp

25°C and 1000 W/m^2

020209-009

Results: IV curve at STC

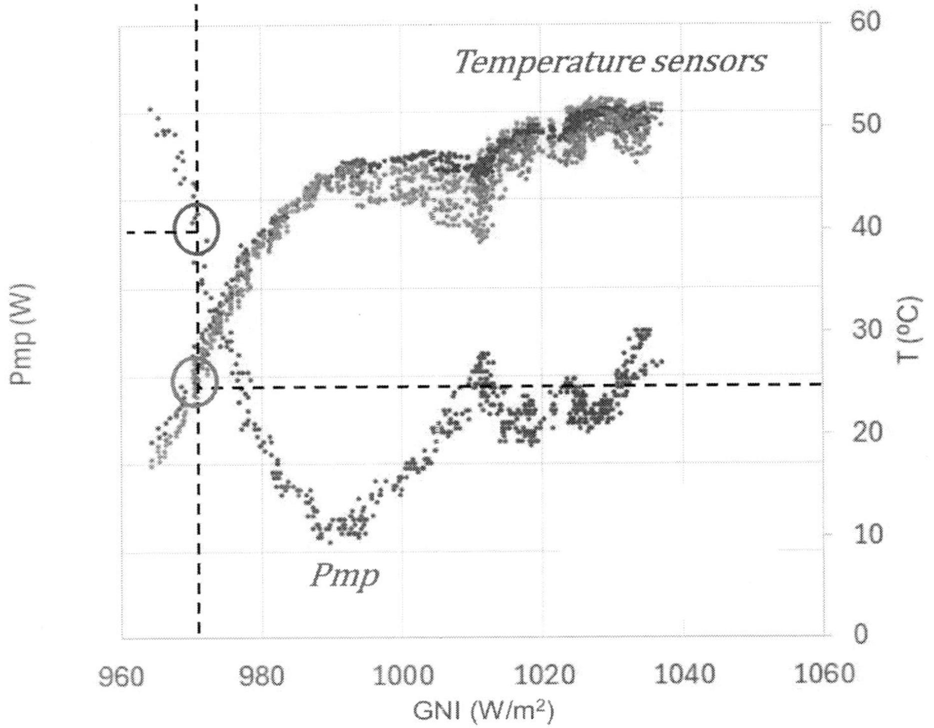

- Outdoor vs. indoor:
  - 0.93 % relative error on Pmp

25°C and 1000 W/m^2

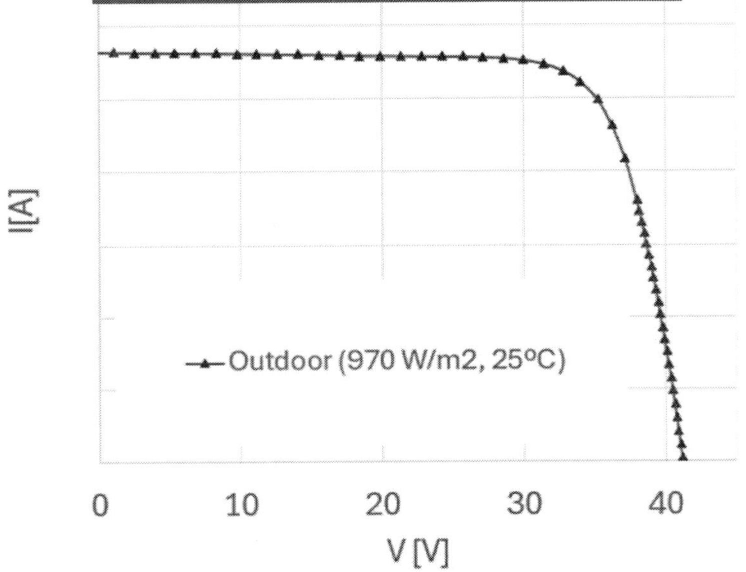

Results: IV curve at STC

INSTITUTO
DE ENERGÍA
SOLAR

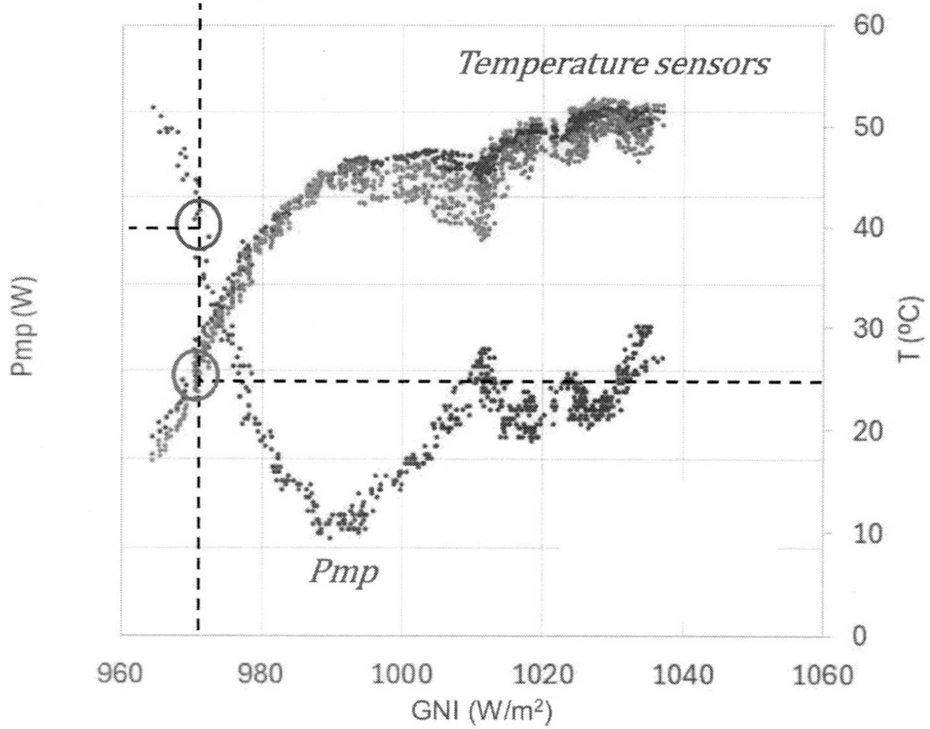

- Outdoor vs. indoor:
  - 0.93 % relative error on Pmp

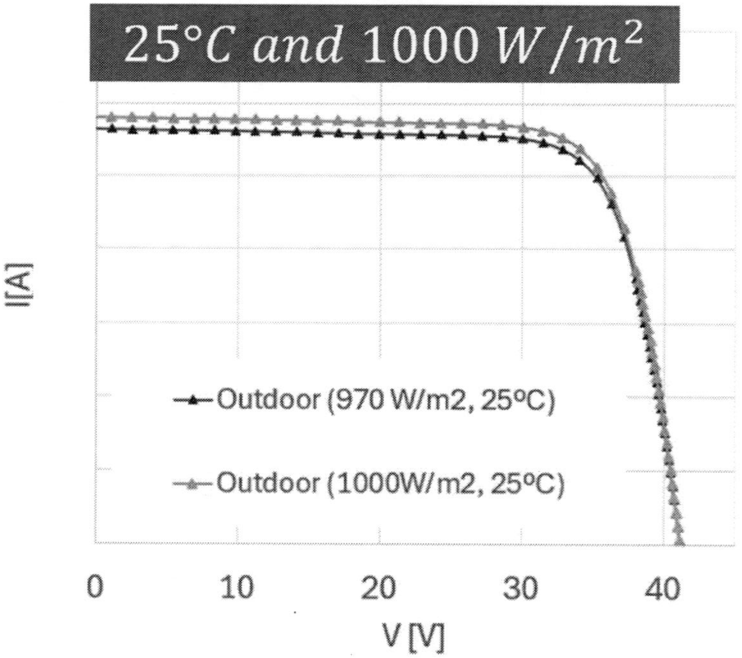

$25°C\ and\ 1000\ W/m^2$

020209-011

Results: IV curve at STC

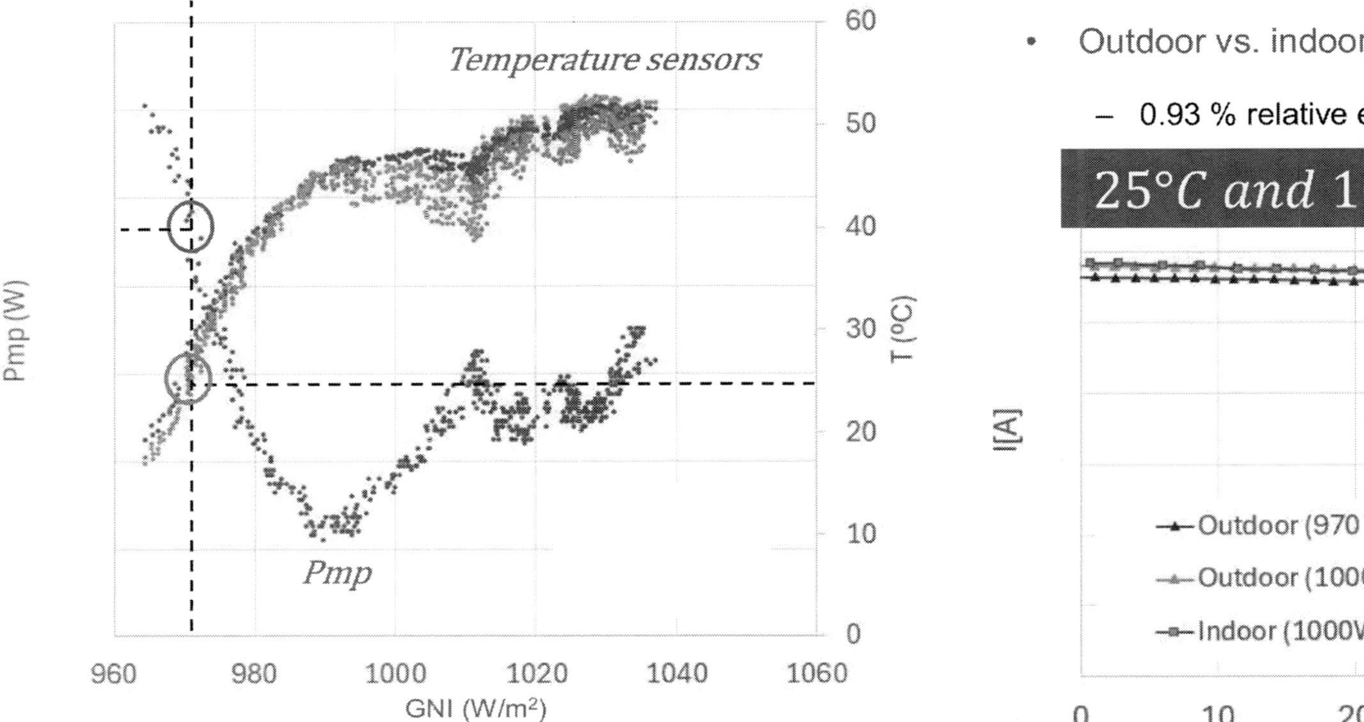

- Outdoor vs. indoor:

  – 0.93 % relative error on Pmp

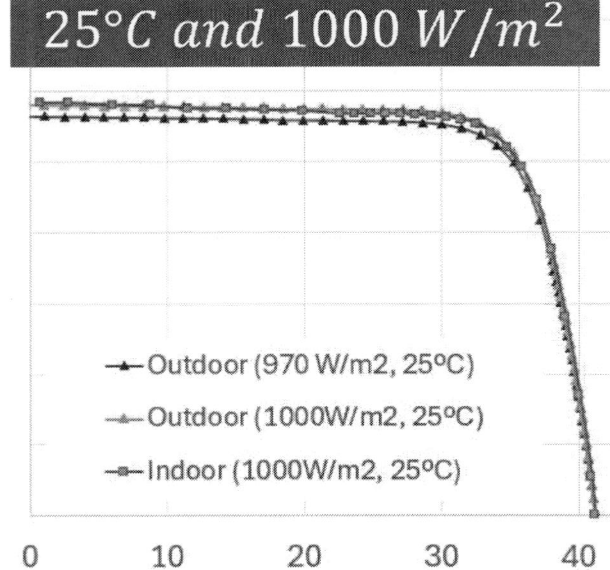

020209-012

Results: Angular response (indoor)

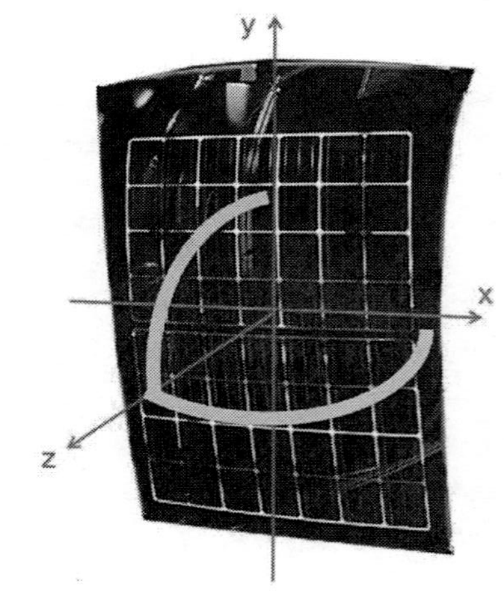

- Indoor IV curve at differents angles of incidence:

  - Vertical and horizontal sweep

  - Collimated light: 1000 W/m2

  - Module temperature: 25 °C

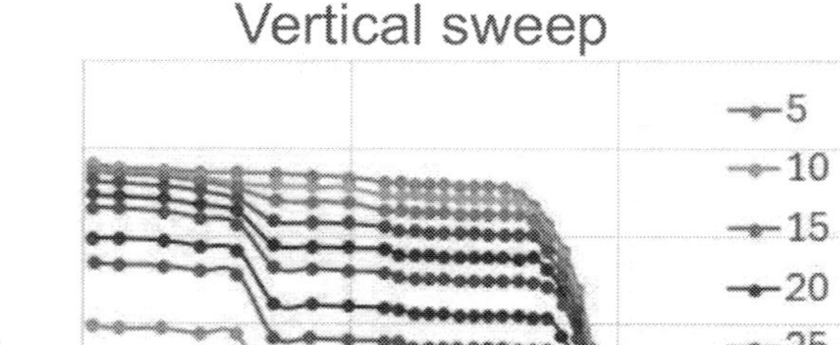

No correction needed!!

Focus on Pmp, not Isc

Vertical sweep

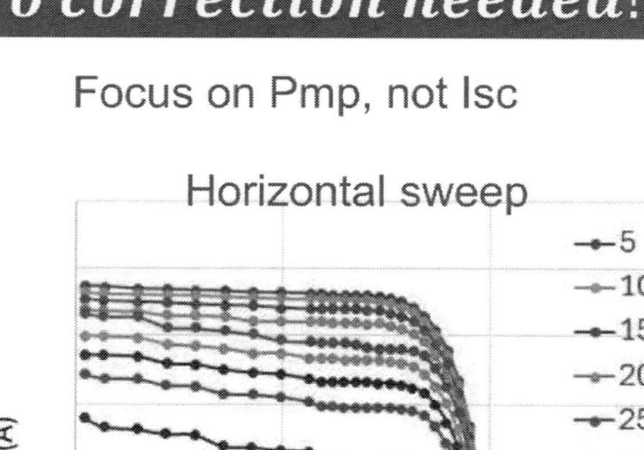

Horizontal sweep

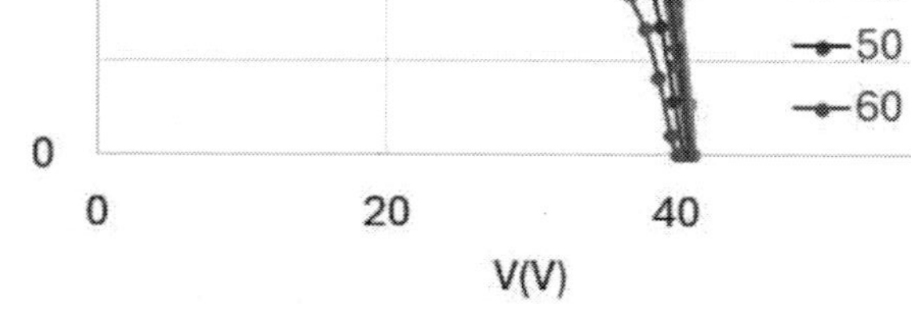

Results: Angular response (outdoor)

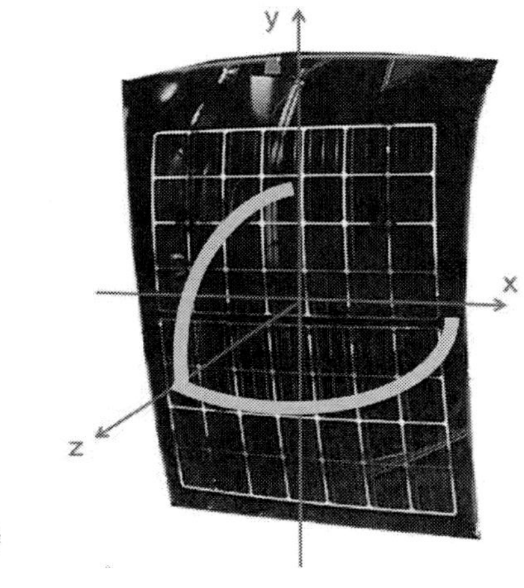

- Outdoor IV curve at differents angles of incidence:

  - Module temperature from 40 to 65 °C

  - Diffuse light from 50 W/m^2 to 130 W/m^2

Correction needed!!

Vertical sweep

Horizontal sweep

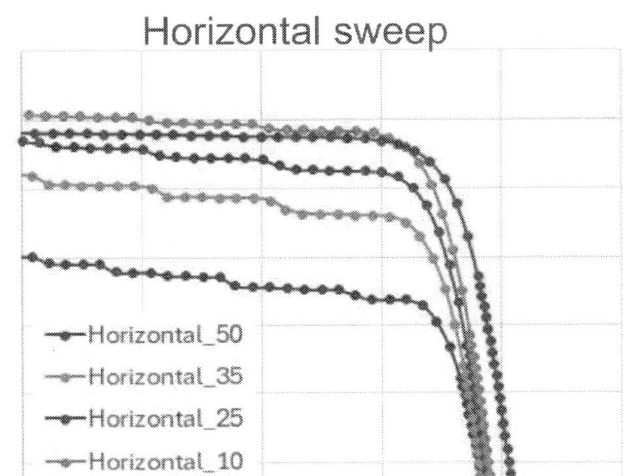

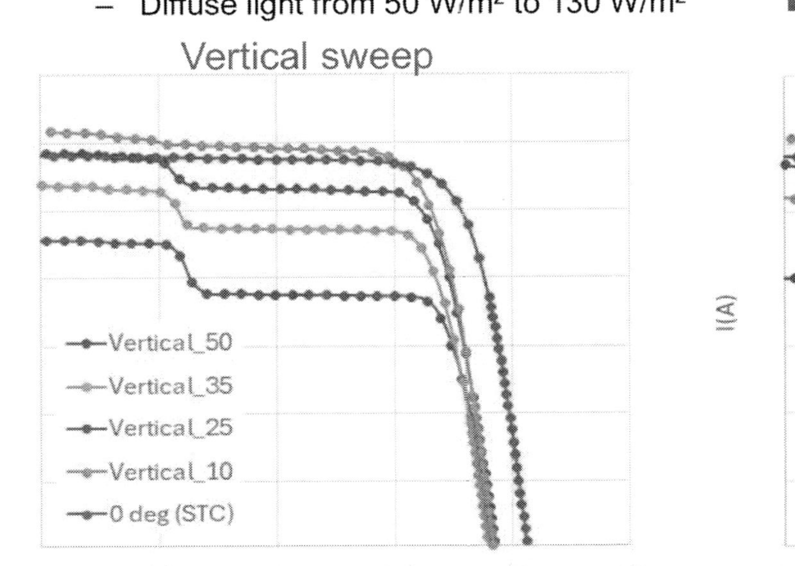

Outdoor angular response

INSTITUTO DE ENERGÍA SOLAR

- Challenges for high angles of incidence!

- Not all angles of incidence are possible:

  - It depends on the Sun elevation and tracker's position (TAz, TEl)

Diffuse component varies for the different positions of the tracker (TAz, TEl)

α and β

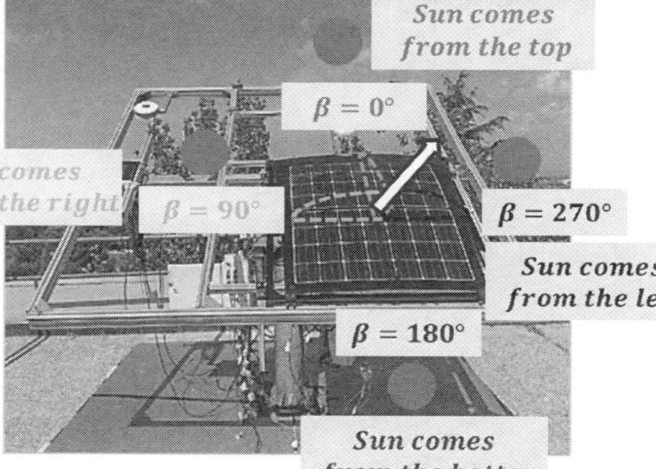

Even with the same α and β, the tracker's position (TAz, TEl) can change due to the different Sun's position

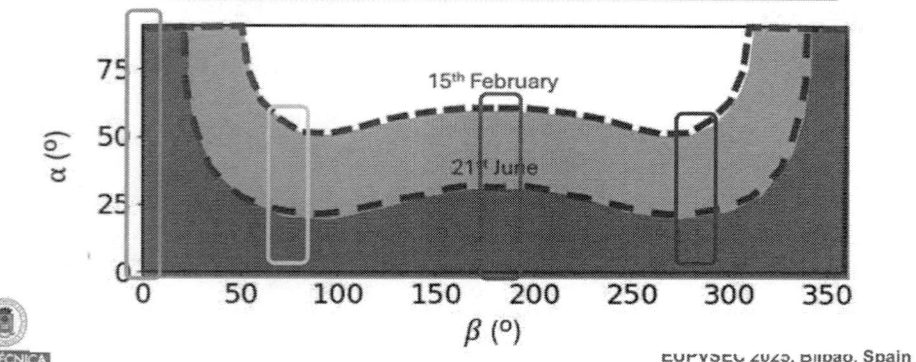

Outdoor angular response

- Challenges for high angles of incidence!

- Not all angles of incidence are possible:

  – It depends on the Sun elevation and tracker's position (TAz, TEL)

Diffuse component varies for the different positions of the tracker (TAz, TEI)

Bigger range!

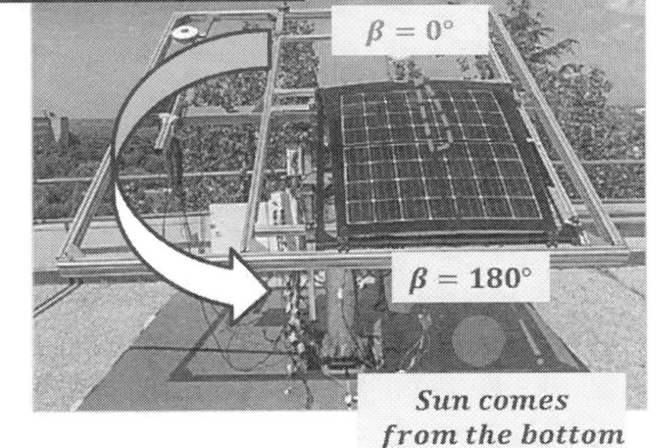

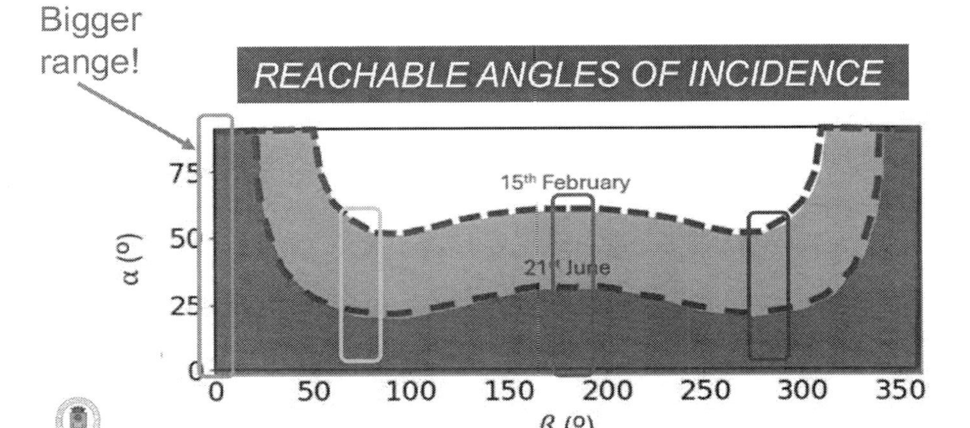

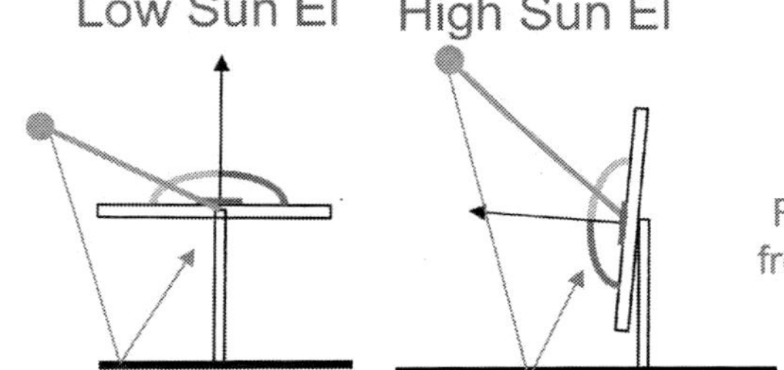

Outdoor angular response: vertical sweep

INSTITUTO
DE ENERGÍA
SOLAR

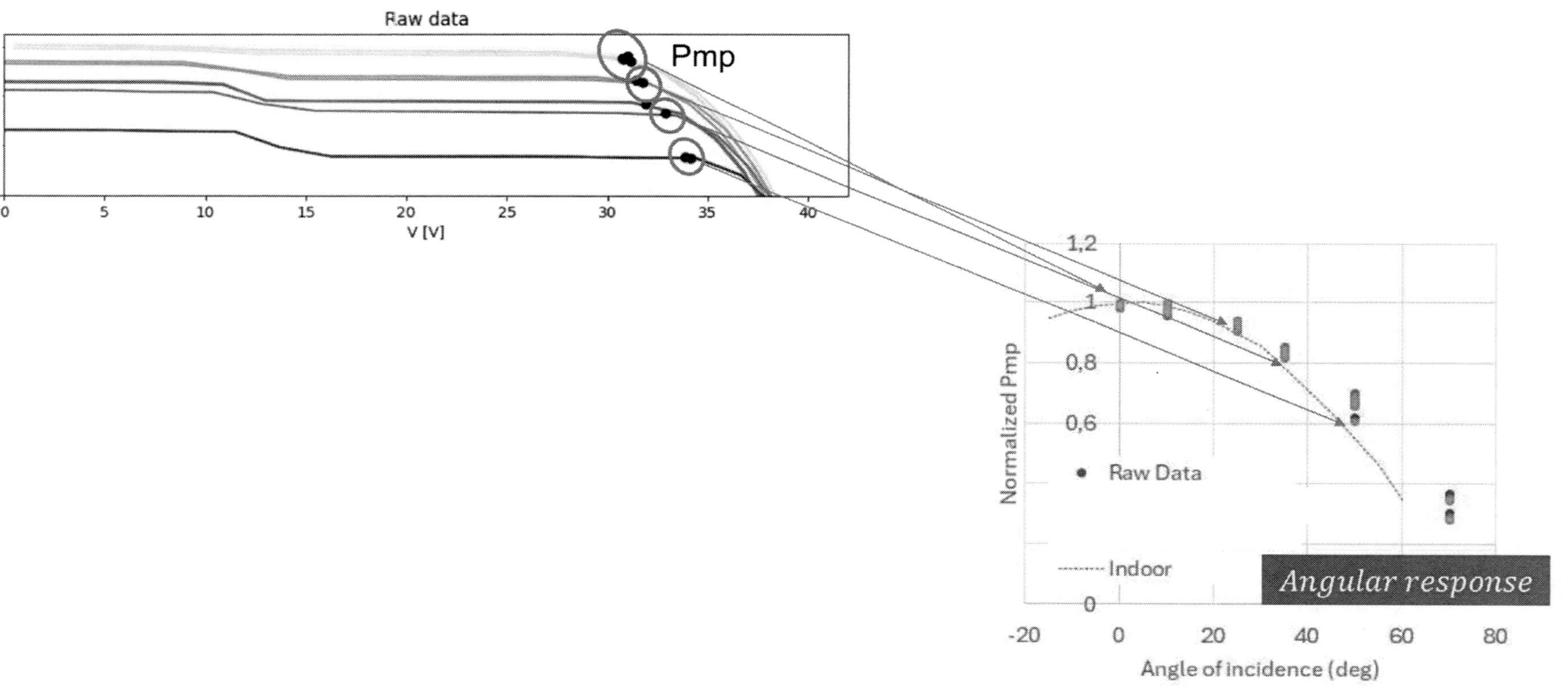

020209-017

Outdoor angular response: vertical sweep

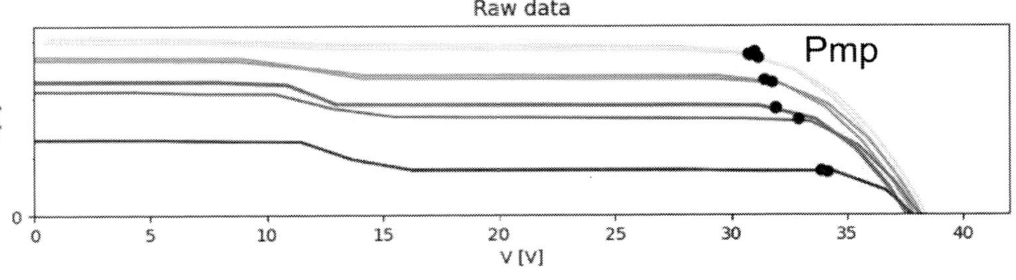

Temperature correction

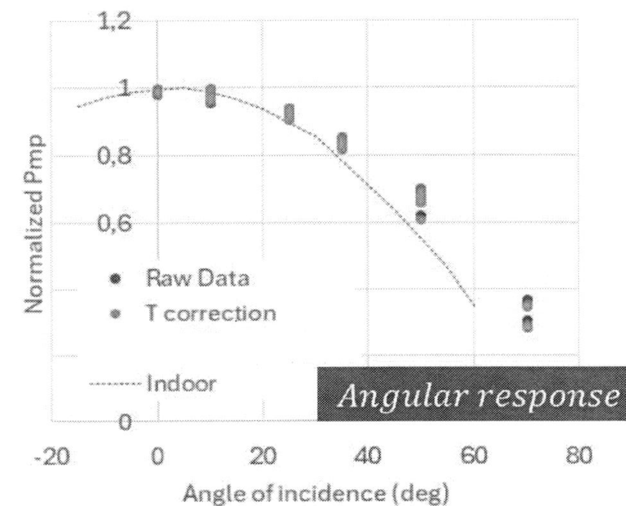

020209-018

Outdoor angular response: vertical sweep

INSTITUTO
DE ENERGÍA
SOLAR

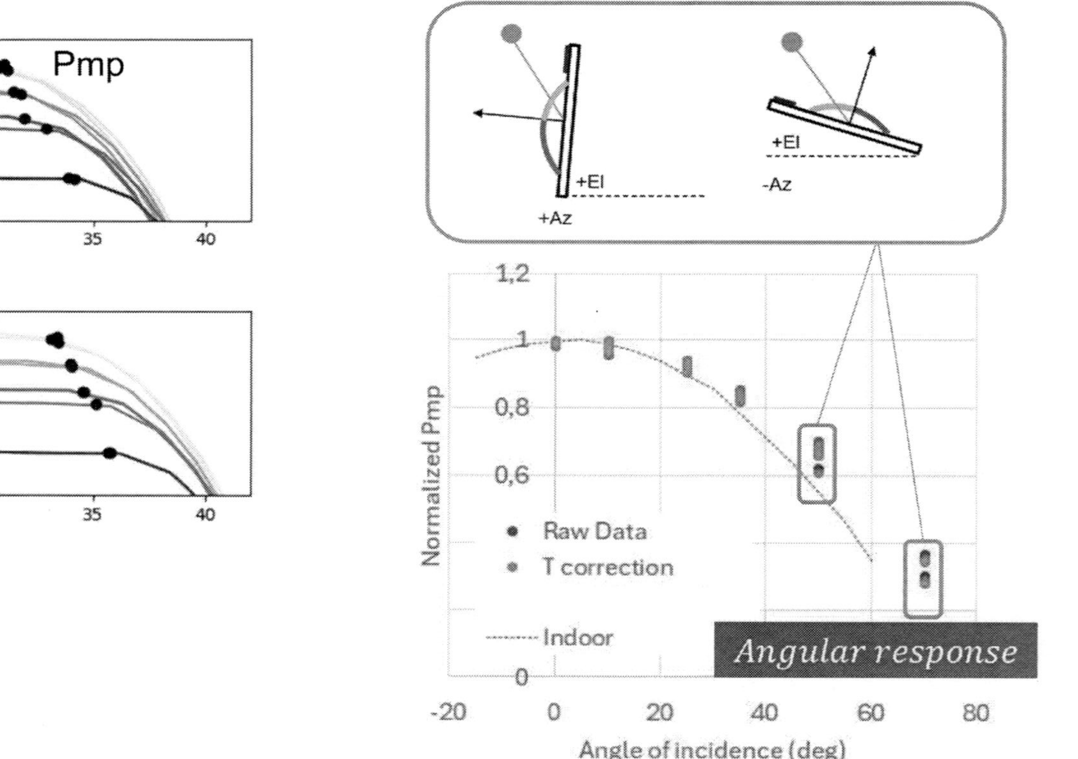

020209-019

Outdoor angular response: vertical sweep

INSTITUTO DE ENERGÍA SOLAR

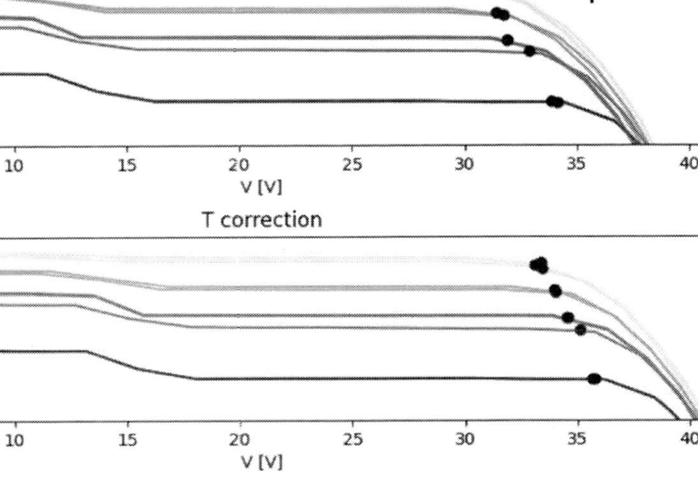

Diffuse on POA is discounted
Irradiance is normalized to 1000W/m²

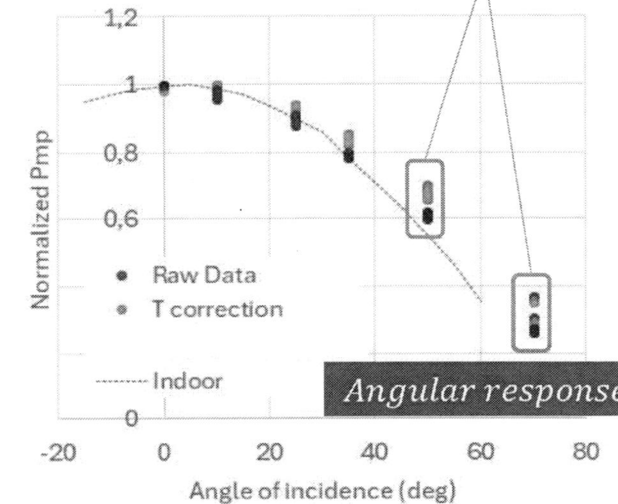

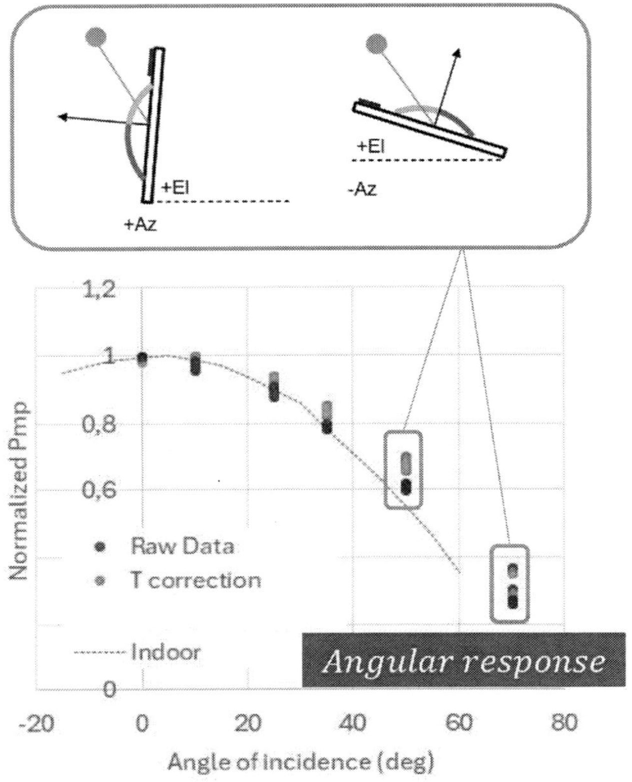

Outdoor angular response: vertical sweep

INSTITUTO
DE ENERGÍA
SOLAR

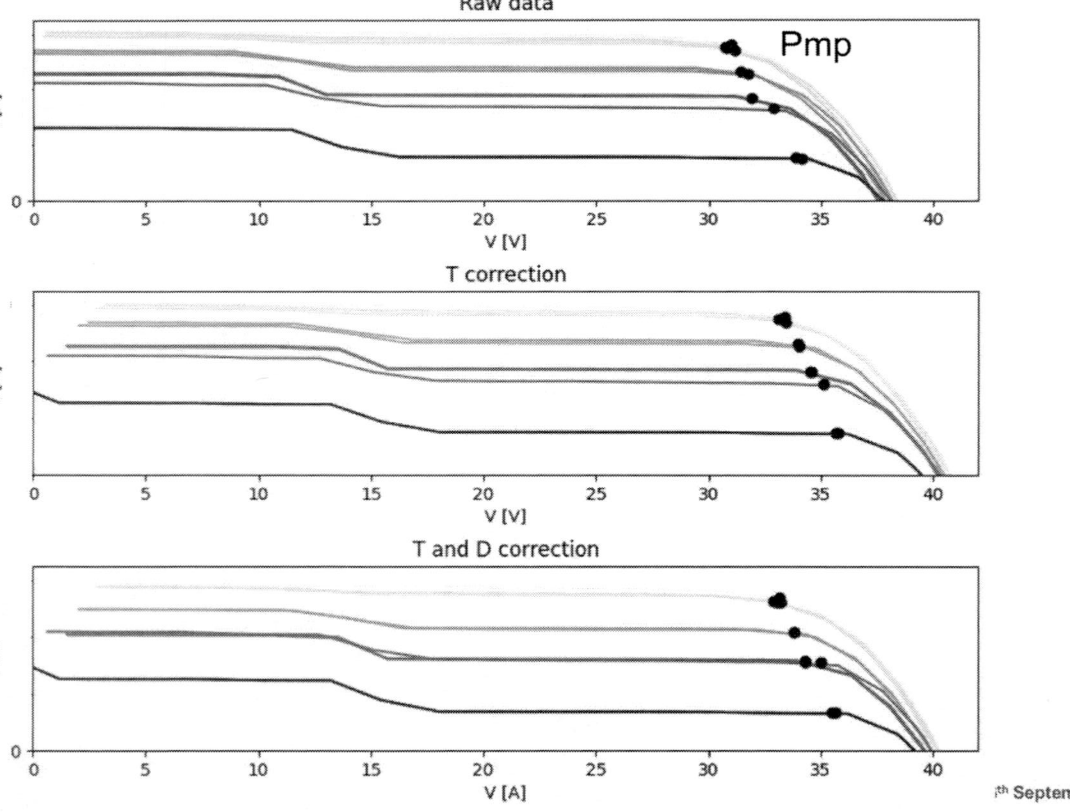

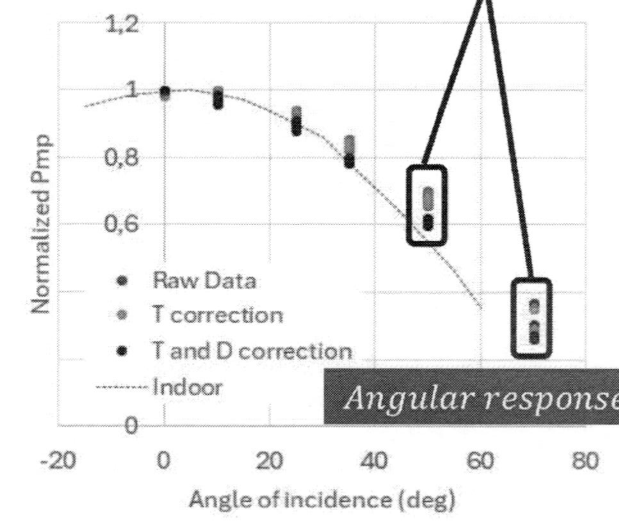

020209-021

Outdoor angular response: vertical sweep

- Possible effect of reflected irradiance:

  – Module more affected by diffuse reflected than reference sensor

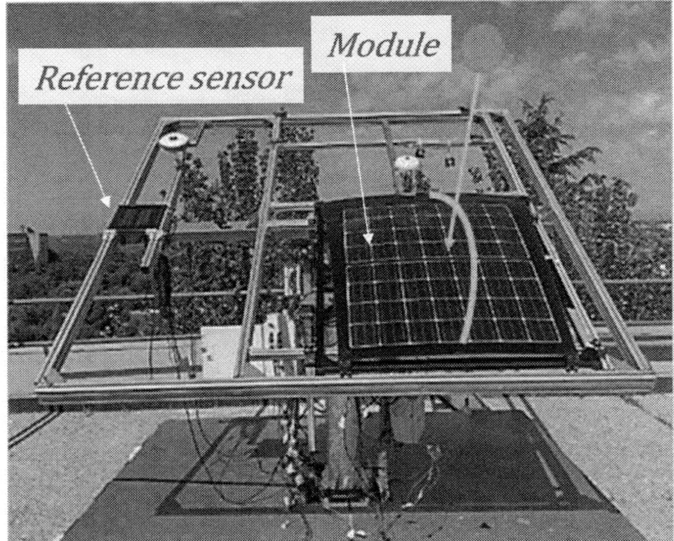

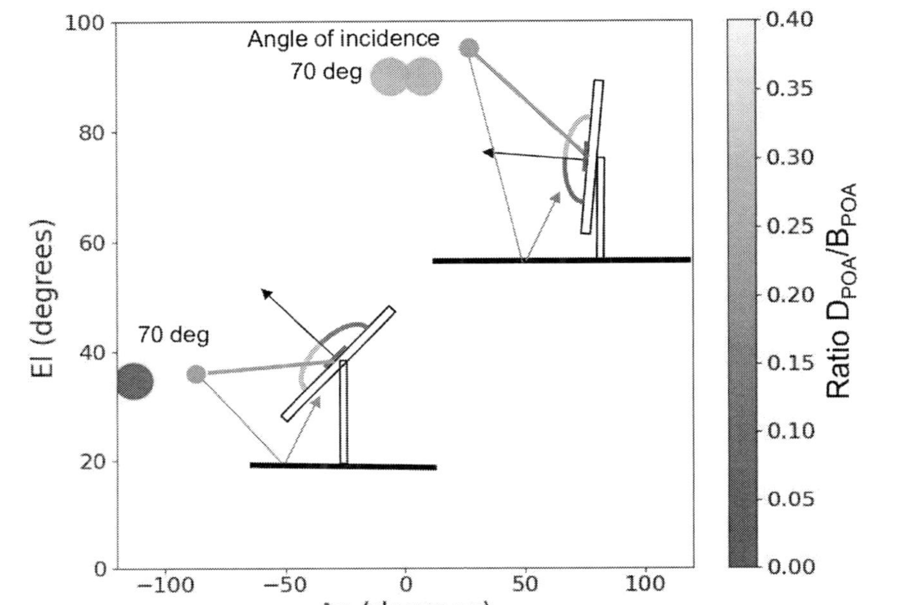

020209-022

Outdoor angular response: vertical sweep

- Possible effect of reflected irradiance:

  - Module more affected by diffuse reflected than reference sensor

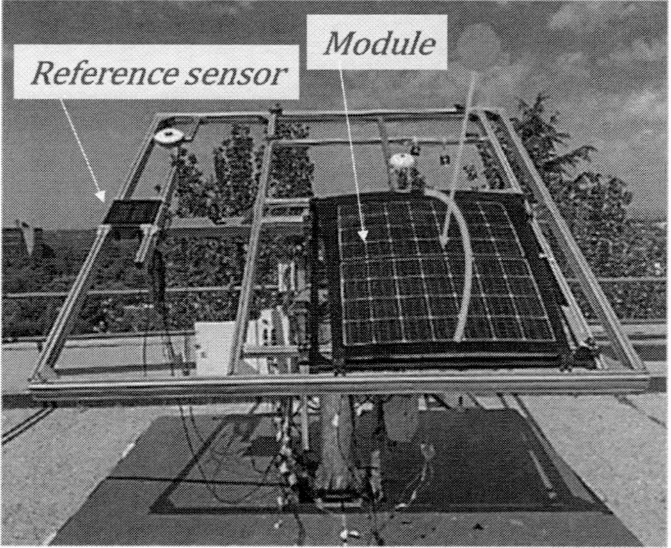

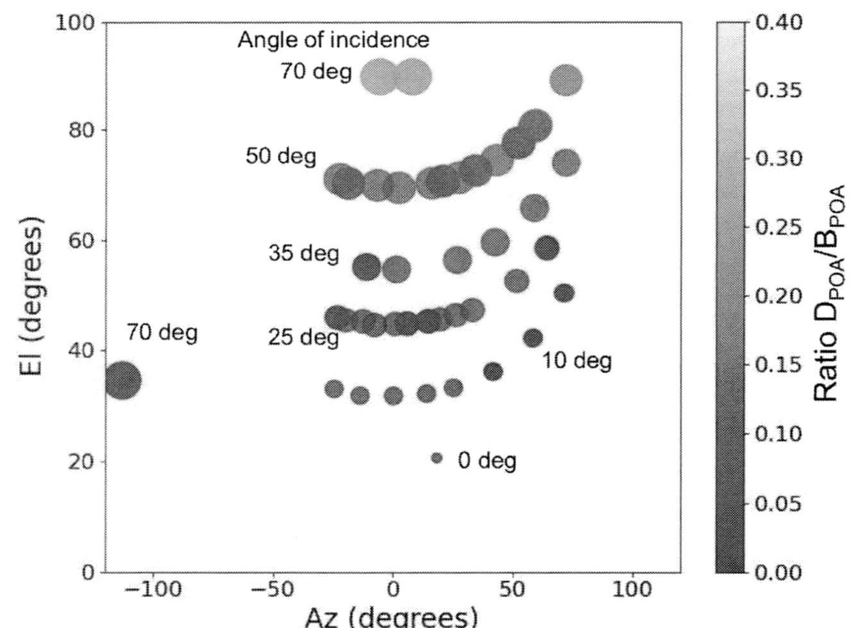

Results: Angular response (vertical sweep)

INSTITUTO
DE ENERGÍA
SOLAR

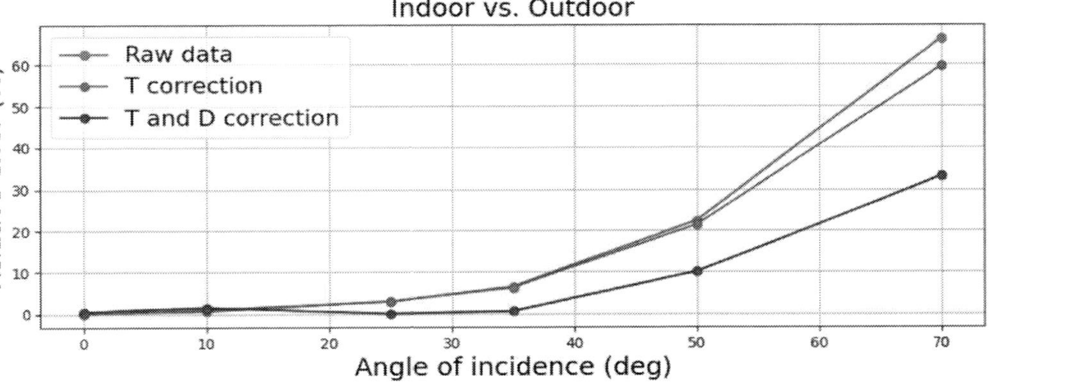

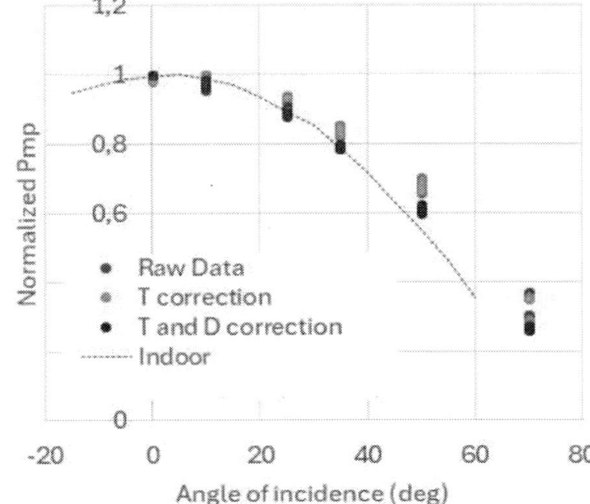

- Additional correction for reflected irradiance is needed

Results: Angular response (vertical sweep)

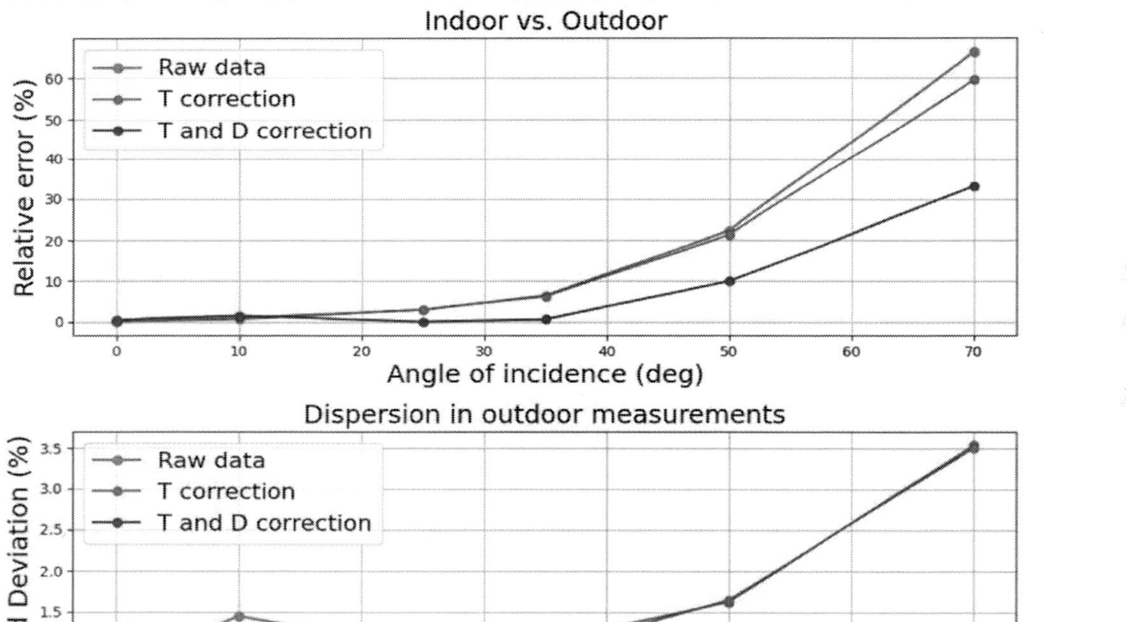

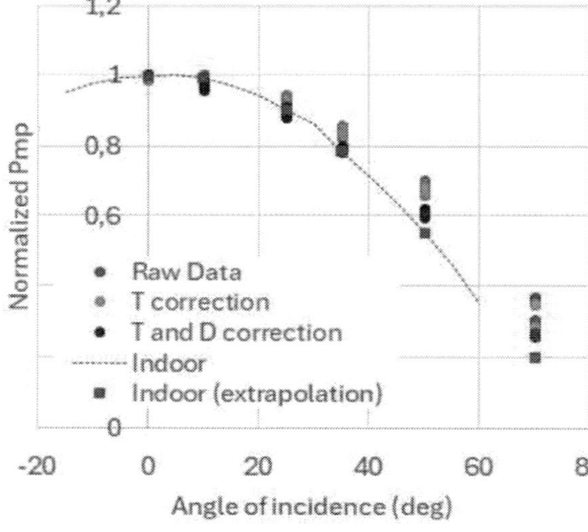

- Measurement dispersion is highly reduced with T and D correction

Conclusions

- A collimated-light solar simulator is effective for VIPV characterization and offers several advantages, both for IV curve at STC and angular response tests:
  - It is less time-consuming.
  - No temperature or diffuse corrections are required.

- Matching results from indoor and outdoor IV curve STC characterization (<1% difference).

- Regarding outdoor angular response characterization:
  - **Not all α and β** combinations can be achieved at a certain **moment of the year**. This can be solved rotating the module.
  - Vertical sweeps ($\beta = 0°$) allow higher angles of incidence, but with **high reflections** on pronounced **tracker elevations**.

- To minimize error and dispersion:
  - Temperature correction **slightly** reduces measurement **dispersion** but does not affect **error**.
  - Diffuse correction affects both **error** and **dispersion**, due to varying levels of diffuse irradiance on the module at different angles.

020209-026

Thank you for your attention

INSTITUTO
DE ENERGÍA
SOLAR

Innovation in photovoltaics since 1979

We gratefully acknowledge the DETEC-PV project, Grant PID2021-128853OB-I00, funded by MCIN/AEI/10.13039/501100011033 and "ERDF A way of making Europe"

The authors express sincere thanks to JEMA and JET program for sponsoring the activities, entrusted by METI (Japan) and carried out under the umbrella of the IEC TC82/PT600 group devoted to Vehicle Integrated Photovoltaic Systems

INSTITUTO
DE ENERGÍA
SOLAR
Innovation in photovoltaics since 1979

ESTIMATING THE ENERGY YIELD OF BIFACIAL PHOTOVOLTAICS WITH THE JRC'S PHOTOVOLTAIC GEOGRAPHIC INFORMATION SYSTEM

N. Taylor[1], T. Lyubenova[1], L. Malarkannan[2], N. Alexandris[1], A. Falangas[3], R. Kenny[1], E.D. Dunlop[1], B. Mihaylov[1]
1) European Commission Joint Research Centre, Ispra, Italy
2) National Physical Laboratory, Teddington, UK
3) TRASIS International, Belgium

ABSTRACT: The European Commission's Joint Research Centre is upgrading its Photovoltaic Geographic Information System (PVGIS) to include energy yield from bifacial photovoltaics. The aim is to provide a reliable method that is suitable for online information systems designed to provide quick and reliable estimates on PV performance, also for non-expert users and with limited data input requirements. A simplified bifacial PV model has been adapted for this purpose. The initial validation with data from south facing tilted and from east-west vertical systems at JRC's European Solar Test Installation in Ispra, Italy, gave encouraging results for the irradiance levels at the rear of the modules (tilted and vertical systems) and for module temperature. The model is implemented in the PVGIS 6 software update, currently under development. The validation should be extended in future, with suitable data from other locations.
Keywords: photovoltaics, bifacial, energy yield

1 INTRODUCTION

As bifacial PV modules become the norm in many applications, it is increasingly important that online tools for energy yield estimates adapt to take account of potential performance gains. The Joint Research Centre's Photovoltaic Geographical Information System (PVGIS) has provided a free web-based service for over 20 years, with on-the-fly calculation power output from hourly values of historic solar radiation and other environmental variables for the requested location and system configuration [1]. The paper describes the extension of this capability in the new PVGIS 6 Python version to cover power generation bifacial PV modules, considering two configurations: a) open-rack systems, typically equator facing with tilted panels, installed either on flat roofs or on open ground, and b) vertical- mounted systems, typically with east-west orientation.

Bifacial PV modules have significant market share and the price difference to monofacial modules has reduced considerably. Depending on the installation, bifacial modules can produce up to 20% more energy in side-by-side comparisons than equivalent monofacial modules. For the bifacial PV technology, the nominal module peak power is the same as for the monofacial module, since it refers only to front-side illumination. In operation, such modules can benefit from any rear-side illumination available, but there is a lack of standardised methods for estimating the impact on annual energy yield.

There is no option for bifacial modules in the current version of PVGIS tool. For equator-facing tilted systems users can input the power value for Bifacial Nameplate Irradiance (BNPI). This can also be estimated from the front side peak power P_STC value and the power bifaciality coefficient, φ as: P_BNPI = P_STC * (1 + φ * 0.135). For vertical installations, users have the option to treat each side of the bifacial module as an independent monofacial device and manually sum of the contribution from each side (back-to-back approach), with the bifaciality factor applied directly to the estimated power output from the side with lower average yearly in-plane irradiation. A previous JRC study [2] compared these simplified approaches, as well as that proposed by the EU's Horizon 2020 PV-Enerate project [3] for estimating effective irradiance on bifacial modules. The results varied in a range of approximately 10% with the back-to-back

approach between the other two. However, the back-to-back cannot be used for tilted systems. This suggests a more detailed approach is required, that users could access via a bifacial PV option in PVGIS.

2 METHODOLOGY

2.1 Bifacial Irradiance

In PVGIS the instantaneous power output is a function of in-plane irradiance and module temperature [4]:

$$P(G', T') = G'(P_{STC,m} + k_1 \ln(G') + k_2 \ln(G')^2 + k_3 T' + k_4 T' \ln(G') + k_5 T' ln(G')^2 + k_6 T'^2) \quad (1)$$

where the normalised in-plane irradiance G' is given by: $G' = \frac{G}{G_{STC}}$ and the module temperature difference T' is given by: $T' = T_{mod} - T_{STC}$. The input irradiance data in the form of two parameters derived from hourly satellite images: SIS = global horizontal irradiance and SID = direct horizontal irradiance. These are used to determine a total in-plane irradiance value on the front surface, from the sum of direct, diffuse and reflected components [5]. For calculating the rear-side irradiance for bifacial modules, the following requirements were set:

- Exploit existing validated approaches
- Simple «infinite shed» geometric model with a default geometry: module height (1 m) and length (2 m)
- Single row i.e. no inter-row shading effects
- Non-uniformity or mismatch effects not considered
- Fast calculation, to support the PVGIS on-the-fly computational approach

On this basis we selected the model proposed by Vogt et al [6]. Their application was for studying energy rating of bifacial modules and only considered an equator-facing tilted system. The approach was therefore extended to cover all orientations and tilts (as well as tracking in the future). Also in our implementation, the transposition of the diffuse light component to the plane of interest is done using the Muneer model instead of the Perez model, since the former is already used in the PVGIS calculations for monofacial modules. The whole process is implemented in Python as a module in the new PVGIS 6 code.

Figure 1 shows a sample calculation of monthly irradiation for an East-West vertical system at the Ispra, Italy location in 2021 and includes results obtained using the NREL view factor algorithm [7] as well as the approach available from PVLIB [8].

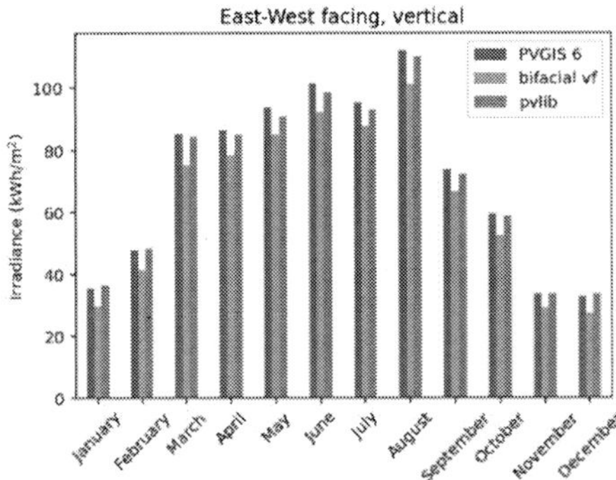

Figure 1: Monthly irradiation estimates for an east-west facing, vertical bifacial PV system in Ispra, Italy, for 2021.

2.2 Bifacial Energy Yield

The PVGIS energy yield estimation process is similar to that used for energy rating in IEC61853 part 3. In applying this to bifacial modules, several aspects need to be considered, as shown in Table 1. Some of the resulting assumptions can be directly supported by JRC experimental data, as shown in Figures 2 and 3.

Table 1: Key aspects in the PVGIS energy yield calculation and the assumptions for bifacial modules

Aspect	PVGIS6 Approach
Reflectance	Use same a_r value front and back
Spectral correction to irradiance	Spectral content: same front & back Spectral response: same front & back
Module operating temperature	Based on front irradiance, ambient T and wind speed (Faiman equation)
Bifaciality ratio	Same for all irradiance and temperature values
Power model	Generic PVGIS model for «crystalline silicon» (calibrated on monofacial modules [9])

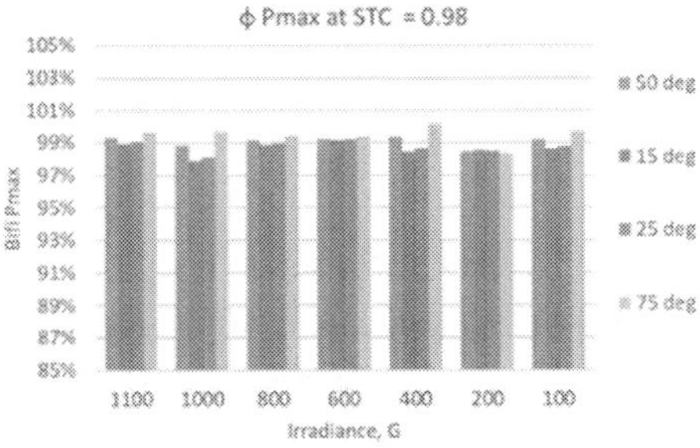

Figure 2: Measured bifaciality ratio values over a broad range of irradiance and temperature values for a PERC module. The variations are minimal.

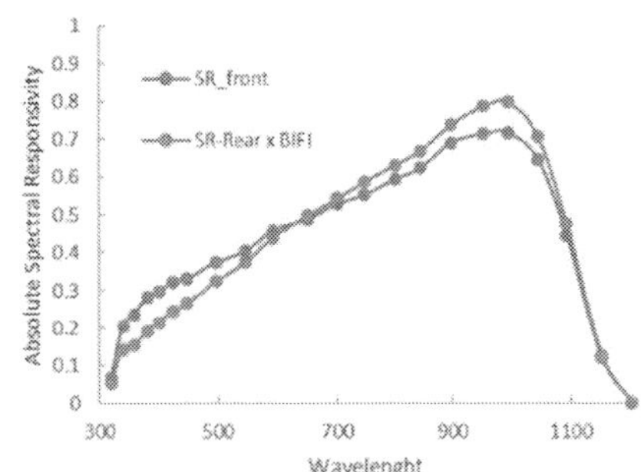

Figure 3: Measured spectral response curves for a PERC module with 0.7 bifaciality ratio, showing good correspondence between the two sides (when corrected for the bifaciality effect).

3. RESULTS

3.1 Irradiance

We compare the PVGIS model estimates with experimental data from the JRC's European Solar Test Installation (ESTI), in particular, the results from long-term monitoring of p-PERC-type bifacial modules with modest bifaciality (0.7) and including both equator-facing, tilted and vertically mounted modules [10]. The albedo is approximately 0.2. An important feature of this system is that it is equipped with over 30 irradiance sensors to monitor both front and rear irradiance values, while temperature measurements are also available for one module in each of the south-facing tilted and the vertical systems.

These system data are complemented by measurements of the global horizontal and beam irradiance from the ESTI meteo tower system. For this validation exercise, the new PVGIS 6 model uses these later measurements as input for the calculation of the in-plane irradiation at the front and rear sides of the system. NB the online version of PVGIS uses either satellite or reanalysis estimates of the horizontal global and beam irradiance as inputs.

Figures 4 and 5 compare the calculated rear side irradiance values with those measured (taking an average of the values form the central sensors, avoiding system edge effects) on a clear summer day (14.8.2021) for the south tilted and the east-west vertical system respectively. For the south-tilted case, the measured value peaks close to 100 W/m^2 (for reference, the corresponding front side irradiance is approximately 800W/m^2). The model overestimates the noon value by approximately 15 W/m^2. For the vertical system there is good agreement both in the morning (when west side in shade and in the afternoon (with west side in direct sunlight).

Figures 6 and 7 show the same comparison for the monthly cumulative values over the full year. For the south-facing tilted system, the model gives higher values in all months, and particularly in the summer. For the whole year, this difference is +10.8%. In the case of the east-west vertical system, the modelled monthly values are slightly below those measured, with negligible differences in the winter months but higher in the summer. The total annual difference is -6.7%.

3.2 Module temperature

The module temperature measurements are compared to values from the PVGIS model (the Faiman equation):

$$T_{mod} = T_{amb} + \frac{G}{u_0 + u_1 * ws}$$

where T_{amb} is ambient temperature, G is the irradiance on the front side, ws is the wind speed, and u_0, u_1 are coefficients for ground-mounted open rack systems. For this validation the ambient temperature is the measured value on site, whereas the online PVGIS tool uses the T_{2m} value from the ERA5 reanalysis data set.

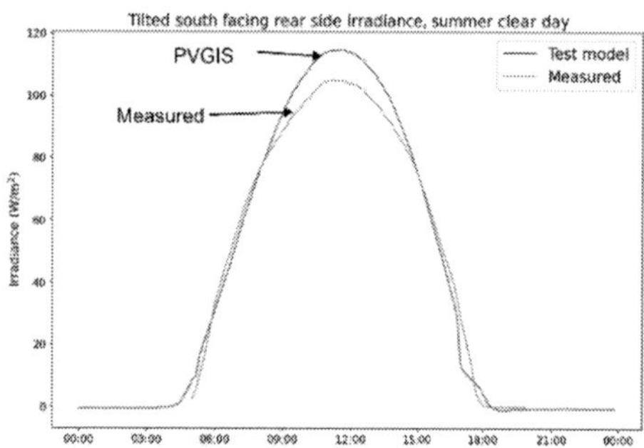

Figure 4: PVGIS6 model and measured irradiance values for the rear side of a south-facing system on a clear day (Ispra, 14.8.2021)

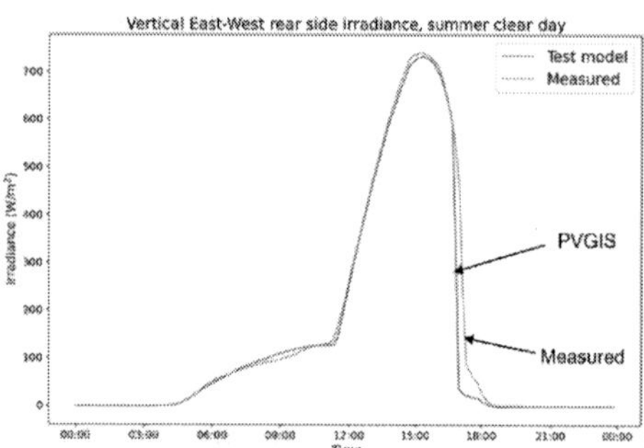

Figure 5: PVGIS6 model and measured irradiance values for the rear (west) side of a vertical system on a clear day (Ispra, 14.8.2021)

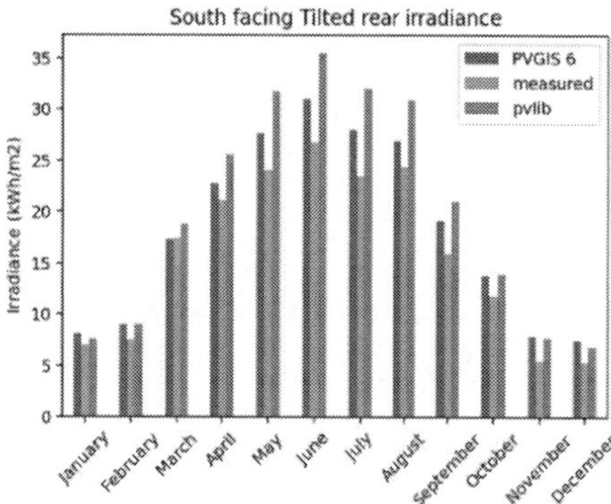

Figure 6: Cumulative month irradiance from the PVGIS6 model and measured values for the rear side of a south-facing system (Ispra, 2021)

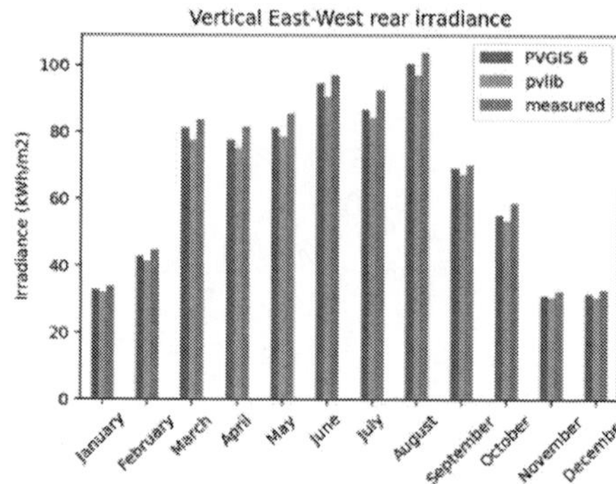

Figure 7: Cumulative month irradiance from the PVGIS6 model and measured values for the rear (west) side of a vertical system (Ispra, 2021)

Figures 8 and 9 compare the calculated and measured values for the same clear summer day (14.8.2021) mentioned above, for the south tilted and the east-west vertical system respectively. Two calculated values are shown: one using the front side irradiance for G and the other with the summed front and rear values for G. For the south-facing tilted system the front-side irradiance approach is closer to the observed values. For the vertical system, this approach leads to underestimates in the afternoon, when the rear side receives direct sunlight. This suggests that it is more appropriate to calculate the module temperature based on the irradiance on the sun-facing side.

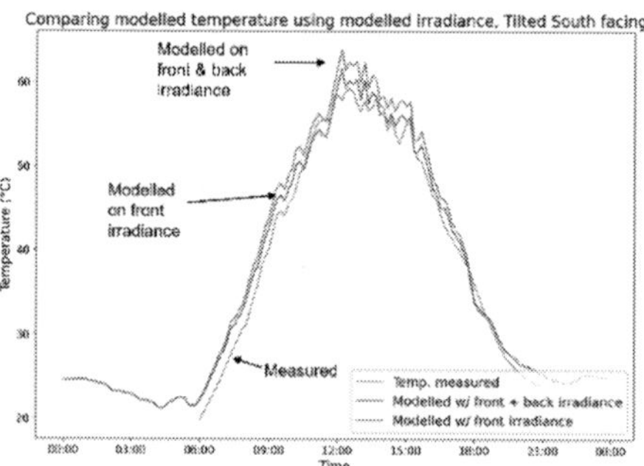

Figure 8: Modelled and measured temperatures for the south-facing tilted system (clear day, Ispra, 14.8.2021)

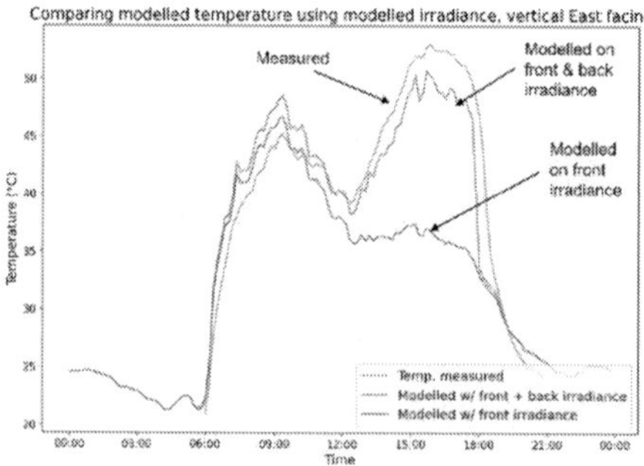

Figure 9: PVGIS6 model and measured temperatures for the vertical system on a clear day (Ispra, 14.8.2021)

3.3 Energy Yield

The final analysis step considers the predicted energy yield ratio i.e. the ratio of the annual energy yield of a south-facing tilted and east-west vertical systems to that of a monofacial south-facing titled system, as a function of bifaciality factor. In the case of the south facing tilted system (Figure 10), for the 0.2 albedo level, the PVGIS bifacial model predicts a modest bifacial yield gain, slightly greater than that which would be predicted using the monofacial model with a nominal module power corresponding to the bifacial nameplate irradiance instead of P_{STC}. However, the bifacial model captures the effect of increased albedo seen in the experimental data, whereas the bifacial nameplate power approach is insensitive to albedo.

The experimental data for the PERC modules with 70% bifaciality and 0.2 albedo indicate a gain of 16%, higher than that estimated by the PVGIS model. For the high albedo case (0.4), the model estimates are closer to the observed gains: bifaciality values of 67-68% (p-PERC glass-glass) result in a gain of around 25%, while the bifaciality of 98% (n-PERC glass-glass) results in an increased performance of 31.2% in comparison to the monofacial device (c-Si).

For the east-west vertical system (Figure 11), the proposed PVGIS bifacial model predicts a higher bifacial yield ratio than the "back-to-back" approach with 2 monofacial modules.

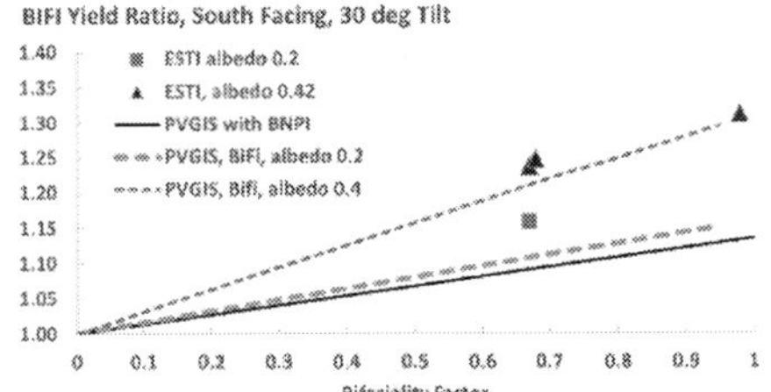

Figure 10: The effect of the module bifaciality and albedo on the bifacial yield ratio for a south-facing tilted system in Ispra, Italy. The high albedo data refers to the experimental work reported in [10].

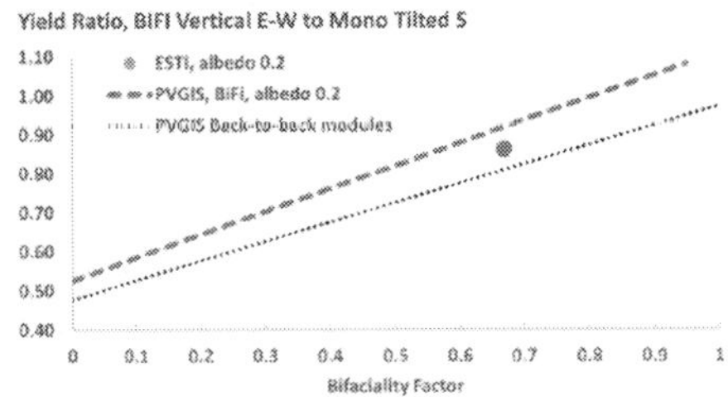

Figure 11: The effect of the module bifaciality on the bifacial yield ratio for an east-west vertical system in Ispra, Italy.

4   CONCLUSIONS

- A simple bifacial PV model has been adapted for the upcoming PVGIS6 software; intended to capture key aspects of bifacial yield gains for small systems designs likely to be of interest for PVGIS users
- An initial validation with data from JRC's European Solar Test Installation gave encouraging results for the irradiance levels at the rear of the modules (tilted and vertical systems) and for module temperature
- On this basis JRC will implement the modified Vogt bifacial model in PVGIS 6, with the option to include alternatives in future
- Extended validation is essential, both with the Ispra data and with data from other locations and systems with suitable monitoring instrumentation.

5. ACKNOWLEDGEMENTS

The authors gratefully acknowledge the collaboration between the European Commission Joint Research Centre and the National Physical Laboratory, UK, which facilitated the study visit of LM to the JRC's Ispra site. Our thanks also to the colleagues of the European Solar Test Installation for their support to the outdoor field measurements and to Diego Pavanello for the calibration of the sensors used in the bifacial PV test stand.

6. DISCLAIMER

The contents of this paper do not necessarily reflect the position or opinion of the European Commission. Neither the European Commission nor any person acting on behalf of the Commission is responsible for the use that might be made of this publication

4   REFERENCES

[1] Photovoltaic Geographical Information System (PVGIS) online tool https://joint-research-centre.ec.europa.eu/photovoltaic-geographical-information-system-pvgis_en

[2] Kakoulaki, G. et al, European transport infrastructure as a solar photovoltaic energy hub, Renewable and Sustainable Energy Reviews, Volume 196, 2024.

[3] Kenny, R. et al, Proposal For The Extension Of The Energy Rating Standard Series IEC 61853 To Bifacial Modules, Proc. 8th World Conference on Photovoltaic Energy Conversion, 2022

[4] Huld, T. et al., "A power-rating model for crystalline silicon PV modules," Sol. Energy Mater. Sol. Cells, vol. 95, no. 12, pp. 3359–3369, 2011

[5] Suri, M. and Hofierka, J. (2004) A New GIS-Based Solar Radiation Model and Its Application to Photovoltaic Assessments. Transactions in GIS, 8, 175-190.

[6] Vogt, M. R. et al, 2023, Developing an energy rating for bifacial photovoltaic modules. Progress in Photovoltaics, 31(12), 1466-1477.

[7] Marion. B. et al, "A Practical Irradiance Model for Bifacial PV Modules".2017 IEEE 44th Photovoltaic Specialists Conference (PVSC), 2017, pp. 1537-1543. doi: 10.1109/PVSC.2017.8366263

[8] PVLIB Bifacial modeling — pvlib python 0.11.2 documentation

[9] Chatzipanagi, A. et al, An Updated Simplified Energy Yield Model for Recent Photovoltaic Module Technologies, Progress In Photovoltaics: Research And Applications, 33, 8, 2025, p. 905-917, 2025

[10] Gracia-Amillo, A. et al, Energy yield analysis of bifacial PV modules: different technologies and configurations, Proc EU PVSEC 2019

AN UPDATE ON ENERGY RATING AMENDMENTS – INTEGRATION OF BIFACIAL MODULES

Stefan Riechelman[1], Hendrik Sträter[1], Ana María Gracia-Amillo[2], Sophie Pelland[3], Anton Driesse[4]

[1]Physikalisch-Technische Bundesanstalt (PTB), Braunschweig, Germany
[2]National Renewable Energy Center (CENER), Pamplona, Spain
[3]Natural Resources Canada (CanmetENERGY), Varennes, Canada
[4]PV Performance Labs, Freiburg, Germany
stefan.riechelmann@ptb.de[1], hendrik.straeter@ptb.de[1], agracia@cener.com[2], sophie.pelland@NRCan-RNCan.gc.ca[3],
anton.driesse@pvperformancelabs.com[4]

ABSTRACT: This work describes the ongoing IEC TC82 WG2's revision of IEC 61853 Photovoltaic (PV) module performance testing and energy rating Parts 1, 3 and 4, with a focus on extending the energy rating standard to bifacial photovoltaic modules. A joint project team has updated the formulae of Part 3 to include backside irradiance and developed preliminary meteorological datasets for Part 4 to support different installation configurations. The clarity of the formulas and instructions has also been improved. These improvements will enable a more accurate and comprehensive energy rating for PV modules. A set of six different bifacial PV modules with different cell technologies and different technical layouts were characterized according to IEC 61853-1 and IEC 61853-2 to verify the extended energy rating series. E present the Climate-Specific Energy Rating (CSER) values calculated using these modules' data and the updated formulas.

Keywords: Energy Rating, Modelling, Testing, Standards

1 INTRODUCTION

The IEC 61853 standard series Photovoltaic (PV) module performance testing and energy rating describe how to perform energy rating calculations to provide a more realistic energy-based rating of PV modules based on predefined generic meteorological data for different climate zones. The series consists of four parts:

IEC 61853-1 (2011) [1] – Measurement of the PV module power matrix for combinations of different temperature and irradiance conditions.

IEC 61853-2 (2016) [2] – Measurement of the PV module spectral responsivity (SR), angular incidence effect (IAM) and thermal coefficients for the estimation of the module's operating temperature.

IEC 61853-3 (2018) [3] – Mathematical formulation of the energy rating, describes how to calculate energy yield and Climate-Specific Energy Rating CSER based on the input data retrieved in the other three parts.

IEC 61853-4 (2018) [4] – Meteorological datasets containing hourly data over one year of six different climate zones.

The standard series has been developed since 1995 and was completed in 2018 [5]. At that time, bifacial modules had a negligible market share, so the developed methods did not cover this type of modules. Today, the share of bifacial modules is about 64 % of all modules sold [6], so the standard series needs to be updated to reflect the characteristics of bifacial PV modules.

In this study, the calculation method in Part 3 of the standard is revised by introducing a rear irradiance component to allow the rating of bifacial modules considering the contribution to the module's performance of the rear side. This updated formula considers the additional irradiance received at the rear of the module. In addition, all necessary intermediate steps to estimate the operating module temperature and the effective irradiance are now defined to take into consideration both sides of the module. In addition to the module mounting configuration assumed in the current standard (20° tilt angle, facing the equator and no rear-side irradiance), three additional settings have been defined in the proposed revision to

61853-3 to reflect the wider use of bifacial solar modules.

In the proposed revision to Part 4 of the standard, for each reference climate data set direct, diffuse and ground-reflected irradiance has been calculated for both sides of the bifacial module for the four different module mounting configurations, needed as input for Part 3.

Part 1 is the oldest part of the series; a lot of references were outdated and have been fixed. Also, the power matrix now is extrapolated already in this part of the series to obtain a regular grid (currently, this is performed in Part 3), to provide the lab performing power matrix measurements the choice to either measure or extrapolate those values of the matrix that were not mandatory before.

2 METHODOLOGY

2.1 Additional module mounting configurations
Table 1: Module mounting configurations according to 61853-3 ED2

	Setting 1	Setting 2	Setting 3	Setting 4
Description	closed rack	open rack	vertical	tracking
Inclination angle β_i	20°	20°	90°	variable
Orientation	Equator	Equator	front to East, rear to West	East/West

The new version of the Energy Rating Standard series must ensure comparability between monofacial and bifacial modules without favoring or discriminating against either type of module. PV modules are currently used in various mounting configurations where the two types of PV modules perform considerably differently. This is considered by introducing different module orientations and inclinations in the form of four new settings as proposed in revision of the standard (see Table 1):

Setting 1 is an equator-facing installation, resembling situations where nearly no irradiance reaches the module from the rear, which is the case for most rooftop-mounted systems. This type of system is therefore abbreviated as closed rack system.

Setting 2 resembles Setting 1, but with rear-side irradiance reaching the module, which is typically the case for ground-mounted installations. This kind of system is therefore called an open rack installation.

Setting 3 is an east-west oriented vertical installation, which is common for agricultural PV, fences or noise barriers.

Setting 4 describes an east-west-oriented single-axis horizontal tracking situation (axis in the direction north-south).

While monofacial and bifacial PV devices will perform similar in rooftop applications due to their severe self-shading, in all other three settings bifacial devices will outperform monofacial devices due to the output power gain from their rear side.

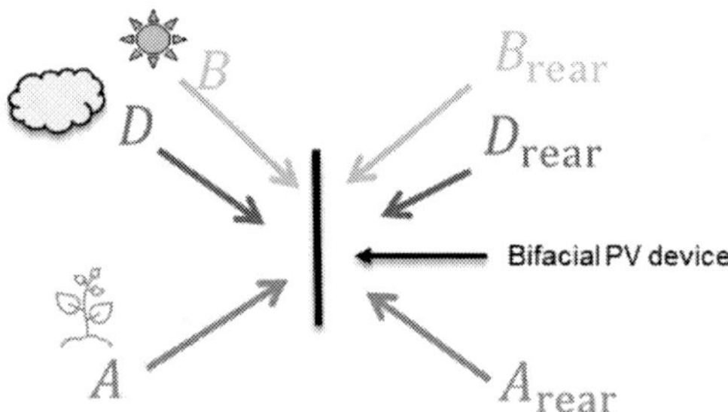

Figure 1: The total irradiance received by a bifacial PV module is given by front- and rear-side direct, diffuse and ground-reflected irradiance.

2.2 Implementing bifacial formulas

The current energy rating standard series do neither consider ground-reflected nor rear-side irradiance. In case of bifacial modules, both front- and rear-side irradiance is crucial for calculating the module power output (see Figure 1). By introducing ground-reflecting irradiance, a formula for angle of incidence (AOI) correction needs to be introduced analogous to the existing ones for direct and diffuse irradiance from [7]:

$$A_{AOI,j} = A_j \cdot \left\{ 1 - exp \left[-\frac{1}{a_r} \left(\frac{4}{3\pi} \left(sin\,\beta_j + \frac{\beta_j - sin\,\beta_j}{1 - cos\,\beta_j} \right) + \right. \right. \right.$$
$$\left. \left. \left. (0.5 a_r - 0.154) \left(sin\,\beta_j + \frac{\beta_j - sin\,\beta_j}{1 - cos\,\beta_j} \right)^2 \right) \right] \right\}$$

where
A_j is the uncorrected in-plane ground-reflected irradiance at hour j,
θ_j is the angle between sun and the normal to the module surface in units of radians at hour j,
β_j is the inclination angle of the module relative to horizontal in units of radians at hour j (constant for Settings 1-3) and
a_r is a fitting parameter provided by the analysis of the angle of incidence measurements, as carried out in IEC 61853-2.

The angle of incidence-corrected broadband in-plane global irradiance $G_{AOI,j}$ for the front side of the module is now calculated as:

$$G_{AOI,j} = B_{AOI,j} + D_{AOI,j} + A_{AOI,j}$$

where
$B_{AOI,j}$ is the angle of incidence (AOI)-corrected direct irradiance,
$D_{AOI,j}$ is the AOI-corrected diffuse irradiance and
$A_{AOI,j}$ is the AOI-corrected ground-reflected irradiance.

Spectral correction of $G_{AOI,j}$ is done as described in [8] to derive the spectrally and angle of incidence-corrected global broadband in-plane irradiance at hour j $G_{SC,AOI,j}$.

To describe the gain of bifacial modules due to rear-side illumination, the concept of equivalent irradiance, G_e, has been introduced according to [9]:

$$G_{e,j} = G_{SC,AOI,j} + \varphi_{P_{max}} \cdot G_{SC,AOI,rear,j}$$

where
$\varphi_{P_{max}}$ is the maximum power bifaciality of the PV module after IEC 60904-1-2,
$G_{SC,AOI,j}$ is the front-side spectrally and angle of incidence-corrected global broadband in-plane irradiance at hour j and
$G_{SC,AOI,rear,j}$ is the rear-side spectrally and angle of incidence-corrected global broadband in-plane irradiance at hour j.

$G_{SC,AOI,rear,j}$ is calculated analogous to $G_{SC,AOI,j}$ by applying AOI and spectral correction procedures to all irradiance values reaching the rear side of a PV module. In case of monofacial modules, $G_{SC,AOI,rear,j}$ is assumed to be 0 for the sake of simplicity. This is also the case for the rear side of Setting 1.

The maximum power bifaciality $\varphi_{P_{max}}$ is used because energy rating is about power losses. Inhomogeneous shading on the rear-side of a PV module due to junction boxes or module frames lead to a power loss and thus a drop in $\varphi_{P_{max}}$. Short circuit bifaciality $\varphi_{I_{sc}}$ is not affected, since $\varphi_{I_{sc}}$ is only affected if all strings of a PV module are shaded to the same extent.

The module temperature is calculated according to:

$$T_{mod,j} = T_{amb,j} + \frac{G_{AOI,j} + G_{AOI,rear,j}}{u_0 + u_1 v_j}$$

$T_{amb,j}$ is the ambient temperature at hour j, given by IEC 61853-4,
v_j is the wind speed at the height of the module at hour j, given by IEC 61853-4,
$G_{AOI,j}$ is the angle of incidence-corrected front-side global broadband in-plane irradiance at hour j,
$G_{AOI,rear,j}$ is the angle of incidence-corrected rear-side global broadband in-plane irradiance at hour j, calculated analogous to $G_{AOI,j}$,
u_0 and u_1 are the module thermal coefficients measured as described in IEC 61853-2, representing the influence of irradiance and the impact of wind speed on module temperature, respectively.

Since $G_{AOI,rear,j}$ is 0 for monofacial modules, the temperature of bifacial PV modules is assumed to be slightly higher due to absorbing more rear-side irradiance. A simplified approach is assumed when the rear-side of monofacial PV modules are considered usually white, while bifacial PV modules absorb rear-side irradiance instead of reflecting it.

2.3 Improving inter- and extrapolation

The calculated parameters $G_{e,j}$ and $T_{\mathrm{mod},j}$ can now be used to determine the equivalent module power $P_{\mathrm{mod},j}\big(G_{e,j}, T_{\mathrm{mod},j}\big)$ for each hour j of the reference climatic datasets by bilinear interpolation and extrapolation from the matrix of power values $P(G,T)$ measured in accordance with IEC 61853-1. In advance to the interpolation, the efficiency matrix $\eta(G,T)$ is derived by $\eta(G,T) = \frac{P(G,T)}{G \cdot A_{\mathrm{mod}}}$ where G is the irradiance value of each individual power value of $P(G,T)$ and A_{mod} is the PV module area in m². The following formulas are now used to derive the efficiency $\eta\big(G_{e,j}, T_{\mathrm{mod},j}\big)$ for each hour j from $\eta(G,T)$ by bilinear interpolation and extrapolation after [10]:

$$\eta\big(G_{e,j}, T_1\big) = \eta(G_1, T_1) + \frac{G_{e,j} - G_1}{G_2 - G_1}\big(\eta(G_2, T_1) - \eta(G_1, T_1)\big)$$

$$\eta\big(G_{e,j}, T_2\big) = \eta(G_1, T_2) + \frac{G_{e,j} - G_1}{G_2 - G_1}\big(\eta(G_2, T_2) - \eta(G_1, T_2)\big)$$

$$\eta\big(G_{e,j}, T_{\mathrm{mod},j}\big) = \frac{T_2 - T_{\mathrm{mod},j}}{T_2 - T_1}\eta\big(G_{e,j}, T_1\big) + \frac{T_{\mathrm{mod},j} - T_1}{T_2 - T_1}\eta\big(G_{e,j}, T_2\big)$$

where in the case of interpolation:

T_1 and T_2 are the temperature grid points of $\eta(G,T)$ left and right of $T_{\mathrm{mod},j}$, respectively, and

G_1 and G_2 are the irradiance grid points of $\eta(G,T)$ below and above $G_{e,j}$, respectively.

And where in the case of extrapolation:

T_1 and T_2 are the temperature grid points of $\eta(G,T)$ closest to $T_{\mathrm{mod},j}$ and

G_1 and G_2 are the irradiance grid points of $\eta(G,T)$ closest to $G_{e,j}$.

A visual example of this method is shown in Figure 2.

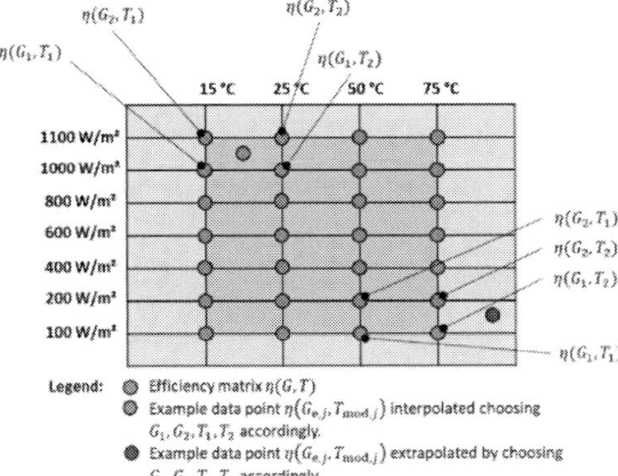

Figure 2: Example on how to choose T_1, T_2, G_1 and G_2, respectively, to interpolate or extrapolate $\eta\big(G_{e,j}, T_{mod,j}\big)$ values.

Note that these formulas allow no missing data points on the power matrix grid. Therefore, in the new edition of the standard a complete power matrix needs to be provided by 61853-1. In the current edition of the standard six points were not mandatory to be measured, since their combination of irradiance and temperature are unlikely to occur. Nowadays measuring those points is often a negligible additional effort, so labs can choose whether they want to measure or to extrapolate these power values. A new extrapolation method for 61853-1 based on [10] has been introduced:

$$P_{1-6}(G,T) = G \cdot \left(\frac{P(G_1,T_1)}{G_1} + \frac{P(G_2,T_2)}{G_2} - \frac{P(G_3,T_3)}{G_3} \right)$$

with values for irradiances and temperatures G_1, G_2, G_3, T_1, T_2 and T_3 taken from Table 2:

Table 2: Values for G_1, G_2, G_3, T_1, T_2 and T_3.

	Power value $P_{1-6}(G,T)$					
	P_1 1100,15	P_2 400/75	P_3 200/50	P_4 200,75	P_5 100,50	P_6 100,75
G_1 (W/m²)	1000	400	200	200	100	100
G_2 (W/m²)	1100	600	400	400	200	200
G_3 (W/m²)	1000	600	400	400	200	200
T_1 (°C)	15	50	25	50	25	50
T_2 (°C)	25	75	50	75	50	75
T_3 (°C)	25	50	25	50	25	50

An example on how to extrapolate missing power matrix values is given in Figure 3.

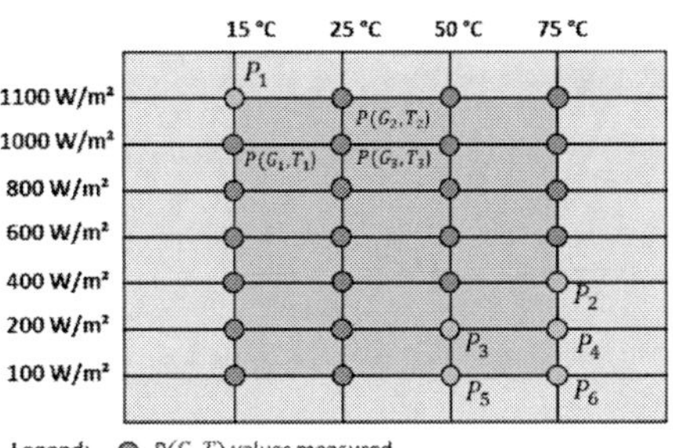

Figure 3: Example on how to extrapolate missing data points based on three nearest neighboring points in the power value grid.

After deriving $\eta\big(G_{e,j}, T_{\mathrm{mod},j}\big)$, the equivalent module power $P_{\mathrm{mod},j}\big(G_{e,j}, T_{\mathrm{mod},j}\big)$ is derived for each hour j by multiplying with the equivalent irradiance $G_{e,j}$ and the module area A_{mod} at each hour j:

$$P_{\mathrm{mod},j}\big(G_{e,j}, T_{\mathrm{mod},j}\big) = \eta\big(G_{e,j}, T_{\mathrm{mod},j}\big) \cdot G_{e,j} \cdot A_{\mathrm{mod}}$$

2.4 Module data

To test the changes of the energy rating procedure, we need measurements on PV modules. Six bifacial modules and one monofacial module were characterized at PTB according to the test procedures described in 61853-1 and 61853-2 and the corresponding proposed revision extended when necessary for bifacial modules. The PV module power matrix and $\varphi_{P_{\mathrm{max}}}$ were measured with an LED-based solar simulator described in [11]. Front- and rear-side spectral responsivity (SR) was also measured with the same setup using a procedure described in [12]. Front- and rear-side incidence angle modifier (IAM, also denoted a_r) measurements were conducted under direct sunlight with an outdoor facility described in [13]. The thermal coefficients were determined with an outdoor test stand described in [14].

Table 3: Values of $\varphi_{P_{max}}$ and a_r of the measured modules.

	Technology Manufacturer	$\varphi_{P_{max}}$	a_{r_front}	a_{r_rear}
1	Heterojunction (HJT)	87.9	0.152	0.169
2	TOPCon white mesh grid	75.5	0.153	0.163
3	TOPCon transparent	78.9	0.154	0.160
4	TOPCon black mesh grid	73.0	0.150	0.175
5	PERC, frameless	70.3	0.153	0.160
6	Back contact (IBC)	41.0	0.153	0.153
7	TOPCon black mono	-	0.153	-

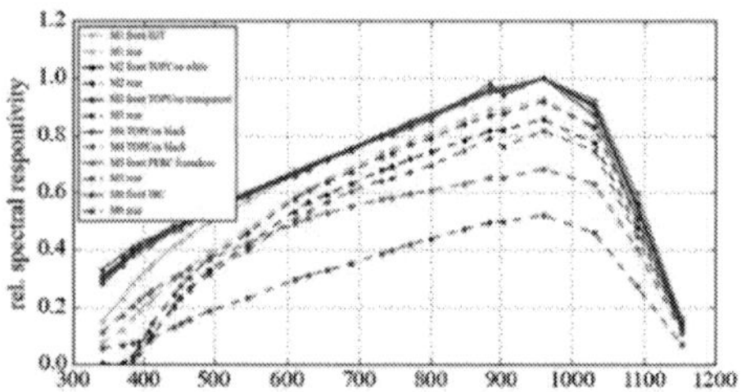

Figure 4: Front- and rear-side spectral responsivity of all measured bifacial PV modules of Table 3.

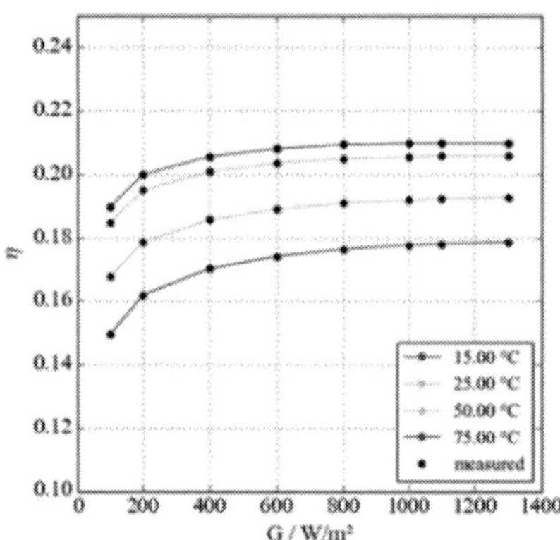

Figure 5: Example power matrix of Module 1 (HJT).

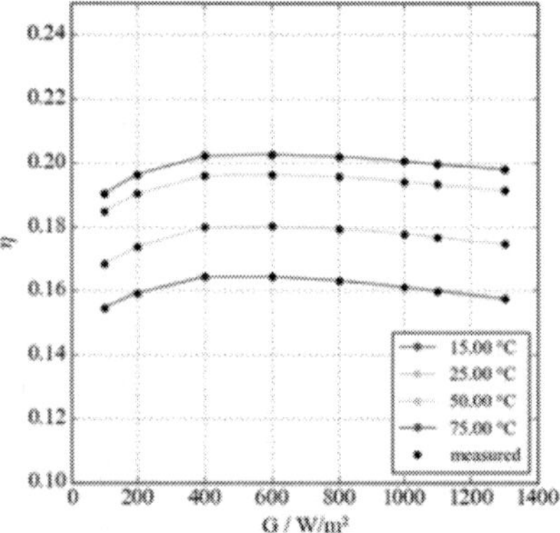

Figure 6: Example power matrix of Module 5 (PERC)

The energy produced by the module over one year ($E_{mod,year}$) is determined as the sum of the hourly energy $E_{mod,j} = P_{mod,j}\left(G_{e,j}, T_{mod,j}\right) \cdot 1\ hour$ produced by the PV module at each hour j over the year:

$$E_{mod,year} = \sum_{j=1}^{j=8760} P_{mod,j}\left(G_{e,j}, T_{mod,j}\right) \cdot 1\ hour,$$

where j ranges from 1 to 8760 in the reference period (one year).

The Climate-Specific Energy Rating $CSER$ is the normalized energy generation for the reference climate profile:

$$CSER = \frac{E_{mod,year} \cdot G_{STC}}{P_{STC} \cdot H_{ref}}$$

where

H_{ref} is the sum of the front-side global in-plane irradiance G_j values over one year of a reference climate period (1 year) given in IEC 61853-4 (kWh/m²),

G_{STC} is the irradiance at standard test conditions (1000 W/m²) and

P_{STC} is the power under standard test conditions in W, taken from the power measurements according to IEC 61853-1.

3 RESULTS AND DISCUSSION

The $CSER$ values are calculated for each climate zone and each of the introduced settings, yielding a total of 24 $CSER$ values for each PV module.

The results for the subtropical arid climate are shown in Figure 7. In Setting 1, the monofacial module is quite close in terms of $CSER$ to all bifacial modules, with values ranging from 0.933 to 0.941. For Setting 2, the $CSER$ values show a strong deviation ranging from 0.943 up to 1.085. Here, a strong correlation to the bifaciality can be observed, with those modules having the highest bifaciality showing the best $CSER$ value. In Setting 3, we observe substantially higher $CSER$ values compared to the monofacial module, since bifacial modules perform way better in this situation. Setting 4 shows the result of the tested modules in a tracking condition, where again the module with the highest bifaciality outperforms the other.

The results for the temperate coastal climate are shown in Figure 8. In Settings 1, 2 and 4 the PERC module performs best – despite having lower bifaciality than the other bifacial devices (with the exception of the IBC device, which is not presented as bifacial device by the manufacturer). The reason for this behavior is the efficiency peak of this module for irradiances at 400-600 W/m². Since the temperate coastal climate dataset contains a lot of low irradiance values, this leads to a particularly high $CSER$ value for the PERC bifacial device.

One of the topics still up to discussion is the definition of the $CSER$, especially the normalization to H_{ref} (front-side global in-plane irradiation). Especially for Setting 3, this yields a very high $CSER$ value for bifacial modules, because of the high rear-side irradiance apparent in this situation used in the hourly energy estimation which is not considered in the normalization. However, this normalization has the advantage that $CSER$ values of monofacial modules stay at a comparable level as they have been in the first version of the standard and that monofacial PV modules can be directly compared to bifacial module performance. However, this way a comparison between different settings is not plausible.

subtropical arid	Setting 1 closed rack	Setting 2 open rack	Setting 3 vertical E/W	Setting 4 tracking
M1 HJT	0.937	1.085	1.703	1.070
M2 TOPCon white	0.936	1.059	1.593	1.043
M3 TOPCon transparent	0.940	1.072	1.633	1.058
M4 TOPCon black	0.941	1.059	1.579	1.045
M5 PERC frameless	0.937	1.046	1.566	1.029
M6 IBC	0.933	1.000	1.272	0.997
M7 TOPCon Mono	0.940	0.943	0.926	0.948

Figure 7: CSER results of all PV modules listed in Table 3 for the subtropical arid climate.

temperate coastal	Setting 1 closed rack	Setting 2 open rack	Setting 3 vertical E/W	Setting 4 tracking
M1 HJT	0.969	1.054	1.842	1.081
M2 TOPCon white	0.961	1.033	1.704	1.056
M3 TOPCon transparent	0.983	1.061	1.782	1.085
M4 TOPCon black	0.990	1.060	1.723	1.081
M5 PERC frameless	0.999	1.068	1.724	1.087
M6 IBC	0.961	1.002	1.347	1.019
M7 TOPCon Mono	0.983	0.985	0.969	0.993

Figure 8: CSER results of all PV modules listed in Table 3 for the temperate coastal climate.

Performing energy rating on bifacial modules is considerably more effort. Thus, parameter sensitivity studies have been performed to analyse if all measurements done with bifacial modules are necessary for the *CSER* outcome. Derived from the use of the concept of equivalent irradiance, higher irradiance values $G_{e,j}$ are reached and thus measured the power matrix up to 1300 W/m² seem necessary. To check if this additional data point is necessary for energy rating, every *CSER* was recalculated without the power values measured at 1300 W/m². Maximum differences were only 0.01 %, so it can be assumed that extending the power matrix to 1300 W/m² is not necessary.

Removing the 75°C data point was also assessed and a very low difference of only 0.02 % was also found compared to the calculations with the full dataset. It is therefore up to discussion, if temperatures up to 75°C are really necessary or if 60°C would be sufficient. This would reduce measurement time and instrument requirements for a lot of measurement labs.

Using equal values for rear-side IAM and front-side IAM yield a bias of up to 0.61 %, while using equal front- and rear- spectral responsivity yields a bias of 0.88 %. This is especially the case for Setting 3, where a substantial amount of rear-side irradiance is apparent over the course of the day. Therefore, it is reasonable to conclude that both rear-side IAM and rear-side SR are to be measured so no bias is introduced.

	remove 1300 W/m²	remove 75 °C	IAM front = IAM rear	SR front = SR rear
M1 HJT	0.01%	0.02%	0.50%	0.35%
M2 TOPCon white	0.00%	0.01%	0.24%	0.88%
M3 TOPCon transparent	0.01%	0.01%	0.15%	0.87%
M4 TOPCon black	0.01%	0.02%	0.61%	0.83%
M5 PERC frameless	0.01%	0.01%	0.15%	0.11%
M6 IBC	0.00%	0.01%	0.01%	0.59%

Figure 9: Changes to CSER values if either data points are removed or front- and rear-side are treated with the same SR or IAM values, those of the front-side.

4 REFERENCES

[1] IEC 61853-1, "Photovoltaic (PV) module performance testing and energy rating - Part 1: Irradiance and temperature performance measurements and power rating," International Electrotechnical Commission, 2011. Accessed: Nov. 20, 2024. [Online]. Available: https://www.vde-verlag.de/iec-normen/217749/iec-61853-1-2011.html

[2] IEC 61853-2, "Photovoltaic (PV) module performance testing and energy rating - Part 2: Spectral responsivity, incidence angle and module operating temperature measurements," International Electrotechnical Commission, 2016.

[3] IEC 61853-3, "Photovoltaic (PV) module performance testing and energy rating - Part 3: Energy rating of PV modules," International Electrotechnical Commission, 2018.

[4] IEC 61853-4, "Photovoltaic (PV) module performance testing and energy rating - Part 4: Standard reference climatic profiles," 2018. [Online]. Available: www.iec.ch

[5] T. Huld, A. G. Amillo, T. Sample, E. D. Dunlop, E. Salis, and R. Kenny, "THE COMPLETED IEC 61853 STANDARD SERIES ON PV MODULE ENERGY RATING, OVERVIEW, APPLICATIONS AND OUTLOOK," in *EU PVSEC 2024*, 2018, pp. 1113–1118. doi: 10.4229/35thEUPVSEC20182018-5DO.9.2.

[6] VDMA, "International Technology Roadmap for Photovoltaics (ITRPV) - 2023 Results," 2024.

[7] N. Martin and J. M. Ruiz, "A new model for PV modules angular losses under field conditions," *International Journal of Solar Energy*, vol. 22, pp. 19–31, 2002, doi: 10.1080/01425910212852.

[8] M. Ruben Vogt et al., "PV Module Energy Rating Standard IEC 61853-3 Intercomparison and Best Practice Guidelines for Implementation and Validation," *IEEE J Photovolt*, 2022, doi: 10.1109/JPHOTOV.2021.3135258.

[9] M. R. Vogt, G. Pilis, M. Zeman, R. Santbergen, and O. Isabella, "Developing an energy rating for bifacial photovoltaic modules," *Progress in Photovoltaics: Research and Applications*, vol. 31, no. 12, pp. 1466–1477, Dec. 2023, doi: 10.1002/pip.3678.

[10] A. Driesse, M. Theristis, and J. S. Stein, "A New Photovoltaic Module Efficiency Model for Energy Prediction and Rating," *IEEE J Photovolt*, vol. 11, no. 2, pp. 527–534, Mar. 2021, doi: 10.1109/JPHOTOV.2020.3045677.

[11] S. Riechelmann, H. Sträter, and S. Winter, "DETERMINATION OF A PV MODULE POWER MATRIX WITH AN LED SOLAR SIMULATOR," in *EU PVSEC 2020*, 2020. doi: 10.4229/EUPVSEC20192019.

[12] H. Sträter, S. Riechelmann, F. Neuberger, and S. Winter, "LED-BASED DIFFERENTIAL SPECTRAL RESPONSIVITY MEASUREMENTS OF PV MODULES," in *EU PVSEC 2019*, 2019.

[13] S. Riechelmann, D. Friedrich, M. Müller, F. Schmaljohann, H. Sträter, and S. Winter, "PRIMARY CALIBRATION OF SOLAR MODULES WITH DIRECT SUNLIGHT," in *EU PVSEC 2022*, 2022, pp. 474–476. doi: 10.4229/WCPEC-82022-3BO.11.2.

[14] M. Schrempf, S. Riechelmann, S. Winter, and L. Stenzig, "Outdoor NMOT test stand with adjustable wind field," in *WCPEC-8*, 2022.

PTB Physikalisch-Technische Bundesanstalt
Braunschweig und Berlin
Nationales Metrologieinstitut

An Update on Energy Rating Amendments – Integration of Bifacial Modules

Stefan Riechelmann, Hendrik Sträter, Ana María Gracia-Amillo, Sophie Pelland, Anton Driesse

[1]PTB, Braunschweig, Germany
[2]CENER, Pamplona, Spain
[3]Natural Resources Canada, Varennes, Canada
[4]PV Performance Labs, Freiburg, Germany

What is Energy Rating?

Standard Test Conditions

- 1000 W/m²
- 25°C module temperature
- AM1.5 spectrum
- 0° incidence angle

Energy Rating

Simple but realistic rating of the performance of PV modules at different climatic conditions, taking into account:

- Ambient temperature
- Direct and diffuse irradiance
- Incidence angle
- Spectral distribution
- Wind speed

Energy Rating Standards (IEC 61853)

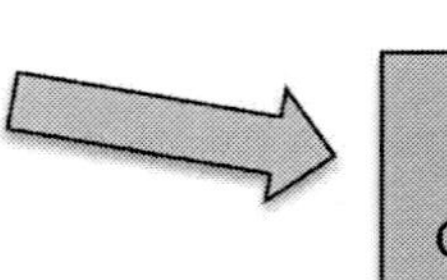

IEC TC82 WG2 currently revises the standards, so what will be new in ED2?

a) Formulas and measurement procedures adapted for supporting bifacial modules
b) Introduction of different module orientations
c) Improvement on inter- and extrapolation

How to adapt the 61853-3 formulas for bifacial modules?

Edition 1:
only front-side irradiance:

B – direct irradiance

D – diffuse irradiance

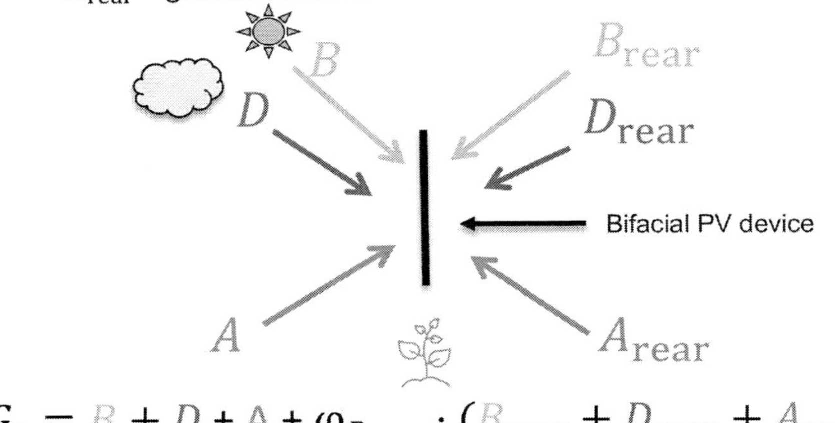

$$G = B + D$$

Edition 2:
Front- and rear-side (equivalent) irradiance:

B – direct irradiance

D – diffuse irradiance

A – ground-reflected irradiance

B_{rear} – direct rear-side irradiance

D_{rear} – diffuse rear-side irradiance

A_{rear} – ground-reflected rear-side irradiance

$$G_{\mathrm{e}} = B + D + A + \varphi_{P_{\max}} \cdot (B_{\mathrm{rear}} + D_{\mathrm{rear}} + A_{\mathrm{rear}})$$

61853-3 ED1: Module orientation and mounting condition

PTB

61853-3 ED1:

- 20° tilt
- equator-facing
- albedo is 0

– No rear-side irradiance (this is similar to a rooftop installation where we have severe self-shading)
– Bifacial modules shine in settings, where rear-side irradiance is apparent

For a fair comparison of monofacial and bifacial modules, we need more settings than this!

61853-3 ED2: Settings with different orientation and mounting conditions

S1	S2	S3	S4
Close rack	open rack	vertical	tracking

	Setting 1	Setting 2	Setting 3	Setting 4
Description	closed rack	open rack	vertical	tracking
Inclination angle β_j	20°	20°	90°	variable
Orientation	Equator	Equator	front to East / rear to West	East/West
Rear-side irradiance	-	+	+++	+

61853-3 ED2: Fixing inter- and extrapolation of module power

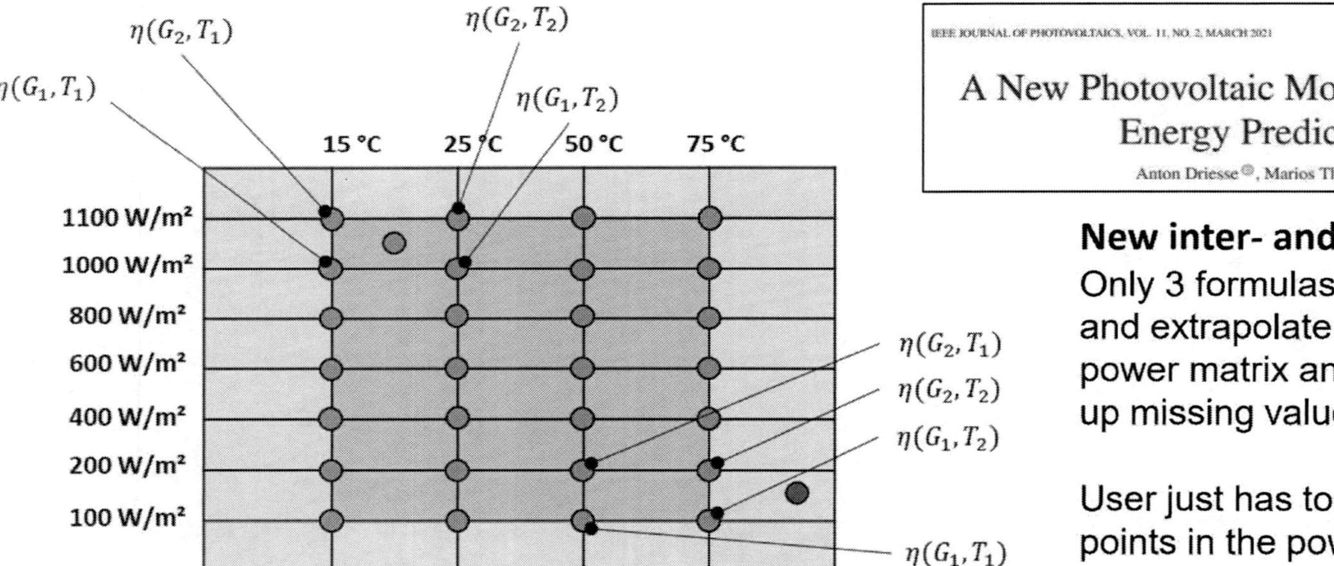

Legend:
- Filled efficiency matrix $\eta(G, T)$
- Example data point $\eta(G_{e,i}, T_{mod,i})$ interpolated by using Formula (11) to (13) 4 and choosing G_1, G_2, T_1, T_2 accordingly.
- Example data point $\eta(G_{e,i}, T_{mod,i})$ extrapolated by using Formula (11) to (13) and choosing G_1, G_2, T_1, T_2 accordingly.

IEEE JOURNAL OF PHOTOVOLTAICS, VOL. 11, NO. 2, MARCH 2021

A New Photovoltaic Module Efficiency Model for Energy Prediction and Rating

Anton Driesse, Marios Theristis, and Joshua S. Stein

New inter- and extrapolation:

Only 3 formulas needed to interpolate and extrapolate module power from power matrix and 2 formulas for filling up missing values of the matrix

User just has to find the four nearest points in the power matrix grid

Matrix has to be fully filled, no NA values. In 61853-1, this points either will be measured or extrapolated.

Testing Edition 2 with measured data

Power matrix (IEC 61853-1)	Spectral responsivity measurements (IEC 61853-2)	Angle of Incidence (AOI) measurements (IEC 61853-2)	Temperature coefficients (IEC 61853-2)
$T=15\text{-}75°C$ and $G=100\text{-}1300\ W/m^2$ (extended irradiance, more steps than in the standard) + φ_{Pmax} measurement.	Front side SR and rear side SR of all devices was measured using an LED-based solar simulator at PTB.	Front side and rear side AOI was measured with direct sunlight.	Temperature coefficients were measured analogous to monofacial modules.

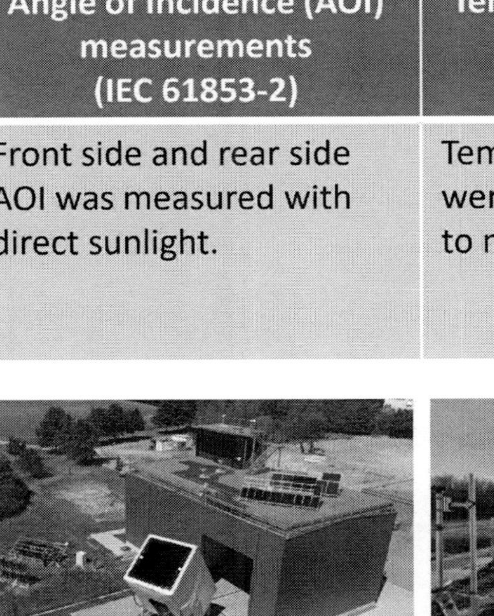

Testing Edition 2 with measured data

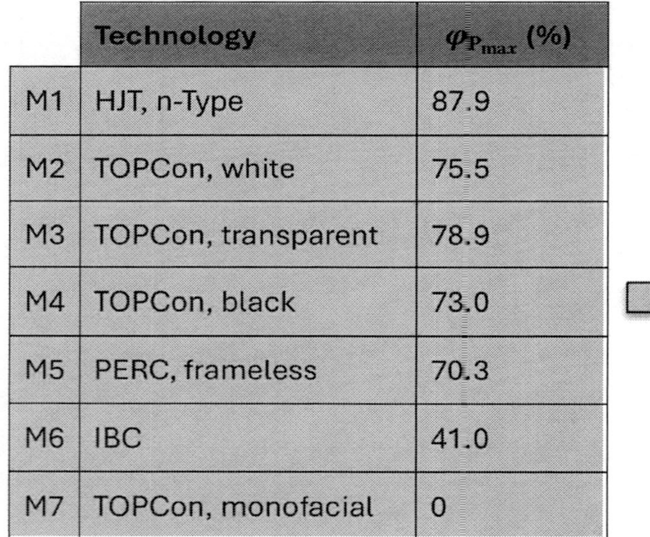

	Technology	$\varphi_{P_{max}}$ (%)
M1	HJT, n-Type	87.9
M2	TOPCon, white	75.5
M3	TOPCon, transparent	78.9
M4	TOPCon, black	73.0
M5	PERC, frameless	70.3
M6	IBC	41.0
M7	TOPCon, monofacial	0

61853-1:ED2, 61853-2:ED2

CSER values of 7 different PV modules in different climates

Tropical arid
albedo: high (0.4)
G: high (2400 kWh/m²)
$T_{amb,day,mean}$: high (22.5 °C)
D/G ratio: low (24 %)

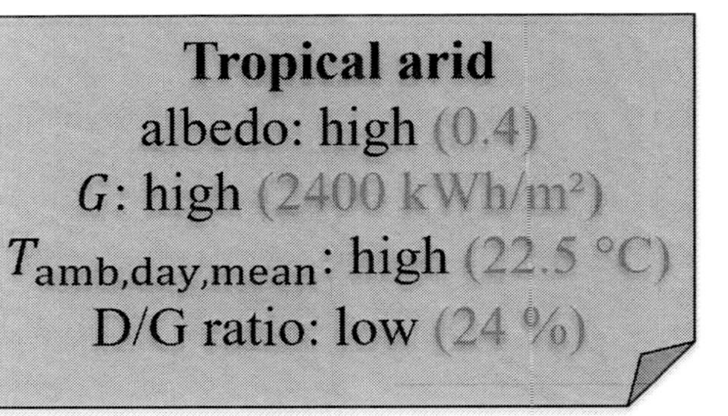

subtropical arid	Setting 1 closed rack	Setting 2 open rack	Setting 3 vertical E/W	Setting 4 tracking
M1 HJT	0.937	1.085	1.703	1.070
M2 TOPCon white	0.936	1.059	1.593	1.043
M3 TOPCon transparent	0.940	1.072	1.633	1.058
M4 TOPCon black	0.941	1.059	1.579	1.045
M5 PERC frameless	0.937	1.046	1.566	1.029
M6 IBC	0.933	1.000	1.272	0.997
M7 TOPCon Mono	0.940	0.943	0.926	0.948

CSER = Climate-Specific Energy Rating

020212-010

CSER values of 7 different PV modules in different climates

Temperate coastal
albedo: medium (0.2)
G: low (1100 kWh/m²)
$T_{amb,day,mean}$: medium (11.3 °C)
D/G ratio: high (51 %)

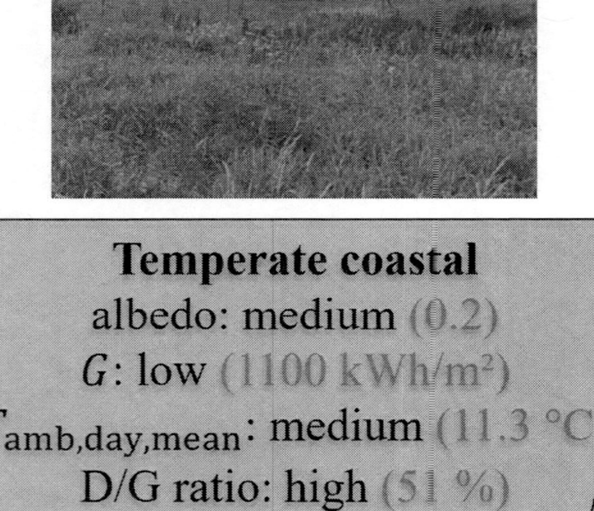

temperate coastal	Setting 1 closed rack	Setting 2 open rack	Setting 3 vertical E/W	Setting 4 tracking
M1 HJT	0.969	1.054	1.842	1.081
M2 TOPCon white	0.961	1.033	1.704	1.056
M3 TOPCon transparent	0.983	1.061	1.782	1.085
M4 TOPCon black	0.990	1.060	1.723	1.081
M5 PERC frameless	0.999	1.068	1.724	1.087
M6 IBC	0.961	1.002	1.347	1.019
M7 TOPCon Mono	0.983	0.985	0.969	0.993

CSER = Climate-Specific Energy Rating

61853 ED2: Parameter studies

That's a lot of effort!
How about some simpler measurements?

	remove 1300 W/m²	remove 75 °C	IAM front = IAM rear	SR front = SR rear
M1 HJT	0.01%	0.02%	0.50%	0.35%
M2 TOPCon white	0.00%	0.01%	0.24%	0.88%
M3 TOPCon transparent	0.01%	0.01%	0.15%	0.87%
M4 TOPCon black	0.01%	0.02%	0.61%	0.83%
M5 PERC frameless	0.01%	0.01%	0.15%	0.11%
M6 IBC	0.00%	0.01%	0.01%	0.59%

(Maximum deviation of all climates and settings)

020212-012

Conclusion

Edition 1

ER module performance under different climatic conditions, monofacial devices only

Edition 2

+ ER performance of monofacial and bifacial modules
+ ER performance under different orientations
+ Clearer and more robust calculations

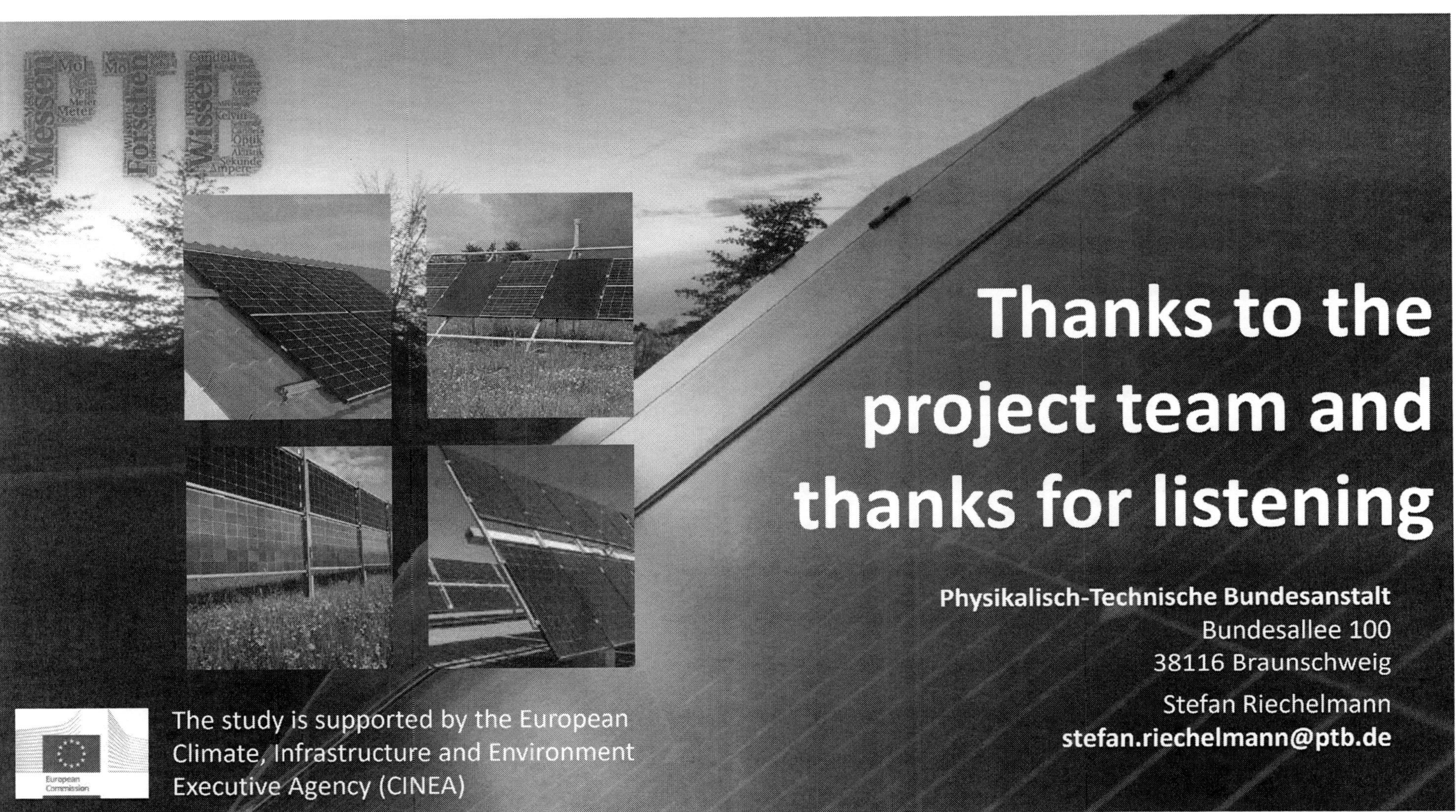
Thanks to the
project team and
thanks for listening
Physikalisch-Technische Bundesanstalt
Bundesallee 100
38116 Braunschweig
Stefan Riechelmann
stefan.riechelmann@ptb.de
The study is supported by the European
Climate, Infrastructure and Environment
Executive Agency (CINEA)

Outdoor Measurements of Perovskite Modules

Hanna Ellis[1], Harald Müllejans and Ewan D. Dunlop

European Commission[2], Joint Research Centre, Ispra, Italy

1 Hanna.Ellis@ec.europa.eu
2 The views expressed are purely those of the presenter and may not in any circumstances be regarded as stating an official position of the Europen Commission

Installation

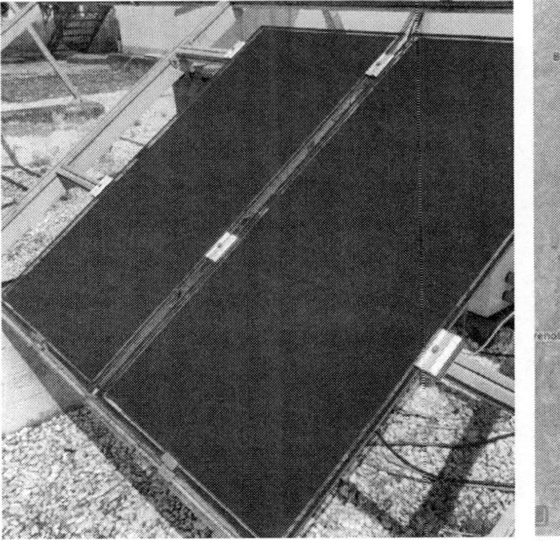

Image from PVGIS

- Single junction Perovskite modules (0.72 m^2)
- No knowledge of the chemical composition or structure
- Northern Italy (humid subtropical climate)
- 45° tilted fixed racks, facing south
- June 2024 to May 2025

Installation

- Reference cell - a ESTI sensor (a crystalline silicon reference cell designed for outdoor monitoring
- Anemometer
- Temperature sensor for ambinent temperature measurements
- Pyranometer
- Monitoring instrumentations:
  - MPPT
  - Four quadrant power supply (BOPA)
  - Multimeters
  - Shunt
  - Relays
  - Labview control software

Indoor Measurement Protocol

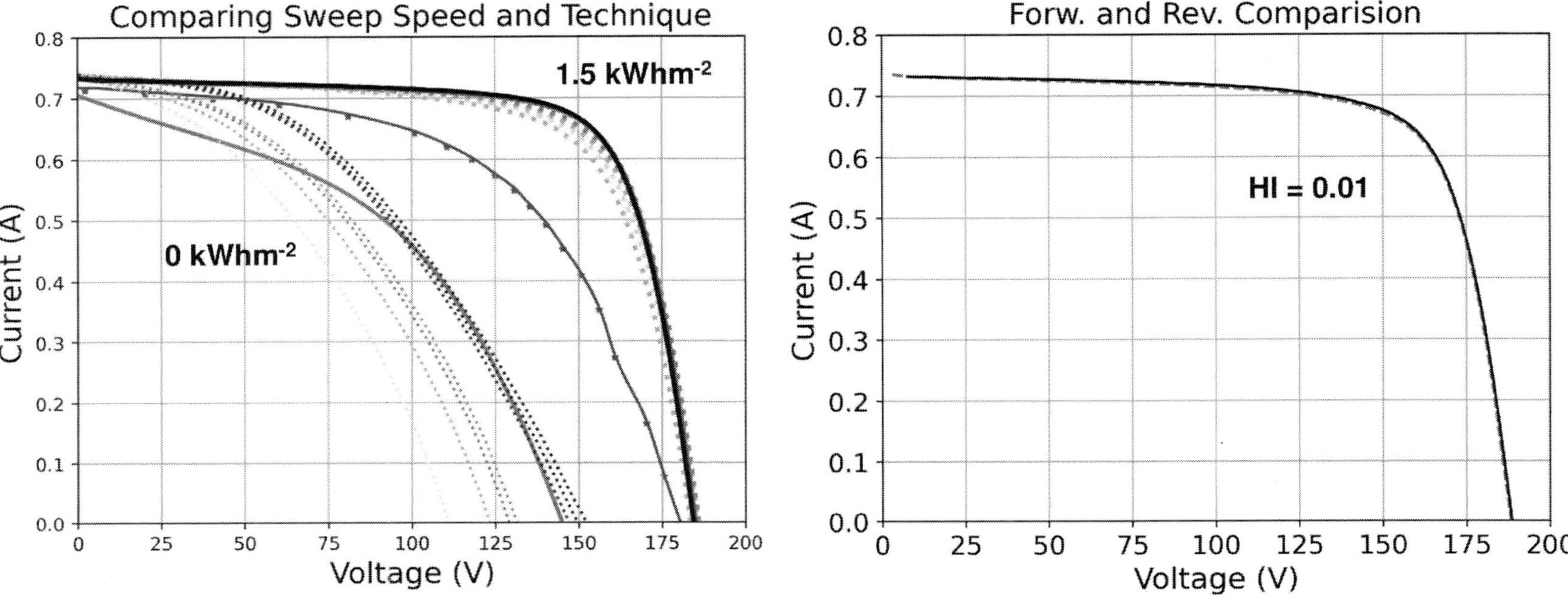

Overall Performance

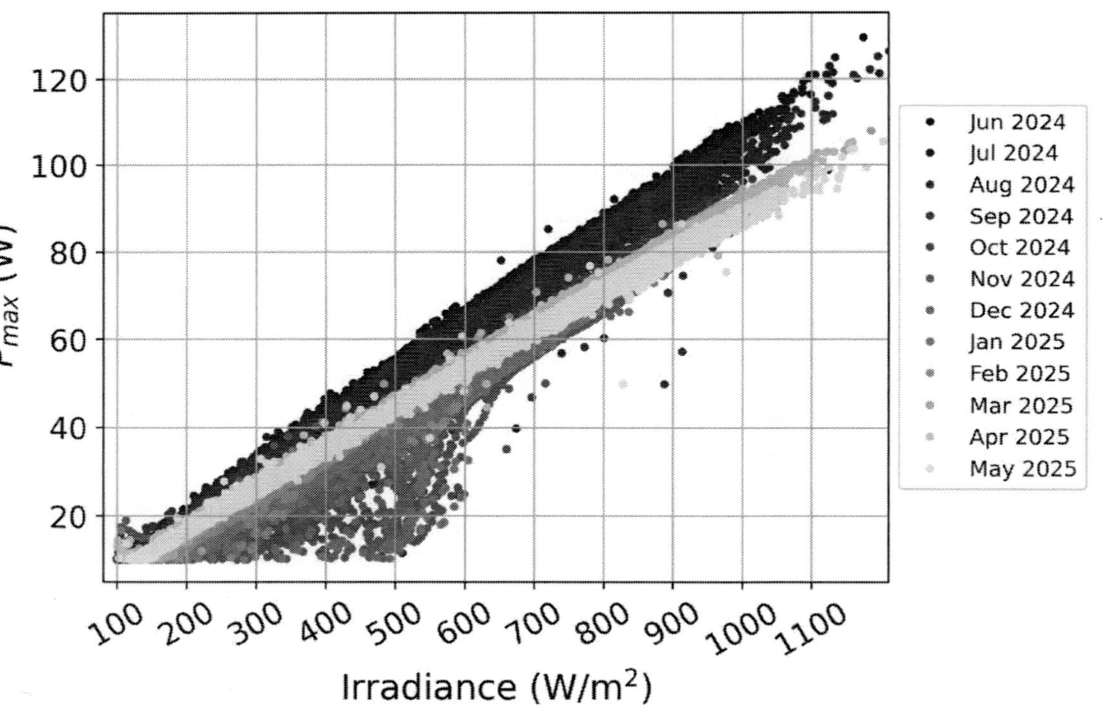

Overall Performance

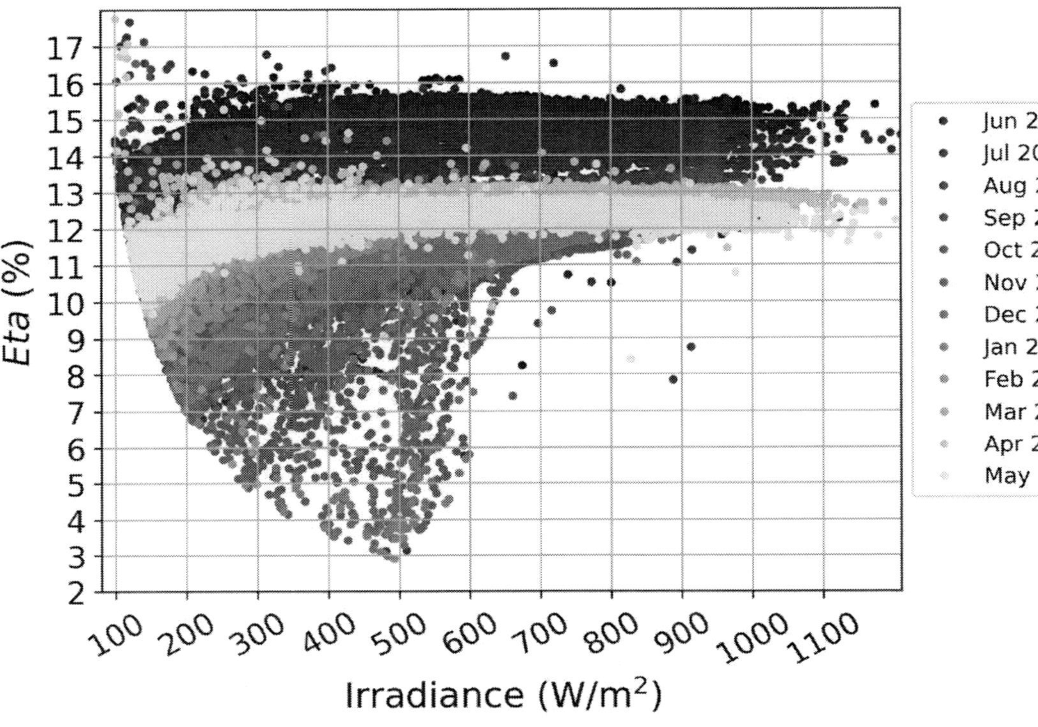

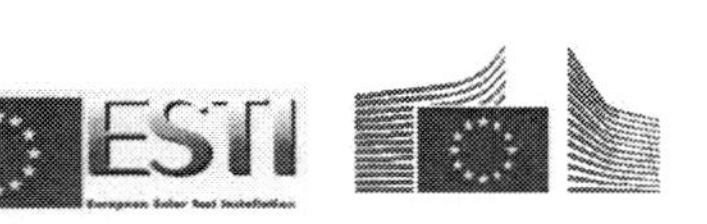

Specific Performance

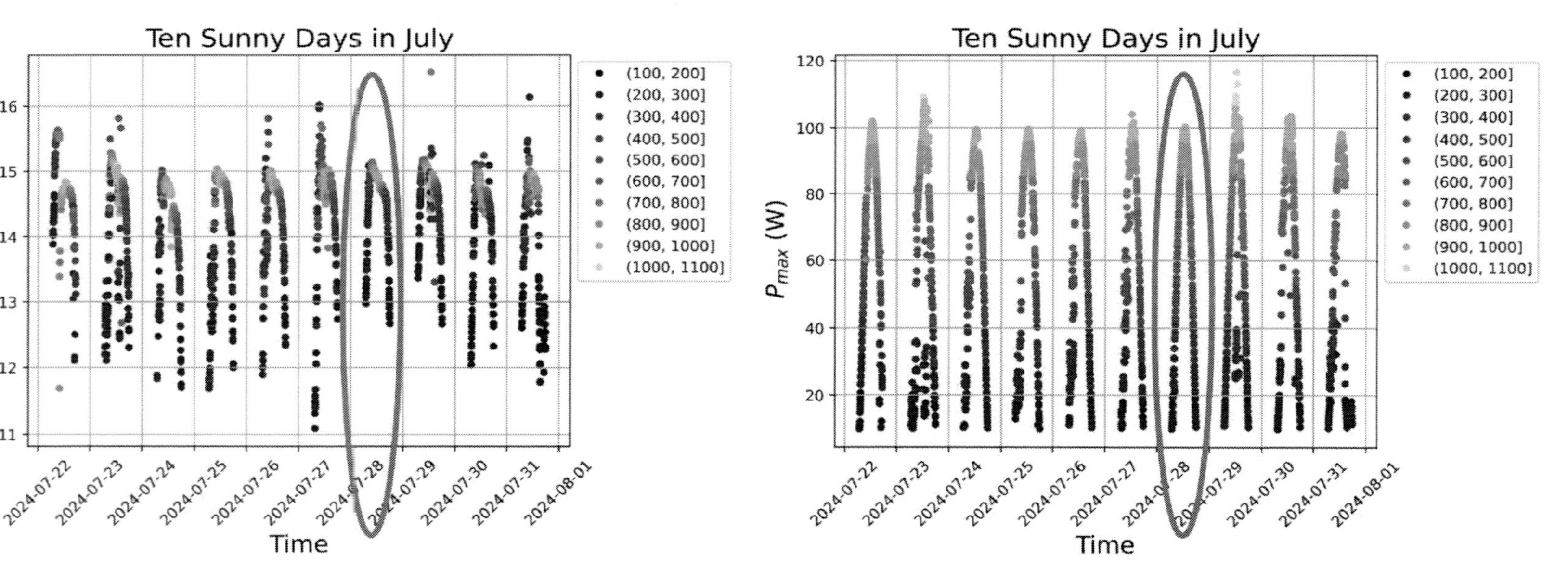

Specific Performance

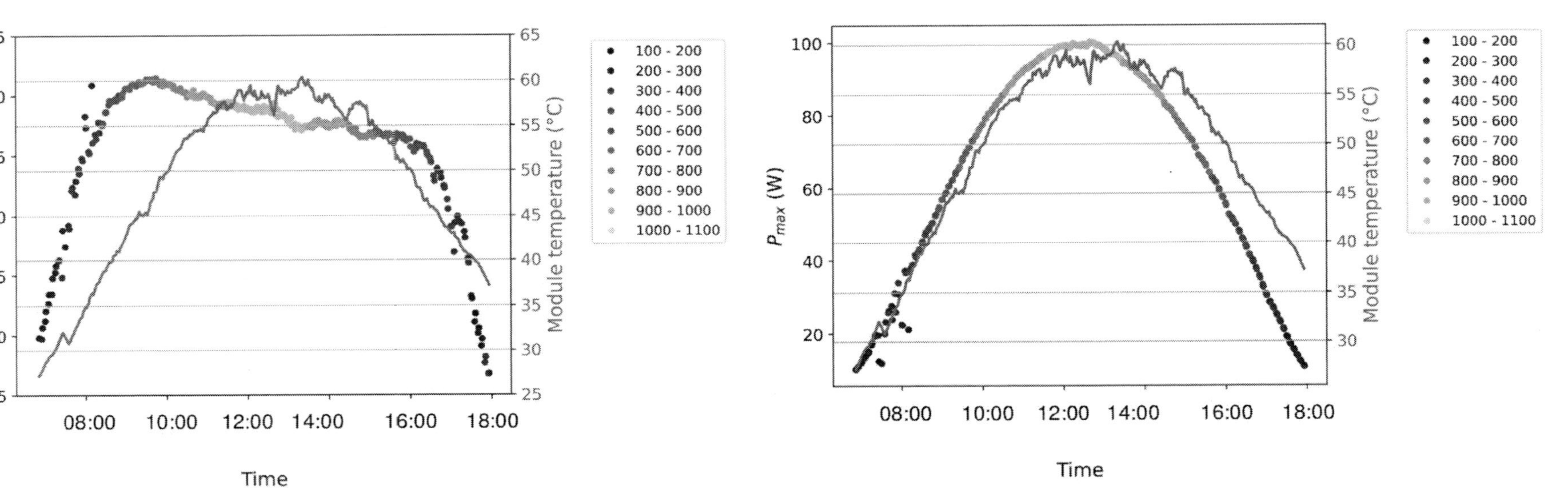

Specific Performance

ESTI
European Solar Test Installation

Temperature Dependency - for 980 - 1020 Wm^{-2}

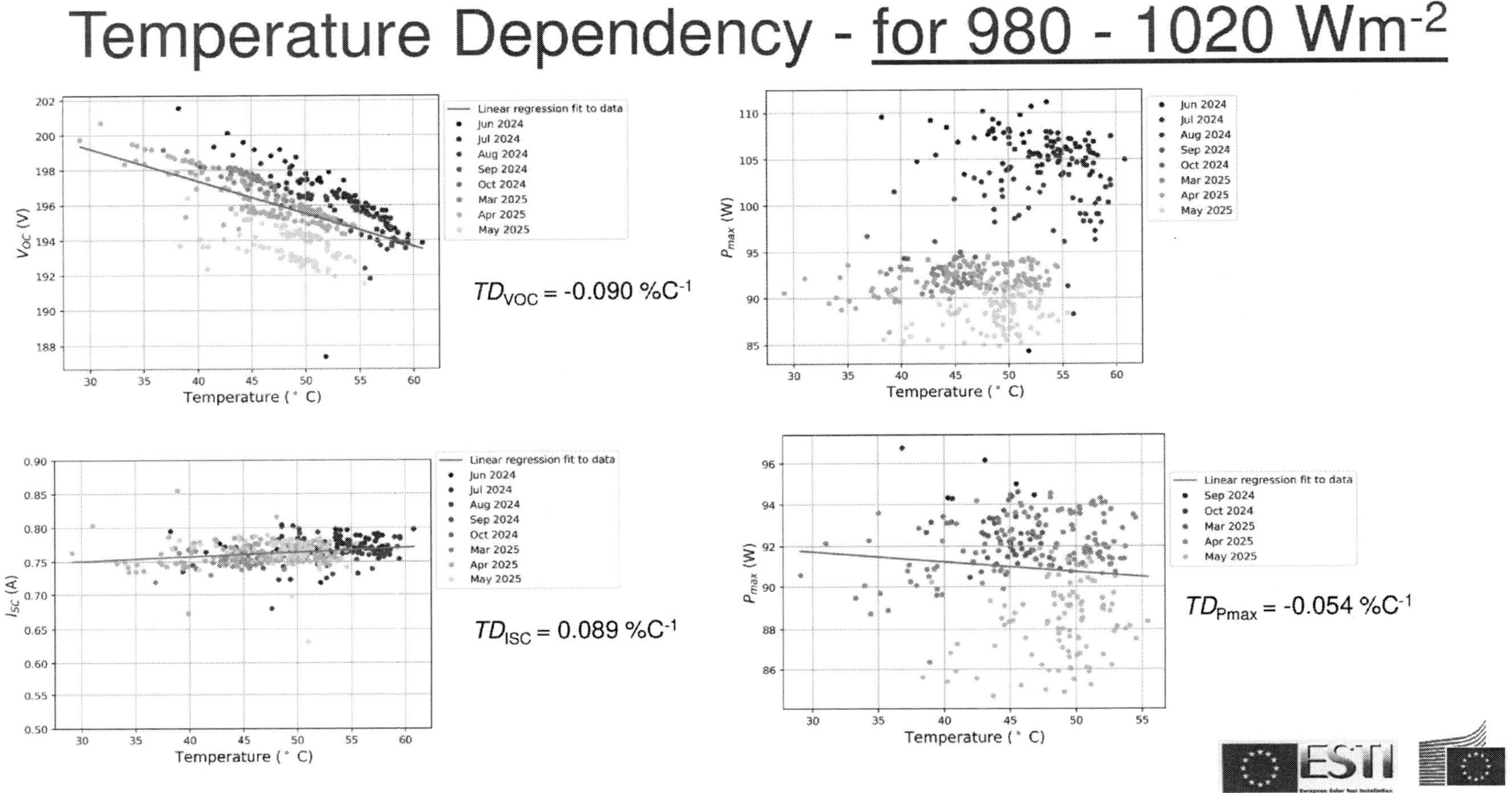

Performance as a Function of Time

Indoor data for 1000 Wm^{-2}

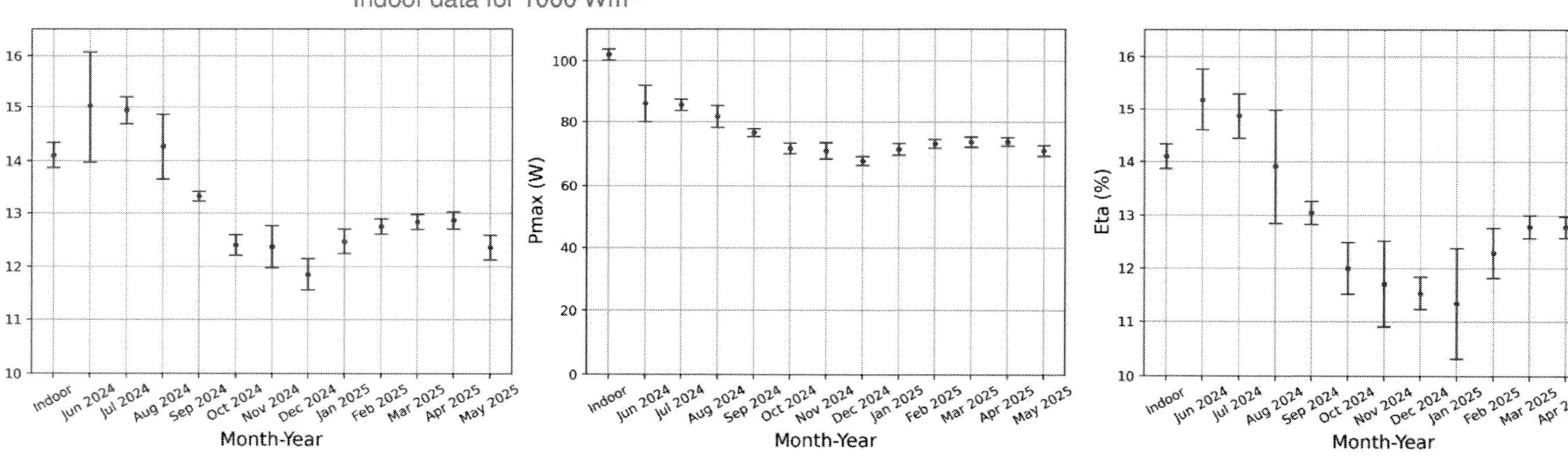

Average eta and P_{max} of binned data for each month with one standard deviation as error bars for every month. **Data filtered between 780 Wm^{-2} and 820 Wm^{-2}.**

Average eta of binned data for each month with one standard deviation as error bars for every month. **Data filtered between 580 Wm^{-2} and 620 Wm^{-2}.**

Conclusions

- Settled values are measured after a certain amount of pre-conditioning (at V_{mpp}) and with a sweep time of, in this case 10 s (= approx 15-19 V/s).
- Temperature dependency was investigated between 980 and 1020 Wm^{-2} as:
  - $TD_{ISC} = 0.089$ %C^{-1}
  - $TD_{VOC} = -0.090$ %C^{-1}
  - $TD_{Pmax} = -0.054$ %C^{-1}
- Performance over time; Module 1 15% $\rightarrow$ 12.5% and Module 2 14% $\rightarrow$ 7.5%

Thank you for listening!

Many thanks to Flavio Nico and Ambrogio Nico for all the help with the outdoor monitoring installation and to the ESTI Team

The JRC – provides independent, evidence-based knowledge and science, supporting EU policies to positively impact society.

For more information and open job positions please visit: **https://joint-research-centre.ec.europa.eu**

JRC is open to cooperation and receiving PhD students and other researchers (as unpaid visiting scientists)

JRC is constantly hiring new staff: **https://recruitment.jrc.ec.europa.eu/**

For further discussions with ESTI please visit our stand F7 !

For the calibrations price list or for requesting information on ESTI services, please contact:
JRC-ESTI-SERVICES@ec.europa.eu

Scientific Project Officer, Hanna Ellis, **Hanna.Ellis@ec.europa.eu**

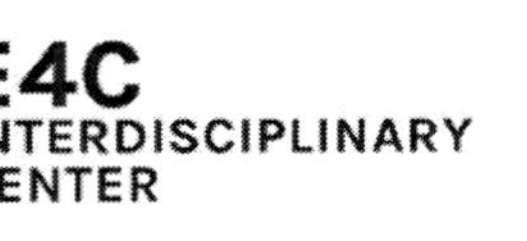

Performance characterization of monofacial and bifacial modules in French Polynesia: Case study of Tahiti

Moira I. Torres Aguilar[1]
Pascal Ortega[2]
Jordi Badosa Franch[3]
Johan Parra[3]

23/09/25

[1] CentraleSupélec, GeePs
[2] University of French Polynesia, GEPASUD
[3] E4C Institut Polytechnique de Paris

Agenda

- **Bifacial PV market**
- **PV Platform**
- **Yield**
- **Bifacial gain**
- **Performance Ratio**
- **Conclusions & Future Work**

2

Bifacial market share

Why is performance characterization of bifacial modules under real-life conditions important?

The market share of bifacial modules has increased from:
50% in 2023 → a projected 73% in 2034

Source: "International Technology Roadmap for Photovoltaics (ITRPV) 2023 Results," VDMA, May 2024.

IEC TS 60904-1-2

Standard specific for bifacial modules

PV performance on islands?

•IEC 60891, IEC60904-X

•Design: IEC 61215-X,
•Safety: IEC 61730

Measurement issues, in particular output power determination

Product qualification testing

PV materials and components

Energy Rating

•IEC 62852, IEC 62790, IEC 62930

•IEC 61853-X

Source: J. Stein et al., "Bifacial Photovoltaic Modules and Systems: Experience and Results from International Research and Pilot Applications," SAND--2021-4835R, IEA--PVPS T13-14:2021, 1779379, Apr. 2021.

020214-003

PV Platform

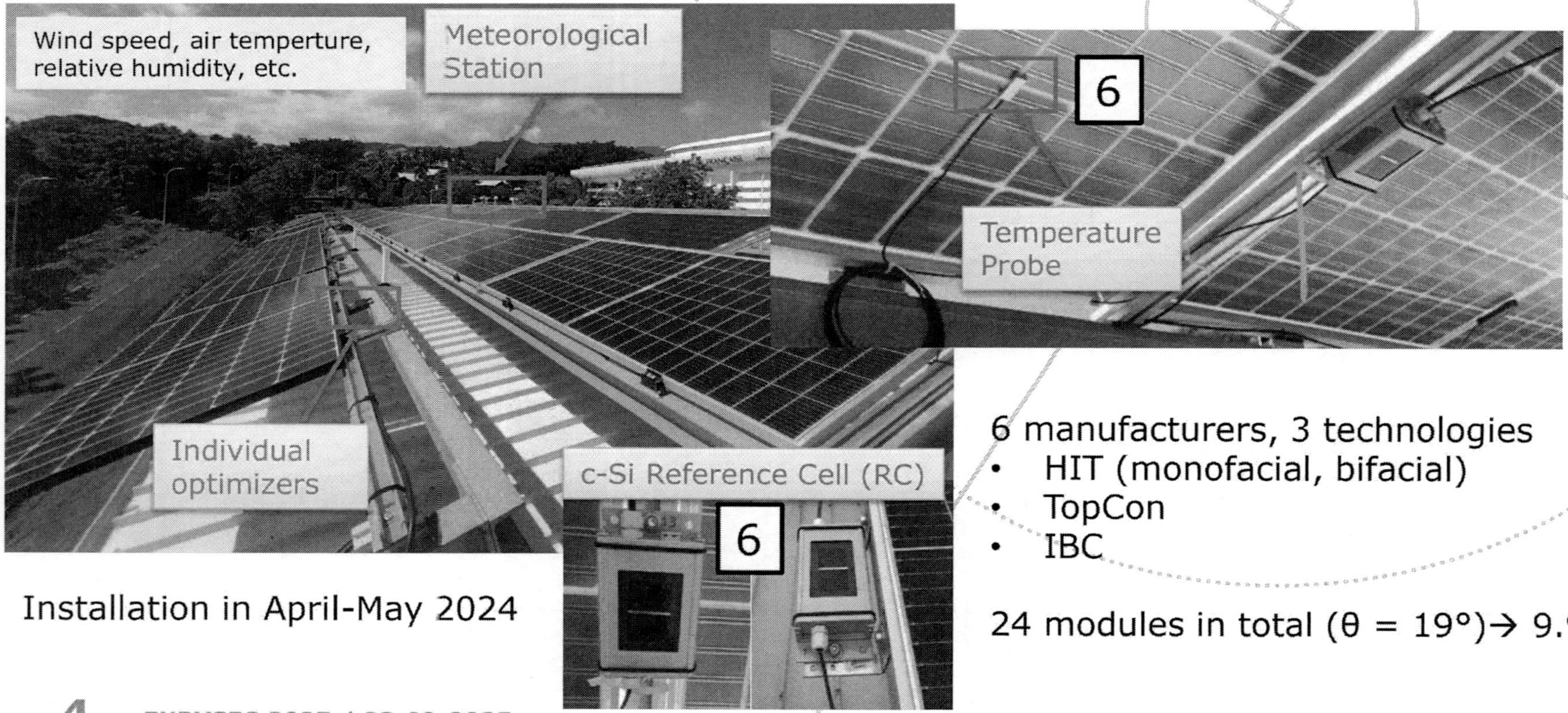

6 manufacturers, 3 technologies
- HIT (monofacial, bifacial)
- TopCon
- IBC

24 modules in total ($\theta = 19°$) → 9.9 kWp

Installation in April-May 2024

PV Platform

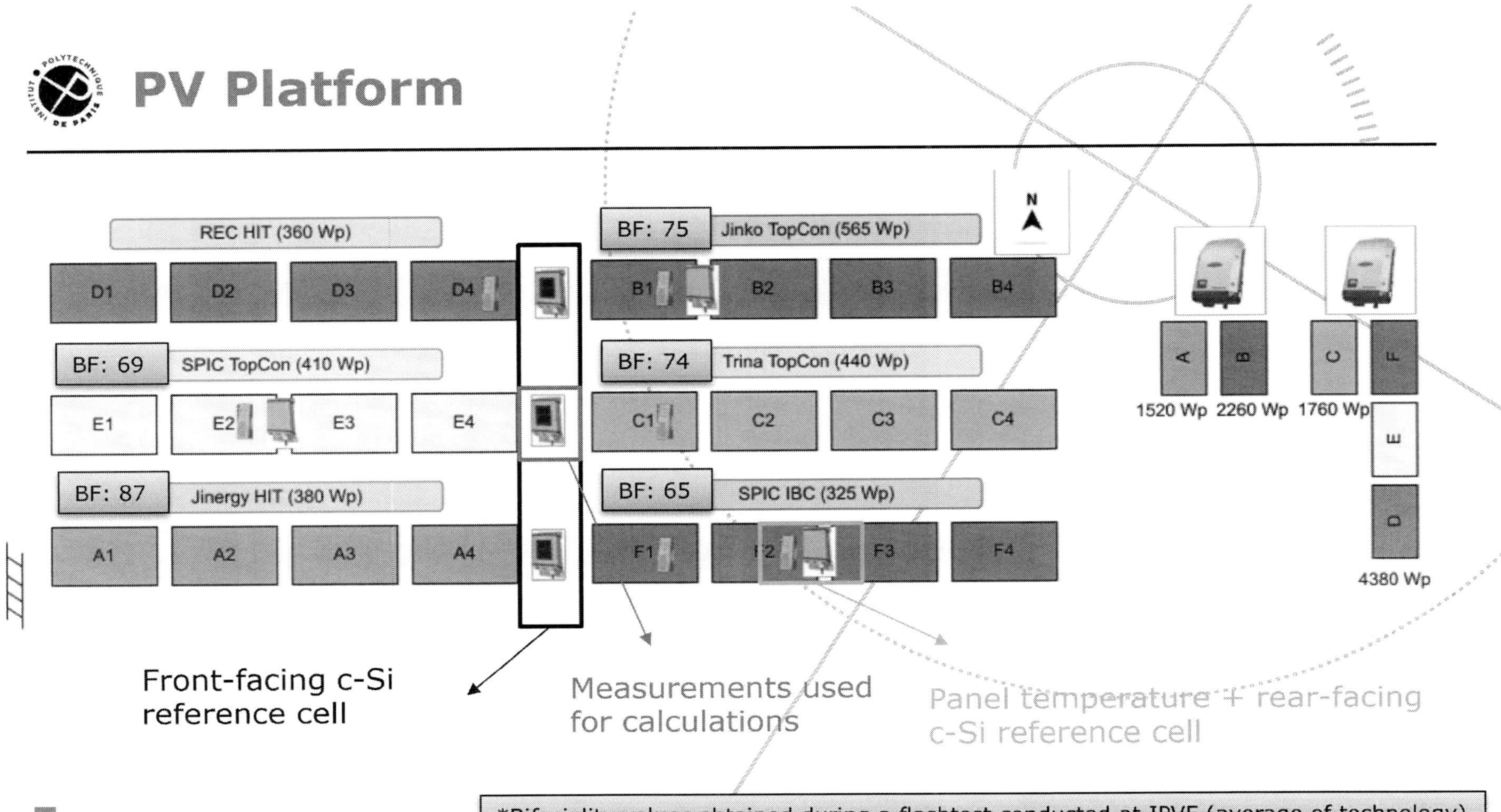

Front-facing c-Si reference cell

Measurements used for calculations

Panel temperature + rear-facing c-Si reference cell

*Bifaciality values obtained during a flashtest conducted at IPVF (average of technology)

020214-005

Performance Characterization

How do these technologies perform in a tropical climate (Tahiti)?

$$Y_M = \frac{\sum P_{meas}}{P_{STC}}$$

$$Y_R = \frac{\sum G_{meas}}{G_{STC}}$$

Module Yield

Reference Yield

$$Performance\ Ratio(PR) = \frac{Y_M}{Y_R}$$

P_{meas} : module power output (W)
P_{STC} : power output under STC conditions (Wp)
G_{meas} : measured plane-of-array irradiance (W/m²)
G_{STC} : irradiance uner STC conditions (1000 W/m²)

020214-006

Reference Yield

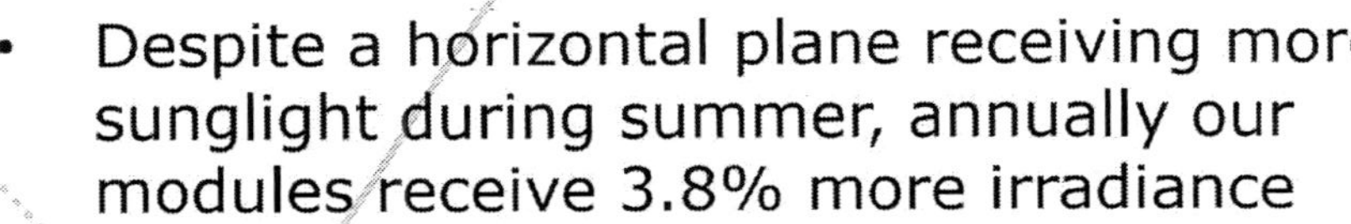

- Our modules benefit from a lower solar elevation angle

- Despite a horizontal plane receiving more sunglight during summer, annually our modules receive 3.8% more irradiance

Module Yield

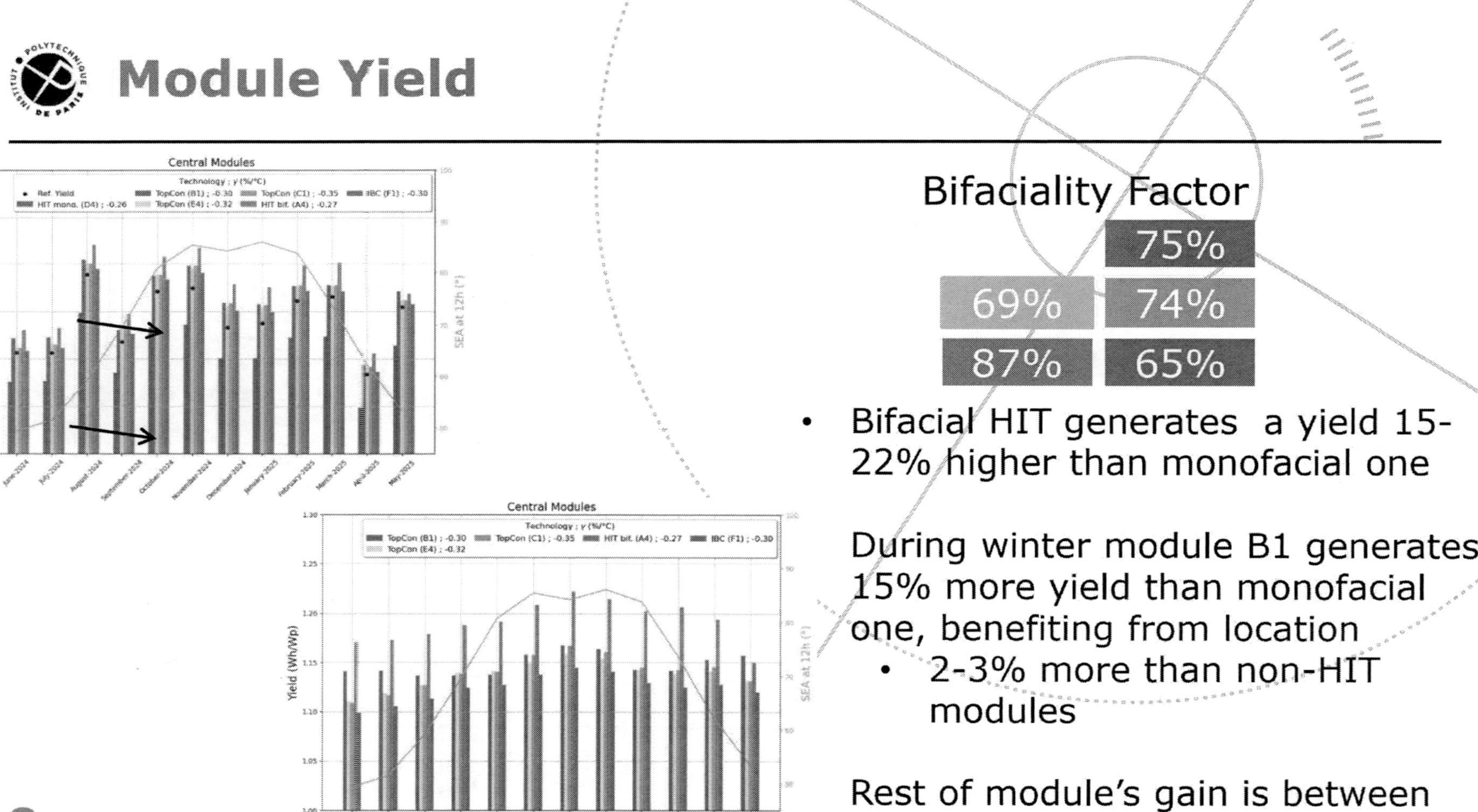

Bifaciality Factor

	75%
69%	74%
87%	65%

- Bifacial HIT generates a yield 15-22% higher than monofacial one

During winter module B1 generates 15% more yield than monofacial one, benefiting from location
- 2-3% more than non-HIT modules

Rest of module's gain is between 10-16%

Temp. Corrected Module Yield

$$Y_M = \frac{\sum P_{meas}}{P_{STC}} \longrightarrow P_{corr} = \frac{P_{meas}}{1 + \gamma(T_{mod} - Tp_{STC})} \Longrightarrow Y_c = \frac{\sum P_{corr}}{P_{STC}}$$

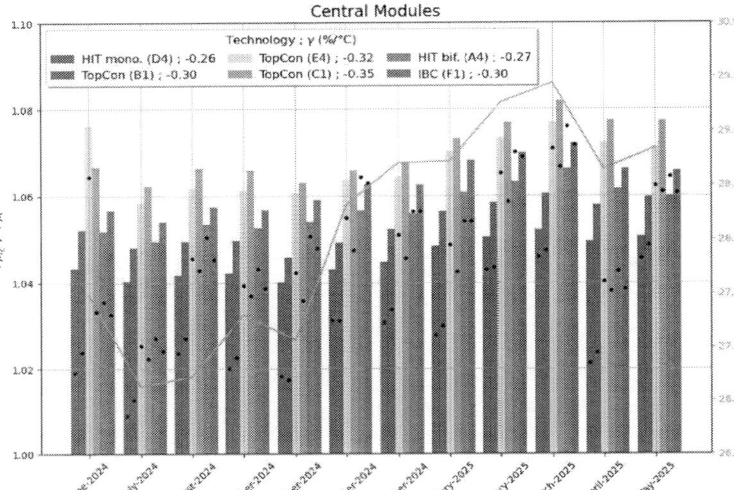

- Due to low temperature variability, thermal losses remain stable throughout the year

- Despite having a higher temperature coefficient, module B1 losses than other modules due to cooling effect

- Due to a low power temperature coefficient, and position, the monofacial module losses 4–5% of yield only

- The average difference in module temperature between the modules located in the first row and the others is 1.7°C

Effect of wind on module temperature

The sea breeze causes a visible difference in T_{mod} between modules of the first row and the rest

10 EUPVSEC 2025 / 23-09-2025

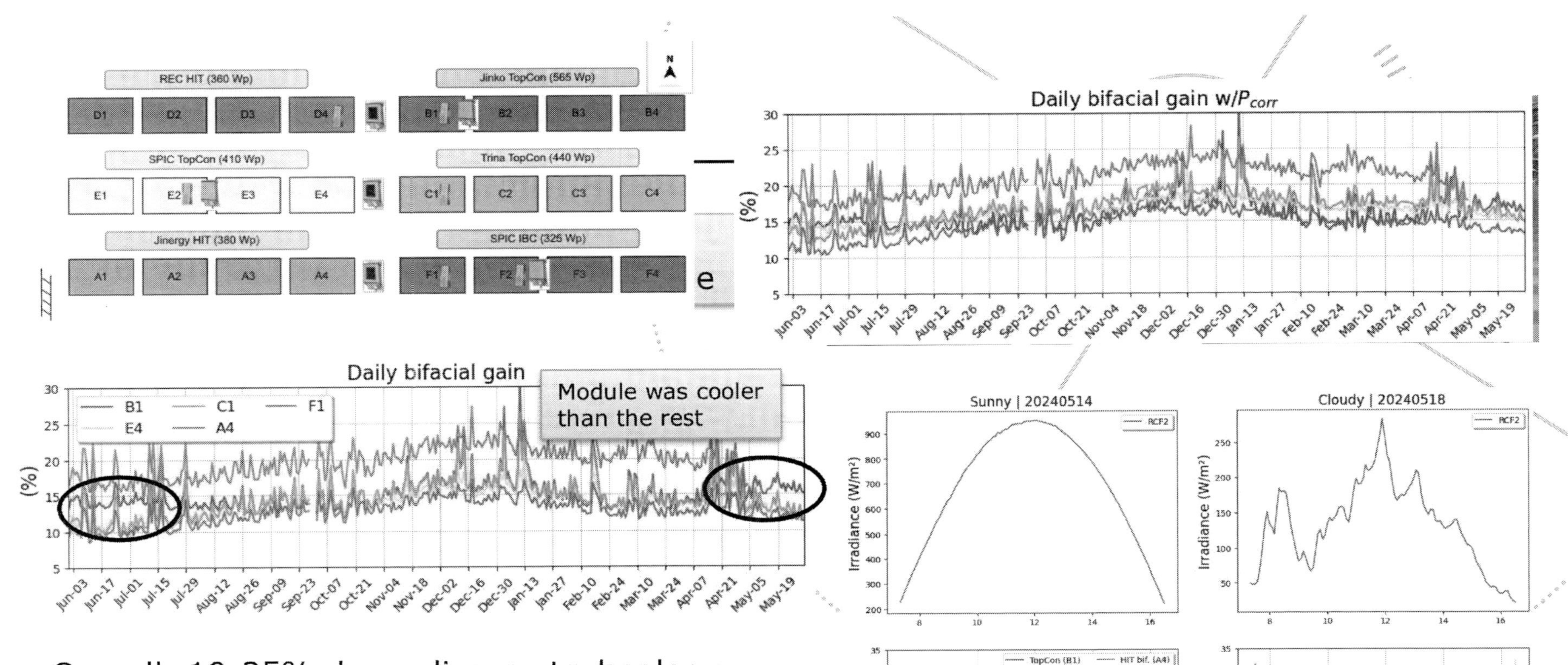

- Overall: 10-25% depending on technology
  - Sunny day: 10-15%
  - Cloudy day: 15-25%
- Bifacial gain increases with sun elevation

020214-011

Daily averaged performance ratio

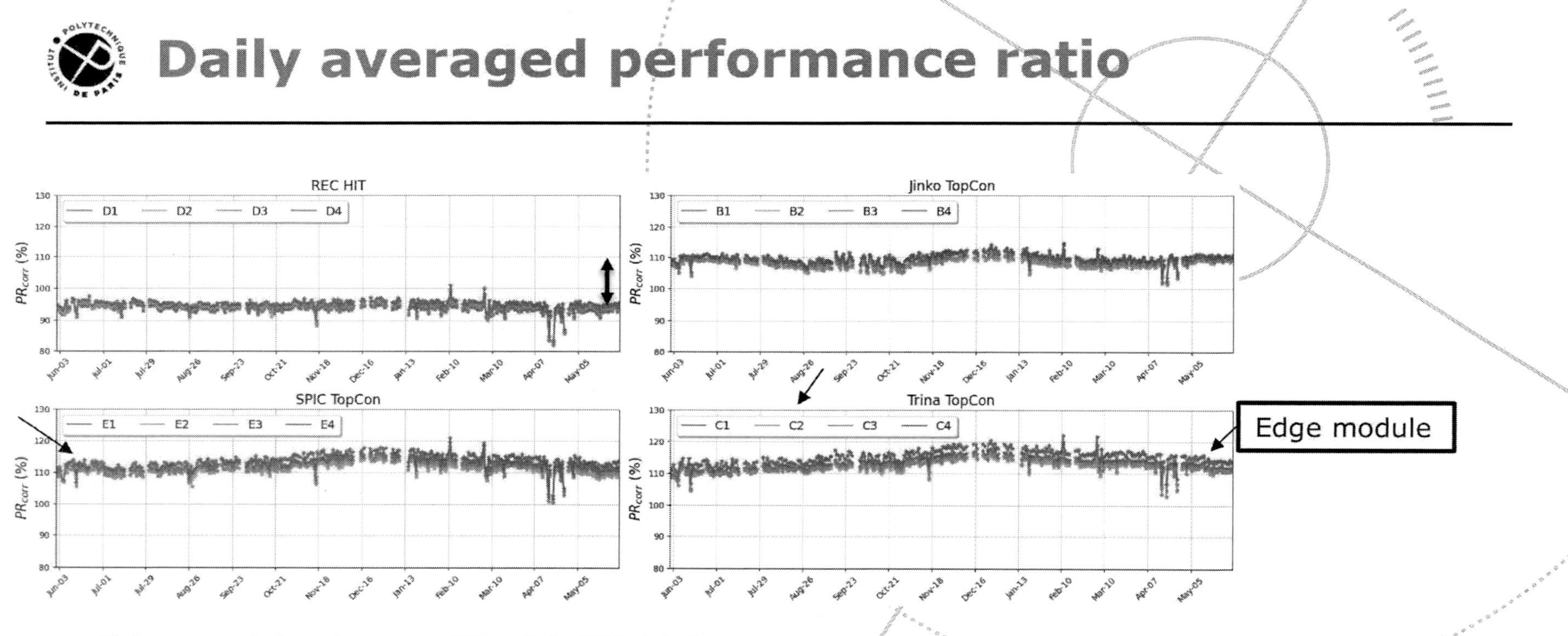

- Edge modules have a PR of 1-2% higher

- PR for bifacial modules is up to 25% higher than that of a monofacial

12 EUPVSEC 2025 / 23-09-2025

Decreased PR due to soiling(?)

Picture taken after one month without rain

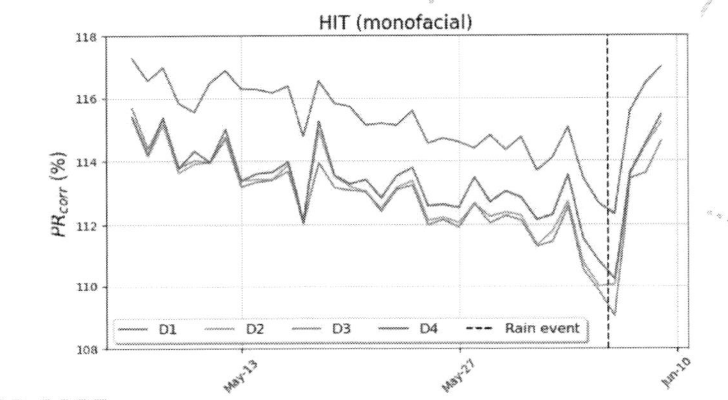

For prolonged periods of time without rain (more than 3 weeks), a decrease in PR of up to 4% has been observed

Performance summary

	HIT (mono) (D4)	TOPCon (B1)*	TOPCon (E4)	TOPCon (C1)	HIT (bif.) (A4)*	IBC (F1)
PR (%)	91 (86-94)	107 (102-109)	109 (104-114)	110 (104-114)	108 (101-115)	104 (98-109)
Yield (Wh/Wp)	1707 (119-160)	1960 (137-182)	1943 (136-180)	1947 (136-180)	2034 (142-188)	1920 (134-178)
Bifacial Gain (%)		15 (13-17)	14 (11-16)	14 (11-17)	19 (15-22)	12 (10-14)

Bifaciality Factor: 75%   69%   74%   87%   65%

Take away messages

- First row modules benefit from:
  - Location
  - Cooling from breeze

- Annually:
  - Bifacial gain: range 12-19% (mean is 14.8%)
  - HIT bifacial yields 19% more than HIT monofacial
  - PR of bifacials is 104-110%, monofacial is 91%

- Modules with a bifacial factor from 65-74% perform similarly (except for front row)

020214-015

Future Work

- Performance characterization of current installation
  - Soiling
  - Degradation

- Modelling
  - Irradiance
  - Power output

- Financial analyses(LCOE, self-consumption,…)

- Performance of experimental cells

020214-016

Data availability

Agrivoltaic

Visit our poster!
4DV.1.18

- 72 TOPCon half-cell bifacial modules (555 Wp, 560 Wp, 565 Wp)
  - 36 equipped with individual optimizers
  - 4 inverters with 18 modules each

17

Rooftop

- Installed in July 2020
- Capacity of 16.3 kWp
- 6 types of panels
- sc-Si reference cell, panel temperature

sc-Si black backsheet
sc-Si white backsheet
sc-Si Q.ANTUM half-cells
Low LID sc-Si PERC half-cells
Low LID sc-Si PERC full-cells
LID Bifacial PERC

18

PhD Offer

PV infrastructure
+
Instrumentation
TE FARE ITO
UPF
UNIVERSITÉ
DE LA POLYNÉSIE FRANÇAISE
Thesis
Vatea SANSINE
(March 2022)
Thesis
Paul MAUGER
(May 2026)
Artificial Intelligence
+
Small scale modelization
Forecasting tool for PV production
Climatology +
Large scale modelization
020214-019

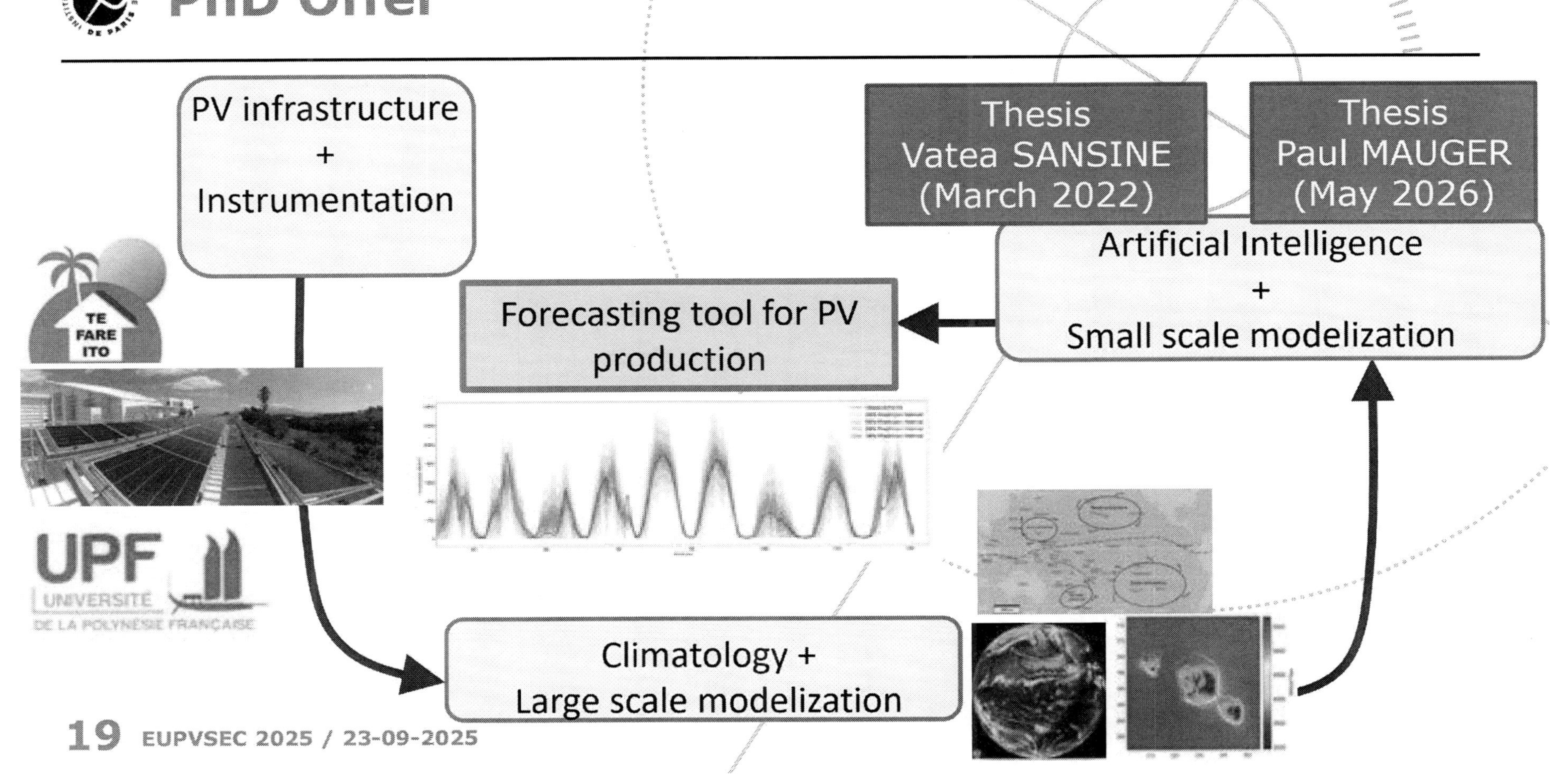

E4C
INTERDISCIPLINARY
CENTER
LMD
Thank you for your attention!
UPF
UNIVERSITÉ
DE LA POLYNÉSIE FRANÇAISE
GePaSud
moira.torres_aguilar@upf.pf
l'
ÉCOLE
POLYTECHNIQUE

STATISTICAL TRENDS IN NOMINAL VS. MEASURED PERFORMANCE OF PV MODULES AND THE IMPACT OF METASTABILITY

Ulli Kräling[1], Daniel Philipp[1], Martin Kaiser[1]
[1]Fraunhofer Institute for Solar Energy Systems ISE
Heidenhofstr. 2, 79110 Freiburg, Germany

ABSTRACT: The Calibration and Testing Laboratory for PV Modules at Fraunhofer ISE has been conducting characterization measurements on modules for many years, placing emphasis on a stable calibration level and measurement precision. In this publication, we statistically analyze measurement data over the past 12 years and specifically examine the development of the performance conformity of the modules with the nameplate values given by the manufacturers. We present the underlying data filters and assess the results in the context of recent technological developments in cell and module technology. Notably, from 2016 to 2023, we observe a continuous trend towards a negative deviation, meaning that the measured performance under standard test conditions (STC) is lower than the promised nominal value by -1.28 % (median). In 2024, we observe stabilization or slight improvement. To contextualize this observation, we also examine the development of initial degradation due to light induced degradation (LID) along the evolution of different solar cell generations. This shows a significant improvement for newer technologies, leading to a trend reversal, where LID affects modules positively, which could be partly attributed to dark-storage induced metastability phenomena.
Keywords: PV Module Performance, Calibration, LID, Metastability, Storage Effect

1 INTRODUCTION

1.1 Background and motivation

The expansion of photovoltaics in Germany, Europe, and worldwide has gained rapid momentum. According to the Federal Network Agency, the installation rates in Germany were 14.1 GW in 2023 [1] and 16.2 GW in 2024 [2]. In the European Union, the installation rates according to the industry association "SolarPower Europe" were 62.8 GW and 65.5 GW, respectively [3]. Globally, the installation rate in 2023 was around 450 GW [4, 5].

This strong PV expansion is occurring in an extremely competitive environment. Especially in the years 2023 and 2024, the global PV market was characterized by significant overcapacity regarding the production of PV cells and modules, leading to a price drop below \$0.1/Wp [5] in some cases.

The reference for assessment of these installation capacities is the sum of the nominal maximum performance of the PV modules installed in the PV systems. This value is often referred to as nominal or nameplate power at maximum power point (P_{nom}), which is determined according to IEC 60904-1 [6] for monofacial PV modules and IEC 60904-1-2 [7] for bifacial PV modules, under standard test conditions (STC), respectively. These conditions are essentially defined by an irradiation of 1000 W/m², a light spectrum corresponding to an Air-Mass Index of 1.5 (AM1.5G), and a module temperature of 25°C [8].

The nominal power P_{nom} has a high significance because it serves as the central reference describing a module type. Accordingly, the price for PV modules is often related to P_{nom} to enable comparative evaluation of different products/manufacturers by giving module prices per Watt Peak (Wp). The calculated energy yield of a PV system also correlates to the nominal power of the modules. Simplified, each percentage increase in nominal power results in a correspondingly higher yield over lifetime, assuming equal secondary module- and system characteristics (temperature and low-light behavior,

bifaciality, system design etc.). Moreover, the P_{nom} is used as reference to capture the aging/degradation of modules: Whether modules perform as expected or if there are indications of quality defects or even claims from the performance warranty is usually assessed based on how much the measured performance under STC deviates from the value in new (initial) condition. Provided that there is no other agreement between buyer and manufacturer, P_{nom} represents the initial value.

Due to the relevance of the nominal performance, laboratories that are capable of measuring module performance accurately and traceable to internationally recognized references are of high importance. Module manufacturers obtain so-called reference modules from such laboratories. These should be precisely characterized modules used by the module manufacturer to adjust the production in-line flasher. In the so-called binning process, each module is measured at the end of the production line and assigned a performance class. In a process commonly referred to by manufacturers as 'positive sorting', the module must achieve at least the value of a certain performance class. The performance class defines the nominal performance of the module that the manufacturer indicates on the nameplate. Consequently, the value, measured by the external lab for the reference module defines indirectly to which performance class a module is assorted. Also, module purchasers often rely on such independent laboratories by having samples from the purchased modules tested to assure that the modules reach the promised performance class.

This study provides a deep statistical evaluation of the measurement data collected at Fraunhofer ISE over a period from 2012 to the first half year of 2025. The focus of the investigation is on the measured module performance P_{MPP} compared to the nominal performance P_{nom} as indicated on the nameplate. Other nameplate values such as short-circuit current I_{SC} and open-circuit voltage V_{OC} will be considered.

10.4229/EUPVSEC2025/3BO.15.4

An additional aspect that is also regarded in this study pertains to the light induced degradation (LID) effect. Since the performance of PV modules is known to experience a slight change during the first operating hours under irradiation, the development of the LID effect is examined regarding various solar cell generations.

Finally, metastable behavior of PV modules with the TOPCon cell technology, which is the leading technology at the moment [9], were analyzed. The focus is on the degradation and recovery behavior of new PV modules (storage effects). While the impact of these variations on the actual yield of a PV system is expected to be rather low, they can superimpose precise measurements and thus lead to errors or misinterpretations if not considered properly.

1.2 Laboratory environment and calibration level

The Fraunhofer Institute for Solar Energy Systems operates an accredited testing laboratory including all relevant performance and reliability standards such as IEC 60904, IEC 61215 and IEC 61730 within the scope of accredited work (certificate D-PL-11140-33-00). For the exact IV-characterization the laboratory holds additionally an accreditation as calibration laboratory (certificate D-K-11140-02-00), which requires the highest level of traceability. The laboratory benefits from the advantageous combination of testing and calibration services. This lab, herein referred to as CalLab PV Modules has been conducting characterization measurements on modules for many years, placing emphasis on a stable calibration level and precision. All calibrations and measurements are directly traceable to national standards via the Physikalisch-Technische Bundestanstalt (PTB) which is the national metrology institute (NMI) of Germany. At CalLab PV Modules, IV-characteristics and the maximum power at STC (P_{MPP}) of the modules are measured in the context of various applications, such as reference modules for production lines, reliability investigations, product certification, and particularly in the context of quality assurance measures for module buyers.

In an accredited calibration laboratory highest standards must be applied to monitor and to minimize unpreventable temporal variations of the calibration level. For the latter interpretation of statistical trends observed in this study, the stability of the calibration level of CalLab PV Modules is shown exemplarily based on results of internal and external measures for the quality assurance.

Figure 1 presents the results of Round Robins (RR) on PV modules between the years 2008 to 2024. It is important to note that the participants as well as the number of PV modules and technologies in the RR have varied across different years. Results of the RR with the international leading PV labs have been published separately [10, 11]. Furthermore, bilateral comparisons with the PTB [12] are included.

The plot illustrates the average, minimum, and maximum deviations of CalLab PV Modules from the respective reference value of the RR. The differences in scatter are influenced by the varying number of participants and the different technologies involved. A central message derived from the data is that, on average, the values reported by CalLab PV Modules have consistently deviated by less than 0.5 % from the reference value since 2009, and notably no significant trends are observable throughout the years.

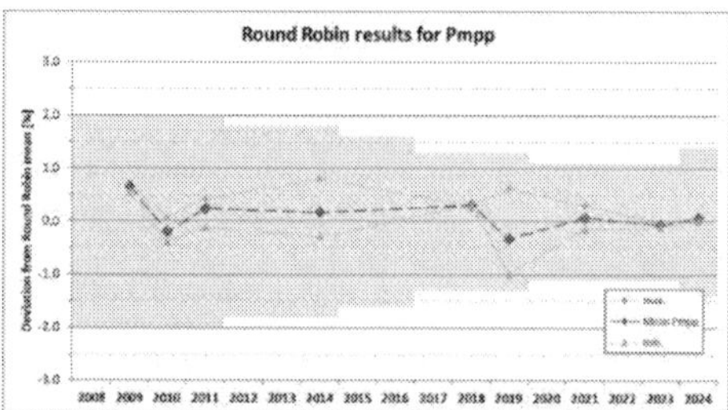

Figure 1: Results of various Round Robins on module level. The average, minimum and maximum deviation of CalLab PV Modules from the respective reference value is provided for each Round Robin campaign. The grey area represents the measurement uncertainty (k=2) of CalLab PV Modules for the measurements.

Figure 2 shows the average deviation of the measured short-circuit current Isc of primary calibrated WPVS reference cells from the calibration value measured by PTB. It shows that the deviation is continuously below 0.5 % and no trend towards higher or lower deviations is visible.

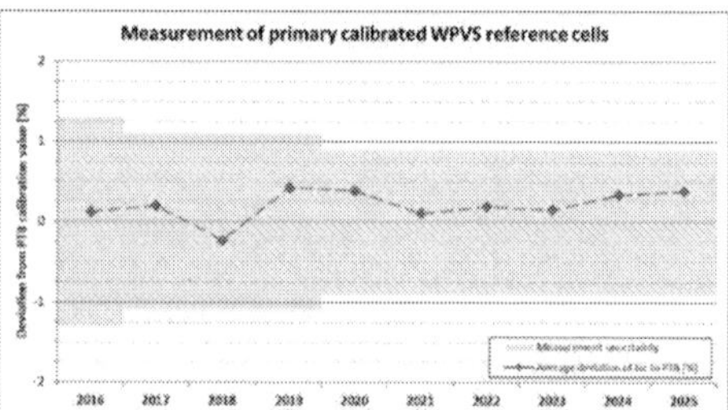

Figure 2: Average deviation of measured short-circuit current Isc of primary calibrated WPVS cells from PTB calibration values.

2 DATA SOURCES AND FILTERING

As described above CalLab PV Modules produces accurate measurement results for its customers since more than a decade [13]. Beside the measurement results, basic characteristics of each module, e.g., manufacturer, module type, module dimensions, and cell material were recorded. Moreover, the nameplate values of the modules were recorded where available.

For this study, measurement results were used in an anonymized way to analyze the development of the measured deviation from nameplate values in the past years. It is to be noted that this is not the first publication of statistical evaluation of measurements and the basic filtering principles have already described [14]. To ensure a good understanding of this study, this data processing, referred to as "basic filter" are explained in detail again below. Additionally, further specific filters were applied for the focused evaluations, which are also described below.

2.1 Basic filter for power at STC evaluations

This study is based on an overall number of 76936 measurements (IV-characteristics at STC) taken between the beginning of 2012 and the first half year of 2025.

Within this period, all measurement results were evaluated using the same inhouse-developed software.

As mentioned above, the modules belong to different types of projects with different objectives. Projects coming from module buyers often include large sets of identical modules of the same type, e.g., from a PV power plant. Projects from manufacturers often include only single modules, e.g., reference modules for the production line. Beside the number of modules per type (i.e. product name), also the number of measurements conducted on an individual module varies sometimes, e.g. since aging tests, such as (LID), light- and elevated temperature-induced degradation (LETID), potential-induced degradation (PID), and others, require module measurements at different states, such as initial (out of the box), interim (after different steps of stressing) and final (very last measurement).

The basic filter ensures the statistical evaluability of the modules in their new (initial) condition. In short, these are the following filtering stages, which are explained in detail further below:

- Inconsistency filter: Filtering out invalid or unusable data
- Initial measurement filter: Filtering out data after pre-treatment
- First appearance filter: Each module (serial number) is considered only once
- Imbalance filter: Avoids statistical distortions due to differing sample sizes

2.1.1 Inconsistency filter

The 1st filter sorts out measurement results with inconsistent data. E.g., target temperature and target irradiance must align with the designated measurement type (e.g. STC). The serial number of the device under test (DUT) in the results information is mandatory to identify repeating measurements. Measurements of the rear side of bifacial modules are also sorted out. Finally, datasets with physically impossible results are excluded, like negative values for short-circuit current I_{SC}, open-circuit voltage V_{OC}, or maximum power P_{MPP}, or fill factor beyond 100 % or efficiencies beyond 30 %. Additional constraints are a current limit of 25 A, a voltage limit of 250 V and a power limit of 800 W. Those results might originate from measurements of defect modules (e.g., due to transportation damage). Incorrect prototypes could also lead to ambiguous IV curves which are sort out. Only measurements with a complete IV curve respectively all relevant electrical parameters are considered.

2.1.2 Initial measurement filter

The 2nd filter only preserves the first measurement – of a specific measurement type like STC – of a DUT within a project. The intention is to obtain only results at initial state of the module. This is the only comparable state across a large set of data because the intermediate state of a module depends on the individual schedule and focus of a project and therefore differs for each project. This also means that the herein presented data was acquired before any stabilization, e.g. by light soaking.

2.1.3 First appearance filter

The 3rd filter removes datasets of recalibrations and other re-measurements. Typically, golden modules are sent to the lab to be recalibrated in regular time intervals. Then, the identical module refers to different projects

respectively orders. To avoid double counting of these modules, only the first appearance of a serial number of a specific module is valid and all subsequent remeasurements of a module are sorted out.

2.1.4 Imbalance filter

In the 4th step, from each module type in a project, only the measurement results closest to the average power for this module type is considered. Hence, the imbalance due to different numbers of modules per project is eliminated. In addition, this paper is focused on general and representative trends in PV module development and not in the presentation of highest possible results.

The filtering steps 1-4 reduced the dataset from 76936 to 6999 measurements which represents 9.1 % of the initial data whereas the variety of module types of the initial dataset is still represented by the filtered dataset. The number of unique module types is only reduced from 4322 to 4272 by the filtering steps.

2.2 Extended filter for power at STC evaluations

Although the basic filter described in Section 2.1 already provides a good evaluation of statistical trends, additional filtering methods were applied to present a more representative picture from the perspective of the module recipients, assuming this view correlates more to the products installed in PV systems. Initially, only measurements with nameplate values are considered, where the deviation to rated values can be evaluated. This reduced the dataset from 6999 to 6344 measurements. Furthermore, additional factors were excluded that could potentially lead to slight statistical distortions when only considering the basic filter. In short, the following filtering steps were added (detailed description follows below):

- Technology filter: Consider only modules based on crystalline silicon cell technology and electrical characteristics typically for most modules installed in PV-plants
- Indoor filter: Exclude modules which were already exposed in PV-plants
- Project filter: Focus only on market relevant modules and assure an unused condition
- Customer filter: Focus only on projects engaged by module recipients
- TOP15 manufacturer filter: Focus on PV modules from established companies only

The effect of the different filters on the size of the dataset is shown in Table I.

2.2.1 Technology filter

The evaluation focused only on crystalline modules. Hence, a technology filter was applied sorting out all datasets which were not based on single-junction mono-Si or poly-Si cell material. The evaluation should represent standard sized modules and exclude any small test samples or cells. So, results are filtered by some module characteristics: the total module area is within 0.5 m² and 4 m² and the number of cells in a module is between 30 and 200 cells. These boundaries exclude small modules as well as oversized or in-series connected modules.

2.2.2 Indoor filter

In some projects, modules from the field are measured before and after cleaning to identify the soiling effect. In these cases, the initial measurement is on the one hand based on a dirty module and on the other hand the modules were already exposed outdoors and are not comparable to new modules. Those kinds of measurements are also sorted out.

2.2.3 Project filter

Measurements from research projects as well as from certification projects are sorted out because these are modules which might not be available on the market or test samples or prototypes. Internal measurements for continuous quality assurance as well as any test measurements are also filtered out.

2.2.4 Customer filter

Measurements ordered by PV module manufacturers are rejected. The modules might be used as reference modules for their production line (golden module) or for R&D purposes. The label on the module is then not relevant and golden modules are only for internal use by the manufacturer. Therefore, any deviation between nameplate and measurement is not relevant for the downstream market.

2.2.5 TOP15 manufacturer filter

The variety of modules manufacturers and their experience is large. Some manufacturers are present on the market for years and some already vanished. Therefore, the final filter considers only the TOP15 manufacturers over the past 7 years (by shipment volume) to have a more consistent dataset and comparable data over the years. Available TOP10 lists from the past years [15–19]. are used to identify TOP15 manufacturers. The explicit mention of individual manufacturer names is deliberately omitted to prevent misinterpretation, for example, arising from whether a specific manufacturer was included in the evaluation or not. This is also considered irrelevant for the results and conclusions of this study.

Table I: Number of datasets per year (YR) after basic filtering (BAS) (section 2.1) and for the extended filter steps: technology (TECH), indoor (INDR), project (PROJ), customer (CUS) and TOP15 manufacturer (T15).

YR	BAS	TECH	INDR	PROJ	CUS	T15
12	696	615	611	518	284	93
13	763	646	623	523	325	73
14	613	500	468	383	219	58
15	542	456	452	370	135	52
16	517	457	455	368	165	86
17	483	428	422	337	167	87
18	428	372	358	271	147	70
19	392	335	320	236	155	93
20	403	367	357	275	158	111
21	339	315	308	203	129	77
22	317	292	279	195	130	73
23	309	293	287	194	126	68
24	371	353	348	286	167	90
25*	171	161	160	122	77	40
Σ	6.344	5.590	5.448	4.281	2.384	1.071

*For 2025 only the first 6 months are considered

2.3 Filtering approach for LID evaluations

To consider the light induced degradation (LID) effect, the standard IEC 61215-2 [20] describes a methodology for the stabilization of PV modules. Slightly simplified, a crystalline silicon-based PV module can be regarded as stable when its performance does not change by more than 1 % over two consecutive light exposures of at least 5 kWh/m². In the laboratory practice this was realized by exposing the module in an initial step to a dose of 20 kWh/m² to degrade the module, followed by two further exposures of 5 kWh/m² to proof the stability with performance measurements at STC in-between. Typically, an initial (out-of-the-box) power measurement was conducted to quantify the LID effect. For the light exposure, an artificial sun-simulator with an irradiance around 1000 W/m² was used. The modules were operated in MPP mode at (50 ± 10) °C.

For the evaluation of the LID effect throughout this study only datasets were considered, for which the full stabilization process as described above was executed, including initial out-of-the-box measurement. These datasets mainly came from product certification or calibration projects. Since the process was only implemented with the 2016 edition of IEC 61215, the earliest datasets date from 2017. Table II shows an overview of 127 datasets where information on the cell technology was available.

Table II: Number of datasets per year and technology for the LID statistics.

YR	PERC	TOPCON	HJT	IBC
17	4			
18	14			
19			1	
20	1			
21	5			
22	6		1	
23	8	13	3	
24	32	21	3	
25*	1	6		8
Σ	71	40	8	8

*For 2025 only the first 6 months are considered

3 RESULTS

3.1 Absolute STC results

Referring to the data filtering described above, this chapter presents the key results of the statistical investigations into the IV- and performance characteristics taken at Standard Test Conditions. It can be assumed that the following data represent currently field-installed modules. While the focus of this publication lay on the deviation of measured to nominal values, the following plots (Figure 3 - Figure 6) shall visualize the development of the mainstream crystalline silicon-based module technology of the past 12 years in general. In these plots, the mean of all data points (dashed line) and the median (solid line), as well as the quantiles for 50 % and 80 % of the datasets, is provided.

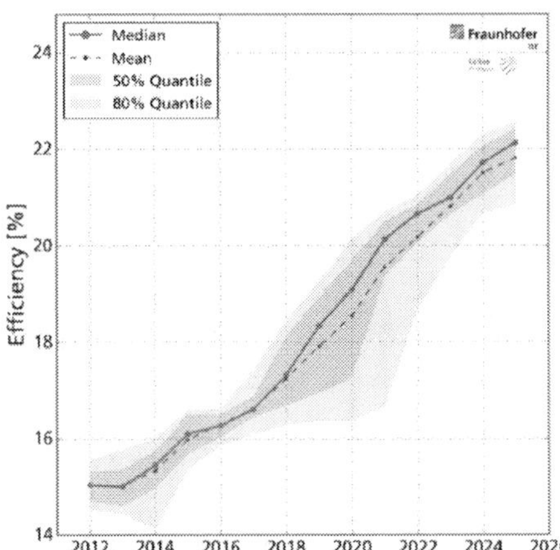

Figure 3: PV module efficiencies over time after filtering.

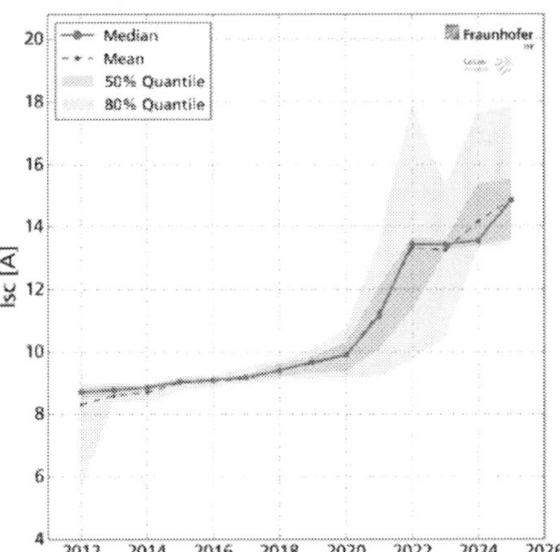

Figure 4: PV module short-circuit current I_{SC} over time after filtering.

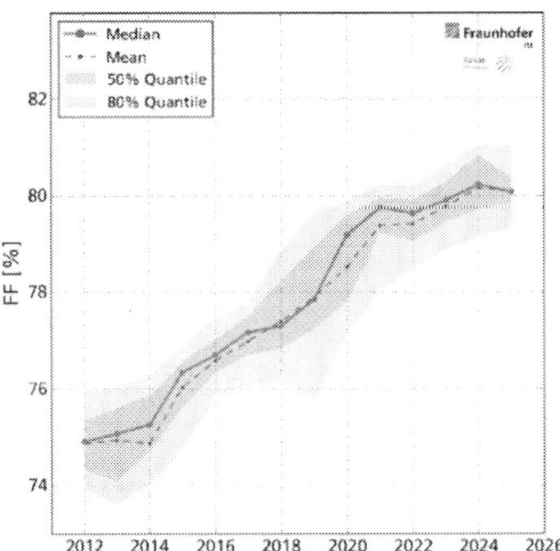

Figure 5: PV module fill factor FF over time after filtering.

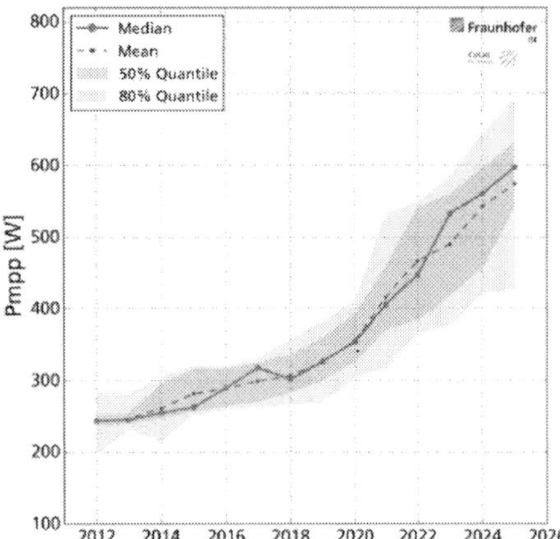

Figure 6: PV module maximum power P_{MPP} over time after filtering.

The efficiency of PV modules increased almost linear from ~15 % to ~22 % within 12 years which corresponds to a rate of 0.6 %/year. The fill factor also increased almost linear from 75 % to 80 % within this period. For I_{SC} and P_{MPP}, the development can be split in two sections: until 2020, the values slightly increased over the years from 8.5 A to 10 A and from 250 W to 350 W for I_{SC} and P_{MPP}, respectively. From 2020 until now, there was a steeper increase up to 15 A for I_{SC} and 600 W for P_{MPP}. Furthermore, the spread – represented by the 80 % quantile – was larger in the section from 2020 until now. Both effects can be explained by higher variation in the module layout and the cells used in the PV modules. Cell dimensions increased which directly affects the I_{SC} and different sizes were available which led to different geometrical layouts. Modules with 5 and 6 cell rows were available, cells are cut into half cells and third cells. In general, module dimensions increased which is directly linked to higher power outputs. There were more options to build a module which is mainly reflected by the higher spread in I_{SC} and P_{MPP}.

The development of V_{OC} over time is not shown because there are no trends visible. Generally, the measured V_{OC} is dominated by the number of cells per module and the interconnection of these cells which was not analyzed systematically in this study.

3.2 Deviation from nominal STC values

Although the extended data filtering is more relevant for the consumer side and thus for the installed PV modules, the deviation of P_{MPP} from P_{nom} is plotted for both filter levels, as the basic filtering (Figure 7) is based on a larger dataset and furthermore to illustrate the impact of the additional filtering (Figure 8). However, in Table III, results are only provided after extended filtering due to the greater practical relevance. The plots show the temporal progression of the percentage deviation over the last 12 years. This is particularly interesting for evaluating developments in the context of other market- and/or technology trends.

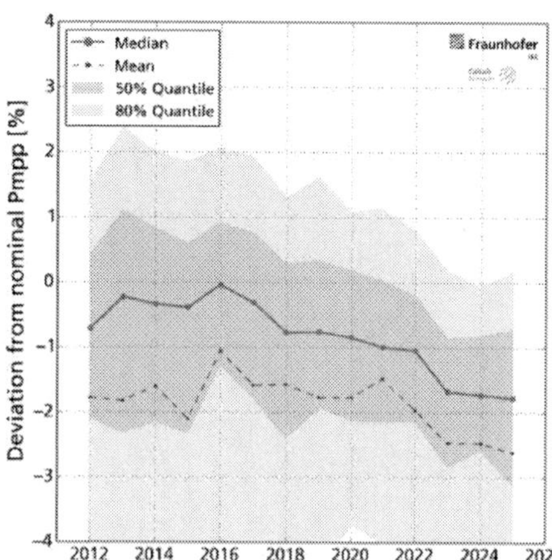

Figure 7: P_{MPP} deviations between measured and nominal value over time (basic filter)

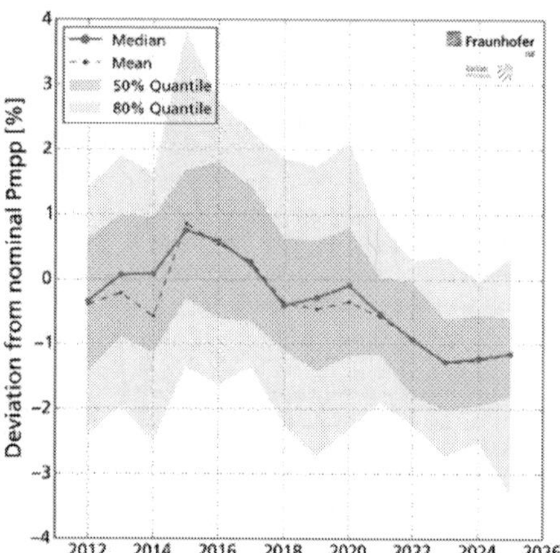

Figure 8: P_{MPP} deviations between measured and nominal value over time (extended filter)

In the extended filter, the median and mean for all examined parameters align well (Figure 8). In contrast, a negative shift in the mean performance deviation compared to the median can be observed in the basic filter (Figure 7). This indicates a stronger influence of negative outliers. Qualitatively, both evaluations show a slight but almost continuous negative trend in performance deviation since around 2016. Notably, the extended evaluation showed, on average, mostly positive values compared to the nominal value in the years up to the year 2017 (e.g., median 2016 at +0.59 %), which reduced to a median value the following years but especially pronounced from 2021 to 2023, ending at -1.28 %. In 2024, this negative trend has halted, and a slight trend reversal was observed towards a median value of -1.15 % in 2025.

In contrast, Figure 9 shows in which ranges nominal (label) power P_{nom} can deviate from results measured by an accredited calibration laboratory, regardless of technical or other external developments.

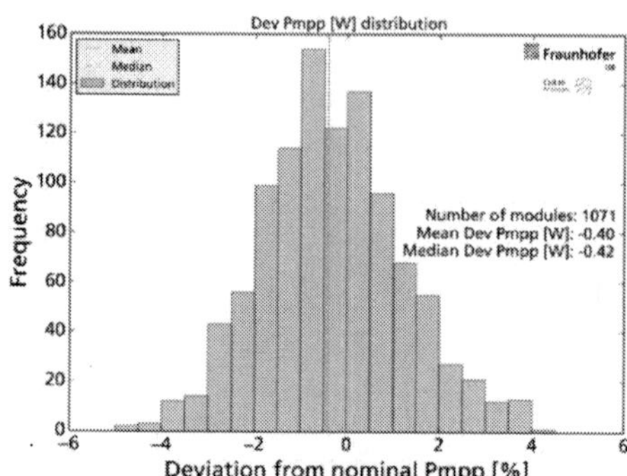

Figure 9: Histogram of deviations between measured and nominal value for P_{MPP} (extended filter)

Regarding V_{OC} and I_{SC} both filter levels convey a very comparable picture. Hence, only the plots for the filtered data are shown in Figure 10 and Figure 11. For V_{OC}, the nominal and measured values overall match best over the entire observation period. In the last 2 years, a slight trend towards somewhat higher measured values compared to the nominal values is noticeable. Notably, I_{SC}, increased over the entire observation period: While the median value in 2012 was still around +1.37 %, it fell below -3 % by 2025. Since this trend does not align with the trend of the performance specification and the V_{OC} remains nearly stable, a corresponding opposite trend is evident in the fill factor, shown in Figure 12.

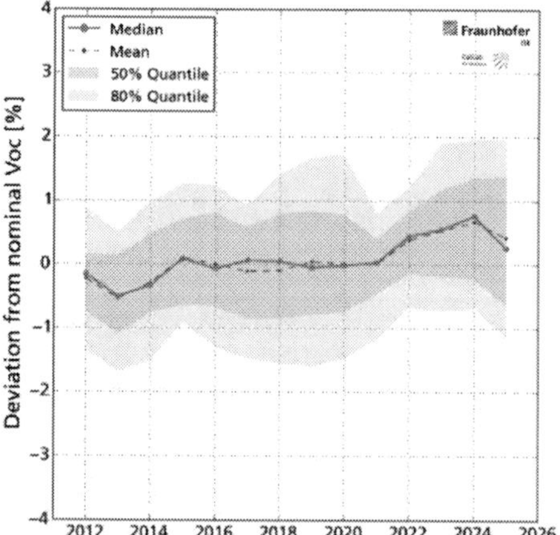

Figure 10: V_{OC} deviations between measured and nominal value over time (extended filter)

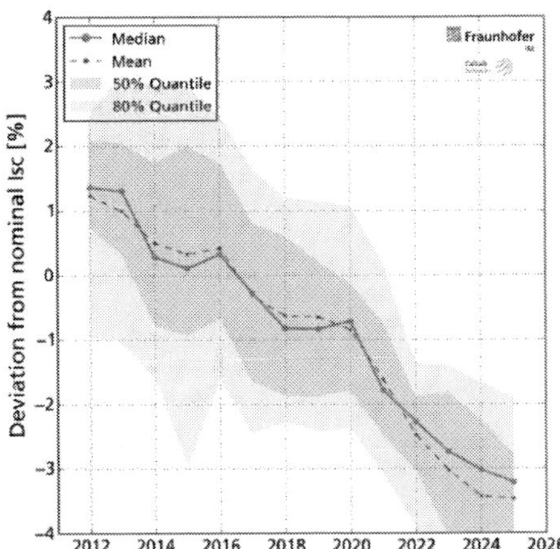

Figure 11: I_{SC} deviations between measured and nominal value over time (extended filter)

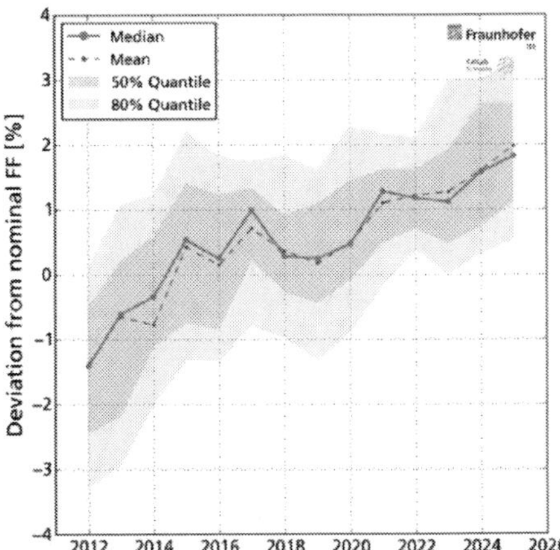

Figure 12: FF deviations between measured and nominal value over time (extended filter)

Table III: Deviation of measured STC parameters from nameplate values per year based on the extended filter TOP15. datasets per year and technology for the LID statistics.

Year	I_{SC} [%]	V_{OC} [%]	P_{MPP} [%]	FF [%]
2012	1.37	-0.16	-0.34	-1.41
2013	1.31	-0.50	0.07	-0.60
2014	0.29	-0.33	0.09	-0.33
2015	0.11	0.09	0.75	0.54
2016	0.33	-0.07	0.59	0.25
2017	-0.28	0.07	0.23	0.99
2018	-0.82	0.05	-0.40	0.29
2019	-0.84	-0.05	-0.28	0.25
2020	-0.71	-0.01	-0.09	0.47
2021	-1.78	0.03	-0.52	1.28
2022	-2.26	0.44	-0.93	1.17
2023	-2.74	0.55	-1.28	1.12
2024	-3.02	0.76	-1.22	1.57
2025	-3.21	0.26	-1.15	1.82

PV module prices are typically defined by \$/Wp which makes the nominal power an important parameter. It is a tradeoff between the profit margin of the PV module manufacturer and the customer who calculates the costs for a PV plant and the return of invest. So, the contract between the manufacturer and the customer plays an important role. The question, if measurement uncertainties of a third-party laboratory are considered or not, can shift the acceptance criteria for measured power output to a lower value. This could somehow explain why the observed deviation in power does not further drop.

In contrast to that, I_{SC} and V_{OC} are not relevant for pricing of PV modules. However, these parameters have high relevance for the inverter design and the string layout. Due to the high temperature coefficient of V_{OC}, the match of V_{OC} is important to align with the inverter requirements and limits for various temperature conditions. As the V_{OC} of a module is mainly defined by the underlying cell technology, the variation of V_{OC} in a production line for a specific module type is typically lower than for I_{SC} and P_{MPP}. So, the manufacturer can set the nameplate value more precisely which is reflected here by small deviations within ± 1 % with no significant trend over time.

I_{SC} is relevant for cabling and ohmic losses as well as for instances of overheating. Therefore, the upper limits are mainly relevant for inverter inputs, and the slight overrating of I_{SC} might be a safety issue. System layout, including inverters and cabling, is based on the high nameplate I_{SC}. We expect no warranty issues due to overcurrent because currents in operation will typically be lower. This could explain why there are higher negative deviations for I_{SC} but it is still unclear why there is a downwards trend over time. A potential reason could be the fact that manufacturers calibrate their inline measurement systems with reference modules to match P_{MPP}. Due to the increase in I_{SC} of the PV modules in the past years, ohmic losses become more relevant. If the module is not connected in 4-wire technology during the measurement, then cable resistance can affect the measurement results and lower the fill factor or P_{MPP}, respectively. These cases lead to the I_{SC} being overrated. The fill factor is not affected by this procedure and is still affected by the ohmic losses. Measurement software usually includes several calibration factors for IV curve correction to overcome these issues. The inline calibration procedures and the application of correction factors by manufacturers are not known. The negative trend could be a consequence of increasing I_{SC} values, ohmic losses in 2-wire connection and missing application of correction factors.

3.2 Light induced degradation

Figure 13 shows the result of the stabilization process according to IEC 61215 [20] for new modules after an initial out-of-the-box measurement. The initial measurement at STC served as reference value, the relative deviation of P_{MPP} in percent after 3 steps of light exposure (20/5/5 kWh/m²) was calculated, and for each year the averaged values are shown, based on the respective number of datasets (see Table II). The results are differentiated according to the cell technology.

The result shows the progress in the past years in preventing LID effects. While early PERC-based technologies show effects of up to -2 % this was reduced within this technology levels below 0.5 %. For TOPCon, HJT and IBC almost no negative LID effects are determined. However, only a low number of HJT based module types are considered here.

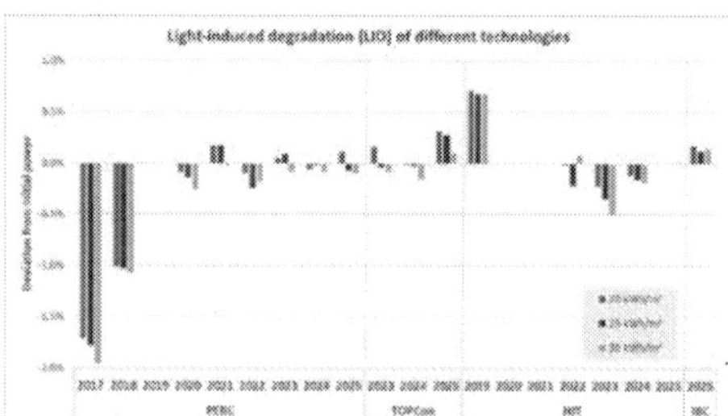

Figure 13: Average deviation of P_{MPP} from initial out-of-the-box result per year and technology. Results after 20, 25 and 30 kWh/m² light-induced degradation (LID) are shown.

3.3 TOPCon metastability effects (storage effect)

The impact of storage conditions on the performance measured on TOPCon based PV cells and modules has been reported in the context of their impact on aging tests. Strong power drops of several percent have been observed especially after UV aging [21, 22].

In contrast, the results presented in this study refer to degradation taking place during ordinary laboratory storage of modules and recovery after short light soaking. The susceptibility of the module types to any storage-based degradation was not known in advance. Some TOPCon module types were chosen from customer projects where the sensitivity to LID and storage effects were investigated. Other TOPCon module types were property of the laboratory and hence, effects could be investigated for a longer period. Consequently, the number of modules examined for each type, as well as the specific experimental approach, is not 100 % identical for all modules.

Figure 14 (top) shows the development of the measured performance of 4 module types (C, D, E, F). Of type C and D one module was tested, of type E two modules, and of type F four modules were tested. The measurement sequence started with an initial light stabilization process as required in IEC 61215 with 20 kWh/m² followed by 2 x 5 kWh/m² (as described in section 2.3). To analyze the impact of this initial light soaking on the storage effect of type E and F the half of the modules were not exposed to this process (E_1, F_1, F_2). After several steps of storage (i.e. not completely dark, ordinary laboratory light), a single short light soaking with 2 kWh/m² using a class B solar simulator and MPP tracking, was conducted to analyze to what extent the short light exposure recovers the storage effect.

Figure 14 (bottom) refers to results of two additional module types (A, B) of which only one module per type was analyzed. In contrast to types C, D, E, F these modules were exposed to several intervals of storage and short light soaking of 2 kWh/m².

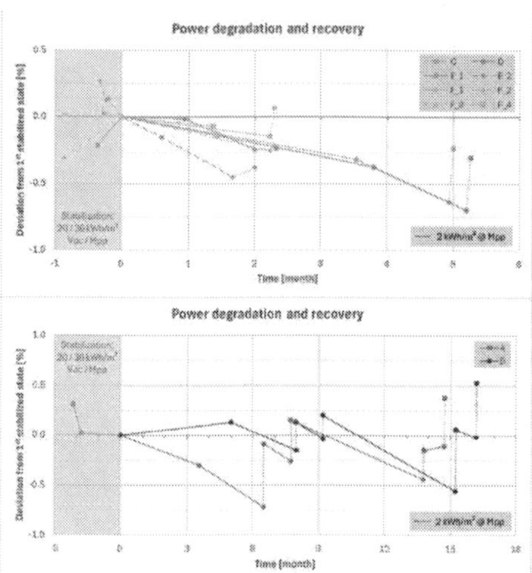

Figure 14: TOPCon degradation over time by lab storage (solid and dashed lines) and recovery by light-soaking of 2 kWh/m² at P_{MPP} (dotted lines) for six different module types. Top: modules with only single recovery step within 6 months; bottom: modules with multiple storage and recovery steps within 18 months.

All module types showed a degradation in power during storage periods. The degradation rate over time is similar for the different modules except for the E_2 which shows stronger degradation and type B, which showed a slight gain after the first 5 months of storage. The storage conditions were not controlled in detail; therefore, this module might have been exposed more to the ambient laboratory light than other modules or any other storage condition might have differed. After this first gain, the module showed similar behavior as the other modules during storage. The storage degradation rate is on average -0.11 % per month. There is no difference observed between stabilized modules and non-stabilized modules.

The short light soaking of 2 kWh/m² at MPP induced a gain in power for all module types. The average gain was +0.24 %. In contrast to the degradation, there was no similar behavior observed for the different module types. The recovery in P_{MPP} ranged from almost no gain (E_1, F_2 – F_4) up to 0.63 % (A, first cycle). Modules of the same type showed different recovery effects. Therefore, a general conclusion per module type is not possible. In addition, the recovery process for the modules was not reproducible: After several cycles of short light soaking (Modules A and B), the resulting power of the modules did not reach the initial stabilized power nor any other reproducible value. The power values even exceeded the initial stabilized power.

4 CONCLUSIONS

The statistical analyses presented in this study are meant to provide an overview of trends regarding the deviation between nominal (nameplate) to precisely measured electrical characteristics of PV modules.

Between the years 2017 to 2023 we observed a continuous negative trend of the deviation between measured and rated power, reaching a median value of -1.28 % in 2023 and stabilizing since then. While on module level the observed deviations result only in few Watts less performance; the aspect becomes relevant considering the effects on a whole energy economy. The filtering and the broad statistical basis for these results allow to assume that the deviation is representative for the overall PV installations in Germany and Europe.

In Germany, 14.1 GW of capacity was installed in 2023 [1], and 16.2 GW in 2024 [2]. When applying the observed deviations to these installation capacities, the resulting shortfall amounts to approximately 180 MW for 2023 and as much as 198 MW for 2024. These deficits are comparable to the capacity of large-scale PV power plants, such as exemplarily the Weesow-Willmersdorf solar park, which has an installed capacity of 187 MW and, according to the operator, supplies electricity to up to 50,000 households [23].

The underlying causes of this pronounced trend toward negative performance deviations remain subject of speculations. However, the intense pricing and competitive pressure faced by manufacturers likely plays a significant role. The presented findings highlight the importance of verifying the promised performance, both to avoid negative discrepancies and, perhaps even more critically, to accurately determine the actual performance level of installed modules. In the case of large-scale power plants, it is often necessary to assess the condition of the modules after years of operation, e.g. due to a planned sale of the facility or because the modules exhibit irregularities. In such cases, it is essential to establish whether the performance has degraded compared to its original state. Referring solely to the nominal value introduces considerable uncertainty and does not allow to evaluate the real annual degradation rate. Operators or installers of such power plants should therefore ensure that performance measurements are conducted in a laboratory that maintains a stable long-term calibration standard and is logistically accessible with manageable effort.

A positive development was observed for the LID effect, where a clear trend towards less initial degradation could be observed since 2018. Currently LID seems hardly to play a role for modern PV modules. Considering the positive power-deviation around the year 2015 in context of the LID development, it could be possible that manufacturers overrated the module power in the years 2015 to 2017 slightly to be more on the safe side considering LID.

The herein provided experimental results on the impact of storage effects are mainly meant to raise awareness of these effects and to provide the observed range of magnitude. Since the power drop occurs during storage, these effects will not be unveiled by the stabilization process according to IEC61215-2:2021, MQT 19. With variations ranging between 0.5 % and 1 % the observed effects lay typically below stability criteria of IEC61215-1-1:2021 which allows a max. difference between highest and lowest value of 1 % related to the average value over three measurements. Notably, this comparison is only meant as orientation since the standard describes stabilization through light exposure. Especially for applications where high precision and reproducibility is required (e.g. round robins, proficiency testing, generation of golden- and silver modules for production lines) it is important to know and to consider these effects. Processes to reduce undesired impacts or wrong interpretations of measured data are currently under development and the provided data shall support these activities.

5 REFERENCES

[1] Bundesnetzagentur, *Zubau Erneuerbarer Energien 2023*. [Online]. Available: https://www.bundesnetzagentur.de/997312

[2] Bundesnetzagentur, *Ausbau Erneuerbarer Energien 2024*. [Online]. Available: https://www.bundesnetzagentur.de/1043738

[3] SolarPower Europe, *EU Market Outlook for Solar Power 2024-2028*. [Online]. Available: https://www.solarpowereurope.org/insights/outlooks/eu-market-outlook-for-solar-power-2024-2028

[4] G. Masson, M. de l'Epine, and I. Kaizuka, "Trends in Photovoltaic Applications 2024," International Energy Agency (IEA), 2024. [Online]. Available: https://iea-pvps.org/trends_reports/trends-in-pv-applications-2024/

[5] IRENA, *Renewable capacity statistics 2025*. [Online]. Available: https://www.irena.org/Publications/2025/Jul/Renewable-energy-statistics-2025

[6] *Photovoltaic devices – Part 1: Measurement of photovoltaic current-voltage characteristics*, IEC 60904-1: 2020-09, International Electrotechnical Commission (IEC), Geneva, Switzerland, 2020.

[7] *Photovoltaic devices – Part 1-2: Measurement of current-voltage characteristics of bifacial photovoltaic (PV) devices*, IEC TS 60904-1-2: 2024-11, International Electrotechnical Commission (IEC), Geneva, Switzerland, 2024.

[8] *Solar photovoltaic energy systems - Terms, definitions and symbols*, IEC TS 61836: 2016-12, International Electrotechnical Commission (IEC), Geneva, Switzerland, 2016.

[9] ITRPV, "International Technology Roadmap for Photovoltaic (ITRPV): 2024 Results," 2025.

[10] D. Dirnberger *et al.*, "Progress in PV Module Calibration - Results of a world-wide intercomparison between four reference laboratories," *Measurement Science & Technology*, 2014.

[11] E. Salis *et al.*, "Improvements in world-wide intercomparison of PV module calibration," *Progress in Solar Energy 1*, vol. 155, pp. 1451–1461, 2017, doi: 10.1016/j.solener.2017.07.081.

[12] Fraunhofer Institute for Solar Energy Systems ISE, *PV module measurement results from Fraunhofer ISE and the German National Metrology Institute (PTB) show high level of agreement*. Freiburg, Germany, 2023. [Online]. Available: https://www.ise.fraunhofer.de/en/press-media/press-releases/2023/pv-module-measurement-results-from-fraunhofer-ise-and-the-german-national-metrology-institute-show-high-level-of-agreement.html

[13] Fraunhofer Institute for Solar Energy Systems ISE, *Fraunhofer ISE's CalLab PV Modules Improves Measurement Uncertainty to Record Value of 1.1 %*. Freiburg, Germany, 2020. [Online]. Available: https://www.ise.fraunhofer.de/en/press-media/press-releases/2020/Fraunhofer-ISEs-CalLab-PV-Modules-Improves-Measurement-Uncertainty-to-Record-Value.html

[14] U. Kräling, P. Gebhardt, M. Kaiser, and D. Philipp, "PV Module Performance Measurements – Statistical Analysis of Technological Trends," 2022, doi: 10.4229/WCPEC-82022-3BO.14.1.

[15] Solar Media Limited, *Top 10 PV module suppliers in 2022 shipped 245GW.* [Online]. Available: https://www.pv-tech.org/top-10-pv-module-suppliers-in-2022-shipped-245gw/

[16] Solar Edition, *Top 10 PV Module Manufacturers in 2020, Based-on Their Module Shipment.* [Online]. Available: https://solaredition.com/top-10-pv-module-manufacturers-in-2020-based-on-their-module-shipment/

[17] RTS Corporation, *PV Module Shipment Ranking in 1H 2024.* [Online]. Available: https://www.rts-pv.com/en/blogs/12764/

[18] SolarQuarter, *2025 Top 20 Global Photovoltaic Module Manufacturers Revealed by PVBL.* [Online]. Available: https://solarquarter.com/2025/06/17/2025-top-20-global-photovoltaic-module-manufacturers-revealed-by-pvbl/

[19] Solar Media Limited, *Top 10 solar module suppliers in 2018.* [Online]. Available: https://www.pv-tech.org/top-10-solar-module-suppliers-in-2018/

[20] *Terrestrial photovoltaic (PV) modules – Design qualification and type approval – Part 2: Test procedures*, IEC 61215-2: 2021-02, International Electrotechnical Commission (IEC), Geneva, Switzerland, 2021.

[21] P. Gebhardt *et al.*, "Stabilization procedures for TOPCon PV modules after UV-induced degradation," *Sol Energ Mat Sol C*, vol. 294, p. 113885, 2026, doi: 10.1016/j.solmat.2025.113885.

[22] T. Karin, "UVID initiates metastability in the dark: how to properly measure unstable SI modules," *PVRW: Photovoltaic Reliability Workshop*, 2025.

[23] EnBW Energie Baden-Württemberg AG, *Größter förderfreier Solarpark Deutschlands eingeweiht*, 2021. [Online]. Available: https://www.enbw.com/presse/enbw-weiht-groessten-solarpark-deutschlands-ein.html

Fraunhofer
ISE
Fraunhofer
CalLab
PV Module
Statistical Trends in Nominal vs. Measured Performance of PV Modules and the Impact of Metastability
—
U. Kräling, D. Philipp, M. Kaiser
EU PVSEC 2025, Session 3BO.15.4
Bilbao, 23.09.2025

Motivation

Negative Deviations from Nominal Power

Nominal power (P_{Nom}) is a key parameter
- to calculate the yield
- to determine the price ($/Wp)

Trend toward negative deviations
- Initial presentation in 2023
- High international attention [1, 2]

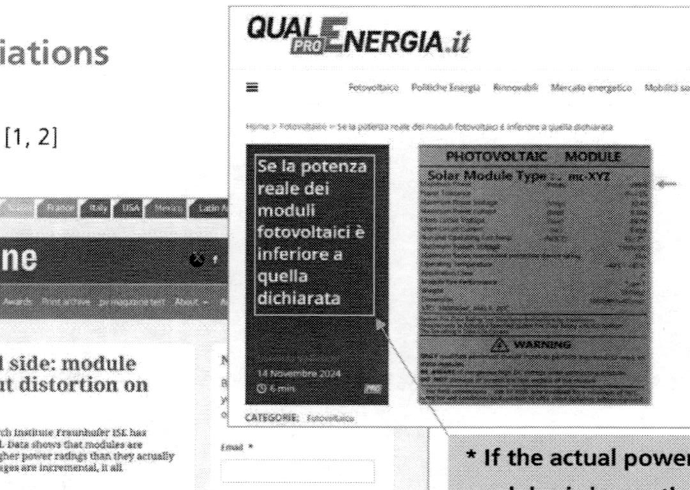

CalLab
PV Modules

−1.3% *

* -1.3% reduction in output corresponds to approximately 820 MWp with 63 GWp of new capacity added in 2023 in Europe!

* If the actual power of the photovoltaic modules is lower than the declared one

[1] https://www.pv-magazine-australia.com/2024/11/02/on-the-small-side-module-power-output-distortion-on-rise/
[2] https://www.qualenergia.it/pro/articoli-pro/potenza-reale-moduli-fotovoltaici-spesso-inferiore-quella-dichiarata/

020216-002

Who we are
CalLab PV Modules, TestLab PV Modules

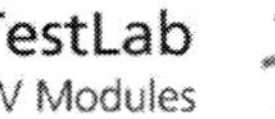

Accredited laboratories for PV modules (ISO/IEC 17025)

- Calibration laboratory
  - STC performance: IEC 60904-1, IEC 60904-1-2

- Testing laboratory
  - Performance, reliability, safety: IEC 61215, IEC 61730

High effort for quality assurance

- Lowest measurement uncertainty
- Stable calibration level
- Reproducible results

Provide high quality services to industry

- Around 6,000 STC measurements per year

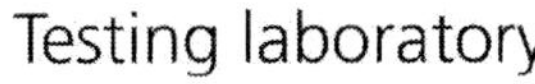

Database

Representative Filtering of STC Measurements [3]

Measurements since 2012 — 76,936 datasets

- Only new PV modules
- 1 PV module per type and order
- With nameplate values
- Crystalline PV modules
- Tier 1 manufacturer

Measurements after filtering — 1,071 datasets

Facts about filtering

- 1.4% of initial datasets
- 79 datasets per year on average
- 662 different module types
- 14 manufacturers

Year	Initial	Filtered
2012	5,332	93
2013	5,964	73
2014	5,534	58
2015	5,553	52
2016	5,032	86
2017	6,990	87
2018	5,296	70
2019	5,541	93
2020	5,983	111
2021	5,791	77
2022	5,940	73
2023	6,072	68
2024	5,834	90
2025 H1*	2,074*	40*
Total	**76,936**	**1,071**

[3] U. Kräling, P. Gebhardt, M. Kaiser, D. Philipp, PV Module Performance Measurements – Statistical Analysis of Technological Trends. 9 pages / 8th World Conference on Photovoltaic Energy Conversion; 498-506 (2022).

Fraunhofer ISE

STC Results
Development of Performance since 2012

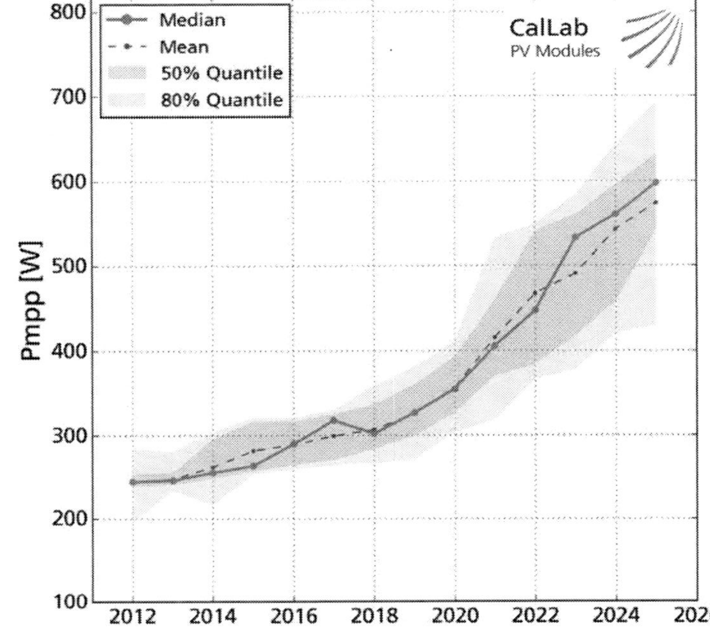

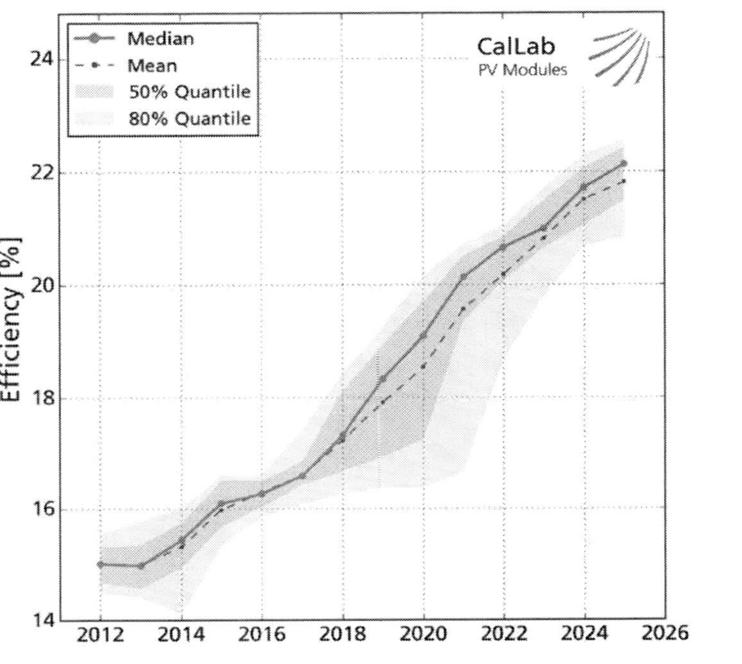

Fraunhofer
ISE

020216-005

STC Results

Performance Deviation from Nameplate since 2012

Significant negative deviation in the last years

- Average deviation in 2025: -1.1%

Stabilized after 2023 (first publication)

- Change from 2023 to 2025: +0.2%

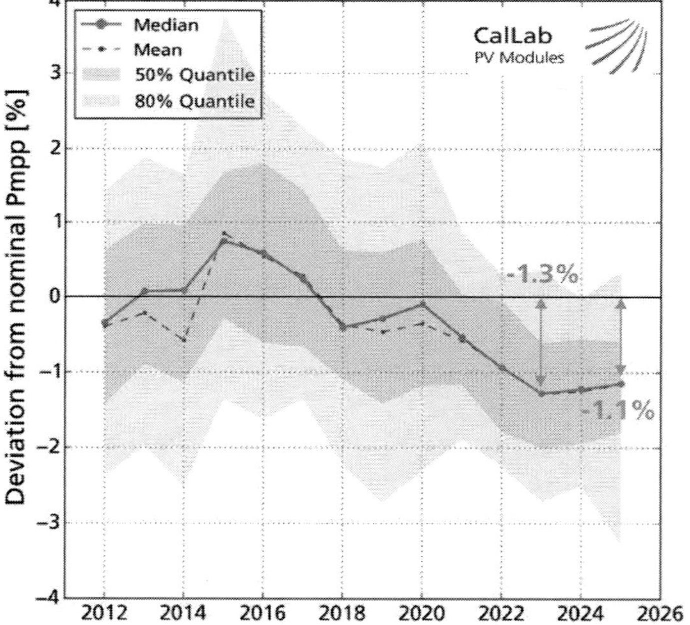

Fraunhofer
ISE

020216-006

Light-Induced Degradation (LID)

Test Sequence

Database: new modules, identical test sequence, PERC and TOPCon

Performance test

20 kWh/m² irradiation
Performance test

5 kWh/m² irradiation
Performance test

5 kWh/m² irradiation
Performance test

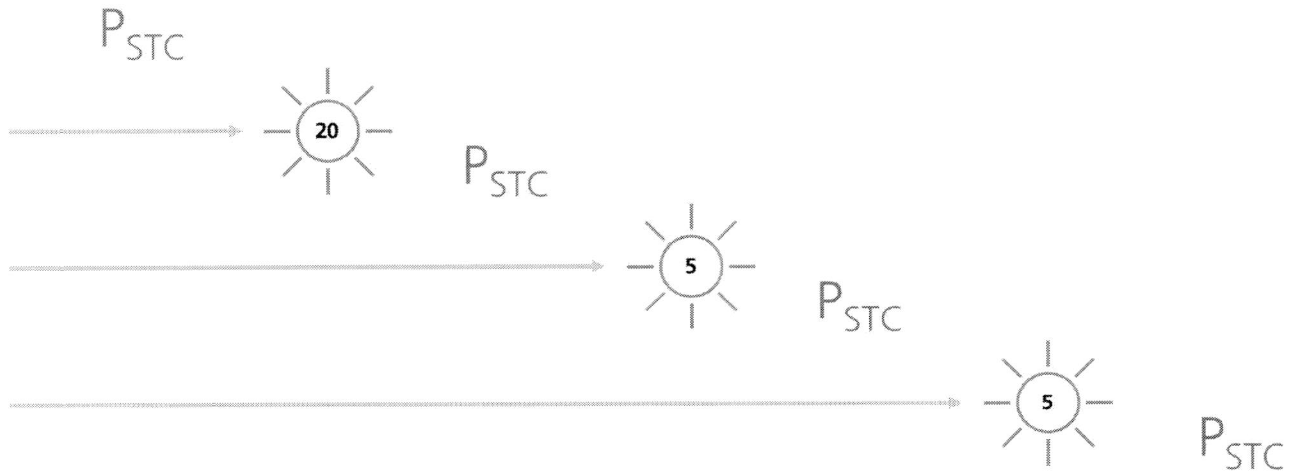

Fraunhofer
ISE

020216-007

Light-Induced Degradation (LID)
Results

Number of modules
- PERC: 71
- TOPCon: 40

„Early"-PERC
- strong LID observed

PERC, TOPCon
- no significant LID
- Partially positive LID

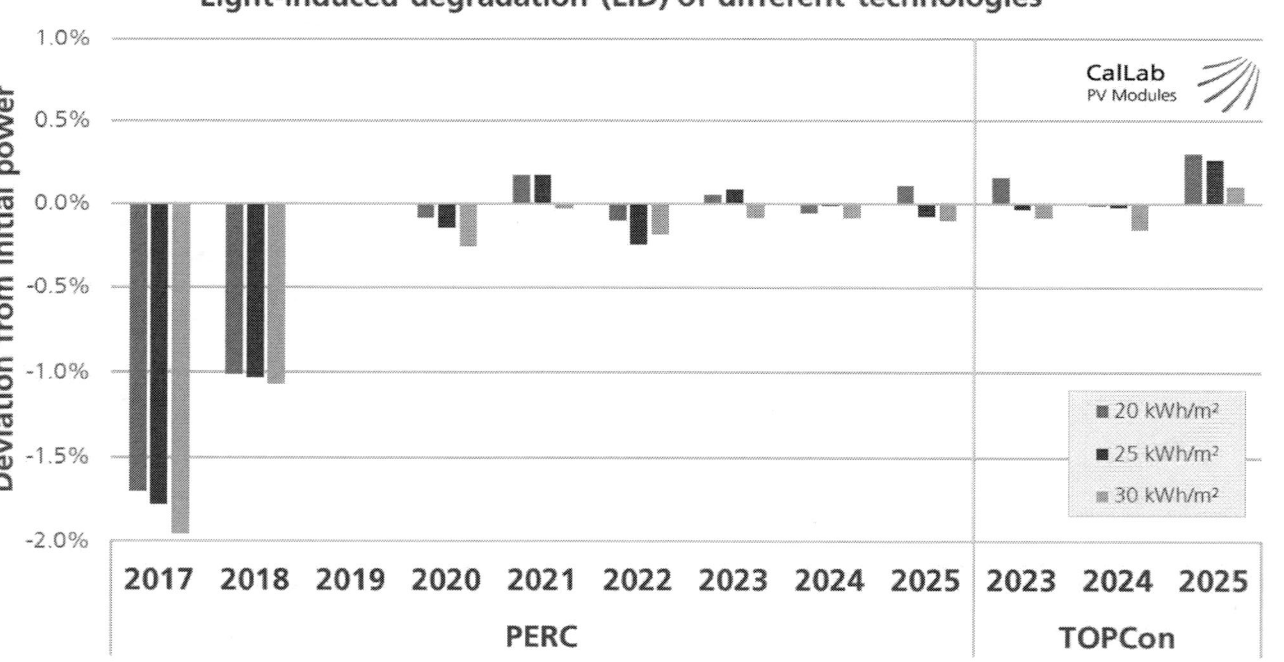

Fraunhofer
ISE

TOPCon Metastability

Test Sequence – Storage and Light Soaking

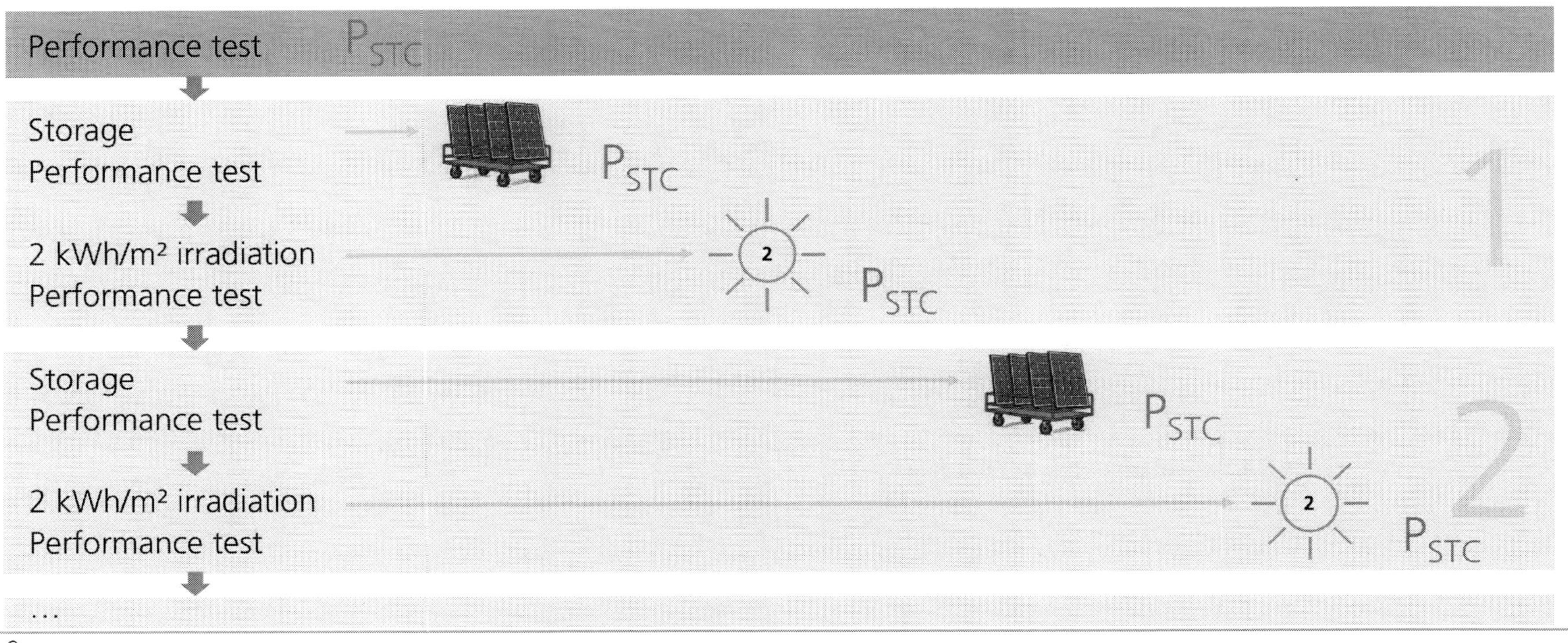

Fraunhofer
ISE

020216-009

TOPCon Metastability – Storage Effects
1 Cycle

4 different module types
- Storage at ordinary lab conditions
- Degradation observed for all types
  - Unstabilized (E1, F1, F2)
  - Stabilized (C, D, E2, F3, F4)

Degradation rate
- -0.1% / month

Recovery
- No general statement
- Range of gains: 0% – 0.4%

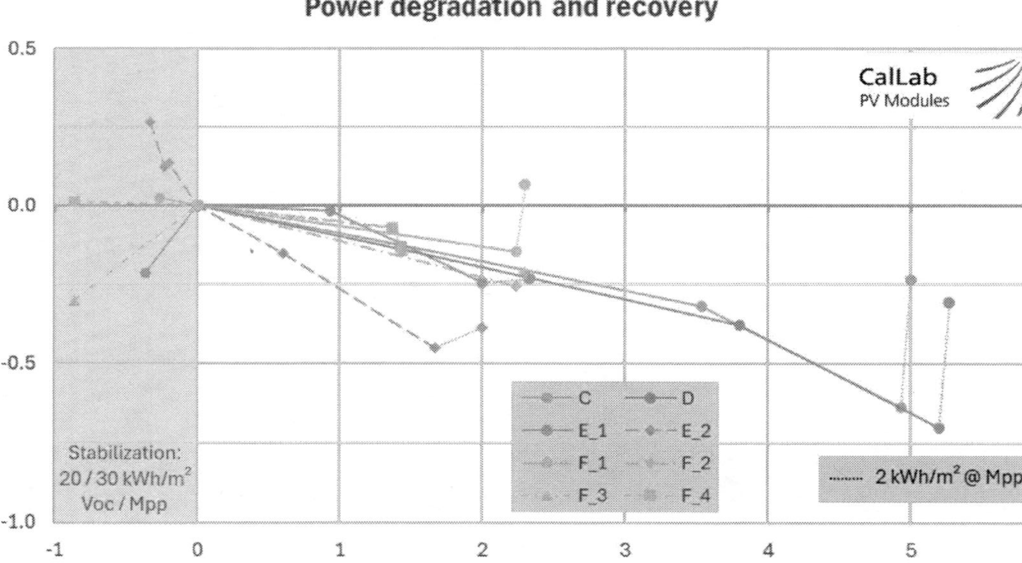

Fraunhofer
ISE

020216-010

TOPCon Metastability – Storage Effects
4 Cycles

2 different module types (stabilized)
- Storage at ordinary lab conditions
- Degradation observed for both types

Degradation rate
- -0.1% / month

Recovery
- No general statement
- Range of gains: 0.2% – 0.6%
- No reproducible result for P_{MPP}

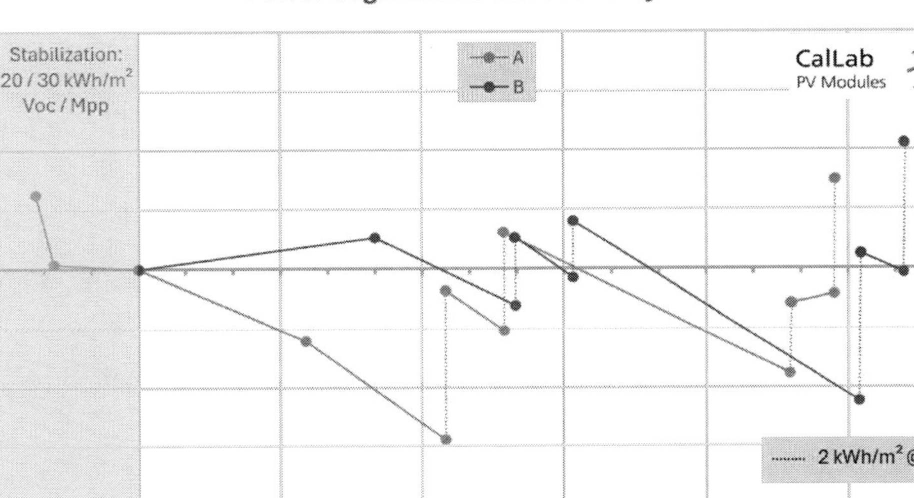

Fraunhofer
ISE

020216-011

Summary and Conclusions

PV module performance in 2025
- Negative deviation stabilized after 2023
- -1.1% P_{MPP} deviation (purchase should be proved independently)
  - ≙ more than a power class (5 W)
  - ≙ ~700 MWp with 64 GWp of new capacity expected for 2025 in Europe [4]

No significant LID for latest PERC / TOPCon

TOPCon storage effects
- Degradation and recovery observed ⟷ stable according to IEC 61215-2 MQT 19.1 (<1%)
- Critical for reference (golden) modules / comparisons

[4] SolarPower Europe (2025): EU Market Outlook for Solar Power. 2025 Mid-Year Analysis.
https://www.solarpowereurope.org/insights/outlooks/eu-market-outlook-for-solar-power-2025-mid-year-analysis.

Fraunhofer
ISE

020216-012

Thank you very much
for your attention

Contack

Dipl.-Ing. Ulli Kräling

**Manager Test and Calibration Lab
(D-PL-11140-33-00 | D-K-11140-02-00)
Department Module Characterization and Reliability
Phone: +49 761 4588-5761
ulli.kraeling@ise.fraunhofer.de**

Fraunhofer ISE
Heidenhofstraße 2
79110 Freiburg
www.ise.fraunhofer.de

FIFTEEN YEARS UNDER THE SUN:
REAL-FIELD DEGRADATION ANALYSIS OF VETERAN PV MODULES

Ioannis (John) A. Tsanakas*, Frédéric Mezzasalma, Maxime Babics, Alexandre Mignonac, Hervé Colin, Romain Couderc, Lionel Sicot, Philippe Marechal, Guillaume Capron, Jérémie Aimé
CEA, Liten, Univ. Grenoble Alpes, Campus INES, 73375 Le Bourget du Lac, France

*corresponding author : ioannis.tsanakas@cea.fr

ABSTRACT: This study presents a 15-year performance analysis of photovoltaic (PV) modules installed at CEA's outdoor test site in Cadarache, southern France. Three PV technologies – polycrystalline silicon (p-Si), amorphous silicon (a-Si), and monocrystalline silicon (m-Si) – have been continuously monitored under real-field conditions to assess their long-term degradation rates and aging mechanisms. The p-Si modules exhibited the highest degradation rate, averaging 2% per year, significantly exceeding the manufacturer's warranty expectations of 0.8% per year. Laboratory flash tests confirmed power losses ranging between -33% and -70% over 15 years. Infrared (IR) imaging identified a single hot spot, but degradation appeared uniformly distributed across all modules. Electroluminescence (EL) analysis revealed extensive microcracks and inactive cell regions, while visual inspections highlighted discoloration, light corrosion, and early signs of delamination. Despite these findings, no critical failures were detected in bypass diodes or electrical connectors. The study underscores the necessity of long-term real-field monitoring to refine predictive models for PV degradation and enhance module durability. Further detailed material analysis is ongoing to confirm intrinsic aging mechanisms and provide deeper insights into PV module reliability over time.

Keywords: *PV systems; PV module; PV degradation; PV module reliability; Fault analysis; IV characterization.*

1 INTRODUCTION: CONTEXT and AIM

Long-term monitoring of photovoltaic (PV) installations provides invaluable insights into real-world performance, degradation rates, and the underlying mechanisms that affect PV module reliability and performance over time. Earlier studies on long-term PV performance analysis in the field, examined the degradation rates of PV modules, revealing variability across different PV technologies and environmental (macro- and micro-climatic) conditions. A comprehensive review by the National Renewable Energy Laboratory (NREL) analyzed various studies and found that crystalline silicon (c-Si) PV modules exhibit degradation rates ranging from 0.4% to 0.5% per year, with system-level degradation rates being higher due to balance-of-system (BOS) components and soiling effects. Similarly, a study focusing on c-Si PV modules in Japan reported degradation rates between 0.01% and 0.47% per year, with an overall annual average of 0.27%. In contrast, other research has identified higher degradation rates under specific conditions. For instance, an analysis of monocrystalline silicon (m-Si) modules, after 20 years of field exposure, indicated a degradation rate of approximately 1.75% per year, much higher than that reported in the aforementioned studies or from that guaranteed from the manufacturers.

These variations underscore the influence of factors such as PV module design, BOM quality, installation practices, and environmental stressors on long-term PV performance. Quantifying and understanding these degradation mechanisms is crucial for improving PV module designs in terms of durability, reliability and weather resilience, as well as for accurately assessing long-term PV energy yields, considering actual PV degradation losses over time. Yet, extended datasets and systematic multiyear PV monitoring studies, particularly for diverse PV technologies and field conditions, remain relatively scarce.

Figure 1: Overview of the studied PV test arrays installed in Cadarache site.

Since its launching in early 00's, CEA's outdoor PV test site in Cadarache has been vital resource to our research, for understanding in-field lifelong performance and aging of PV modules. The site is located in southern France, about 30km north-east of Aix-en-Provence, in a region with generally little rainfall ("hot dry-summer" climate, classified as *Csa*, per the Köppen climate classification). This research focuses on three distinct technologies (Fig. 1): polycrystalline silicon (p-Si), amorphous silicon (a-Si), and monocrystalline silicon (m-Si).

Each system, rated at 1 kWp, has been continuously monitored under identical environmental and operational conditions. These systems are paired with SMA SWR1100E inverters and complemented by an array of high-precision environmental sensors to capture irradiance, wind speed, temperature, and other key parameters. The primary objectives of this study are:

1. To quantify long-term performance degradation rates for different PV technologies under real-field conditions, for the case of Cadarache site and climate characteristics.
2. To identify and analyze mechanisms (physico-chemical, electrical, thermal, optical) responsible for module aging.
3. To bridge the gap between field performance data and laboratory findings.

2 METHODOLOGY – APPROACH

The PV systems at Cadarache have been monitored continuously since 2008, providing a wealth of long-term performance data. Electrical parameters such as DC voltage (U_{dc}), DC current (I_{dc}), AC power (P_{ac}), and inverter efficiency (η_i) are logged alongside environmental conditions, enabling a comprehensive assessment of system performance. Monitored environmental parameters include: i) *irradiance* (measured using multiple pyranometers and reference cells installed both in-plane and horizontally; ii) *temperature* (both ambient and at PV module level, using precision sensors); *wind speed* (recorded to assess cooling effects on module temperature and its impact on efficiency). Standardized performance indicators are calculated, including reference yield (Y_r), array yield (Y_a), system losses (L_s), and performance ratio (PR), providing an integrated view of energy production efficiency. To identify thermal anomalies, regular thermal imaging surveys were conducted. These images help detect potential issues such as hot spots, which could be indicative of early-life or mid/end-life faults, such as cell cracks or bypass diode failures.

To complement field measurements, selected modules were dismantled and subjected to indoor (laboratory) characterization at CEA-INES premises, to enable a deeper understanding of material degradation and failure mechanisms. The characterization methods include:

- Flash Tests (IV characterization, under standard test conditions (STC), employing a A+ PASAN solar simulator) to quantify power loss, compare against baseline measurements and identify known IV patterns related to faults (if any);
- Electroluminescence (EL) imaging, to identify potential cracks and their propagation, inactive regions, etc.;

- Visual inspections, to document physical damage such as discoloration, delamination, corrosion;
- Component-level forensics: Ongoing "autopsies" involving microscopic and material analyses of PV components.

The p-Si modules, which exhibited the highest degradation rate, were prioritized for in-depth analysis. Laboratory autopsies focus on uncovering intrinsic and extrinsic factors contributing to performance loss. Results from these analyses are compared with thermal imaging, IV curve measurements, and field data to establish correlations and identify dominant degradation pathways. This holistic methodology ensures a robust understanding of aging mechanisms.

3 RESULTS and DISCUSSION

Overall results (Fig. 2) from field-monitored data indicate significant performance degradation for p-Si modules, with an average annual degradation rate of 2%. This value is considerably higher than the 0.8% annual degradation rate specified by the manufacturer. In contrast, m-Si and a-Si modules showed lower degradation rates, with m-Si modules demonstrating better long-term stability.

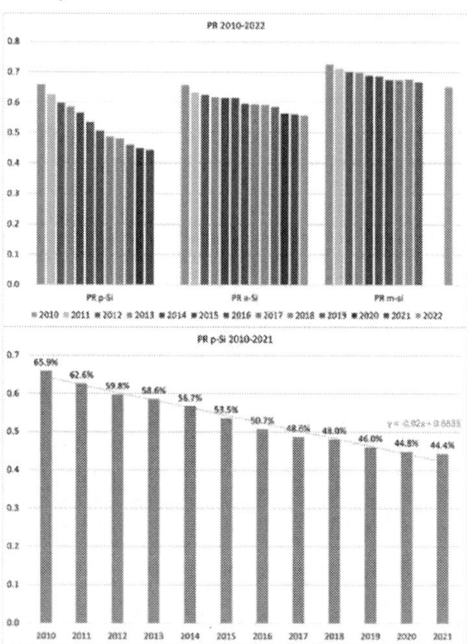

Figure 2: Top: Evolution of PR for the studied modules (2010–2022). Bottom: PR decrease for the p-Si modules for the same period.).

Comparative IV curve measurements taken in 2008 and 2023 revealed substantial reductions in current output for p-Si modules (Fig. 3). Flash tests confirmed power losses ranging between -33% and -70%, suggesting both intrinsic material degradation and external environmental factors as contributors. In quantitative terms, higher losses are derived from significant drop in the P_{mpp}, fill factor (FF) and I_{mpp}, corresponding up to -41%, -36% and 27%

respectively, in direct correlation with a significant increase of the series resistance (R_s) by up to 2.6× times its initial value, while the shunt resistance (R_{sh}) has been decreased by up to 5.4× times from its initial value.

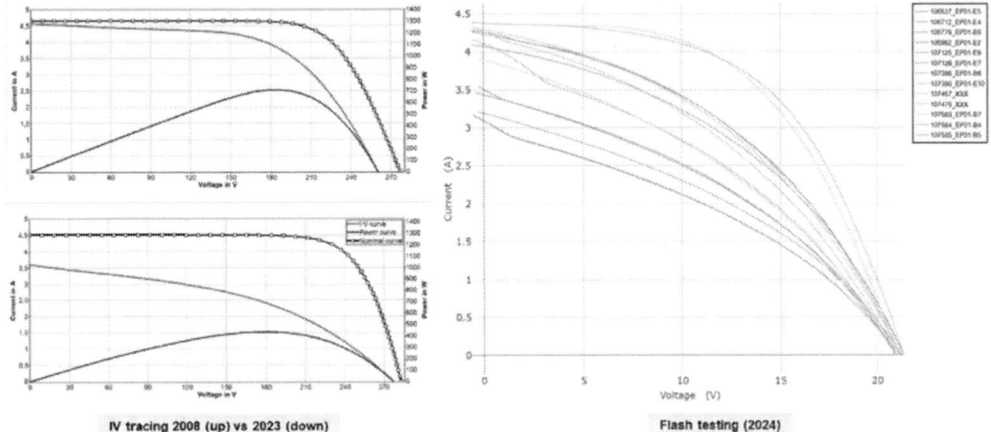

Figure 3: Left: I-V and P-V characteristics comparison (2008 vs. 2023) for the p-Si modules, through in-field IV tracing. Right: Indoor flash tests results for all p-Si modules in 2024, i.e. after 15 years completed with field exposure.

Further field inspections, via IR imaging, identified one module with a hot spot (Fig. 4), but no significant localized failures were observed in other modules. This supports the hypothesis that performance loss is generally uniform across all modules. EL analysis further revealed extensive microcracks and inactive cell regions, correlating with the observed power loss.

Figure 4: Examples of IR images obtained for one of the studied p-Si modules, suggestive of an occurring hot spot.

Visual inspections (Fig. 5) identified some signs of discoloration and burnt marks from localized overheating (in the case of the aforementioned hot spot) and light corrosion in the junction boxes, as well as some suspected – yet not confirmed, starting delamination. On the other hand, bypass diodes and electrical connectors were found to be in good condition, ruling out major failures in these components. None of the (suspected) cell cracks was visible by naked eye.

A detailed material analysis of the p-Si modules is underway to investigate intrinsic aging mechanisms and confirm potential faults, suspected through the IR, EL and visual inspections. Early observations suggest that the degradation is not confined to specific cells but is distributed, rather uniformly, across all modules in the array.

On the basis of these results and discussion, key takeaways (so far) can be summarized in the following:

1. **Degradation Rates**: The p-Si modules exhibited a degradation rate of 2% per year, significantly higher than warranty expectations. In contrast, m-Si and a-Si modules showed better durability under the same environmental conditions.
2. **Mechanisms of Degradation**: Laboratory analyses confirmed that power losses in p-Si modules are primarily due to uniform cell degradation, as evidenced by EL imaging and IV curve measurements. External factors such as thermal cycling, UV exposure, and material aging likely contributed to the observed trends.
3. **Thermal and Visual Observations**: Despite some visible damage (discoloration and delamination), no critical failures were found in bypass diodes or junction boxes. The uniformity of degradation suggests systemic aging mechanisms rather than isolated defects.
4. **Relevance for Industry**: The findings underscore the importance of real-world, long-term monitoring for validating manufacturer warranties and improving predictive models for PV performance.

The study, so far, sets the stage for a deeper exploration and understanding of the degradation mechanisms occurring in the studied PV modules, as they approach the end of their service life. More detailed and comparative results, including further characterization techniques, comprehensive discussion and sensitivity analysis, are ongoing and will be included in a future work.

Figure 5: Examples of degradation and faults identified or suspected during visual inspection, for the case of p-Si modules.

4 CONCLUSIONS - OUTLOOK

This study provides a comprehensive 15-year performance evaluation of polycrystalline, monocrystalline, and amorphous silicon PV modules exposed to real-field conditions at CEA's Cadarache test site. Results reveal a markedly higher degradation rate for polycrystalline silicon modules ($\approx$2%/year) compared to manufacturer warranty expectations, with cumulative power losses between -33% and -70%. Infrared and electroluminescence analyses confirmed that degradation is largely uniform across modules, dominated by microcracks, inactive cell regions, and increased resistive losses, while bypass diodes and connectors remained intact. In contrast, monocrystalline and amorphous silicon modules exhibited lower degradation rates, underlining the importance of both technology choice and bill of materials quality for long-term PV durability.

The findings demonstrate the critical value of long-term field monitoring in complementing laboratory tests and refining predictive models for PV reliability. By correlating outdoor performance data with laboratory diagnostics, this study highlights systemic degradation pathways that cannot be captured by short-term testing alone. Future work will expand on the ongoing material-level analyses to pinpoint intrinsic aging mechanisms and validate failure hypotheses.

Looking ahead, these insights can support:

- improved module design and material selection to enhance resilience against thermal cycling, UV exposure, and environmental stressors,
- more accurate degradation models for lifetime energy yield predictions, and
- updated warranty and reliability frameworks aligned with field-verified performance.

Ultimately, the results contribute to a more robust understanding of PV module lifetimes in real-world conditions, helping bridge the gap between manufacturer guarantees and field realities, and reinforcing the importance of continuous, multi-year monitoring for the sustainable deployment of PV technologies.

ACKNOWLEDGEMENTS

Part of this work has been carried out in the framework of the Horizon Europe CACTUS project. CACTUS project has received funding from the European Union's Horizon Europe research and innovation programme under grant agreement No. 101132182. Part of this work was also supported by the French National Program "Programme d'Investissements d'Avenir - INES.2S" under Grant Agreement ANR ANR-10-IEED-0014 0014-01.

TOWARDS ENHANCED RELIABILITY OF BUSBAR-FREE IBC SOLAR CELL INTERCONNECTIONS BY NON-CONDUCTIVE ADHESIVE REINFORCEMENT

Tudor Timofte[1], Tobias Messmer[1], Karl Wienands[1], Joris Libal[1], Stephan Großer[2], Matthias Pander[2],
Giuseppe Galbiati[3], Tobias Nitsche[3], Daniel Buckland[3], Andreas Halm[1]
[1] ISC Konstanz, Rudolf-Diesel-Straße 15, 78467 Konstanz, Germany
[2] Fraunhofer-Center für Silizium-Photovoltaik CSP, Otto-Eißfeldt-Str. 12, 06120 Halle (Saale), Germany
[3] Henkel AG & Co. KGaA, Henkelstraße 67, 40589 Düsseldorf, Germany

ABSTRACT: Current crystalline silicon solar cell metallization layouts feature pad busbars and have (compared to total available interconnection ribbon area) a reduced available surface for soldering or gluing the narrow copper ribbons (rectangular cross section) or wires (round cross section). For further reduction of silver consumption, an emerging trend implies omitting totally the busbars from cell's metallization, which means that (usually silver-plated) interconnection copper tracks are bonded directly to cell's fingers and SixNy coated surface [1]. At interdigitated back contact (IBC) solar cell ZEBRA [2], the thermo-mechanical stress during and after interconnection process is higher than for front-back contacted solar cells [3]. Removing completely the busbars at this cell type would therefore pose exceptional challenges for a robust stable interconnection [4]. One promising approach implies point fixing additionally the connected ribbons to the cell surface by non-conductive adhesive (NCA) pads [5]. In this work, we describe the investigation of ECA formulations as electrical connection, in combination with NCA formulations, which will reinforce mechanically the interconnection. The reliability of interconnection was investigated at mini-module level by temperature-cycling test (TCT). The goal of this experiment is to shape a cell interconnection process and testing sequence, and to identify suitable ECA-NCA formulations for a technical and economical competitive ECA pad –NCA pad connection procedure for busbar-free IBC ZEBRA solar cells. The process addresses also environmental aspects, since the interconnection is lead-free, and add additional options for cell-ribbon separation [6].

Keywords: electrically conductive adhesive, cell interconnection, back contact solar cell, reliability

1 INTRODUCTION

From previous tests, it is known that interconnection of busbar-free IBC ZEBRA cells by silver coated copper ribbons with electrically conductive adhesives (in form of continuous or interrupted line) might cause massive power losses [4], usually related to defects at cell's interconnection, such as adhesive and cohesive breakage. An example of good interconnection (for IBC ZEBRA half cells with busbars) and faulty interconnection (at busbar-free IBC ZEBRA half cells), both prepared with same ECA material, stringing process and continuous ECA line geometry, is presented in form of electroluminescence (EL) imaging at fig.1 below. The affected interconnection patterns are revealed by dark stripes at image B, on the right side, which signalize total or partial decoupled cell areas from the current flow.

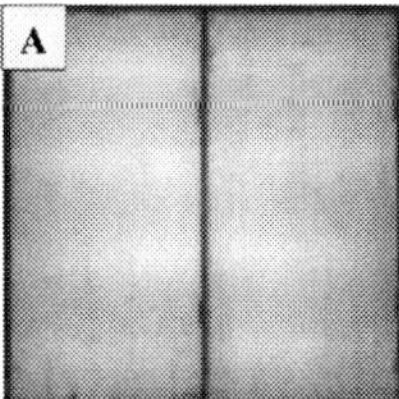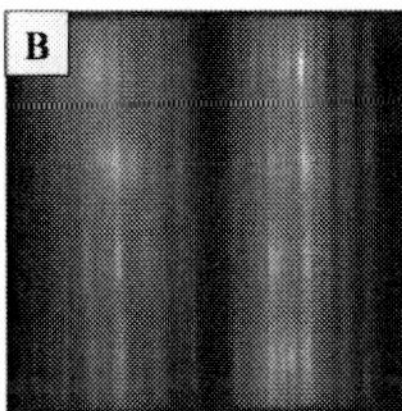

Figure 1. ECA interconnection at IBC cells **with** busbars (image A, left) and faulty ECA interconnection at IBC cells **without** busbars (image B, right)

Since it is clear for tested adhesives that neither ECA lines, nor ECA pads can provide a sufficiently strong interconnection at busbar-free solar cells, which could withstand the (thermo-) mechanical stress occurring during production and operational environment [4], a further reliable mechanical stabilization is necessary. This could be achieved by suitable non-conductive adhesives.

Therefore, several ECAs and NCAs were considered for testing the capability of dispensing these in the required size and shape by a micro dispensing unit and for testing the adhesion of ribbons to the busbar-free IBC ZEBRA cell after full curing of the adhesive bonds. At an initial test, ECA and NCA pads were dispensed alternating by a XYZ transport and dispensing system. Following, ribbon attachment and down-holder positioning were accomplished manually or in semi-automatic mode (cut and stretched ribbons were attached by a robot arm to cell with ECA- and NCA-pads), whereas curing took place on a heating plate. The resulted samples were highly impacted by several issues (cracks in the ECA, interconnection offsets, contamination of electrical path by NCA, detachments at the interconnection interfaces, etc.), which translated into a high power loss after production and during ageing tests. The aim of the presented work is to mitigate and avoid such issues, by the following systematic approach:

- ECAs and NCAs were selected by defined Interconnection geometry and process, considering full curing and highest interconnection adhesion force;

- optimization of cell interconnection (stringing) by additional automatized processes, to improve accuracy, process stability and reproducibility of material deposition and interconnection pattern, as well as to avoid contaminations between NCA and ECA.

The characterization and qualification imply a sequence containing the following tests for: ribbon-cell adhesion peel test, cross-linking degree, electroluminescence, IV flash characterization, accelerated ageing (temperature cycling test) and microstructure analysis, like X-ray imaging [7], scanning electron microscope (SEM) cross sections and optical microscope cross section inspections.

2   EXPERIMENTAL SETUP

For the planned experiment, several materials, processes and characterization techniques were used, which will be described below.

2.1 Materials

Halved monocrystalline IBC ZEBRA solar cells produced on M6 wafers (166.0 x 166.0 mm) with busbars (only for soldering reference) and for the rest of testing groups, without busbars (metallization only with contacting fingers at 1.0 mm pitch and specific ZEBRA cell insulation patterns: the light brown pads at fig. 2), however with six interconnection patterns per polarity, were used.

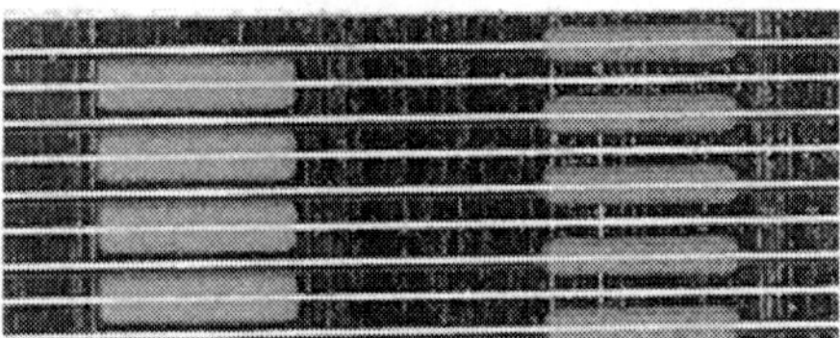

Figure 2. Section of the busbar-free IBC ZEBRA cell, containing two interconnection patterns (light brown pad rows), each belonging to a different polarity

The soldering interconnection was made with 0.40 x 0.20 mm $Sn_{60}Pb_{40}$ coated copper photovoltaic (PV) ribbons (max. thickness of $Sn_{60}Pb_{40}$ coating in range 18.7 – 19.8 μm); whereas for ECA-NCA interconnection 0.50 x 0.24 mm Ag100 coated copper ribbons were used.

For soldering, a rosin-free, low residue industrially available soldering flux (with isopropanol solvent) was used.

Two electrically conductive adhesives (ECA 01 and ECA 02) were introduced in the test plan, both with high content of silver filler particles and both based on acrylic resins, available as a (frozen) mix (viscosity ECA 01: 28400 mPa.s at shear rate 15 s^{-1}, thixotropic index: 2.6 and viscosity ECA 02: 14600 mPa.s at shear rate 15 s^{-1}, thixotropic index: 4.2).

For the mechanical reinforcement of the interconnection three epoxy based non-conductive adhesives were initially tested, whereas from the tested ones, only one (NCA 01) proved to achieve acceptable and stable adhesion to solar cell and ribbon; this glue was considered for further testing (viscosity NCA 01: 4000-7000 mPa.s at shear rate 10 s^{-1}, thixotropic index: 3.5 – 4.5).

For the production of mini-modules toughened solar glass with 250.0 x 250.0 x 3.2 mm size, without anti reflective coating and with a non-geometrically aligned structure pattern, was chosen.

As encapsulation material, a standard PV industrial grade, ethylene vinyl acetate resin (EVA), with low UV cutoff and fast curing properties was used.

For the electric contacts of mini-modules a 5.0 x 0.30 mm copper PV bussing ribbon with $Sn_{60}Pb_{40}$ coating (max. thickness of $Sn_{60}Pb_{40}$ coating: ~15 - 25 μm) was chosen.

At rear side of the mini-module an industrially available, 370 μm transparent PV backsheet with cross-section structure: PET-PET-Primer was added.

2.2 Processes

According to previous experience, a process improvement was considered necessary. The chosen strategy was to implement at most of processing steps automated high precision positioning procedures, in order to improve the accuracy for the ECA and NCA pads location, as well as to ensure a reproducible aspect ratio of the dispensed ECA and NCA pads (round shaped pads).

The dispensing of ECA and NCA was made by a home-made processing robot, fitted with an accurate XYZ axes Linax linear motor system from Jenny Science AG, and with a double micro dispensing unit MDS 1560 (with DST®) from VERMES Microdispensing GmbH, hence enabling sequential dispensing of the two materials. The targeted shape, size and aspect ratio of ECA and NCA pad deposition was obtained and optimized by varying the key process parameters of the device (nozzle size, cartridge and actuator pressure, jetting head temperature, tappet open time, tappet close time, distance to target, speed, etc.).

Two types of dispensing were tested:

- continuous ECA or NCA line for identification of pad geometry (width and height was transferred from line to pad patterns) and adhesion tests at the busbar-free cells;
- ECA pads and NCA pads, dispensed alternating at the interconnection pattern (the target position of ECA pads being concentric to contacting fingers, whereas the NCA pads target position being concentric to insulation pads, to which these were dispensed).

For the qualification of the ECA-NCA interconnection approach, several variation (A, B, C, D) of interconnection type and geometry were designed and tested (fig.3).

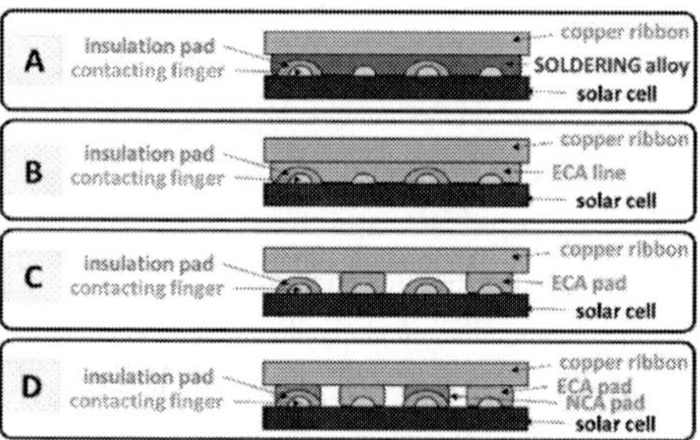

Figure 3. Schematic cross section segment representation of the tested types of interconnections at interdigitated busbar-free back contact ZEBRA solar cell

At Table 1 are presented the main features of the above-mentioned interconnection variations.

Table I: Main designed (target) characteristics of the tested interconnection types

Test group ID	A	B	C	D
Connection type	solder	glue	glue	glue
Connection width (μm)	400	500	500	500
Connection thickness (μm)	20	20	20	20
Ribbon width (μm)	400	500	500	500
Ribbon thickness (μm)	240	200	200	200
Ribbon coating	$Sn_{60}Pb_{40}$	Ag	Ag	Ag
ECA pad location	centered to contacting fingers			
ECA pad diameter (μm)	400	400	400	400
ECA pad height (μm)	50	50	50	50
NCA pad location	centered to insulation pad			
NCA pad diameter (μm)	400	400	400	400
NCA pad height (μm)	50	50	50	50

Indeed, mainly at ECA and NCA pad geometries (diameter, height) considerable, but still acceptable variations from the target value and position offsets were observed; these are caused by an interaction of hardware specific features and material properties (viscosity, surface tension, etc.).

After printing of ECA and NCA pad patterns on the half busbar-free cells, these were immediately transferred to an industrial TeamTechnik TT2100 stringer with IR soldering (the IR heating was not used for curing of ECA and NCA), which was adapted, as follows:

1. a previously implemented semiautomatic R&D mode was used, which implied positioning the cell manually on conveyor, all other assembly and transport processes being applied automatically;

2. with a dedicated spacer, the half IBC ZEBRA cell with ECA and NCA pads on, was mounted at assigned position, being hold by vacuum at transport belt system;

3. a subsystem then stretched, picked and applied the ribbons over the patterns with ECA and NCA pads, together with the down-holders;

4. the fastest possible cycle time (1.6 s) was set, and the isothermal curing time was achieved by stopping the cell assembly (cell with ECA and NCA having ribbons and down-holders on top) on transport belt at heating zone with highest set temperature and dwell for 300s;

5. for transferring fastest possible the sample assembly to the defined setup temperature for optimal curing (+190°C), the first two heating plates were switch off;

5.1 at fig.4 below is presented the heating plate setup.

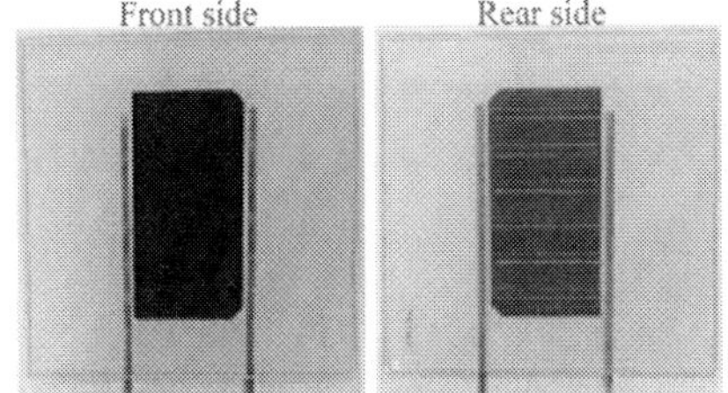

Figure 4. Schematic setup temperature of the curing path

Usually, a considerable offset between the setup temperature and real temperature at sample level occurs. Therefore, to determine the real temperature of the process, a temperature profile was acquired with a DataPaq Q18 data logger and type K thermocouples attached at six positions to the blades of the down-holders. According to the temperature profile measurement, in the quasi-isothermal part of the process, approximately 1 min. after arrival of sensor assembly at curing location, the average temperature of the process was 156.3°C (std.dev. = 16.6°C).

Furthermore, for a better distribution of applied pressure during curing, the process was adapted by adding a stack of three cells under the down-holder, together with a Teflon-coated foil (to avoid accidental gluing of these cells by ECA or NCA from the sample).

Each of the stringed half-cells was laminated at a laboratory membrane laminator into mini-modules of glass-backsheet type, with a single EVA encapsulation film layer on each side of the half-cell (fig. 5).

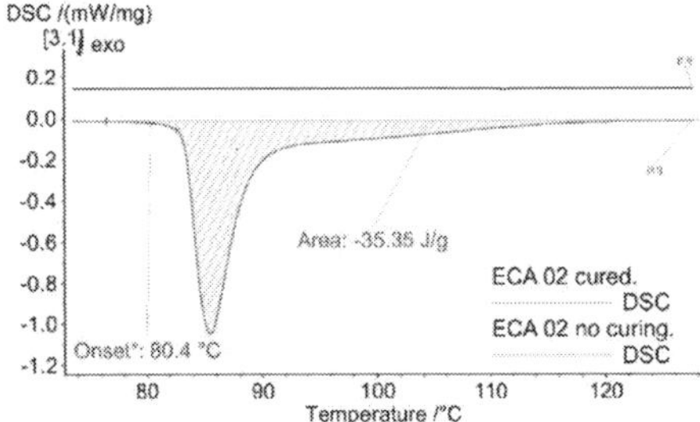

Figure 5. Mini-module type (glass-backsheet) used for testing ECA-NCA strings with IBC ZEBRA half-cells

The lamination recipe was defined to reach a highest possible cross-linking degree for the tested EVA encapsulation material: 145°C temperature setup; 1260 s total lamination time (360s evacuation step and 900s with stepwise-applied pressure of 1000mbar).

The samples (mini-modules) were subjected to accelerated ageing, by applying a temperature cycling test profile, according to IEC 61215 norm, without current injection, in temperature range – 40°C / + 85°C.

<u>3. Characterization techniques</u>

A NETZSCH 214 Polyma DSC device, using Nitrogen as protective and purge gas, was implemented to verify the full cross-linking of ECAs, NCAs and of EVA encapsulation material.

Peel force measurements between ribbon and cell were made at a Zwick Roell BT1-FR0.5TN.D14 digital force testing unit, with special mounting adapter for cells with attached ribbons, at 180° peel angle and 150mm/min peel speed setup.

Electroluminescence was recorded at a homemade EL-PL measurement device.

The mini-modules were measured at an AAA h.a.l.m. GmbH flasher, using 4 point contacting at STC (flasher irradiance 1000 W/m², 25°C ± 2°C).

3D images were obtained by an Olympus LEXT OLS 4000 laser confocal microscope.

For magnetic field imaging (MFI), a homemade system equipped with an MFI-sensor from DENKweit was used.

X-Ray images were acquired with a PHOENIX NANOMEX 180NF X-ray inspection system.

X-Ray and MFI were measured at samples without any accelerated ageing. Cross section analysis was made using contrast mode microscopy (bright field / dark field) at metallographic polished samples.

Scanning electron microscopy has been performed at a HITACHI SU-70 analytical FE-SEM device.

3 RESULTS

For the curing pattern at stringer, DSC measurements (of samples sent through the stringer process) confirmed full curing for ECA01, ECA02 and NCA01 (no residual exothermal cross-linking peak after stringer process) [8]. At fig.6 below is presented the DSC diagram of ECA02, demonstrating full curing (no residual exothermal peak at the blue line). For the ECA01 and NCA01 the same procedure was implemented, with confirmed full curing.

Figure 6. DSC diagram of uncured and cured ECA 02

In addition, DSC measurements were made also for cured encapsulation material (EVA) and no residual cross-linking peak could be detected as well, confirming a high or full cross-linking degree [9].

For the production of strings with different

interconnections pad arrangements, it was necessary to define at first a suitable geometry for the ECA and for the NCA interconnection patterns. This was made by considering two aspects:

- avoiding contamination with ECA and NCA at the components of the stringer, therefore allowing a maximal width of ECA and NCA before curing as wide as the ribbon width;
- achieving best possible adhesion to ribbon and to substrate with a defined curing process, by increasing the width and height of ECA and NCA interconnections.

Following this procedure, the 3D profile of the ECA lines was recorded, to identify the width range and the height range. It was noticed that width of ECA in range 400µm (+/-60µm) is favorable for a good adhesion to ribbon and to busbar-free solar cell at samples with continuous interconnection line (fig.7). The line height associated to this width depends on one side on the properties of the uncured ECA and NCA pastes (like viscosity, thixotropic index, etc.), and also on the dispensing process; at the trials presented in this paper it was in the range 50-80 µm.

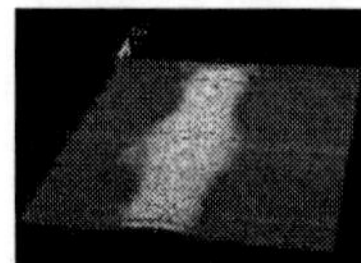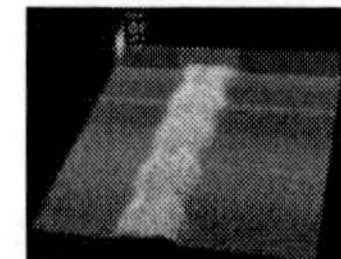

Figure 7. 3D microscopy for ECA line on busbar-free IBC solar cell: ECA 01 (left),   ECA 02 (right)

With the identified ECA and NCA width and height, samples with continuous ECA and NCA lines and optimized stringing process were produced with busbar-free ZEBRA cells, to test elaborately the adhesion.

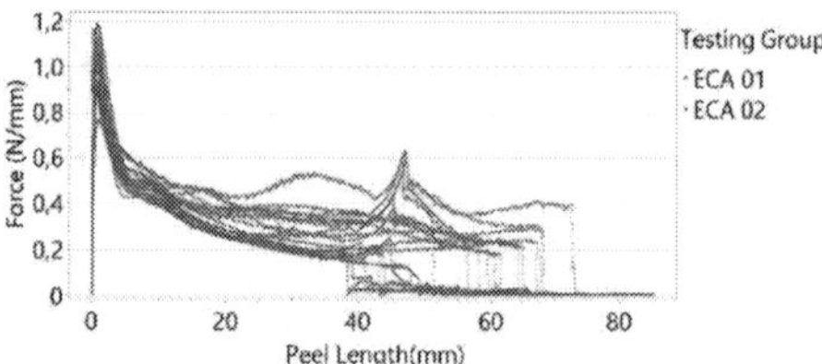

Figure 8. Peel force diagram for the tested ECAs without any data filter

The full peel diagrams from fig.8 required processing, by removing the first and last part of graph, to avoid artefacts. Hence, the data within first 10 and approx. last 40mm was removed. The sorted data below (fig.9) depict the peel force range for the two tested ECAs at busbar-free ZEBRA IBC cells. Despite general low adhesion, the ECA02 was selected for further trials, since the peel force was by approx. 50% higher compared to the peel force at ECA 01 sample during same test.

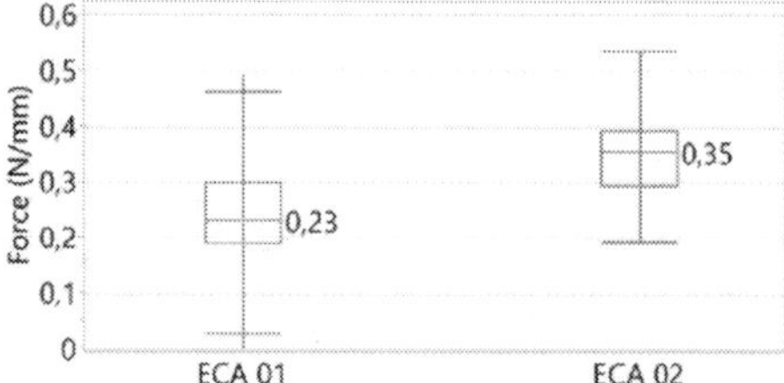

Figure 9. Peel force analysis for ECA 01 and ECA 02

At NCA testing, only one candidate proved suitable for further testing (NCA 01), the others being disqualified due to low viscosity, or due to extremely low peel forces to substrate. A short optimization trial for NCA curing process provided best results of adhesion at a setup temperature of 190°C and 300s dwell time, translated into 0.63 N/mm median value peel force between ribbon and busbar-free solar cell.

After these test results, only ECA 02 and NCA 01 were considered for the ECA-NCA process testing, which means: alternating ECA round pads with NCA round pads at interconnection. The geometry of both pad types (ECA, NCA) was defined same, with a target diameter width at 400 µm and with a target height in range 40-60 µm. The process at dispensing robot was adjusted to create reproducible alternating ECA and NCA pads, without contamination. The schematic plan of the ECA-NCA alternating interconnection is shown at fig.10.

Figure 10. Representation of the ECA pad – NCA pad interconnection at busbar-free ZEBRA cell (top view)

At the optimized setup for ECA pad trails could be determined by 3D confocal laser microscopy that the diameter of pads is in range 298 µm/ ± 39 µm, to which corresponds a pad height of approx. 130 µm/ ± 5 µm. For NCA, the height of the pads could not be determined with the same method, due to strong light reflection, curved NCA surface and material transparency. In contrast, the width of NCA pads could be determined by this measurement method, since this feature addresses the 2D image. The measured width for NCA in the presented NCA-ECA process is in range 487 µm/ ± 7 µm. At the fig.11, a magnified cell segment with alternating ECA and NCA pads is presented.

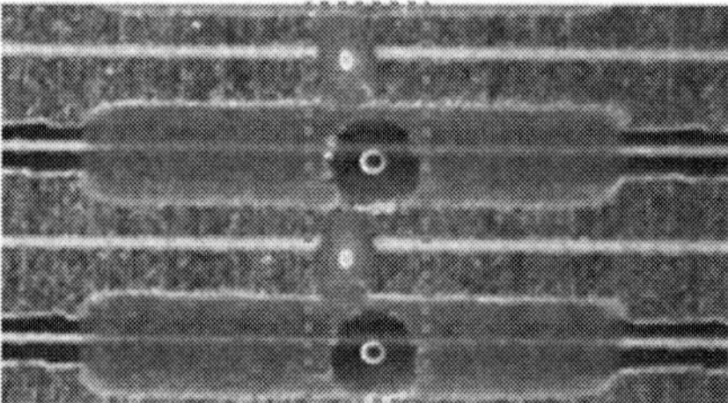

Figure 11. Microscope image of a cell segment with alternating NCA and ECA pads at the positive polarity interconnection pattern (the orange interrupted line marks the location of the ribbon, which will be added)

After lamination of the strings (at least three minimodules considered at each group), these were characterized by EL and by IV before and after accelerated ageing (TCT). Due to poor performance (multiple electrical interruptions at stringed samples detected by EL), ECA 01 was excluded from further testing. Differences at the robustness of cell interconnections can be observed at the EL images at fig.12, in initial state, as well as during ageing. Soldering interconnection (A), as well as continuous ECA line (B) behave stable up to 100 TCT (no change at EL image, no dark sectors). However, at test group with ECA pads (C) and group with ECA and NCA pads (D), affected interconnection regions (dark zones) can be observed, mentioning that NCA mechanical stabilization lead to a clear improvement (EL image similar to ECA line or soldered test groups).

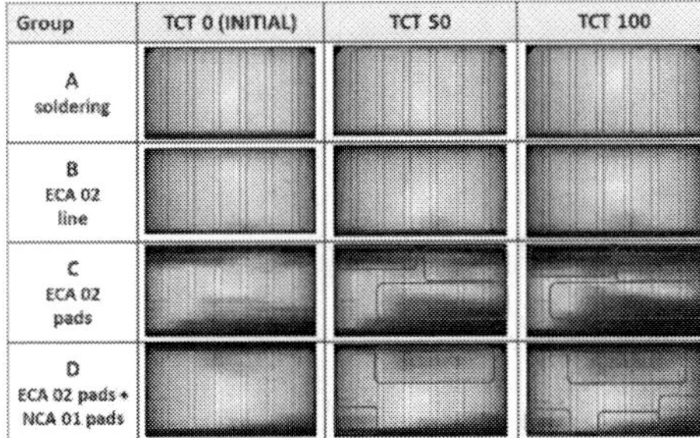

Figure 12. Electroluminescence imaging of relevant samples from each group at initial state, after 50, and after 100 cycles TCT ageing.

After EL characterization the mini-modules were characterized by IV measurements (at STC conditions), before and after temperature cycling test. The relative changes to initial state (in percentage) of main electrical parameters at IV measurement: short circuit current (Isc), open circuit voltage (Voc), fill factor (FF) and power at maximum power point (Pmpp), are presented at fig.13. An ageing level of 100 cycles TCT is not sufficient to make predictions or statements for the long-term stability. Nevertheless, several observations can be made after 100 cycles TCT regarding the susceptibility of interconnection to thermomechanical stress: the soldered interconnection at cells with busbars provide a stable behavior with a small change at the IV parameters (0.6% Pmpp loss). In addition, the testing group with continuous ECA02 line provides as well a stable behavior, with 0.5% Pmpp loss to initial. On the other hand, the samples with ECA02 pads interconnection had 12.0% Pmpp loss to initial, therefore disqualified, since it exceeded the allowed maximal power loss of 5% (according to IEC 61215 norm [10]). The clear confirmation of functionality for this proof of concept, regarding the reinforcement of interconnection by NCA is delivered by the testing group with alternating ECA-NCA pads, which has a Pmpp loss of 4.2% after 100 cycles TCT.

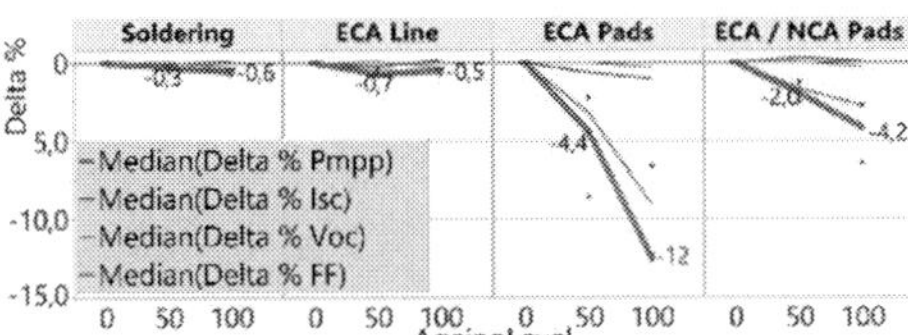

Figure 13. Relative change (percentage) to initial state at main IV parameters of tested interconnection variations during temperature cycling test (TCT)

An analysis of the electrical parameters indicate that current (Isc) and voltage (Voc) do not change considerably during the applied accelerated ageing. The fill factor, FF, (red line at fig.13) is the parameter, which affects at most the low and high changes of Pmpp parameter (blue line at fig.13). The fill factor decreases when series resistance and, or shunt resistance of the solar cells increase; furthermore, for a solar module, the fill factor will include also the effects of electrical resistances (usually series resistances) caused by cell interconnections. Since degradations of cell metallization or at cell interconnection usually lead to an increase of series resistance, and since electroluminescence and microscopy confirm degradations at cell interconnection as well, it is demonstrated together with the IV measurement data, that the reduction of power parameter Pmpp is caused by an increase of series resistance, due to damage at cell interconnection.

The good and faulty interconnection regions were identified at provided samples by MFI [11] [12] and X-ray imaging. These methods correlated provide a more sensitive and specific approach for identification of faulty interconnections compared to EL imaging. Regions of interest (for cross sectioning) were extracted on localized positions and prepared for optical and for scanning electron microscopy. By the analysis was observed that an offset of ribbons to the ECA-NCA pads occurred at certain samples (fig.14). The cause for this misalignment is the manual positioning of cell on stringer's conveyor. Such offsets are responsible for weaker adhesion, since less surface is available for the connection between components.

Figure 14. X-ray imaging exposes the offset ribbon – pad pattern of a sample region with ECA pad interconnection

The process was improved considerably, providing acceptably homogeneous thickness at interconnection and the previously observed ECA-NCA contamination issue could not be detected at this trial.

However, the main issue detected at the produced samples was a certain considerable offset of ECA pads to the position for contacting the fingers (fig.15). This is considered as one of main causes for the relatively high power drop during the TCT tests, since at certain contacting positions either the ECA pads barely contact with their edges the fingers, or fail to contact the finger.

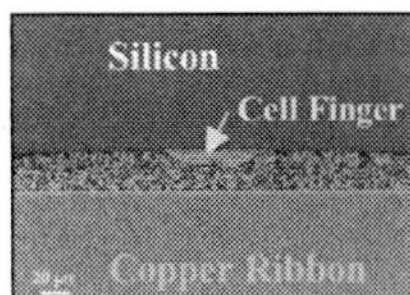

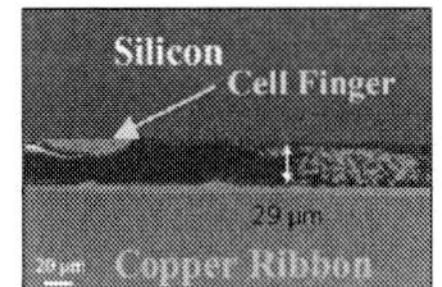

Figure 15. Cross-section of localized good (left) and faulty (right) interconnection (SEM image)

Given the good results from these trials, implementation at the industrial level could be expected in the short- or mid-term. The next step involves testing in a fully automated industrial environment, for which an estimated Cost of Ownership (CoO) calculation has been performed. For this CoO calculation, a scenario based on an ECA with low silver filler content and a price of pure silver of 1300 € /kg was considered. Based on our experimental results, the CoO calculations have been performed for two different amounts of ECA per cell: 40mg and 113mg (for M10 full cell size with 10 busbars per polarity). This considerable ECA weight difference at samples with same or similar ECA dispensing pattern and geometry can be explained by high differences of the density of the tested ECAs.

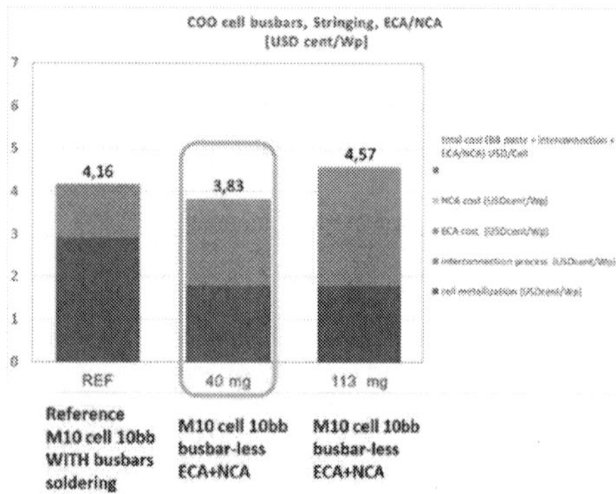

Figure 16. CoO ECA-NCA cell interconnection process calculations, in comparison with soldering process (left)

The CoO results shown in fig.16 include the following cost items: paste for busbars ("cell metallization"), total cost of tabbing-stringing process, excluding cost of the ribbons ("interconnection process"), cost of ECA and NCA respectively, whereas the NCA cost is negligible.

Further tests must explore the further reduction of printed ECA quantity at this interconnection type.

Dedicated FEM simulations revealed that highest shear forces within interconnection layers are distributed over a length of approx. 20mm from each edge (perpendicular to interconnection ribbons) of cell towards inner part of the cell. These mechanical tensions are introduced by the thermomechanical stress, which occurs during or after interconnection process, due to different coefficients of thermal expansion, mainly between copper from interconnection ribbons and bulk silicon of solar cell.

4 SUMMARY

The tested continuous interconnection ECA line (with ECA02 material) proved stable up to 100 cycles TCT, which emphasizes the importance of the material choice at this process (since previous tests [4] failed). However, a continuous ECA line would imply a high silver consumption, which would not be practicable at industrial scale. Therefore, it was proven during this experiment that a NCA reinforcement can be used and this allow the ECA-NCA interconnection with tested materials and process to withstand 100 cycles TCT accelerated ageing (power loss at 4.2%, still below 5% to initial). The high power loss is assigned mainly to observed ECA-NCA-cell-ribbon offsets (this create sensitive low contact surface interconnection, which fail during TCT test/ confirmed by EL imaging): light spread of dark regions in the EL images), which will be addressed at future process

optimizations. The takeaway message is that the reported ECA-NCA interconnection process has high chances to pass at least 1x IEC norm requirements at accelerated ageing level, if the process will be optimized (mostly regarding positioning precision and reproducibility for ECA and NCA pads). In the same time is also economically attractive, offering the potential to reduce cell interconnection process and material costs by at least 7.9% (compared to standard soldering process at cells with busbars).

5 ACKNOWLEDGEMENT

The authors express their gratitude to German Federal Ministry for Economic Affairs and Energy in the frame of Indifiduell Project (contract no.: 03EE1185) for funding, and thank to Henkel AG & Co. KGaA, Fraunhofer-Center für Silizium-Photovoltaik CSP, and all partners and colleagues, which contributed, for very good collaboration.

6 REFERENCES

[1] G. Beaucarne, et al. – doi: 10.1016/j.egypro.2015.03.302
[2] A. Halm, et al. – doi: 10.4229/27thEUPVSEC2012-2AO.2.1
[3] A. Halm, et al. doi: 10.4229/EUPVSEC20172017-2CV.2.91
[4] T. Timofte, et al. – doi: 10.4229/WCPEC-82022-3CO.4.5
[5] G. Beaucarne, et al. – doi: 10.1016/j.egypro.2016.10.087
[6] A. Hartwig, et al. – doi: 10.1142/S0960313193000188
[7] R. Hanke et al. – doi: 10.1016/j.nima.2008.03.016
[8] T.Geipel et al. – doi: 10.1016/j.egypro.2013.07.287
[9] Ch. Hirschl et al. – doi: https://doi.org/10.1016/j.solmat.2013.04.022
[10] IEC norms 61215-1/-2:2021 and IEC 61730-2:2016
[11] S. Großer et al. - doi: 10.1051/epjpv/2023029
[12] S. Großer et al. - doi: 10.4229/WCPEC-82022-3DV.3.17

Towards enhanced reliability of busbar-free IBC solar cell interconnections by non-conductive adhesive reinforcement

Tudor Timofte[1], Tobias Messmer[1], Raphael Shanmugam[1], Karl Wienands[1], Joris Libal[1], Stephan Großer[2], Matthias Pander[2], Giuseppe Galbiati[3], Tobias Nitsche[3], Daniel Buckland[3], Andreas Halm[1]

[1] ISC Konstanz, Rudolf-Diesel-Straße 15, 78467 Konstanz, Germany

[2] Fraunhofer-Center für Silizium-Photovoltaik CSP, Otto-Eißfeldt-Str. 12, 06120 Halle (Saale), Germany

[3] Henkel AG & Co. KGaA, Henkelstraße 67, 40589 Düsseldorf, Germany

Content

- Motivation
- BB vs BB-less Metallization Layout
- Challenge
- Proposed approach
- Tested laboratory process
- Design of Experiment
- Results
- Cost Calculations
- Conclusions

020219-002

Motivation: Why no busbars (BB)? Why use ECA & NCA ?

- Module **price** trend[1]

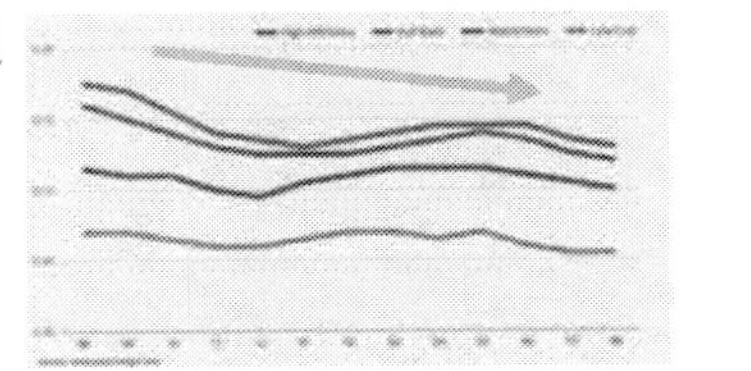

ECA = Electrically Conductive Adhesive
NCA = Non Conductive Adhesive

- Towards **Pb-free** interconnection[2]

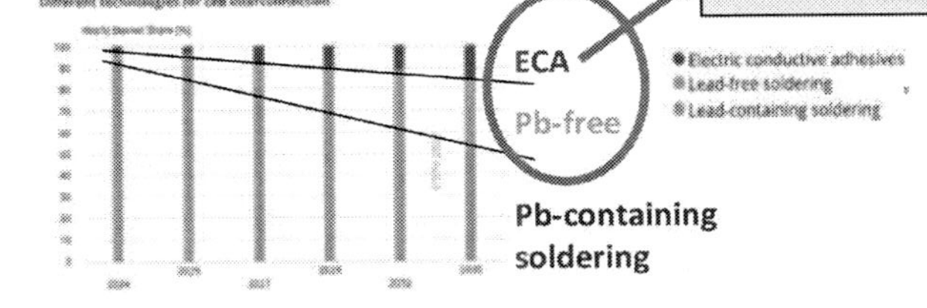

- Demand for **low temperature interconnections**
  - for ex. Tandem-Perovskite solar cells demand processing temperatures < 150°C [3]

- **Environmental aspects & Recyclability**
  - interconnection which can be coupled to recycling processes (for ex. solvent separation, thermal decomposition, etc.)

[1] Source: www.pvexchange.com (price trend 08.2024 – 08.2025)
[2] Source: www.vdma.eu / ITRPV 2025
[3] A. De Rose et al., DOI: 10.1016/j.solmat.2023.112515

Busbar (BB) vs. Busbar (BB)-less Cell Metallization Layout

- **@ Cell Level (trend to reduce further considerably silver consumption)**
  - From BB Pads to BB-less (soldering or ECA will take over the role of BB as well)

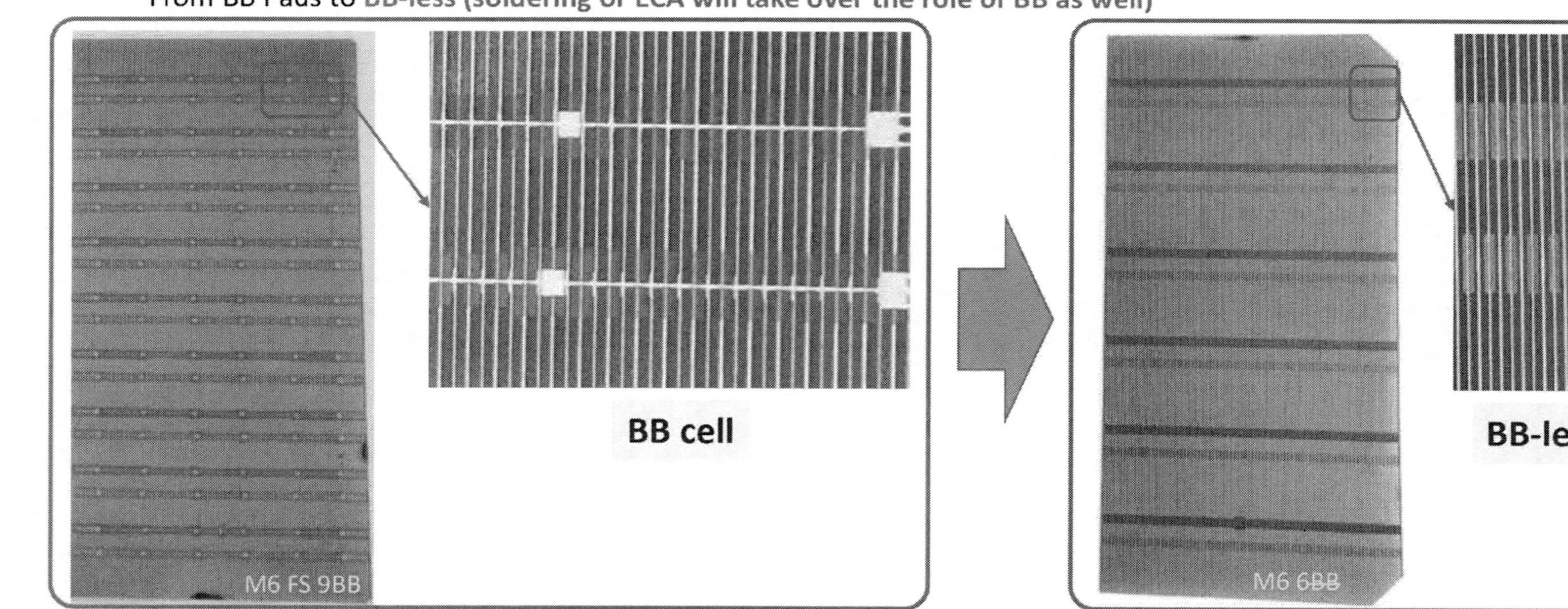

Challenge at BB-less Cell Interconnection

- PV specific ECA is a market proven solution for connection of solar cells <u>with busbars</u>
- Interconnection of busbar-less cell with ECA (or solder paste) pose new challenges:
  - <u>no standard soldering</u> with solder alloy coated ribbons possible for BB-less cells
  - <u>different contacting interface</u> (textured surface with SixNy coating and cell fingers instead of busbars)
  - <u>additional freedom for deformations</u> due to thermo-mechanical stress

half cells (G1 wafer size) **with busbars**[*]
Epoxy ECA line interconnection (~ 0.42mg/cm)
ECA Dispensing, Assembly and Curing at industrial stringer
(setup: 180°C / T ramp to target temp. = 15s/ dwell at target temp. = 35s)

EL

half cells (G1 wafer size) **without** busbars (**busbar-less**[*])
Epoxy ECA line interconnection (~ 0.42mg/cm)
ECA Dispensing, Assembly and Curing at industrial stringer
(setup: 180°C / T ramp to target temp. = 15s/ dwell at target temp. = 35s)

EL

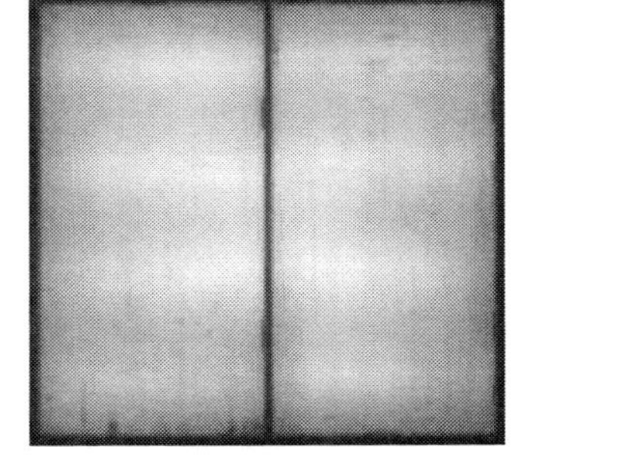

Dark areas and stripes indicate multiple electric interruptions at cell interconnection and cell metallization

*Previous tests made in the frame of Zquadrat Project

Proposed approach (schematic cross section of an IBC ZEBRA solar cell with interconnection)

Classic interconnection

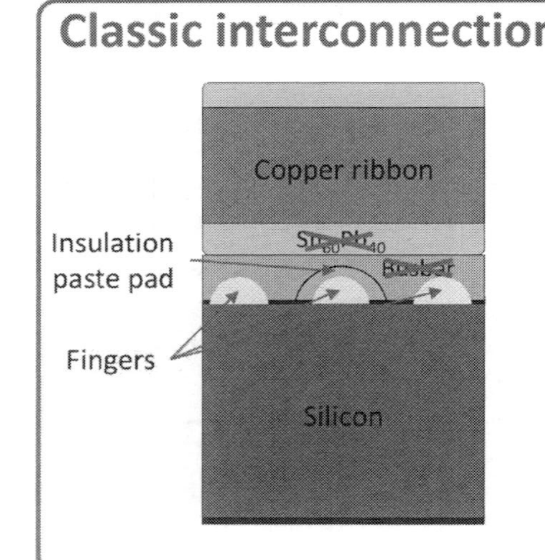

ECA interconnection

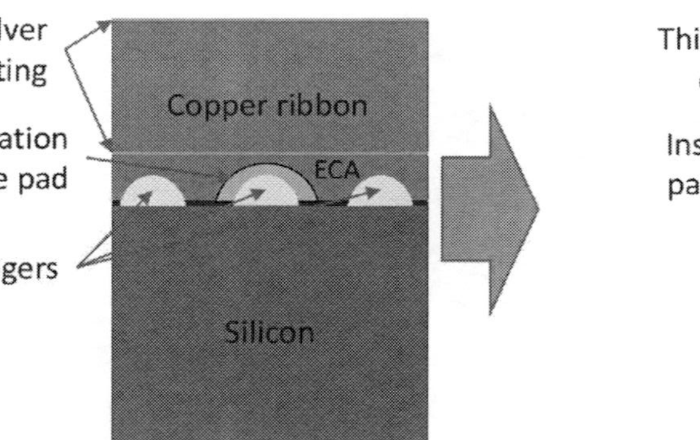

ECA-NCA interconnection

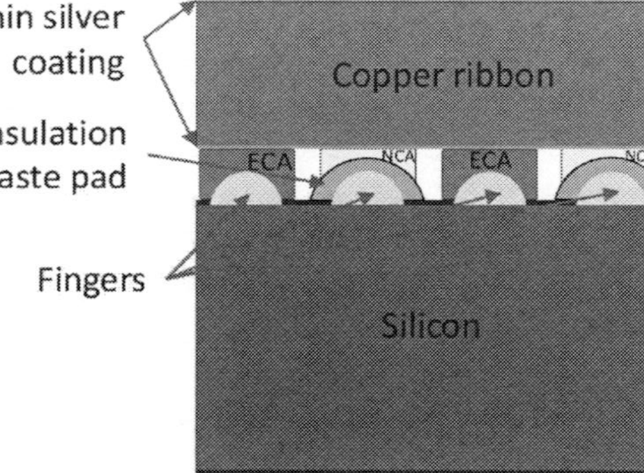

020219-006

Proposed approach (schematic cross section of an IBC ZEBRA solar cell with interconnection)

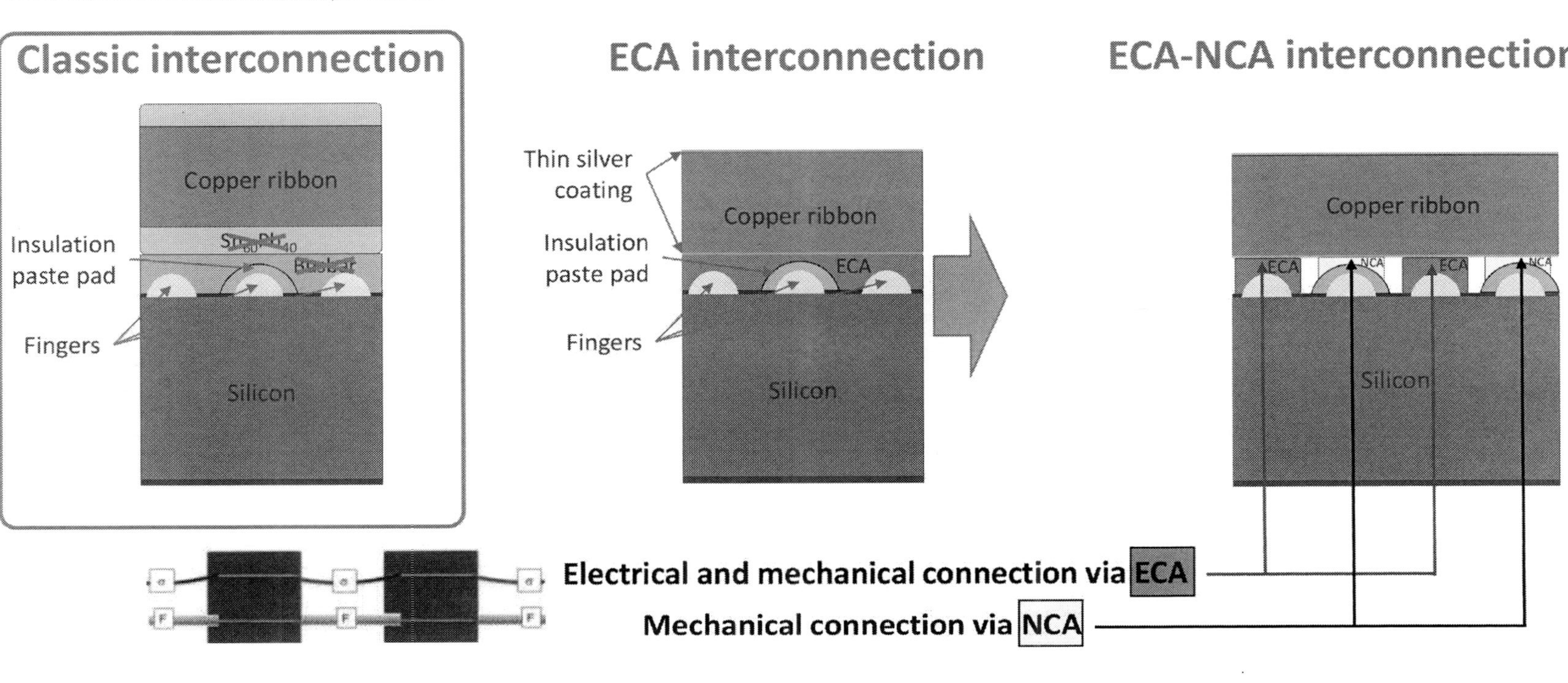

020219-007

Proposed and tested approach

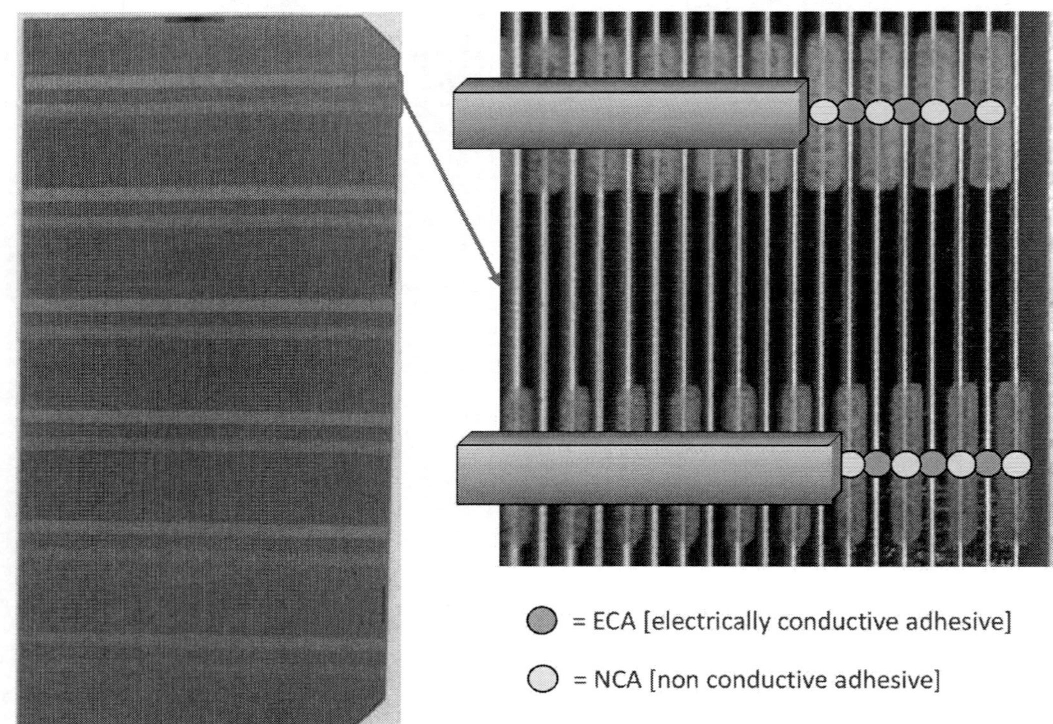

Systematic approach:

1. **Test of an ECA sampling contingent** (acryl based) at BB-less ZEBRA cells:
   * Develop process for ECA dispensing, assembly cell-ECA-ribbon fixation and curing schedule
   * Test adhesion, ECA cross linking and compatibility

2. **Test of an NCA sampling contingent** (epoxy based) at BB-less ZEBRA cells:
   * Develop process for ECA dispensing, assembly cell-ECA-ribbon fixation and curing schedule
   * Test adhesion, NCA cross linking and compatibility

3. **Test of an ECA and NCA** (epoxy and acryl based) at BB-less ZEBRA cells:
   * Develop process for ECA dispensing, assembly cell-ECA-ribbon fixation and curing schedule
   * Test adhesion, ECA cross linking and compatibility

020219-008

Issues noticed at ECA-NCA interconnection trials

- **Test Setup:**
  - ECA pads + NCA pads
  - Micro dispensing at robot unit
  - Manual assembly after ECA and NCA dispensing
  - Curing at heating plate with down-holder
  - Curing schedule: setup temperature = 180°C / dwell time = 360

Connection type: ECA + NCA

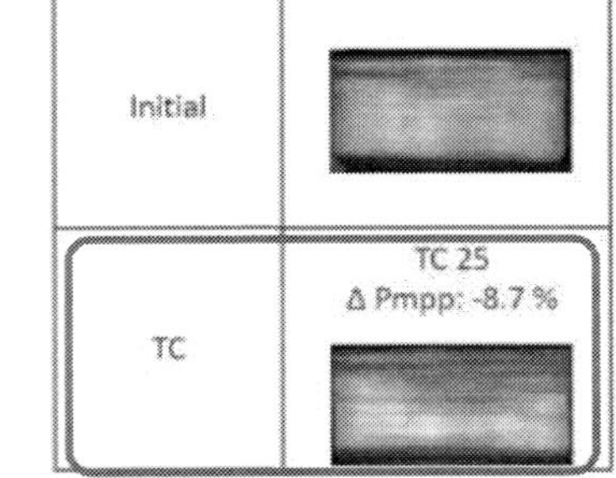

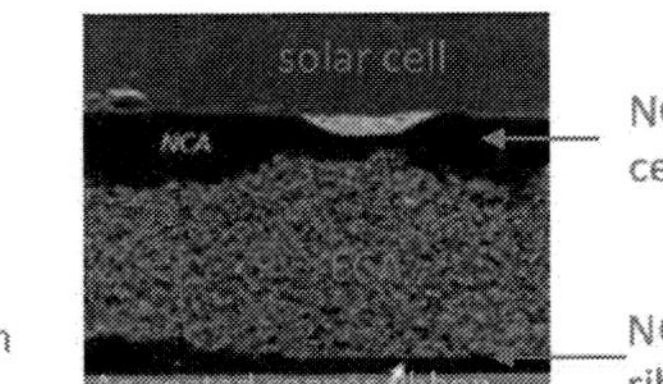

T. Meßmer et al., MIW 2024

- **Identified causes for the sensitivity/ fail of the ECA-NCA interconnection**
  - Contact failure localization by MFI[4,5] + X-ray and target preparation of cross-sections for SEM

[4] S. Großer, M. Schak, T. Timofte and M. Turek, "Assessment of ECA to Ribbon Interconnection Stability by Current Path and Power Loss Imaging", 8th World Conference on Photovoltaic Energy Conversion Milano (2022) DOI: 10.4229/WCPEC-82022-3DV.3.17

[5] S. Großer, M. Pander, U. Zeller and B. Jäckel, "Local resolution of currents through electrical joints consisting of materials with different conductivity" EPJ Photovoltaics, 14 (2023) DOI: 10.1051/epjpv/2023029

Fraunhofer CSP

020219-009

Test Lab Process: Dispensing, Assembly and Curing

Jetting continuous lines or pads for ECA & NCA

- XY pick and place unit with optical alignment
- Integrated micro jet dispensing units

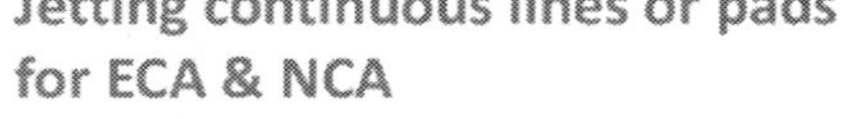

See poster: R. Shanmugam et al., 3.AV.1.29

Assembly cell - ECA/NCA - ribbon

TeamTechnik Stringer TT 2100
Adapted semiautomatic process for ECA curing
cell with ECA lines **mounted manually on conveyor**

1st Ribbon set added automatically on ECA lines on cell

Down-holder and 2nd ribbon set added automatically on cell

Curing procedure

TeamTechnik Stringer TT 2100

- only heat plate curing, without IR heating
- Heating pattern setup (°C):

- Dwell time at 190°C heating area: 300s
- Temperature profile:

020219-010

Design of Experiment

Glas - backsheet mini-module used for testing of IV characteristics, EL and accelerated ageing (TCT)

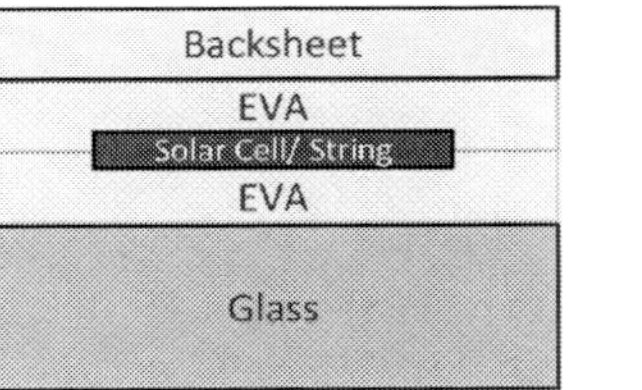

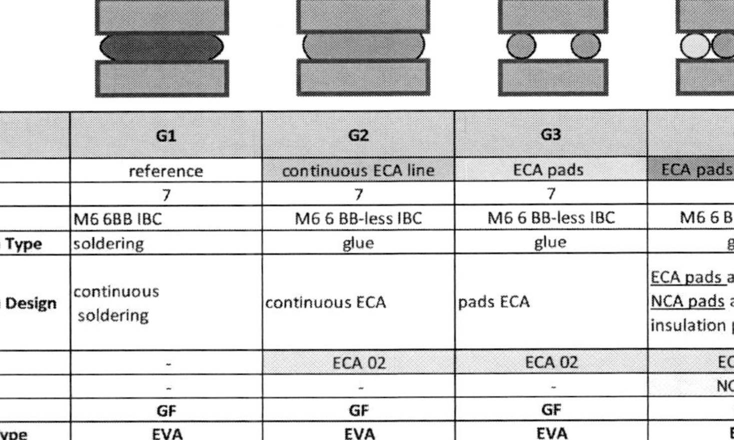

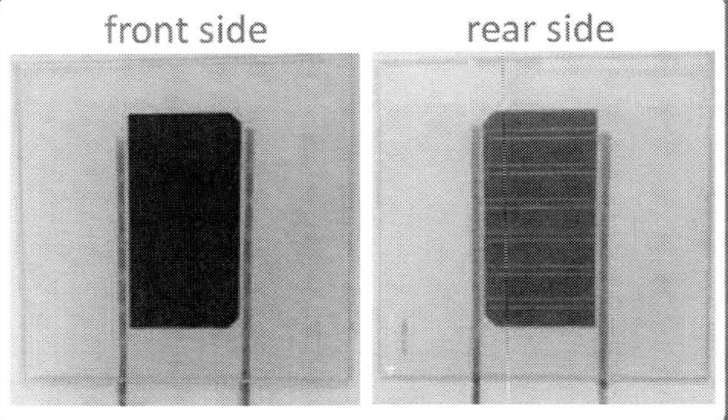

Testgroup	G1	G2	G3	G4
Purpose	reference	continuous ECA line	ECA pads	ECA pads + NCA pads
Nr of samples	7	7	7	7
Cell type	M6 6BB IBC	M6 6 BB-less IBC	M6 6 BB-less IBC	M6 6 BB-less IBC
Interconnection Type	soldering	glue	glue	glue
Interconnection Design	continuous soldering	continuous ECA	pads ECA	ECA pads at all fingers NCA pads at all insulation pads
ECA_	-	ECA 02	ECA 02	ECA 02
NCA_	-	-	-	NCA 01
Module Type	GF	GF	GF	GF
Encapsulation Type	EVA	EVA	EVA	EVA

Characterization:

- Visual inspection
- Electroluminescence (EL)
- Sun simulator flash (IV)
- MFI + X-ray + cross-section analysis by SEM

Ageing:

- Temperature Cycling Test according to IEC 61215 (- 40°C/+85°C, without current injection)
- Stages: 0 (initial), 8 cycles, 50 cycles, 100 cycles (ongoing), 200 cycles (ongoing), etc.

020219-011

Microscopy: good vs. faulty dispensing

Section of a cell (only plus interconnection polarity at image below) with dispensed ECA pads and NCA pads
(same process target/ similar parameters compared to previous presented results / ECA = epoxy based)

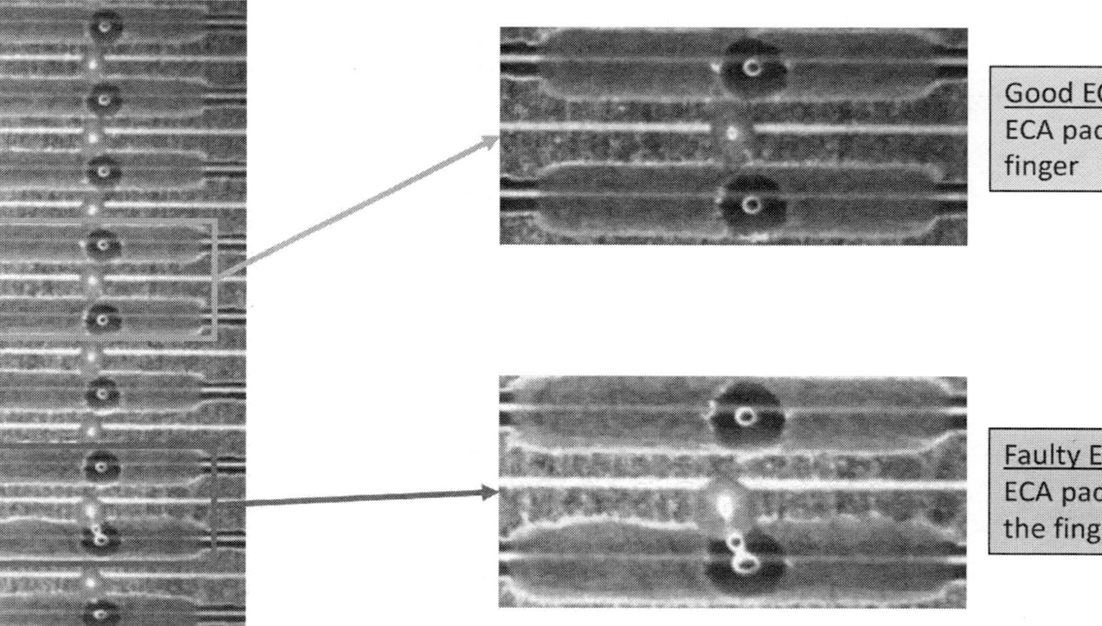

Accelerated Ageing (Temperature Cycling Test)

EL changes after 8 and 50 cycles TCT

Group	Description	TCT 0 (INITIAL)	TCT 8	TCT 50
G1 soldering	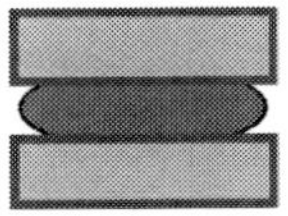	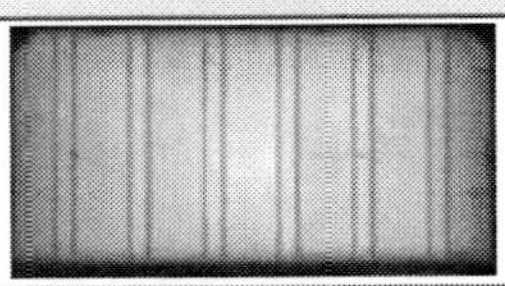		
G2 ECA 02 line	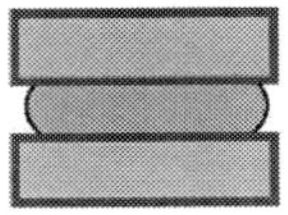			
G3 ECA 02 pads	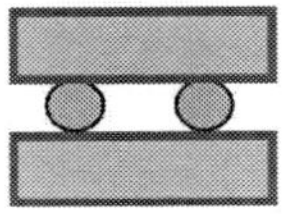	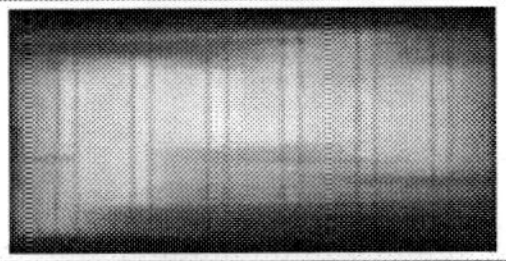	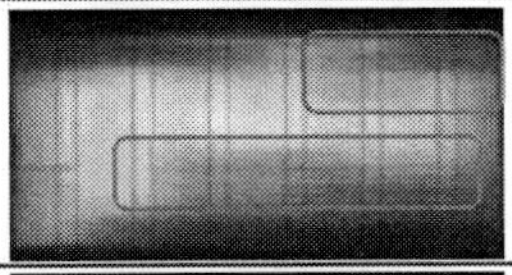	
G4 ECA 02 pads + NCA 01 pads	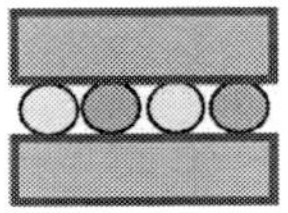		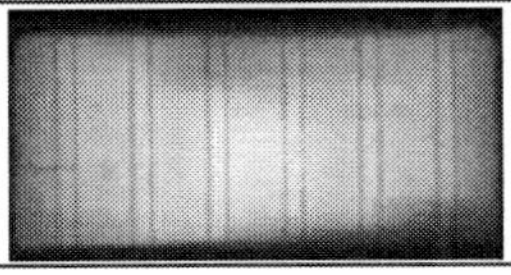	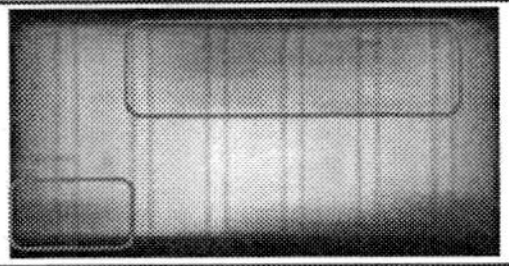

020219-013

IV parameters rel. (%) change after 8, 50 cycles TCT

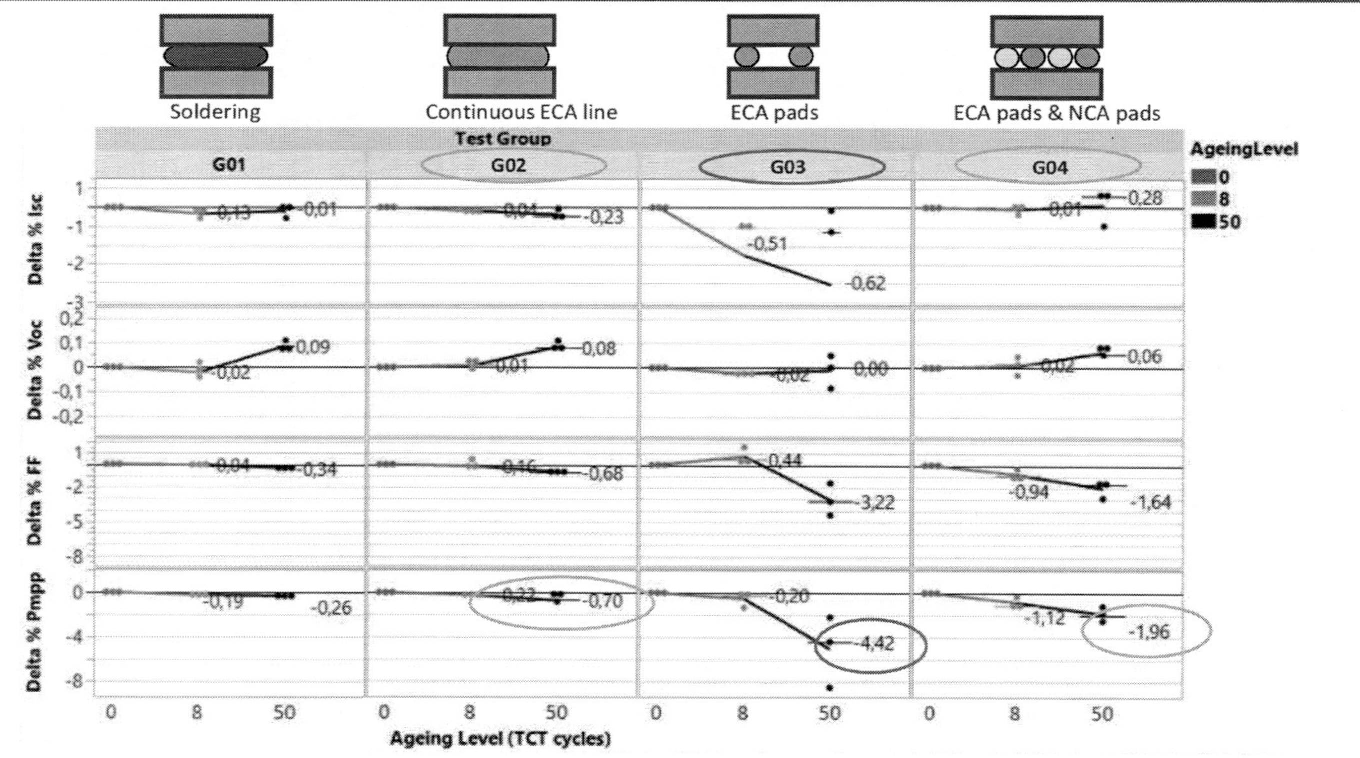

Inspection of interconnection at good and faulty locations

Rear view of sample with marked positions for longitudinal and perpendicular cross section at interconnection (selection made by using **X-ray scan and MFI**):
F = faulty contact / G = good contact

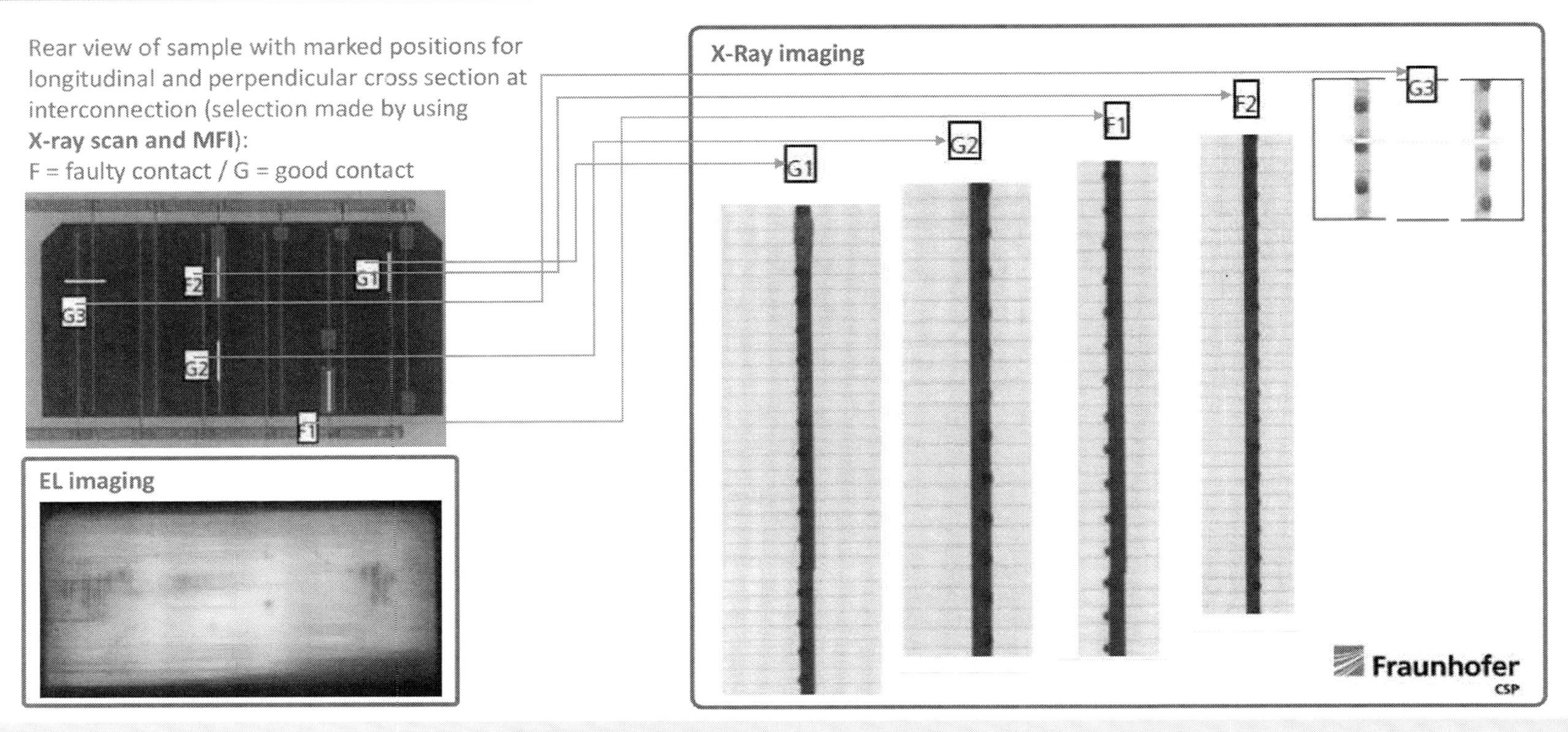

020219-015

Inspection of interconnection at good and faulty locations

Good
interconnection
position

Position G1:
Position G1:

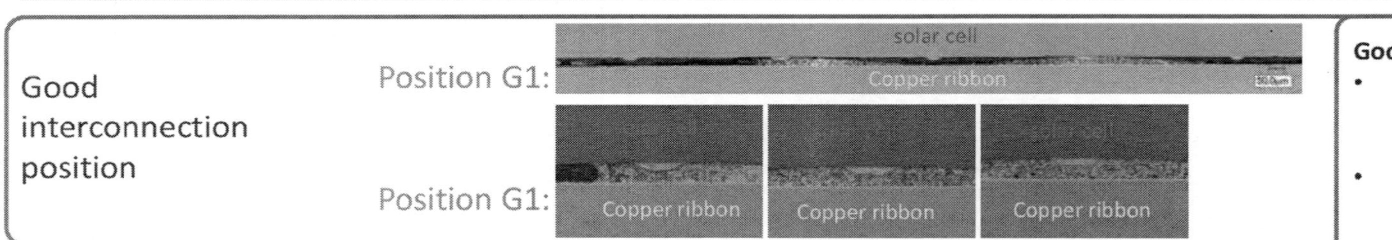

Faulty
interconnection
position

Position F1:
Position F1:

Good
interconnection
position

Position G3:   ECA: NCA:

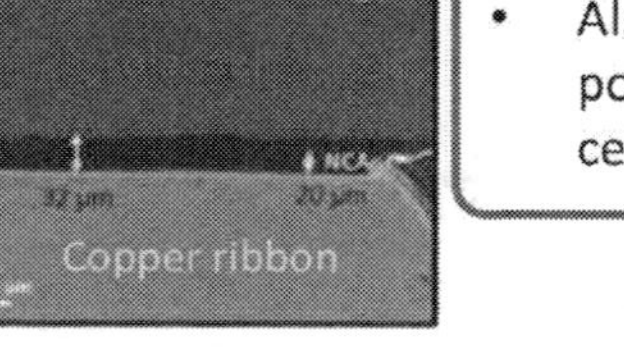

Good points:
- Jetting position accuracy for ECA and NCA pads improved
- Improved homogeneity of pressing during curing
- No NCA between ribbon and contacting fingers (cross contamination avoided)

Bad points:
- Still certain offset to cell finger of ECA and NCA pads
- Also offset observed at positioning of ribbon to cell

Estimative Cost Calculation (CoO)

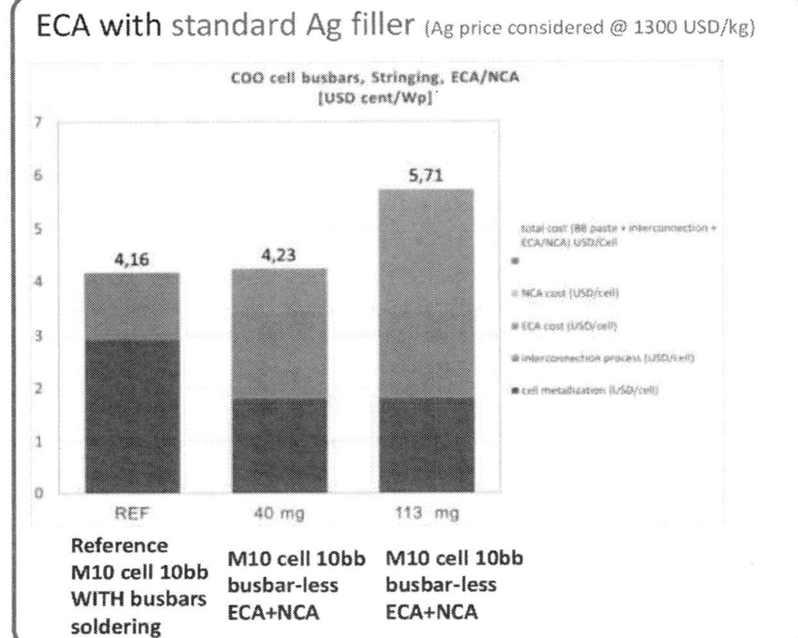

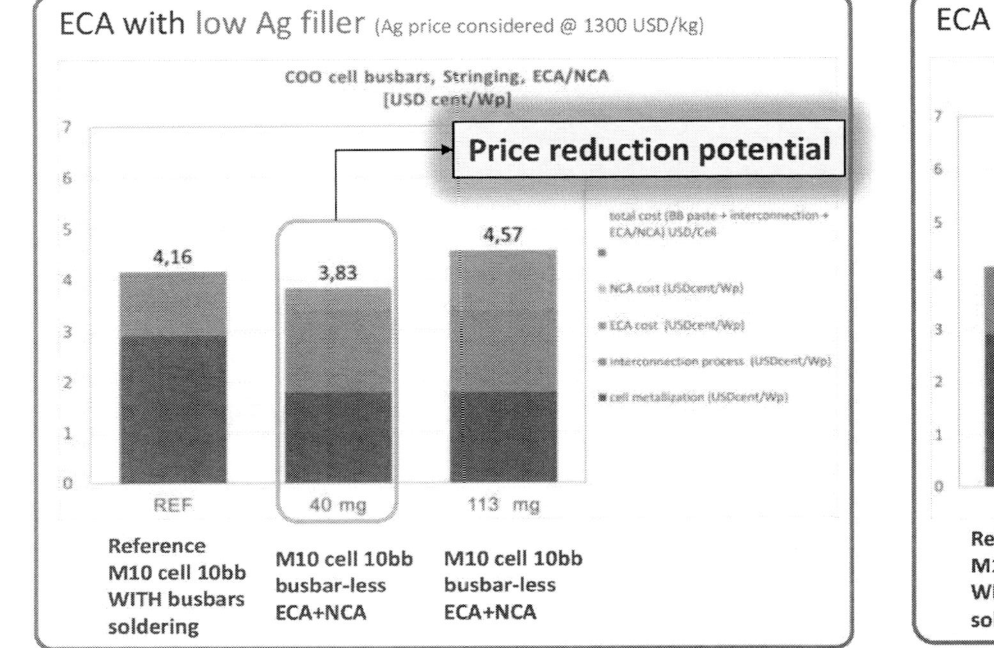

020219-017

Summary

- ECA pad – NCA pad interconnection for BB-less IBC ZEBRA cell successfully tested and optimized
  - Improved processing supported by contact microstructure analysis (Fraunhofer CSP)
- Best ECA-NCA material & process setup pass TCT50 with 1.9% power loss to initial (less power drop expected by improving the positioning accuracy of ECA and NCA pads)
- FEM simulations reveal peak of thermo-mechanical stress along the ribbon at soldered or glued interconnection in range of cell edges
  - Possible process optimization: reinforcing with NCA pads only ~ 20 mm length from both cell edges towards cell centre
- Further tests are ongoing and planned for further optimization and qualification of materials and processes at semi industrial process equipment, also including the setup solder paste – NCA interconnection at BB-less IBC cell
- The CoO calculation indicate the opportunity for cost saving (~ 8%) at BB-less cell with ECA and NCA interconnection compared to classic soldering approach at cells with busbars

Acknowledgments

The authors thank to

Supported by:

 for funding, on the basis of a decision by the German Bundestag

 and  for fruitful collaboration.

Furthermore many thanks to all colleagues and other partners involved in testing and general support!

Project Indifiduell: 03EE1185

Visit ISC Konstanz! 21st -24th October, 2025

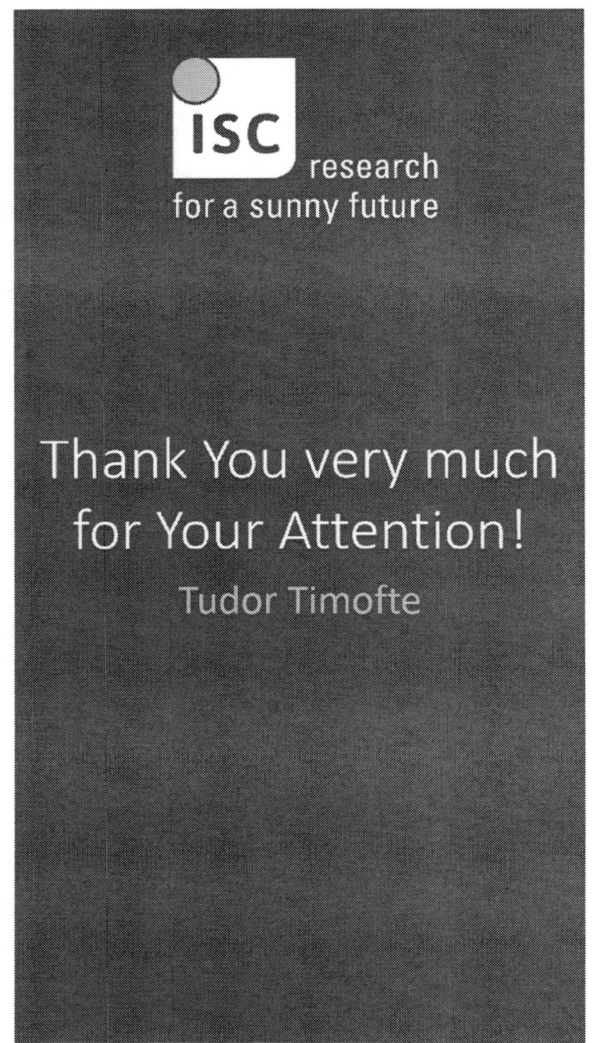

© ISC Konstanz e.V.   Tudor Timofte, 42nd EU PVSEC, Bilbao, Spain, 22-26 September 2025

Contact resistance limitations in conductive adhesive and solder paste modules

Daniel Tune[1], M. Ignacia Acevedo Devoto[1], Raphael Shanmugam[1], Karl Wienands,[1] Nils Kopp[2],

Carina Hallensleben[2], Rihoko Kizukuri[2], Matthias Helbig[1], Andreas Halm[1]

[1] International Solar Energy Research Centre (ISC) Konstanz

[2] TAMURA-ELSOLD GmbH, Ilsenburg, Germany

ABSTRACT: The reduction of conductive adhesive (ECA) or low temperature solder paste (LTS) in photovoltaic (PV) modules offers a potential path to lowering material costs and reducing the use of limited materials. However, reducing the amount of ECA or LTS beyond a certain threshold results in increased contact resistance due to the reduced total contact area and this detrimentally affects the fill factor (FF) due to series resistance losses. Additionally, insufficient interconnection material can compromise the mechanical strength of the connections, making them less capable of withstanding subsequent handling or thermal cycling stresses. In this study, we employ both simulation models and experimental measurements on minimodules to examine the effects of reducing ECA and LTS amount on contact resistance and FF in both shingled interconnections. To ensure adequate mechanical stability, we incorporate non-conductive adhesive (NCA), which allows us to explore lower material volumes where increases in contact resistance begin to significantly degrade module performance. Our results demonstrate that the strategy of combining reduced ECA or LTS with NCA can offer substantial cost and material savings without sacrificing performance or reliability. The simulation model developed in this work serves as a valuable tool for determining the minimum required amount of interconnection material based on material properties, providing essential guidelines for further optimizing interconnection materials and costs in PV modules while maintaining both the efficiency and durability of the modules.

Keywords: Solder paste, Conductive adhesive, Shingling, Module Integration

1 INTRODUCTION

The aim of this work is to further explore the limits to strategies of reducing the amount of ECA or LTS in PV module interconnections. The approach involves analytical simulations of the interconnects to predict the dependence of the module performance on the amount of ECA or LTS and then manufacturing and measuring the performance of strings of interconnected solar cells and dedicated test structures to validate the output of the simulation models. ECA or LTS are applied on the busbars of solar cells and then these are used to assemble test samples and one-cell-equivalent minimodules using standard industrial production processes. Mechanical properties of the ECA or LTS interconnects are assessed and the performance of the minimodules is measured before and after accelerated aging tests.

The market prevalence of modules that use ECA interconnects is increasing and it has been previously shown that LTS can also be used in some applications where ECA is used, but the relatively high cost of some ECAs and the use of limited materials such as bismuth or silver in LTS and silver in ECAs creates an impetus for exploring ways to reduce the amount of the materials used (in addition to general cost-down considerations). However, this must be done in a way that does not detrimentally impact the performance or reliability of the modules or, better, provides improvements. In this work, we use an innovative approach of adding NCA to provide mechanical reinforcement of ECA or LTS interconnects, allowing a much lower amount of these materials to be used since they are only required to provide the necessary electrical functionalities.

This study addresses the question of how much further the amount can be reduced before the electrical resistance of the interconnects causes a detrimental increase in the series resistance of the modules and corresponding decrease in FF and power output. This can be caused primarily by the limited contact area (contact resistance), the thickness of the bonding material (bulk resistance), or the distance charges must travel along the busbar (busbar resistance) and depends also on the magnitude of the current that must be passed through each interconnect, itself a function of the cell size, cell efficiency, and number of busbars/shingle strips per cell.

2 EXPERIMENTAL

The test platform used in this work consists of a G1 6BB PERC shingled minimodule, wherein the conductive adhesive or solder paste is applied between the inner five shingle overlaps (Figure 1). For convenience in the production and to avoid the influence of differences on the string ends, tin-lead solder-coated copper ribbons are used for the end connectors. The modules are made in a glass-backsheet configuration using POE encapsulant. After initial IV and EL testing, the modules are loaded into damp-heat or temperature cycling climate chambers and retested periodically. Commercially available conductive and non-conductive adhesives are deposited by jet dispensing (Vermes) and solder paste is applied via stencil printing.

10.4229/EUPVSEC2025/3CO.10.6
020220-001

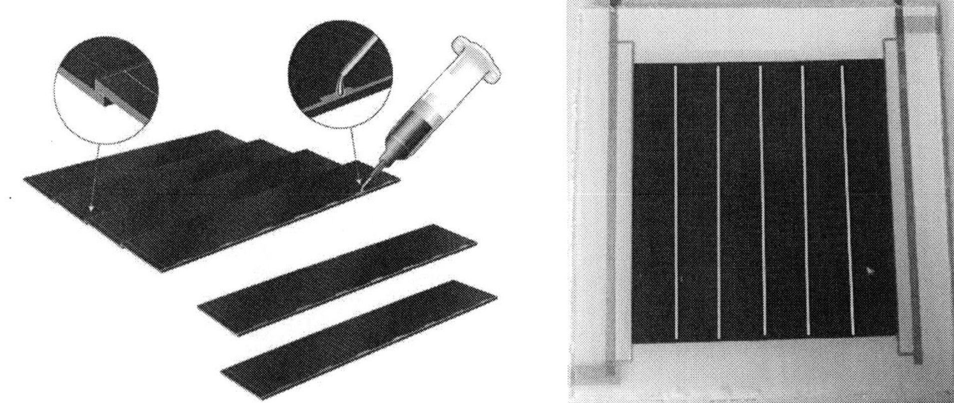

Figure 1. The test platform used in this work, consisting of shingled minimodules with five lines of conductive adhesive or solder paste as indicated by yellow lines in the image on the right. For convenience in the manufacturing, end connectors are attached using standard tin-lead solder-coated ribbons. The modules are laminated in a glass-backsheet configuration using POE encapsulant (*left image credit: Nagase-Chemtex*).

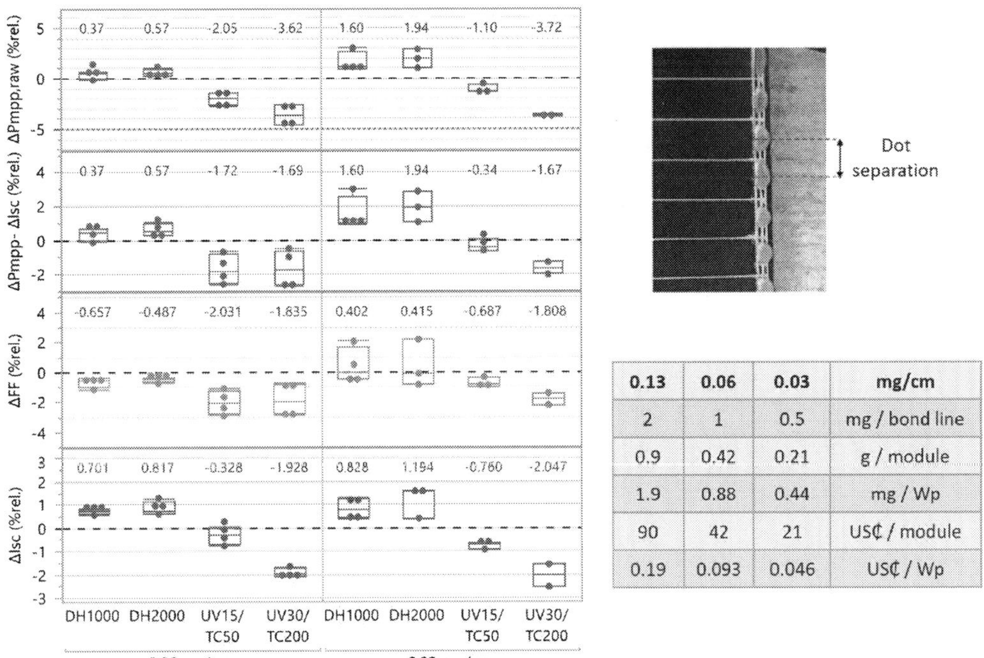

0.13	0.06	0.03	mg/cm
2	1	0.5	mg / bond line
0.9	0.42	0.21	g / module
1.9	0.88	0.44	mg / Wp
90	42	21	US¢ / module
0.19	0.093	0.046	US¢ / Wp

Figure 2. Initial work to reduce the amount of ECA by exchanging continuous lines for a line of dots and varying the dot separation. The relative change of the IV characteristics of modules made with either 0.06 mg/cm or 0.03 mg/cm after climate chamber accelerated aging are shown on the left. The photograph in the upper right shows an example of the deposited ECA dots on the shingle busbar and the table in the lower right gives a breakdown of the associated material consumption and costs extrapolated for the modelled module.

3 RESULTS

3.1 ECA Reduction Strategies

Transitioning from continuous adhesive lines to discrete dots or pads offers a straightforward route to material reduction (**Figure 2**). Jet-dispensing allowed for flexibility and easy control of pad mass and separation. IV data obtained from minimodule tests demonstrated that even with starkly reduced adhesive volume, no significant power losses occurred after 2000 h damp-heat exposure (even some small gains, as often seen with ECA bonds). Combined UV/TC accelerated aging revealed yellowing of the encapsulant used, as seen visually and in the decrease of ISC. However, even after correcting for this, a power loss of ~1.7% was still observed after TC400. It should be noted that this power loss depends strongly on the bill of materials used, with previous work demonstrating losses of only 0.5% to TC720 with other material combinations.

Extrapolating these amounts to the case of an M10, 7BB shingled module with 23% efficiency and providing 460 W power output at STC allows for an estimate of the ECA material costs of as low as 0.046 US¢/Wp, which is a 75% cost reduction *vs.* the widely quoted amount of 2 mg ECA per G1 shingle bond line.

3.2 Low-Temperature Solder (LTS) reduction and NCA Reinforcement

LTS pastes, widely used in microelectronics, offer excellent mechanical and electrical properties, and are readily printable or dispensable. Their integration into PV modules has been validated in conductive backsheet designs and is here extended to shingled modules. SBAC solder paste was provided by Tamura-Elsold GmbH within the framework of a German publicly funded project.

As shown in **Figure 3**, material reduction via stencil printing demonstrated a clear 'less-is-better' trend, with pad size and spacing influencing both electrical resistance and mechanical strength in the range of 2.2 mg/cm to 0.59 mg/cm. Further reductions in the amount were not possible due to a lack of mechanical stability in subsequent processing steps – the shingles simply fell apart during handling.

To overcome these mechanical strength limitations, the LTS interconnects were reinforced with non-conductive adhesive (NCA) as first suggested by Beaucarne in 2016.[1] Two commercial NCAs were tested, with either high (400–600 MPa) or low (40–60 MPa) elastic modulus. Using this strategy, the amount of LTS was reduced by half to 0.32 mg/cm. Thermal cycling tests showed modest improvement in the power loss to TC600 in both NCA cases, while damp-heat stability to 3000 h was significantly improved. Cost analysis indicates that such reinforced solder joints are competitive with silver-based ECAs.

3.3 Modelling the Lower Electrical Limit of ECA Amount

To guide further work to reduce the amount of ECA, we developed a numerical model using our previously demonstrated technique used to determine the contact resistivity of ECA-based interconnects.[2-4] The model uses the known geometrical parameters of the ECA pads in the interconnect combined with the measured electrical parameters (**Figure 4**) and is used to estimate the resistance contributions of the interconnects to the total series resistance of the module. Based on this, and knowledge of the cell output properties and characteristic resistance (**Figure 5**), it is possible to estimate the cell-to-module (CTM) loss of FF for a given amount and contact geometry of the ECA in the interconnect.

As shown in **Figure 6**, the model output reveals that the contact resistance dominates the FF loss within the modelled range of ECA-BB contact resistivities (corresponding to the values we have measured from commercial ECAs and industry standard BB metallisation pastes). This dependency is amplified when the thickness of the ECA pad (i.e. the distance between adjacent cells in a shingle overlap, or between the BB and ribbon) is increased. The amplification is understood on the basis that, for a given ECA amount, a thicker pad entails a smaller contact area. Surprisingly, for the two orders of magnitude range of ECA bulk resistivities that we measure from commercial ECAs, very little effect on the FF loss is estimated.

Additional modelling as shown in **Figure 7** highlighted the importance of busbar line resistance when the ECA amount is very small i.e., when the pads are widely spaced, demonstrating that at very low adhesive amounts, BB resistance between pads cannot be neglected, as it increases series resistance and reduces fill factor.

3.4 Reliability and Performance

To test the model predictions for varying amounts of ECA in the interconnects, several groups of minimodules were produced and the electroluminescence images of them are shown in **Figure 8**. To avoid inadvertent contact between BBs between the ECA pads, NCA was first deposited between the pads and cured to produce an insulating region. ECA and further NCA were then deposited according to amounts specified in the figure, and these were cured before the shingles strings were made into minimodules.

Significant losses were observed, especially for the smaller amounts, and these were generally consistent with the predictions of the model. However, for the highest amount, the FF loss due to the ECA contact resistance was a smaller contribution to the total FF loss, with the losses due to the BB line resistance dominating in this case (**Figure 9**).

To further test the model predictions, a similar range of minimodules were produced using the same techniques (**Figure 10**). In these modules, the amount of ECA was held relatively constant but the separation between the pads of ECA was varied from two pads of ECA per bond line to 16 pads of ECA per line. In this case, as observed in the EL images, the definition between conducting and non-conducting regions was less well defined than for the amount variation experiments. **Figure 11** shows the IV characteristics of the modules and the corresponding model predictions. As with the amount variation tests, the correlation between the model predictions and the IV results shows an overestimation by the model, especially for the lowest amounts and smallest separations, indicating either inadequacies in the model, or poor interconnect quality, or a combination of both. Nevertheless, the small underestimation of the FF loss by the model is not considered to limit its usefulness in guiding and informing module development in R&D or production environments.

We note that in the three cases of shortest pad separation, champion minimodules achieved fill factors of ~79%, comparable to modules made with continuous lines containing eight times more ECA, giving confidence that, with further process optimisation, such low FF losses could also be achieved at high yield for these very small amounts of ECA. We further note that the material cost of the NCA is smaller by at least a factor of ten than the ECA, meaning that significant cost reductions can be expected to accompany reduced ECA material consumption, despite the addition cost of the NCA support material.

4   SUMMARY AND OUTLOOK

This study investigated the electrical and mechanical limitations of reducing the amount of silver-based ECAs in PV module interconnects, assessed the potential of LTS pastes with NCA reinforcement, and demonstrated a numerical model capable of estimating the FF loss at module level for a given amount and application of conductive material in PV interconnects. The following conclusions can be drawn:

- Substantial reductions in ECA or LTS consumption are possible, especially when combined with NCA reinforcement.
- Contact resistivity dominates the electrical limitation of how little conductive material is required, while bulk resistivity plays a lesser role.
- Modelling confirms that pad thickness and BB resistance are also critical factors to consider when reducing adhesive quantities.
- A strong business case exists for ECA and LTS interconnects, supporting reduced cost and silver dependency in PV module manufacturing.

Overall, both ECA and LTS interconnects demonstrate excellent prospects for future module designs, provided that careful attention is paid to pad design, contact resistivity, and the use of mechanical reinforcement strategies.

ACKNOWLEDGEMENT

This work was funded by the German Federal Ministry of Economic Affairs and Energy (BMWE) as part of the BIG project with reference number 03EE1116A.

REFERENCES

1.Beaucarne (2016) DOI: 10.1016/j.egypro.2016.10.087
2.Devoto et al. (2023) DOI: 10.1016/j.solmat.2023.112490
3.Devoto et al. (2023) DOI: 10.1016/j.solmat.2023.112518
4.Devoto et al. (2024) DOI: 10.1002/pip.3787

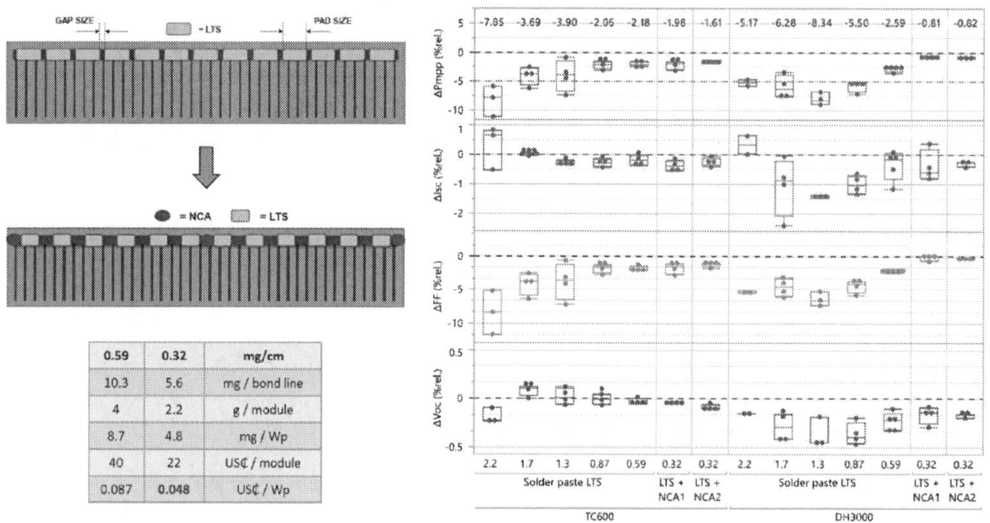

Figure 3. The strategy of reducing the amount of LTS in the interconnects by first reducing pad size and separation and then by including NCA as mechanical support. The changes in the IV characteristics to TC600 and DH3000 show significant reductions in power losses through both strategies and the associated cost breakdown for the modelled M10 wafer size module clearly demonstrate cost competitiveness with ECA-based interconnects.

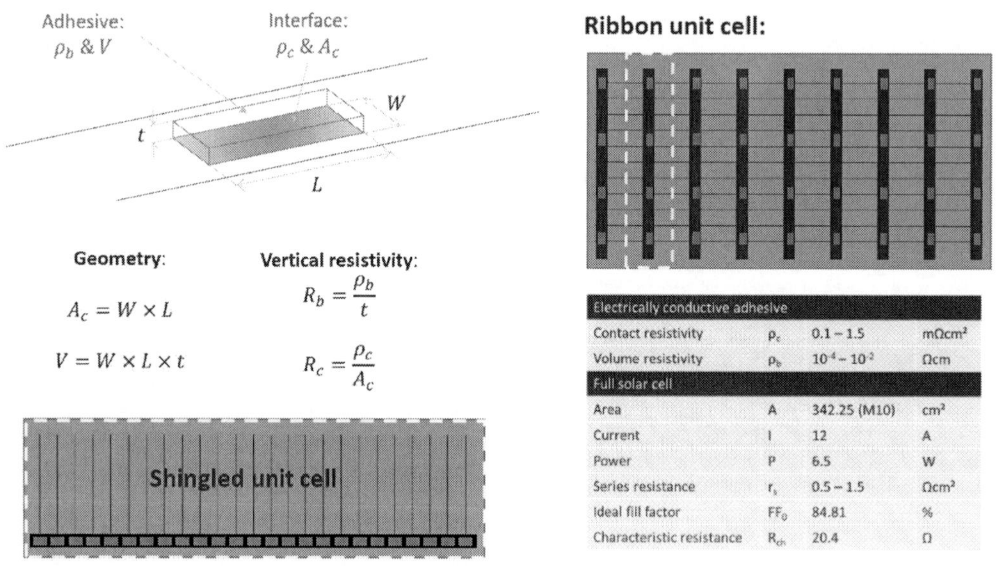

Figure 4. Aspects of the numerical model developed to estimate the CTM loss of FF for a given geometry and set of electrical characteristics of the ECA in the interconnect. The model is applicable to either shingled or ribbon-interconnected modules and is used to simulate an M10-wafer-size module with the parameters shown in the table on the bottom right.

Parameter	Sym.	Eq. (Shingle)	Eq. (Ribbon)	Unit
Total contact area **per unit cell**	A_c	$N_{pad} \cdot W \cdot L$		cm^2
Contact resistance / interface / bond line	R_c	ρ_c / A_c		Ω
ECA bulk / volume resistance	R_b	$\rho_b \cdot H / A_c$		Ω
Contact resistance component of *series resistance* **per unit cell**	$R_{c/s}$	$2 \cdot R_c$	$4 \cdot R_c$	Ω
ECA bulk resistance component of *series resistance* **per unit cell**	$R_{b/s}$	R_b	$2 \cdot R_b$	Ω
Contact resistance component **normalized** *for series resistance*	$r_{c/s}$	$R_{c/s} \cdot A_{BB}$		Ωcm^2
ECA bulk resistance component **normalized** *for series resistance*	$r_{b/s}$	$R_{b/s} \cdot A_{BB}$		Ωcm^2
How much of the **series resistance** would this amount of **contact resistivity** be?		$r_{c/s} / r_s$		%
How much of the **series resistance** would this amount of **ECA bulk resistivity** be?		$r_{b/s} / r_s$		%
Cell series resistance **normalized** *for cell characteristic resistance (1 cm²)*	$r_{z/ch}$	r_s / R_{CH}		-
Module series resistance **normalized** *for cell characteristic resistance (1 cm²)*	$R_{m/ch}$	$(r_z + r_{c/s} + r_{b/s}) / R_{CH}$		-
Cell fill factor	FF_z	$FF_0 \cdot (1 - 1.1 \cdot r_{z/ch}) + r_{z,ch}^2 / 5.4$		%
Module fill factor	FF_m	$FF_0 \cdot (1 - 1.1 \cdot r_{m/ch}) + r_{m,ch}^2 / 5.4$		%
Fill factor absolute loss (cell to module)	ΔFF	$FF_m - FF_z$		%

Figure 5. Parameters used in the numerical model for shingled and ribbon-interconnected modules.

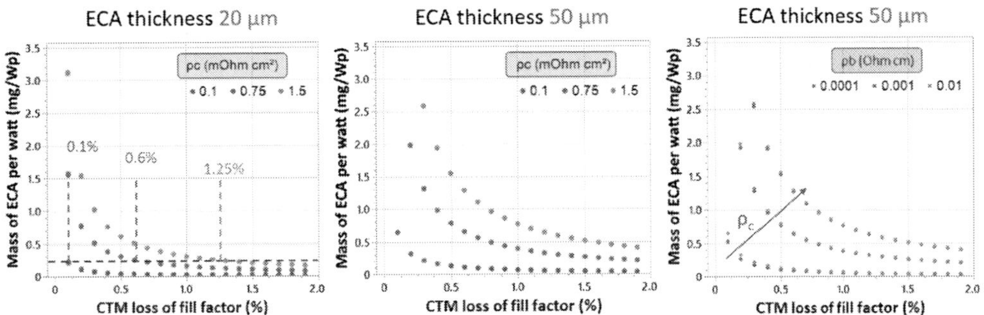

Figure 6. Examples of the model output showing the relationship between the CTM loss of FF and the amount of ECA in the interconnect. The left plot shows the difference in FF loss estimated for an amount of 0.23 mg/Wp and for the three different modelled ECA-BB contact resistivities. The middle plot shows how the amount required for a certain FF loss is amplified when the thickness of the ECA pad is increased. The plot on the right shows the same as the middle plot but overlays the difference between different bulk resistivities (in different colours), revealing very little effect of the bulk resistivity on the estimated FF loss (the coloured data points are all mostly in the same place).

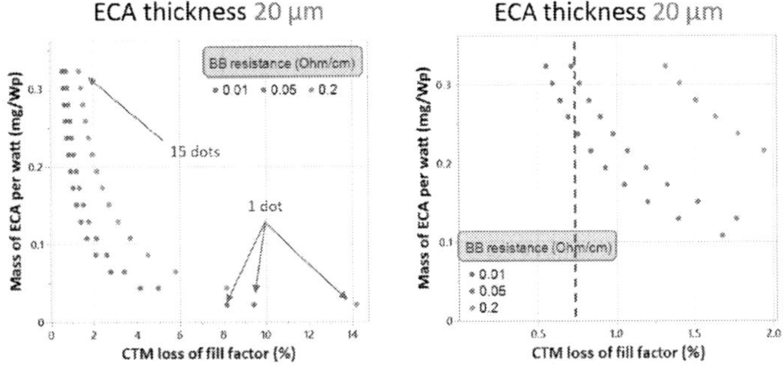

Figure 7. The model output as before but including the effects of the BB line resistance between the ECA pads.

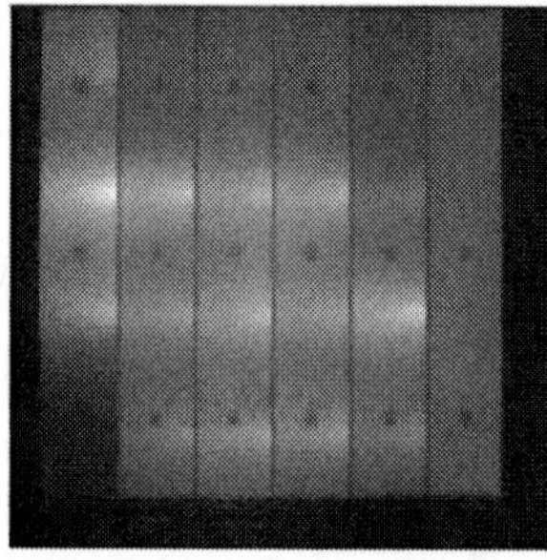
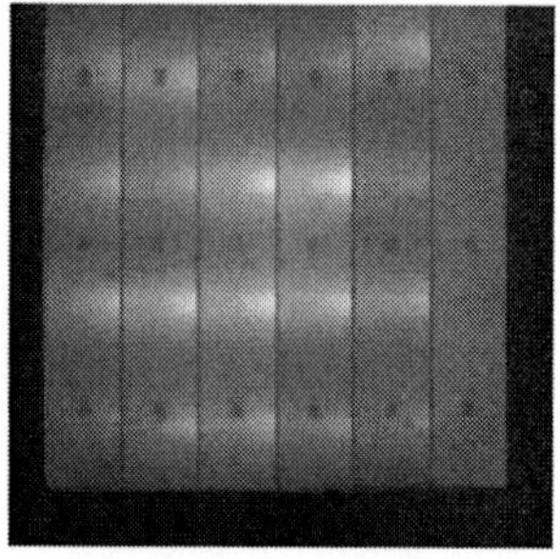
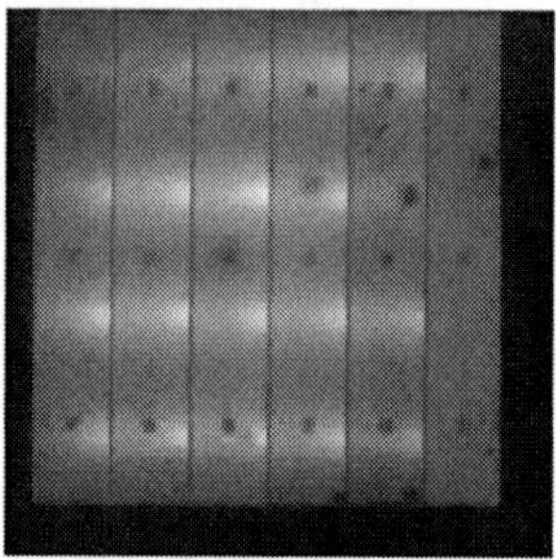

Figure 8. Representative EL images of the three types of minimodules produced to test the estimations of the numerical model for different amount of ECA in the interconnects. The three rectangular features on the back of each shingle stripe are connection pads used in an unrelated investigation and can be ignored (the same print screens were used).

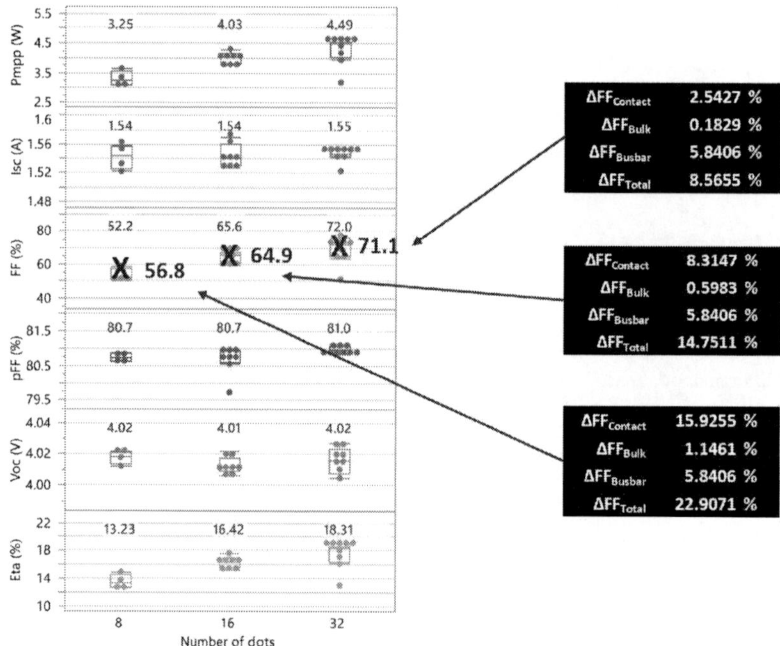

Figure 9. IV characteristics of the minimodules used to test the model predictions for varying amounts of ECA in the interconnects, including the breakdown of the resistance contributions predicted by the model for each case.

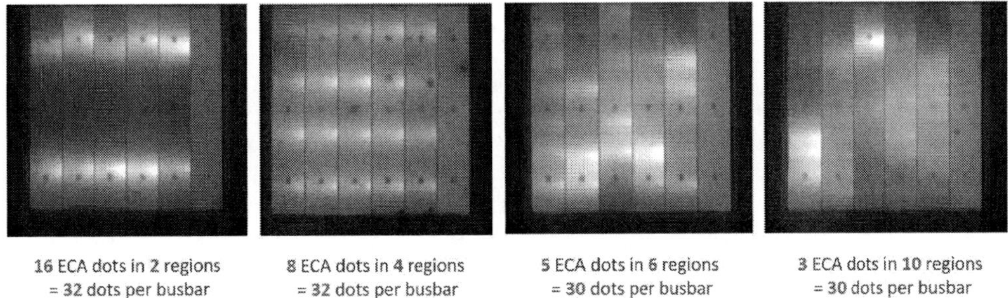

Figure 10. Representative EL images of the four types of minimodules produced to test the estimations of the numerical model for different ECA pad separations in the interconnects.

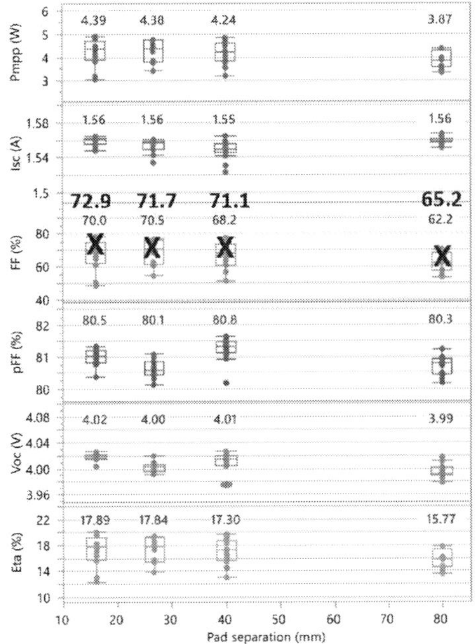

Figure 11. IV characteristics of the minimodules used to test the model for varying ECA pad separations.

PROCESS AND DESIGN FREEDOM ENABLED BY BACK-CONTACT SOLAR CELLS MINIMIZING THE INACTIVE MODULE AREA

Andreas Halm, Daniel Tune, Karl Wienands, Tudor Timofte, Tobias Messmer
International Solar Energy Research Center (ISC) Konstanz,
Rudolf-Diesel Str. 13-15, 78467 Konstanz, Germany

ABSTRACT:
We present three process and design novelties that enable higher module efficiencies by decreasing solar modules inactive area:
i)   a gapless stringing procedure
ii)   a gapless string layup
iii)   a cross connection behind the active cell matrix
All above mentioned innovations are applied for stringed back contact solar cells called Zebra cells which are in house developed all screen-printed IBC solar cells. Yet they are relevant for most wire interconnected BC type cells. The main improvement is an increased module efficiency achieved by reduction of inactive module area. Another advantage of the gapless stringing approach is the uniform aesthetic module appearance relevant to BIPV applications without the necessity to mask interconnection ribbons, especially in the case of applying a black background and/or colored module glass.
To show the validity of our approach we have assembled several mini-modules and a full-size module demonstrator in different configurations applying the above-mentioned novelties. A simple geometric calculation shows the potential of inactive area reduction and also factors in shading of cells due to overlaps that are necessary for the practical realization of the gapless approach.

Keywords: IBC cell, gapless stringing, gapless layup

1   INTRODUCTION

To increase the PV module efficiency and provide uniform aesthetic module appearance we explore approaches to eliminate inactive module area by processing stringed IBC solar cells into modules eliminating cell-to-cell gaps and string gaps. Our new module matrix is called "full gapless" (applied for patent). Cell gaps are eliminated by overlapping neighboring cell edges in string direction.

Since for most IBC cell concepts all interconnection ribbons run along one cell side, no front to back transfer of the ribbon is needed making overlapping of neighboring cells feasible. The absence of front side metallization further enables overlapping between neighboring strings and similarly as for cell to cell connection, during cross connection of neighboring strings the cross connector can run on one cell side making it possible to relocate it to behind the active cell matrix. Industry is starting to adopt our innovations. Different realizations of the area reduction are described in the following as single points.

2   EXPERIMENTAL AND RESULTS

2.1 Geometrical calculations

The fraction of inactive module area in stringed c-Si modules is considerable. The physical dimensions of a typical commercial rooftop module containing 54 M10 half cells are 1722 mm x 1134 mm (see e.g. [1]). 8.5% of the module area is not contributing to power generation. Details on geometrical parameters (e.g. cell gap, bussing width, etc) to calculate module dimensions, area reduction potentials and shading fractions are given in table 1 in the appendix. The calculations show for the M10 case that 4.6% of the inactive area result from frame and safety margin (1500V case) and cannot be avoided. The remaining 3.9% are avoidable and are distributed the following (with the assumptions given in table 1): the sum of top busing, center busing (incl j-box) and bottom bussing accounts for 2.1%, the cell gaps and string gaps both for 0.9% respectively. That opens a potential for 3.9%

in module area reduction. Without overlap that would yield in a 4% relative increase in module efficiency. In reality, introducing the overlaps to realize the full gapless layout and at the same time shrinking the overall module area this vale cannot be reached. Applying 0.7 mm cell to cell overlap and 1 mm string to string overlap leads to 1.6% shaded area (0.7% for cell gaps, 0.9% for string gaps) in this example versus a 2.9% (1.6% for cell gaps, 1.3% for string gaps) in module area reduction. It has to be mentioned that the efficiency gain reachable by this approach is mainly relevant for black background or true bifacial modules.

2.2 relocation of rear bussing behind cell matrix

For relocating the cross connection behind the active cell matrix, cells are locally isolated against the busing. Mini-modules with single half cells, M6, Zebra, 6 busbars have been assembled semi-manual at ISC to show a proof of concept how to realize the bussing behind cell matrix concept. Aiko solar already sells a commercial module featuring a similar approach [2]. Lab results shown here are realized by locally applying Kapton tape or similar materials as insulation layer between bussing and ribbon (group 1,2 Figure 2). In one case we add another layer on the cell surface before stringing to enable horizontal movements (group 3 Figure 22). A sketch of group 3 configuration is given in Figure 1.

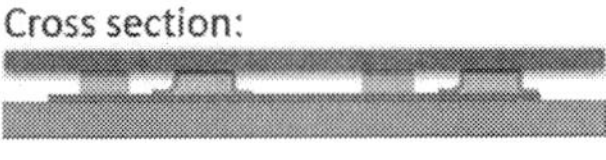

Cross section:

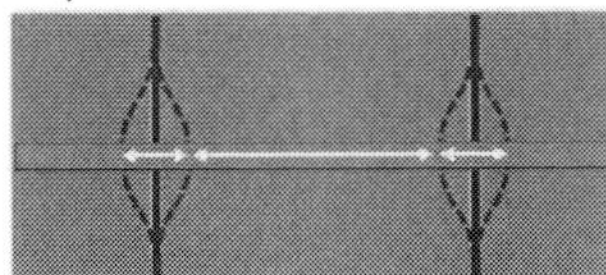

Top view:

Figure 1: cross section and top view of isolation configuration by Kapton tape of group 3

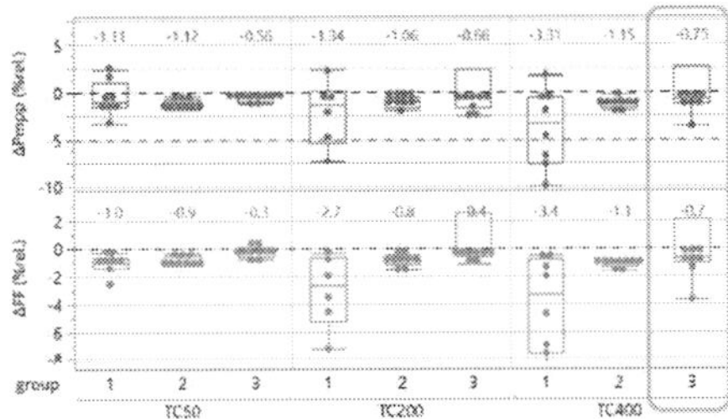

Figure 2: tempearture cycle test reults of relative change in power and fill factor for mini modules in different test configurations

Climate chamber results of mini-modules tested in temperature cycling (according to 61215, no current injection) are promising. Best group shows a moderate degradation of 0.7% relative after TC400.

2.3 assembly of low voltage/high current strings to avoid the butterfly gap

Another method to avoid the butterfly gap enabled by rear side stringing is the combination of parallel and series connected cells in a string (Figure 3). This method was not yet realized experimentally.

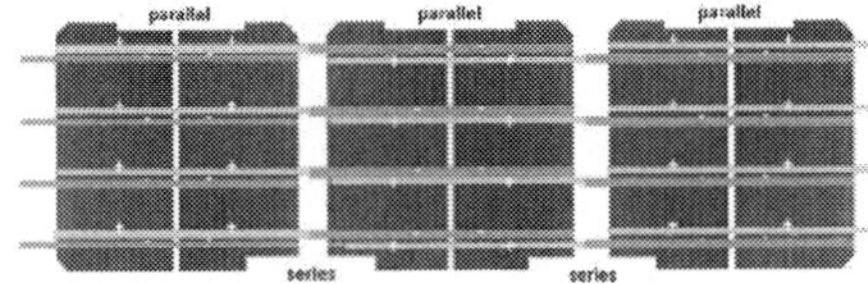

Figure 3: combination of parallel and series connected half cell; the amount of cells per bypass diode in a string can be doubled due to the parallel connection

2.4 gapless stringing by cell to cell overlaps

The gapless stringing process is compatible with standard back contact stringing equipment. At ISC Konstanz we use a teamtechnik TT2100 IR stringing tool and an overlap in the range of 0.7 to 1mm. The overlap is merely mechanical. If sorted correctly, non-passivated edges of the half cells in the string can always be placed below uncut edges. In this fashion, edge recombination effects can be reduced since the non-passivated edge of the cell is not illuminated. EL pictures of the full-size module below that cracking at the cell edges is no issue.

Figure 4: picture of a gapless string assembled by IR soldering on a TT2100 stringer machine at ISC Konstanz

2.5 gapless layup

String gaps vanish by introducing a discrete overlap of 1 to 2mm between strings in horizontal direction during module layup. At ISC the process is done manually. A combination of cell- and string overlap can be seen in Figure 5. For this gapless layup, the strings are alternating slightly shifted in vertical direction to avoid cell overlap regions directly on top of each other, aiming for integrity of the cells under thermo-mechanical stresses. An isolation layer screen printed at the cell edges inhibits shunting between cells of neighboring strings.

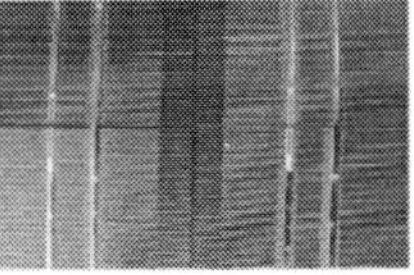

Figure 5: cell to cell overlap in vertical direction and string to string overlap in horizontal direction; to electrically isolate the neighboring strings, an isolation layer is screen printed at the cell edges

Applying the gapless layup (1 mm overlap) with gapless strings (1 mm overlap), a120 half-cell module with M6 Zebra cells, 23.1% average efficiency was assembled to demonstrate the efficiency increase with the full gapless approach.

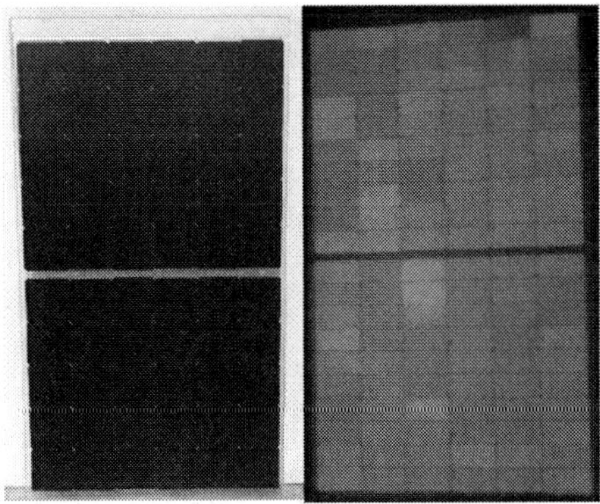

Figure 6: left: Photo of a bifacial module assembled with gapless stringing and gapless layup; right: EL picutre of the module reavling no critical damages or cracks that can be attributed to the overlap scenario

The overall efficiency of the module is with 20.6 % 0.1% absolute higher than the reference module (1 mm cell gap and 2 mm string gap). Geometrical dimensions for both modules are given in table 1. IV results and CTM ratio are compared in the following tables 2 and 3.

Table 1: geometrical calculations on the area fractions of a standard M10 rooftop module and an M6 IBC module. For both types different configurations in layup are represented with according shaded area fractions and reduction of total area compared to a standa

configuration	Nr of half cells in Module	cell width (mm)	cell length (mm)	Nr of cells in string	cell to cell gap (mm):	with cross connector (busing) mm	distance cell edge to busing (mm)	width diode center gap (mm)	creepage distance (mm):	String gap (mm)	additional width/length due to frame (mm)	framed module length (mm)	framed module width (mm)	total module area (m²)	reduced module area by overlapping (%)	shaded area due to cell overlaps (mm²)	shaded area due to string overlaps (mm²)	shaded fraction of total cell active area due to shading (%)
M10 case study																		
standard	108	182	91	9	1	5	1	24	11	2	5	1722	1134	1.953	0.0%			0
no frame, no creepage margin	108	182	91	9	1	5	1	24	0	2	0	1690	1102	1.862	4.6%			
no diode and bussing area	108	182	91	9	1	0	0	0	11	2	5	1686	1134	1.912	2.1%			
gapless cell stringing: theory	108	182	91	9	0	5	1	24	11	2	5	1706	1134	1.935	0.9%			
gapless string layup: theory	108	182	91	9	1	5	1	24	11	0	5	1722	1124	1.936	0.9%			
gapless cell stringing: overlap	108	182	91	9	-0.7	5	1	24	11	2	5	1694.8	1134	1.922	1.6%	-12230.40		-0.7%
gapless string layup: overlap	108	182	91	9	1	5	1	24	11	-1	5	1722	1119	1.927	1.3%		-16540	-0.9%
M6 experimental																		
standard	120	166	83	10	1	5	3	30	8.4	2	4	1748.8	1030.8	1.803	0			0
gapless cell stringing	120	166	83	10	-1	5	2	35	8.4	2	4	1715.8	1030.8	1.769	1.9%	-17928.00		-1.1%
gapless string layup	120	166	83	10	1	5	2	35	8.4	-1	4	1751.8	1015.8	1.779	1.3%		-16780	-1.0%
no diode and bussing area	120	166	83	10	1	0	0	0	8.4	2	4	1702.8	1030.8	1.755	2.6%			

Table 2,3: comparison of IV results and CTM ratio for full gapless module vs. a standard reference; CTM ratio is also given assuming a same FF level for reference and full gapless module

	Isc [A]	Uoc [V]	FF [%]	Pmpp[W]	Eta [%]	Area (m²)
reference	11.17	41.44	79.7	369.2	20.5	1.803
Full-gapless	10.86	41.51	79.1	356.5	20.6	1.731

	CTM power (%)	CTM eta (%)
reference	2.85	11.4
Full-gapless	6.17	10.9
Full-gapless (FF adapted)	5.45	10.2

As expected, the CTM ratio in power for the full gapless approach is higher compared to the reference due to shading. Yet, the CTM ratio for efficiency and the overall efficiency for the full gapless module is higher due to the reduced overall module area.

3 SUMMARY

The paper shows design possibilities reducing the active module area and hence increase module efficiency that are applied with stringed back contact solar cells. The novelties can be adapted independently of each other, some can already be found in commercially available modules [2].

4 ACKNOWLEDGEMENTS

This project has received funding from the European Union's Horizon Europe research and innovation programme under grant agreement No.101084256

5 REFERENCES

[1]https://www.luxor.solar/files/luxor/download/datasheets/LX_EL_N-Type_NR_BW_M108_420-440W_182_DE.pdf

[2]https://aikosolar.com/static/pdfjs/web/viewer.html?file=/wp-content/uploads/2025/08/Neostar-3P54_AIKO-A-MCE54Mw_470-500W-1762%C3%971134%C3%9730_DsDr_EN.pdf

6 APPENDIX

3CO.11.3: Techno-economic analysis of a suitable module BOM for different climatic conditions

EUPVSEC 2025
Session 3CO.11: Innovative Module Design and Characterization
24.09.2025

Sraisth, Julian Reichle, Mehul Rawal, Gourab Das, Xinyang Li, Hardik Gohil, Wolfgang Jooß

RCT Solutions GmbH

One-Stop
Renewable
Solutions
Partner

Agenda

RCT solutions

- ❑ Motivation
- ❑ Different Climate Zones
  - ❑ Their impact
  - ❑ Solutions to mitigate its impact
- ❑ BOM Selection and its Impact
  - ❑ Cost of Ownership, CoO ($/Wp)
  - ❑ Levelized Cost of Electricity (LCOE)

Images Source: Sraisth

020222-002

Motivation

Module Degradation: Using a standard PV module for different climate regions is not a solution – Modules degrade differently in different climates.
[J. Ascencio-Vásquez, et al., https://doi.org/10.3390/en12244749]

OBBBA - One Big Beautiful BOM for All Applications

It is not a solution

Solution
Suitable BOMs for Different Climate Zones & Conditions (SBDCZC)

Images: Sraisth

020222-003

Köppen–Geiger PV Climate Classification

RCT solutions

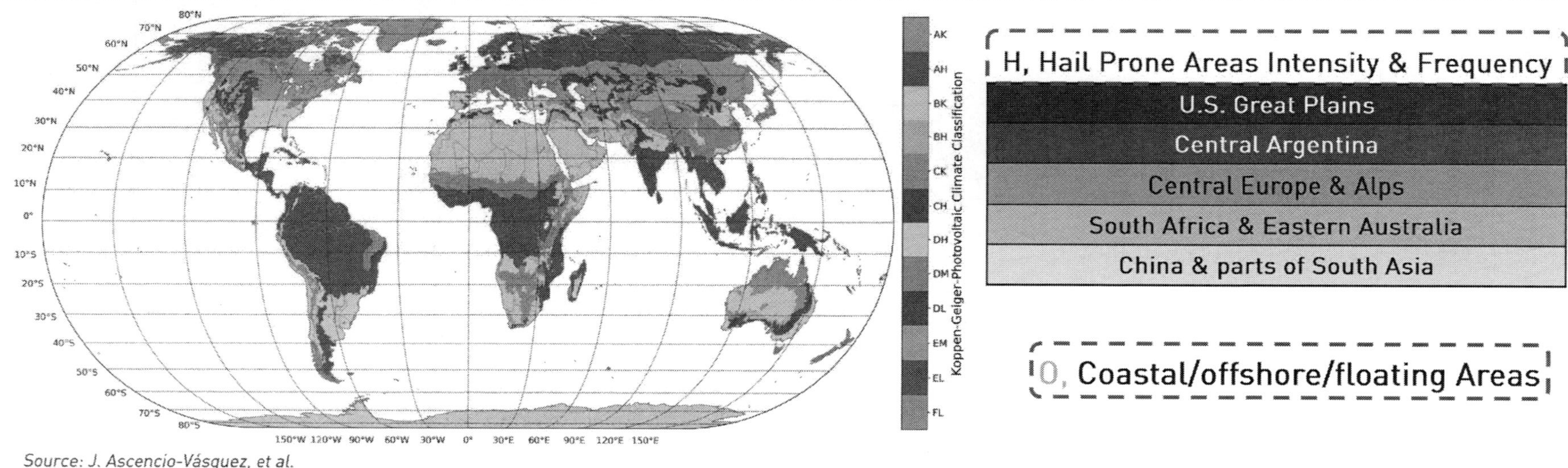

Source: J. Ascencio-Vásquez, et al.

H, Hail Prone Areas Intensity & Frequency

U.S. Great Plains
Central Argentina
Central Europe & Alps
South Africa & Eastern Australia
China & parts of South Asia

O, Coastal/offshore/floating Areas

The dominant climate class by land area:
B, Arid (30.2%)
E, Cold (24.6%)
A, Tropical (19.0%)
C, D, Temperate (13.4%)
F, Polar (12.8%)

[https://koeppen-geiger.vu-wien.ac.at/present.htm]
[https://koeppen-geiger.vu-wien.ac.at/pdf/Paper_2006.pdf]
[J. Ascencio-Vásquez, et al., https://doi.org/10.1016/j.solener.2019.08.072]
[M.C. Peel et al.,https://doi.org/10.5194/hess-11-1633-2007]
[https://yaleclimateconnections.org/2022/03/hailstorms-and-climate-change-what-to-expect/]

020222-004

Different Climate Conditions Impact

IEA-PVPS: Optimisation of Photovoltaic Systems for Different Climates. DOI:10.69766/QSYC8858]
IEA-PVPS: Degradation and Failure Modes in New Photovoltaic Cell and Module Technologies /https://doi.org/10.69766/ATBD2730]

RCT solutions

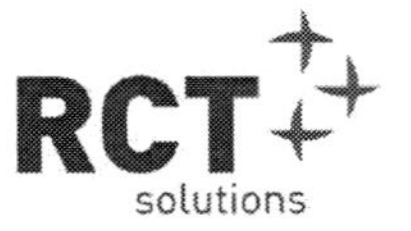

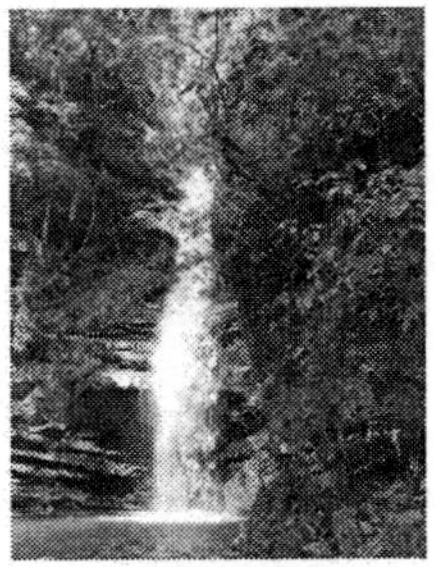

Tropical

- High humidity
- Intense sunlight
- Frequent rain

- **Moisture ingress**
- **Delamination**
- **Corrosion- PID**

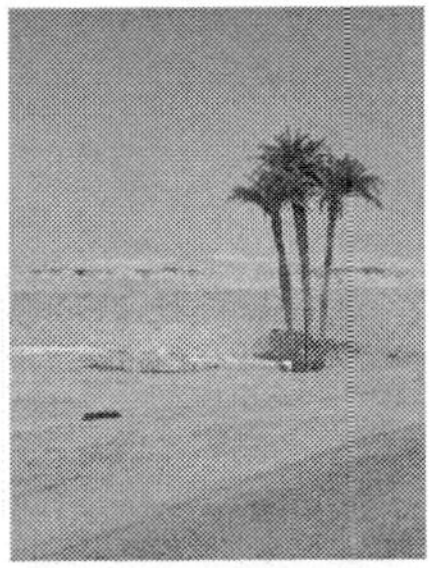

Arid

- High temperatures
- Intense sunlight
- Dust accumulation

- **Module efficiency reduction**
- **Shading losses**
- **Hot Spot**
- **Thermal Stress**
- **Sandstorms can abrade module surfaces**

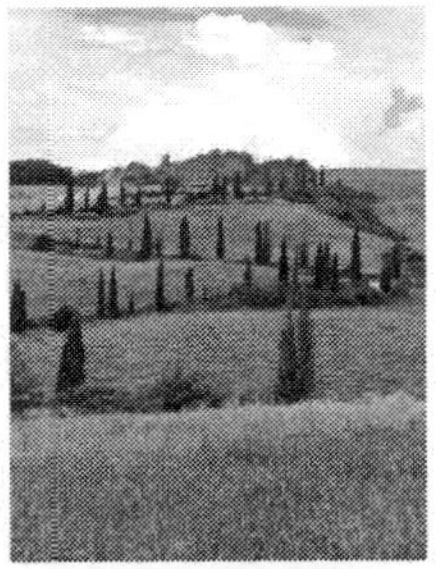

Temperate

- Freeze-thaw cycles
- Semi-arid conditions
- Rain
- Snow

- **Moisture ingress**
- **Delamination**

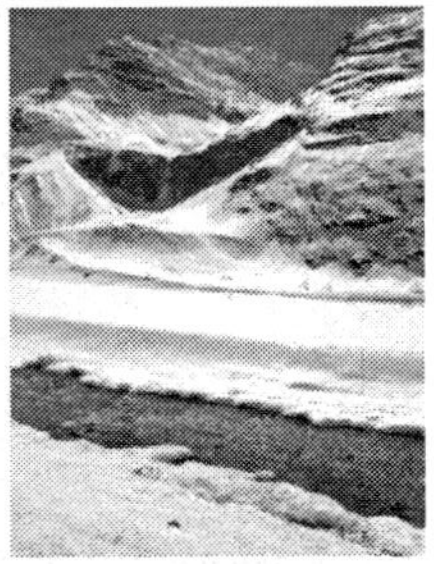

Cold/Polar

- Reduced amount of sunlight hours
- Low temperatures
- Thin Atmosphere
- Intense Sunlight

- **UV-related degradation**
- **Moisture Ingress**
- **Mechanical load issues.**

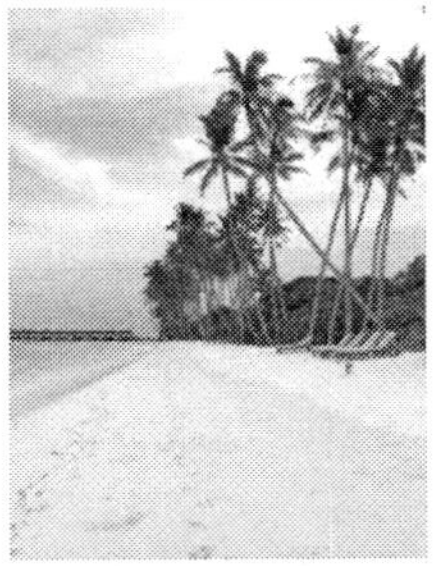

Coastal/Floating

- High humidity
- Salt mist
- Strong winds

- **Corrosion in module frames and electrical components.**
- **Mechanical stress.**
- **UV-related degradation**

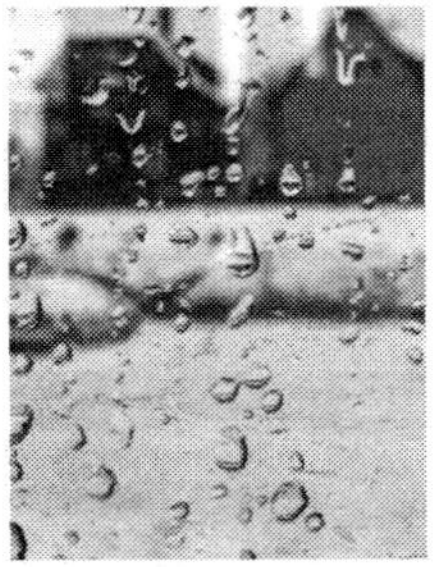

High Hail Impact and Storms

- Hails
- Strong winds
- Rain

- **Glass breakages**
- **Microcracks**

Images Source: Sraisth

Different Climate Conditions Solutions

IEA-PVPS: Optimisation of Photovoltaic Systems for Different Climates. DOI:10.69766/QSYC8858]
IEA-PVPS: Degradation and Failure Modes in New Photovoltaic Cell and Module Technologies /https://doi.org/10.69766/ATBD2730]
[Aksel K. Öz, et al., DOI: 10.1016/j.solmat.2025.113735]

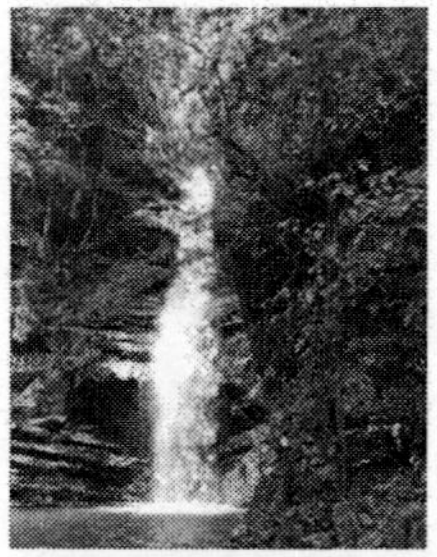

Tropical

- Moisture-resistant encapsulants.
- Improved module sealing
- Improved coatings
- Sealed Junction-box

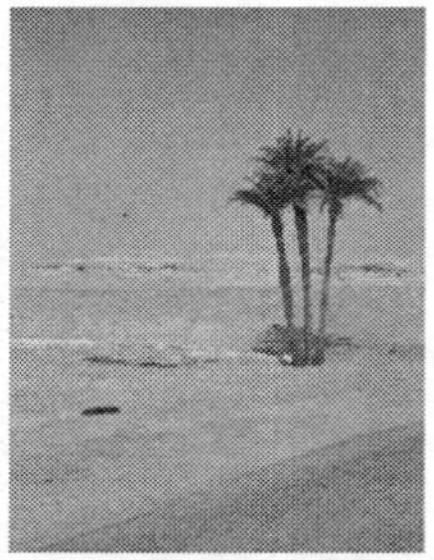

Arid

- Anti-soiling coatings.
- Advanced thermal management materials
- Frameless design/anti-dust Frame design

Regular cleaning systems

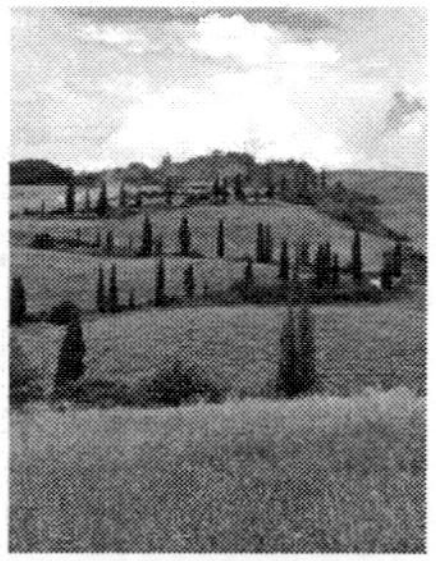

Temperate

- Materials that tolerate freeze-thaw cycles.
- Good sealing
- Moisture-resistant encapsulants.

Optimized module tilt for snow shedding

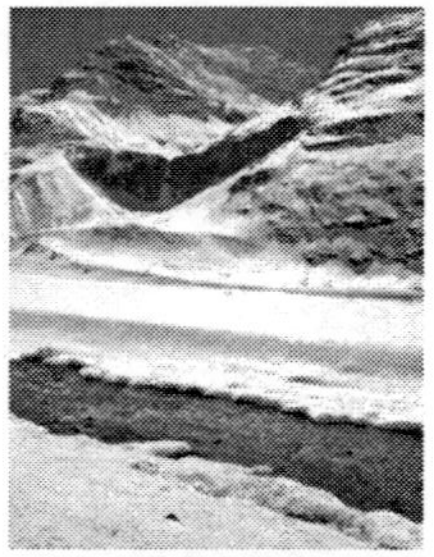

Cold /Polar

- Materials that perform well in low-light
- Improved structural stability like steel frames
- UV-resistant materials and protective coatings

Higher module tilt to facilitate snow shedding

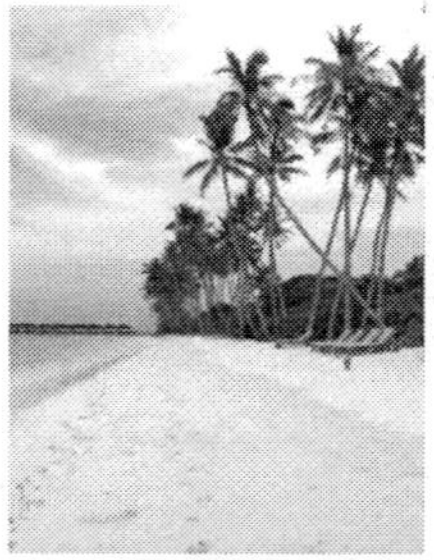

Coastal/Floating

- Corrosion-resistant materials and coatings
- Thick anodized aluminum or stainless steel for frames.
- Sealed Junction-Box

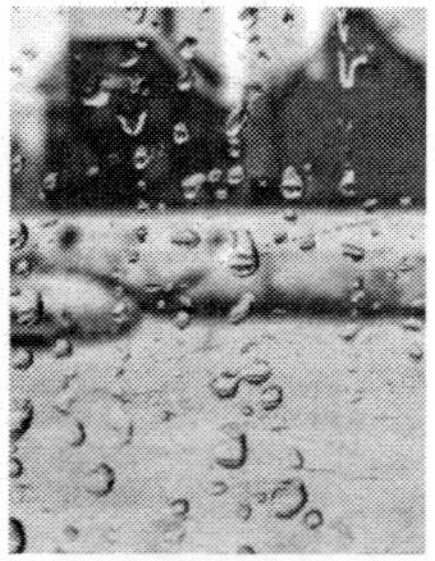

High Hail Impact and Storms

- Thicker glass
- Thicker frames

Tracker system to avoid direct hail impact

020222-006

Cost Impact: Total Cost of Ownership ($/Wp)

Standard BOM

- ARC GG 2mm front glass
- 2mm rear glass
- EPE – front side
- EVA – rear side
- Al Frame AA15
- TOPCon Cells

Change Proposal in BOMs for different modules

- ARC GG 3.2 mm front glass (E, H)
- Anti-soiling coated front glass (A, B)
- 3.2 mm rear Glass (E, H)
- PIB Sealant (A, O)
- UV-Conversion POE (A, B, C, D, E)
- POE on rear side (A, B, C, D, E)
- Steel Frame (A, E, H)
- Composite Frame (O)
- Double-insulated Junction-Box (A, O)
- Thicker Frames 35mm (All)
- Anti-soiling Frame design (B)
- HJT Cells (A, B)
- BC Cells (E)

Base Assumptions for Cost Calculations

- Factory in Western Europe
- Other CAPEX
- 5-Year Depreciation of Equipment
- 1 GW Production Factory
- EU Tariffs Included

LCOE Calculation

[J. Reichle et al., 2023, A Comprehensive Study of Silicon Solar Cell Technologies Across the Globe for Sustainable Integrated Manufacturing, ISBN 3-936338-88-4]

020222-007

Cost Impact: Material Costs /Module vs Module Cost/Wp

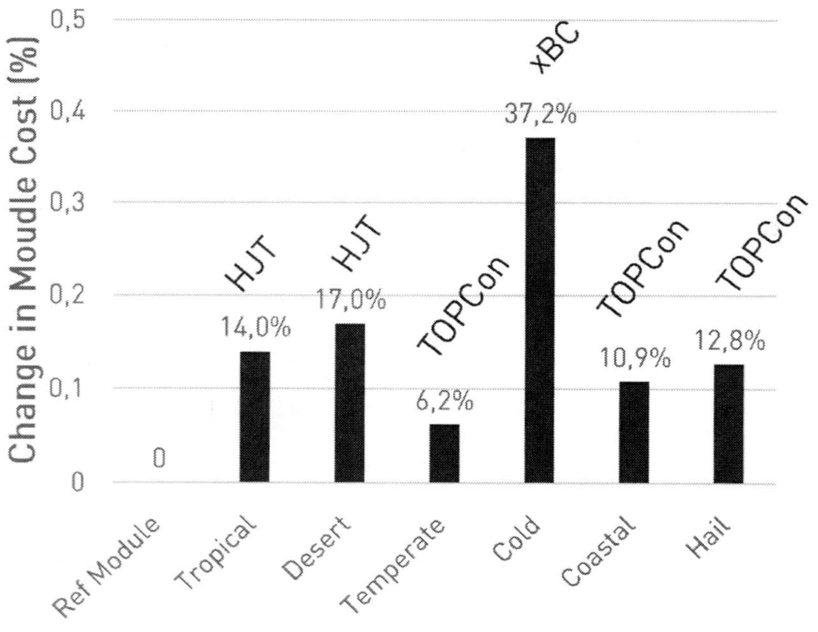

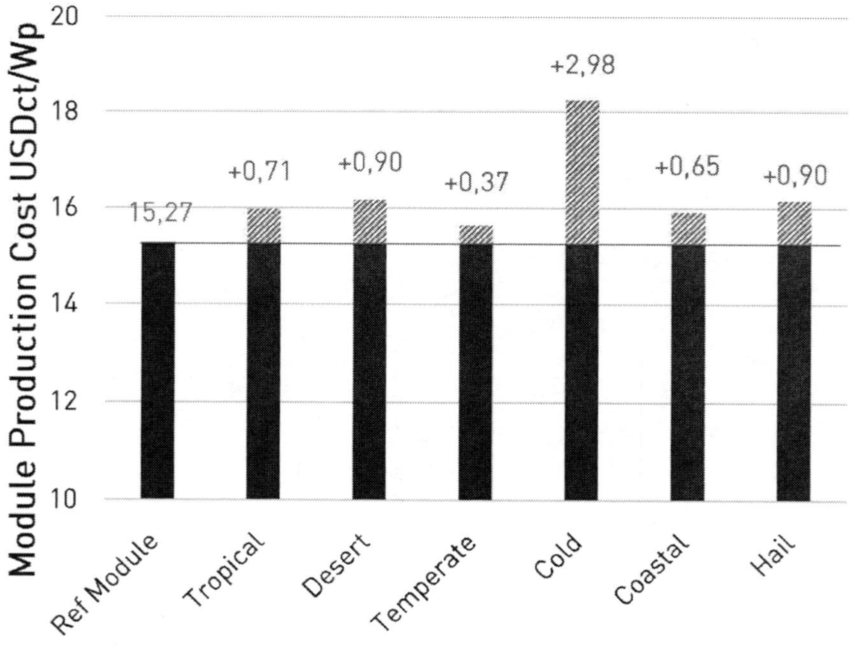

020222-008

Case 1: Tropical

- In hotter US climates, modules degrade on avg **0.88%/yr**, where **HJT degrades on avg 0.735%/yr**.

[D.C. Jordan, et al., https://doi.org/10.1002/pip.3566]

- Along the equator line, degradation above **1.4%/yr** is observed. On average, a **tropical climate has 1.03%/yr**.

[J. Ascencio-Vásquez, et al., https://doi.org/10.3390/en12244749]

- In another study, data from the Sub-Saharan tropical climate in Ghana, **up to 3.19%/yr**.

[D. Atsu et al., https://doi.org/10.1016/j.renene.2020.08.021]

Reported rate of degradation of PV modules for different locations and methodologies.

[D. Atsu et al.]

Location	Duration	Technology	Method applied	Degradation rate (%/year)
Perth, Australia	19 months	c-Si	MPPTs (continuous measurement)	0.5–2.7
Perth, Australia	19 months	pc-Si	MPPTs (continuous measurement)	1.0–2.9
Colorado, USA	8 years	c-Si	Regression model	0.75
Singapore	3 years	a-Si	Statistical decomposition method (applying the locally weighted scatterplot smoothing)	2
Japan	10 years	a-Si	Regression analysis	3.51
Netherlands	44 months	c-Si	Seasonal and Trend decomposition using Locally Weighted Scatterplot Smoothing (Loess) (STL) technique	1.35
Morocco	3 years	c-Si	IV Tracer and Translation equations	2.6
Morocco	3 years	pc-Si	IV Tracer and Translation equations by IEC 60891	3.41
India	22 years	c-Si	IV Tracer and Translation equations by IEC 60891	1.9
Thailand	4 years	pc-Si	Simple Linear regression model	1.7
Malaga, Spain	12 years	c-Si	Translation equations	0.7
Koforidua, Ghana	**12 years**	**c-Si**	IV Tracer and Translation equations	**3.19**

Solutions:
- Edge sealant PIB
- Anti-soiling coated glass
- GG configuration
- UV-conversion POE
- Anti-corrosive coatings
  Steel Frame
- Double-insulated J-Box

020222-009

CoO impact on the LCOE Case 1: Tropical

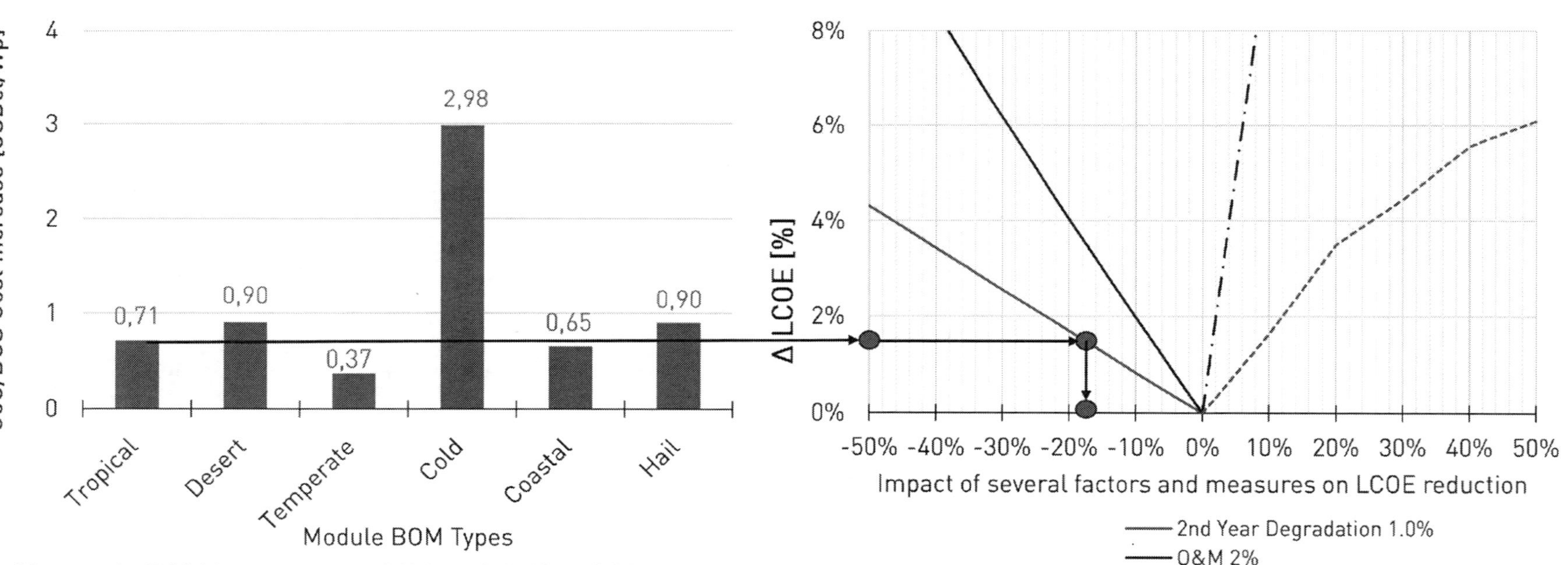

- Change in BOM leads to an **additional 1.6% LCOE.**
- Minimum 17% lower degradation is required, reducing degradation from **1,0%/yr to ~0.8%/yr**, to compensate for the additional LCOE. HJT degrades on average **0.735%/yr** [D.C. Jordan, et al., https://doi.org/10.1002/pip.3566] + improved BOM

020222-010

Case 2: Desert

- There is up to **0.9%/yr degradation** observed in the MBR Solar park, UAE.

[S. Kumar et al., DOI: 10.4229/EUPVSEC2023/3AV.2.27]

- **Cracking, chalking, and yellowing** were observed for glass-backsheet modules in Qatar.

[A. A. Abdallha et al., DOI: 10.4229/WCPEC-82022-3DV.1.10] and G.Orenski publicaitons

- **HJT modules showed the lowest soiling-induced energy loss** among tested module types in both fixed (2.3%) and HSAT (-0.24%) installations in the Atacama Desert in Chile.

[A. Taquichiri et al., DOI: 10.4229/EUPVSEC2023/4CV.1.20]

- **5% degradation** observed due to Soiling in Qatar. A higher oxygen content in the ARC layer and a double ARC layer contribute to achieving a higher Isc. Additionally, coating combined with a high tilt angle helps reduce the soiling effect.

[B. Aissa, et al., DOI: 10.4229/EUPVSEC2023/3AV.2.20]

Solutions:
- Anti-soiling coated glass
- HJT cells
- GG configuration
- Anti-soiling frame design on short side

+0,90 USDct/Wp

020222-011

CoO impact on the LCOE Case 2: Desert

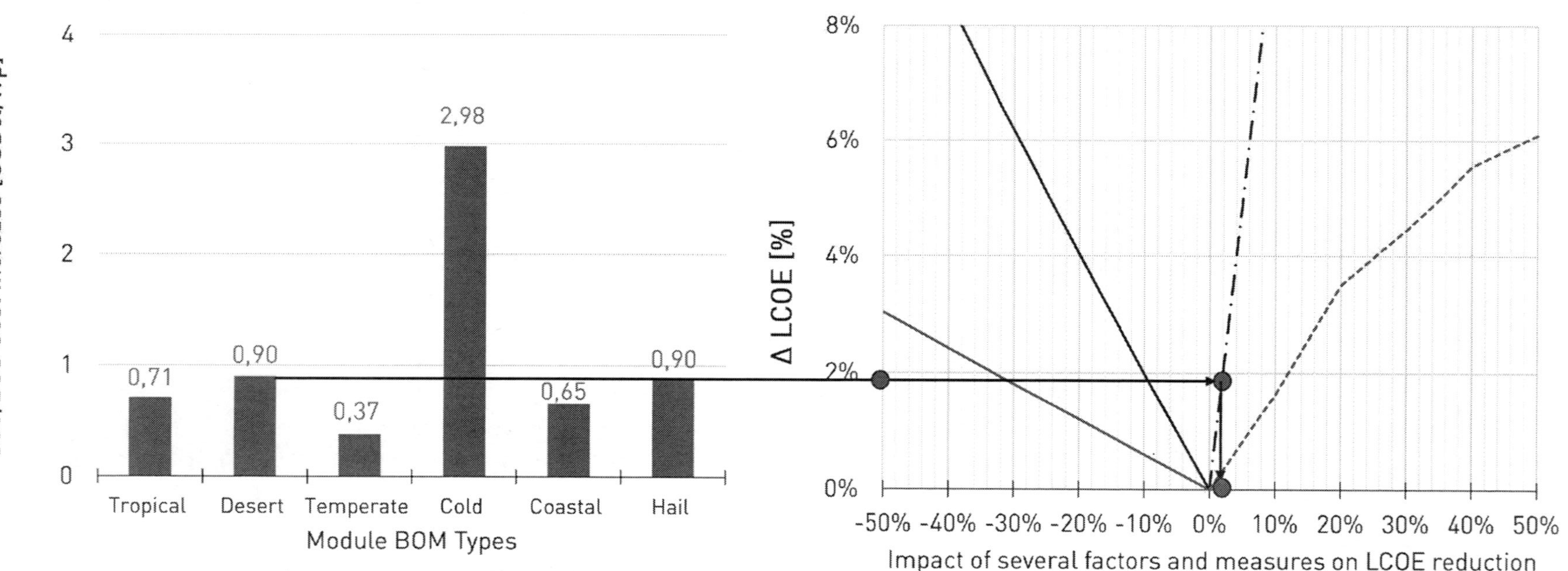

> Minimum **2% extra energy yield is required to compensate for the additional 1.8% LCOE. This is already observed in the HJT module type, with an energy yield of more than 4% compared to PERC** [A. Taquichiri et al., DOI: 10.4229/EUPVSEC2023/4CV.1.20] + **improved BOM.**

020222-012

Local Production Impact on CoO. Case 2: Desert

RCT solutions

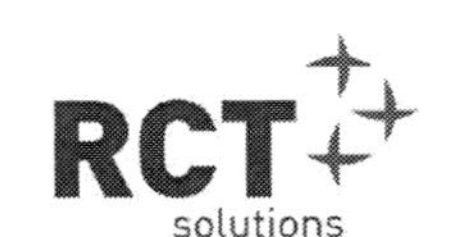

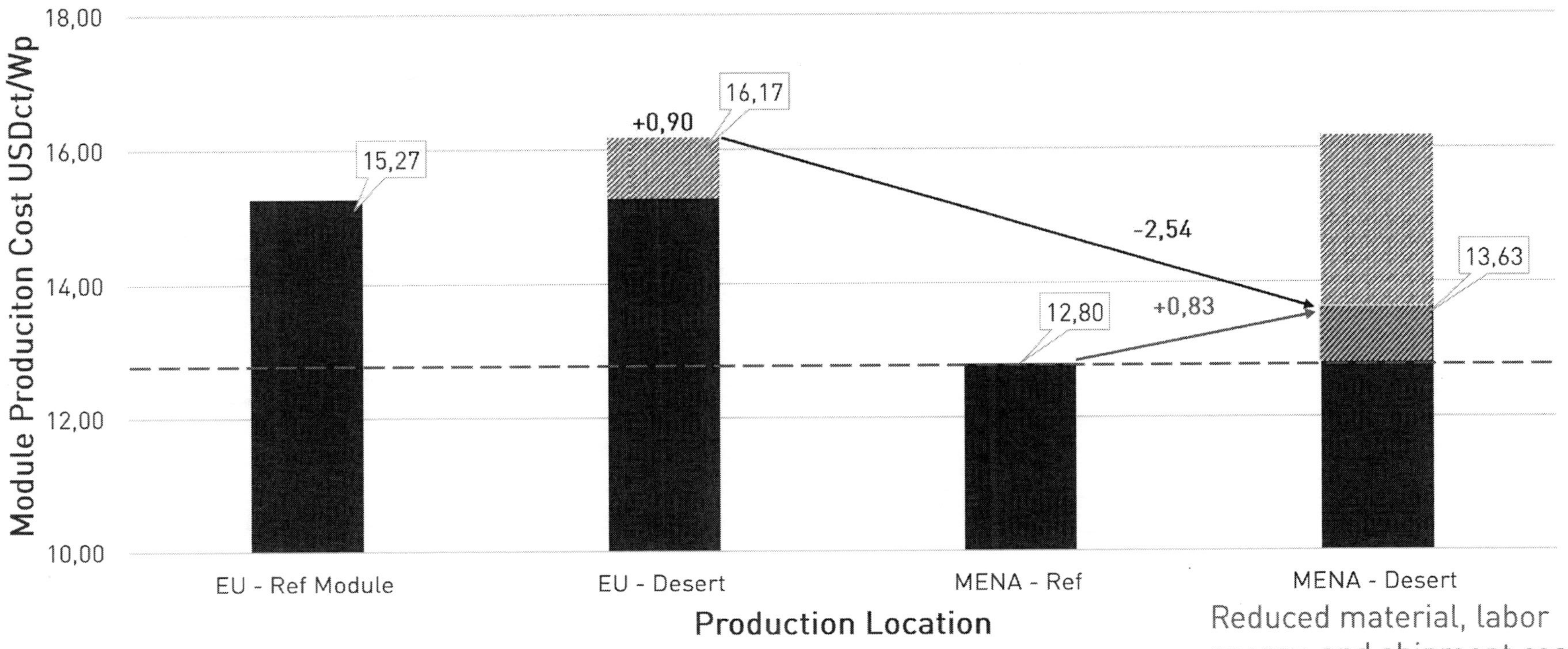

Reduced material, labor energy, and shipment cost

Case 3: Hail Impact

- **GCube Insurance** study claims that 54% of total solar losses in the USA came from hail-related insurance claims.

[https://www.pv-magazine.com/2025/09/19/hail-damage-to-solar-projects-1-of-filed-claims-but-over-50-of-total-losses/]

- **Thicker glasses** on the front, 3.2mm, have higher hail resilience than the 2mm glass.

[Module Glass Impacts Hail Resiliency — RETC, LLC]

- **CFV Labs Study**: Thinner glass and larger module trend leads to more failures, where the rate of breakage pressure is reduced by 70%.

[T. Billie, et al., https://grndwork.com/pv-module-testing-cfv-labs/]

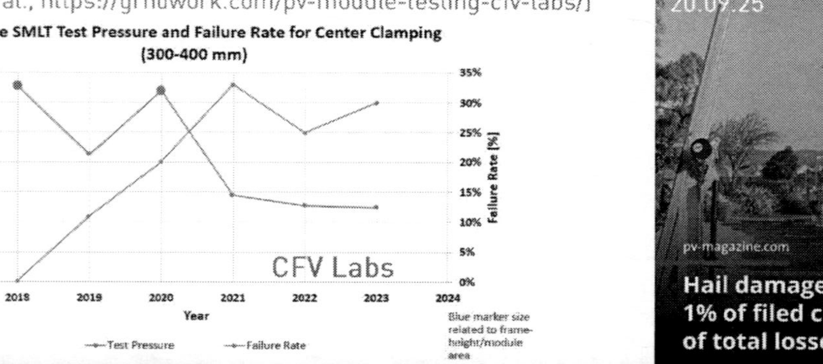

Solutions:
- Steel Frame
- Thicker Frame 35 mm
- Thicker Glass
- GG configuration

→ +0,90 USDct/Wp

020222-014

CoO impact on the LCOE. Case 3: Hail

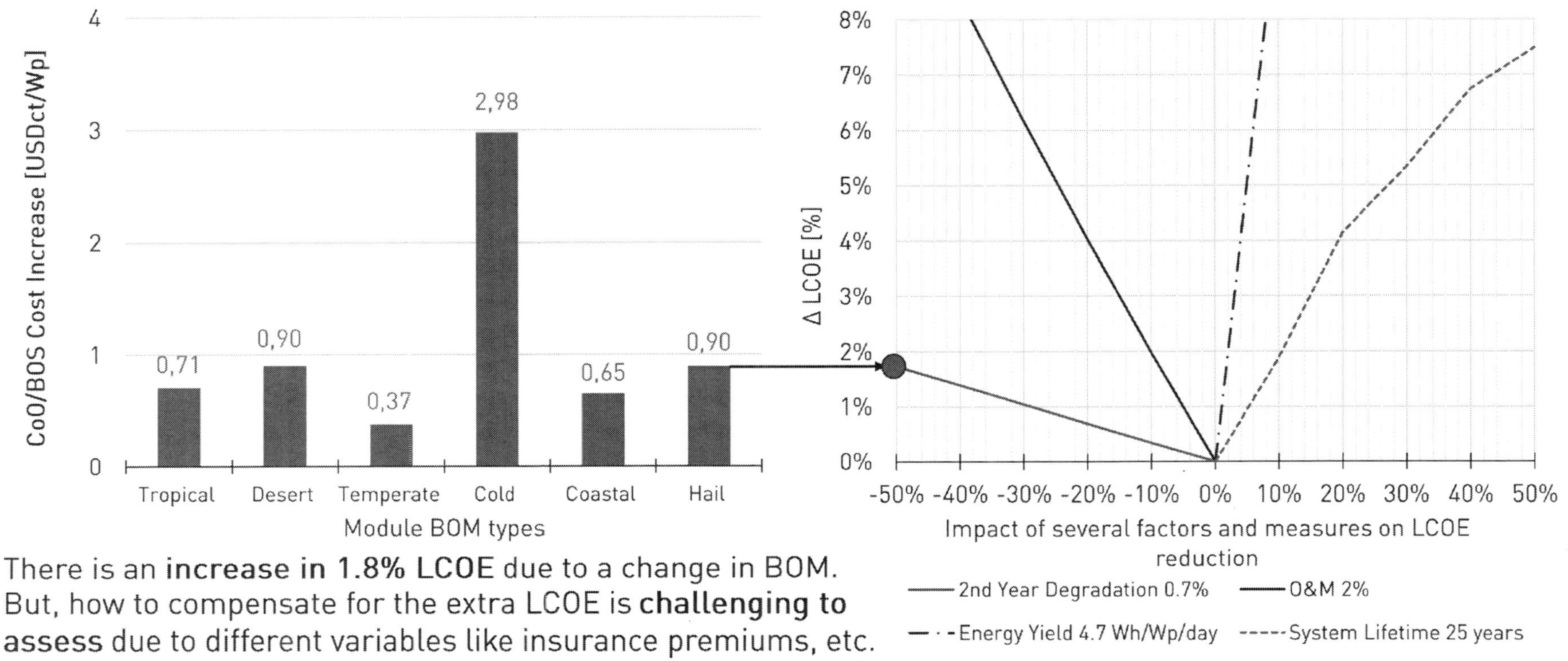

➢ There is an **increase in 1.8% LCOE** due to a change in BOM.
➢ But, how to compensate for the extra LCOE is **challenging to assess** due to different variables like insurance premiums, etc.

020222-015

Local Production Impact on CoO. Case 3: Hail

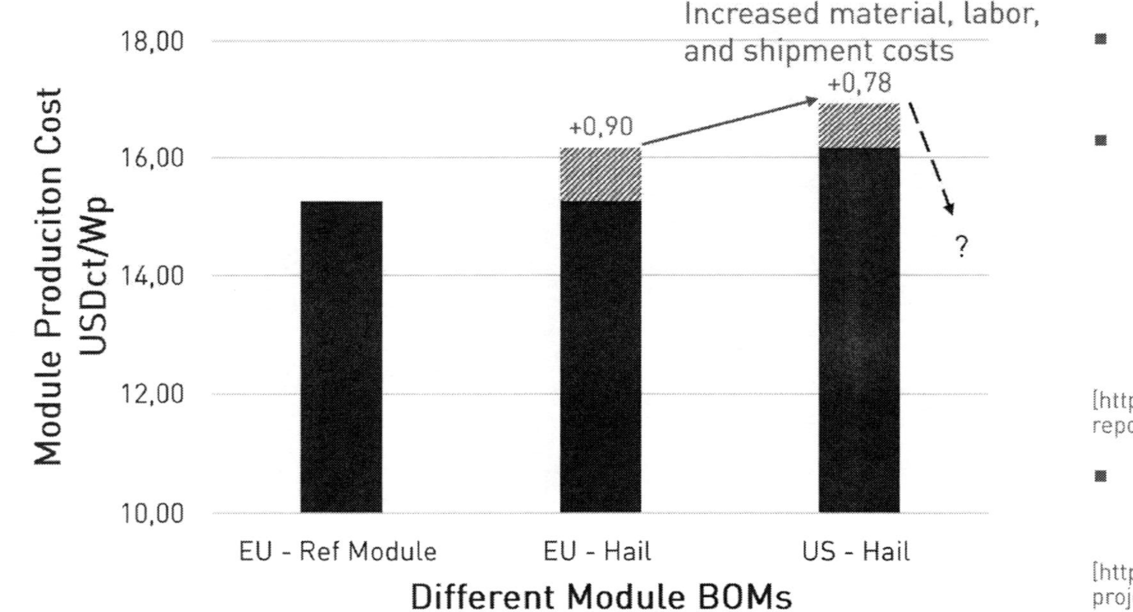

- Currently, the US installation stands at ~**255 GW**. [SEIA.org]

- Wood Mackenzie Power & Renewables U.S. Solar Market Insight Q3 2025 predicts **168 GW utility installation in the next 5 years, considering the** low-case scenario from 0BBBA.

[https://seia.org/research-resources/solar-market-insight-report-q3-2025/]

- Project loss affected due to Hail is >50% of all losses.

[https://www.pv-magazine.com/2025/09/19/hail-damage-to-solar-projects-1-of-filed-claims-but-over-50-of-total-losses/]

➢ Local production will be suitable for hail-free PV module BOM production, especially considering the **well-established steel industry and glass industry**.

020222-016

Summary

- There is potential to work on an **improved BOM that can withstand different climate conditions** and reduce the degradation rates.
- The assumed changes in BOM for different climates result in an additional **0.37 USDct/Wp to 2.98 USDct/Wp.**
- The **costs/Wp will increase the LCOE,** which can be **compensated by robust modules or improved systems,** withstanding the effect of severe climate conditions.
- The impact of higher climate-specific BOM cost on Module cost can be compensated by **producing locally,** specific to the climate zone.

Key Message: Extra cost for a reliable climate-specific BOM can be financially viable.

Outlook

- CTM Analysis (Standard BOM vs Different BOMs suitable for different climatic conditions).
- Detailed Energy Yield/loss Analysis.
- Using a suggested suitable BOM and testing in labs for long-term stability.

020222-017

Thank you

RCT Solutions GmbH
Line-Eid-Strasse 1
D-78467 Konstanz, Germany

Phone +49 15143176023
sraisth@rct-solutions.com
http://www.rct-solutions.com

This presentation was selected by the Sc. Committee of the EU PVSEC 2025 for submission of a full paper to one of the EU PVSEC's collaborating peer-reviewed journals.

INDOOR CHARACTERIZATION AND ANALYSIS OF REVERSE BREAKDOWN BEHAVIOR OF SOLAR CELLS WITH DIFFERENT CELL ARCHITECTURES

Bengt Jaeckel[1]*, Jens Froebel[1], Matthias Pander[1], Andreas Maixner[2], Hamed Hanifi[2]
[1] Fraunhofer Center for Silicon Photovoltaics CSP, Otto-Eißfeldt-Straße 12, 06112 Halle (Saale), Germany
[2] AESOLAR, Messerschmittring 54, 86343 Koenigsbrunn, Germany
*e-mail: bengt.jaeckel@csp.fraunhofer.de

ABSTRACT: With TOPCon cell technology becoming mainstream in 2025 and HJT/BC increasing their market share, too, cell strings now operate at higher voltages and current densities and exhibit different reverse-bias behavior than legacy PERC/Al-BSF.
We experimentally compare reverse characteristics of five c-Si cell architectures (Al-BSF, PERC, TOPCon, HJT, IBC) using mini-modules and mini-strings measured from 100 to 1.300 W/m^2 at 25°C with a four-quadrant long-pulse flasher. TOPCon and HJT show pronounced hysteresis in the 1st quadrant but no relevant hysteresis in reverse; bifacial front and rear behavior is essentially identical. The key findings are that typical reverse breakdown voltage for Al-BSF is around -14 V, PERC between -21 and -24 V, HJT around -30 V, TOPCon between -44 and -49 V and for BC between -4 and -5 V. Illumination-dependent reverse current is strong for PERC, low for Al-BSF, very low for HJT and IBC, and overall low for TOPCon, considering more relevant voltages very low. Under full shading scenarios TOPCon and HJT strings with ≥24 cells per bypass diode are generally feasible as string voltages remain below reverse breakdown voltage onset. However, under partial shading (~50% coverage), PERC is most critical due to illumination-enhanced reverse current, while TOPCon/HJT dissipate less power. IBC breaks down early and therefore dissipates less power due to low breakdown voltage. Implications for hot-spot risk, bypass design, and applications with recurring shading (C&I, BaPV, BiPV) are discussed.

Keywords: hot-spot, partial shading, reverse bias, reliability, energy loss

1 INTRODUCTION

PV technology evolved from 3-busbar to multi-wire with more than 20 wires per cell in less than one decade. Their layouts changed from full cell configurations of 3×20 (–24) cells per strings to half-cut serial/parallel with typically 108–156 cells, modifying and increasing voltage and current [1]. New n-type designs (TOPCon, HJT, BC) behave differently in reverse than legacy p-type Al-BSF/PERC.
Under (partial) shading, a cell can be forced into reverse bias and dissipate power, potentially causing local or areal hot spots depending on reverse current paths and localization mechanisms such as edge shunts, grain boundaries/impurities, or areal pn-junction breakdown [2]-[16].
Larger cells (M10/G12) and >20 cells per bypass diode require re-evaluating reverse breakdown voltage onset in general and as a function of illumination [17]-[21].

The current standard for hot-spot testing, IEC 61215-2 [22] hot-spot test (MQT 09) is based on understanding of Al-BSF and PERC cell concepts, not of today's high-power cell types and module layouts. The standard test assumes a "fault"-scenario, not a "daily use" scenario. In C&I, BaPV, BiPV, partial shading is routine. Over 20 years, localized heating can exceed 7000h, while tests (even "extended" MQT 09) cover only hours. Higher façade/roof temperatures raise risk additionally and is tried to include for "fault"-scenario testing in IEC TS 63126 [23]. A stricter hot-spot protocol is under discussion; experiments show >200°C under partial shading [17][19]. The technical background is that heating occurs when power from (n−1) cells is dissipated in one (partially) shaded cell, setting the string in reverse bias operation in the shaded cell. Reverse current flow paths include edge shunts, defects/grain boundaries, and area-wide junction breakdown. Multi crystalline Al-BSF is more prone to

localized heating due to its material [10].
Partial shading (20–80%) is common and it was found experimentally that most heating occurs near ~50% shade[17][19].
Herin the focus is set to study reverse breakdown at 25°C. Higher cell temperature will alter the numbers given here typically to lower numbers. However, the trend is same as shown exemplary in the result section.

2 EXPERIMENTAL SETUP

Mini-modules and mini strings per technology were fabricated including 4-point contacts for more precise measurement at expected high currents. IV-curves were measured with an A+A+A+ HALM flasher using long pulses (up to 150 ms) and multi-flash configurations to mitigate hysteresis. To cover all regions a possible four-quadrant sweep from forward bias into reverse breakdown was configured. Irradiance was measured from 100 to 1300 W/m^2 at 25°C, including the use of a neutral density filter (ND) for low irradiance while maintaining near-AM1.5 spectrum. Additionally dark IV-curves were measured with each measurement run. For TOPCon and HJT hysteresis was checked, and their bifacial front and rear side behavior was measured separately. EL images pre- and -post confirmed no damage during testing. For TOPCon cells multiple batches were checked to test for cell manufacturing induced spread in reverse breakdown behavior.

3 RESULTS

3.1 Al-BSF cells

Al-BSF cell served as a baseline, as many module designs and the IEC 61215-2 hot-spot test criteria were basically developed with this technology in mind. The sample was a multi-crystalline 3-BB cell. IV curves at 25°C taken in the dark (D-IV) and from 100 to 1300 W/m² in 100W/m²-steps were swept from 1st quadrant to reverse until breakdown occurred without inducing damage (see Figure 1 a) left side). After subtracting Isc to highlight illumination effects (see Figure 1 b) left side), a slight irradiance-dependent increase in reverse current is visible between about −5 V and breakdown. Reverse breakdown voltage onset occurs at approximately −14 V, consistent with expectations for multi-crystalline Al-BSF.

3.2 PERC cell

Two mono-crystalline PERC samples were investigated to capture the technology evolution from full to half cells: a 5-BB M3 full cell (≈2020) and a 9-BB M6 half-cut cell (≈2024) were measured as it is described for the Al-BSF cell (see Figure 1 a) right side).
The reverse breakdown voltage is around -21 to -24 V, with the newer half-cell about 1-2 V higher voltages. A strong illumination-enhanced reverse current between about -5 V and breakdown is clearly visible, significantly larger than for Al-BSF (see Figure 1 and note the different x- and y-axis scaling).

3.3 TOPCon cell

TOPCon cells were examined for hysteresis, bifaciality, and manufacturing spread. TOPCon cells show pronounced hysteresis in the 1st quadrant if IV-curve sweep is too fast (~10ms), but no relevant hysteresis in reverse was observed. Front and rear sides behave similarly in reverse (see [24]).
M10 half-cut, 16-wire cells from different manufacturing dates were investigated and a quite large spread in reverse breakdown voltage onset was observed, ranging

absolutely from -39 V to around -48 V (see Figure 2 left side and [24]). The irradiance dependence starts at around -20 V, significantly higher compared to PERC and even close to reverse breakdown the additional current is very small.

3.4 HJT cells

M6 half-cut HJT cell was tested (see Figure 2 right side). As with TOPCon, HJT exhibits 1st quadrant hysteresis under rapid sweeps but no observable hysteresis in reverse. Front and rear reverse behavior was very similar. The measured reverse breakdown onset was determined to be around -30 V with essentially no irradiance dependence in the range tested.

3.5 IBC cells

IBC technology was assessed using an 8-cell R&D string. The presented voltages were normalized per cell (Figure 3). IV-curves largely overlap across irradiance, with minor spread between -1 and -3 V likely due to the series interconnection. The key difference vs. other technologies is the very early breakdown at about -4.5V per cell and a negligible irradiance dependence in reverse breakdown voltage behavior.
While breakdown is reached at low reverse voltage, the resulting power density is small, which limits heating severity making such cells great candidates for shade-prone locations.

More details and a closer look into the rear and front side behavior of bifacial cells is given in [24].

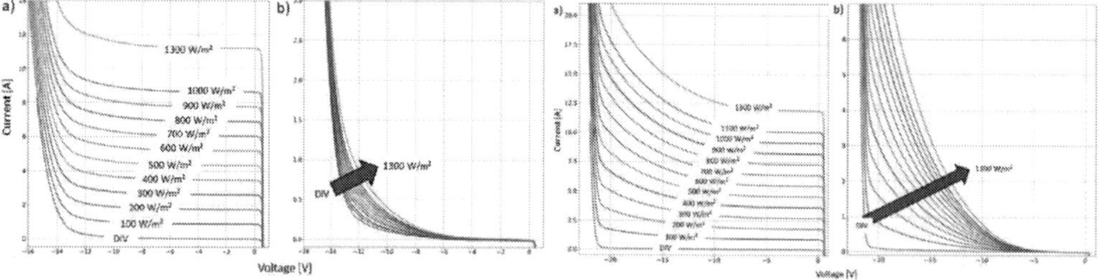

Figure 1: IV-curves a) under different irradiance levels and b) IV-curves where Isc is subtracted to show extra impact on irradiance on reverse voltage behavior.; left: Al-BSF, right: PERC, both full cells.

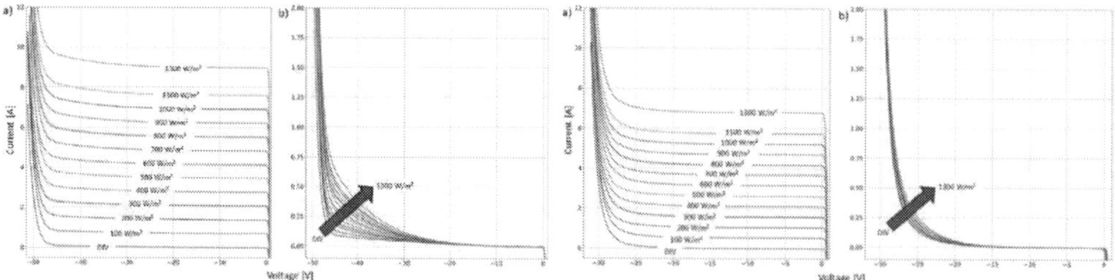

Figure 2: IV-curves a) under different irradiance levels and b) IV-curves where Isc is subtracted to show extra impact on irradiance on reverse voltage behavior.; left: TOPCon, right: HJT, both half cells.

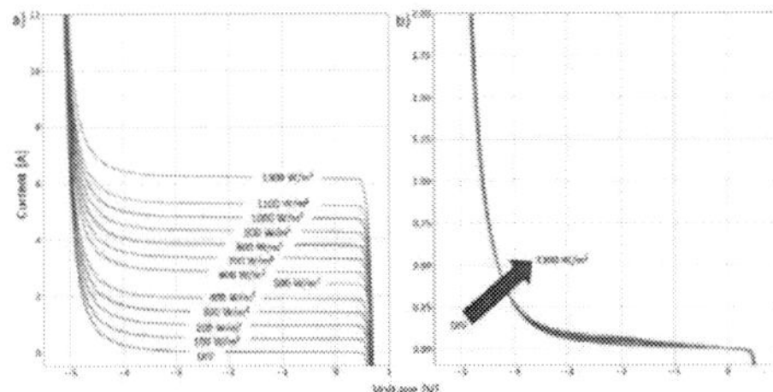

Figure 3: IV-curves from an IBC cell: a) under different irradiance levels and b) IV-curves where Isc is subtracted to show extra impact on irradiance on reverse voltage behavior.

4 DISCUSSION and CONCLUSIONS

4.1 Full-shading implications:

High reverse breakdown voltages for TOPCon (-39 … -49 V) and HJT (≈-30 V) means available series voltage per bypass section typically remains below the threshold voltage, preventing breakdown and limiting heat generation and dissipation. Thus, full-shading hot spots are unlikely for TOPCon and HJT at today's number of cells in series.

However, PERC also has higher reverse breakdown voltages (21…-24 V) than Al-BSF (≈-14 V) and 24 cells per bypass are feasible for PERC with no significant risk. IBC breaks down early (-4…-5 V), so breakdown under full shading is frequent, but low reverse breakdown voltages limits power density.

4.2 Partial shading

Real hot-spot risk is governed by partial shading (20–80 % coverage) and is quite common, and temperatures often peak near ~50 % coverage. Reverse breakdown voltages decrease with temperature (see exemplary for PERC in Figure 4), further support heating. The critical differentiator is the illumination-enhanced reverse current between roughly -5 V and reverse breakdown voltages with strongest impact for PERC, a slight impact for Al-BSF, low for TOPCon, very low impact for HJT, while IBC showed a negligible impact.

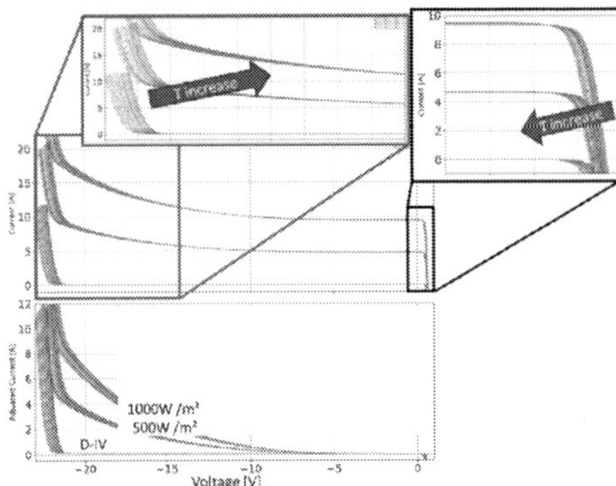

Figure 4: Temperature dependence of IV-curves for PERC cell technology.

4.3 Hysteresis and bifaciality

TOPCon and HJT show pronounced first-quadrant hysteresis if swept rapidly. No relevant hysteresis was observed in reverse, and front- and rear- sides behave similarly in reverse direction for both. Hence, hysteresis and bifaciality do not significantly affect reverse-bias conclusions.

4.4 Manufacturing spread and process control

The investigated TOPCon cells showed significant batch-to-batch spread in Reverse breakdown voltages (-39 V to -48 V) despite identical box sorting, consistent with known process sensitivities for other cell types. In-line metrology and specifications for reverse-bias behavior are advisable in addition to standard forward IV parameters.

4.5 Implications for design and testing

Because partial shading is a recurrent use case in C&I, BaPV, and BiPV, reducing cells per bypass diode lowers potential thermal peaks, long lasting and extra increased operation temperatures and impact energy generation negatively. Relying solely on full-shading criteria can be misleading: PERC's strong illumination-enhanced reverse current makes it most prone to hot spots near ~50% shading, while TOPCon and HJT have in comparison a negligible impact by illumination. MQT 09 reflects earlier generations and rare-fault assumptions. For modern high-power layouts and recurring shading, extended protocols (e.g., "severe hot-spot test") are needed.

The cross-technology comparison of five cell types / generations highlights three drivers of hot-spot risk: 1) reverse breakdown voltage, 2) illumination-dependent reverse current in the pre-breakdown regime, and c) manufacturing spread that shifts reverse breakdown to lower values.

5 OUTLOOK

Figure 4 shows exemplary the temperature dependence of PERC cell technology. Similar experiments were done and are still conducted on other technologies to achieve a more comprehensives picture, including definition of reverse breakdown voltage onset temperature coefficients (TC). The extent on how such TCs are impacted by irradiance is ongoing work.

6 ACKNOWLEDGEMENTS

This work was funded by the Federal Ministry for Economic Affairs and Climate Action (BMWK) under grant 03EE1180 (SegmentPV).

7 REFERENCES

[1] International Technology Roadmap for Photovoltaic (ITRPV), 15th Edition, 2024

[2] J. W. Bishop, Computer simulation of the effects of electrical mismatches in photovoltaic cell interconnection circuits, Solar Cells, 1988, vol. 25, pp. 73-89, DOI:10.1016/0379-6787(88)90059-2

[3] J. W. Bishop, Microplasma breakdown and hot-spots in silicon solar cells, Solar cells, 1989, 26 (4), 335-349.

[4] M. Danner, Reverse characteristics of commercial silicon solar cells-impact on hot spot temperatures

and module integrity, Conference Record of the Twenty Sixth IEEE Photovoltaic Specialists Conference - 1997, IEEE, PVSC-97, 1997, pp. 1137-1140, DOI:10.1109/pvsc.1997.654289

[5] W. Herrmann, Hot spot investigations on PV modules-new concepts for a test standard and consequences for module design with respect to bypass diodes, IEEE Photovoltaic Specialists Conference - 1997,
DOI:10.1109/PVSC.1997.654287

[6] W. Herrmann, Operational Behaviour of Commercial Solar Cells under Reverse Biased Conditions, EU-PVSEC, 1998.

[7] M. C. Alonso-Garcia, Analysis and modelling the reverse characteristic of photovoltaic cells, Solar Energy Materials & Solar Cells, 2006, vol. 90, pp. 1105-1120

[8] D. Lausch, Identification of pre-breakdown mechanism of silicon solar cells at low reverse voltages, Applied Physics Letters, 2010, 97, 073506

[9] C. Reichel, Investigation of electrical shading effects in back-contacted back-junction silicon solar cells using the two-dimensional charge collection probability and the reciprocity theorem, Journal of Applied Physics, 2011-01, vol. 109,
DOI:10.1063/1.3524506

[10] O. Breitenstein, Understanding junction breakdown in multi-crystalline solar cells Journal of Applied Physics, 2010,
DOI:https://doi.org/10.1063/1.3562200

[11] H. Yang, Investigation of the Relationship between Reverse Current of Crystalline Silicon Solar Cells and Conduction of Bypass Diode, International Journal of Photoenergy, 2012, vol. 2012, pp. 1-5,
DOI:10.1155/2012/357218

[12] K. A. Kim, Photovoltaic hot spot analysis for cells with various reverse-bias characteristics through electrical and thermal simulation, IEEE 14th Workshop on Control and Modeling for Power Electronics (COMPEL), IEEE, 2013,
DOI:10.1109/compel.2013.6626399

[13] J. Bauer, Hot spots in multi-crystalline silicon solar cells: avalanche breakdown due to etch pits, Physica status solidi (RRL) – Rapid Research Letters, 2009-03, vol. 3, pp. 40-42,
DOI:10.1002/pssr.200802250.

[14] F. Dauzou, Electrical behaviour of n-type silicon solar cells under reverse bias: Influence of the manufacturing process, Solar Energy Materials and Solar Cells, 2012-09, vol. 104, pp. 175-179,
DOI:10.1016/j.solmat.2012.04.046

[15] V. Shanmugam, Impact of the manufacturing process on the reverse-bias characteristics of high-efficiency n-type bifacial silicon wafer solar cells, Solar Energy Materials and Solar Cells, 2019, vol. 191, pp. 117-122,
DOI:10.1016/j.solmat.2018.11.014

[16] J. Qian, Two-Dimensional Hot Spot Temperature Simulation for c-Si Photovoltaic Modules Physica status solidi (a), 2018, vol. 215,
DOI:10.1002/pssa.201800429

[17] B. Jaeckel, Hotspottest und reale Teilverschattung von modernen High-Density HD-Modulen: eine Wahrscheinlichkeits- und Risikobetrachtung, PV Symposium Bad Staffelstein, 2021

[18] E. Oezkalay, The effect of partial shading on the reliability of photovoltaic modules in the built-environment, EPJ Photovoltaics, 2024, vol. 15, 7, DOI:10.1051/epjpv/2024001.

[19] R. Witteck, Hot Cells in High-Power Photovoltaic Modules with Solar Cells from Larger Silicon Wafer Formats Eu-PVSEC, 2021,
DOI:10.4229/EUPVSEC20212021-4AV.1.25

[20] C. Clement, Illumination Dependence of Reverse Leakage Current in Silicon Solar Cells," 49th IEEE Photovoltaic Specialists Conference, 2021, vol. 11, pp. 1285-1290,
DOI:10.1109/jphotov.2021.3088005

[21] C. Clement, Design of shading- and hotspot-resistant shingled modules, Progress in Photovoltaics: Research and Applications, 2021, DOI:10.1002/pip.3507

[22] IEC 61215-2, Crystalline silicon terrestrial photovoltaic (PV) modules - Design qualification and type approval, (2016, 2022)

[23] IEC TS 63126, Guidelines for qualifying PV modules, components and materials for operation at high temperatures, 2020,
https://webstore.iec.ch/en/publication/59551

[24] B. Jaeckel, Characterization and analysis of reverse breakdown voltage onset of solar cells with different cell architectures, EPJ Photovoltaics, 2025

3CO.11.5

Indoor characterization and analysis of reverse breakdown behavior of solar cells with different cell architectures

—

Bengt Jaeckel, Jens Froebel, Matthias Pander, Andreas Maixner, and Hamed Hanifi
Fraunhofer Center for Silicon Photovoltaics CSP, Otto-Eissfeldt-Str. 12, 06120 Halle (Saale), Germany
AESOLAR, Messerschmittring 54, 86343 Königsbrunn, Germany

Reverse Bias Characterization
Outline

1. **Motivation**

2. **Experimental setup**

3. **Cell architecture results**
   - Al-BSF, PERC, TOPCon, HJT, (I)BC

4. **Conclusions & Outlook**

Outdoor partial shading test setup at Fhg CSP

Image: https://enterfea.com/thermal-loads/

25.09.2025

- Informationsklassifizierung -

Fraunhofer
CSP

020224-002

Reverse Bias Characterization
Motivation

> Solar cell and module technology changed (60 full cells to 144+ half cells)

> Cell **efficiency increases, so do Voc voltages** (eff. 14% to 25+%)

> Cells got significant larger, and number of busbars increased (2 → 20+)

> Cells get **more temperature sensitive**

> Modules are significant less expensive!

> Modules are **mounted in more (partial) shade prone areas**

> **Partial shading is more critical** compared to full cell shading

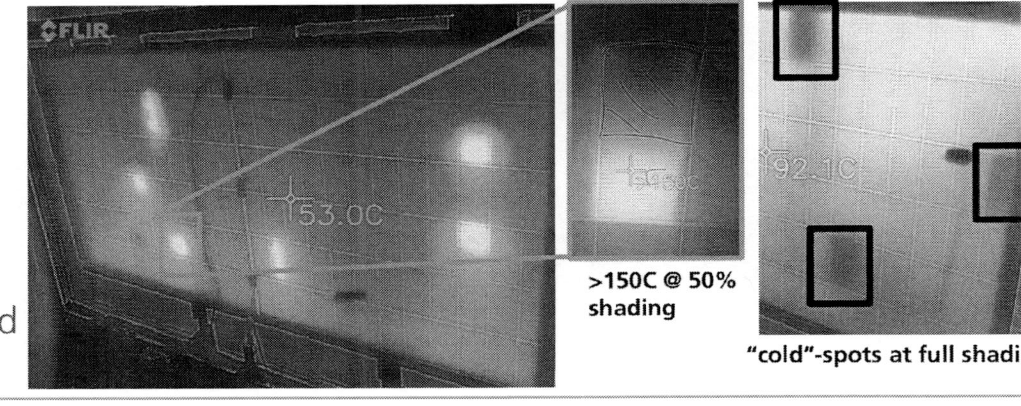

Fraunhofer
CSP

020224-003

Reverse Bias Characterization

Motivation – full shading of one cell

- Typical look at a solar cell / module!

- Power is produced and current flow is "normal"

- For normal operation this is sufficient!

- BUT: **under (full) shading** the IV / PU diagram changes as shaded cell goes into reverse and **becomes a consumer**

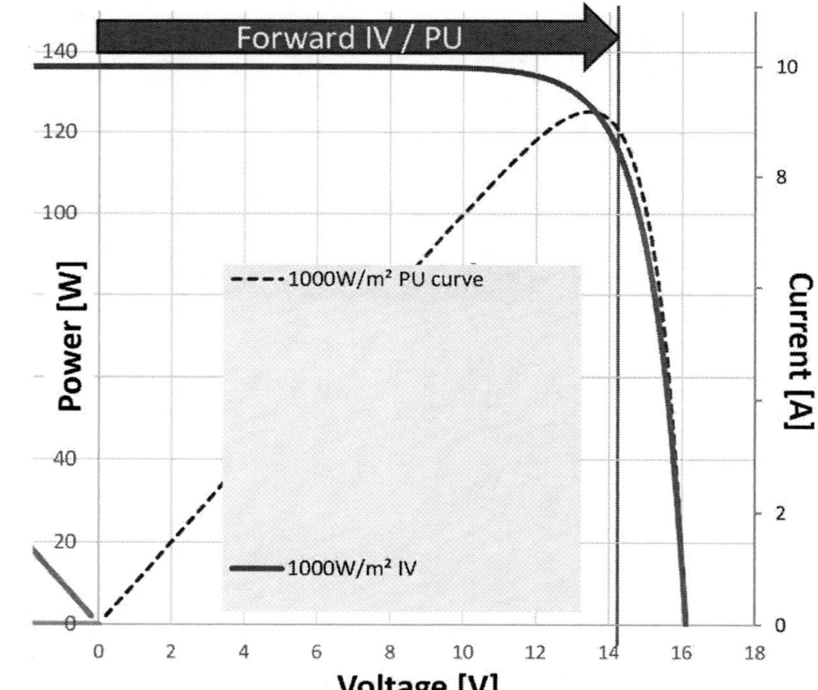

- Informationsklassifizierung -

Fraunhofer
CSP

020224-004

Reverse Bias Characterization

Motivation – full shading of one cell

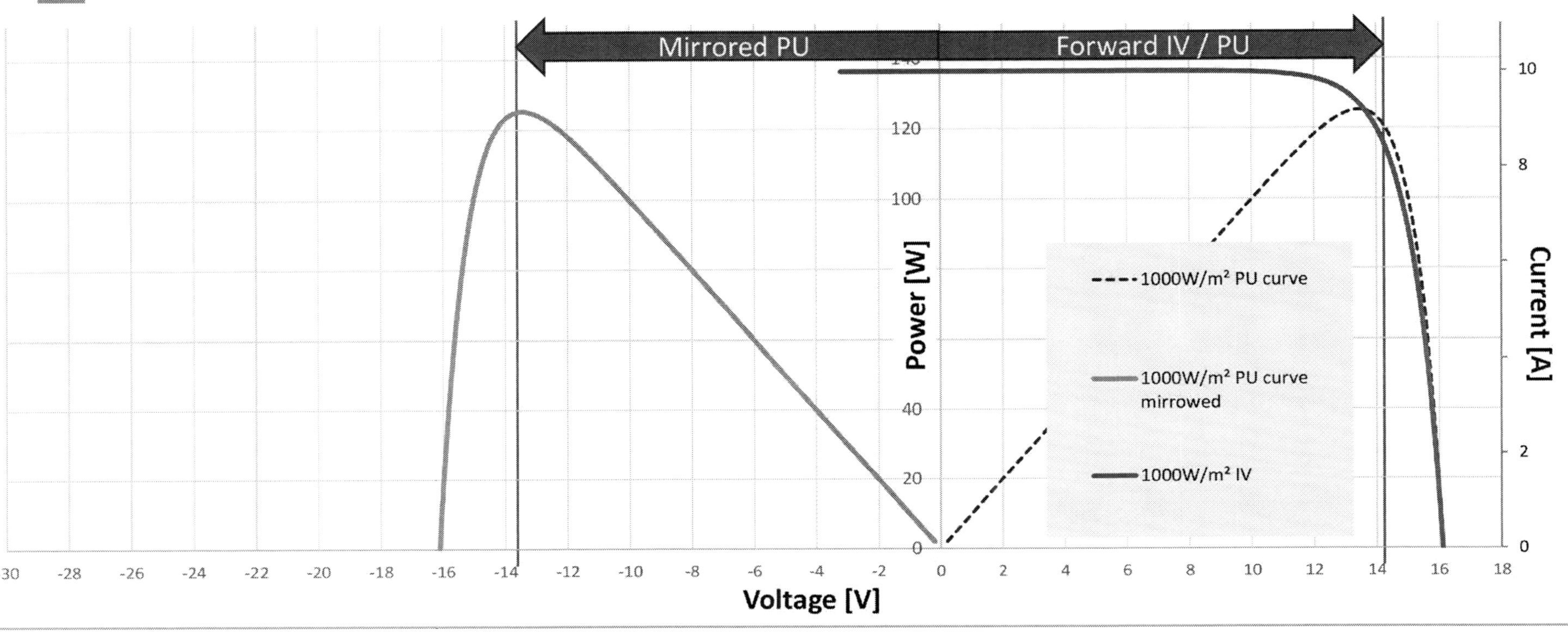

25.09.2025

- Informationsklassifizierung -

Fraunhofer
CSP

020224-005

Reverse Bias Characterization

Motivation – full shading of one cell

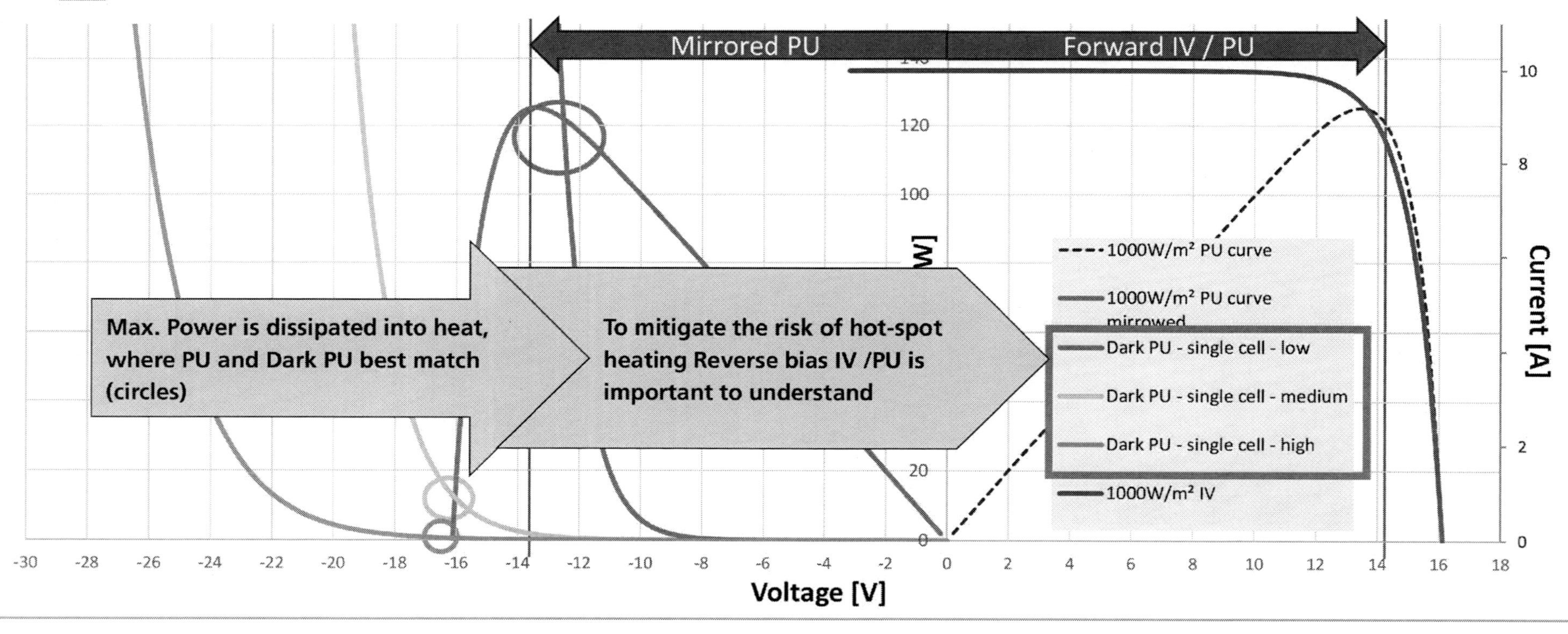

Fraunhofer
CSP

020224-006

Reverse Bias Characterization

Experimental setup

- Mini-modules and mini strings per technology

- IV-curves were measured with an long pulse A+A+A+ halm.

- 4-quadrant IV sweeps from forward bias into reverse breakdown

- Irradiance: 0 (DIV), 100 to 1300 W/m² at 25°C in 100W/m² steps

- EL images pre- and -post confirmed no damage during testing

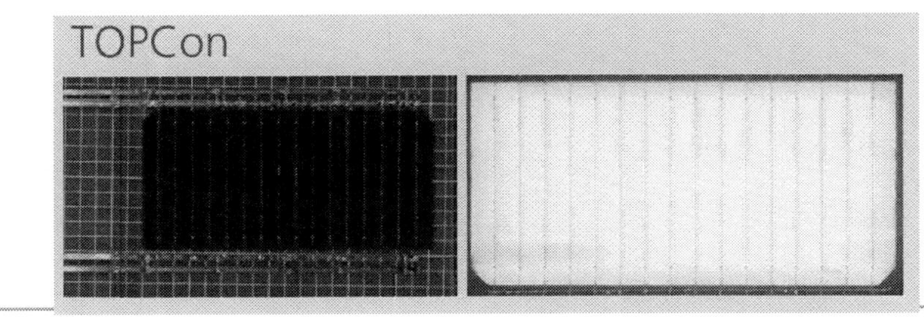

Fraunhofer
CSP

Reverse Bias Characterization

Investigated cell architectures - Overview

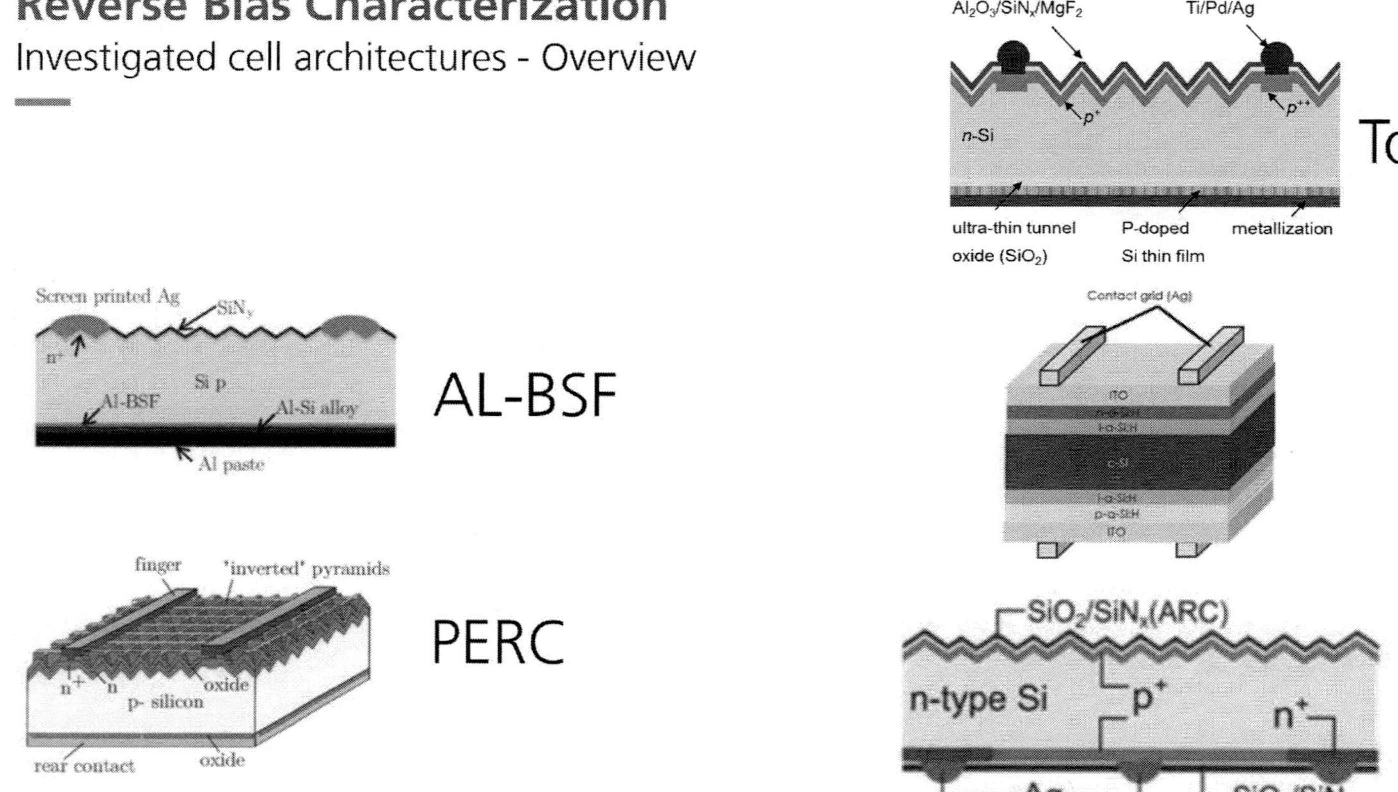

020224-008

Reverse Bias Characterization
Results – Al-BSF

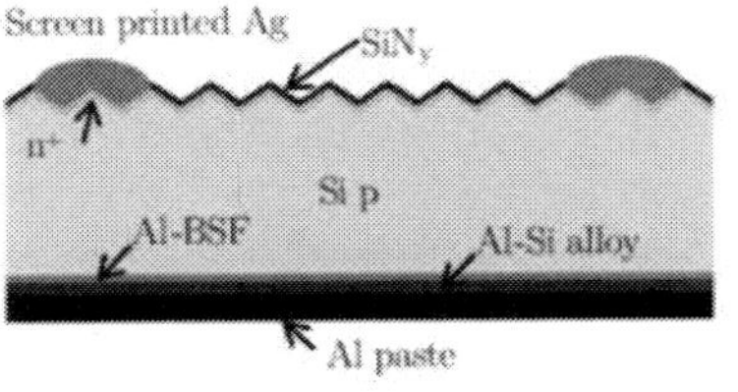

AL-BSF

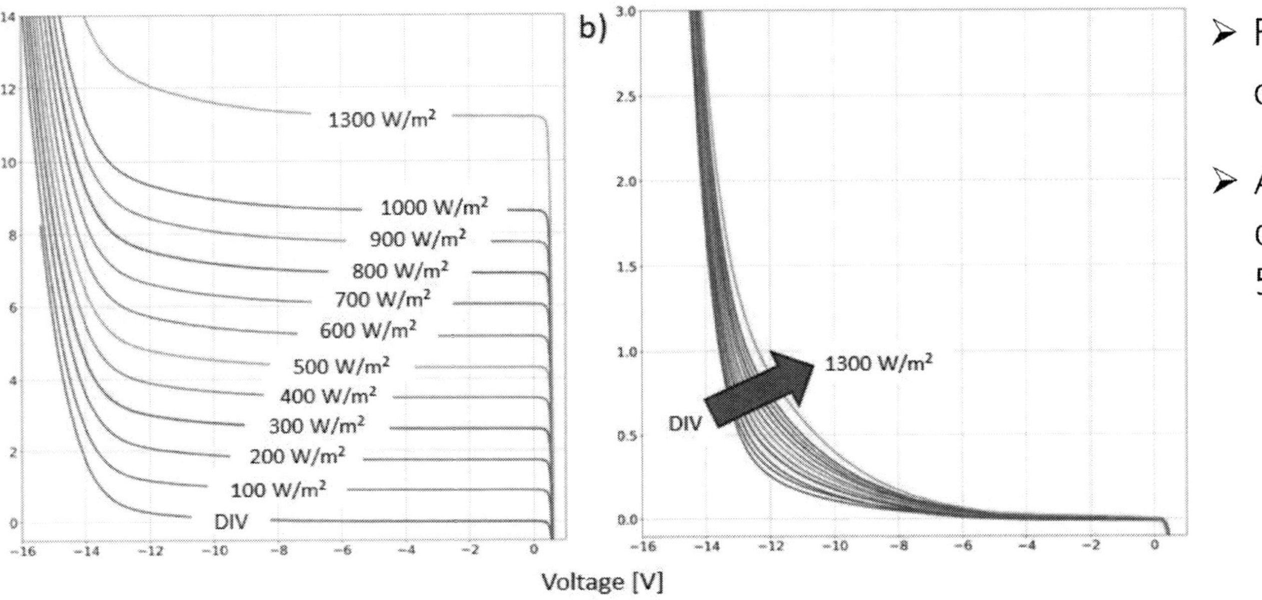

➢ Reverse breakdown voltage onset at **~-14V**

➢ A little irradiance dependence in range from -5V to -13V

Reverse Bias Characterization
Results – PERC

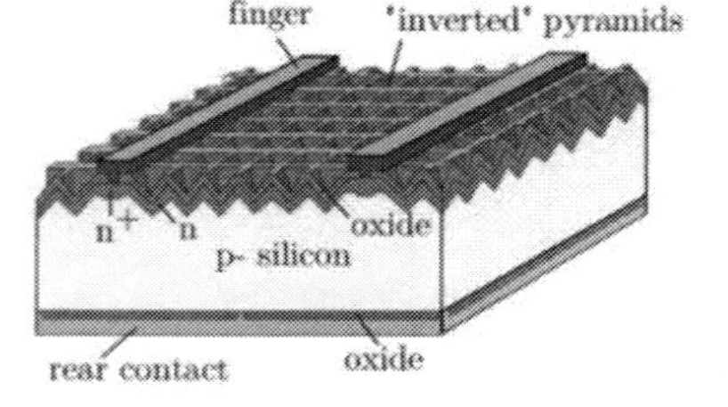

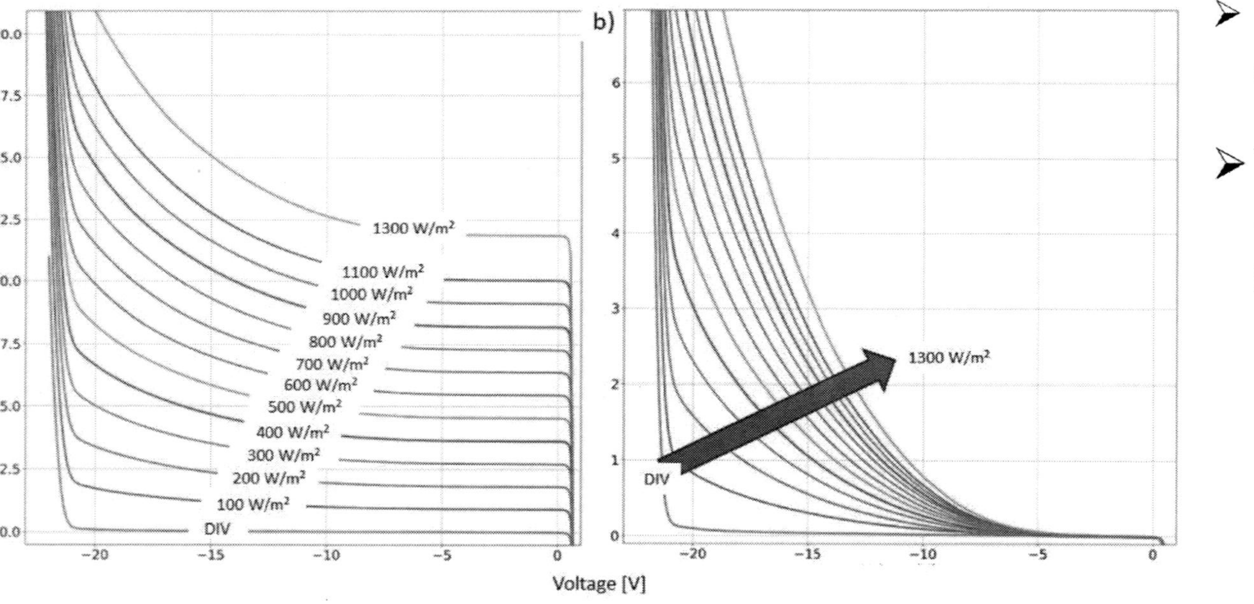

> Reverse breakdown voltage onset at **-21 to -24 V**

> **Very strong irradiance** dependence in range from -5V to -21V

020224-010

Reverse Bias Characterization
Results – TOPCon - BIFACIAL

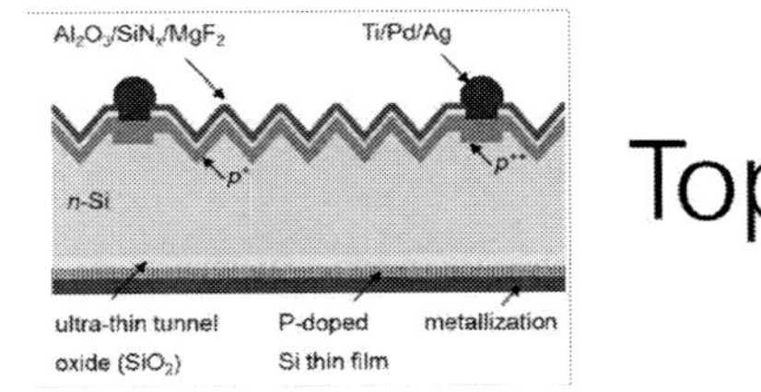

Topcon

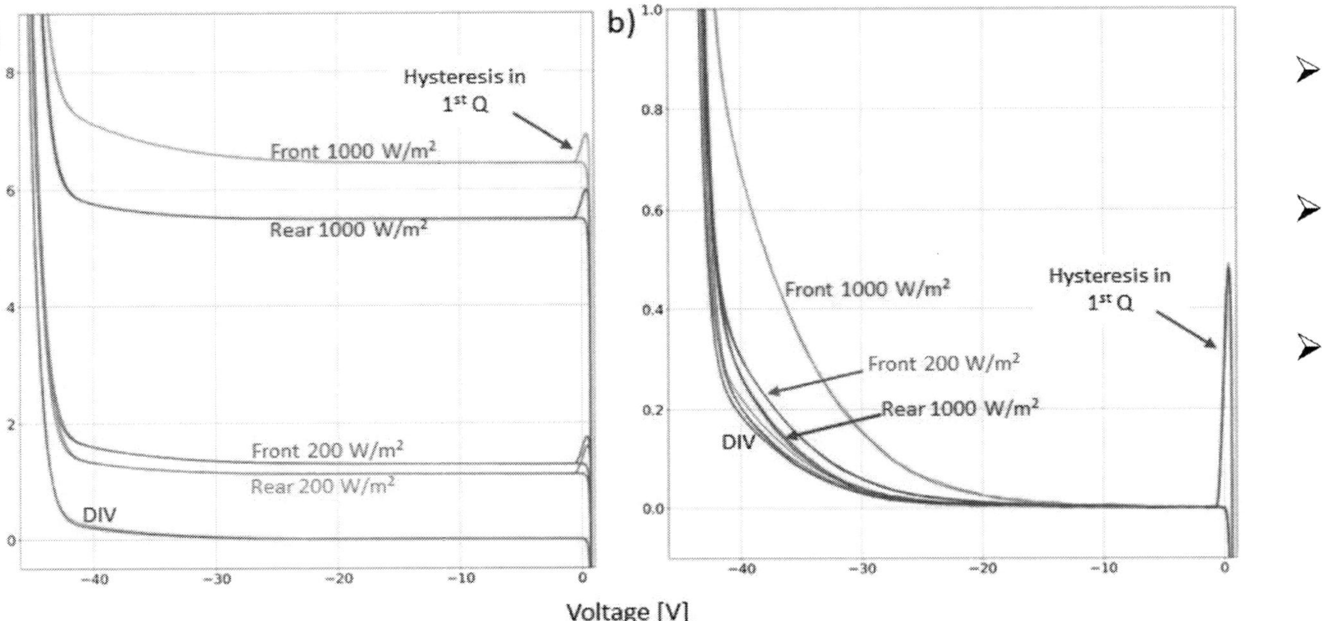

- Hysteresis is front direction √

- **NO hysteresis in reverse**

- Front side has slightly higher irradiance dependence compared to rear side

Fraunhofer
CSP

020224-011

Reverse Bias Characterization
Results – TOPCon

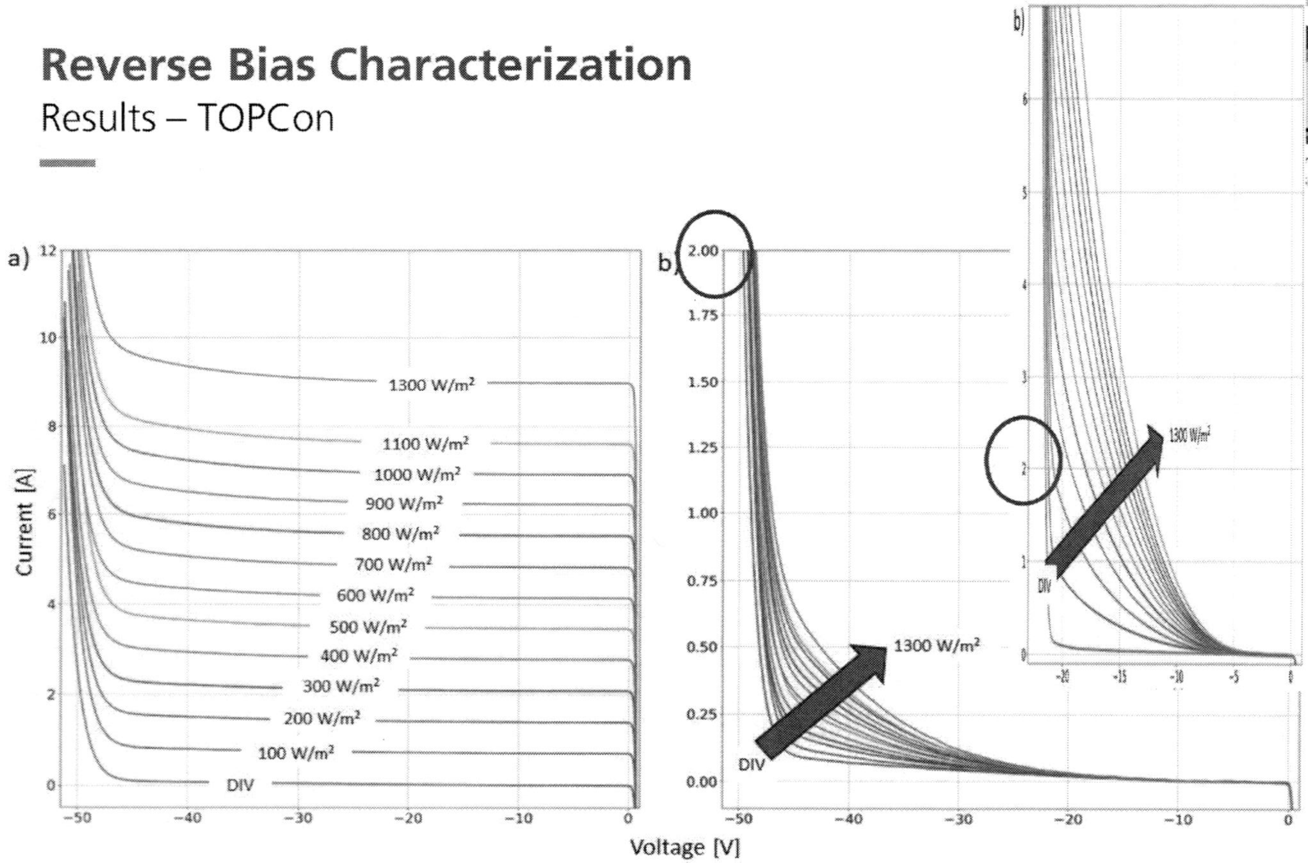

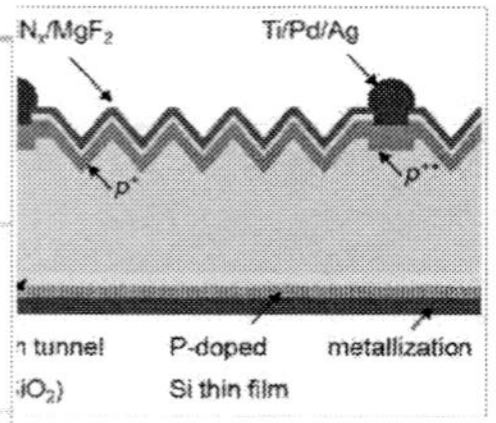

Topcon

➢ Reverse breakdown voltage onset at **-39 to -48 V**

➢ **Quite low irradiance dependence** in range from -20V to -48V

➢ Irradiance dependence starts at **quite different voltage**!!!

Reverse Bias Characterization
Results – (I)BC

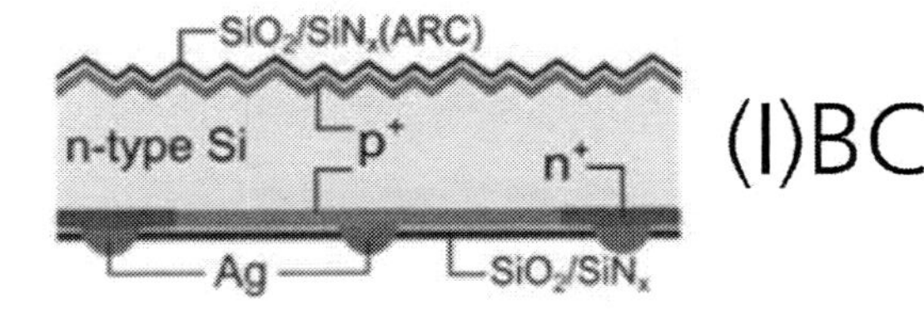

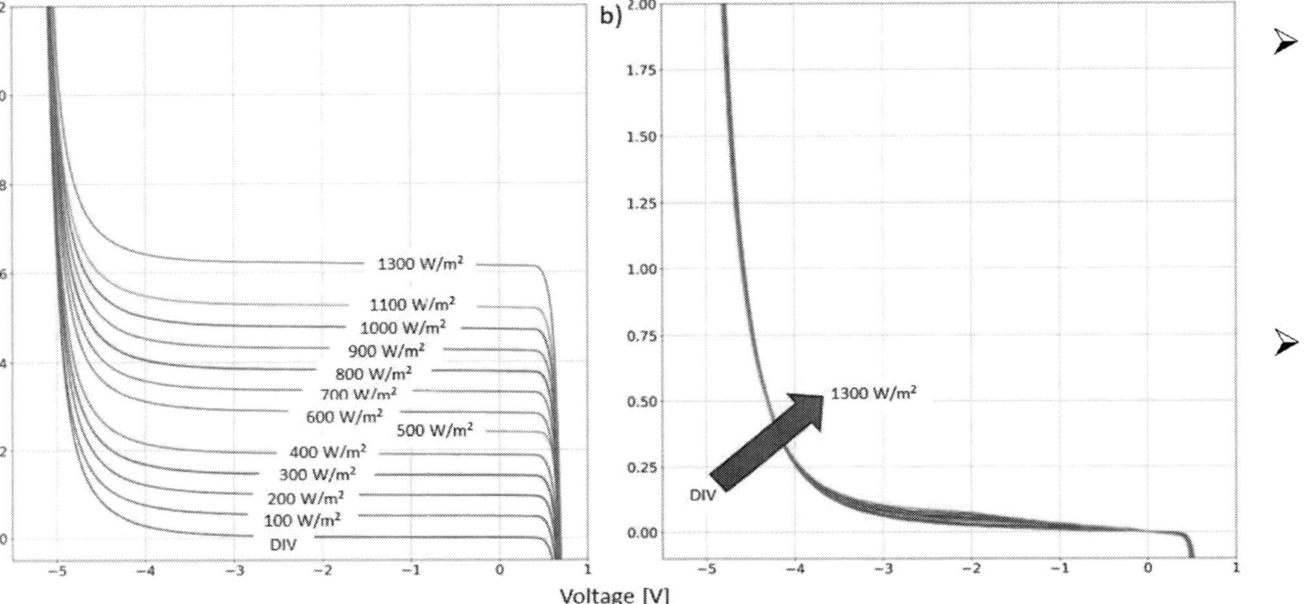

- Reverse breakdown voltage onset at **~-4.5 V, significant lower compared** to other technologies

- **No irradiance dependence**

Fraunhofer
CSP

020224-013

Reverse Bias Characterization

Impact on temperature: Example: PERC

> Temperature dependent IV curves taken at 1000, 500W/m² and in the dark

> Range: 30-70°C

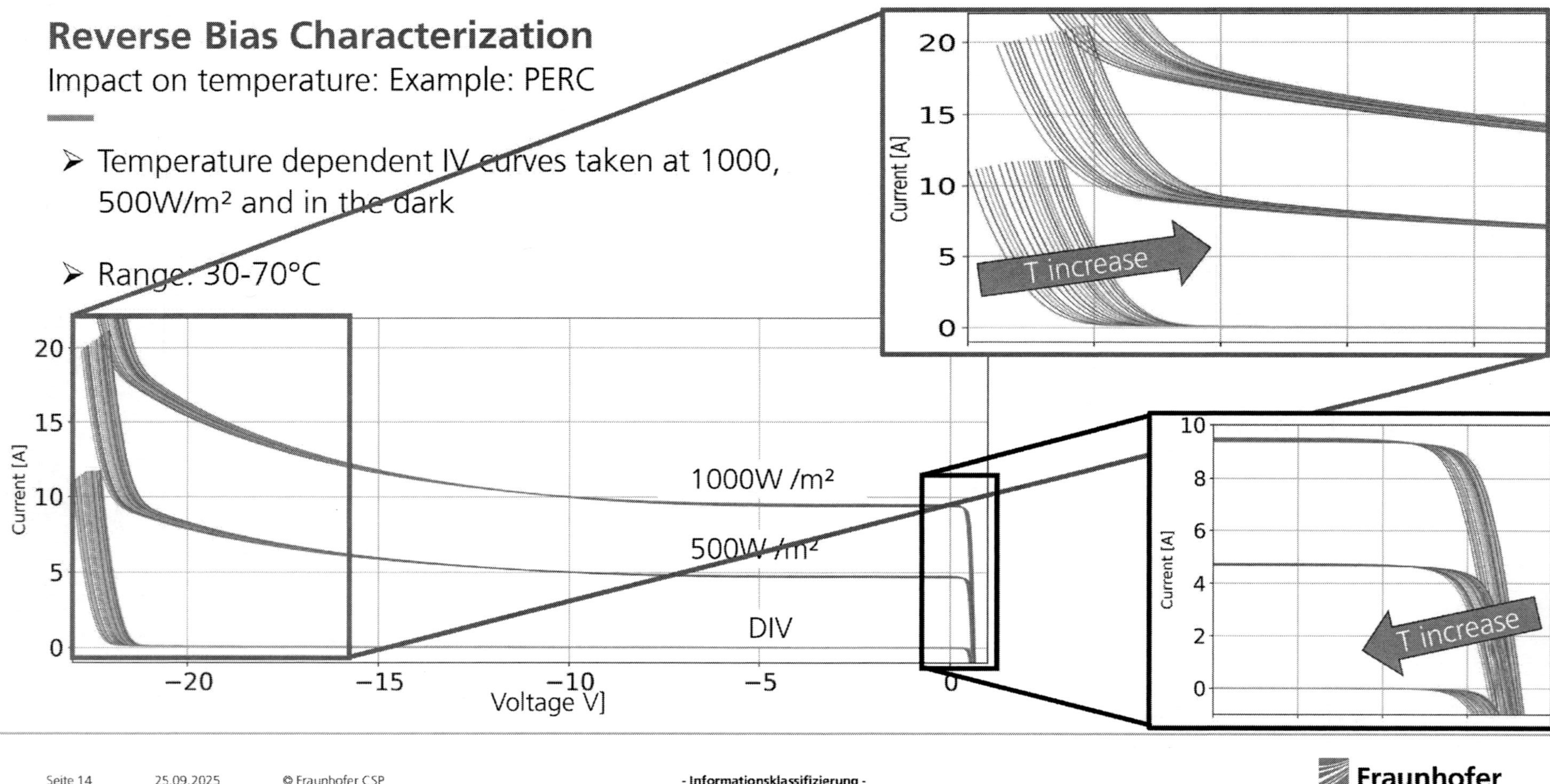

020224-014

Reverse Bias Characterization

Summary

1 PERC shows very string Irradiance dependence while IBC alomost none

2 Breakdown voltage of TOPCon is significant higher compared to PERC, HJT is sort of in the middle.

3 IBC shows quite different behavior (as expected)

4 Reverse Breakdown voltage is reduced with increasing temperatures
Outlook: reverse breakdown temperature coefficient (TC)
determination and rel. / abs. comparison to standard TCs

- Informationsklassifizierung -

Fraunhofer
CSP

020224-015

Thank you for your attention!

Contact
Dr. Bengt Jaeckel
Group manager PV Modules, Components and Manufacturing
Bengt.jaeckel@csp.fraunhofer.de

Fraunhofer CSP
Otto-Eißfeldt- Straße 12
06120 Halle (Saale)
www.csp.fraunhofer.de

Funding:
Project SegmentPV (#03EE1180)

Fraunhofer
CSP

Fraunhofer Center for Silicon
Photovoltaics CSP

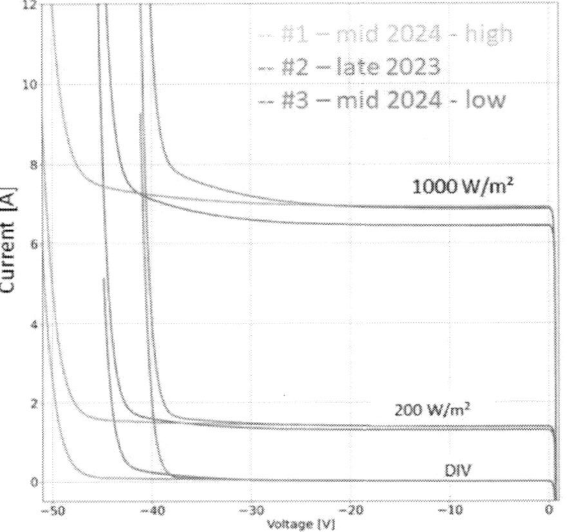

Publication note:

A detailed Paper on Mission Profiles will be published in EPJ as invited paper of EU Pvsec later this year. Please check journal webpage or contact Bengt Jäckel

**Title:
„Characterization and Analysis of Reverse Breakdown Voltage onset of Solar Cells with Different cell Architectures"**

IBC4EU: European Back Contact Technology

Dr. Florian Buchholz

3CP.1

42nd EUPVSEC, Bilbao, Spain

24.09.2025

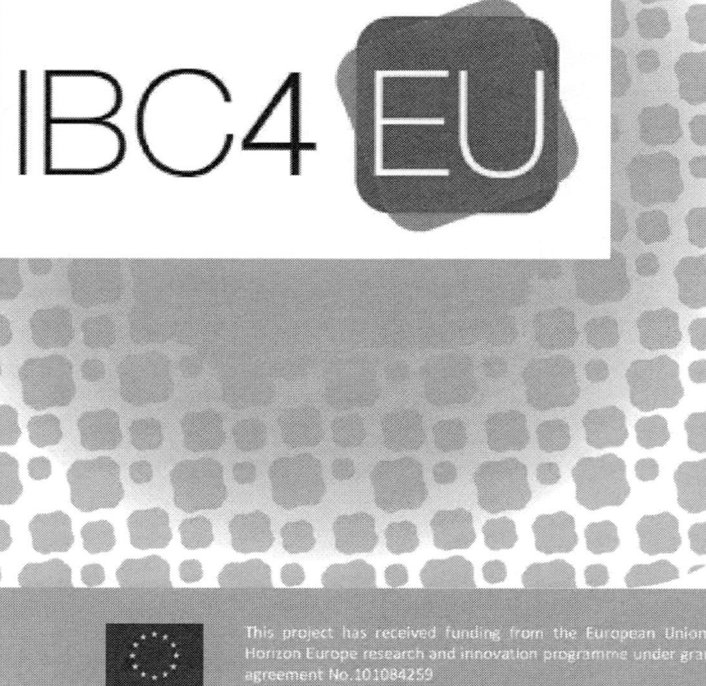

This project has received funding from the European Union's Horizon Europe research and innovation programme under grant agreement No.101084259

TOPCon takes over, what's next?

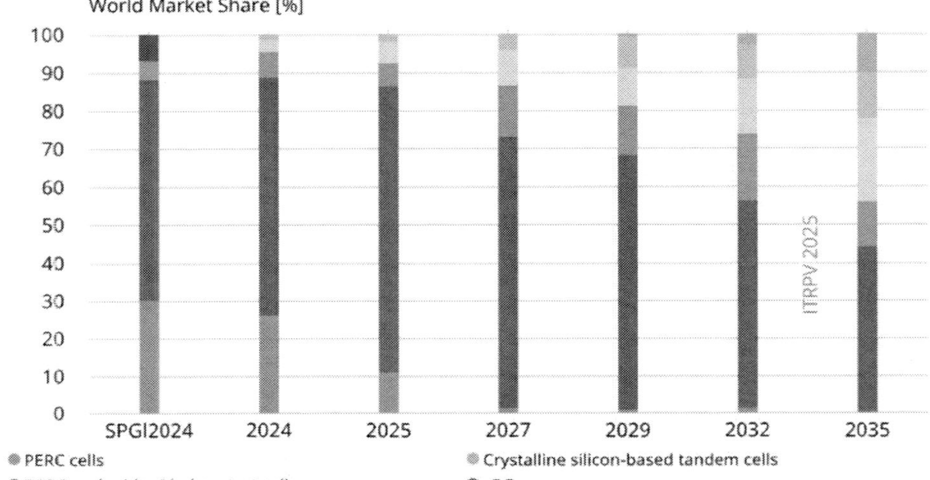

020225-002

IBC4 EU

TOPCon takes over, what's next?

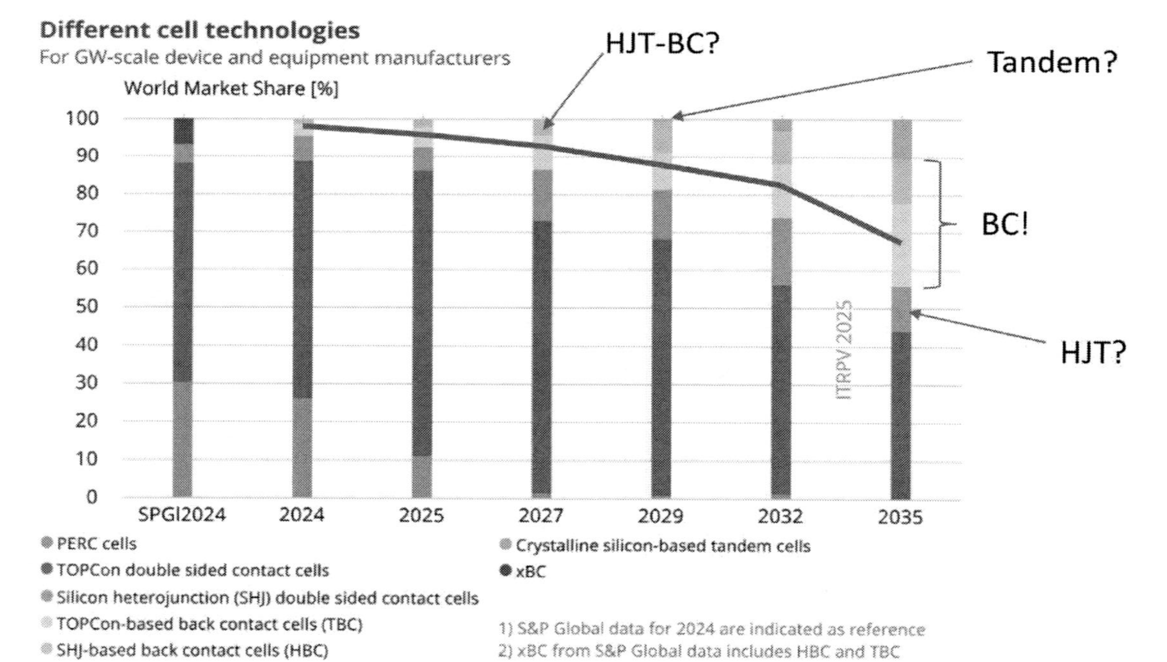

020225-003

Why Back Contact?

IBC4 EU

020225-004

IBC4EU Project

- Virtual pilot line

Project Partners

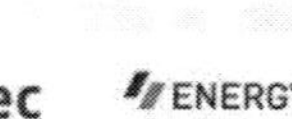

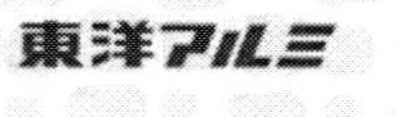

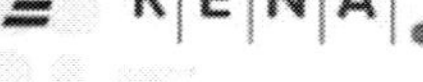

Associated Partners

- Funded by Horizon Europe
- European and non-European partners
- Across the whole value chain

020225-005

IBC4EU Project

- Virtual pilot line

Silicon Wafers

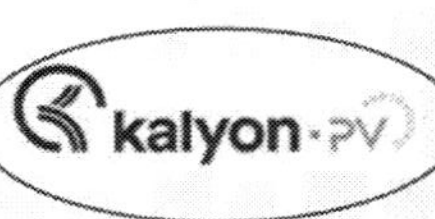

IBC4EU Project

- Virtual pilot line

Silicon Wafers

Solar Cells

F. Buchholz, 3CP.1 - 42nd EU-PVSEC 2025, Bilbao, Spain

020225-007

IBC4EU Project

IBC4 EU

- Virtual pilot line

Silicon Wafers → Solar Cells → Modules

020225-008

IBC4EU Project

- Virtual pilot line

Silicon Wafers
↓
Solar Cells
↓
Modules
↓
Recycling

020225-009

IBC4EU Project

- Virtual pilot line

Industry
4.0

Techno-
economic
evaluation

Silicon Wafers

Solar Cells

Modules

Recycling

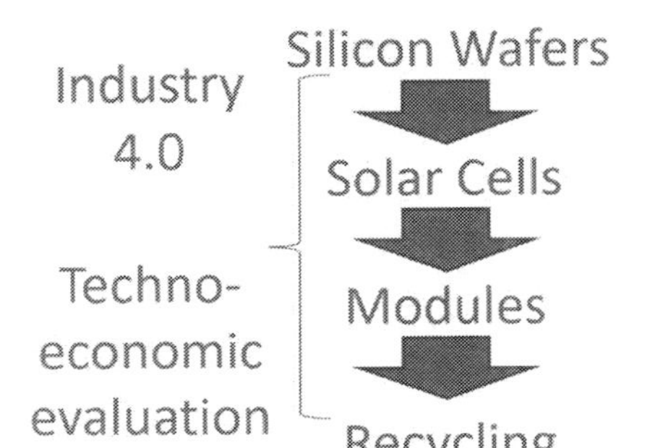

Silicon Wafers

- Tungsten wire with 38 µm diameter tested in production (4 bricks)

- Kerf loss decreases below 60 µm (with 140 µm wafer thickness)

- No wire ruptures

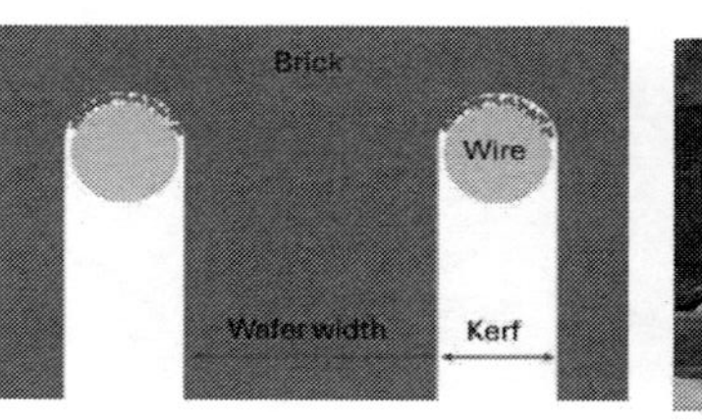

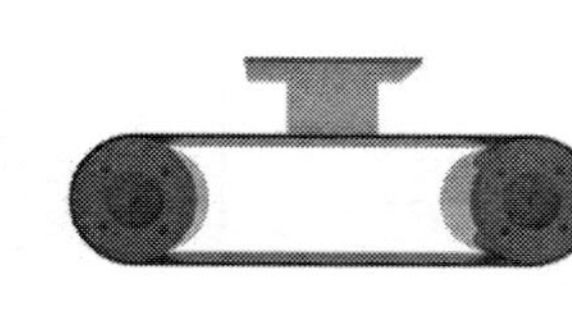

Solar Cells

IBC4 EU

ISFH · kalyon·PV

ISC research for a sunny future · FuturaSun® anticipate tomorrow

POLO

- Very lean POLO IBC process flow on p-type wafers

polyZEBRA

- Process largely based on TOPCon processes on n-type wafers

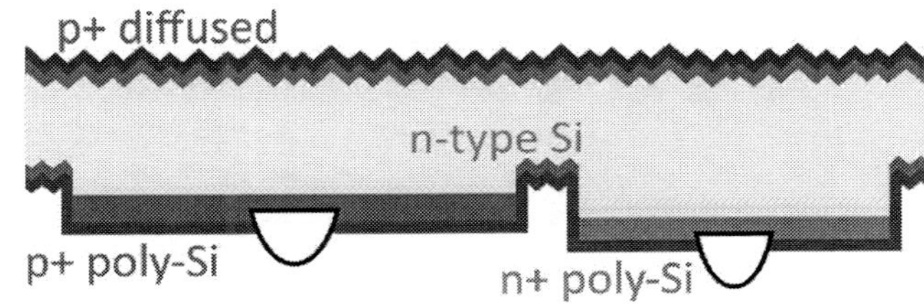

020225-012

Solar Cells

POLO IBC process at Kalyon PV

1. Texturing
2. Rear polishing
3. **Local** PECVD SiO_xN_y / n-a-Si   New !
4. Thermal Anneal
5. Front AlO_x/SiN_y
6. Rear AlO_x/SiN_y
7. Laser contact opening
8. Al and Ag screen printing
9. Firing

- POLO IBC technology licensed by ISFH to Kalyon PV in 2024. Technology transfer started

020225-013

Solar Cells

POLO IBC

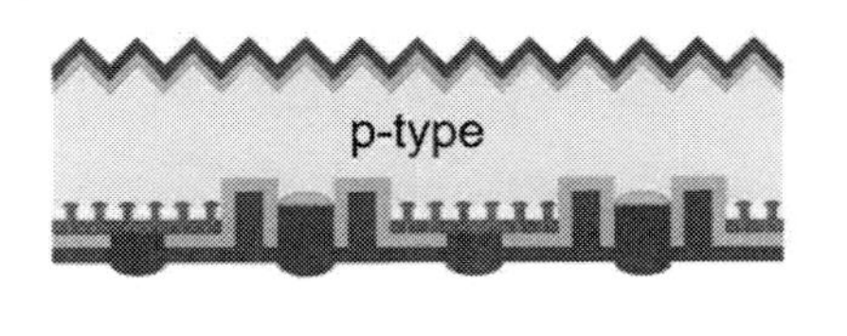

- ## Most recent results

Date	Efficiency [%]	Voc [mV]	Jsc [mA/cm2]	FF [%]
08/2024	23.9	720	41.1	80.5
01/2025	24.1*	723	40.8	81.5
08/2025	24.5*	726	41.2	82.0

Lower poly annealing temp and addition of contact pads

Improved ARC and narrower Ag fingers

- Improvement potential to 25% by reducing high Ag to n-poly-Si contact resistance[1]
  - More details: 1BO.3

* Independently confirmed by ISFH CalTeC
[1] V. Mertens et al., Solar RRL 8, 2300919 (2024)

020225-014

Solar Cells

polyZEBRA

Step #		
1	SDE +cleaning	alkaline wet bench
2	SiO_2+a-Si(n)	PECVD
3	SiNx mask	PECVD
4	Local ablation	Laser
5	Alkaline poly-Si removal +clean	alkaline wet bench
6	SiO_2+a-Si(i)	PECVD
7	B-diffusion (B2B)	BCl_3 tube furnace
8	local activation	Laser
9	texturing	alkaline wet bench
10	B-diffusion	BCl_3 tube furnace
11	Wet chemical cleaning	batch wet bench
12	AlOx (double side coating)	ALD (or PE-ALD)
13	SiNx	PECVD
14	SiNx	PECVD
15	Screen printing Ag	SP, dryers, FF furnaces, Ag paste
16	Screen printing Cu	SP, dryers, FF furnaces, snap curing Cu paste

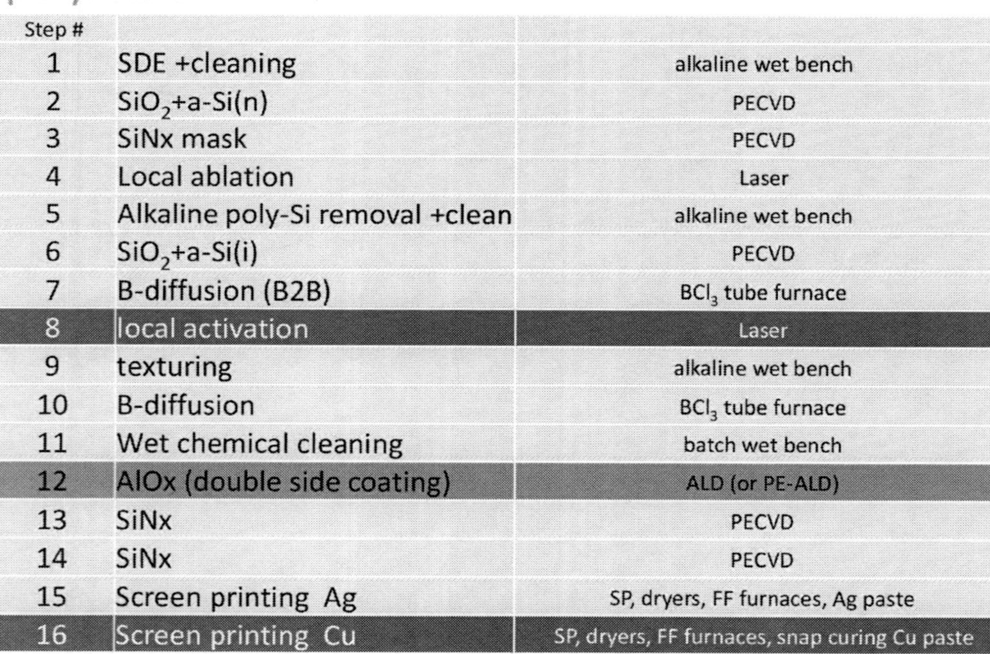

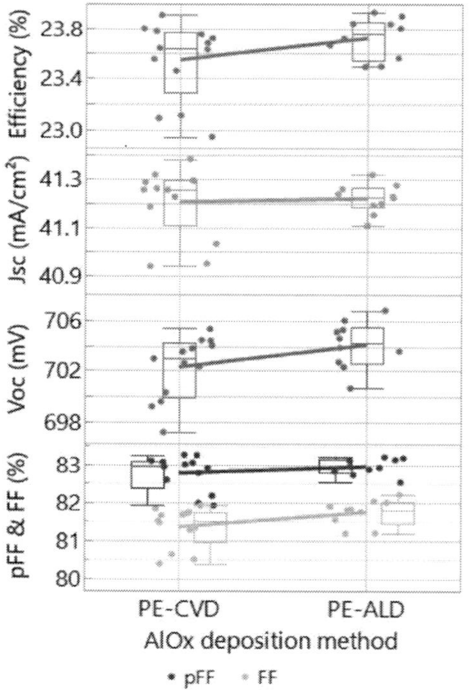

F. Buchholz, 3CP.1 - 42nd EU-PVSEC 2025, Bilbao, Spain

020225-015

Solar Cells

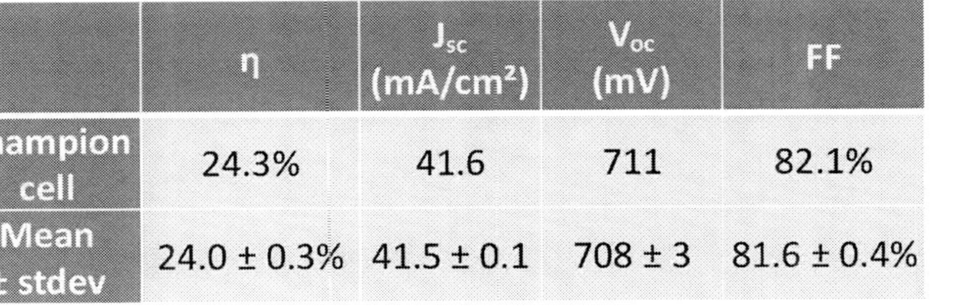
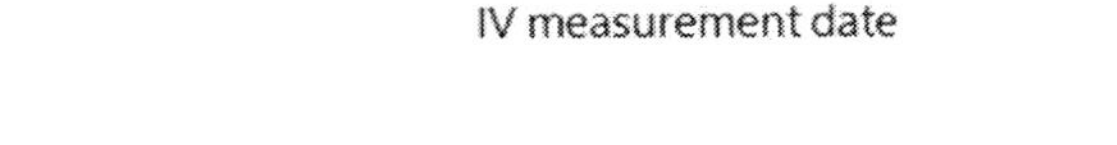

polyZEBRA

	η	J_{sc} (mA/cm²)	V_{oc} (mV)	FF
Champion cell	24.3%	41.6	711	82.1%
Mean ± stdev	24.0 ± 0.3%	41.5 ± 0.1	708 ± 3	81.6 ± 0.4%

- Best polyZEBRA cell batch so far (with Cu BB)
- +0.2% compared to previous reported data
- Main gain in pFF (thus FF) from real **passivating contacts** and **PE-ALD AlO$_x$**

More details: 1CV.2

020225-016

Solar Cells

polyZEBRA

- BC has more freedom for metallization
- Cu to replace most of the silver
- Screen printing based
- No HT sintering
- Less than 4 mg/Wp have been demonstrated on ZEBRA

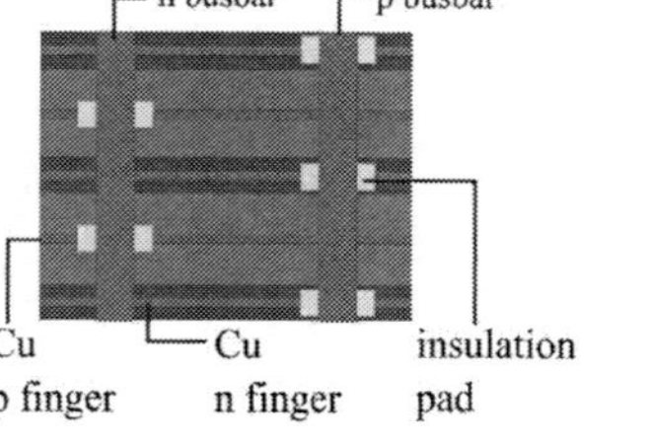

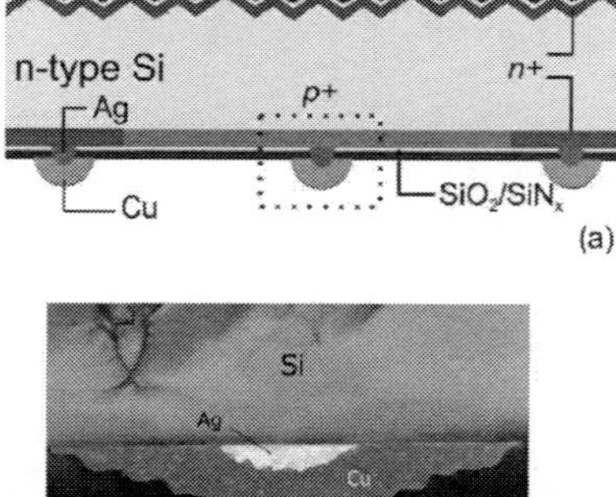

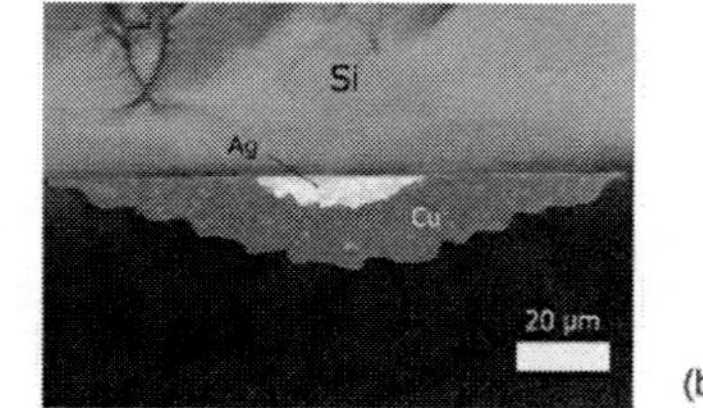

More details 1.AO.5.4

DE10 2022 118 063, pending

Ning, et al. SILICONPV 2022, Vol. 2826. No. 1. AIP Publishing LLC, 2023.
Rudolph et al. *Solar Energy Materials and Solar Cells* 264 (2024): 112603;
Rudolph et al. AIP Conference Proceedings. Vol. 2709. No. 1. AIP Publishing LLC, 2022

020225-017

Solar Cells

ISC's BC technology

- **10 2010 024 834** granted
- **10 2012 207 764** granted
- **3 104 397** granted
- **3 982 421** pending
- **4 092 760** pending
- **4 195 299** pending
- **10 2022 118 063** pending
- **25 169 642.3** pending

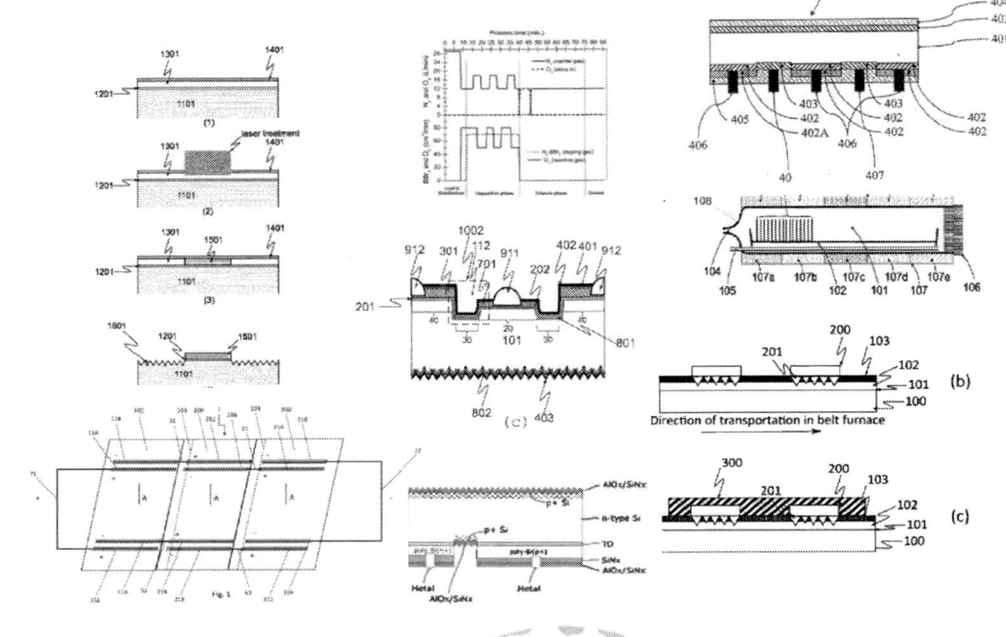

IBC4 EU

Modules

Interconnection of IBC cells

ENERGYRA®
TNO innovation for life

Conductive backsheet

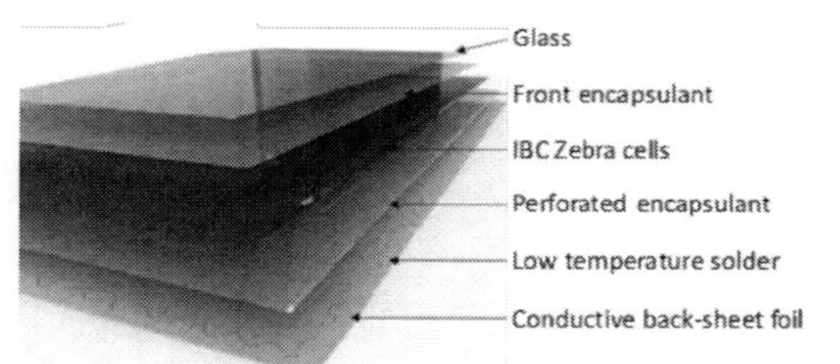

Stringing interconnection

3D Multi-Ribbon[1]

[1] R. Van Dyck et al, Prog Photovolt Res Appl 2021; 29: p.507

020225-019

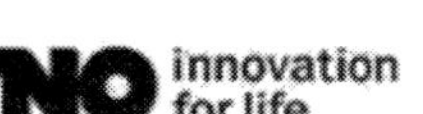

Modules

Light transmitting conductive substrate (LTCS):

- Interconnection of ZEBRA cells
- Interconnection tracks integrated to the rear-side glass
- Cells-to-LTCS electrical contact via conductive adhesive
- Module assembly based on a "pick & place" process

Front-side (left) and rear-side (right) of TNO's bifacial module
(132 ½-cut IBC cells)

TNO's pick and place robot assembling a bifacial module

020225-020

Modules

Light transmitting conductive substrate (LTCS):

> High performance of this prototype module demonstrates the potential of the LTCS interconnection technology
>> P_{max} > 410Wp (132 M6 half cells)
>> Bi-faciality   = 76.5%
>> CtM FF loss   ≈ 2%abs (estimation)

> Performance estimation with front glass:
>> P_{max} ≈ 388Wp
>> Bi-faciality   ≈ 81.2%

> TC already demonstrated on 400x400mm modules

020225-021

Modules

Module based on Cu-metallized cells

Full Size Module (120 M6 half cells)

- Standard soldering (Tabber), glass-glass
- Similar power as silver reference module
  Slightly lower FF
- Bifaciality lower because of thicker fingers

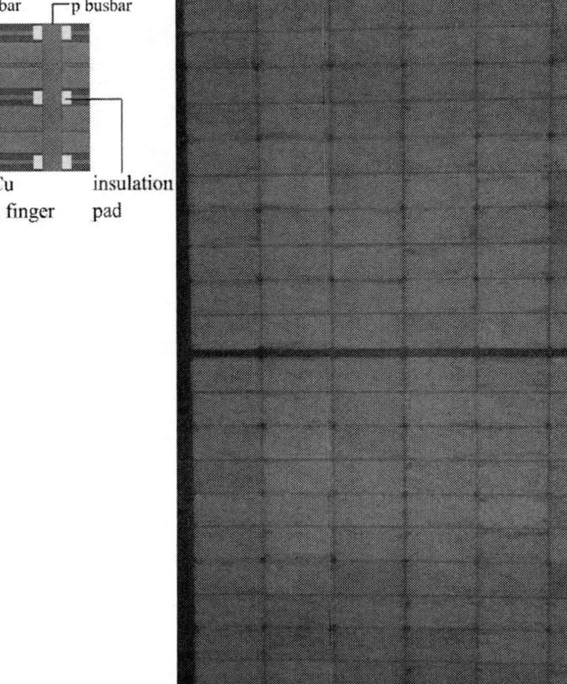

	Isc [A]	Uoc [V]	FF [%]	Pmpp[W]
Ref_Ag_front	11.17	41.44	79.73	**369.24**
Cu-Zebra_front	11.11	41.54	79.31	**365.94**

See ISC Konstanz booth in this exhibition

020225-022

Modules

Gapless technology

- Tabbing and stringing based
- Cell to cell overlap common practice

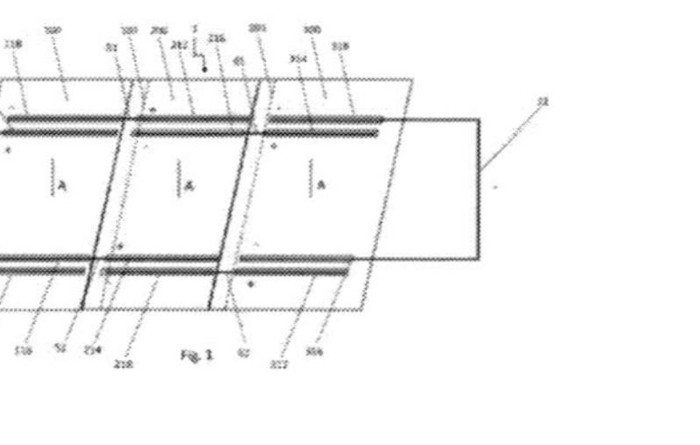

EP 4 092 760, pending

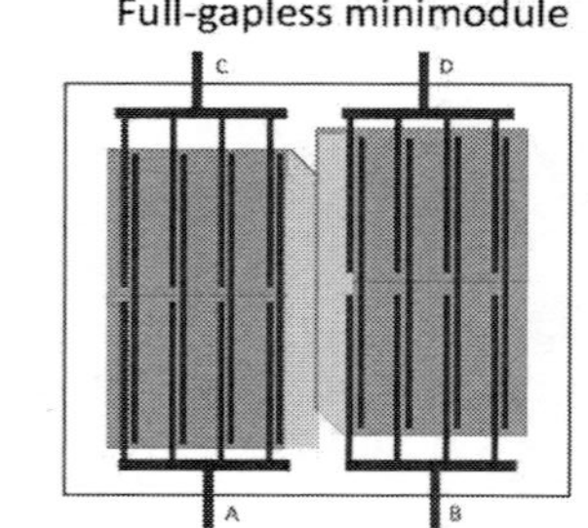

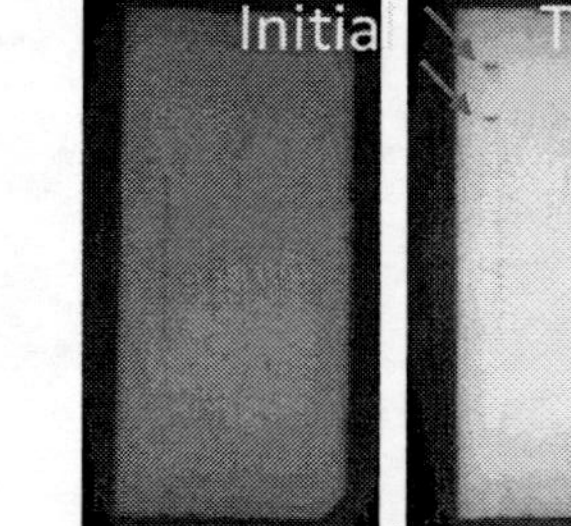

020225-023

Modules

Gapless technology

- Tabbing and stringing based

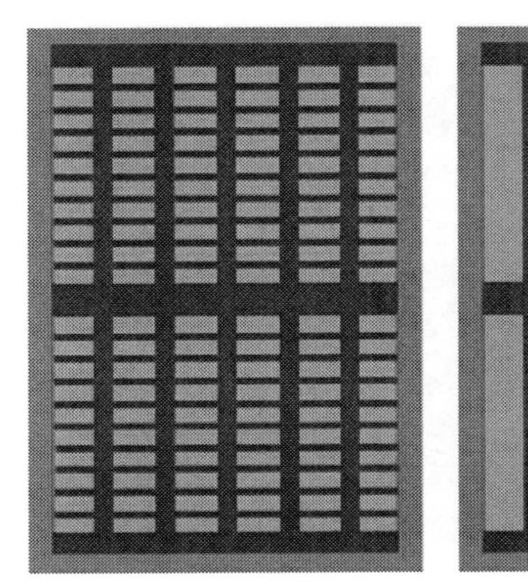
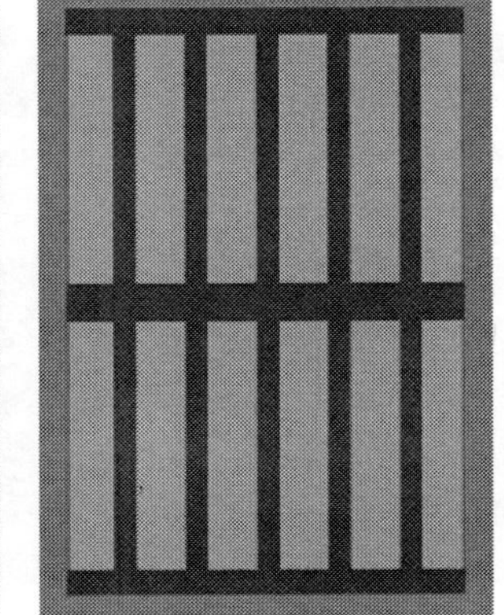

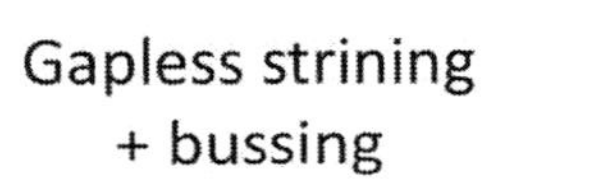
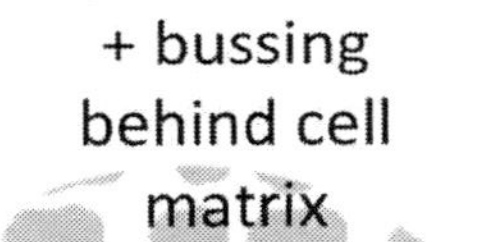
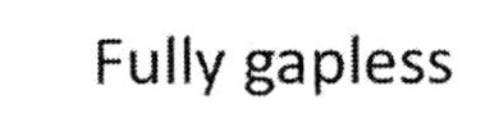

020225-024

IBC4 EU

Modules

gapless stringing

Overlap of ~0.7 mm leads to cell shading

gapless string layup

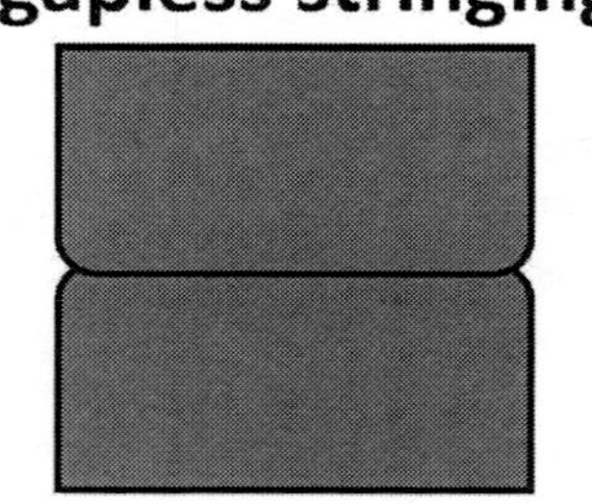

Overlap of ~1 mm leads to cell shading

More details: 3CO.11.2

	Area reduction (%)*	Shading fraction (%)*
Butterfly gap and bussings	2.1	
Cell gaps (for 0.7 mm overlap)	1.6	0.7
String gaps (for 1 mm overlap)	1.3	0.9

» net efficiency increase for M10 HC, 54 cell module 3.5 % rel.

020225-025

Recycling

ZEBRA Mini module from TNO:

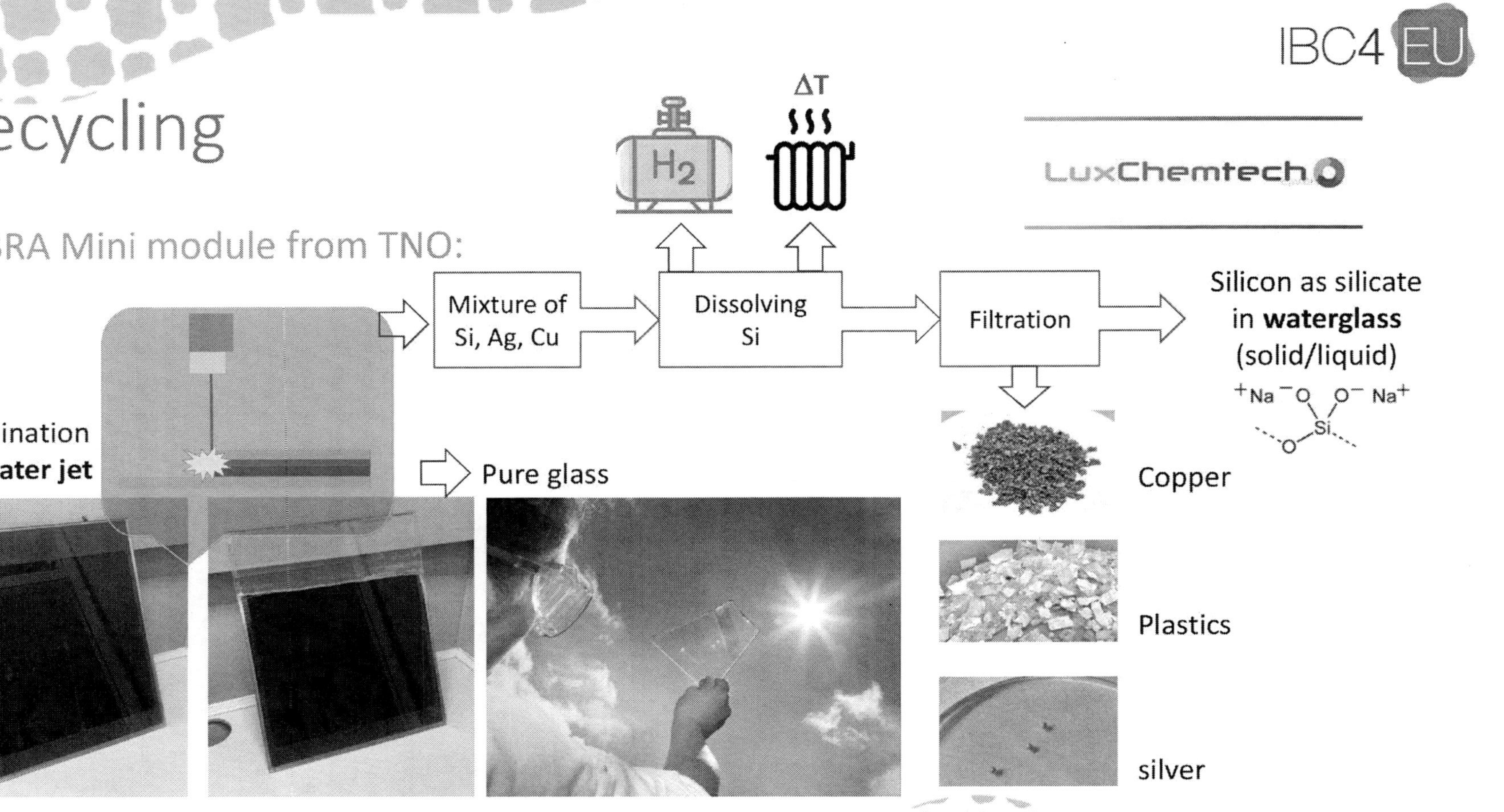

020225-026

IBC4EU technology

- Close to state of the art TOPCon / PERC
- Low breakdown voltage
- Strong family of patents and applications
- Potential >25% efficiency
- Full gap-less module
- Cu Ready
- Multiple promising approaches for module interconnection

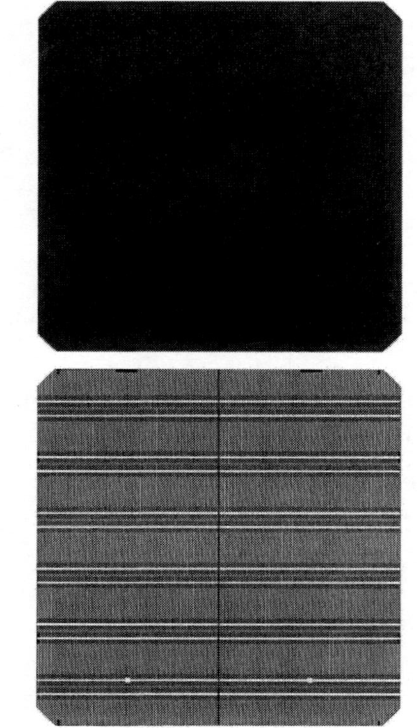

020225-027

Why European Back Contact?

- IP → multiple ways of making it, no general blocking patents (c.f. TOPCon)
- Innovation driven, slightly more complex
- IBC4EU approach: low cost, low silver, EU-owned
- De-risking the EU's energy supply
- Potential for an EU / non-Chinese supply chain
- Long-term suply of stable form factors
- Allow for highest quality and service

From niche to mainstream?

see last talk of this session (**CP.1.4**) and IBC4EU side event (**PV Made in the EU: How Do Companies Die and How Can They Thrive**)!

020225-028

IBC4 EU

Thank you!

Dr. Florian Bucholz, ISC Konstanz

florian.buchholz@isc-konstanz.de

https://x.com/Ibc4EU

https://www.linkedin.com/showcase/ibc4eu/
https://www.linkedin.com/in/dr-florian-buchholz-90789675/

This project has received funding from the European Union's Horizon Europe research and innovation programme under grant agreement No.101084259

Visit ISC Konstanz!  21st -24th October, 2025

Events in Konstanz (details: www.isc-konstanz.de)

- IBC4EU/EMPOWER workshop 21st /22nd October
- M&M (Module and Material) workshop 23rd /24th October
- 20 years of ISC Konstanz – party! 23rd October evening from 7pm
- Energy worlds 24th October, afternoon

24.09.2025

020225-030

Outdoor Performance and Reliability of Perovskite (Pk)-Silicon (Si) Tandems:

>1 year of Monitoring in the NEXUS Project

Atse Louwen[1,2], Jordi Veirman[1], Alexander Astigarraga[1], Juan Josè Stivanello[1], David Moser[1,3], Perrine Carroy[4], Vincent Barth[4], Delfina Muñoz[4], Markus Lenz[5] Anika Sidler[5], Jorge Ferrando[6], Maximiliano Alejandro Senno[6], Henk Bolink[6], Talat Özden[7], Hisham Nasser[7], Shuaifeng Hu[8], Xinyi Shen[8], Henry Snaith[8]

[1]Eurac Research, Bolzano, Italy

[2]RISE Research Institutes of Sweden

[3]Becquerel Institute Italia

[4]CEA INES, Le Bourget-du-Lac, France

[5]Fachhochschule Nordwestschweiz, Basel, Switzerland

[6]Universitat de València, Valencia, Spain

[7]ÖDTU-GÜNAM, Ankara, Türkiye

[8]University of Oxford, Oxford, United Kingdom

EU-PVSEC – Bilbao - 2025

Background

NEXUS is a HE project that started Nov. 2022

- Developing **solvent-free (fully evaporated), sustainable** Pk-Si tandems: **In-free, low Ag**
- High efficiency devices: >33% cells, >30% modules

In NEXUS, we also test the
outdoor performance + reliability:

- Testing outdoor in 4 locations
- Collecting rainwater runoff to test for any Pb leaching

Eurac Research have been testing different Pk-Si samples outdoor since late July 2024.

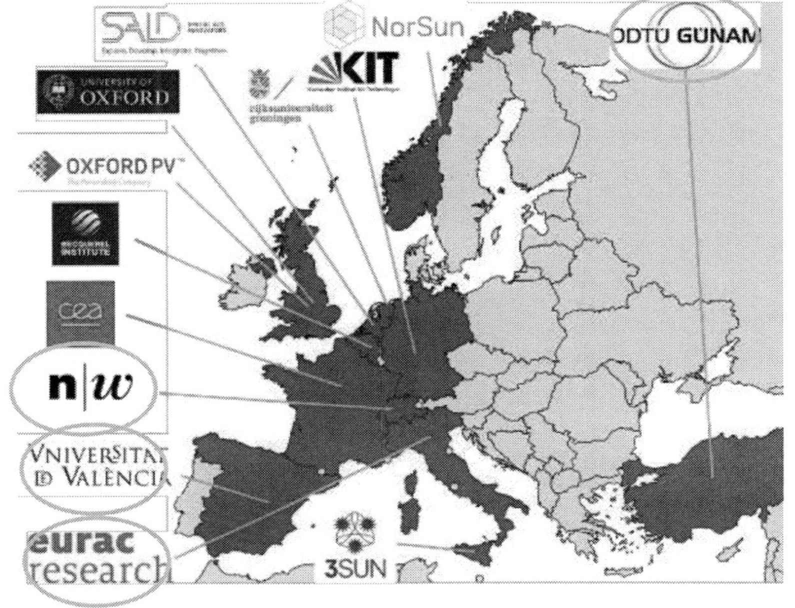

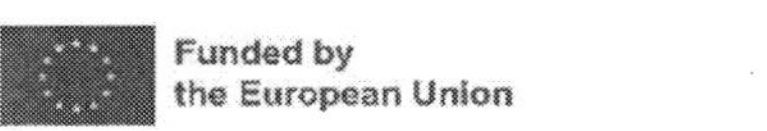
Funded by
the European Union

25/09/2025   2

020226-002

Why outdoor monitoring?

- **Field-relevant** data (all stressors!)
- Precious **feedback for cell/ module** improvements
- Basis for **Degradation Rate, Energy Yield** (kWh/kWp) and **LCOE** (€/kWh) calculations
  - → **Bankability** assessment
- Supports **standardisation**

More outdoor data are needed for Perovskite (Pk)-Si tandems

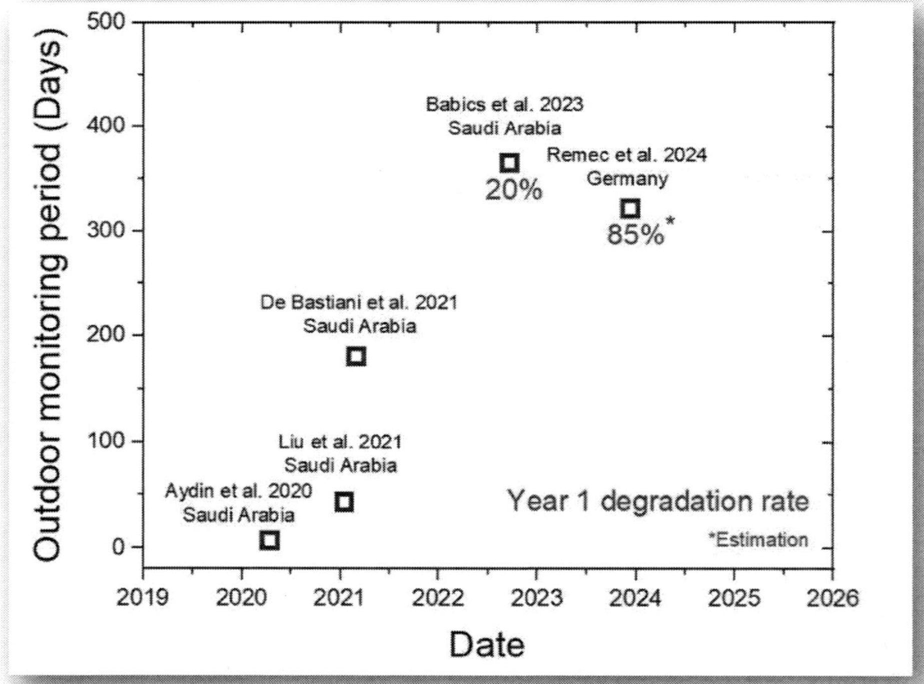

Funded by the European Union

020226-003

Measurement setup @ Eurac

- Electrical data measured with µMPPT setup for low current/power levels
  - V_{mp}, I_{mp}, P_{mp}

- Complemented with measurements:

  - <u>Operating conditions</u>: irradiance components, temperature, etc.

  - <u>Rainwater runoff</u>: measured, filtered, refrigerated for analysis to assess presence of **Pb**

n|w Fachhochschule Nordwestschweiz

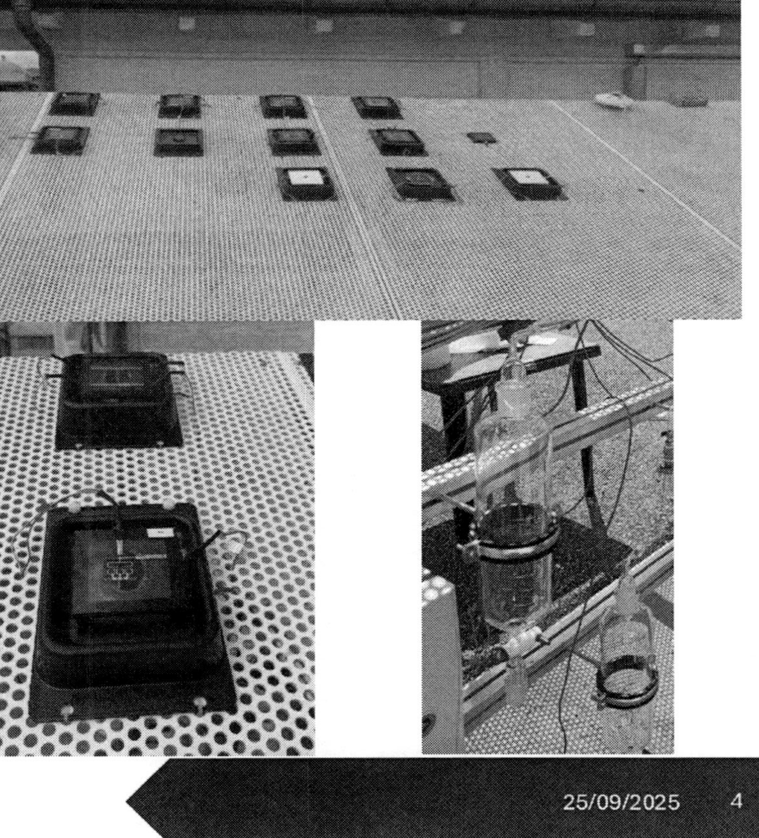

Funded by the European Union

25/09/2025   4

020226-004

Samples

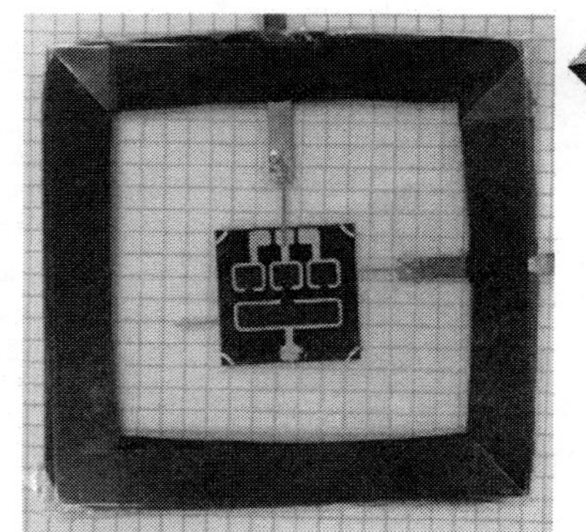

- 9 Pk-Si samples with HJT bottom cell + HJT cell as Reference
- Two types of bottom cells:
  - Polished wafers
  - (nano)-textured wafers
- Different perovskite deposition approaches
  - 4 Hybrid process (solution-based + evaporation)
  - 5 Fully evaporated
- Edge sealant used to avoid moisture ingress

- Labelling:

  Batch# +

Pk Deposition	Wafer surface state
H = Hybrid	P=Polished
E= Evaporated	(n)T=(nano)Textured

Main module BOM	
Front cover	100 x 100 x 3mm glass
Encapsulant	TPO
Rear cover	100 x 100 x 3mm glass
Edge sealant	PIB 10mm x 650µm
ECA	Acrylate
Ribbons	800 x 200µm

Funded by the European Union

25/09/2025 5

020226-005

Results – Performance Ratio (PR) over 13 months

- Benchmark is "stable"

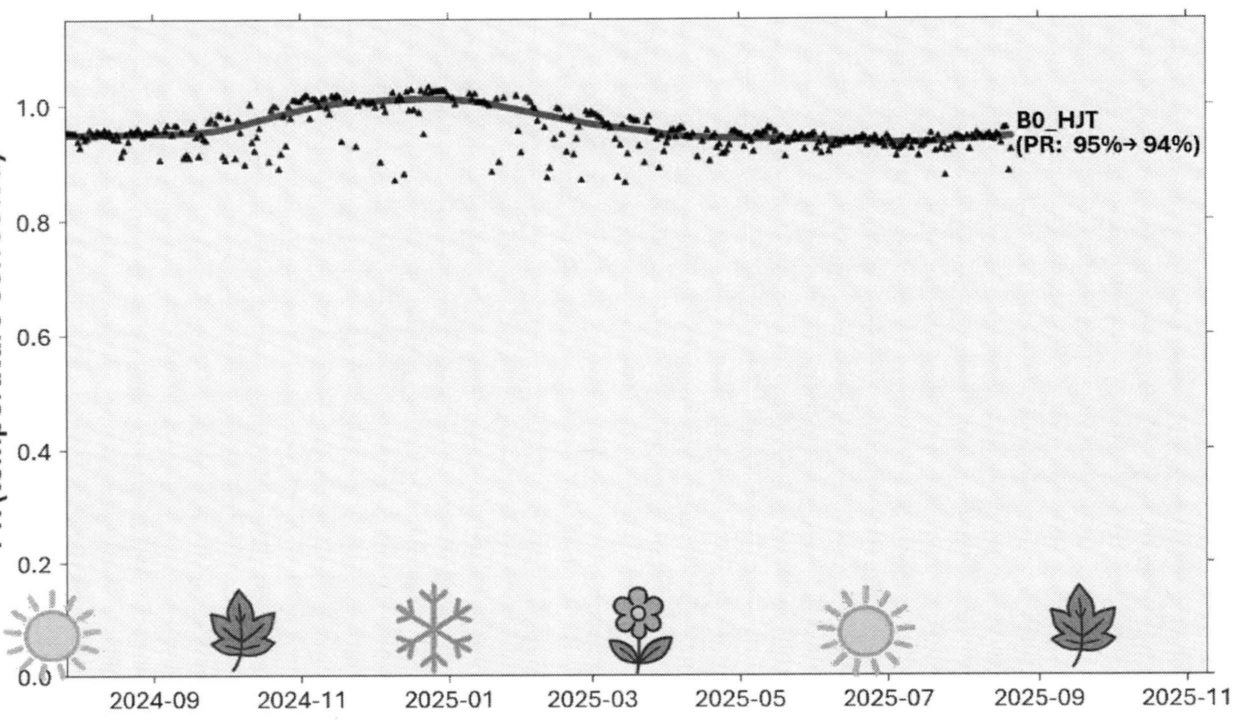

Performance Ratio (PR):
Delivered energy / what the
module should deliver

(given irradiance and Pmax)

Funded by
the European Union

25/09/2025

6

020226-006

Results – Performance Ratio (PR) over 13 months

- Benchmark is "stable"
- **Hybrid** samples: seasonal fluctuations + degradation

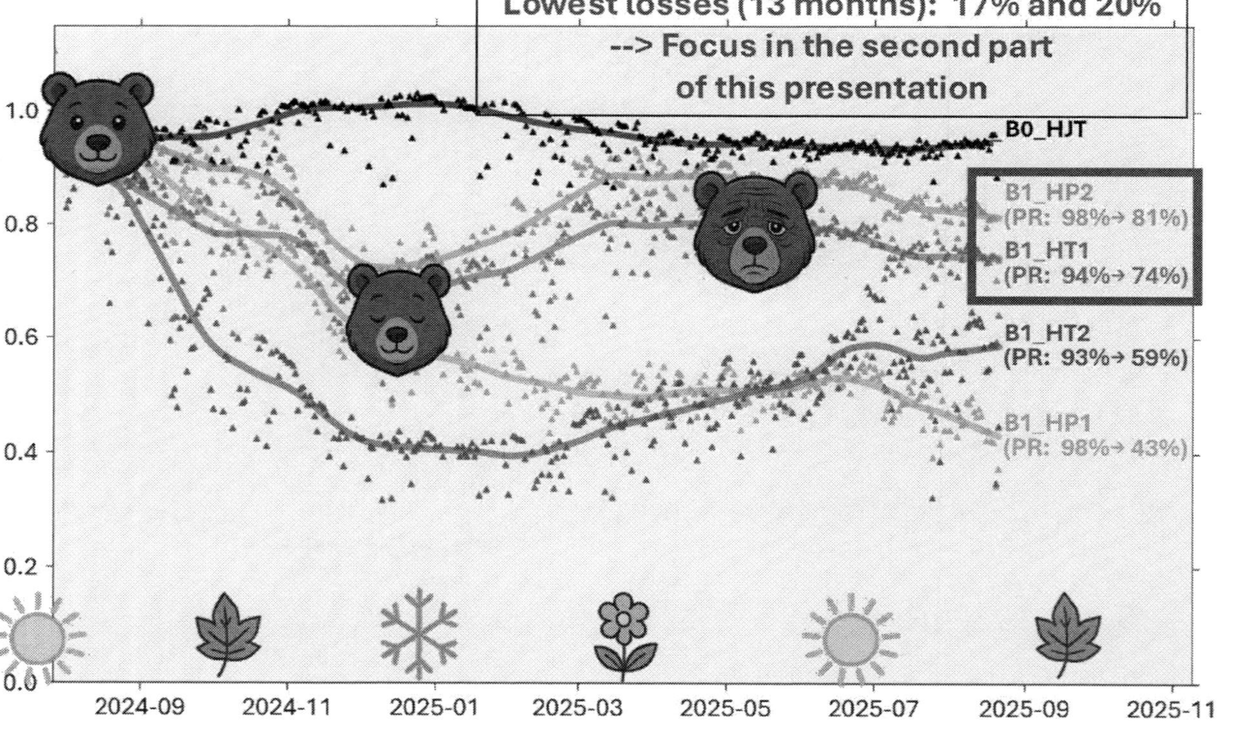

Funded by the European Union

25/09/2025   7

Results – Performance Ratio (PR) over 13 months

- Benchmark is "stable"
- Hybrid samples: seasonal fluctuations + degradation
- **Evaporated** samples: mixed behaviours

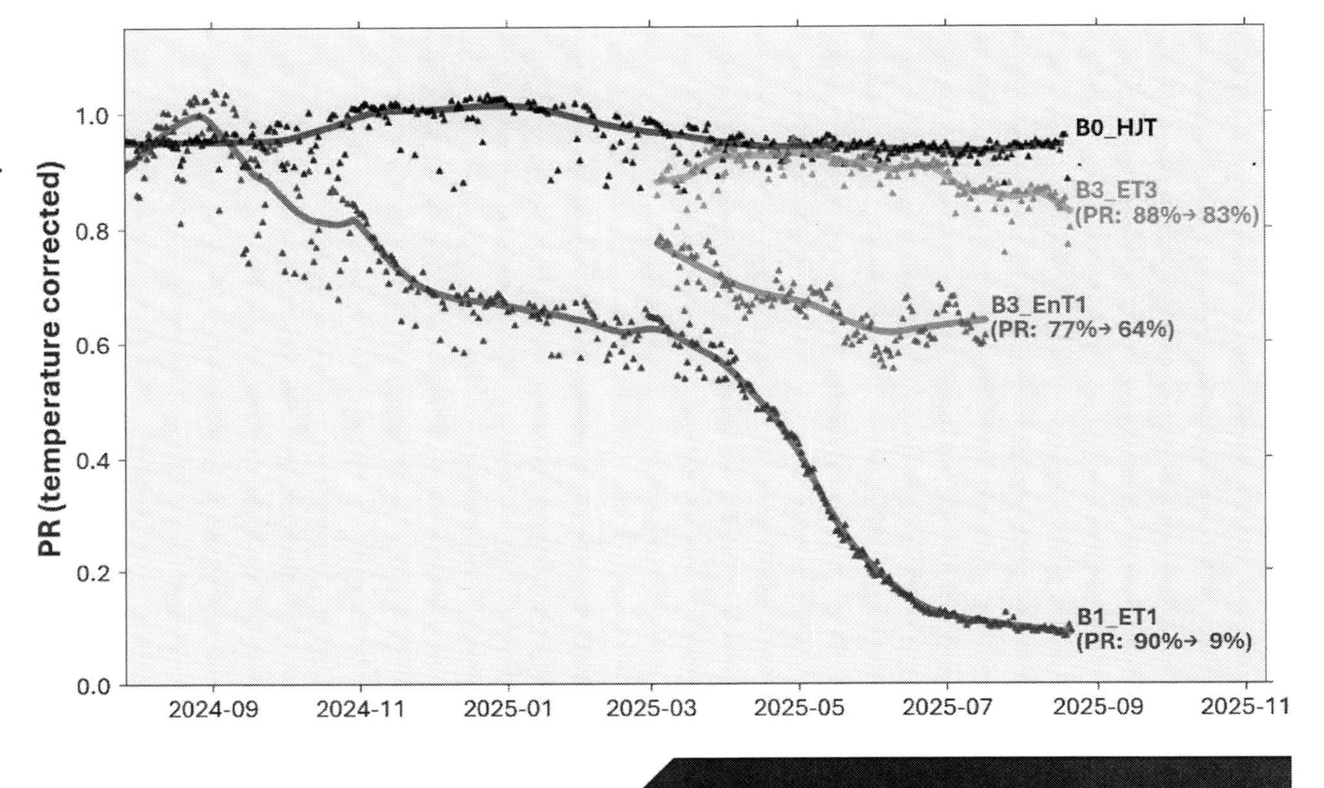

Funded by the European Union

020226-008

Results – Performance Ratio (PR) over 13 months

- Benchmark is "stable"
- Hybrid samples: seasonal fluctuations + degradation
- Evaporated samples: mixed behaviour
- Some samples **failed** due to various reasons

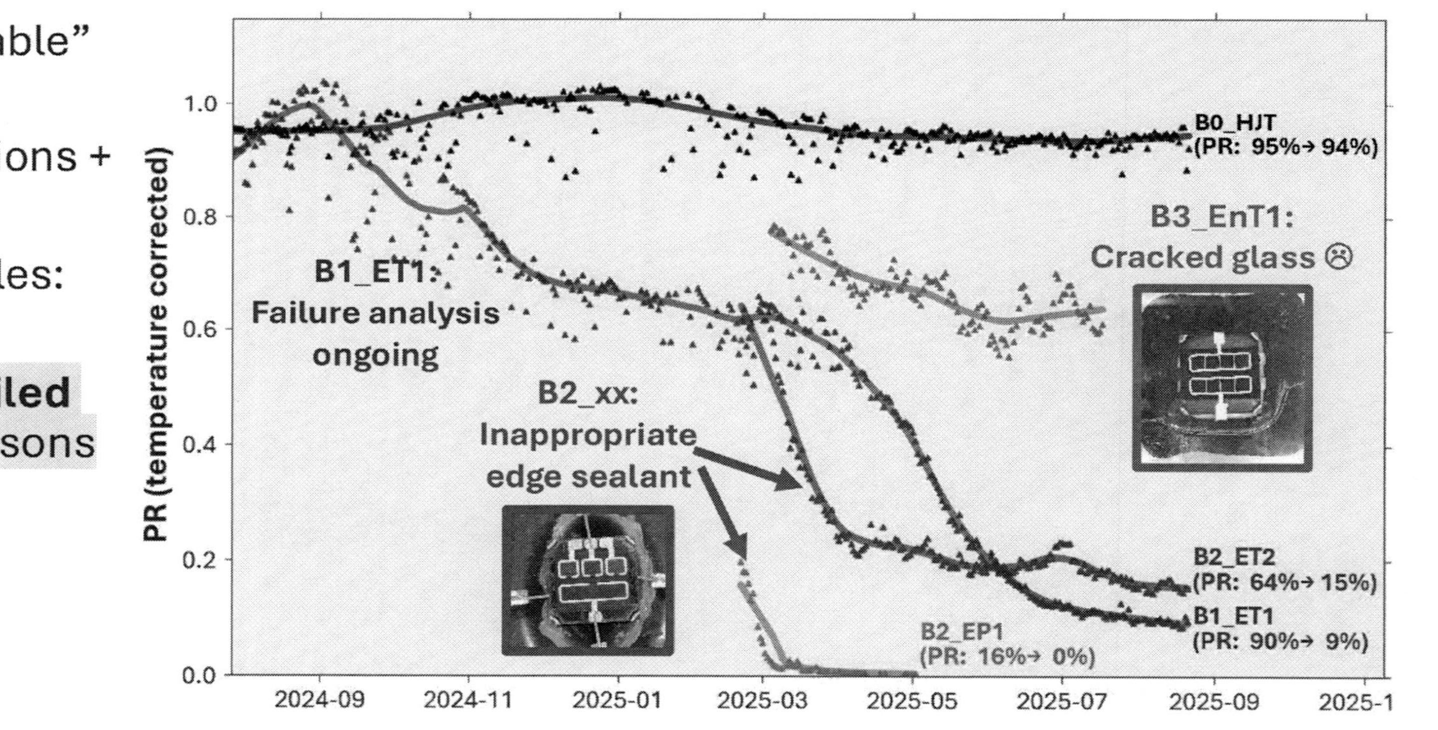

Funded by the European Union

020226-009

Results – first *PR* correlation with irradiance

- Benchmark is "stable"
- Hybrid samples: seasonal fluctuations + degradation
- Evaporated samples: mixed behaviour
- Some samples failed due to various reasons
- Most samples show low *PR* during low *irradiance* days

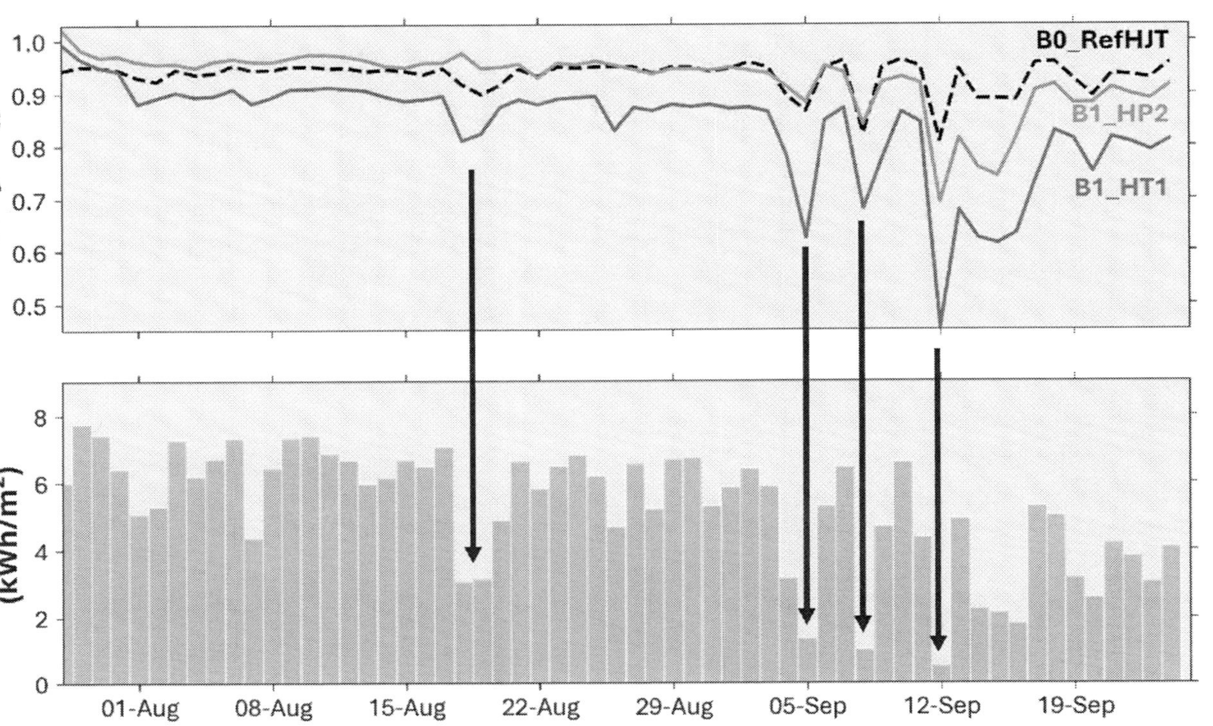

GPOA= Global Plane Of Array irradiance

Funded by the European Union

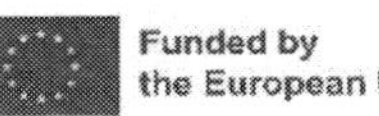

25/09/2025   10

020226-010

Results – *PR* correlation with irradiance

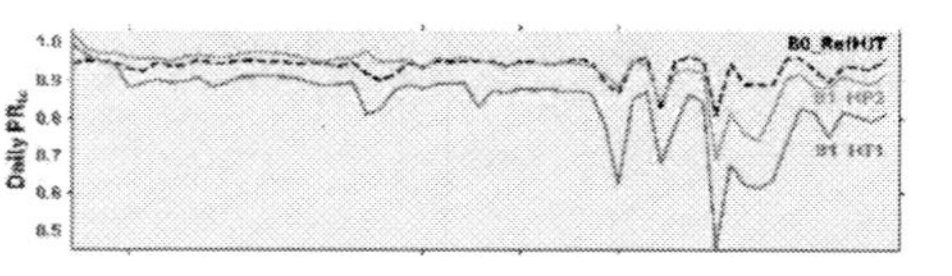

- Drop in **PR** in low irradiance days confirmed throughout the monitoring period

- Long-term aging: magnitude of daily PR variation decreases
(screened by background deg?)

Origin of the drop at low irradiance ???

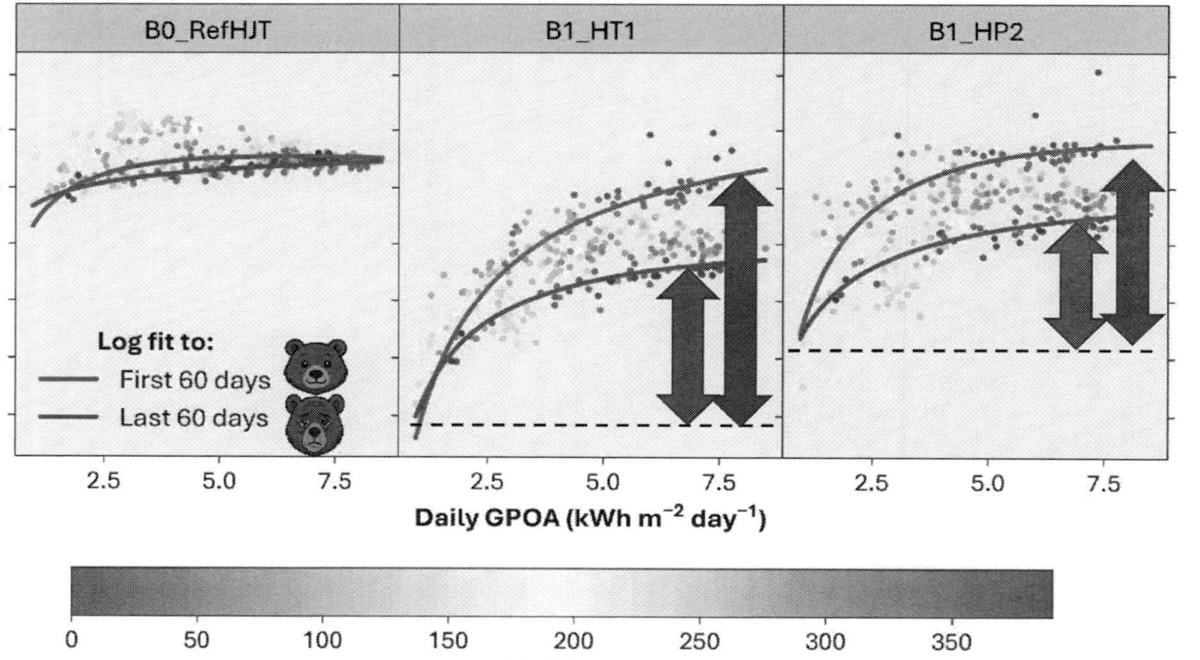

Funded by the European Union

GPOA= Global Plane Of Array irradiance

25/09/2025   11

020226-011

Results – Light soaking behaviour

- On <u>early-life</u> **sunny** days:
  - B1_HP2 on par with HJT once sun is out
  - B1_HT1 shows full recovery after some hours
- On <u>early-life</u> **cloudy** days
  - B1_HP2 now needs recovery
  - B1_HT1: fails to recover

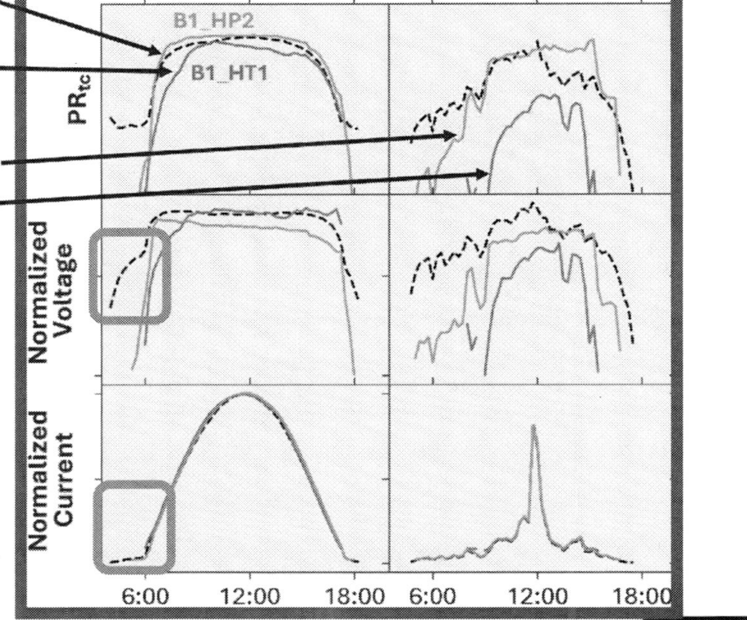

020226-012

Results – Light soaking behaviour

- On <u>early-life</u> **sunny** days:
  - B1_HP2 on par with HJT once sun is out
  - B1_HT1 shows full recovery after some hours
- On <u>early-life</u> **cloudy** days
  - B1_HP2 now needs recovery
  - B1_HT1: fails to recover
- On <u>late-life</u> **sunny** days
  - B1_HP2 needs now to recover
  - B1_HT1 similar but w/ degr.
- On <u>late-life</u> **cloudy** days
  - Both devices similar, but with degradation

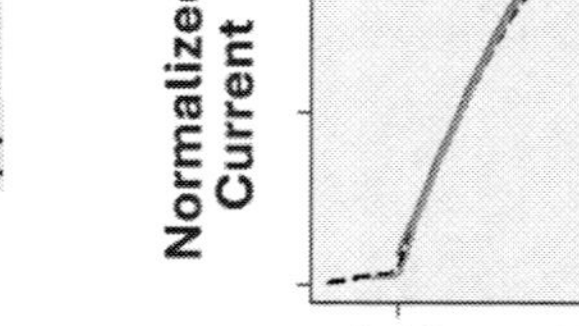

Funded by the European Union

25/09/2025   13

020226-013

Light-soaking effect (LSE)

- Metastability well-known at lab level

- LSE reported in most recent outdoor studies on SJ Pk [1-4], Pk-Si tandems [5-7]

- Also observed on Pk-CIGSe [8]

Effect not specific to NEXUS devices

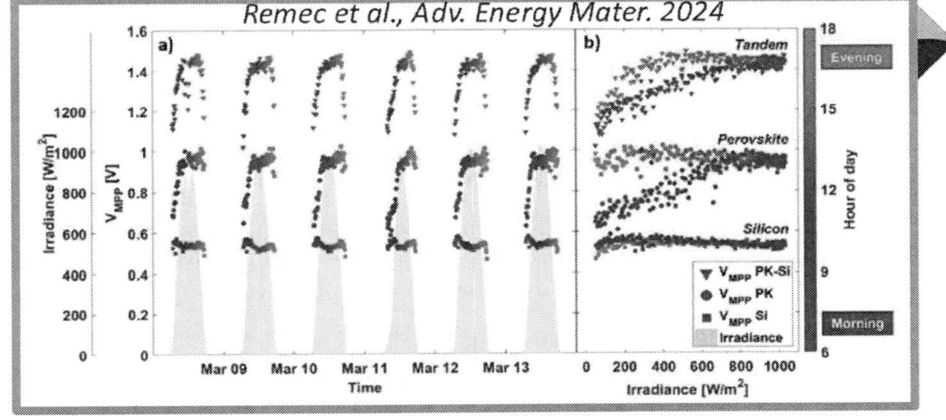

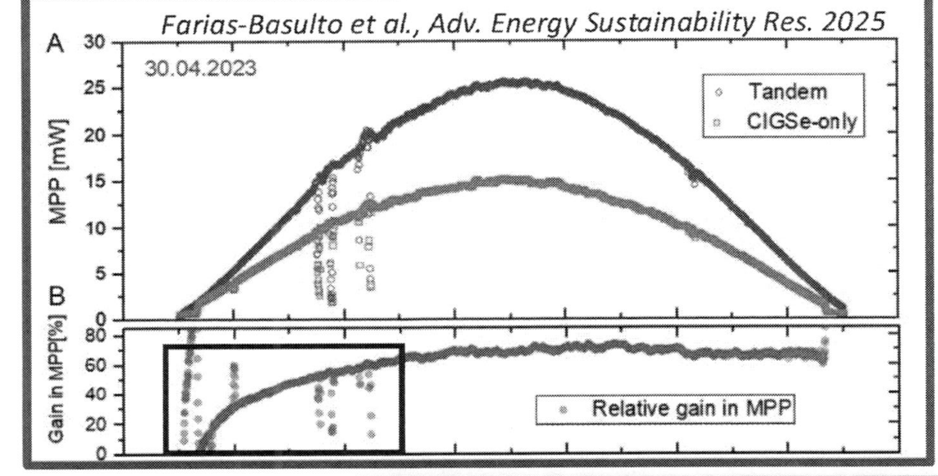

[1] Deceglie et al., IEEE JPV 15, **2025**
[2] Gupta et al., Adv. Energy Mater. **2025**
[3] Remec et al., Adv. Energy Mater. **2025**
[4] Bovesecchi et al, PIP, **2025**
[5] De Bastiani et al., ACS Energy Letters 6 (**2025**)
[6] Babics et al., Cell Reports Physical Science 4, **2023**, 101280
[7] Remec et al., Adv. Energy Mater. **2024**, 14, 2304452
[8] Farias-Basulto et al., Adv. Energy Sustainability Res. **2025**, 2500162

Funded by the European Union

020226-014

Light-soaking effect (LSE) vs "hard" degradation

- Rough estimate of the contribution to the energy loss:

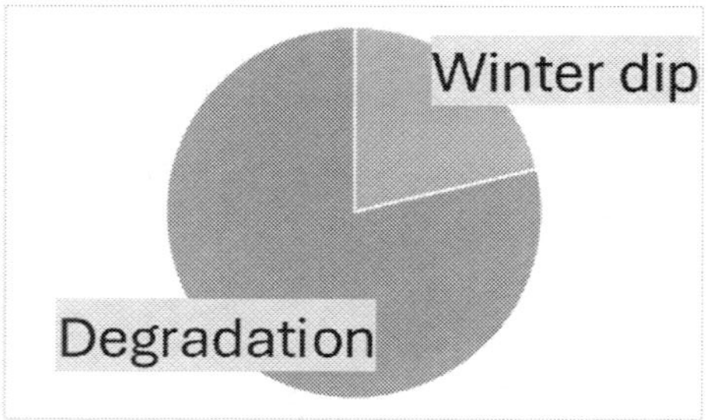

- Contribution of winter dip loss << "hard" non-reversible degradation!

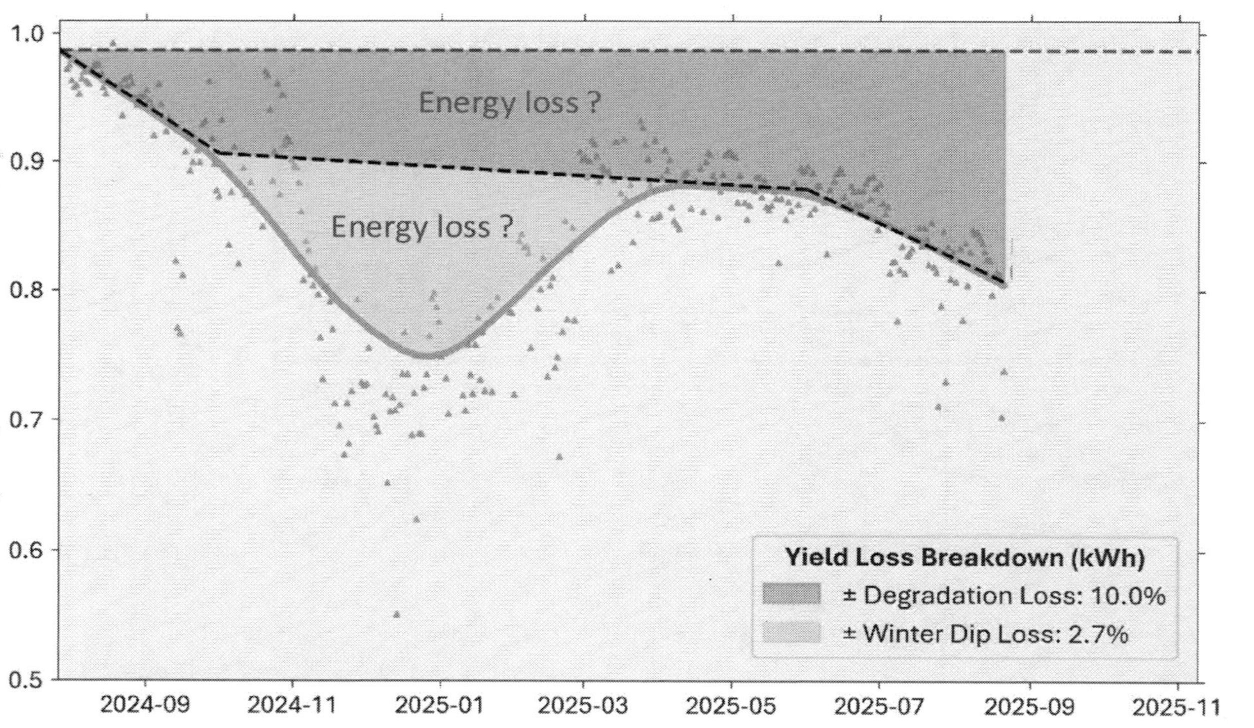

Funded by the European Union

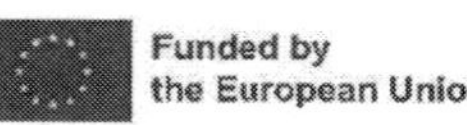

25/09/2025   15

020226-015

Conclusions and outlook

- ~13 months monitoring NEXUS Pk-Si tandem cells

- <u>For the tested devices, in Bolzano:</u>

  - Least unstable device: **14% Year-on-Year degradation**

    → Positive learning curve, but necessary improvements!

  - Clear **diurnal metastability**. **Device** & **climate**-dependent.

  - Contributes to **seasonality** effects with **lower PR in winter**

  - Main Energy Yield killer = **non-reversible losses** (metastability losses 2nd order)

- <u>Next</u>: Forensics for failure mode analysis, extend monitoring period
(GEN3 samples promising !)

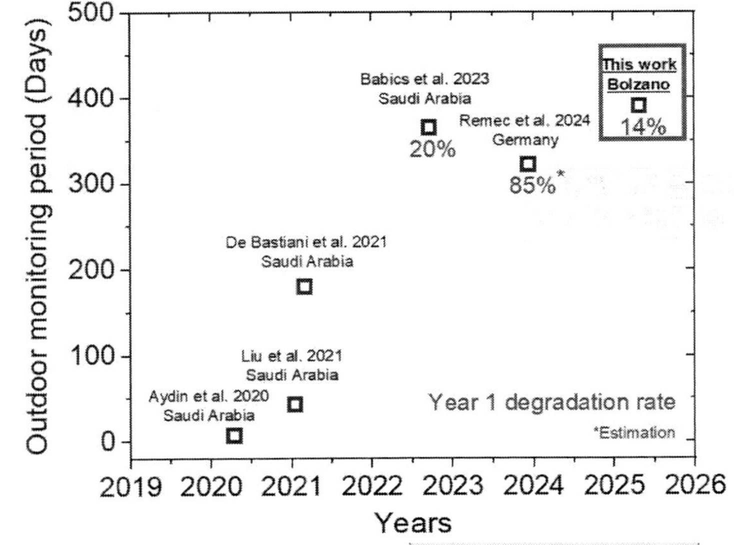

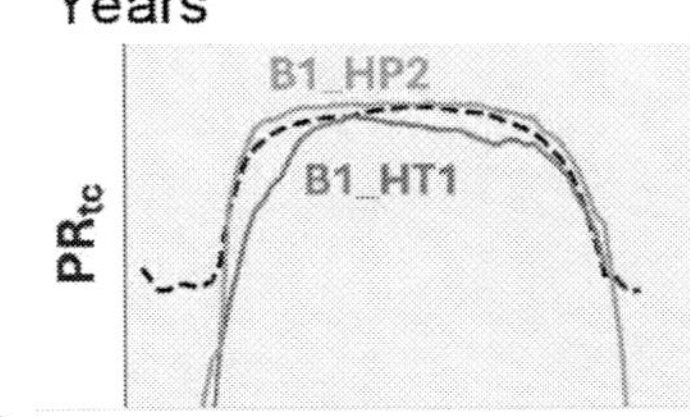
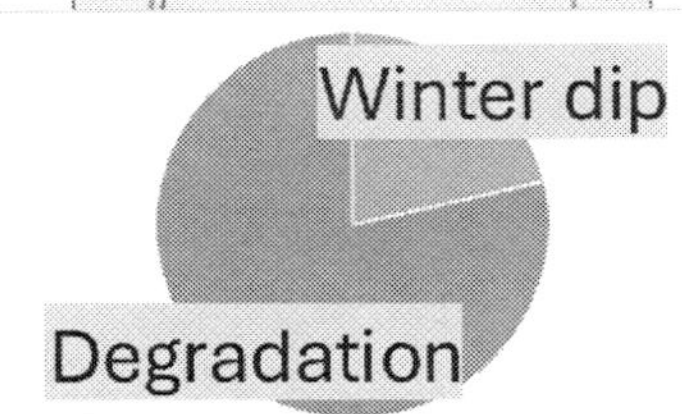

Funded by
the European Union

25/09/2025   16

020226-016

NEXUS

Thanks for your attention!

Project coordinator
Perrine Carroy
CEA
Perrine.CARROY@cea.fr

Project Partner
Jordi Veirman
Eurac Research
Jordi.Veirman@eurac.edu

Technical questions --> atse.louwen@ri.se

Funded by the European Union. Views and opinions expressed are however those of the author(s) only and do not necessarily reflect those of the European Union or RIA. Neither the European Union nor the granting authority can be held responsible for them.

NEXUS project has received funding from the European Union's Horizon Europe research and innovation program under grant agreement No. 101075330.

Project Partners

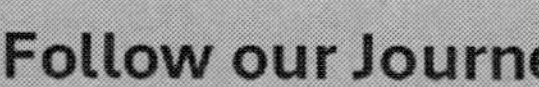

Funded by
the European Union

Follow our Journey!

EU PVSEC
22 — 26
September
BEC
Bilbao Exhibition Centre
Bilbao
Spain
EU
PVSEC
2025
42nd European
Photovoltaic Solar Energy
Conference and Exhibition
030001-001

Conference Highlights

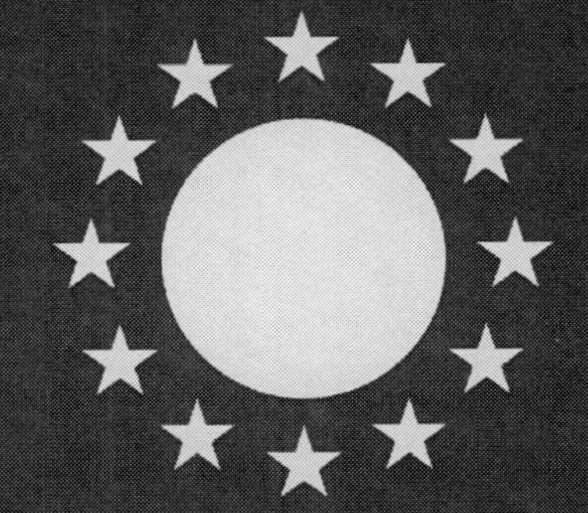

Robert Kenny
European Commission Joint Research Centre
EU PVSEC Technical Programme Chair

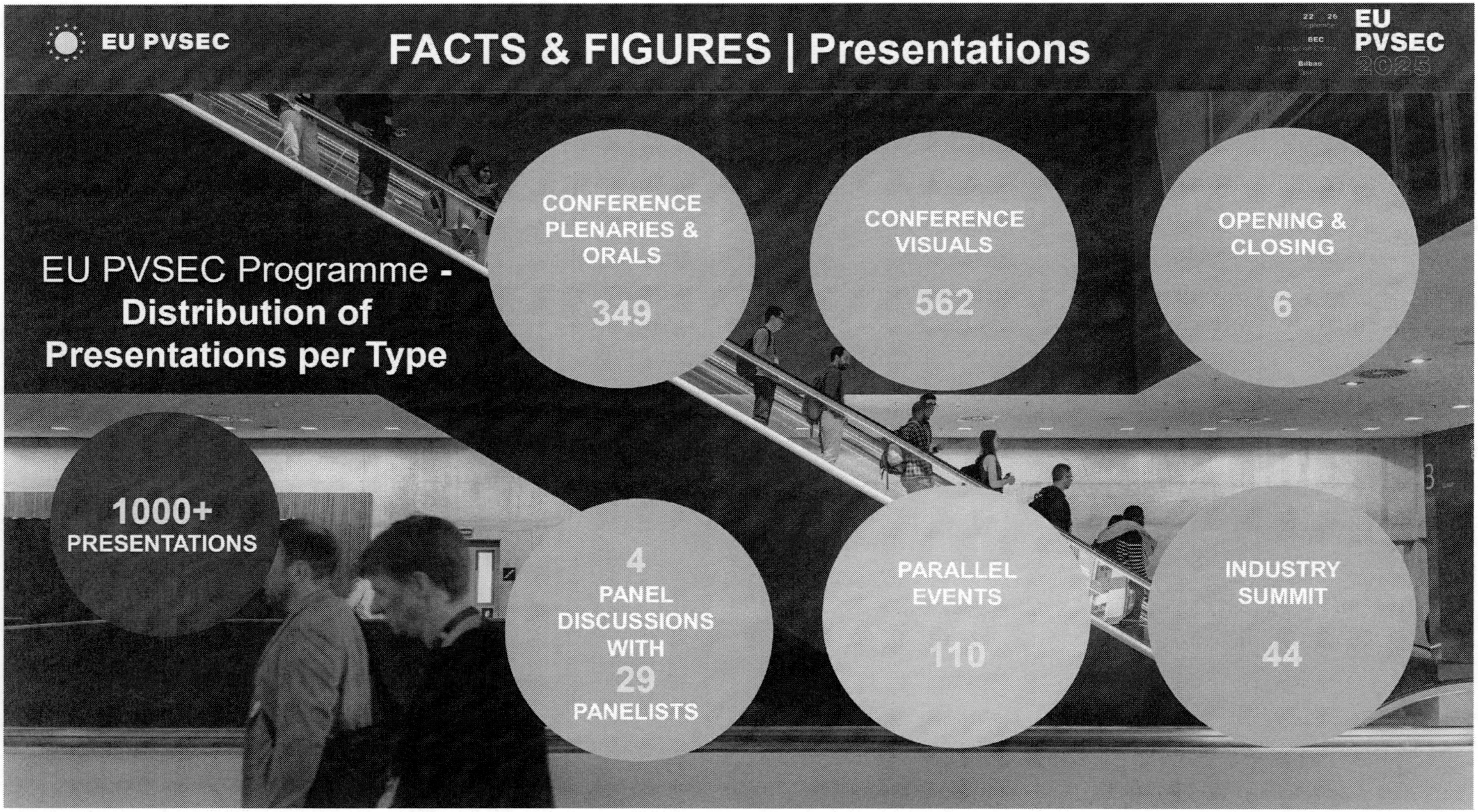

EU PVSEC
FACTS & FIGURES | Presentations
EU PVSEC
2025
EU PVSEC Programme -
Distribution of
Presentations per Type
CONFERENCE PLENARIES & ORALS
349
CONFERENCE VISUALS
562
OPENING & CLOSING
6
1000+
PRESENTATIONS
4
PANEL DISCUSSIONS WITH
29
PANELISTS
PARALLEL EVENTS
110
INDUSTRY SUMMIT
44
030001-004

EU PVSEC
FACTS & FIGURES | Presentations
EU PVSEC 2025
EU PVSEC Scientific Conference Programme - Distribution of Presentations per Topic
TOPIC 5:
Photovoltaics in the Energy Transition
18%
TOPIC 1:
Silicon Materials and Cells
12%
TOPIC 2:
Thin Films and New Concepts
20%
TOPIC 3:
Photovoltaic Modules
18%
TOPIC 4:
Photovoltaic Systems
32%

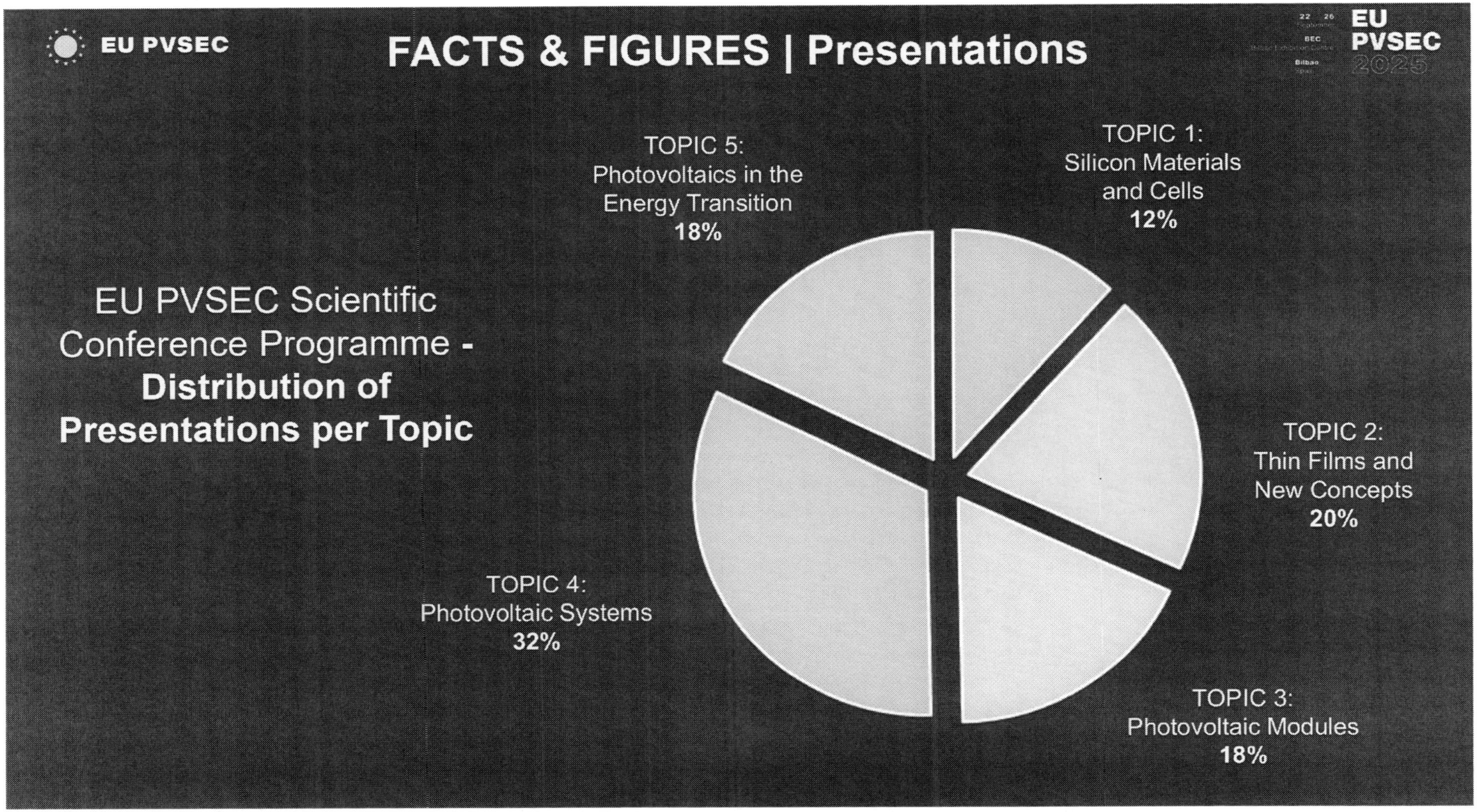

EU PVSEC

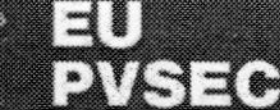

FACTS & FIGURES | Participants

EU PVSEC 2025

22 26 September

BEC

Bilbao Spain

Participants by Countries

Top 10

No	Country	Participants
1	Germany	310
2	Spain	270
3	France	108
4	Italy	90
5	The Netherlands	76
6	South Korea	67
7	Switzerland	62
8	Japan	55
9	Belgium	44
10	Norway	35

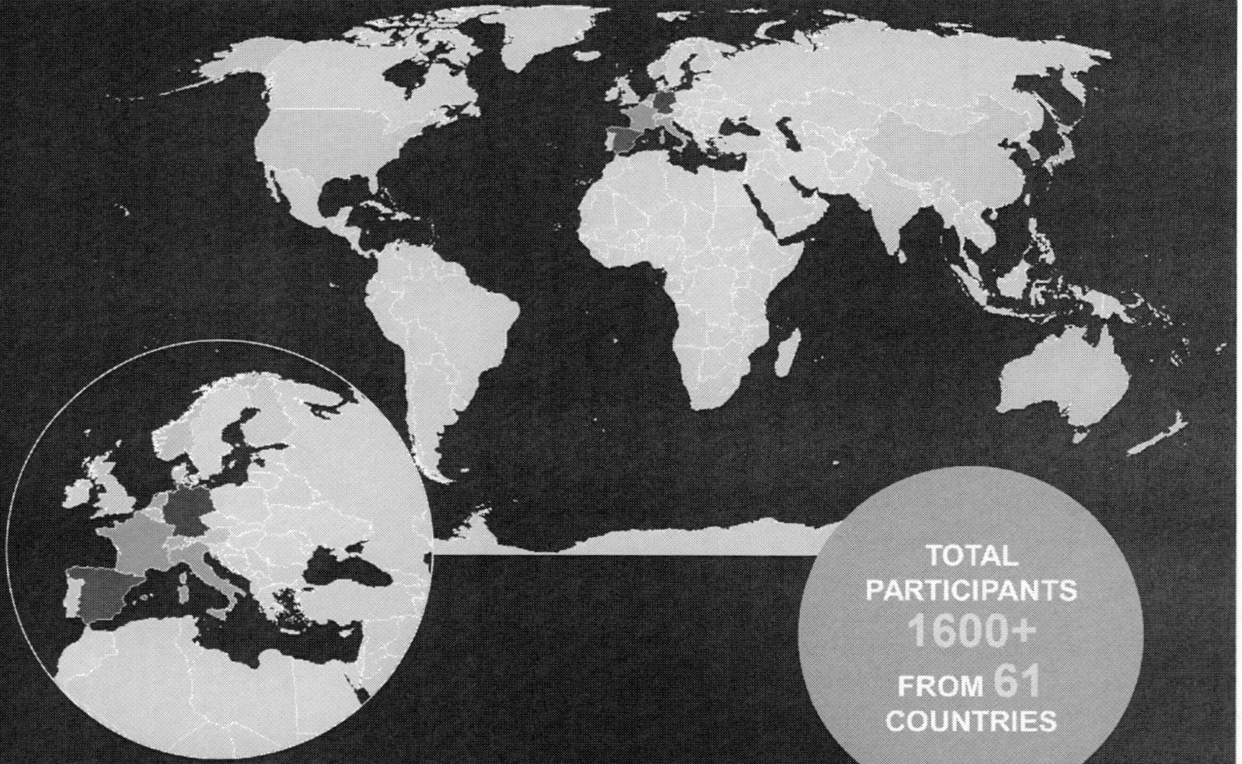

TOTAL PARTICIPANTS 1600+ FROM 61 COUNTRIES

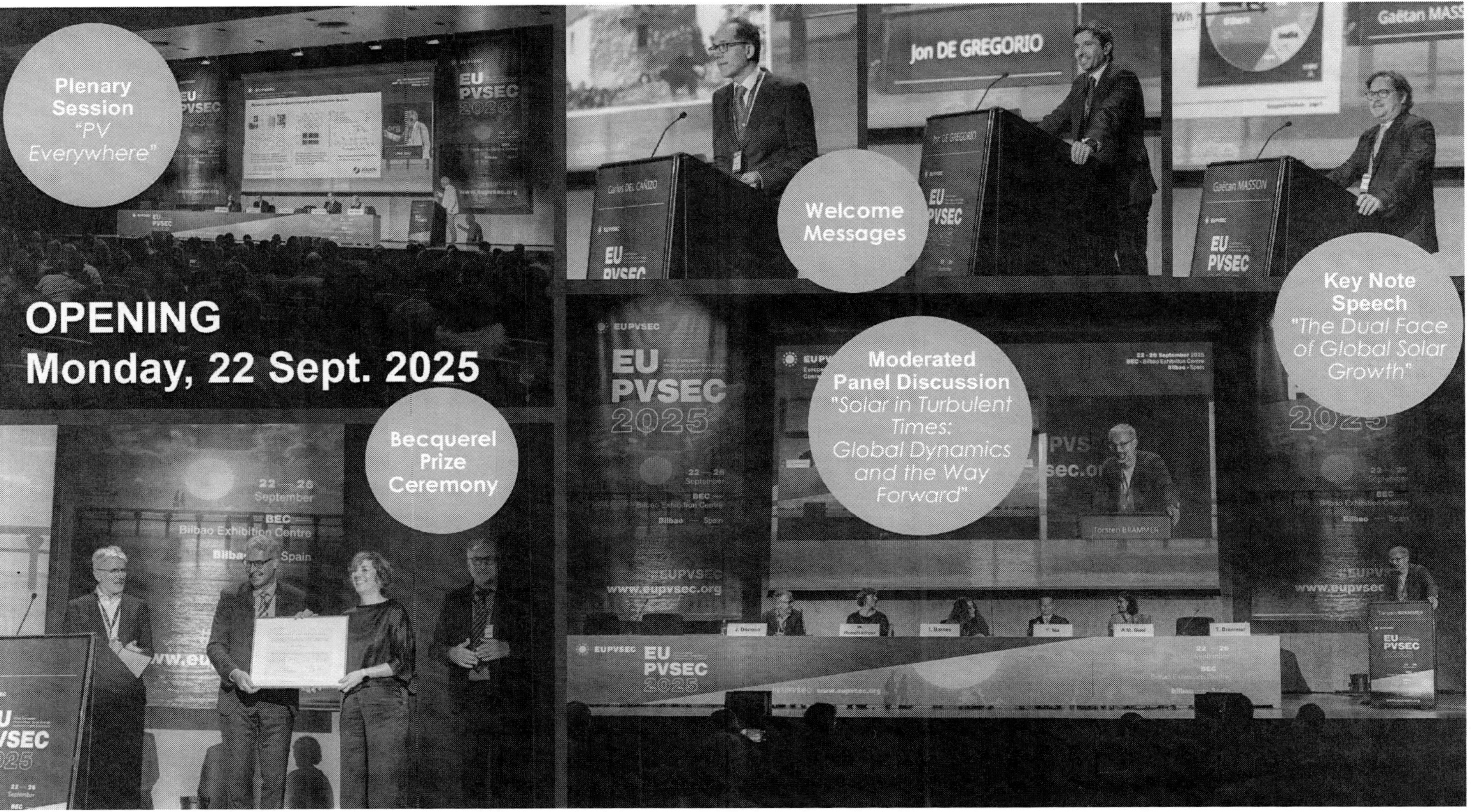

Plenary Session "PV Everywhere"
OPENING
Monday, 22 Sept. 2025
Becquerel Prize Ceremony
Welcome Messages
Moderated Panel Discussion "Solar in Turbulent Times: Global Dynamics and the Way Forward"
Key Note Speech "The Dual Face of Global Solar Growth"
Jon DE GREGORIO
Gaëtan MASSON
Carlos DEL CAÑIZO
Torsten BRAMMER

EU PVSEC
PANEL DISCUSSIONS
EU PVSEC 2025

BO.13 Reliability and Bankability in PV
"The rapid developments of PV technology require increased attention to be paid to reliability testing."

CO.7 Challenges and Opportunities of PV up to 2030
"PV Technology is already reliable and cost effective, and even though improvements are welcome, key blockages are storage and grid strengthening. AI and robotics are essential to meet the scale of developments needed."

DO.13 Scalability and Manufacturability Prospects in Europe for New Technologies
"The prospects for reaching the 30GW target for PV module manufacturing in Europe were discussed and policy measures proposed."

CONFERENCE

KEY MESSAGES

Cross-cutting themes emerged throughout the programme, showcasing how solar technologies can be applied everywhere, from traditional to emerging fields.

- Sustainability and circularity remain central, with research focused on reducing material use, such as replacing silver with copper, and advancing end-of-life management of modules.

- Ensuring long-term stability and predictable energy yield is equally essential, with studies of degradation mechanisms such as UVID carried out.

- The role of AI across the PV value chain is rapidly expanding, from design to operations and maintenance, including drone applications.

CONFERENCE

Enhancements in IV measurement procedures

- Michael Rauer, Fraunhofer ISE: 1AO.4.5 *Universal Contacting Approaches for the Characterization of Solar Cells*
- Shuai Nie, UNSW: 1AO.4.6 *Contact-Free J-V: a Simple Technique for Universal State-of-the-Art Solar Cells*

Replacement of critical by sustainable materials:

- Reduced Ag consumpion e.g. by replacing by Cu (plating)
- In-free SHJ solar cells and Pero-Si tandems

CONFERENCE

TOPIC 1: SILICON MATERIALS AND CELLS

Great advance in understanding of UV induced degradation and Hydrogen related degradation

- Excellent PLENARY by Bram Hoex (presenting for Muhammad Umair Khan), UNSW: 1CP.3.5 *Understanding the Root Cause of UV-Induced Degradation in TOPCon and PERC Solar Cells*

Further high quality orals:

- Christina Hollemann, ISFH: 1AO.4.2 *Mitigating UV-Induced Degradation: Impact of PECVD and PEALD AlOx Layers Deposited in a Tube-Type Direct Plasma-Enhanced Chemical Vapor Deposition System*
- Hugo Lajoie, CEA: 1AO.4.3 *New Insights on UV-Induced Degradation of SHJ Solar Cells*
- Byungsul Min, ISFH: 1BO.3.6 *UV Stable Passivation Stack with Plasma-Enhanced Atomic Layer Deposition of Aluminum Oxide from an Industrial Tube-Type Direct Plasma-Enhanced Chemical Vapor Deposition System*
- Wolfram Kwapil, Fraunhofer ISE: 1AO.5.6 *Impact of Illumination on Solar Cell Properties: Insights into Atomic Hydrogen Release*

EU PVSEC
22 26 December
SEC
Bilbao
EU PVSEC
2025

CONFERENCE

TOPIC 1:
SILICON
MATERIALS
AND CELLS

Advances in TOPCon and SHJ technology → Pushing the Limits of Performance

- Fantastic keynote lecture (PLENARY) on heterojunction solar cells by Dr. Guangtao Yang, Trina: 1CP.1.1 *Silicon Surface and Interface Study for >27% Efficient SHJ Solar Cell*
    - Deep insight into technological aspects eg. influence of rear side polishing on cell performance
    - Very high efficiencies for both-sides contacted HJT > 27%
    - Issues with CAPEX, sustainibility (Ag, In)
    - Pero-Si tandem cells on large area and modules

Late News Presentation on 27.8% efficient back contact silicon solar cells by Hua Wu, Longhi: 1DO.9.1 *Hybrid Interdigitated Back Contact Silicon Solar Cells with Superior Efficiency*

Late News Presentation as TOPCon for Bottom Solar Cells in Pero-Si Tandem devices by Jana Polzin-Isabelle Polzin, Fraunhofer ISE: 1DO.9.3 *Silicon Solar Cells – From High Efficiency Single-junction to Bottom Cells in Two-Terminal Perovskite-Silicon Tandem Devices*

EU PVSEC
EU PVSEC 2025

CONFERENCE

TOPIC 1:
SILICON
MATERIALS
AND CELLS

Further high quality orals:

• Hua Wu, Longhi: 1DO.9.1 Hybrid Interdigitated Back Contact Silicon Solar Cells with Superior Efficiency
• Daming Chen, Trina: 1AO.5.1 Large Area i-TOPCon Solar Cells with 25.9% Record Efficiency
• Maysa Sarsour, UNSW: 1AO.6.1 Evaluating Silicon Heterojunction Solar Cell Stability under Industrial Illuminated Hydrogenation Conditions

Bottom cell optimization for Pero-Si tandems

030001-013

CONFERENCE

**TOPIC 2:
THIN FILMS
AND NEW
CONCEPTS**

A lot of focus on the long-term stability improvement and upscaling of tandem devices based on a variety of materials (hence not only pero-Si).

Many companies (e.g. Hanwha Q-cells, Oxford PV, Microquanta Seminconductor, Jinko Solar, Longi, etc. non-exhaustive list) presented impressive results on industrial size single-junction pero modules and pero-based tandem modules. A highlight here was the plenary talk from Hanwha Q-cells showing a record large area (M10) pilot-scale Pk/Si tandem cell of 28.6% efficiency.

In the field of pero-Si tandems, there is clearly more focus on improving the stability of the tandem devices than before with many contributions doing in-depth investigations into the different degradation mechanisms that can occur in pero-Si tandems.

In this respect, 2DO9.5 presented a consensus statement about reliability testing of perovskite-based tandems that is endorsed by specialists worldwide from both industry and research and presents a kind of minimum that should be done in terms of testing and reporting concerning the stability and lifetime of perovskite-based tandem devices.

More and more advanced characterization methods for perovskite and perovskite - silicon tandem solar cells are being used, hyperspectral imaging methods identify non-uniformities by layer for processing development.

Another clear trend is that pero-TOPCon cells are nearing the same record efficiencies as pero-Heterojunction cells. A highlight talk here was the certified 34.22% efficiency perovskite/ topcon tandem solar cell(1cm2) by Jinko Solar 2CO2.1

Another highlight was the 30.5% triple junction pero/pero/silicon cell by EPFL (2CO2.3)

In the field of perovskite single junction devices, 2DO.7.3 showed perovskite devices with remarkable reliability, withstanding 4 years of outdoor exposure. The degradation mechanism is attributed to the diurnal behaviour, also verified and replicated with indoor experiments.

2AO3.6 investigated experimental degradation and recovery of perovskite solar cells, improving the comprehension of instability's dynamics, to extend the lifetime of devices.

In the field of compound semiconductors, there were many presentations on alternative materials for perovskite in tandems. In this way, first monolithic (AgCu)(InGa)Se2 on Si tandem cells were demonstrated as well as 16.1% semitransparent Ag doped Cu(InGa)S2 sulfide top cells.

An exciting highlight in this field was 2BO8.2 in which UPC Barcelona achieved 18% efficiency under indoor lighting for kesterite solar cells with alkali doping

EU PVSEC
EU PVSEC
2025

CONFERENCE

TOPIC 3:
PHOTOVOLTAIC
MODULES

"Reliable packaging to Maximize the energy yield from high efficiency cells"

big theme: Optimizing module materials and packaging for long lifetime and predictable energy yield from high efficiency cells. The industry and research community are moving quickly to assess and improve reliability.

• Understanding, accelerated testing, and mitigating UV-ID in n-type cells and modules

• How do you develop accelerated tests for constantly changing BOMs - new encapsulants, new metallization, thinner glass, and high efficiency cells

CONFERENCE

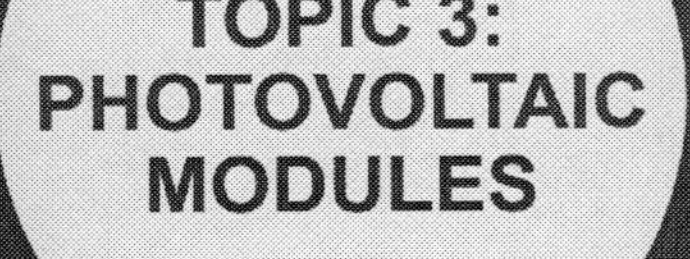

- Degradation and metastability in packaged perovskite tandems - understanding energy yield and realistic degradation rates

- Characterization out of the lab and into the field and factory - accurate outdoor performance, online quality control measurements for encapsulant cross linking

- Reducing silver content and metallization temperatures - reliability of low temperature and low silver metallization

- Developing glass qualification requirements to minimize breakage

CONFERENCE

EU PVSEC

EU
PVSEC
2025
22 26
BEC
Bilbao

TOPIC 4:
PHOTOVOLTAIC
SYSTEMS

Advances in O&M of PV systems

(4CV.1) focuses on fault detection, cleaning optimization, soiling (and snow 4CO.8), UAV for autonomous monitoring and digital twin.

Data driven and AI based O&M (4CO.9) including a medicine-like workflow in Autonomous multi-AI agent system for health monitoring: a fully automated O&M pipeline with field robotics (4CO.9.4 D. Moser, EURAC)

030001-020

PV Everywhere from space to agricultural applications like integration in vineyards (Mo, Opening plenary) and many other **integrated options** as we have seen throughout the week. On Thursday (4DO.4) agriPV, noise barriers and floating integrated systems. AgriPV technologies (4DO.2), BIPV

PV needs solar energy. **Solar resource and forecasting** (Mo, 4AO.7-9 & Tu 4BV.3). Shortly IEA PVPS T16 will publish minute irradiance data, some including GT over 220 stations worldwide with. Same format and quality controlled. (*Worldwide solar radiation measurement database with quality-control added value*, Anne Forstinger CSP Services, 4AO.7.1)

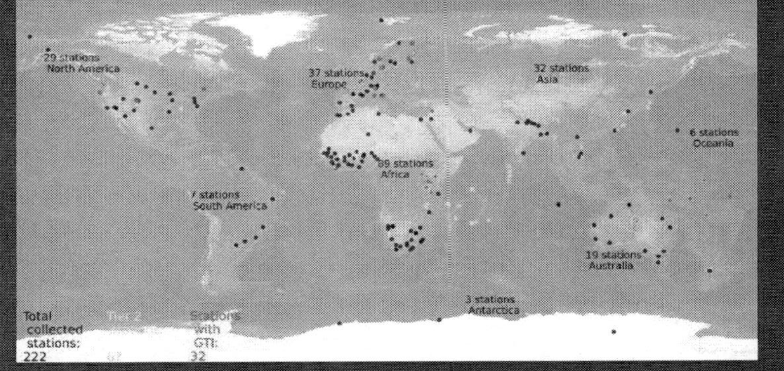

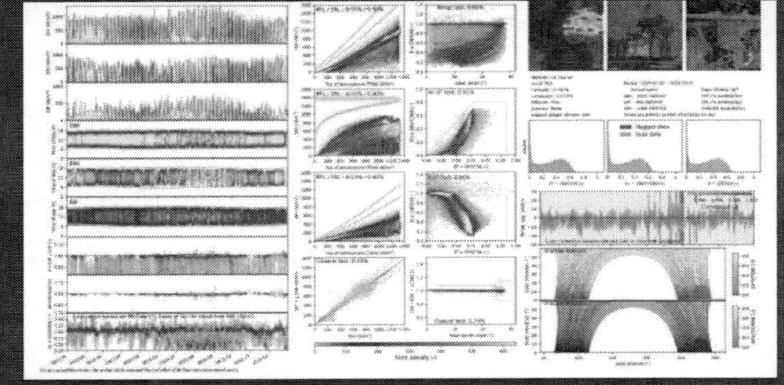

(4BV.3). Poster winner 4BV.3.12 *Advancing Very Short-Term Solar Irradiance Forecasting in Africa: A Low-Cost Sky Imaging and Machine Learning-Based Approach*, implications for PV deployment and grid integration (Martin Ansong, KIT). Runner-up 4BV.3.25 *Evaluating the Suitability of Köppen-Geiger Climate Classifications for Photovoltaic Systems: Micro-climate Analysis and Risk Assessment Maps*, with worldwide distribution of humidity related risk assessment for PV performance (Pavan Kumar Panda, Anhalt University of Applied Sciences).

Integrated PV

BIPV (4BO.16) examples of coloured modules (which was main topic of the poster session along with fire concerns of BIPV, 4BV.4), lightweight solutions (4BO.5) and modelling partial shading effects 4BO.17.1, *Modelling partial shading at the cell level on PV modules,* Jean-Paul Calin, ENSTA) and 4BO.17.3, *Comparing the energy yield and degradation rates of smart PV modules compared to conventional PV system designs in shaded urban scenario's,* Youri Blom, TU DELF.

AgriPV 4DO.2 the room was fully packed showing the interest in the topic. 5 talks were on new ways of sharing light (2 spectral splitting before the PV conversion, 2 semitransparent PV modules both c-Si and CdTe, 1 on downshifting encapsulate) + 1 new AgrivPV like application with Algae instead of crops.

4DO.4 also included AgriPV and **Others types of integration like noise barriers and floating.** In addition to performance other aspects like (*Hydrological and ecological effects on floating PV,* Konstantin Ilgen, FHO ISe) have been highlighted this week

BOS and tracking systems (4DO.1) focused on backtracking strategies and terrains with complex topography.

4DO.1.4

4DO4.2

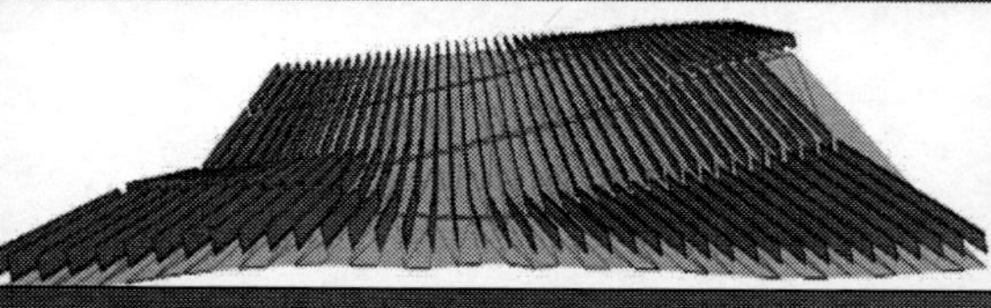

CONFERENCE

Reliability of PV systems

Several presentations focused long-term monitored degradation, failure modes and degradation modes identification techniques (non-destructive, aerial images, AI-based)

4BO.6.1 *Three decades, three climates: insights and lessons on PV reliability.* Good BOM offer very high reliability in power production, with 30-35 years old modules showing 0.24% degradation rate per year.

4BO.6.3 *Non-destructive detection of water ingress in solar modules using NIR spectroscopy* (Oleksandr Mashkow HI ERN) proved near-infrared absorption (NIRA) technique to detect water ingress in modules in the field, which correlated with the module degradation.

4BO.7.2 *Robust PV performance loss rate calculation for high latitudes* (Lauri Karttunen, Meteo Inst Helsinki) and 4BO.7. 3 *Detailed analysis of degradation rates of operating PV assets in tropical climate conditions* (Xioaqi Xu, Seris Singapore) Performance loss rates reported for high latitudes and tropics based on solid data sets. PLR in the tropics -1.4%/year

4DO.3.6 PV system design and assessment highlighted how inverter safety issues are extremely important and how more research about inverter safety and reliability is needed.

EU PVSEC
22 26 September
EU
BEC
PVSEC
Bilbao Spain
2025

CONFERENCE

TOPIC 5:
PHOTOVOLTAICS
IN THE ENERGY
TRANSITION

Main topics of interest :

• Flexibility

• Artificial intelligence

• EoL management

CONFERENCE

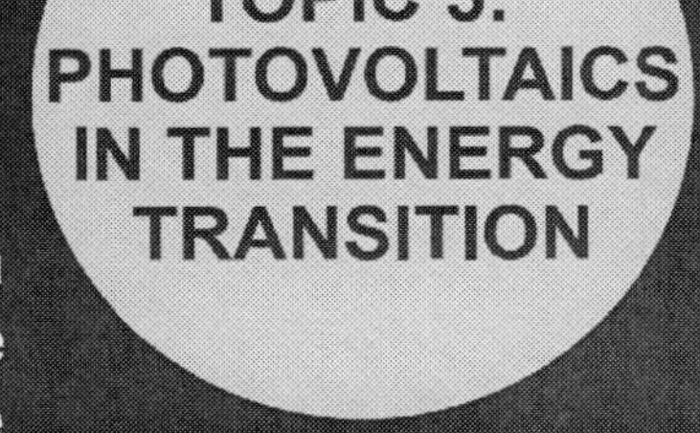

5.1 Grid Integration and Flexibility Enablers (2 sessions)

- Smoothing effect related to different orientations of PV systems in a given area allows 10 to 15% additional hosting capacity of the distribution grid compared to the conservative calculation that consists in summing the AC power. Such accurate calculation enabled by high resolution large area images and LIDAR and induces therefore very low costs.

5.2 Sustainability of PV (4 sessions)

- New inventories LCI and LCA for emerging technologies even though lack of data for perovskites, LCA showing a way for low environmental Impacts with technology improvement and localisation. / Technological improvements will contribute to the reduction of environmental Impact / Grid Efficiency has an Impact on the environmental Footprint.

- Manufacturing optimization / Reuse & recycling: results from the perspective of economic performance – would it convince manufacturer to consider it if economic benefit ?

- EoL Management /recycling -> emerging field attracting lots of activities / mainly EU projects (EVERPV / ICARUS / QASAR) – highlight on polymer, interesting question came up and to be debated for the next decade: is it worth it to consider polymer (EVA/ backsheet) recycling ?

- Major progress in methodology and indicators to assess sustainable design & circularity and improve transparency recyclability index, technical recyclability, digital passport)

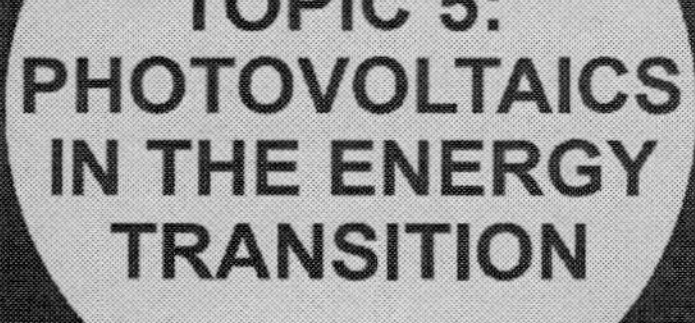

CONFERENCE

5.3 Scenarios for Renewables, Policy, Global Challenges (1 session)

- wide scope of contributions on the way to massive, medium- to long-term PV deployment -> should not be taken for granted despite positive projections since there can be limiting factors such as public acceptance / regulatory restrictions and effect of climate change

5.4 Costs, Economics, Finance and Markets (1 session)

- Annual installed capacity over 400 GWp / total cumulative installed capacity worldwide over 2.1 TWp / Clear mismatch between PV module installations rate worldwide and PV module production rate leading to bunch of inventories and drastically reduced prices.

5.6 Societal Challenges; Citizens' Participation, Awareness (1 session)

- data and analysis in gender aspects are emerging in PV! (poster session) + Highlight on innovation in education! On example that targets students & skilled workers -> mobile Lab for advanced experimental training PV-related to bring skills and characterization tools everywhere.

PARALLEL EVENTS
Collaborat Network
Diversity
Prejudice
Justificat
Change
Needs -Profile Match
Avoid Blind Spots
Job Cocs?
Integration
Lack of Attractivn
Resilience (People + Company)
Creativity
Different Communicat°
Internal Friction
More Efforts

- Perovskite Innovation Roundtable: Driving EU Leadership in Perovskite Innovation
- Women in PV presents: Leading with Inclusion – Embracing the 6 Traits of Inclusive Leadership
- Unlocking the Potential of Integrated Photovoltaic Systems - European R&D Approach
- Why Do PV Plants Perform Lower than Expected? (Estimating losses by backtracking algorithms in undulating terrain & Analysis of the loss chain and identification of deviations from initial expectations)
- PV Made in the EU: How Do Companies Die and How Can They Thrive?

22 — 26
September
BEC —
Bilbao Exhibition Centre
Bilbao — Spain
EU PVSEC
42nd European
Photovoltaic Solar Energy
Conference and Exhibition
2025
EXHIBITION FORUM
INDUSTRY SUMMIT
The road to a sustainable future

Industry Summit Opening (session I)

Session Title: Solar PV production in Europe - the way forward

Moderators: Begoña Molinete, Walburga Hemetsberger

Key Takeaway:

This session discussed the state of play of European manufacturing projects and whether there is enough European support. It was clear that political support is further lacking – only 3 Member States have developed schemes to support European manufacturing. While the Net Zero Industry Act is helpful to diversify supplies, it will not particularly support European manufacturing.

All panellists agreed that apart from further policy support (financing, derisking) collaboration is the way forward.

EU PVSEC

EU PVSEC 2025
22 – 26 SEP
Bilbao

Session II
Session Title: International corporations in the light of changing geopolitics
Moderators: Radovan Kopecek, Puzant Baliozian

Key takeaway:
EU machine builders are still supporting mostly Indian but also US and EU projects with their technology and expertise. The major arguments for choosing EU tech are quality, training, support and low OPEX.

Session III
Session Title: PV Systems: How do we get the produced electricity in Europe into the grid?
Moderators: Catarina Augusto, Peter Fath

Key Takeaway:
Hybrid PV + storage systems (co-located or distributed) are essential for integrating PV into electricity grids. Storage adds flexibility and stabilizes the grid, making it a cornerstone of resilient energy systems; while the technology is mature, scalable and bankable revenue models remain the key gap for widespread deployment.

LIST OF EXHIBITORS
(in alphabetical order)

Company name	Country
2nd Cycle FlexCo	Austria
9-Tech	Italy
Avalon ST / Pasan	Switzerland
BASQUENERGY Cluster	Spain
Becquerel Institute	Belgium
ECOPROGETTI	Italy
EKIENERGY	Spain
ESMC Pavilion	Belgium
Eternal Sun I WAVELABS	The Netherlands
EU PVSEC Startup Pavilion	
European Commission JRC	Italy
exateq	Germany
FLUXiM AG	Switzerland
G2V Optics	Canada
GALEA	Spain
halm elektronik	Germany
HighLine Technology	Germany
IEA PVPS	
Innovations in Optics, Inc.	United States of America
ISC Konstanz	Germany
LAB14	Germany
MBJ Solutions	Germany
Mondragon Assembly	Spain
Nagase Chemtex America	United States of America
NEO Messtechnik Holding	Austria
ODTÜ GÜNAM	Türkiye
Phoenixolar	China
PSE Instruments	Germany
PVsyst	Switzerland
RCT Future	Germany
RCT Solutions	Germany
RENA	Germany
ReNewPV-CA21148 / 5GSOLAR	Estonia
SALD B.V.	The Netherlands

SCIPRIOS	Germany
SEMILAB	Hungary
SINGULUS TECHNOLOGIES	Germany
Sinton Instruments	United States of America
SOLAR MATERIALS	Germany
SolarNL	The Netherlands
Soli Tek R&D	Lithuania
TAMURA ELSOLD	Germany
TECNALIA	Spain
The Netherlands Pavilion	The Netherlands
TNO	The Netherlands
University of the Basque Country	Spain
Vector Energy	Spain
VON ARDENNE	Germany
WCPEC-9	South Korea
WIP Renewable Energies	Germany
ZSW	Germany

We thank the EU PVSEC 2025 Sponsors

Platinum

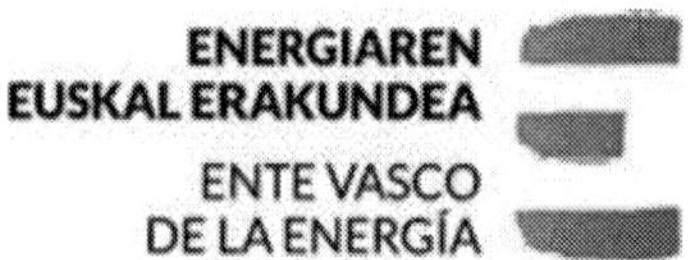

Gold

Silver

Bronze

AUTHORS OF EU PVSEC 2025 PROCEEDINGS PAPERS

Aghamohammadi, Amirhossain   020356
Amirkabir University of Technology, Tehran, Iran

Aguirre, Aranzazu   020064
Hasselt Unversity, Genk, Belgium

Ahmadi, Mehdi   020066
CNR-IMM, Catania, Italy

Aiello, Andrea   020255
ACCA Software, Cosenza, Italy

Aimé, Jérémie   020217, 020311
CEA / INES, Le Bourget-du-Lac, France

Aissa, Brahim   020042, 020075, 020108, 020109, 020146, 020147
QEERI, Doha, Qatar

Aizpurua, Jon   020139
Tecnalia, Donostia - San Sebastián, Spain

Akbayrak, Serdar   020020
Necmettin Erbakan University, Konya, Türkiye

Akram, M. Waqar   020164
Hohai University, Changzhou, China

Al Katrib, Mirella   020116
IPVF, Palaiseau, France

Alam, Habeel   020394
Lancaster University, Lancaster, United Kingdom

Alberts, Vivian   020229
DEWA, Dubai, United Arab Emirates

Albuquerque, Daniel P.   020464
Centre for New Energy Technologies, Sacavém, Portugal

Alet, Pierre-Jean   020238, 020544
CSEM, Neuchâtel, Switzerland

Alexandris, Nikos   020210
European Commission JRC, Ispra, Italy

Alfieri, Felice   020497
Viegand Maagøe, Copenhagen, Denmark

Ali, Adnan   020147
QEERI, Doha, Qatar

Allen, Vince   020048
SunDrive Solar, Kurnell, Australia

Alloji, Esma   020020
Necmettin Erbakan University, Konya, Türkiye

Almeida Silva, José   020565
University of Évora, Évora, Portugal

Almuneau, Guilhem   020074
LAAS-CNRS, Toulouse, France

Alonso, Ricardo   020197, 020198, 020353, 020358
TECNALIA, Derio, Spain

Alonso-Montesinos, Joaquín   020100
University of Almeria, Almeria, Spain

Alonso-Montesinos, Joaquín	020336
University of Almería, La Cañada de San Urbano, Spain

Álvarez Hervás, José Domingo	020336
University of Almería, La Cañada de San Urbano, Spain

Alvarez, José	020040, 020058
CNRS, Gif-sur-Yvette, France

Álvarez, Marta	020300
CENER, Sarriguren, Spain

Álvarez-Pérez, Guillem	020062
IPVF, Palaiseau, France

Alvaro Høye, Ingar	020443
Solkraft Sør, Øyslebø, Norway

Alves e Silva, Kiane	020439, 020535, 020567, 020575
UPM, Madrid, Spain

Amaro e Silva, Rodrigo	020490
University of Lisbon, Lisbon, Portugal

Amatriain, Irati	020392
CENER, Sarriguren, Spain

Anamiati, Gaetana	020448, 020481
GreenPowerMonitor a DNV company, Barcelona, Spain

Anaya, Julian	020191, 020205
University of Valladolid, Valladolid, Spain

Ancillao, Andrea	020079
Polytechnic University of Turin, Turin, Italy

Anderlini, Alessandro	020155
Coveme, Gorizia, Italy

Andersen, Nanna L.	020250
DTU, Roskilde, Denmark

Andersen, Nanna Lysgaard	020306
DTU, Roskilde, Denmark

Andrade-Arvizu, Jacob	020094
IREC, Barcelona, Spain

Andreozzi, Federico	020494
University of Rome Tor Vergata, Rome, Italy

Anefnaf, Ikram	020093
University of Verona, Verona, Italy

Ansong, Martin	020272
KIT, Eggenstein-Leopoldshafen, Germany

Antognini, Luca	020196
PVsyst, Geneva, Switzerland

Antoine, C.	020508
IMDEA Nanoscience Institute, Madrid, Spain

Antón, Ignacio	020209, 020246, 020257, 020453, 020459
UPM, Madrid, Spain

Antonucci, Daniele	020551
Eurac Research, Bolzano, Italy

Apostoleris, Harry   020487
EPRI, Dubai, United Arab Emirates

Arakawa, Hayato   020436
NIED, Shinjo, Japan

Aranguren, Gerardo   020289, 020353
UPV/EHU, Bilbao, Spain

Arbaretaz, Sebastien   020317
CEA INES, Le Bourget-du-Lac, France

Ardissone, Bastien J. J.   020396
PV Lighthouse, Coledale, Australia

Arduino, Daniele   020079
Polytechnic University of Turin, Turin, Italy

Ariolli, Daniela Maria Godinho   020325
BayWa r.e, Rome, Italy

Ariza Camacho, Maria Jesus   020100
University of Almeria, Almería, Spain

Armstrong, Alona   020394
Lancaster University, Lancaster, United Kingdom

Arribat, Mathieu   020074
LAAS-CNRS, Toulouse, France

Arrizabalaga, Igor   020139
Tecnalia, Donostia - San Sebastián, Spain

Artegiani, Elisa   020057, 020089, 020093
University of Verona, Verona, Italy

Arumughan, Jayaprasad   020569
ISC Konstanz, Konstanz, Germany

Asaa, Shu-Ngwa   020393
imo-imomec, Genk, Belgium

Ascencio-Vásquez, Julián   020371
Univers, Courbevoie, France

Askins, Steve   020209, 020257
UPM, Madrid, Spain

Assaid, El Mahdi   020171
University of Chouaib Doukkali, El Jadida, Morocco

Aste, Niccolò   020249
Polytechnic University of Milan, Milan, Italy

Astigarraga, Alexander   020226
Eurac Research, Bolzano, Italy

Athienitis, Andreas   020248
Concordia University, Montreal, Canada

Aurrekoetxea, Olaia   020302
TECNALIA, Saint Sebastian, Spain

Awadallah, Carlos   020536
Wattkraft, Madrid, Spain

Azkona, Nekane   020055, 020097, 020153, 020287
UPV/EHU, Bilbao, Spain

Azzopardi, Brian 020318, 020334, 020520
FIR, Birkirkara, Malta

Azzopardi, Carmel 020334
FIR, Birkirkara, Malta

Babich, Francesco 020551
Eurac Research, Bolzano, Italy

Babics, Maxime 020217
CEA / INES, Le Bourget-du-Lac, France

Babin, Markus 020249, 020250, 020306, 020477
DTU, Roskilde, Denmark

Bachour, Dunia A. 020275, 020278
QEERI, Doha, Qatar

Bachour, Dunia 020291
QEERI, Doha, Qatar

Baderiya, Naman 020390
MARIN, Wageningen, The Netherlands

Badosa Franch, Jordi 020214
Polytechnic Institute of Paris, Palaiseau, France

Baeck, Pieter-Jan 020511
Flemish Institute for Technological Research (VITO), Genk,
Belgium

Bai, Jianbo 020164
Hohai University, Changzhou, China

Bailache, Simon 020303
CSTB, Marne-la-Vallée, France

Bakhtiari, Afshin 020121
AESOLAR, Koenigsbrunn, Germany

Balafoutis, Athanasios T. 020464
CERTH, Athens, Greece

Bald, Juan 020514
AZTI, PASAIA, Spain

Baldacchino, Alex J. 020065
UNSW, Sydney, Australia

Baležentienė, Skirmantė 020380
The Applied Research Institute for Prospective
Technologies, Vilnius, Lithuania

Baležentis, Algirdas 020380
The Applied Research Institute for Prospective
Technologies, Vilnius, Lithuania

Ballif, Christophe 020467
CSEM, Neuchâtel, Switzerland

Ballif, Christophe 020251
EPFL, Neuchâtel, Switzerland

Bandaru, Narendra 020039, 020043, 020104
Aarhus University, Aarhus, Denmark

Bang, Ole   020043
Technical University of Denmark, Copenhagen, Denmark

Barakel, Damien   020188
Toulon University, Marseille, France

Baraket, Mira   020039
ATLANT 3D, Taastrup, Denmark

Baranek, Philippe   020060
EDF R&D, Palaiseau, France

Barchi, Grazia   020485, 020489, 020544
Eurac Research, Bolzano, Italy

Bardizza, Giorgio   020181
TÜV Rheinland Italia, Milan, Italy

Bardizza, Giorgio   020208
TÜV Rheinland Solar, Cologne, Germany

Bardizza, Giorgio   020144
TÜV Rheinland, Cologne, Germany

Barguès, Anna   020505
Becquerel Institute France, Lyon, France

Barguès, Anna   020558
Becquerel Institute, Brussels, Belgium

Barnscheidt, Verena   020063, 020114
ISFH, Emmerthal, Germany

Barretta, Chiara   020325
PCCL, Leoben, Austria

Barrionuevo, Bruno   020464
CERTH, Athens, Greece

Barroso, João   020565
University of Évora, Évora, Portugal

Barrou, Alexis   020467
CSEM, Neuchâtel, Switzerland

Barrutia, Laura   020446, 020536
UPM, Madrid, Spain

Barth, Vincent   020134
CEA / INES, Le Bourget-du-Lac, France

Barth, Vincent   020019
CEA, Le Bourget-du-Lac, France

Barth, Vincent   020226
CEA/ INES, Le Bourget-du-Lac, France

Bartholomäus, Martin   020346
DTU, Roskilde, Denmark

Bartolo, Brian   020334
FIR, Birkirkara, Malta

Basta, Beata   020068
Roltec, Poznań, Poland

Basta, Marek   020068
Roltec, Poznań, Poland

Battisti, Kurt 020255
A-Null Development, Vienna, Austria

Bauhuis, Gerard 020067
Radboud University, Nijmegen, The Netherlands

Baumann, Kerstin 020470
bifa Umweltinstitut, Augsburg, Germany

Baumann, Sara 020063
ISFH, Emmerthal, Germany

Baumann, Ulrike 020006
ISFH, Emmerthal, Germany

Baur, Carsten 020246
European Space Agency, Noordwijk, The Netherlands

Beaucarne, Guy 020384
Dow Silicones Belgium, Seneffe, Belgium

Becker, Carl 020331
DLR, Almería, Spain

Behrensdorff Poulsen, Peter 020037
DTU, Lyngby, Denmark

Beinert, Andreas J. 020123
Fraunhofer ISE, Freiburg, Germany

Bejat, Timea 020225, 020500
CEA, Le Bourget-du-Lac, France

Belawadi, Aditya Girish 020231
Fraunhofer ISE, Freiburg, Germany

Belferkous, Brahim Anis 020325
PCCL, Leoben, Austria

Bellmann, Martin 020495, 020510
SINTEF, Trondheim, Norway

Bellvert, Eduard 020139
Tecnalia, Donostia - San Sebastián, Spain

Beltran-Condori, Sonia 020129, 020417
University of Antofagasta, Antofagasta, Chile

Belzunce, María Jesús 020514
AZTI, PASAIA, Spain

Bendix, Peter 020388
Next2Sun Technology, Dillingen, Germany

Bengoechea, Jaione 020181, 020300
CENER, Sarriguren, Spain

Bermudez Benito, Veronica 020146
QEERI, Doha, Qatar

Bermudez-Garcia, Anderson 020246
Thales Alenia Space, Cannes, France

Berrian, Djaber 020492
Belectric, Kolitzheim, Germany

Berson, Solenn 020134
CEA / INES, Le Bourget-du-Lac, France

Bolink, Henk J.   020226
University of Valencia, Paterna, Spain

Bonal, Victor   020085
UAM, Madrid, Spain

Bonnet, Martin   020141
University of Applied Science Cologne, Cologne, Germany

Bonnet-Eymard, Bénédicte   020251
CSEM, Neuchâtel, Switzerland

Borgers, Tom   020225
IMEC, Genk, Belgium

Borgna, Luciano   020369
BFH, Burgdorf, Switzerland

Borie, Benjamin   020039
ATLANT 3D, Taastrup, Denmark

Borowski, Peter   020307
Avancis, Munich, Germany

Borriello, Aniello   020378
ENEA, Portici, Italy

Borzi, Giovanni   020019
Enginsoft, Padua, Italy

Bosch, Elina   020252, 020543, 020564, 020573
Becquerel Institute, Brussels, Belgium

Bosma, Theo   020571
DNV, Arnhem, The Netherlands

Bothe, Karsten   020236
ISFH, Emmerthal, Germany

Bou-Nassif, Liliane   020338
CETHIL, Villeurbanne, France

Bouchier, Daniel   020058
CNRS, Palaiseau, France

Bouguerra, Sara   020156, 020294, 020389, 020393
imec, Genk, Belgium

Bourdin, Vincent   020406
CNRS, Paris, France

Bourgeois, Antoine   020102
SERIS, Singapore, Singapore

Bovesecchi, Gianluigi   020494
University of Rome Tor Vergata, Rome, Italy

Brabec, Christoph J.   020117
HI ERN, Erlangen, Germany

Bradford, David Roy   020077
Newcastle University, Newcastle upon Tyne, United
Kingdom

Brailovsky, Peter Henri   020475
Fraunhofer ISE, Freiburg, Germany

Braña, Alejandro F.   020508
Autonomous University of Madrid, Madrid, Spain

Brandstätter, Andreas   020227
Lenzing Plastics, Lenzing, Austria

Braun, Christian   020457
Luxembourg Institute of Science and Technology, Esch-sur-
Alzette, Luxembourg

Brecl, Kristijan   020269, 020319
University of Ljubljana, Ljubljana, Slovenia

Bredemeier, Dennis   020240
Leibniz University Hannover, Hannover, Germany

Breitenbücher, Marian   020225
Highline Technologies, Freiburg, Germany

Brendel, Rolf   020006, 020008, 020236, 020240, 020260,
ISFH, Emmerthal, Germany   020482

Brendstrup Møller, Clara Bolette   020028
DTU, Roskilde, Denmark

Bretzel, Tamara   020195
Fraunhofer ISE, Freiburg, Germany

Breyer, Christian   020479
LUT University, Lappeenranta, Finland

Brito, Miguel   020457
University of Lisbon, Lisbon, Portugal

Brivio, Elisabetta   020462
RSE, Milan, Italy

Brockmann, Lukas   020063
ISFH, Emmerthal, Germany

Brodnicke, Linda   020296
ETH, Zurich, Switzerland

Brueckner, Emanuel   020063
ISFH, Emmerthal, Germany

Bründlinger, Roland   020369
AIT, Vienna, Austria

Brun, Gonzalo   020414, 020517
ENDEF, Zaragoza, Spain

Bruno, Maddalena   020452
Fraunhofer ISE, Freiburg, Germany

Buceta, Alicia   020300
CENER, Sarriguren, Spain

Bucher, Christof   020179, 020322, 020359, 020369, 020386
BFH, Burgdorf, Switzerland

Buchholz, Florian   020035, 020225, 020569
ISC Konstanz, Konstanz, Germany

Buchmann, Johanna   020309
Berlin University of Applied Sciences, Berlin, Germany

Buck, Thomas   020033
ISC Konstanz, Konstanz, Germany

Buckland, Daniel
Henkel, Düsseldorf, Germany
020119, 020218

Buddana, Viswa Harinath
DLR, Oldenburg, Germany
020482

Bühlmann, Gian-Luca
ZHAW, Winterthur, Switzerland
020385

Buerhop, Claudia
HI ERN, Erlangen, Germany
020149, 020150, 020377

Buerhop-Lutz, Claudia
HI ERN, Erlangen, Germany
020185, 020230

Burgers, Antonius R.
TNO, Petten, The Netherlands
020405

Burri, Matthias
BFH, Burgdorf, Switzerland
020179

Busto, Chiara
Eni, Novara, Italy
020521

Butrichi, Fabio
University of Milano-Bicocca, Milan, Italy
020087

Butt, Nauman
Lahore University of Management Sciences, Lahore, Pakistan
020394

C. Tavares, Fabiele
Federal University of Rio de Janeiro, Duque de Caxias, Brazil
020090

Cabal, Raphael
University Grenoble Alpes, Le Bourget-du-Lac, France
020034

Caballero, Luis Jaime
UPM, Madrid, Spain
020501, 020508

Caballero, Raquel
CSIC, Madrid, Spain
020094

Caballero, Raquel
IO-CSIC, Madrid, Spain
020085

Cabecinha, Vasco
Nova University Lisbon, Lisbon, Portugal
020565

Cabello, Fatima
IO-CSIC, Madrid, Spain
020085

Caçapietra Pires da Silva, Lucas Teixeira
PUCRS, Porto Alegre, Brazil
020025

Caccavelli, Dominique
CSTB, Bussy-Saint Georges, France
020551

Caccivio, Mauro
SUPSI, Mendrisio, Switzerland
020204, 020574

Caffari, Francesca
ENEA, Ispra, Italy
020551

Calabrese, Nicolandrea
ENEA, Ispra, Italy
020551

Calin, Jean-Paul   020251
ENSTA Paris, Palaiseau, France

Çalışkan Arslan, Meriç   020006, 020135
Kalyon PV, Ankara, Türkiye

Caluori, Philip   020455
Virtual Vehicle, Graz, Austria

Camara, Assa   020274
Solargis, Bratislava, Slovakia

Cambarau, Werther   020139
Tecnalia, Donostia-San Sebastián, Spain

Campana, Pietro Elia   020381
Mälardalen University, Västerås, Sweden

Campos Guzman, Laura   020331
DLR, Almería, Spain

Cancro, Carmine   020378
ENEA, Naples, Italy

Canesse, Auriane   020196
PVsyst, Geneva, Switzerland

Cañizo, Carlos   020097
IES-UPM, Madrid, Spain

Cano, Francisco J.   020139
Tecnalia, Donostia - San Sebastián, Spain

Cano, Lucía   020127
ENDEF, Zaragoza, Spain

Cánovas, Enrique   020508
IMDEA Nanoscience Institute, Madrid, Spain

Cao, Han   020263
SERIS, Singapore, Singapore

Capitaine, Anna   020116
IPVF, Palaiseau, France

Cappelle, Jan   020329, 020351
KU Leuven, Ghent, Belgium

Capron, Guillaume   020217
CEA / INES, Le Bourget-du-Lac, France

Carballo López, José Antonio   020336
University of Almería, La Cañada de San Urbano, Spain

Cardenas, Luis Alejandro   020339, 020546
National University of Colombia, Bogotá, Colombia

Carmo, Paulo   020304, 020420
University of Évora, Évora, Portugal

Carrasco, Luis Miguel   020439, 020535, 020567
UPM, Madrid, Spain

Carrillo Mejía, Luis   020279
District University of Bogotá, Bogotá, Colombia

Carrillo, Rafael E.   020238
CSEM, Neuchâtel, Switzerland

Carroy, Perrine   020226
CEA/ INES, Le Bourget-du-Lac, France

Carstens, Justus   020003
ISC Konstanz, Konstanz, Germany

Cartenì, Fabrizio   020378
University of Naples Federico II, Naples, Italy

Casappa, Michele   020087
National Research Council, Parma, Italy

Casasola Paesa, Marta   020389
Hasselt University, Diepenbeek, Belgium

Castilla Nieto, María del Mar   020336
University of Almería, La Cañada de San Urbano, Spain

Castillo Patton, Daniel Jason   020326
Enertis Applus+, Madrid, Spain

Castro, Luis Guilherme   020530
Casa dos Ventos, Fortaleza, Brazil

Castro, Rui   020464
University of Lisbon, Lisbon, Portugal

Castro-Gallardo, Fernando   020417, 020422
University of Antofagasta, Antofagasta, Chile

Cavaco, Afonso   020304, 020565
University of Évora, Évora, Portugal

Cebecauer, Tomas   020274
Solargis, Bratislava, Slovakia

Çekerek, Gamze   020006
Kalyon PV, Ankara, Türkiye

Celik, Duygu   020551
WIP Renewable Energies, Munich, Germany

Çeliktaş, Melih Soner   020559
Ege University, İzmir, Türkiye

Centazzo, Massimo   020006
EnPV, Karlsruhe, Germany

Centeno Brito, Miguel   020421, 020490
University of Lisbon, Lisbon, Portugal

Cereceda, Eneko   020055, 020097, 020153, 020287
UPV/EHU, Bilbao, Spain

Ceretti, Mattia   020204
SUPSI, Mendrisio, Switzerland

Cesar, I.   020405
TNO, Petten, The Netherlands

Ceuppens, Ignas   020302
BUILD'UP, Aarschot, Belgium

Chatterji, Nithin   020071
SVNIT, Surat, India

Chen, Daniel   020048
SunDrive Solar, Kurnell, Australia

Chen, Syh-Homg   020161
ITRI, Hsinchu, Taiwan

Chen, Xiang   020111
Hohai University, Changzhou, China

Cheung, Kak Pong   020313
Kiel University of Applied Sciences, Kiel, Germany

Chhapia, Gaurang   020492
Belectric, Kolitzheim, Germany

Chiba, Takahiro   020436
Hokkaido University of Science, Sapporo, Japan

Chichignoud, Guy   020495
13Institut Polytechnique De Grenoble, Grenoble, France

Chicote, Beatriz   020289
Mondragon University, Arrasate-Mondragon, Spain

Chiesa, Matteo   020487
Khalifa University, Abu Dhabi, United Arab Emirates

Chini de Freitas, Felipe   020023
PUCRS, Porto Alegre, Brazil

Cho, Yunae   020045
KIER, Daejeon, South Korea

Choi, Kwan Bum   020102
SERIS, Singapore, Singapore

Chouder, Aissa   020301
University of M'sila, M'sila, Algeria

Chowdhury, Gofran   020276, 020544
3E, Brussels, Belgium

Christ, Anja   020063
ISFH, Emmerthal, Germany

Chrkavy, Daniel   020262
Solargis, Bratislava, Slovakia

Chueh, Wei-Lo   020021
TSEC, Hsinchu, Taiwan

Ciesla, Alison   020065
UNSW, Sydney, Australia

Cirimele, Vincenzo   020314
University of Bologna, Bologna, Italy

Clausing, Roland   020063, 020114
ISFH, Emmerthal, Germany

Clochard, Laurent   020031
Nines Photovoltaics, Dublin, Germany

Clochard, Laurent   020007
Nines Photovoltaics, Dublin, Ireland

Clyncke, Jan   020472, 020513
PV CYCLE, Brussels, Belgium

Coşkun, Özlem   020006, 020027, 020225
Kalyon PV, Ankara, Türkiye

Colberts, Fallon 020389
Zuyd University, Heerlen, The Netherlands

Colin, Hervé 020217, 020262
CEA / INES, Le Bourget-du-Lac, France

Collin, Stéphane 020074
C2N, Palaiseau, France

Colwell, Jack 020048
SunDrive Solar, Kurnell, Australia

Comak, Mertcan 020003
ISC Konstanz, Konstanz, Germany

Connolly, James Patrick 020058, 020060
CNRS, Gif-sur-Yvette, France

Cordeiro, Diogo 020464
EDP, Lisbon, Portugal

Cornago, Iñaki 020392
CENER, Sarriguren, Spain

Cornaro, Cristina 020494
University of Rome Tor Vergata, Rome, Italy

Correa, Guillermo 020412
Gonvarri MS R&D, Corvera - Asturias, Spain

Correia, Joana 020565
University of Évora, Évora, Portugal

Couderc, Romain 020217, 020311, 020546
CEA / INES, Le Bourget-du-Lac, France

Coutel, John 020244
SOLAÏS, Valbonne, France

Cowan, Don 020230
Kiwa PI Berlin, Hudson, United States of America

Cox, Joel D. 020250
SDU Climate Cluster, Odense, Denmark

Cox, Joel D 020306
SDU Climate Cluster, Odense, Denmark

Coz, Pier Luigi 020246
European Space Agency, Noordwijk, The Netherlands

Crespo, Carolina 020490
University of Lisbon, Lisbon, Portugal

Cristiane Pan, Aline 020548
UFRGS, Tramandaí, Brazil

Cristóbal, Ana Belén 020491, 020535, 020575
UPM, Madrid, Spain

Crozier McCleland, Jacqueline 020185, 020344
Nelson Mandela University, Port Elizabeth, South Africa

Cuadra, Juan Manuel 020318
CENER, Sarigurren, Spain

Cui, Jindan 020320, 020525
Tokyo University of Science, Tokyo, Japan

Culot, Dominique 020384
Dow Silicones Belgium, Seneffe, Belgium

Curon, Jonathan 020384
Dow Silicones Belgium, Seneffe, Belgium

Cusenza, Maria Anna 020466
RSE, Milan, Italy

D. Pinto, Luciana 020090
Federal University of Rio de Janeiro, Rio de Janeiro, Brazil

Daenen, Michael 020156, 020389, 020393
imec, Genk, Belgium

Dagla, Anastasia 020276
3E, Brussels, Belgium

Dahle, Arne 020225, 020495
Norsun, Oslo, Norway

Dahlioui, Dounia 020443
University of Agder, Grimstad, Norway

Dalibor, Thomas 020307
Avancis, Munich, Germany

Dalla Maria, Enrico 020485
Eurac Research, Bolzano, Italy

Dalla Torre, Francesco 020010
Applied Materials, Treviso, Italy

Dalmazzone, Didier 020251
ENSTA Paris, Palaiseau, France

Damon, Keanu 020382
7SecondSolar, Cape Town, South Africa

Danelli, Andrea 020462, 020466
RSE, Milan, Italy

Darsene Dimd, Berhane 020270
SINTEF, Trondheim, Norway

Das, Gourab 020005, 020222, 020463
RCT Solutions, Konstanz, Germany

Dasilva-Villanueva, Nerea 020014, 020501, 020508
UPM, Madrid, Spain

Daßler, David 020313
Fraunhofer CSP, Halle, Germany

Daßler, David 020355
Fraunhofer IMWS, Halle, Germany

Daume, Darwin 020361
pvnode, Rosenheim, Germany

Davidsen, Rasmus Schmidt 020028, 020039, 020043
Aarhus University, Aarhus, Denmark

De Almeida, Laura 020074
LAAS-CNRS, Toulouse, France

De Biasio, Martin   020504
Silicon Austria Labs, Villach, Austria

De Blasi, Mariam   020378
Enel Green Power, Pisa, Italy

de Graaf, Gertjan J.   020405
TNO, Petten, The Netherlands

de Groot, Koen M.   020405
TNO, Petten, The Netherlands

De Gruijter, Alvaro   020254
Eurac Research, Bolzano, Italy

de Jong, Minne M.   020169, 020425
TNO, Eindhoven, The Netherlands

De Jong, Richard   020156, 020294, 020389
imec, Genk, Belgium

de l'Epine, Mélodie   020252, 020505, 020543, 020564
Becquerel Institute France, Lyon, France

de l'Epine, Melodie   020225, 020334, 020520, 020558
Becquerel Institute, Brussels, Belgium

de l'Epine, Melodie   020570
IEA PVPS Task 1, Lyon, France

de la Casa Higueras, Juan   020269
University of Jaén, Jaén, Spain

de la Viuda, Eva   020205
University of Valladolid, Valladolid, Spain

de Meatza, Iratxe   020495
CIDETEC, San Sebastián, Spain

De Rose, Angela   020123
Fraunhofer ISE, Freiburg, Germany

De Rose, Jonas   020010
Fraunhofer ISE, Freiburg, Germany

Debastiani Benato, Betina   020019
AMIRES, Prague, Czech Republic

Deepti,   020563
SRM University, Sonipat, India

Del Campo, Valeria   020311
Federico Santa María Technical University, Valparaiso,
Chile

del Cañizo, Carlos   020014, 020501, 020507, 020508
UPM, Madrid, Spain

Del Pero, Claudio   020249
Polytechnic University of Milan, Milan, Italy

Del Pozo, Alberto   020197, 020198
TECNALIA, Derio, Spain

del Prado Santamaria, Rodrigo   020191, 020376
DTU, Roskilde, Denmark

del Ser, Javier   020358
UPV/EHU, Bilbao, Spain

Delgado-Sanchez, Jose Maria
University of Seville, Seville, Spain
020089

Delli Veneri, Paola
ENEA, Naples, Italy
020378

Denafas, Julius
Solitek, Vilnius, Lithuania
020225, 020353

Deniz, Engin
Ege University, İzmir, Türkiye
020559

Denke, Sebastian
ISFH, Emmerthal, Germany
020236

Dentz, Laurie
CNRS, Palaiseau, France
020058

Derin Gure, Pinar
ODTU GUNAM, Ankara, Türkiye
020513, 020521, 020556

Derj, Anyssa
IPVF, Palaiseau, France
020116

Dessì, Alessio
CNR-ICCOM, Sesto Fiorentino, Italy
020077

Devenson, Jan
Center for Physical Sciences and Technology (FTMC),
Vilnius, Lithuania
020157

Dhimish, Mahmoud
DTU, Roskilde, Denmark
020346, 020376

Di Matteo, Alfredo
Enel Green Power, Catania, Italy
020010

Diab, Mohanad
Eurac Research, Bolzano, Italy
020203

Diano, Marcello
M2M Engineering, Naples, Italy
020378

Diaz, Roberto
Notio Association, Toledo, Spain
020300

Díaz, Sara
CENER, Sarriguren, Spain
020365, 020366

Dietrich, Andreas
DiSUN Deutsche Solarservice, Werder, Germany
020355

Díez Alcántara, Eduardo
UCM, Madrid, Spain
020501

Díez, Eduardo
UCM, Madrid, Spain
020508

Dimd, Berhane Darsene
SINTEF, Trondheim, Norway
020495, 020510

Ding, Kaining
FZJ, Jülich, Germany
020233

Ding, Kung
Hohai University, Changzhou, China
020111

Dittmann, Sebastian
Anhalt University of Applied Sciences, Köthen, Germany
020318

Dittrich, Arne 020240
ISFH, Emmerthal, Germany

Dizier, Antoine 020373
INES, Le Bourget-du-Lac, France

Djeukeu, Ivanol Jaurece 020050
halm elektronik, Frankfurt am Main, Germany

Dobreva, Petja 020193
University of Namibia, Windhoek, Namibia

Dörenkämper, Maarten 020169
TNO, Eindhoven, The Netherlands

Dörn, Markus 020255
A-Null Development, Vienna, Austria

Doi, Minh Thong 020317
CEA INES, Le Bourget-du-Lac, France

Domínguez, César 020209, 020246, 020257
UPM, Madrid, Spain

Donadello, Alessandro 020485, 020489
Edyna, Bolzano, Italy

Donėlienė, Jolanta 020157
Applied Research Institute for Prospective Technologies,
Vilnius, Lithuania

Donoso, José 020570
UNEF, Madrid, Spain

Doppler, Christian 020455
Virtual Vehicle, Graz, Austria

dos Reis, Givaldo 020348
University of São Paulo, São Paulo, Brazil

dos Santos, Jeremias 020409
University of Évora, Évora, Portugal

Doucet, Jean-Baptiste 020074
LAAS-CNRS, Toulouse, France

Dovesi, Roberto 020060
Academy of Sciences of Turin, Torino, Italy

Driesse, Anton 020211, 020293, 020452
PV Performance Labs, Freiburg, Germany

Duarte, Dorivaldo 020418, 020565
University of Evora, Évora, Portugal

Dubois, Sebastien 020034
University Grenoble Alpes, Le Bourget-du-Lac, France

Dubravskij, Piotr 020157
Applied Research Institute for Prospective Technologies,
Vilnius, Lithuania

Dubravskij, Piotr 020380
Modern E-Technologies, Vilnius, Lithuania

Duerinckx, Filip 020064, 020225
Hasselt Unversity, Genk, Belgium

Düz, Cansel   020135
Kalyon PV, Ankara, Türkiye

Dullweber, Thorsten   020006, 020007, 020008, 020225
ISFH, Emmerthal, Germany

Dunlop, Ewan D.   020173, 020210, 020213
European Commission JRC, Ispra, Italy

Dupon, Olivier   020294
imec, Genk, Belgium

Dupuis, Julien   020188
EDF R&D, Moret Loing Orvanne, France

Dutykh, Denys   020338
Khalifa University, Abu Dhabi, United Arab Emirates

Duzellier, Sophie   020073
University of Toulouse, Toulouse, France

Dypvik Sødahl, Elin   020340
IFE, Kjeller, Norway

Ebert, Matthias   020426
Fraunhofer CSP, Halle, Germany

Ebert, Matthias   020355
Fraunhofer IMWS, Halle, Germany

Ebner, Rita   020318, 020334, 020521
AIT, Vienna, Austria

Echeverria, Oihane   020139
Tecnalia, Donostia - San Sebastián, Spain

Eder, Gabriele C.   020160, 020162, 020249, 020500, 020504
OFI, Vienna, Austria

Eelma, Tonis   020302
IBS, Tartu, Estonia

Efthymiou, Venizelos   020544
EPL Technology Frontiers, Dhali, Cyprus

Egan, Renate   020048
UNSW, Sydney, Australia

Egido, Miguel-Ángel   020407
UPM, Madrid, Spain

Eidtmann, Maximilian   020385
ZHAW, Winterthur, Switzerland

Eijgelaar, Marcel   020571
DNV, Arnhem, The Netherlands

Eikelboom, Erik   020225
Futurasun, Citadella, Italy

Einhaus, Roland   020312
ZSW, Stuttgart, Germany

Eisenacher, Matthias   020141
University of Applied Science Cologne, Cologne, Germany

Eiternick, Stefan
Fraunhofer CSP, Halle (Saale), Germany
020004, 020052

Ekins-Daukes, Nicholas J.
UNSW, Sydney, Australia
020065

El Ainaoui, Khadija
Green Energy Park, Benguerir, Morocco
020171

El mrabet, Yasmine
Green Energy Park, Benguerir, Morocco
020171

Elgaili, Mohamed
QEERI, Doha, Qatar
020166

Elhamaoui, Said
Green Energy Park, Benguerir, Morocco
020171

Ellis, Hanna
European Commission JRC, Ispra, Italy
020213

Engelen, Tine
Hasselt University, Diepenbeek, Belgium
020389

Erber, Alexander
BFH, Burgdorf, Switzerland
020386

Eryılmaz, Hande
ODTÜ-GÜNAM, Ankara, Türkiye
020521

Escudero, Ana
IaSol, Zaragoza, Spain
020414

Esmailifar, Seyyed Majid
Amirkabir University of Technology, Tehran, Iran
020335, 020356, 020374, 020375

Espinosa, Nieves
University of Murcia, Murcia, Spain
020497, 020506

Essam T. Mohammed, Sarah
EU SOLARIS, Almeria, Spain
020546

Esteras, Miguel
TECNALIA, Derio, Spain
020358

Eyhorn, Steffen
Fraunhofer ISE, Freiburg, Germany
020369

Fabel, Yann
DLR, Almería, Spain
020235, 020237, 020239

Fabris, Francesca
Futurasun, Citadella, Italy
020225

Faes, Antonin
CSEM, Neuchâtel, Switzerland
020251

Falangas, Alexandros
TRASIS International, Brussels, Belgium
020210

Fang, Xue
Tokyo University of Science, Tokyo, Japan
020525

Fano, Vanesa
UPV/EHU, Bilbao, Spain
020055, 020097, 020153, 020287

Farhat, Mohammad   020428
Australian University, Kuwait City, Kuwait

Farina, Andrea   020066
CNR-IFN, Milan, Italy

Farrias-Basulto, Guillermo   020101
HZB, Berlin, Germany

Fath, Moritz   020463
RCT Solutions, Konstanz, Germany

Fath, Peter   020005, 020463
RCT Solutions, Konstanz, Germany

Fava, Henrique   020565
University of Évora, Évora, Portugal

Feichtner, Markus   020255
Sonnenkraft Energie, St. Veit/Glan, Austria

Feichtner, Markus   020160
Sonnenkraft Energy, St. Veit/Glan, Austria

Feldbacher, Sonja   020136, 020500
PCCL, Leoben, Austria

Feldhof, Anne Maren   020522
University of Applied Science Cologne, Cologne, Germany

Fernandes, Cláudia   020464
Centre for New Energy Technologies, Sacavém, Portugal

Fernández Solas, Álvaro   020331
DLR, Almería, Spain

Ferrando, Jorge   020226
University of Valencia, Paterna, Spain

Ferreira, Catarina G.   020250
SDU Climate Cluster, Odense, Denmark

Ferreira, Catarina   020306
SDU Climate Cluster, Odense, Denmark

Ferrero, Sergio   020079
Polytechnic University of Turin, Turin, Italy

Feuerherdt, Niels   020309
Berlin University of Applied Sciences, Berlin, Germany

Fialho, Luis   020203, 020254, 020261, 020304, 020403,
Eurac Research, Bolzano, Italy   020409, 020418, 020420, 020565

Figueroa, Andrés   020339
National University of Colombia, Bogotá, Colombia

Fischer, Stefan   020495
SGL Carbon, Meitingen, Germany

Fleischanderl, Martin   020136
voestalpine Stahl, Linz, Austria

Fleury, Perine   020513, 020521
Biosphere Solar, Delft, The Netherlands

Flouchi, Imane   020171
Green Energy Park, Benguerir, Morocco

Fodor, Nikoletta   020521
SolarPower Europe, Brussels, Belgium

Fontani, Daniela   020066
CNR-INO, Florence, Italy

Forster, Jacob   020135
Fraunhofer ISE, Freiburg, Germany

Forstinger, Anne   020331
CSP Services, Cologne, Germany

Franch, Jordi Badosa   020406
Ecole Polytechnique, Palaiseau, France

Franchi, Daniele   020077
CNR-ICCOM, Sesto Fiorentino, Italy

Franquet, Erwin   020259, 020428
Côte d'Azur University, Nice, France

Frasson, Nicola   020019
Applied Materials, San Biagio di Callalta, Italy

Freer, Solomon   020396
PV Lighthouse, Coledale, Australia

Freitag, Marina   020077
Newcastle University, Newcastle upon Tyne, United
Kingdom

Freund, Timo   020312
EnBW, Karlsruhe, Germany

Friansyah, Rizal   020376
DTU, Roskilde, Denmark

Friesen, Gabi   020160, 020249, 020574
SUPSI, Mendrisio, Switzerland

Friesen, Thomas   020249
Megasol Energie, Deitingen, Switzerland

Fritz Muñoz, Benjamín   020099
UPV, Valencia, Spain

Froebel, Jens   020121, 020142, 020192, 020223
Fraunhofer CSP, Halle, Germany

Frontini, Francesco   020249, 020253
SUPSI, Mendrisio, Switzerland

Fuentealba-Vidal, Edward   020129, 020311, 020342, 020417, 020422
University of Antofagasta, Antofagasta, Chile

Füreder-Kitzmüller, Friedrich   020136
voestalpine Stahl, Linz, Austria

Fuertes Marrón, David   020014, 020501, 020507, 020508
UPM, Madrid, Spain

Fuertes, David   020097
IES-UPM, Madrid, Spain

Furnari, Alessandro   020010
Enel Green Power, Catania, Italy

Fuß, Michael   020206
MBJ Solutions, Ahrensburg, Germany

Gabor, Andrew M.   020166
BrightSpot Automation, Boulder, United States of America

Gaete, Martin   020311
University of Antofagasta, Antofagasta, Chile

Gafert, Michael   020369
AIT, Vienna, Austria

Gageot, Tristan   020040
CEA / INES, Le Bourget-du-Lac, France

Gainza, Eusebio   020392
ALLOTARRA, Allo, Spain

Galarza, Alejandra   020461
IPVF, Palaiseau, France

Galbiati, Giuseppe   020119, 020218
Henkel, Düsseldorf, Germany

Galdikas, Algirdas   020157
Applied Research Institute for Prospective Technologies,
Vilnius, Lithuania

Galiana, Beatriz   020085
Charles III University of Madrid, Madrid, Spain

Galiazzo, Marco   020019
Applied Materials, San Biagio di Callalta, Italy

Gall, Stefan   020101
HZB, Berlin, Germany

Gallmetzer, Sandra   020261, 020509
Eurac Research, Bolzano, Italy

Galparsoro, Ibon   020514
AZTI, PASAIA, Spain

Gamarra, Ana Rosa   020502
CIEMAT, Madrid, Spain

Ganter, Alissa   020296
ETH, Zurich, Switzerland

Gaona García, Elvis Eduardo   020279
District University of Bogotá, Bogotá, Colombia

Garabetian, Thomas   020551
SolarPower Europe, Brussels, Belgium

García Campos, Enrique   020336
University of Almería, La Cañada de San Urbano, Spain

García, Fernando   020326
UC3M, Madrid, Spain

García, Sonia   020139
Tecnalia, Donostia - San Sebastián, Spain

García-Cañas, Alejandro   020257
IMDEA Nanoscience, Madrid, Spain

García-Salinas, María José   020100
University of Almeria, Almería, Spain

Garcia-Sanchez, Almudena   020246, 020257
UPM, Madrid, Spain

Garg, Vivek   020069, 020071, 020081
SVNIT, Surat, India

Garraín, Daniel   020502
CIEMAT, Madrid, Spain

Gasse, Hugues   020073
University of Toulouse, Toulouse, France

Gassner, Anika   020160, 020162, 020500, 020504
OFI, Vienna, Austria

Gatti, Cesare   020541
PedersoliGattai, Milan, Italy

Gattu, Apoorva   020003
ISC Konstanz, Konstanz, Germany

Gautier, Damien   020505
Becquerel Institute, Brussels, Belgium

Gauvin, Xavier   020302
Bouygues Construction, Saint-Quentin-en-Yvelines, France

Ge, Hua   020249
Concordia University, Montreal, Canada

Gebhardt, Paul   020195
Fraunhofer ISE, Freiburg, Germany

Geerligs, L. J.   020030
TNO, Petten, The Netherlands

Gehrlein, Janek   020522
University of Applied Science Cologne, Cologne, Germany

Geier, Jutta   020234
PCCL, Leoben, Austria

Geml, Fabian   020031
University of Konstanz, Constance, Germany

Genovese, Maria   020378
Enel Green Power, Pisa, Italy

Georghiou, George E.   020534
University of Cyprus, Nicosia, Cyprus

Germani, Simone   020302
CEI, Milan, Italy

Getsiou, Maria   020181
Directorate General for Research and Innovation, Brussels,
Belgium

Geymayer, Lukas   020136
voestalpine Stahl, Linz, Austria

Ghahremani, Amirreza   020335, 020374
Amirkabir University of Technology, Tehran, Iran

Ghennioui, Abdellatif   020171
Green Energy Park, Benguerir, Morocco

Ghosh, Saptak   020519
CSTEP, Bengaluru, India

Girardi, Pierpaolo   020462, 020466
RSE, Milan, Italy

Giroux-Julien, Stephanie   020338
CNRS, Villeurbanne, France

Gissler, Antoine   020060
EDF R&D, Palaiseau, France

Göckeritz, Robert   020119
Fraunhofer CSP, Halle, Germany

Gohil, Hardik   020222
RCT Solutions, Konstanz, Germany

Gomes de Venuto, Vitor   020025
PUCRS, Porto Alegre, Brazil

Gomez Trillos, Juan Camilo   020482
DLR, Oldenburg, Germany

Gomez-Lazaro, Emilio   020562
University of Castilla-La Mancha, Albacete, Spain

Gonnella, Gabriella   020249, 020254
Eurac research, Bolzano, Italy

González Pérez, Sara   020151
ULL, San Cristóbal de La Laguna, Spain

González Rodríguez, Brais   020243
University of Vigo, Vigo, Spain

González, Miguel Ángel   020205
University of Valladolid, Valladolid, Spain

González-Díaz, Benjamín   020151
ULL, San Cristóbal de La Laguna, Spain

Goraya, Baljeet Singh   020475
Fraunhofer ISE, Freiburg, Germany

Gordillo, Gerardo   020110
National University of Colombia, Bogotá, Colombia

Gordon, Ivan   020521
imec, Genk, Belgium

Gottschalg, Ralph   020158
Anhalt University of Applied Sciences, Köthen, Germany

Gottschalg, Ralph   020056, 020201, 020229, 020233, 020284,
Fraunhofer CSP, Halle, Germany   020574

Govaerts, Jonathan   020019
imec, Genk, Belgium

Gracia Amillo, Ana María   020211
CENER, Pamplona, Spain

Gracia Amillo, Ana María   020318
CENER, Sarigurren, Spain

Gracia Amillo, Ana María   020181, 020365, 020366, 020497
CENER, Sarriguren, Spain

Gregory, Geoffrey   020006
EnPV, Karlsruhe, Germany

Greslou, Olivier 020551
CSTB, Bussy-Saint Georges, France

Grommes, Eva-Maria 020522, 020523
University of Applied Science Cologne, Cologne, Germany

Grosser, Stephan 020119, 020142, 020218
Fraunhofer CSP, Halle, Germany

Grünsteidl, Stefan 020307
Avancis, Munich, Germany

Gruginskie, Natasha 020067
Radboud University, Nijmegen, The Netherlands

Guedea, Isabel 020127, 020517
ENDEF, Zaragoza, Spain

Gülsoy, Eren Cihan 020521
METU, Ankara, Türkiye

Gümüs Çiftci, Burcu 020027
Kalyon PV, Ankara, Türkiye

Guerra, Gerardo 020448, 020481
GreenPowerMonitor a DNV company, Barcelona, Spain

Guidetti, Giulia 020541
Green Horse Advisory, Milan, Italy

Guillemoles, Jean François 020062
IPVF, Palaiseau, France

Guillevin, Nicolas 020225
TNO, Petten, The Netherlands

Gunbas, Gorkem 020113
ODTÜ-GÜNAM, Ankara, Türkiye

Gupta, Akshit 020551
Eurac Research, Bolzano, Italy

Gutierrez, Jose Ruben 020055, 020097, 020153, 020287
UPV/EHU, Bilbao, Spain

Gutjahr, Astrid 020030
TNO, Petten, The Netherlands

Haaland, Petry Kristine Nøttum 020476
NTNU, Trondheim, Norway

Haase, Felix 020063
ISFH, Emmerthal, Germany

Hadiwidjaja, Stella 020102
SERIS, Singapore, Singapore

Hadjipanayi, Maria 020064
University of Cyprus, Nicosia, Cyprus

Haedrich, Ingrid 020195, 020231
Fraunhofer ISE, Freiburg, Germany

Hämmer, Matthias 020470
bifa Umweltinstitut, Augsburg, Germany

Hafidi, Elias   020511
Inflights BV, Brussels, Belgium

Hagemann, Elizabeth M.   020416
Nelson Mandela University, Port Elizabeth, South Africa

Hallais, Géraldine   020058
CNRS, Palaiseau, France

Halle, Lasse   020359
BFH, Burgdorf, Switzerland

Hallensleben, Carina   020220
TAMURA-ELSOLD, Ilsenburg, Germany

Halm, Andreas   020218, 020220, 020221
ISC Konstanz, Konstanz, Germany

Halme, Janne   020249
Aalto University, Espoo, Finland

Hamada, Toshiyuki   020190
Osaka Electro-Communication University, Osaka, Japan

Hammer, Annette   020239
DLR, Oldenburg, Germany

Hamouda, Frederic   020058
CNRS, Palaiseau, France

Hanifi, Hamed   020121, 020125, 020137, 020223
AESOLAR, Koenigsbrunn, Germany

Hansen, Per-Anders   020017, 020503
Institute for Energy Technology, Kjeller, Norway

Harit, Amit Kumar   020064
Hasselt Unversity, Genk, Belgium

Harrison, Samuel   020225
CEA, Le Bourget-du-Lac, France

Hashem, Ahmad   020056, 020201
Anhalt University of Applied Sciences, Köthen, Germany

Hategan, Sergiu Mihai   020283
West University of Timisoara, Timisoara, Romania

Hauch, Jens   020117, 020149, 020150
HI ERN, Erlangen, Germany

Hauer, Martin   020255
Bartenbach, Vienna, Austria

Haverkamp, Helge   020008
centrotherm international, Blaubeuren, Germany

Hee Lee, Sang   020045
KIER, Daejeon, South Korea

Heidrich, Robert   020233
Fraunhofer CSP, Halle, Germany

Heikkinen, Kyösti   020423
VTT Technical Research Centre of Finland, Oulu, Finland

Heiser, Moritz   020230
Kiwa PI Berlin, Berlin, Germany

Helbig, Matthias ISC Konstanz, Konstanz, Germany	020220
Helten, David CSP Services, Cologne, Germany	020331
Hennig, Carsten saferay holding, Berlin, Germany	020313, 020355
Hennig, Patrick Kiel University of Applied Sciences, Kiel, Germany	020313
Heras, Jesús Wattkraft, Madrid, Spain	020536
Hermle, Martin Fraunhofer ISE, Freiburg, Germany	020475
Hernández Mora, Johann Alexander District University of Bogotá, Bogotá, Colombia	020279, 020441
Hernández, Jaime J. IMDEA Nanoscience, Madrid, Spain	020257
Hernández, Johann Francisco José de Caldas District University, Bogota, Colombia	020526
Herodotou, Panayiotis University of Cyprus, Nicosia, Cyprus	020534
Herrera Leon, Fernando Augusto National University of Colombia, Bogotá, Colombia	020339, 020546
Herrero, Leire Tecnalia, Donostia - San Sebastián, Spain	020139
Herrero, Rebeca UPM, Madrid, Spain	020209, 020453, 020459
Herrmann, Werner TÜV Rheinland Solar, Cologne, Germany	020208
Herteleer, Bert KU Leuven, Ghent, Belgium	020329, 020351
Herteleer, Bert SUPSI, Mendrisio, Switzerland	020574
Hessler-Wyser, Aïcha EPFL, Neuchâtel, Switzerland	020251
Heydari, Azim Eurac Research, Bolzano, Italy	020485
Hinken, David ISFH, Emmerthal, Germany	020236
Hladys, Bertrand CEA, Grenoble, France	020010
Hoex, Bram UNSW, Sydney, Australia	020065
Hofer, Leo BFH, Burgdorf, Switzerland	020322
Hoffmann, Erik EnPV, Karlsruhe, Germany	020006

Hogan Almeida, Rita
UPM, Madrid, Spain

020535, 020567

Hollemann, Christina
ISFH, Emmerthal, Germany

020008

Holovský, Jakub
Czech Technical University, Prague, Czech Republic

020107

Honrubia-Escribano, Andrés
University of Castilla-La Mancha, Albacete, Spain

020562

Hopp, Tobias
Sunman Energy, Frankfurt, Germany

020384

Horn, Jonas
halm elektronik, Frankfurt am Main, Germany

020050

Horta, Pedro
University of Évora, Évora, Portugal

020304, 020403, 020409, 020418, 020420, 020565

Hosatte, Mikaël
SEGTON Advanced Technology, Versailles, France

020068

Hoß, Jan
ISC Konstanz, Konstanz, Germany

020004, 020035

Hossain, Mohammad Istiaque
QEERI, Doha, Qatar

020042, 020075, 020108, 020109, 020146, 020147

Hou, Yi
SERIS, Singapore, Singapore

020102

Hsiao, Pei-Chieh
UNSW, Sydney, Australia

020048

Hsieh, Cho Fan
ITRI, Hsinchu, Taiwan

020083, 020161, 020163

Hu, Shuaifeng
University of Oxford, Oxford, United Kingdom

020226

Huang, Chris
SunDrive Solar, Kurnell, Australia

020048

Huang, Gan
KIT, Eggenstein-Leopoldshafen, Germany

020272

Huang, Lu-Jan
TNO, Leiden, The Netherlands

020425

Huang, Tzu-Yen
National Synchrotron Radiation Research Center, Hsinchu, Taiwan

020096

Hügi, Matthias
BFH, Burgdorf, Switzerland

020322

Huemer, Martin
University of Linz, Linz, Austria

020227

Huerta, Hugo E.
TUAS, Turku, Finland

020286, 020400

Hüttl, Bernd
Coburg University of Applied Sciences, Coburg, Germany

020361

Hulik Jansova, Marketa   020274
Solargis, Bratislava, Slovakia

Hung, Tzu Han   020552
ITRI, Taipei City, Taiwan

Hutterer-Tik, Thomas   020347
Watt Analytics, Vienna, Austria

Hwang, Hye-Mi   020324, 020357, 020561
KIER, Daejeon, South Korea

Iglesias, Unai   020139
Tecnalia, Donostia - San Sebastián, Spain

Ikeda, Kazuaki   020436
AIST, Koriyama, Japan

Infante, Paulo   020420
University of Évora, Évora, Portugal

Isabella, Olindo   020515
TU Delft, Delft, The Netherlands

Ishikawa, Ryousuke   020106, 020115
Tokyo City University, Setagaya, Japan

Iwaszko, Victorien   020495
ROSI Solar, Saint-Martin-d'Hères, France

Izquierdo-Roca, Victor   020094
IREC, Barcelona, Spain

J. N. Soares, Guillermo   020090
Federal University of Rio de Janeiro, Duque de Caxias,
Brazil

Jacob, Julieu   020302
METABUILD, Berlin, Germany

Jacobs, Ayesha   020382
Zutari, Cape Town, South Africa

Jaeckel, Bengt   020056, 020119, 020121, 020140, 020142,
Fraunhofer CSP, Halle, Germany   020175, 020192, 020201, 020223, 020229

Jäger Waldau, Arnulf   020570
European Commission, Rome, Italy

Jäger, Philip   020006
ISFH, Emmerthal, Germany

Jäggi, Adrian   020179
BFH, Burgdorf, Switzerland

Järventausta, Pertti   020445
Tampere University, Tampere, Finland

Jaffré, Alexandre   020058
CNRS, Gif-sur-Yvette, France

Jahn, Ulrike   020521, 020574
Fraunhofer CSP, Halle, Germany

Jahn, Ulrike 020355
Fraunhofer IMWS, Halle, Germany

Jahreis, Sophia 020142, 020192
Fraunhofer CSP, Halle, Germany

Jakomin, Roberto 020090
Federal University of Rio de Janeiro, Duque de Caxias, Brazil

Jakubik, Martin 020274
Solargis, Bratislava, Slovakia

Jakuza, Paola 020089
University of Padova, Padova, Italy

Jalkh, Judy 020455
Virtual Vehicle, Graz, Austria

Jandl, Ralf 020204
FFHS, Zurich, Switzerland

Jankovec, Marko 020197
University of Ljubljana, Ljubljana, Slovenia

Jaworczak, Kamil 020402
Technology Innovation Institute, Abu Dhabi, United Arab Emirates

Jensen, Adam R. 020267
DTU, Kongens Lyngby, Denmark

Jeong, Jungi 020323
K-water, Daejeon, South Korea

Jeong, Kyung Taek 020045
KIER, Daejeon, South Korea

Jeong, Minsoo 020045
KIER, Daejeon, South Korea

Jeronimo, Pedro 020010
CEA, Grenoble, France

Jiang, Zonghan 020158, 020201
Anhalt University of Applied Sciences, Köthen, Germany

Jimenez, Maria 020302
Onyx Solar, Avila, Spain

Jimeno, Juan Carlos 020055, 020097, 020153, 020287, 020289, 020353
UPV/EHU, Bilbao, Spain

Jo, Hyunsik 020323
K-water, Daejeon, South Korea

Job, Enzo 020231
Fraunhofer ISE, Freiburg, Germany

Johnson, Mark Robert 020546
Institut Laue-Langevin (ILL), Grenoble, France

Joo, Dongmyoung 020449
KETI, Wonmi-gu, South Korea

Jooss, Wolfgang 020005, 020222, 020463
RCT Solutions, Konstanz, Germany

Joseph, Daniel Christopher   020123
Fraunhofer ISE, Freiburg, Germany

Joshi, Deepak   020069, 020081
SVNIT, Surat, India

Joss, David   020359, 020369, 020386
BFH, Burgdorf, Switzerland

Jouini, Anis   020034
ECM Technologies, Grenoble, France

Jouttijärvi, Sami   020286, 020298, 020398
University of Turku, Turku, Finland

Joziak, Roman   020230
Kiwa PI Berlin, Berlin, Germany

Ju, Young-Chul   020324, 020357, 020561
KIER, Daejeon, South Korea

Jugo, Josu   020437
UPV/EHU, Leioa, Spain

Junge, Sebastian   020008, 020482
ISFH, Emmerthal, Germany

Kaaya, Ismail   020156, 020294, 020389, 020393
imec, Genk, Belgium

Kähler, Jan-Dirk   020482
Centrotherm International, Blaubeuren, Germany

Kahraman, Mert   020027
Kalyon PV, Ankara, Türkiye

Kainz, Konrad   020430
AIT, Vienna, Austria

Kaiser, Martin   020215
Fraunhofer ISE, Freiburg, Germany

Kaizuka, Izumi   020570
RTS Corporation, Tokyo, Japan

Kajari-Schröder, Sarah   020063
ISFH, Emmerthal, Germany

Kallioharju, Kari   020444, 020445
TUAS, Tampere, Finland

Kalliojärvi, Heidi   020194
Tampere University, Tampere, Finland

Kalshetty, Mahesh   020519
CSTEP, Bengaluru, India

Kaltenbach, Thomas   020195
Fraunhofer ISE, Freiburg, Germany

Kamphues, Joshua   020031
University of Konstanz, Constance, Germany

Kandiyoti-Eskenazi, Selin   020467
CSEM, Neuchâtel, Switzerland

Kang, Min Gu   020045
KIER, Daejeon, South Korea

Kapetanovic, Viktor   020367
Nextracker, Fremont, United States of America

Karhu, Juha   020286
Finnish Meteorological Institute, Helsinki, Finland

Kari, Thøger   020191, 020376
DTU, Roskilde, Denmark

Karimy, Hedayatullah   020052
Fraunhofer CSP, Halle (Saale), Germany

Karttunen, Lauri   020298, 020398
University of Turku, Turku, Finland

Kasper, Ruth   020167, 020232
University of Applied Sciences Cologne, Cologne, Germany

Katouli, Tannaz   020195
Fraunhofer ISE, Freiburg, Germany

Kaufmann, Kai   020355
DENKweit, Halle, Germany

Kawabata, Rudy   020092
PUC-Rio, Rio de Janeiro, Brazil

Kemp, Linda   020390
MARIN, Wageningen, The Netherlands

Kenchington, Ian   020225, 020474, 020558
Becquerel Institute, Brussels, Belgium

Kenny, Robert   020210
European Commission JRC, Ispra, Italy

Khan, Abeer Ali   020513
First Solar, Mainz, Germany

Khosravi, Arash   020381
Mälardalen University, Västerås, Sweden

Kikkert, Benjamin W. J.   020405
TNO, Petten, The Netherlands

Kilickaya, Seda   020020
ODTÜ-GÜNAM, Ankara, Türkiye

Kim, Jin-Hong   020449
KETI, Wonmi-gu, South Korea

Kim, Jun-Tae   020249
Kongju National University, Chungnam, South Korea

Kim, Kihwan   020112
KIER, Daejeon, South Korea

Kim, Seok Won   020449
KETI, Wonmi-gu, South Korea

Kim, Yong-Jin   020045
KIER, Daejeon, South Korea

Kinge, Sachin   020117
Toyota Motors Europe, Brussels, Belgium

Kolahi, Mohammad   020356, 020375
University of Isfahan, Isfahan, Iran

Konagai, Makoto   020106, 020115
Tokyo City University, Setagaya, Japan

Kono, Toru   020484
Hitachi, Kokubunji, Japan

Konu, Christopher Bruce   020132
HTW Berlin, Berlin, Germany

Kopecek, Radovan   020569
ISC Konstanz, Konstanz, Germany

Kopp, Nils   020220
TAMURA-ELSOLD, Ilsenburg, Germany

Korkmaz Arslan, Melisa   020020
ODTÜ-GÜNAM, Ankara, Türkiye

Korpås, Magnus   020476
NTNU, Trondheim, Norway

Kortetmäki, Aki   020444, 020445
TUAS, Tampere, Finland

Koskela, Juha   020444, 020445, 020554
Tampere University, Tampere, Finland

Kossen, Eric J.   020030
TNO, Petten, The Netherlands

Kowalski, Julia   020237
RWTH, Aachen, Germany

Kräling, Ulli   020215
Fraunhofer ISE, Freiburg, Germany

Kraft, Thomas M.   020423
VTT Technical Research Centre of Finland, Oulu, Finland

Krainer, Diana Maria   020430
AIT, Vienna, Austria

Krasilnikov, Inga   020379
Tel Aviv University, Tel Aviv, Israel

Krever Lopes, Bruno   020023
PUCRS, Porto Alegre, Brazil

Kribus, Abraham   020379
Tel Aviv University, Tel Aviv, Israel

Krishnan, Sasikumar   020361
Coburg University of Applied Sciences, Coburg, Germany

Kroon, Jan   020225
TNO, Petten, The Netherlands

Kuan, Ta-Ming   020021, 020053
TSEC, Hsinchu, Taiwan

Kubicek, Bernhard   020281, 020318, 020334, 020347, 020430
AIT, Vienna, Austria

Kucuk, E. Busra   020030
TNO, Petten, The Netherlands

Lachowicz, Agata 020039
CSEM, Neuchâtel, Switzerland

Lahr, Simon 020388
Next2Sun Technology, Dillingen, Germany

Lahr, Simon 020411
Next2Sun, Dillingen, Germany

Lajunen, Antti 020400
University of Helsinki, Helsinki, Finland

Lambertz, Andreas 020233
FZJ, Jülich, Germany

Lamblot, Hervé 020302
Sunstyle, Paris, France

Lamghari, Fouad 020402
Fujairah Research Centre, Fujairah, United Arab Emirates

Lamminaho, Jani 020250, 020306
SDU Climate Cluster, Odense, Denmark

Landaas, Christian 020495
Northern Silicon, Meråker, Norway

Landberg, Lars 020448
DNV Denmark, Hellerup, Denmark

Landberg, Lars 020481
DNV Denmark, Hellerup, Spain

Landes, Dieter 020361
Coburg University of Applied Sciences, Coburg, Germany

Landová, Lucie 020107
Czech Technical University, Prague, Czech Republic

Lansade, David 020073
University of Toulouse, Toulouse, France

Lappalainen, Kari 020194, 020528, 020537
Tampere University, Tampere, Finland

Lara, Yolanda 020127, 020414, 020517
ENDEF, Zaragoza, Spain

Larionova, Yevgeniya 020006, 020007, 020225
ISFH, Emmerthal, Germany

Låstad, Jonas 020011
NTNU, Trondheim, Norway

Laurens-Berge, Clarisse 020034
University Grenoble Alpes, Le Bourget-du-Lac, France

Laurikėnas, Paulius 020353
Solitek, Vilnius, Lithuania

Lauwaert, Johan 020064
Ghent University, Ghent, Belgium

Lazaro-Castrillon, Luna 020085
IO-CSIC, Madrid, Spain

Le Bossenec, Hugo 020116
IPVF, Palaiseau, France

Leza, Baurin 020412
Gonvarri MS R&D, Corvera - Asturias, Spain

Lezaca, Jorge 020239
DLR, Oldenburg, Germany

Li, Xinyang 020222
RCT Solutions, Konstanz, Germany

Li, Yung-Chih 020021
TSEC, Hsinchu, Taiwan

Li, Yuxuan 020001
East China University of Science and Technology,
Shanghai, China

Libal, Joris 020218, 020474
ISC Konstanz, Konstanz, Germany

Lichtenberger, Janine 020430
AIT, Vienna, Austria

Lițiu, Andrei Vladimir 020551
EPB Center, Rotterdam, The Netherlands

Lin, Shih-Chieh 020021
TSEC, Hsinchu, Taiwan

Lindahl, Johan 020486, 020532
Becquerel Sweden, Knivsta, Sweden

Linder, Johannes 020492
Belectric, Kolitzheim, Germany

Lindfors, Anders 020286
Finnish Meteorological Institute, Helsinki, Finland

Lindig, Sascha 020371
Univers, Courbevoie, France

Linke, Jonathan 020004, 020035, 020225
ISC Konstanz, Konstanz, Germany

Linß, Volker 020033
VON ARDENNE, Dresden, Germany

Lipovšek, Benjamin 020047
University of Ljubljana, Ljubljana, Slovenia

Lippke, Benjamin 020180, 020230
Kiwa PI Berlin, Berlin, Germany

List-Kratochvil, Emil 020101
HZB, Berlin, Germany

Litrico, Grazia 020010
Enel Green Power, Catania, Italy

Liu, Cui 020001
East China University of Science and Technology,
Shanghai, China

Liu, Dongyang 020063
ISFH, Emmerthal, Germany

Liu, Han-Chang 020350
ITRI, Tainan, Taiwan

Liu, Huiping   020495
GRÄNGES, Finspång, Sweden

Liu, Mengdi   020144, 020208
TÜV Rheinland, Shanghai, China

Liu, Yung-Tsung   020053, 020083
ITRI, Hsinchu, Taiwan

Livera, Andreas   020534
University of Cyprus, Nicosia, Cyprus

Lizin, Sebastien   020513, 020521
UHasselt, Hasselt, Belgium

Llarena, María Elena   020151
ITER, Granadilla de Abona, Spain

Loeckenhoff, Ruediger F.   020416
AZUR SPACE Solar Power, Heilbronn, Germany

Löhning, Martha   020063
ISFH, Emmerthal, Germany

Löhr, Johannes   020063, 020114
ISFH, Emmerthal, Germany

Lokhat, Ismaël   020262
Cythelia Energy, La Motte-Servolex, France

Lokhat, Ismael   020373
Trace Software, Saint-Romain-de-Colbosc, France

Lombardo, Salvatore   020066
CNR-IMM, Catania, Italy

Long, Yean-San   020053, 020083
ITRI, Hsinchu, Taiwan

Longo, Giulia   020099
UPV, Valencia, Spain

Lopes Gomes, Carlos Javier   020432, 020434
Sunveon, Madrid, Spain

Lopes, Ana Patrícia   020464
University of Lisbon, Lisbon, Portugal

López Cuéllar, Juan Manuel   020501
UCM, Madrid, Spain

López Dalmau, Daniel   020432, 020434
Sunveon, Madrid, Spain

López, Nuria   020451
DTU, Roskilde, Denmark

Lorenz, Dieter   020206
MBJ Solutions, Ahrensburg, Germany

Lorenzo Pigueiras, Eduardo   020363
UPM, Madrid, Spain

Lorenzo, Celena   020337, 020536
UPM, Madrid, Spain

Lorenzo, Eduardo   020439, 020446
UPM, Madrid, Spain

Maiz, Alexander 020437
UPV/EHU, Vitoria-Gasteiz, Spain

Majak, Martyna 020068
Roltec, Poznań, Poland

Makrides, George 020534
University of Cyprus, Nicosia, Cyprus

Malarkannan, Lavanya 020210
National Physical Laboratory, Teddington, United Kingdom

Malcorps, Philippe 020276
3E, Brussels, Belgium

Malik, Stephanie 020313
Fraunhofer CSP, Halle, Germany

Malik, Stephanie 020355
Fraunhofer IMWS, Halle, Germany

Maliutina, Kristina 020141
University of Applied Science Cologne, Cologne, Germany

Malo, Javier 020209
UPM, Madrid, Spain

Mancini, Simone 020425
TNO, Eindhoven, The Netherlands

Mandiola, Gotzon 020514
AZTI, PASAIA, Spain

Manganiello, Patrizio 020389
Hasselt University, Diepenbeek, Belgium

Manganiello, Patrizio 020294
imec, Genk, Belgium

Manito, Alex 020348
University of São Paulo, São Paulo, Brazil

Manochehrian, Rasoul 020539
Frankfurt University of Applied Sciences, Frankfurt am
Main, Germany

Manzolini, Giampaolo 020261
Polytechnic University of Milan, Milan, Italy

Maqsood, Ayman 020101
HZB, Berlin, Germany

Marangis, Demetris 020534
University of Cyprus, Nicosia, Cyprus

Marcos-Castro, Ana 020297
CIEMAT, Madrid, Spain

Marechal, Philippe 020217
CEA / INES, Le Bourget-du-Lac, France

Marí Soucase, Bernabé 020099
UPV, Valencia, Spain

Markert, Jochen 020231
Fraunhofer ISE, Freiburg, Germany

Marquardt, Cornelia 020063
ISFH, Emmerthal, Germany

Marteau, Baptiste ECM Technologies, Grenoble, France	020034
Martín Rueda, Javier UPM, Madrid, Spain	020535
Martín, Francisco José UPM, Madrid, Spain	020459
Martín, Francisco UPM, Madrid, Spain	020209
Martín-Chivelet, Nuria CIEMAT, Madrid, Spain	020297
Martín-Rueda, Javier UPM, Madrid, Spain	020337, 020363
Martínez González, Mario Enertis Applus+, Madrid, Spain	020326
Martinez, Juan Ignacio Becquerel Institute Spain, San Sebastian, Spain	020252
Martinez, Oscar University of Valladolid, Valladolid, Spain	020191, 020205
Martínez-Barbeito, María ieco.io, Vigo, Spain	020243
Maruyama, Rodrigo P. University of São Paulo, São Paulo, Brazil	020154, 020348
Marzo, Aitor University of Granada, Granada, Spain	020311, 020546
Mashkov, Oleksandr HI ERN, Erlangen, Germany	020149, 020150, 020377
Massaro, Lorenzo PedersoliGattai, Milan, Italy	020541
Masson, Gaëtan Becquerel Institute, Brussels, Belgium	020474, 020558, 020564, 020573
Masson, Gaëtan IEA PVPS Task 1, Brussels, Belgium	020570
Mateos, Yeray UPV/EHU, Bilbao, Spain	020055, 020153
Maturi, Laura Eurac Research, Bolzano, Italy	020249, 020254, 020551
Mayer-Ullmann, Philipp AIT, Vienna, Austria	020430
Mazzoleni, Stefano University of Naples Federico II, Naples, Italy	020378
McIntosh, Keith R. PV Lighthouse, Coledale, Australia	020396
McNab, Shona UNSW, Sydney, Australia	020065
Meereboer, Martijn Energyra, Westknollendam, The Netherlands	020225

Meier, Rico 020132
HTW Berlin, Berlin, Germany

Meixner, Michael 020050
halm elektronik, Frankfurt am Main, Germany

Mekhaldi, Bouchra 020406
Ecole Polytechnique, Palaiseau, France

Melges de Andrade, Adnei 020154
University of São Paulo, São Paulo, Brazil

Melino, Francesco 020314
University of Bologna, Bologna, Italy

Mellone, Celeste 020541
Green Horse Advisory, Rome, Italy

Menard, Lionel 020291
MINES Paris, Nice, France

Mencaraglia, Denis 020058
CNRS, Gif-sur-Yvette, France

Menchaca, Iratxe 020514
AZTI, PASAIA, Spain

Mendes Ferreira Gomes, Amanda 020548
UFSC, Florianopolis, Brazil

Mendikoa, Iñigo 020514
Tecnalia, BRTA, Derio, Spain

Meneghini, Matteo 020089
University of Padova, Padova, Italy

Ménézo, Christophe 020317
LOCIE, Le Bourget-du-Lac, France

Menghini, Mariela 020508
IMDEA Nanoscience Institute, Madrid, Spain

Mercade Ruiz, Pau 020448, 020481
GreenPowerMonitor a DNV company, Barcelona, Spain

Merino, Amanda 020040
CEA / INES, Le Bourget-du-Lac, France

Merino, José Manuel 020085
UAM, Madrid, Spain

Mermoud, André 020196
PVsyst, Geneva, Switzerland

Merodio, Pablo 020337
UPM, Madrid, Spain

Mertens, Jan 020389
imec, Genk, Belgium

Mertens, Verena 020006, 020008
ISFH, Emmerthal, Germany

Meßmer, Marius 020031
Fraunhofer ISE, Freiburg, Germany

Messmer, Tobias 020218, 020221, 020225
ISC Konstanz, Konstanz, Germany

Messner, Christian
AIT, Vienna, Austria
020369

Mettner, Larissa
ISFH, Emmerthal, Germany
020063, 020114

Meusel, Manuel
Fraunhofer CSP, Halle (Saale), Germany
020052

Meyer, Kevin
ISFH, Emmerthal, Germany
020260

Meza, Carlos
Anhalt University of Applied Sciences, Köthen, Germany
020318, 020334, 020426, 020520

Mezzasalma, Frédéric
CEA / INES, Le Bourget-du-Lac, France
020217

Micha, Daniel
CEFET/RJ, Petrópolis, Brazil
020092

Michael, Poland
Nelson Mandela University, Port Elizabeth, South Africa
020193

Miclea, Paul-Tiberiu
Fraunhofer CSP, Halle, Germany
020233

Midtgård, Ole-Morten
NTNU, Trondheim, Norway
020476

Miettunen, Kati
University of Turku, Turku, Finland
020286, 020298, 020398

Migan-Dubois, Anne
CNRS, Gif-sur-Yvette, France
020406

Mignonac, Alexandre
CEA / INES, Le Bourget-du-Lac, France
020217

Mignonac, Alexandre
CEA, Cadarache, France
020334

Mignonac, Alexandre
CEA, Saint-Paul-Lez-Durance, France
020318

Miguel Laborda, María
IaSol, Zaragoza, Spain
020414

Mihailetchi, Valentin Dan
ISC Konstanz, Konstanz, Germany
020033

Mihailetchi, Valentin
ISC Konstanz, Konstanz, Germany
020225

Mihaylov, Blago
European Commission JRC, Ispra, Italy
020210

Milani, Emanuele
Marelli Europe, Venaria Reala, Italy
020495

Milesi, Frédéric
CEA, Grenoble, France
020068

Min, Byungsul
ISFH, Emmerthal, Germany
020008, 020482

Mirandona López, Haritz
Sunveon, Madrid, Spain
020432, 020434

Moradi Sizkouhi, Amirmohammad 020356, 020375
Concordia University, Montreal, Canada

Moradi Zavie Kord, Soroush 020400
University of Helsinki, Helsinki, Finland

Morales, Sergio 020491
UPM, Madrid, Spain

Morantes Quintana, Giobertti Raul 020551
Eurac Research, Bolzano, Italy

Mordvinkin, Anton 020233
Fraunhofer CSP, Halle, Germany

Moreda, Guillermo P. 020407
UPM, Madrid, Spain

Morin, Claire 020551
SolarPower Europe, Brussels, Belgium

Morisset, Audrey 020068
CSEM, Neuchâtel, Switzerland

Morlier, Arnaud 020156
Hasselt University, Genk, Belgium

Morlier, Arnaud 020294, 020389
imec, Genk, Belgium

Mortazavifar, Leila 020056, 020158, 020201, 020284
Anhalt University of Applied Sciences, Köthen, Germany

Moruno, Ricardo 020209, 020453
UPM, Madrid, Spain

Mosel, Frank 020015
PVA TePla, Wettenberg, Germany

Moser, David 020573
Becquerel Institute Italy, Trento, Italy

Moser, David 020316
Becquerel Institute, Bolzano, Italy

Moser, David 020254
Bequerel Institute, Trento, Italy

Moser, David 020203, 020226, 020261, 020325, 020485, 020489, 020546
Eurac Research, Bolzano, Italy

Mouhoubi, Felicia 020134
CEA / INES, Le Bourget-du-Lac, France

Müllejans, Harald 020208, 020213
European Commission JRC, Ispra, Italy

Müller, Alexander 020119
Fraunhofer CSP, Halle, Germany

Müller, Larissa 020523
University of Applied Sciences Cologne, Cologne, Germany

Mugica, Maikel 020139
Tecnalia, Donostia - San Sebastián, Spain

Mujovi, Fahradin 020251
CSEM, Neuchâtel, Switzerland

Mukherjee, Srijani 020338
CEA / INES, Le Bourget-du-Lac, France

Mukhtar, Mariyam 020057
University of Verona, Verona, Italy

Mulder, Peter 020067
Radboud University, Nijmegen, The Netherlands

Muller, Matthew 020314
NREL, Denver, United States of America

Munkhammar, Joakim 020532
Uppsala University, Uppsala, Sweden

Muñoz Cerón, Emilio 020269
University of Jaén, Jaén, Spain

Muñoz, Delfina 020040, 020311, 020546
CEA / INES, Le Bourget-du-Lac, France

Muñoz, Delfina 020521
CEA, Le Bourget-du-Lac, France

Muñoz, Delfina 020226
CEA/ INES, Le Bourget-du-Lac, France

Muñoz, Ildefonso 020365, 020366, 020392
CENER, Sarriguren, Spain

Muñoz, Jesús Ángel 020508
UCM, Madrid, Spain

Muñoz-García, Miguel-Ángel 020407
UPM, Madrid, Spain

Murano, Giovanni 020551
ENEA, Ispra, Italy

Murillo, Asier 020497
CENER, Sarriguren, Spain

Musembi, Robinson J. 020272
University of Nairobi, Nairobi, Kenya

Nabipouor, Mohammad 020426
Anhalt University of Applied Sciences, Köthen, Germany

Nagel, Henning 020475
Fraunhofer ISE, Freiburg, Germany

Nakamura, Kyotaro 020046
Toyota Technological Institute, Nagoya, Japan

Nanno, Ikuo 020190
Nanno Energy Research Center, Yamaguchi, Japan

Nargelienė, Viktorija 020157
Center for Physical Sciences and Technology (FTMC),
Vilnius, Lithuania

Narsi Patel, Hitarth 020069
SVNIT, Surat, India

Narvarte, Luis 020337, 020446, 020491, 020535, 020536,
UPM, Madrid, Spain 020567, 020575

Nascimento, Lucas   020377
Solar Energy Research Laboratory Fotovoltaica/ UFSC,
Florianópolis, Brazil

Nasebandt, Lasse   020063
ISFH, Emmerthal, Germany

Nasser, Hisham   020226
ODTÜ-GÜNAM, Ankara, Türkiye

Naveiro, José Manuel   020414
ENDEF, Zaragoza, Spain

Nazififard, Mohammad   020259, 020428
Côte d`Azur University, Nice, France

Nejim, Ahmed   020058
SILVACO, St. Ives, United Kingdom

Nel, Paul   020382
7SecondSolar, Cape Town, South Africa

Nelson, Jenny   020394
Imperial College London, London, United Kingdom

Neuba, Adam   020114
Paderborn University, Paderborn, Germany

Neuber, Viola   020031
Fraunhofer ISE, Freiburg, Germany

Neuhaus, Holger   020123, 020140
Fraunhofer ISE, Freiburg, Germany

Neumaier, Lukas   020504
Silicon Austria Labs, Villach, Austria

Neussl, Vassilissa   020318, 020430
AIT, Vienna, Austria

Neykova, Neda   020107
Czech Technical University, Prague, Czech Republic

Nezhad, Mahyar   020230
Kiwa PI Berlin, Hudson, United States of America

Nguyen, Viet Xuan   020008
centrotherm international, Blaubeuren, Germany

Nicolet-dit-Félix, Kléber   020251
EPFL, Neuchâtel, Switzerland

Nicot-Senneville, Zoltan   020102
SERIS, Singapore, Singapore

Nielsen, Michael P.   020065
UNSW, Sydney, Australia

Nissen, Hauke   020313
Wattmanufactur, Galmsbüll, Germany

Nitsche, Tobias   020119, 020218
Henkel, Düsseldorf, Germany

Nobre, André M.   020263
PV Doctor, Singapore, Singapore

Noels, Serge   020472
PV CYCLE, Brussels, Belgium

Özkalay, Ebrar 020160, 020204
SUPSI, Mendrisio, Switzerland

Ogura, Atsushi 020046
Meiji University, Kanagawa, Japan

Ohdaira, Keisuke 020131
JAIST, Ishikawa, Japan

Ohshita, Yoshio 020046
Toyota Technological Institute, Nagoya, Japan

Ojala, Aleksi 020554
Solarigo Systems, Pirkkala, Finland

Okawa, Hayato 020115
Tokyo City University, Setagaya, Japan

Okel, Lars A. G. 020030
TNO, Petten, The Netherlands

Oksanen, Jani 020067
Aalto University, Espoo, Finland

Oliosi, Michele 020196
PVsyst, Geneva, Switzerland

Olivares, Douglas 020311
University of Antofagasta, Antofagasta, Chile

Olivares, Gregorio 020365, 020366, 020392
CENER, Sarriguren, Spain

Oliveira Santos, João Victor 020188
EDF R&D, Moret Loing Orvanne, France

Oliveira, Helena 020420
University of Évora, Évora, Portugal

Oller Westerberg, Amelia 020570
Becquerel Sweden, Knivsta, Sweden

Ollo, Olatz 020139
Tecnalia, Donostia - San Sebastián, Spain

Oozeki, Takashi 020436, 020525
AIST, Koriyama, Japan

Opatovsky, Martin 020241, 020262
Solargis, Bratislava, Slovakia

Oreski, Gernot 020136, 020234, 020325, 020500, 020574
PCCL, Leoben, Austria

Ortega, Eneko 020055, 020153, 020287, 020353
UPV/EHU, Bilbao, Spain

Ortega, Eneko 020289, 020437
UPV/EHU, Leioa, Spain

Ortega, Pascal 020214
University of French Polynesia, Faa'a, French Polynesia

Ortiz-Pena, Aaron 020562
University of Castilla-La Mancha, Albacete, Spain

Ory, Daniel 020188
EDF R&D, Palaiseau, France

Ory, Daniel   020116
EDF, Palaiseau, France

Osman, Alaa   020006
ISFH, Emmerthal, Germany

Osuna, Jose Antonio   020358
MAGTEL, Córdoba, Spain

Osvald, Oliver   020274
Solargis, Bratislava, Slovakia

Otaegi, Aloña   020055, 020097, 020153, 020287
UPV/EHU, Bilbao, Spain

Otnes, Gaute   020169
Institute for Energy Technology, Kjeller, Norway

Otto, Nicolas   020101
HTW, Berlin, Germany

Otto, William   020390
MARIN, Wageningen, The Netherlands

Ou, Chao-Wei   020350
National Chin-Yi University of Technology, Taichung,
Taiwan

Ovaitt, Silvana   020314
NREL, Denver, United States of America

Ovaitt, Silvana   020574
NREL, Golden, United States of America

Oviedo Hernandez, Guillermo   020325
BayWa r.e, Rome, Italy

Ozer, Shay   020379
Agricultural Research Organization, Rishon LeZion, Israel

P. Pires, Maurício   020090
Federal University of Rio de Janeiro, Rio de Janeiro, Brazil

Pabiou, Herve   020338
CETHIL, Villeurbanne, France

Pabst, Elena   020312
ZSW, Stuttgart, Germany

Paiva, Lúcio   020530
Casa dos Ventos, Fortaleza, Brazil

Palais, Olivier   020188
Toulon University, Marseille, France

Palitzsch, Wolfram   020225, 020495
LuxChemTech, Freiberg, Germany

Palomino, Laura   020491, 020535
UPM, Madrid, Spain

Pamir Aly, Shahzada   020229
DEWA, Dubai, United Arab Emirates

Pamula, Bindu   020069
SVNIT, Surat, India

Panda, Pavan Kumar   020284
Anhalt University of Applied Sciences, Köthen, Germany

Pandar, Matthias   020229
Fraunhofer CSP, Halle, Germany

Pander, Matthias   020121, 020142, 020175, 020192, 020218,
Fraunhofer CSP, Halle, Germany   020223, 020232

Panduri, Fabio   020322
BFH, Burgdorf, Switzerland

Pantoja, Jaime   020526
Francisco José de Caldas District University, Bogota,
Colombia

Papantoni, Veatriki   020482
DLR, Oldenburg, Germany

Paraficz, Danuta   020204
FFHS, Zurich, Switzerland

Paraskeva, Vasiliki   020064
University of Cyprus, Nicosia, Cyprus

Pardo, Eduardo   020414
Tecnova, Almeira, Spain

Parfeniukas, Karolis   020039
ATLANT 3D, Taastrup, Denmark

Parion, Jonathan   020064
Hasselt Unversity, Genk, Belgium

Park, Hyeonwook   020112
KENTECH, Naju-Si, South Korea

Parmar, Richa   020429
NISE, Gurugram, India

Parra, Johan   020406
Ecole Polytechnique, Palaiseau, France

Parra, Johan   020214
Polytechnic Institute of Paris, Palaiseau, France

Parrilla, Carlos G.   020402
Fujairah Research Centre, Fujairah, United Arab Emirates

Pascual Gallego, Valero   020407
UPM, Madrid, Spain

Pasquier, Mathis   020451
DTU, Roskilde, Denmark

Passaro, Marcello   020513
Sunzest Solar, Rotterdam, The Netherlands

Patel, Dharm   020355
Fraunhofer IMWS, Halle, Germany

Paul, Ananta   020250, 020306
SDU Climate Cluster, Odense, Denmark

Paulescu, Marius   020283
West University of Timisoara, Timisoara, Romania

Paviet-Salomon, Bertrand   020068, 020467
CSEM, Neuchâtel, Switzerland

Payno, David   020085, 020094
UAM, Madrid, Spain

Pearce, Pheobe   020065
UNSW, Sydney, Australia

Peche, René   020468, 020495
bifa Umweltinstitut, Augsburg, Germany

Pehlivanli, Ezgi   020521
METU, Ankara, Türkiye

Peibst, Robby   020006, 020063, 020114
ISFH, Emmerthal, Germany

Pelfort Ojer, Marta   020241
Solargis, Bratislava, Slovakia

Pelland, Sophie   020211
Natural Resources Canada, Varennes, Canada

Pelle, Martina   020249, 020254
Eurac Research, Bolzano, Italy

Peña-Bermudez, Julian   020110
University of the Caribbean, Santo Domingo, Dominican
Republic

Peng, Cheng-Yu   020350
National Chin-Yi University of Technology, Taichung,
Taiwan

Pera, David   020457
Luxembourg Institute of Science and Technology, Esch-sur-
Alzette, Luxembourg

Perani, Martina   020204
FFHS, Zurich, Switzerland

Peraticos, Elias   020064
University of Cyprus, Nicosia, Cyprus

Pereda, Ainhoa   020198, 020358
TECNALIA, Derio, Spain

Pereira Fialho, Luis Andre   020509
Eurac Research, Bolzano, Italy

Pereira, Sara   020403, 020418, 020565
University of Évora, Évora, Portugal

Pérez García, Manuel   020336
University of Almería, La Cañada de San Urbano, Spain

Pérez, Ernesto   020339
National University of Colombia, Bogotá, Colombia

Pérez, Jairo   020412
Gonvarri AgroTech, Corvera - Asturias, Spain

Pérez, Jorge   020412
Gonvarri AgroTech, Corvera - Asturias, Spain

Pérez, Luis   020412
Gonvarri MS R&D, Corvera - Asturias, Spain

Perez, Richard   020494
University at Albany, Albany, United States of America

Perez-Astudillo, Daniel   020275, 020278, 020291
QEERI, Doha, Qatar

Pérez-García, Manuel   020100
University of Almería, Almería, Spain

Pérez-Rodríguez, Alejandro   020085, 020094
IREC, Barcelona, Spain

Pernas, Tomás   020412
Gonvarri AgroTech, Corvera - Asturias, Spain

Pernau, Thomas   020008
centrotherm international, Blaubeuren, Germany

Perrin, Marion   020544
Energy Pool, Le Bourget-du-Lac, France

Pervan, Nikolina   020136, 020234
PCCL, Leoben, Austria

Peter Amalathas, Amalraj   020107
University of Jaffna, Jaffna, Sri Lanka

Peter, Kristian   020569
ISC Konstanz, Konstanz, Germany

Peters, Ian Marius   020230, 020263
Forschungszentrum Jülich, Erlangen, Germany

Peters, Ian Marius   020149, 020150, 020377, 020574
HI ERN, Erlangen, Germany

Petersons, Karlis   020250, 020306
Stensborg, Roskilde, Denmark

Petkovski, Emil   020571
DNV, Arnhem, The Netherlands

Petzschmann, Jonas   020312
ZSW, Stuttgart, Germany

Pfau, Jan Hendrik   020240
Leibniz University Hannover, Hannover, Germany

Pfeiffer, Oliver   020141
University of Applied Science Cologne, Cologne, Germany

Pfeiffer, Oliver   020140
University of Applied Sciences Cologne, Cologne, Germany

Philipp, Daniel   020215, 020231
Fraunhofer ISE, Freiburg, Germany

Pierro, Marco   020489, 020494
Eurac Research, Bolzano, Italy

Pieters, Bart E.   020180
FZJ, Jülich, Germany

Pieterse, Marco   020495
Chemconserve, Bussum, The Netherlands

Pietralunga, Silvia Maria   020066
CNR-IFN, Milan, Italy

Pietsch, Veith Aquila Capital, Hamburg, Germany	020331
Pilat, Eric CEA / INES, Le Bourget-du-Lac, France	020311
Pilat, Eric CEA INES, Le Bourget-du-Lac, France	020317
Pillai, Akhildev Becquerel Institute, Brussels, Belgium	020558
Pinheiro, Philippe Luxembourg Institute of Science and Technology, Esch-sur-Alzette, Luxembourg	020457
Pinho Almeida, Marcelo University of São Paulo, São Paulo, Brazil	020348
Pinto, Cristina Leyre CENER, Sarriguren, Spain	020497
Pinto, Luciana UFRJ, Rio de Janeiro, Brazil	020092
Pitaval, Sébastien SOLAÏS, Valbonne, France	020244
Pitz-Paal, Robert DLR, Cologne, Germany	020237, 020331
Plakhotnyuk, Maksym ATLANT 3D, Taastrup, Denmark	020039
Platero Gaona, Carlos A. UPM, Madrid, Spain	020332
Plaza, Caroline Becquerel Institute France, Lyon, France	020543, 020564, 020573
Polacchi, Cristina Eurac Research, Bolzano, Italy	020509, 020513
Polo, Jaime CENER, Sarriguren, Spain	020300
Polo, Jesús CIEMAT, Madrid, Spain	020297
Polverini, Davide Directorate General for Internal Market, Industry, Entrepreneurship and SMEs, Brussels, Belgium	020181
Polverini, Davide European Comission, Brussels, Belgium	020497
Pongthanacharoenkul, Nattapark Kiwa PI Berlin, Berlin, Germany	020230
Poortmans, Jef Hasselt Unversity, Genk, Belgium	020064
Popescu, Lacramioara ISC Konstanz, Konstanz, Germany	020068
Pospischil, Maximilian Highline Technologies, Freiburg, Germany	020225

Poulsen, Peter B.
DTU, Copenhagen, Denmark
020039

Poulsen, Peter B.
DTU, Roskilde, Denmark
020250, 020265, 020267, 020376, 020451

Poulsen, Peter Behrensdorff
DTU, Roskilde, Denmark
020028, 020306, 020346

Pourshafi, Pouya
AESOLAR, Koenigsbrunn, Germany
020121, 020125, 020137

Pozza, Cristian
Eurac Research, Bolzano, Italy
020551

Prakash, Jai
NISE, Gurugram, India
020429

Prando, Davide
Edyna, Bolzano, Italy
020485, 020489

Prasad, Manjunath
ISC Konstanz, Konstanz, Germany
020225

Pravettoni, Mauro
Technology Innovation Institute, Abu Dhabi, United Arab Emirates
020402

Preis, Pirmin
ISC Konstanz, Konstanz, Germany
020003

Preu, Ralf
Fraunhofer ISE, Freiburg, Germany
020475

Preuschoff, Jonas
HTW, Berlin, Germany
020101

Protti, Alexander Aguilar
Fraunhofer ISE, Freiburg, Germany
020140

Protti, Alexander
Fraunhofer ISE, Freiburg, Germany
020137

Provost, Marion
IPVF, Palaiseau, France
020116

Puel, Jean Baptiste
IPVF, Palaiseau, France
020062

Puertas López, Antonio Manuel
University of Almeria, Almeria, Spain
020100

Puttock, Claire
Nextracker, Fremont, United States of America
020367

Queste, Samuel
Marie and Louis Pasteur University, Besançon, France
020068

Quiroz, Mónica
Qualifying Photovoltaics, Madrid, Spain
020328

R. Ledesma, Javier
UPM, Madrid, Spain
020363

Rabanal Arabach, Jorge   020183
University of Antofagasta, Antofagasta, Chile

Rabanal-Arabach, Jorge   020129, 020342, 020417, 020422
University of Antofagasta, Antofagasta, Chile

Rabiei, Hossein   020063
ISFH, Emmerthal, Germany

Rachdi, Lazhar   020035, 020068
ISC Konstanz, Konstanz, Germany

Radzevicius, Aurimas   020225
Valoe Cells, Vilnius, Lithuania

Rafiee, Hossein   020539
Frankfurt University of Applied Sciences, Frankfurt am
Main, Germany

Raginskis, Justinas   020380
Kaunas University of Technology, Kaunas, Lithuania

Raievska, Oleksandra   020117, 020149
HI ERN, Erlangen, Germany

Rajan, S. Prithivi   020262
LuciSun, Villers-la-Ville, Belgium

Rajkiewicz, Katarzyna   020551
NAPE, Warsaw, Poland

Rakotoniaina, Jean Patrice   020311
CEA / INES, Le Bourget-du-Lac, France

Ramachandran Nair, Jishnu   020233
Fraunhofer CSP, Halle, Germany

Ramesh, Santhosh   020389
imec, Genk, Belgium

Ramírez Ledesma, Javier   020535
UPM, Madrid, Spain

Ramirez, S.   020396
PV Lighthouse, Coledale, Australia

Rampino, Stefano   020087
National Research Council, Parma, Italy

Ramspeck, Klaus   020050
halm elektronik, Frankfurt am Main, Germany

Ranisch, Tadeus   020101
HTW, Berlin, Germany

Ranta, Samuli   020286, 020400
TUAS, Turku, Finland

Ranta, Samuli   020298, 020398
Turku University of Applied Sciences, Turku, Finland

Raposo, Mauro   020565
University of Évora, Évora, Portugal

Ratnagiri, Abhinav   020367
Nextracker, Fremont, United States of America

Raugewitz, Annika   020063, 020114
ISFH, Emmerthal, Germany

Raval, Mehul   020005, 020222, 020463
RCT Solutions, Konstanz, Germany

Razanajao, Aina   020244
SOLAÏS, Valbonne, France

Razi, Umair   020085
IREC, Barcelona, Spain

Recart, Federico   020097
UPV/EHU, Bilbao, Spain

Redondo Cuevas, Marta   020332
UPM, Madrid, Spain

Redondo, Juan Manuel   020209
UPM, Madrid, Spain

Rehan, Muhammad   020112
KIER, Daejeon, South Korea

Rehman, Anees ur   020111, 020164
Hohai University, Changzhou, China

Reichart, Hannah   020167, 020232
University of Applied Sciences Cologne, Cologne, Germany

Reichel, Christian   020123, 020137, 020140
Fraunhofer ISE, Freiburg, Germany

Reichle, Julian   020005, 020222, 020463
RCT Solutions, Konstanz, Germany

Reinders, Angele   020253
TU Eindhoven, Eindhoven, The Netherlands

Reindl, Thomas   020263
SERIS, Singapore, Singapore

Reis, Luiz Filipe   020530
Casa dos Ventos, Fortaleza, Brazil

Rémondeau, Paul   020251
EPFL, Neuchâtel, Switzerland

Renard, Charles   020058
CNRS, Palaiseau, France

Rende, Fedele   020255
ACCA Software, Cosenza, Italy

Rennhofer, Marcus   020180, 020281, 020318, 020334, 020347,
AIT, Vienna, Austria   020430

Rentsch, Jochen   020475
Fraunhofer ISE, Freiburg, Germany

Rerat, Michel   020060
IPREM, Pau, France

Reshef, Liad   020379
Agricultural Research Organization, Rishon LeZion, Israel

Revol, Inès   020074
LAAS-CNRS, Toulouse, France

Reyal, Jean-Pierre   020303
SemperStyl, Eragny, France

Riaño, Sandra
TECNALIA, Derio, Spain
020197, 020358

Richards, Bryce S.
KIT, Karlsruhe, Germany
020272

Riechelman, Stefan
PTB, Braunschweig, Germany
020181

Riechelmann, Stefan
PTB, Braunschweig, Germany
020177, 020199, 020211

Riedel-Lyngskær, Nicholas
DTU, Roskilde, Denmark
020451

Rienäcker, Michael
ISFH, Emmerthal, Germany
020063

Rindert, Sören
Kiwa PI Berlin, Berlin, Germany
020230

Ríos Moral, Lucía
UCM, Madrid, Spain
020501

Ríos-Ledesma, Felipe
UPM, Madrid, Spain
020446

Ripke, Melanie
ISFH, Emmerthal, Germany
020006

Riva, Roland
CEA, Le Bourget-du-Lac, France
020495

Rivas Rodríguez, José Manuel
Enertis Applus+, Madrid, Spain
020326

Robledo, Jesús
LuciSun, Villers-la-Ville, Belgium
020262

Rodríguez Lucas, Delia
EkiLabs, Boston, United States of America
020407

Rodríguez Plaza, José Luis
Autonomous University of Madrid, Madrid, Spain
020508

Rodríguez Rodríguez, Araceli
UCM, Madrid, Spain
020501

Rodríguez Salazar, David Leonardo
District University of Bogotá, Bogotá, Colombia
020441

Rodríguez, Araceli
UCM, Madrid, Spain
020508

Rodríguez, Diego Julián
Francisco José de Caldas District University, Bogota, Colombia
020526

Rodríguez, Isabel
IMDEA Nanoscience, Madrid, Spain
020257

Rodriguez, Sonia Maria
UPV/EHU, Leioa, Spain
020289

Rodríguez, Velia
UPV/EHU, Bilbao, Spain
020097

Rodríguez-Conde, Sofía
Enertis Applus+, Madrid, Spain
020326

Rodríguez-Gallegos, Carlos D. 020149, 020150
SERIS, Singapore, Singapore

Rodríguez-Romero, Sebastián 020342, 020417, 020422
University of Antofagasta, Antofagasta, Chile

Rodziewicz, Hanna 020498
Gdansk University of Technology, Gdansk, Poland

Römer, Udo 020006, 020063
ISFH, Emmerthal, Germany

Röver, Ingo 020225
LuxChemTech, Freiberg, Germany

Rojas, Christian A. 020422
Federico Santa María Technical University, Valparaíso,
Chile

Rojas-Henríquez, Katalina 020129
University of Antofagasta, Antofagasta, Chile

Román, Eduardo 020139
Tecnalia, Donostia - San Sebastián, Spain

Romeo, Alessandro 020057, 020089, 020093
University of Verona, Verona, Italy

Romer, Pascal 020231
Fraunhofer ISE, Freiburg, Germany

Roodt, Roelof 020185
Nelson Mandela University, Port Elizabeth, South Africa

Roosloot, Nathan 020169
Institute for Energy Technology, Kjeller, Norway

Rosca, Victor 020030
TNO, Petten, The Netherlands

Rosen, Isaac 020225
Copprint, Jerusalem, Israel

Rosenfeld, Lavi 020379
Agricultural Research Organization, Rishon LeZion, Israel

Rosina, Konstantin 020241
Solargis, Bratislava, Slovakia

Rossa, Carlos 020432, 020434
Sunveon, Madrid, Spain

Rouffie, Brice 020068
SEGTON Advanced Technology, Versailles, France

Roulleau, Lea 020303
CSTB, Marne-la-Vallée, France

Rousset, Jean 020116
EDF, Palaiseau, France

Roy, Shantanu 020519
CSTEP, Bengaluru, India

Rudolph, Dominik 020003, 020068
ISC Konstanz, Konstanz, Germany

Rudzikas, Matas 020380
The Applied Research Institute for Prospective
Technologies, Vilnius, Lithuania

Rüther, Ricardo 020377
Solar Energy Research Laboratory Fotovoltaica/ UFSC,
Florianópolis, Brazil

Rüther, Ricardo 020548
UFSC, Florianopolis, Brazil

Ruf, Manuel 020455
Robert Bosch, Stuttgart, Germany

Ruiz Donoso, Elena 020331
DLR, Almería, Spain

S. Sousa, Graciana 020090
Federal University of Rio de Janeiro, Rio de Janeiro, Brazil

Safarian, Jafar 020011
NTNU, Trondheim, Norway

Sah, Dheeraj 020039
Aarhus University, Aarhus, Denmark

Sahin, Hasret 020479
LUT University, Lappeenranta, Finland

Saito, Kimihiko 020106
Tokyo City University, Setagaya, Japan

Salem, Mohammad 020428
Australian University, Kuwait City, Kuwait

Salerno, Giorgia 020077
University of Milano-Bicocca, Milan, Italy

Salis, Fabio 020541
Iberdrola, Rome, Italy

Salvador, Antonio 020358
MAGTEL, Córdoba, Spain

Sample, Tony 020213
European Commission JRC, Ispra, Italy

Samuolienė, Giedrė 020380
The Lithuanian Research Centre for Agriculture and
Forestry, Kaunas, Lithuania

San José, Luis Javier 020209, 020453
UPM, Madrid, Spain

Sánchez de León Peque, Miguel 020243
ieco.io, Vigo, Spain

Sanchez Garcia, Alfredo 020270
SINTEF, Trondheim, Norway

Sanchez, Hugo 020056, 020158, 020284
Anhalt University of Applied Sciences, Köthen, Germany

Sanchez, Jesus 020437
UPV/EHU, Vitoria-Gasteiz, Spain

Sanchez, Laura
UPV/EHU, Leioa, Spain
020437

Sánchez, Yudania
IREC, Barcelona, Spain
020085

Sanchez-Friera, Paula
Solkeys, Gijón, Spain
020412, 020513, 020521

Sanchez-Ruiz, Alain
UPV/EHU, Vitoria-Gasteiz, Spain
020437

Sansavini, Giovanni
ETH, Zurich, Switzerland
020296

Sansoni, Paola
CNR-INO, Florence, Italy
020066

Santamaría Fernández, Susanna
TECNALIA, Derio, Spain
020249

Santamaría-Sancho, Juan
UPM, Madrid, Spain
020363

Santos, Jose Domingo
TECNALIA, Derio, Spain
020197, 020198, 020358

Santos, Rodrigo
Casa dos Ventos, Fortaleza, Brazil
020530

Sanz Martinez, Asier
Tecnalia, Bilbao, Spain
020546

Sanz, Asier
Tecnalia, BRTA, Derio, Spain
020514

Sanz, Asier
TECNALIA, Derio, Spain
020197

Sanz-Cuadrado, Cristina
UPM, Madrid, Spain
020575

Sanz-Saiz, Carlos
CIEMAT, Madrid, Spain
020297

Sarafijanovic-Djukic, Natasa
FFHS, Regensdorf, Switzerland
020204

Saretti, Angelica
Polytechnic University of Bari, Bari, Italy
020301

Sarkadi, Monika
ISC Konstanz, Konstanz, Germany
020569

Sauer, Thomas
EXXERGY, Gräfelfing, Germany
020140

Saura, Juan Antonio
University of Murcia, Murcia, Spain
020506

Savisalo, Tuukka
Valoe, Mikkeli, Finland
020225

Saw, Min Hsian
Technology Innovation Institute, Abu Dhabi, United Arab
Emirates
020402

Saxena, Anmol Ratan
NIT, Delhi, India
020429

Sayed, Abdullah Abu Kiwa PI Berlin, Berlin, Germany	020180, 020230
Scaltrito, Luciano Polytechnic University of Turin, Turin, Italy	020079
Scerri, Kenneth University of Malta, Msida, Malta	020334
Schading, Steve University of Agder, Grimstad, Norway	020443
Schäfer, Aysim Next2Sun Technology, Dillingen, Germany	020388
Schäfer, Sebastian Frankfurt University of Applied Sciences, Frankfurt am Main, Germany	020539
Schenk, Paul Fraunhofer CSP, Halle, Germany	020192
Schermer, John Radboud University, Nijmegen, The Netherlands	020067
Scherret, Jacqueline A-Null Development, Vienna, Austria	020255
Schifferegger, Raffael OFI, Vienna, Austria	020162
Schimanke, Sabrina ISFH, Emmerthal, Germany	020006
Schirmer, Yoko HTW, Berlin, Germany	020101
Schläger, Christian Leibniz University Hannover, Hannover, Germany	020240
Schlatmann, Rutger HTW, Berlin, Germany	020101
Schmidt Davidsen, Rasmus Aarhus University, Aarhus, Denmark	020037, 020104
Schnaus, Dominik TUM, Garching, Germany	020237
Schneider, Andreas University of Applied Sciences Gelsenkirchen, Gelsenkirchen, Germany	020129, 020183
Schneider, Astrid TU Wien, Vienna, Austria	020255
Schneider, Friedrich LPKF SolarQuipment, Suhl, Germany	020482
Schneider, Marc Gabriel University of Applied Science Cologne, Cologne, Germany	020522
Schneiderlöchner, Eric VON ARDENNE, Dresden, Germany	020033
Schnierer, Branislav Solargis, Bratislava, Slovakia	020262

Schönau, Maximilian   020361
Coburg University of Applied Sciences, Coburg, Germany

Schönau, Maximilian   020544
smartblue, Munich, Germany

Schönheits, Markus   020468, 020470
bifa Umweltinstitut, Augsburg, Germany

Schranz, Christian   020255
TU Wien, Vienna, Austria

Schrempf, Michael   020199
PTB, Braunschweig, Germany

Schrijvers, Patrick   020390
MARIN, Wageningen, The Netherlands

Schröter, Nick   020142
Fraunhofer CSP, Halle, Germany

Schubert, Martin C.   020475
Fraunhofer ISE, Freiburg, Germany

Schubnel, Baptiste   020238
CSEM, Neuchâtel, Switzerland

Schüler, Marc Andre   020388
Next2Sun Technology, Dillingen, Germany

Schüler, Marc Andre   020411
Next2Sun, Dillingen, Germany

Schueler, Nadine   020015
Freiberger Instruments, Freiberg, Germany

Schulte-Huxel, Henning   020008, 020260
ISFH, Emmerthal, Germany

Schultz, Christof   020101
HTW, Berlin, Germany

Schulz, Philip   020060
IPVF, Palaiseau, France

Schulze, Achim   020361
Rosenheim Technical University of Applied Sciences,
Rosenheim, Germany

Schulze, Patricia S.C.   020475
Fraunhofer ISE, Freiburg, Germany

Schwenke, Almut   020495
SGL Battery Solutions, Meitingen, Germany

Sciuto, Marcello   020010
Enel Green Power, Catania, Italy

Scognamiglio, Alessandra   020541
ENEA, Naples, Italy

Scognamiglio, Alessandra   020378
ENEA, Portici, Italy

Sedaghat, Ahmad   020428
Australian University, Kuwait City, Kuwait

Seiffert, Christoph   020169
Institute for Energy Technology, Kjeller, Norway

Seiffert, Daniela 020008
centrotherm international, Blaubeuren, Germany

Seitz, Matthias 020468
bifa Umweltinstitut, Augsburg, Germany

Selj, Josefine H. 020169
Institute for Energy Technology, Kjeller, Norway

Senno, Maximiliano Alejandro 020226
University of Valencia, Paterna, Spain

Senturk, Bilge 020556
ODTU GUNAM, Ankara, Türkiye

Setien, Eneko 020198
TECNALIA, Derio, Spain

Šetkus, Arūnas 020157
Center for Physical Sciences and Technology (FTMC),
Vilnius, Lithuania

Shaaban, Ahmed 020402
Technology Innovation Institute, Abu Dhabi, United Arab
Emirates

Shah, Syed Fawad Ali 020112
KENTECH, Naju-Si, South Korea

Shanmugam, Raphael 020218, 020220
ISC Konstanz, Konstanz, Germany

Sharma, Rajesh Kumar 020071, 020081
SVNIT, Surat, India

Sharma, Sushma 020563
SRM University, Sonipat, India

Shen, Xinyi 020226
University of Oxford, Oxford, United Kingdom

Shen, Zhenjue 020001
YIST, Jiangyin, China

Shin, Donghyeop 020112
KIER, Daejeon, South Korea

Shin, Woo Gyun 020324, 020357
KIER, Daejeon, South Korea

Shin, Woo-gyun 020561
KIER, Daejeon, South Korea

Shirai, Yasuhiro 020115
NIMS, Tsukuba, Japan

Shirazi, Elham 020544
University of Twente, Enschede, The Netherlands

Shishavan, Amir Asgharzadeh 020367
Nextracker, Fremont, United States of America

Shishido, Hirotaka 020106
Tokyo City University, Setagaya, Japan

Shochet, Ofer 020225
Copprint, Jerusalem, Israel

Shyong, Yung-Jen   020163
ITRI, Hsinchu, Taiwan

Sicot, Lionel   020217
CEA / INES, Le Bourget-du-Lac, France

Sidler, Anika   020226
School of Life Sciences FHNW, Muttenz, Switzerland

Siebert, Michael   020206
ISFH, Emmerthal, Germany

Siefer, Gerald   020246
Fraunhofer ISE, Freiburg, Germany

Sierra, Daniel   020491
UPM, Madrid, Spain

Sigounis, Anna-Maria   020248, 020249
Concordia University, Montreal, Canada

Søiland, Anne-Karin   020495
ReSiTec, Kristiansand, Norway

Silva, José A.   020304, 020409, 020420
University of Évora, Évora, Portugal

Silva, José   020403
University of Évora, Évora, Portugal

Silvestre, Santiago   020301
UPC, Barcelona, Spain

Simeunovic, Jelena   020238
CSEM, Neuchâtel, Switzerland

Simón-Allué, Raquel   020127, 020414, 020517
ENDEF, Zaragoza, Spain

Singh, Ravi   020571
DNV, Arnhem, The Netherlands

Sinha, Amish Kumar   020463
RCT Solutions, Konstanz, Germany

Sinopoli, Alessandro   020042
QEERI, Doha, Qatar

Sivaramakrishnan Radhakrishnan, Hariharsudan   020064
Hasselt Unversity, Genk, Belgium

Sivaramakrishnan, Hariharsudan   020225
IMEC, Genk, Belgium

Snaith, Henry   020226
University of Oxford, Oxford, United Kingdom

Søndenå, Rune   020503
Institute for Energy Technology, Kjeller, Norway

Sobajima, Yasushi   020131
Gifu University, Gifu, Japan

Soler Toledo, Denet   020509
University of Antofagasta, Antofagasta, Chile

Solomon, Asfaw A.   020479
LUT University, Lappeenranta, Finland

Solórzano, Jorge   020328
Qualifying Photovoltaics, Madrid, Spain

Sondoqah, Mousa   020316
Becquerel Institute, Bolzano, Italy

Sondoqah, Mousa   020261
Eurac Research, Bolzano, Italy

Song, Hee-eun   020045
KIER, Daejeon, South Korea

Spagnolo, Sofia   020462, 020466
RSE, Milan, Italy

Spataru, Sergiu V.   020265, 020267, 020283, 020376, 020451
DTU, Roskilde, Denmark

Spataru, Sergiu Viorel   020346
DTU, Roskilde, Denmark

Spera, Fabian   020411
Next2Sun, Dillingen, Germany

Spihola, Jan   020355
DiSUN Deutsche Solarservice, Werder, Germany

Sraisth,   020005, 020222
RCT Solutions, Konstanz, Germany

Sraisth, Sraisth   020463
RCT Solutions, Konstanz, Germany

Staňková, Tereza   020107
Czech Technical University, Prague, Czech Republic

Steckenreiter, Verena   020063
ISFH, Emmerthal, Germany

Stegemann, Bert   020309
Berlin University of Applied Sciences, Berlin, Germany

Stegemann, Bert   020101
HTW, Berlin, Germany

Stellbogen, Dirk   020312
ZSW, Stuttgart, Germany

Stensborg, Jan F.   020250
Stensborg, Roskilde, Denmark

Stensborg, Jan   020306
Stensborg, Roskilde, Denmark

Stieldorf, Karin   020255
TU Wien, Vienna, Austria

Stierstorfer, Johannes   020225
WIP - Renewable Energies, Munich, Germany

Stierstorfer, Johannes   020551
WIP Renewable Energies, Munich, Germany

Stivanello, Juan José   020226
Eurac Research, Bolzano, Italy

Stoicescu, Liviu   020198
Solarzentrum Stuttgart, Stuttgart, Germany

Stowhas-Villa, Alejandro 020422
Federico Santa María Technical University, Valparaiso,
Chile

Stoyanova Lyubenova, Teodora 020173
European Commission JRC, Ispra, Italy

Sträter, Hendrik 020211
PTB, Braunschweig, Germany

Strey, Jessica 020063, 020114
ISFH, Emmerthal, Germany

Strömberg, Rich 020472
University of Alaska, Fairbanks, United States of America

Stroyuk, Oleksander 020185
HI ERN, Erlangen, Germany

Stroyuk, Oleksandr 020117, 020149, 020150
HI ERN, Erlangen, Germany

Suárez Sánchez, Sergio 020326
Enertis Applus+, Madrid, Spain

Subasi, Dilara Maria 020475
Fraunhofer ISE, Freiburg, Germany

Sudbury, Ben A. 020396
PV Lighthouse, Coledale, Australia

Suemitsu, Issei 020484
Hitachi, Kokubunji, Japan

Suhonen, Riikka 020423
VTT Technical Research Centre of Finland, Oulu, Finland

Sulca, Kabir Paúl 020191, 020205
University of Valladolid, Valladolid, Spain

Svatos, Jan 020250
DTU, Roskilde, Denmark

Sylla, David 020063
ISFH, Emmerthal, Germany

Syre Wiig, Marie 020340
IFE, Kjeller, Norway

Szarek, Magda 020298, 020398
University of Turku, Turku, Finland

Taghipour Kani, Ghaem 020335, 020374
Amirkabir University of Technology, Tehran, Iran

Takahashi, Kanji 020106
Tokyo City University, Setagaya, Japan

Talvi, Micke 020528
Tampere University, Tampere, Finland

Tanahashi, Tadanori 020436
AIST, Koriyama, Japan

Tang, Kai 020011
SINTEF, Trondheim, Norway

Tang, Torben   020028
IPU P/S, Virum, Denmark

Tang, Torben   020037
IPU, Virum, Denmark

Tayebjee, Murad J. Y.   020065
UNSW, Sydney, Australia

Taylor, Nigel   020210
European Commission JRC, Ispra, Italy

Tellez Rodriguez, Eduardo   020230
Kiwa PI Berlin, Berlin, Germany

Teppe, Andreas   020005
RCT Solutions, Konstanz, Germany

Terheiden, Barbara   020031
University of Konstanz, Constance, Germany

Terrados, Cristian   020205
University of Valladolid, Valladolid, Spain

Thakur, Dhruv Singh   020071, 020081
SVNIT, Surat, India

Theocharides, Spyros   020371
Univers, Courbevoie, France

Thomas, Jean   020169
Ciel et Terre, Lille, France

Thorning, Jacob K.   020267, 020283
DTU, Roskilde, Denmark

Thorsteinsson, Sune   020039
DTU, Copenhagen, Denmark

Thorsteinsson, Sune   020037
DTU, Lyngby, Denmark

Thorsteinsson, Sune   020028, 020249, 020250, 020265, 020306, 020477
DTU, Roskilde, Denmark

Timofte, Tudor   020218, 020221
ISC Konstanz, Konstanz, Germany

Ting, San-Yu   020161, 020163
ITRI, Hsinchu, Taiwan

Tissier, Corentin   020238
CSEM, Neuchâtel, Switzerland

Tönies, Alexandra   020523
University of Applied Sciences Cologne, Cologne, Germany

Tomšič, Špela   020047
University of Ljubljana, Ljubljana, Slovenia

Tong, Yongfeng   020108, 020109
QEERI, Doha, Qatar

Topič, Marko   020047, 020269, 020319
University of Ljubljana, Ljubljana, Slovenia

Torabi, Narges   020089
University of Verona, Verona, Italy

Torelly, Guilherme 020092
PUC-Rio, Rio de Janeiro, Brazil

Torre, Gorka 020437
UPV/EHU, Leioa, Spain

Torres Aguilar, Moira Itzel 020214
CentraleSupélec, Gif-sur-Yvette, France

Torres Aguilar, Moira Itzel 020406
CNRS, Gif-sur-Yvette, France

Torres Silva, Nicole 020546
ATAMOSTEC, Santiago, Chile

Torres, Oscar 020110
National University of Colombia, Bogotá, Colombia

Tosi, Irene 020037
IPU, Virum, Denmark

Tran Caliste, Thu Nhi 020546
European Synchrotron Radiation Facility (ESRF), Grenoble,
France

Treberspurg, Christoph 020255
Treberspurg und Partner Ziviltechniker, Vienna, Austria

Treberspurg, Martin 020255
Treberspurg und Partner Ziviltechniker, Vienna, Austria

Trefzer, Aaron 020135
Fraunhofer ISE, Freiburg, Germany

Trifiletti, Vanira 020087
University of Milano-Bicocca, Milan, Italy

Trigo-Gonzalez, Mauricio 020342, 020422
University of Antofagasta, Antofagasta, Chile

Tsai, Min-An 020053, 020083, 020161, 020163
ITRI, Hsinchu, Taiwan

Tsanakas, Ioannis (John) A. 020262
CEA / INES, Le Bourget-du-Lac, France

Tsanakas, Ioannis (John) A. 020544
CEA, Le Bourget-du-Lac, France

Tsanakas, Ioannis (John) 020546
CEA / INES, Le Bourget-du-Lac, France

Tsanakas, Ioannis (John) 020317
CEA INES, Le Bourget-du-Lac, France

Tsanakas, Ioannis (John) 020513, 020521
CEA, Le Bourget-du-Lac, France

Tsanakas, Ioannis 020217, 020338
CEA / INES, Le Bourget-du-Lac, France

Tsanakas, Ioannis 020500
CEA, Le Bourget-du-Lac, France

Tsanakas, John A. 020311
CEA / INES, Le Bourget-du-Lac, France

Tseberlidis, Giorgio 020093
University of Milano Bicocca, Milan, Italy

Tseberlidis, Giorgio 020087
University of Milano-Bicocca, Milan, Italy

Tsoi, Konstantin 020113
ODTÜ-GÜNAM, Ankara, Türkiye

Tsombou, Francois M. 020402
Fujairah Research Centre, Fujairah, United Arab Emirates

Tsuno, Yuki 020436
AIST, Koriyama, Japan

Tsunoda, Jun 020484
Hitachi, Kokubunji, Japan

Tsunoda, Jun 020186
Hitachi, Tokyo, Japan

Tulinski, Lona 020385
ZHAW, Winterthur, Switzerland

Tune, Daniel 020220, 020221, 020225
ISC Konstanz, Konstanz, Germany

Turcu, Mircea 020063
ISFH, Emmerthal, Germany

Turek, Marko 020004, 020052
Fraunhofer CSP, Halle (Saale), Germany

Ueda, Yuzuru 020320, 020525
Tokyo University of Science, Tokyo, Japan

Ujvari, Gusztav 020318, 020430
AIT, Vienna, Austria

Ulbikaitė, Vaidvilė 020157
Applied Research Institute for Prospective Technologies,
Vilnius, Lithuania

Ulbikas, Juras 020225
Protechnology, Vilnius, Lithuania

Ulyashin, Alexander G. 020011
SINTEF, Oslo, Norway

Unsur, Veysel 020020
ODTÜ-GÜNAM, Ankara, Türkiye

Urban, Harald 020255
TU Wien, Vienna, Austria

Useni, Yannick 020393
University of Lubumbashi, Lubumbashi, Congo (DRC)

Uzuner, Bahri Eren 020113
ODTÜ-GÜNAM, Ankara, Türkiye

Väisänen, Kaisa-Leena 020423
VTT Technical Research Centre of Finland, Oulu, Finland

Vaicikauskas, Viktoras 020157
Center for Physical Sciences and Technology (FTMC),
Vilnius, Lithuania

Valaski, Rogério   020090
National Institute of Metrology Quality and Technology,
Rio de Janeiro, Brazil

Valencia, Felipe   020342, 020546
AtamosTec, Santiago, Chile

Vallerotto, Guido   020209, 020246, 020257
UPM, Madrid, Spain

van Aken, Bas B.   020405
TNO, Petten, The Netherlands

van der Heide, Arvid   020472
imec, Genk, Belgium

van der Zee, Friso F.   020405
Wageningen University and Research, Wageningen, The
Netherlands

Van Dyck, Rik   020225
IMEC, Genk, Belgium

van Dyk, E. Ernest   020193, 020416
Nelson Mandela University, Port Elizabeth, South Africa

van Dyk, Ernest E.   020344
Nelson Mandela University, Port Elizabeth, South Africa

Van Overstraeten, Julien   020543
Becquerel Institute France, Lyon, France

Van Overstraeten, Julien   020252
Becquerel Institute, Brussels, Belgium

vanBaal, Rene   020492
Belectric, Kolitzheim, Germany

Vanhanen, Tuomas   020225
Valoe, Mikkeli, Finland

Vargas, Renzo   020348
University of São Paulo, São Paulo, Brazil

Varney, Valérie   020522
University of Applied Science Cologne, Cologne, Germany

Varney, Valérie   020523
University of Applied Sciences Cologne, Cologne, Germany

vas Dyk, Ernest   020185
Nelson Mandela University, Port Elizabeth, South Africa

Vasconcelos, Letícia   020530
Casa dos Ventos, Fortaleza, Brazil

Vavilkin, Tatjana   020302
Soltech, Genk, Belgium

Vázquez Adán, Alejandra   020501
UCM, Madrid, Spain

Vázquez, A.   020508
UCM, Madrid, Spain

Veas, Christian   020136, 020234
PCCL, Leoben, Austria

Vecino, Fernando Román
DTU, Roskilde, Denmark
020346

Veerman, Sebastian
ISC Konstanz, Konstanz, Germany
020035

Vega de Seoane, José Maria
Becquerel Institute Spain, San Sebastian, Spain
020252

Vega de Seoane, Jose
Becquerel Institute, Brussels, Belgium
020546

Vega-Herrera, Jorge
University of Antofagasta, Antofagasta, Chile
020342

Vehus, Tore Sandnes
University of Agder, Grimstad, Norway
020443

Veirman, Jordi
Eurac Research, Bolzano, Italy
020203, 020226, 020254

Velasco, Angel
Nextracker, Fremont, United States of America
020367

Veludo, Jorge
Galp Energia, Lisbon, Portugal
020317

Veneri, Alessandro
University of Verona, Verona, Italy
020093

Vergura, Silvano
Polytechnic University of Bari, Bari, Italy
020301

Verlinden, Pierre
YIST, Jiangyin, China
020001

Vermang, Bart
Hasselt Unversity, Genk, Belgium
020064

Vernay, Christophe
SOLAÏS, Valbonne, France
020244

Vero, Giuseppe
Polytechnic University of Bari, Bari, Italy
020301

Veronese, Elisa
Eurac Research, Bolzano, Italy
020513

Veurman, Welmoed
ISFH, Emmerthal, Germany
020063

Viani, Lucas
Enertis Applus+, Madrid, Spain
020326

Vicente-Laiglesia, Pablo
European Climate, Infrastructure and Environment
Executive Agency, Brussels, Belgium
020181

Vidal de Oliveira, Aline
Solar Energy Research Laboratory Fotovoltaica/ UFSC,
Florianópolis, Brazil
020377

Vidal, Beatriz Muñoz
IaSol, Zaragoza, Spain
020414

Vidal-Fuentes, Pedro
IREC, Barcelona, Spain
020094

Videla-Magnata, Natalia   020129
Universidad de Antofagasta, Antofagasta, Chile

Videla-Magnata, Natalia   020417
University of Antofagasta, Antofagasta, Chile

Vilches, Anna Morales   020388
Next2Sun Technology, Dillingen, Germany

Villalonga Palou, Joan Tomás   020432, 020434
Sunveon, Madrid, Spain

Villén, Raúl   020127, 020414, 020517
ENDEF, Zaragoza, Spain

Villodas, Aritz   020198
TECNALIA, Derio, Spain

Vincent, Laetitia   020058
CNRS, Palaiseau, France

Vincent, Robin   020196
PVsyst, Geneva, Switzerland

Viorel Spataru, Sergiu   020191
DTU, Roskilde, Denmark

Viriyaroj, Bergpob   020298
Aalto University, Espoo, Finland

Viti, Valeria   020541
Legance, Milan, Italy

Vitoshkin, Helena   020379
Agricultural Research Organization, Rishon LeZion, Israel

Vögeli, Pascal   020385
ZHAW, Winterthur, Switzerland

Vogt, Malte R.   020515
TU Delft, Delft, The Netherlands

Vogt, Thomas   020482
DLR, Oldenburg, Germany

Vollbrecht, Joachim   020063, 020114
ISFH, Emmerthal, Germany

Voltan, Alessandro   020010
Applied Materials, Treviso, Italy

von Friedeburg, Christoph   020557
CF Energy Research-Consulting-Operation, Berlin,
Germany

Voronko, Yuliya   020162, 020249
OFI, Vienna, Austria

Vorster, Frederik J.   020193, 020344, 020416
Nelson Mandela University, Port Elizabeth, South Africa

Vorster, Frederik   020185
Nelson Mandela University, Port Elizabeth, South Africa

Vuillon, Laurent   020338
CNRS, Chambery, France

Vulic, Natasa   020296
Univesity of Applied Arts and Sciences Northwestern
Switzerland, Muttenz, Switzerland

Vumbugwa, Monphias   020185, 020193, 020344
Nelson Mandela University, Port Elizabeth, South Africa

Waibel, Christoph   020511
Flemish Institute for Technological Research (VITO), Genk,
Belgium

Wakabayashi, Ryo   020484
Hitachi, Kokubunji, Japan

Wakazono, Kouzen   020131
Gifu University, Gifu, Japan

Wallner, Gernot M.   020227
University of Linz, Linz, Austria

Walpita, Harsha   020169
University of Oslo, Kjeller, Norway

Walsh, Yoselyn   020520
Costa Rica Institute of Technology, Cartago, Costa Rica

Wambach, Karsten   020468, 020470
bifa Umweltinstitut, Augsburg, Germany

Wang, Chia-Chen   020549
ITRI, Hsinchu, Taiwan

Wang, Shuo   020286, 020400
TUAS, Turku, Finland

Wang, Tzuya   020549
ITRI, Hsinchu, Taiwan

Wang, Xiaolin   020381
Mälardalen University, Västerås, Sweden

Wannenwetsch, Jann   020312
EnBW, Karlsruhe, Germany

Wargocki, Pawel   020551
DTU, Roskilde, Denmark

Waschl, Alfred   020255
buildingSMART, Vienna, Austria

Weber, Thomas   020180, 020230
Kiwa PI Berlin, Berlin, Germany

Weeber, Arthur W.   020515
TU Delft, Delft, The Netherlands

Wei, Wenpeng   020484
Hitachi, Kokubunji, Japan

Weihs, Philipp   020281
BOKU, Vienna, Austria

Weinrich, Frank   020177
PTB, Braunschweig, Germany

Weiß, Marius   020361
Coburg University of Applied Sciences, Coburg, Germany

Wellens, Christine   020135
Fraunhofer ISE, Freiburg, Germany

Whyatt, Duncan   020394
Lancaster University, Lancaster, United Kingdom

Wienands, Karl   020218, 020220, 020221
ISC Konstanz, Konstanz, Germany

Wiesenfarth, Maike   020246
Fraunhofer ISE, Freiburg, Germany

Wietler, Tobias   020063
ISFH, Emmerthal, Germany

Wilbert, Stefan   020235, 020237, 020239, 020331
DLR, Almería, Spain

Willers, Guido   020201
Fraunhofer CSP, Halle, Germany

Wilson, Helen R.   020249
Fraunhofer ISE, Freiburg, Germany

Winter, Renate   020063
ISFH, Emmerthal, Germany

Winter, Stefan   020177, 020181
PTB, Braunschweig, Germany

Wirtz, Wiebke   020260
ISFH, Emmerthal, Germany

Witkowska, Agnieszka   020498
Gdansk University of Technology, Gdansk, Poland

Wittmer, Bruno   020196
PVsyst, Geneva, Switzerland

Wolf, Andreas   020031
Fraunhofer ISE, Freiburg, Germany

Wong, Craig   020230
Kiwa PI Berlin, Berlin, Germany

Wu, Li-Guo   020021
TSEC, Hsinchu, Taiwan

Wu, Yu   020030
TNO, Petten, The Netherlands

Wyss, Philippe   020068
CSEM, Neuchâtel, Switzerland

Xiong, Weizhen   020320
Tokyo University of Science, Tokyo, Japan

Xu, Jiahui   020001
YIST, Jiangyin, China

Xu, Wenhao   020144, 020208
TÜV Rheinland, Shanghai, China

Xu, Xiaoqi   020263
SERIS, Singapore, Singapore

Xu, Yu SERIS, Singapore, Singapore	020263
Xuereb, Steven Kiwa PI Berlin, Berlin, Germany	020180, 020230
Yadav, Shivendra SVNIT, Surat, India	020071, 020081
Yamaguchi, Yosuke Hitachi, Kokubunji, Japan	020484
Yanagida, Masatoshi NIMS, Tsukuba, Japan	020115
Yanar, T. Meriç Kalyon PV, Ankara, Türkiye	020027
Yang, Donggeon K-water, Daejeon, South Korea	020323
Yang, Hyoung-Kyu KETI, Wonmi-gu, South Korea	020449
Yde, Leif Stensborg, Roskilde, Denmark	020250, 020306
Ye, JiaYi SERIS, Singapore, Singapore	020102
Yerci, Selcuk ODTÜ-GÜNAM, Ankara, Türkiye	020113
Ylikunnari, Mari VTT Technical Research Centre of Finland, Oulu, Finland	020423
Ylinen, Marko Satakunta University of Applied Sciences, Pori, Finland	020444
Ylipaino, Juho TUAS, Tampere, Finland	020444, 020445, 020554
Yılmaz, Büşra Kameleon Solar, Roosendaal, The Netherlands	020521
Yordadov, Georgi imec, Diepenbeek, Belgium	020389
Younes, Kareem Khalifa University, Abu Dhabi, United Arab Emirates	020487
Yu, Cheng-Yeh TSEC, Hsinchu, Taiwan	020021, 020053
Yu, Shusen Ecole Polytechnique, Palaiseau, France	020406
Yuan, Xiao YIST, Jiangyin, China	020001
Yun, Jae Ho KENTECH, Naju-si, South Korea	020112
Zaimi, Mhammed University of Chouaib Doukkali, El Jadida, Morocco	020171

Zanatta Britto, João Victor   020025
PUCRS, Porto Alegre, Brazil

Zanesco, Izete   020023, 020025
PUCRS, Porto Alegre, Brazil

Zaror, Yasmin   020225
WIP - Renewable Energies, Munich, Germany

Zarzalejo, Luis F.   020237, 020331
CIEMAT, Madrid, Spain

Zekri, Atef   020146
QEERI, Doha, Qatar

Zerafa, Steve   020334
PIXAM, Msida, Malta

Zhang, Geng   020001
Jolywood (ShanXi) Solar Technology, Taiyuan, China

Zhang, Jingwei   020111
Hohai University, Changzhou, China

Zhang, Kai   020233
FZJ, Jülich, Germany

Zhang, Wenjing   020001
YIST, Jiangyin, China

Zhang, Wuai   020101
HZB, Berlin, Germany

Zhang, Yating   020144, 020208
TÜV Rheinland, Shanghai, China

Zhou, Qilin   020102
SERIS, Singapore, Singapore

Zhu, Junjie   020017
Institute for Energy Technology, Kjeller, Norway

Ziaullah, Abdul Wahab   020278, 020291
QEERI, Doha, Qatar

Zilles, Roberto   020154, 020348
University of São Paulo, São Paulo, Brazil

Zimmermann, Iwan   020116
IPVF, Palaiseau, France

Zubillaga, Oihana   020139
Tecnalia, Donostia - San Sebastián, Spain

Zugasti, Eugenia   020334
CENER, Pamplona, Spain

Zugasti, Eugenia   020300
CENER, Sarriguren, Spain

Zwahlen, Theo   020369
BFH, Burgdorf, Switzerland

KEYWORDS OF EU PVSEC 2025 PROCEEDINGS PAPERS

3D GIS	020457
3D Microstructure	020119
3D Shading Model	020432
Accelerated Aging	020254
Accuracy	020276
Adhesion	020384
Adhesive	020384
Adhesives	020127
Adoption vs. Implementation	020563
Aesthetic	020306
Africa	020272
AgBiS2	020071
Agri-photovoltaics	020396
Agriculture	020409
AgriPV	020464
Agrivoltaic	020398, 020407, 020541
Agrivoltaics	020378, 020379, 020388, 020394, 020400, 020402, 020403, 020409, 020412, 020543, 020565
Albedo	020443
Albedo Measurement	020287
Alkaline Leaching	020011
All-Sky Imagers	020267
AlN	020131
Alternative Materials	020020
Aluminium Frame Removal	020497
Aluminium-backed Modules	020192
Aluminum Oxide	020008
Amorphous Silicon	020043
Amorphous Silicon Carbide Crystallization	020079
Ancillary Services	020571
Anion Exchange	020117
Anomaly Detection	020358
Antimony	020140
Antimony Selenide	020087
Antimony-Doping	020015

BIPV	020250, 020260, 020300, 020302, 020304, 020306
BIPV Modelling	020297
BIPV Shading	020297
Bishop Model	020056
Bogotá	020441
Boron Diffusion	020025
BSF Sheet Resistance	020025
Buffer Layers	020087
Building Attached Photovoltaics	020477
Building Energy Efficiency	020259
Building Information Modelling (BIM)	020255
Building Integrated Photovoltaics (BIPV)	020255
Building Integrated PV (BIPV)	020303
Building Renovation	020551
Building-Integrated	020252
Building-Integrated Photovoltaics	020254, 020257, 020477, 020556
Building-Integrated Photovoltaics (BIPV)	020192, 020551
Building-integrated PV	020298
Buried Contact (BC)	020037
Business Models	020564
Bussing	020129
Bypass Diode	020455
Bypass Diodes	020121, 020153
c-Si	020300
c-Si Cell	020131
Cable Layout Optimisation	020382
Calibration	020215
CAMS	020291
Catadioptric Concentrator	020246
CBTS	020069
Cd-free	020087
CdTe	020499
Cell Efficiency	020060
Cell Interconnection	020218
Ceramic	020300
Chalcogenides	020085

Characteristics Addition	020081
Characterization	020050, 020119, 020121, 020151, 020166, 020459
CIGS	020097
CIGS/Perovskite Solar Cell	020104
Circular Economy	020141, 020504, 020510, 020517
Circularity	020470, 020472, 020507, 020517
Citizen Participation	020491, 020575
Clay	020300
Clean Firm Power	020487
Clean Transportation	020428
Cleaning	020332
Cleaning Frequency	020348
Cleaning Optimization Asset Management	020339
Clear-sky	020278
Clear-Sky Detection	020340
Climate Change	020402
Climate-dependent Degradation	020150
Climate-responsive Design	020259
Climate-Specific PV O&M	020546
Cloud Detection	020267
Clustering	020243
Co-Extruded EPE	020135
Co-Visibility	020244
Collective Self-consumption	020490
Color Stability	020254
Colored Photovoltaics	020556
ColorFoil	020306
Comfort	020302
Compact Furnace	020025
Comparative Life Cycle Assessment (LCA)	020303
Competitiveness	020573
Compliance	020444
Composite Encapsulant	020139
Composites	020498
Computational Efficiency	020432
Computer Vision	020336, 020511
COMSOL	020104

Decarbonization   020559
Deep Learning   020272, 020336
Deep Reinforcement Learning (DRL)   020356
Defect Detection   020164, 020377
Defects   020166, 020376
Degradation   020115, 020233
Degradation Monitoring   020361
Degradation Rate   020186
Degree of Cross-Linking   020135
Delamination   020497
Demand Response   020554
Density Functional Theory   020071
DHI   020291
Different Climate Zones   020318
Diffuse Light   020066
Diffuser   020306
Digital Elevation Modelling (DEM)   020244
Digital Surface Modelling (DSM)   020244
Digital Twin (DT)   020375
Digitalization   020544
Direct Irradiance   020283
Direct Sunlight Method (DSM)   020177
Distribution Grid   020537
DNI   020278, 020291
Dockerized Architecture   020491
Dose   020053
Double Perovskites   020117
Downshifting   020233
DPSS Q-switched Laser   020079
Drift-diffusion   020060
Driving Behavior   020455
Drone Inspections   020376
Dueling Deep Q-Network   020356
Durability   020302
Durability Enhancement   020161
Dye Sensitized Solar Cells   020100
Dynamic Shading   020453

Early Anomaly Detection   020338

ECA	020119
Ecodesign	020470
Ecology Index	020468
Economic Feasibility	020394
Economic Valuation	020492
Economic Value Assessment	020486
Education	020548
Education for Sustainable Development (ESD)	020569
Educational Resources	020100
Effects of Temperature and Irradiance	020171
Efficiency Forecast	020279
EL Images Outdoors	020186
EL Imaging	020185, 020510
EL Signal-to-Noise Ratio	020191
Electric Buses	020422, 020457
Electric Mobility	020420
Electric Vehicle Charging	020441
Electric Vehicle Charging Infrastructure	020526
Electrical Mismatch	020265
Electrically Conductive Adhesive	020218
Electricity Demand Coverage	020562
Electricity Market	020332
Electricity Price	020298
Electroluminescence	020188, 020201, 020205, 020206
Electroluminescence (EL) Images	020164
Electrolyzer	020426
Electron Multiplication	020068
Emitter Sheet Resistance	020025
Encapsulant Defects	020157
Encapsulants	020150
Encapsulation	020227
End-of-life PV	020510
Energy Balance	020439
Energy Communities	020445, 020535, 020575
Energy Community	020567
Energy Curtailment	020492
Energy Loss	020223

Grating Structure	020104
Green Hydrogen	020426
Green Purchase Behavior	020523
Greenhouses	020412
Grid Capacity	020486
Grid Integration	020530
Grid Services	020536
Grid-friendly PV Generation	020388
Ground Reflectors	020443
G–T Performance Matrix	020361
GTFS	020457
Half-Cut Cell Module	020193
Headroom Setting	020525
Heat Transfer Modelling	020127
Hemispheric Cameras	020267
Heterojunction	020010, 020515
Heterojunction PV Modules	020173
High Latitude	020400
High-Efficiency	020013
Home Energy Management System	020490
Hor Mirror	020379
Hosting Capacity	020537
Hot Electrons	020013
Hot-Spot	020223
Hotspot	020056
HP-RTM Process	020139
Hybrid Models	020358
Hybrid Photovoltaic-Thermal (PV-T) Collector	020127
Hybrid Photovoltaic-thermal (PVT) Collectors	020517
Hybrid Power Plants	020487, 020530
Hyperspectral Imaging	020504
IAM	020446
IBC	020006, 020055
IBC Cell	020221
IEA PVPS	020570

Lightweight	020384
Long-Term Degradation Rate	020181
Low Intensity Low Temperature (LILT)	020246
Low-Cost Sky Imager	020272
Low-energy Secondary Generation and Multiplication	020013
Luminescence	020206
Machine Learning	020337, 020342, 020355, 020434, 020510, 020522
Machine Learning (ML)	020317
Machine Learning Model	020279
Manufacturing	020007, 020558
Market	020570
Market Potential	020252
Market Uptake	020556
Market Value	020539
Mask	020031
Mass Production	020021
Material Classification	020504
Material Qualification	020574
Maximum Power Line	020449
Maximum Power Point Tracking	020437, 020449
McClear	020278
Mechanical Load Test	020167
Mechanical Loads	020231
Mediterranean Climate PV Performance	020334
Metal Recovery	020501, 020508
Metallization	020020, 020028
Metastability	020215
MgO	020131
Micro-Concentrator Optics	020257
Microalgae	020378
Microclimate	020403, 020565
Microinverter	020386
Minimum Sustainable Price	020482
Mismatch	020056, 020396
Mismatch Losses	020432
Mitigation strategies	020573

Modeling	020265
Modelling	020211, 020250
Module Array Design	020394
Module Degradation	020344
Module Design	020154
Module Inspection	020205
Module Integration	020220
Module Reliability	020254
Module Testing for Lifetime	020574
Modules	020129
Modules Testing	020157
Monitoring	020336, 020346, 020403, 020565
Monolithic Interconnection	020094
Monte Carlo Simulation	020441
MPPT	020422, 020453, 020455
MQTT Protocol	020491
Multi-Dwelling Buildings	020445
Multi-junction Solar Cell	020416
Multi-orientation Analysis	020192
Multi-Site Measurements	020334
Multi-Site PV Plant	020525
Multi-source Solar Simulator	020102
Multiple Linear Regression	020342
Nanocrystalline Silicon	020040
Nanostructure	020001
Nanostructures	020068
Natural Language Processing	020522
Near-infrared Absorption Spectroscopy	020149
Negative Electricity Prices	020492
Negative prices	020573
Neural Network	020186
Ni Contacts	020020
Non-destructive Analysis	020504
Non-Uniform UV Illumination	020158
Nordic	020443
Novel Module Structure	020131

Pinholes	020028
Plane-of-Array Irradiation	020348
pLCA	020515
Plug and Play Photovoltaics	020386
Plug-In Photovoltaics	020386
Policy Impacts	020309
Pollution Variables	020279
POLO BJ	020482
Poly Si	020021
Poly-Si	020008, 020035
Polyaniline	020498
Polymer Degradation	020149, 020150
Polymer Properties	020157
Polynomial Surface	020525
Polysilicon	020006, 020031
PolyZEBRA	020035
Positional Effects	020416
Potential-Induced Degradation	020265
Power Fluctuations	020528
Power Loss	020201
Power Optimizers	020359
Power Output Prediction	020338
Power Reserve	020571
Power System Balancing	020554
Predictive Modelling	020317
Production	020050
Profitability	020388
PSC	020083
Public Buildings	020562
Pump Controllers	020429
PV	020252
PV and Buildings	020301
PV Architecture	020453
PV Array Simulator Assessment	020369
PV Degradation	020217, 020329
PV Digital Twin	020319
PV Fault Diagnosis	020351
PV Fire Performance	020359
PV Integration	020139

Ray-tracing	020250
RCA	020230
Re-Use	020472
Real Monitoring Data	020562
Real-Time Monitoring	020335
Recyclability	020470
Recycling	020468, 020470, 020495, 020499, 020501, 020504, 020507, 020508
Regulatory Constraints	020543
Relative Angular Response (RAR)	020459
Reliability	020144, 020169, 020206, 020218, 020223, 020230, 020233, 020260, 020574
Remote Meteorological Data	020320
Remote Sensing	020486, 020511, 020532
Renewable Energy	020309, 020428
Renewable Energy Communities (REC)	020491
Renewable Energy Integration	020259
Renewable Energy Policy	020549, 020552
Repair	020129, 020511
RES	020476
Research Infrastructures	020546
Reserve Markets	020554
Reserve Power	020525
Residential	020304
Residential Photovoltaic Systems	020294
Residential PV	020490
Resistivity Distribution	020015
Resource	020276
Reuse	020472
Reverse Bias	020056, 020223
Risk	020573
Roll-to-Roll Sputtered System	020306
ROMP	020141
Roof Tile	020300
Round-Robin Study	020262
S-shape	020064
Safety and Quality	020444
Safety Assessment	020386

Salt Spray Corrosion	020161
SAS Quality	020369
Satellite-Derived	020286
Sb-Perovskite	020081
Sb2Se3	020085
SCAPS	020069
SCAPS-1D	020081
School	020548
Screen-Printed Silver	020048
Sealant	020384
Seasonal and Location Coefficient (Temperature and Irradiation)	020180
Second Life	020472
Second-life	020517
Secondary Materials	020468
Segmentation	020188
Selective Emitter	020023
Self-consumption	020298, 020421, 020445
Self-Consumption Systems	020439
Self-sufficiency	020421
Semi-Quantitative UVF	020158
Sensor-free Framework	020320
Sensorisation	020418
Sensors	020403, 020565
Sentiment Analysis	020522
Shading Analysis	020262, 020412
Shading Losses	020434
Shading Removal	020319
Shading-induced Losses	020432
Shared Transportation	020441
Shingled HJT	020254
Shingling	020220
Short-Term Variability	020241
Shunt Resistance	020201
Si heterojunction	020106
Si Modules	020188
Si Solar Cells	020020
Signal Modulation	020205
Silica	020495

Silicon	020007, 020058, 020097, 020468, 020495, 020501, 020507, 020508, 020515
Silicon Heterojunction	020040
Silicon Heterojunction Cell	020046
Silicon Kerf	020495
Silicon Photovoltaics	020144
Silicon Solar Cell	020001, 020013, 020023
Silicon Solar Cells	020006, 020068
Silicone	020384
Silver Recovery	020498
Simulation	020255, 020301
Simulation Acceleration	020243
Single-Axis Tracker Reliability	020314
Sizing Optimization	020530
Smart City	020420
Smart Energy System	020544
Smart Inverter IV Tracing	020361
SMARTS2	020278
Social Cognitive Career Theory (SCCT)	020569
Social Housing	020564
Social Innovation	020575
Social Risks	020505
Socio-Economics	020476
Software Tool	020183
Soil	020403, 020565
Soiling	020311, 020332, 020339, 020361
Soiling Loss Modeling	020317
Soiling Losses	020311, 020348
Soiling Mitigation	020311
Solar	020188, 020276
Solar Array Simulator Evaluation	020369
Solar Cell	020007, 020053, 020083
Solar Cells	020090, 020501, 020508
Solar Energy	020526
Solar Glass	020140
Solar Irradiance	020286
Solar Irradiance Forecasting	020267
Solar Irradiation	020412

Solar Mandate	020551
Solar Modules	020157
Solar Panel Reliability	020154
Solar Photovoltaic Technology	020569
Solar Photovoltaics	020479, 020564
Solar Power	020571
Solar Power Plant	020539
Solar PV	020476, 020549, 020552, 020559, 020573
Solar PV Systems in Buildings	020562
Solar Radiation	020275, 020283
Solar Railways	020421
Solar Resource Variability	020241
Solar Silicon	020011
Solar Water Pumping System	020429
Solder Paste	020220
Solid-State Reaction	020117
Solvent Additives	020096
Soxhlet Extraction	020135
Space	020053
Spatial Planning Integration	020552
Spatio-Temporal Analysis	020338
Spectral Composition	020416
Spectral Irradiance	020283
Spectral Mapping	020149
Spectroscopy	020227
Spectrum Splitting	020379
Stability	020096
Stakeholder Analysis	020556
Stall Detection	020314
Stance Detection	020522
Standardisation	020472
Standards	020211, 020444
STC Parameters	020183
Storage	020429, 020535
Storage Effect	020215
Storage System	020539
Stress Profile	020355
Structural Electronics	020423
Structuring	020031

Thermal Effects   020416
Thermal Image   020193
Thermal Stress   020153, 020260
Thermally Conductive Filler   020131
Thermomechanical Test   020497
Thermophotonics   020067
Thin Film   020071, 020180
Thin Films   020069, 020087
Thin-film   020094
Thin-Film Devices   020067
Thin-Film Solar Cells   020085
Tilt   020532
TOPCon   020010, 020021, 020028, 020031, 020037
TOPCON PV Modules   020229
Tracking Irradiation Gain   020363
Tracking Systems   020402
Transparency   020574
Transparent Conducting Oxide   020046
Tree Shading   020294

UAV-Based Monitoring   020335, 020374
Ultrasonic Characterization   020132
Ultraviolet Fluorescence   020158
Ultraviolet-Fluorescence Imaging   020185
Urban Planning   020420, 020526
Urban Shadowing   020457
Utility-Scale Photovoltaics   020348
Utility-Scale Solar PV   020382
UV Exposure   020229
UV Fluorescence   020166
UV Instability   020229
UV Laser Annealing   020079
UV Laser Scribing   020043
UV-Vis Spectroscopy   020081

Vacuum Refining   020011
Vacuum Thermal Evaporation   020558
Vacuum-Assisted Processing   020079
Validation   020390

Value Chain   020505
Vehicle Integrated Photovoltaics   020459
(VIPV)
Vehicle-Integrated Photovoltaics   020453, 020457
Vehicle-Integrated Photovoltaics   020422
(VIPV)
Vertical Bifacial PV   020262
Vertical PV   020388, 020400
Very Short-term Solar Forecasting   020272
Vibration Durability   020417
VIPV   020417, 020455
Virtual Power Plant   020554
Virtual Power Plants   020535
Visual inspection   020169, 020185

Water Quality   020418
Weather Station   020371
Weather Variables   020279
Wet Etching   020028

Yield   020180, 020307, 020396
YOLO Classifiers   020335, 020374

ZnSnO   020085

WIP – Renewable Energies
Sylvensteinstr. 2
81369 Munchen
Germany

ISBN 979-8-3313-2987-7